Level 3

Teacher's Book

A Resource for Planning and Teaching

Volume 2

HOUGHTON MIFFLIN

Boston • Atlanta • Dallas • Denver • Geneva, Illinois • Palo Alto • Princeton

Goals

of the program

What We Believe

. . . from the authors of *Math Central*

- **Thinking, reasoning,** and **problem solving** are essential to a mathematics program.
- Ongoing assessment should be presented in a variety of formats to **meet individual needs.**
- **Technology** supports and enhances mathematical instruction.
- Frequent, ongoing communication with **parents** is vital to a successful mathematics program.

Authors

Kindergarten

Patsy F. Kanter
Consultant, Teacher, Author
New Orleans, Louisiana

Janet G. Gillespie
Title 1 Specialist, Consultant, Author
Woodlawn Elementary School
Portland, Oregon

Grades 1–6

Laurie Boswell
Profile Jr./Sr. High School
Bethlehem, New Hampshire

Dr. Juanita V. Copley
Associate Professor of Education
University of Houston
Houston, Texas

Dr. Robert Gyles
Community School District 4
New York, New York

Audrey L. Jackson
Assistant Principal
Parkway School District
St. Louis, Missouri

Edward Manfre
Mathematics Education Consultant
Albuquerque, New Mexico

Mary Esther Reynosa
Elementary Mathematics Curriculum Specialist
Edgewood School District
San Antonio, Texas

Dr. Jean M. Shaw
Professor of Elementary Education
University of Mississippi
University, Mississippi

Dr. Lee Stiff
Associate Professor of Mathematics Education
North Carolina State University
Raleigh, North Carolina

Dr. Charles Thompson
Professor of Mathematics Education
University of Louisville
Louisville, Kentucky

Consultants and Contributing Authors

Dr. Carole Basile
University of Houston
Houston, Texas

Cindy Chapman
Inez Science and Technology Magnet School
Albuquerque, New Mexico

Dr. Deborah Ann Chessin
University of Mississippi
University, Mississippi

Dr. Richard Evans
Plymouth State College
Plymouth, New Hampshire

Dr. Karen Karp
University of Louisville
Louisville, Kentucky

Casilda Pardo
Armijo Elementary School
Albuquerque, New Mexico

Caitlin Robinson
Mitchell Elementary School
Albuquerque, New Mexico

Photography Credits
© 1996 PhotoDisc, Inc. p. T25
Tony Scarpetta pp. T6, T7, T29
Parker/Boon Productions pp. T5, T28, T30
Allan Landau Photography pp. T5, T26

Printed in the U.S.A.

ISBN: 0-395-91752-2

123456789-B-04 03 02 01 00 99 98

Teacher Reviewers

Judy Anderson
Shoreline School District
Seattle, WA

Mee Mee Ashba
Woodview Elementary School
Houston, TX

Susan Ashcraft
Broadmor School
Tempe, AZ

Rebekah I. Baker
Shadeland Elementary School
Anderson, IN

Phyllis Bardo
Oak Forest Elementary School
Houston, TX

Mitzie R. Beavert
Valley Ridge Elementary School
Lewisville, TX

Judy Curran Buck
Plymouth State College
Plymouth, NH

Judith Burrell
Charles C. Bell Elementary School
Asheville, NC

Pat Butler
Evans Elementary School
Tempe, AZ

Jan Caldwell
Candler Elementary School
Candler, NC

Rick Callan
Bunker Hill Elementary School
Indianapolis, IN

Anita Carter
Fort Worth ISD
Northeast Instructional Team
Fort Worth, TX

Alma Chavez
Denver Elementary School
Fort Worth, TX

Michelle Cullom
Hawthorne Elementary School
Tulsa, OK

Nora Fabela
Bilingual/ESL
Irving ISD
Irving, TX

Dr. Beverly J. Ferrucci, Ph.D.
Chair, Mathematics Department
Keene State College
Keene, NH

Dixie Finley
Santa Fe Elementary School
Moore, OK

James George
Governor's Ranch School
Littleton, CO

Katherine Hebert
Office of Curriculum Support
School District of Philadelphia
Philadelphia, PA

Kim Heutzenroeder
Cedar Brook Elementary School
Houston, TX

JoAnn Hiser
Broadmor School
Tempe, AZ

Robyn Jamison
Longwood Elementary School
Naperville, IL

Linda Jensen
Rice School
Houston, TX

Mary Fran Johnson
Burris Laboratory School
Muncie, IN

Robin Jones
Laird Elementary School
Tempe, AZ

Cindy Kibler
Evans Elementary School
Tempe, AZ

Mark Kreiter
Gordon Gregory Middle School
Naperville, IL

Sue Larsen
Governor's Ranch School
Littleton, CO

Navor Ledesma
Denver Elementary School
Fort Worth, TX

Linda Lee
Roberts Elementary School
Houston, TX

Martha Mackay
Pinson Elementary School
Pinson, AL

Carol McBride
Creekside Elementary School
Lewisville, TX

Daisy McKenzie
Houston ISD
Northwest Area
Houston, TX

Maria Moon
Fort Worth ISD
Northeast Instructional Team
Fort Worth, TX

Patricia Morgan
T. H. Watkins Elementary School
Lake Charles, LA

Lidia Morris
Hubbard Elementary School
Fort Worth, TX

Rebecca Navarra
Independence Elementary School
Independence, LA

Nancy Neusbaum
Math Specialist
Cumberland Valley S. D.
Mechanicsburg, PA

Delores Oakes
St. Agatha School
Buffalo, NY

Kimberly Orchard
Wood Elementary School
Tempe, AZ

Mary Jeanne Overcash
St. Susanna School
Mason, OH

Brenda Pedersen
West University Elementary School
Houston, TX

Jimmie Rios
Fort Worth ISD
Northwest Instructional Team
Fort Worth, TX

Stuart P. Robertson, Jr., M. Ed.
E.G. Sherburne School
Pelham, NH

Tracy Schallaci
Buffalo Creek Elementary School
Houston, TX

Janet Shew
Halls Ferry School
Florissant, MO

S. Paul Short
Curriculum Coordinator
Sarasota County Schools
Sarasota, FL

Barbara Stevens
Loge Elementary School
Boonville, IN

Melva Lea Stewart
Dalton Elementary
Baton Rouge, LA

Traci Szaz
Our Lady of the Sacred Heart
Reading, OH

Sherri Travisano
Thew Elementary School
Tempe, AZ

Marlene Tuchman
Thomas D. Gregg Elementary School #15
Indianapolis, IN

Stephanie Walton
Roberts Elementary School
Houston, TX

Caryn Weeks-Davis
Bustoz-Elementary School
Tempe, AZ

Amy White
Parkway Elementary School
Lewisville, TX

Jeannie Wilson
Woodbrook Elementary School
Carmel, IN

Dr. Karol Yeatts
Leewood Elementary
Miami, FL

Welcome

A mathematics program should offer teachers and students a balance of experiences – direct instruction and cooperative learning; hands-on activities and paper and pencil tasks; real-world applications along with investigations, projects, math games, and basic facts practice.

Math Central is *math power*—it's what students need to become confident thinkers and problem solvers for today's world and tomorrow's challenges. With *Math Central* students develop a strong foundation in skills and concepts and learn to investigate, reason, and explain. *Math Central* is the headquarters for active learning.

Content

Visual models support and illuminate concepts, bringing them to life for your students. In *Math Central,* content and instruction are carefully sequenced from concrete to connecting to symbolic stages. Integrated and comprehensive, *Math Central* reflects the Curriculum and Evaluation Standards developed by the National Council of Teachers of Mathematics.

Accessibility

With *Math Central,* your classroom becomes a community of math learners. In this flexible and balanced program, you'll find alternative approaches that respond to today's diverse classrooms. *Math Central* has the solid instruction and purposeful practice you want, with opportunities to select techniques that meet the needs of all your students.

Practice and Review

Math Central provides ample, ongoing practice and review. Throughout the program, students are encouraged to draw on their prior knowledge and assess their own progress as they venture into new mathematical territory.

Real-Life Connections

Students learn mathematics that springs from real-life situations—from home, school, community, and the information age. They become consumers, scientists, designers, and explorers of the future, as they discuss and apply mathematical ideas.

Ease of Use

Math Central's clear step-by-step organization gives you and your students information at a glance. Your instructional time is maximized, because what you need is at your fingertips. Your students' learning time is focused, because what they need to learn and do is clear and easy to understand. And, because of the clear instructional pathways, home-school partnerships are strengthened as family members participate in students' mathematical experience.

HOUGHTON MIFFLIN math CENTRAL

math center *components*

- Gameboards
- Playing Cards
- Activity Cards
- How-To Cards
- Teacher's Guide
- Workmats
- Blackline Masters
- Student Manipulatives

Hands on Learning

The Math Center provides an exciting array of materials designed to help students work on their own or in pairs to practice and reinforce the skills and concepts taught in *Math Central*.

Each lesson in the program has a corresponding Math Center activity. There are two sets of materials, one for Levels 1–2 and one for Levels 3–6. Each Math Center includes a Teacher's Guide for modeling student activities and for setting up and using the Math Center. Activity cards give students directions for working independently.

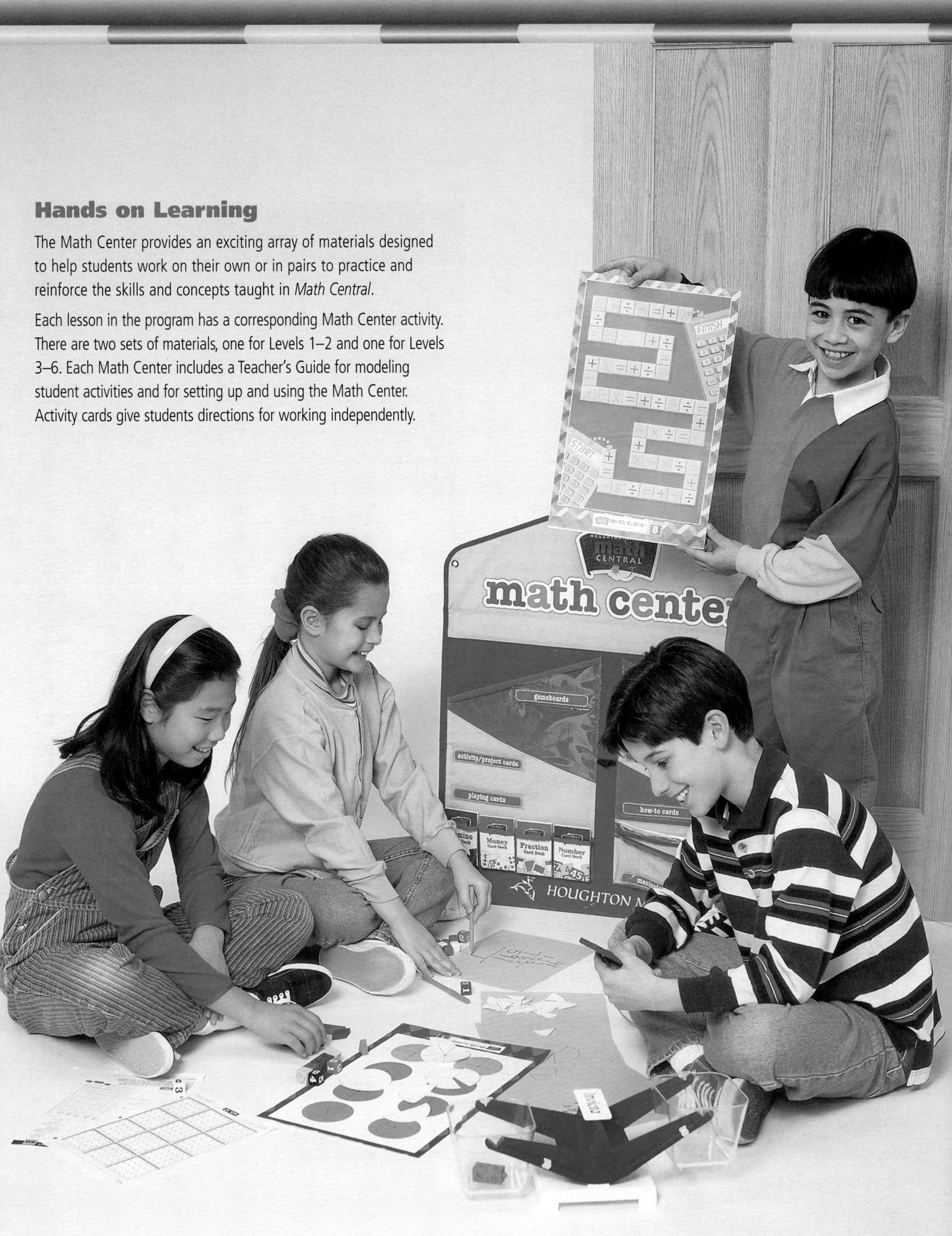

Components

	K	1	2	3	4	5	6
Student Book, Levels 1–6		●	●	●	●	●	●
Student Book with Student Manipulatives Kit, Levels 1–6		●	●	●	●	●	●
Teacher's Book, Levels K–6	●	●	●	●	●	●	●
One, Two, Buckle My Shoe: A Read Aloud Anthology, Levels 1–2 Poems, Rhymes, Songs, and Chants for Math		●	●				
Literature/Trade Book Bookshelves, Levels K–6	●	●	●	●	●	●	●
Math Central Kindergarten Package, Level K includes Teacher's Edition	●						
Kindergarten Activity Book, Level K	●						
Practice Worksheets, Levels 1–6 includes Teacher's Annotated Edition		●	●	●	●	●	●
Enrichment Worksheets, Levels 1–6 includes Teacher's Annotated Edition		●	●	●	●	●	●
Reteaching Worksheets, Levels 1–6 includes Teacher's Annotated Edition		●	●	●	●	●	●
Assessments, Levels K–6	●	●	●	●	●	●	●
Performance Assessments, Levels 1–6		●	●	●	●	●	●
Standardized Testing: New Formats, Levels 3–6				●	●	●	●
Practice and Assessment Skillpads, Levels 1–6		●	●	●	●	●	●
Language Connections, Levels 1–6		●	●	●	●	●	●
Teaching Resources, Levels K–6	●	●	●	●	●	●	●
Overhead Transparencies, Levels K–6	●	●	●	●	●	●	●
Family Involvement, Levels 1–6 (English and Spanish)		●	●	●	●	●	●
Problem of the Day, Levels 1–6 includes BLMs and Answer Key		●	●	●	●	●	●
Problem of the Day Flip Charts, Levels 1–6		●	●	●	●	●	●
Math Center, Levels 1–6		●	●	●	●	●	●
Daily Cumulative Review, Levels 1–6 includes Teacher's Annotated Edition		●	●	●	●	●	●
Just the Facts, Levels 1–6		●	●	●	●	●	●
Daily Lesson Plans, Levels K–6	●	●	●	●	●	●	●
Classroom Manipulatives Kit, Levels K–6	●	●	●	●	●	●	●
Overhead Manipulatives Kit, Levels K–6	●	●	●	●	●	●	●
Student Manipulatives Kit, Levels K–6	●	●	●	●	●	●	●
Activity Kit, Levels 1–2		●	●				
***Houghton Mifflin Education Place* Mathematics Center, Levels K–6**	●	●	●	●	●	●	●
Calculators, Levels K–6	●	●	●	●	●	●	●
MathKeys®, Levels K–6	●	●	●	●	●	●	●

Manipulatives

Suggestions for alternatives to the program materials are listed below each manipulative.

	Problem Solving	Algebra	Ratios, Proportions, Percent	Decimals	Whole Numbers	Patterns, Relations, Functions	Geometry	Statistics, Graphing, Probability	Fractions	Measurement
Attribute Blocks seashells, leaves, pasta, buttons	●		●			●	●		●	●
Blank Cubes dot cubes and labels	●	●		●	●	●		●	●	●
Centimeter Linking Cubes small snap-together blocks	●	●	●	●	●	●	●	●	●	●
Circular Protractors	●		●				●	●		●
Clock Dials clockface with two lengths of string, for the hour and minute hands, stapled to the center	●					●			●	●
Color Tiles ceramic tiles, colored index cards cut into squares	●	●	●		●	●	●	●		●
Connecting Cubes jumbo paper clips, pasta and string, beans glued on sticks	●	●	●		●	●	●	●	●	●
Fraction Models homemade bars made from grid paper or construction paper	●		●	●		●			●	
Geoboards	●					●	●		●	
Geometric Solids cans, cones, boxes, balls, solids made of modeling dough or clay	●					●	●			●
Links jumbo paper clips, ziti macaroni and string, hair ties, rubber bands	●	●			●	●			●	●
Money Set: Coins and Bills real coins, buttons	●	●	●	●	●	●		●		●
Number Cubes/Spinners dot cube, number cards, blocks, spinners	●	●	●	●	●	●	●	●	●	●
Pattern Blocks shapes cut out of felt, shapes cut out of colored cardboard	●					●	●		●	●
Pan Balance clothes hanger, clothespins, and paper cups with string	●	●			●					●
Place-Value Blocks grid paper cutouts, coins, meter stick	●		●	●	●	●				●
Tenths, Hundredths, and Thousandths Squares centimeter grid paper cutouts	●	●	●	●		●			●	
Triman™ Compass	●		●				●			●
Two-Sided Counters coins, washers, or beans with one side painted	●	●	●		●	●		●		

Scope and Sequence

In the Program...

Problem Solving

Problem Solving	K	1	2	3	4	5	6
PROBLEM SOLVING STRATEGIES							
Steps—Understand, Plan, Try It, Look Back		●	●	●	●	●	●
Act It Out	●	●	●	●	●	●	●
Draw a Picture	●	●	●	●	●	●	●
Look for a Pattern	●	●	●	●	●	●	●
Systematic Guess and Check	●	●	●	●	●	●	●
Make a Table	●		●	●	●	●	●
Make a List	●		●	●	●	●	●
Work a Simpler Problem				●	●	●	●
Work Backward				●	●	●	●
Write an Equation						●	●
PROBLEM SOLVING APPLICATIONS							
Using Strategies		▲	▲	▲	▲	▲	▲
Listen to the story	▲	▲	▲				
Using data							
from pictures and maps	●	●	●	●	●	●	●
from graphs, charts, tallies, and tables	●	●	●	●	●	●	●
outside resources				▲	▲	▲	▲
Picture stories/problems	●	●	●	▲			
Using operation sense, number sense, and measurement sense	▲	▲	▲	▲	▲	▲	▲
Create Your Own (Problem formulation)	▲	▲	▲	▲	▲	▲	▲
Draw a picture story	▲	▲	▲	▲			
DECISION MAKING							
Classifying and sorting		▲	▲	▲	▲	▲	▲
Choose appropriate tool							
model the problem	●	●	●	●	●	●	●
calculator/computer			●	●	●	●	●
Choose the operation	●	●	●	▲	▲	▲	▲
Choose a computation method							
use paper and pencil				●	●	●	●
use estimation				●	●	●	●
use mental math			●	●	●	●	●
use technology				●	●	●	●
Estimate or exact?				●	●	●	●
Logical reasoning	●		●	●	●	●	●
Not enough information	●	●	●	●	●	●	●
Extra information	●	●	●	▲	▲	▲	▲
Does it make sense? (reasonableness)		▲	▲	▲	▲	▲	▲
Decide what to do with the remainder				●	●	●	●

KEY Teach and Apply ● Practice and Apply ▲

In Level 3...

Problem Solving

PROBLEM SOLVING STRATEGIES

Steps—Understand, Plan, Try It, Look Back 6
Act It Out 6, 7, 24, 25, 33, 268, 269
Draw a Picture 45, 47, 49, 65, 69, 126–129, 288, 289, 292, 293, 339
Look for a Pattern 24, 48, 49, 62, 63, 138, 162, 163, 234, 235, 256, 257, 262, 263, 323
Guess and Check 106, 107, 112, 113, 115, 198, 199, 212, 213
Make a Table 162, 163, 178, 179
Make a List 354, 355, 368, 369
Work a Simpler Problem 384, 385, 396, 397
Work Backward 322, 323, 336, 337

PROBLEM SOLVING APPLICATIONS

Using Strategies 24, 25, 32, 33, 62, 63, 70, 71, 112–115, 128, 129, 138, 148, 149, 178, 179, 182, 183, 212, 213, 218, 219, 256, 257, 262, 263, 292–295, 336–339, 368–371, 396, 397, 402, 403, 430, 431
Using data (operation, number, and measurement sense)
from pictures and maps 2, 3, 5, 11, 19, 21, 23, 32, 33, 48, 49, 62, 63, 67–69, 75, 89, 91, 93, 94, 96, 103, 110, 112, 113, 126, 129, 161, 175, 177, 167, 179, 183, 193, 199, 204, 209, 211, 213, 215, 217, 218, 219, 234, 235, 239, 243, 254–257, 261–263, 287–289, 323, 325, 338, 339, 353, 357, 360, 367, 368–370, 427, 429, 431
from graphs, charts, tallies, and tables 3, 17, 29, 60, 105, 109, 111, 115, 125, 127, 129–138, 143, 146–147, 149, 201, 212, 254, 255, 280, 289, 290, 293, 311, 335, 336, 371, 383, 385, 397, 400, 401, 403, 415, 431
from outside resources 39, 83, 120–125, 147, 155, 225
Create Your Own (Problem formulation) 3, 9, 31, 33, 47, 49, 57, 69, 71, 77, 89, 115, 129, 133, 135, 137, 143, 145, 167, 197, 204, 211, 229, 233, 241, 253, 255, 257, 261, 268, 269, 275, 280, 287, 293, 295, 321, 339, 369, 387, 390, 397, 413, 425
Draw a picture story 1, 141, 270, 271

DECISION MAKING

Classifying and sorting 26, 27, 30, 31, 52, 66, 67, 229, 231, 234, 235, 237, 239, 241, 243, 248–251, 253, 268, 269, 277, 287, 328, 329
Choose the operation 22, 23, 28, 29, 51, 167, 193, 204, 210, 244, 280
Choose a computation method 9, 17, 21, 29, 390
use paper and pencil 91, 111, 244, 390
use estimation 76, 77, 93, 95, 390
use mental math 91, 111, 195, 204, 244, 280, 387, 390, 395, 427, 429
use technology 175, 181, 204, 280, 390
Choose appropriate computation tool
model the problem 1, 7, 25, 61, 160, 166, 195, 280
calculator/computer 181, 204, 395, 400, 401, 431
Estimate or exact? 76, 77, 92, 204, 244, 280, 390
Logical reasoning 52, 61, 101, 203, 243, 251, 313
Not enough or extra information 12
Does it make sense? 3, 9, 15, 94–96, 108–110, 138, 168, 327, 360, 420
Decide what to do with the remainder 418–420, 427

Type printed in red indicates that a topic is being introduced for the first time.

In the Program...

Whole Number Concepts

COUNTING

	K	1	2	3	4	5	6
Concrete experiences—groups and numbers	●	●	●	▲	▲	▲	▲
One-to-one correspondence and comparing numbers	●	●	▲	▲	▲	▲	▲
Numbers to 10—counting and writing	●	▲	▲				
Ten frame		●	●	▲	▲		
Numbers to 100—counting and writing	●	●	●	●	▲	▲	▲
Counting on the number line	●	●	●	●	●	▲	▲
Counting on, counting back, counting up	●	●	●	▲	▲	▲	▲
Skip counting							
by 2s, 3s, 4s, 5s, and 10s	●	●	●	▲	▲	▲	▲
by 25s, 50s, and 100s			●	●	▲	▲	▲
Number patterns and sequences	●	●	●	▲	▲	▲	▲
Patterns in the Hundreds Chart		●	●	▲			
Ordinal numbers	●	●	●	▲	▲	▲	▲
Making tally marks	●	●	●	●	●	▲	▲

PLACE-VALUE CONCEPTS

	K	1	2	3	4	5	6
Groups of 10 or 100		●	●	●	●	▲	▲
Place value—models and forms							
2- and 3-digit numbers		●	●	●	▲	▲	▲
Thousands				●	●	▲	▲
Millions and beyond					●	●	▲
Place value and money			●	●	▲	▲	▲

NUMBER SENSE

	K	1	2	3	4	5	6
Names for numbers	●	●	●	▲	▲	▲	▲
Making a ten or a hundred		●	●	●	▲		
Regrouping in addition and subtraction		●	●	●	▲	▲	▲
Comparing—more, fewer, same, most, fewest, greater, less	●	●	●	▲	▲	▲	▲
Using <, >, = to compare			●	●	▲	▲	▲
Ordering numbers—before, after, between	●	●	▲	▲	▲	▲	▲
Ordering numbers—greatest, least	●	●	●	●	●	▲	▲
Rounding numbers to the nearest 10 or 100				●	●	▲	▲
Rounding larger numbers						●	●
Numbers and numerals throughout the world	●	●	●	●	●	●	●
Interpreting remainders				●	●	▲	▲

NUMBER THEORY

	K	1	2	3	4	5	6
Even and odd numbers	●	●	●	●	▲	▲	▲
Factors			●	●	▲	▲	
Greatest common factor					●	●	▲
Multiples					●	●	▲
Least common multiple					●	●	▲
Prime factorization					●	●	●
Factor trees						●	●
Rules for divisibility					●	●	▲
Finding least common denominators						●	●
Figurate numbers				●	●	●	●
Finding reciprocals						●	●

KEY Teach and Apply ● Practice and Apply ▲

In Level 3...

Whole Number Concepts

COUNTING

Concrete experiences—groups and numbers 8, 9, 16, 17, 26, 27, 45, 58, 59, 86, 87, 101
One-to-one correspondence 26, 27
Ten frame 16, 17
Numbers to 100—counting and writing 4, 5, 40
Counting on the number line 4, 5, 58, 59
Counting on, counting back, counting up 4, 5, 20, 21
Skip counting
by 2s, 3s, 4s, 5s, and 10s 64, 65, 72–75 130, 156, 157, 173, 176, 177, 196, 197, 332–335
by 25s, 50s, and 100s 64, 65
Number patterns and sequences 4, 5, 7, 9, 49, 64, 65, 72, 73, 130, 173, 176, 177, 196, 197, 378, 379
Ordinal numbers 5
Making tally marks 122–125, 130–133, 141–147, 154, 155

PLACE-VALUE CONCEPTS

Groups of 10 or 100 42–45, 86, 87, 100, 101
Place value—models and forms
2- and 3-digit numbers 46, 47, 86, 87, 100, 101
Thousands 50, 51
Place value and money 66, 67

NUMBER SENSE

Names for numbers 5, 7–11, 16, 17, 20, 28, 29, 43, 45, 175, 190, 191, 383, 425
Making a ten or a hundred 16, 18, 20, 21, 28, 29, 42–44, 86, 87, 100, 101
Regrouping in addition and subtraction 86, 87, 100, 101
Comparing—more, fewer, same, most, fewest, greater, less 60, 61, 96, 109, 131
Using <, >, and = to compare 11, 60, 61, 175, 276, 277, 383, 425
Ordering numbers—before, after, between 4, 5
Ordering greatest to least, least to greatest 60, 61, 125, 132–137, 363
Rounding whole numbers to the nearest 10 or 100 58, 59, 92–95, 108, 109
Numbers and numerals throughout the world
American sign language 55
Ancient Brahmi numerals 171
Ancient Greek numerals 283
Ancient Egyptian numerals 63, 283
Aztec numbers 14
Babylonian numbers 362
Fulani number words 15
Maasai hand signals 55
Maya numerals 62
Roman numerals 316
Viking runes 295
Interpreting remainders 418–420, 427

NUMBER THEORY

Even and odd numbers 7, 61, 109, 161, 165, 431
Factors 160, 161, 192, 193
Arrays for numbers 158, 159, 172, 173, 200

In the Program...

Whole Number Computation

Addition and Subtraction

BASIC FACTS

	K	1	2	3	4	5	6
Tools—concrete/pictorial models and technology	●	●	▲	▲	▲		
Readiness—counting more than, less than	●	●	●				
Readiness—names for numbers	●	●	▲	▲			
Meaning and vocabulary of addition	●	●	●	▲	▲	▲	▲
Meaning and vocabulary of subtraction	●	●	●	▲	▲	▲	▲
Part/Part Whole		●	●	▲			
Writing and solving addition and subtraction number sentences	●	●	●	●	▲	▲	▲
Picture stories	●	●	●	▲			
Number sentences with missing addends		●	●	●	▲	▲	▲
Basic fact strategies	●	●	●	●	▲		
Horizontal and vertical forms	●	●	●	▲	▲		
Making and using an Addition Table			●	▲			
Addition and subtraction are related	●	●	●	●	▲	▲	▲
Addition-subtraction fact families	●	●	●	●	▲		
Properties of addition		●	●	●	●	▲	▲
Three or more addends		●	●	●	●	▲	▲
Rules for subtraction			●	●	●	▲	▲

USING PLACE–VALUE CONCEPTS

	K	1	2	3	4	5	6
Tools—concrete/pictorial models and technology		●	●	●	●	▲	▲
Adding 2- and 3-digit numbers without regrouping		●	●	▲			
Adding with regrouping ones, tens, and hundreds		●	●	●	▲	▲	▲
Three or more addends			●	●	▲	▲	▲
Subtracting 2- and 3-digit numbers without regrouping		●	●	▲	▲		
Subtracting with regrouping hundreds, tens, and ones		●	●	●	▲	▲	▲
Subtracting from zeros			●	●	●	▲	▲
Estimating sums and differences			●	●	●	●	▲
Checking addition and subtraction			●	●	●	▲	▲
Adding and subtracting larger numbers				●	●	●	▲
Mental math patterns in addition and subtraction		●	●	●	●	▲	▲
Expressions and equations						●	●

Multiplication and Division

BASIC FACTS

	K	1	2	3	4	5	6
Tools—concrete/pictorial models and technology	●	●	●	●	●	▲	▲
Readiness—equal groups	●	●	●	●	▲	▲	▲
Skip–counting and multiplication		●	●	▲			
Repeated addition		●	●	●	●	▲	▲
Readiness for division—groups and leftovers	●	●	●	●	●	▲	▲
Repeated subtraction				●	●	▲	▲
Arrays			●	●	●	▲	▲
Meaning of multiplication			●	●	●	●	●
Basic facts strategies				●	●	▲	▲
Writing and solving number sentences			●	●	●	▲	▲
Number sentences with missing factors				●	●	▲	▲
Horizontal and vertical forms			●	●	●	●	●
Meaning of division			●	●	●	▲	▲
Multiplication and division are related				●	●	●	●
Fact families				●	●	▲	▲
Properties of multiplication			●	●	●	●	▲
Making and using the Multiplication Table				●	●	▲	
0 and 1 in multiplication and division			●	●	●	●	▲
Rules for division				●	●	●	▲
Remainder in division				●	●	▲	▲
Fractional parts and division		●	●	●	●	▲	▲

KEY Teach and Apply ● Practice and Apply ▲

In Level 3...

Whole Number Computation

ADDITION AND SUBTRACTION

BASIC FACTS

USING PLACE–VALUE CONCEPTS

MULTIPLICATION AND DIVISION

BASIC FACTS

In the Program...

Whole Number Computation

USING PLACE-VALUE CONCEPTS

	K	1	2	3	4	5	6
Tools for multiplication—models and technology				●	●	▲	▲
Multiplying by 1–digit numbers				●	●	▲	▲
Multiplication patterns—multiples of 10, 100, or 1000				●	●	●	▲
Multiplying by 2-digit numbers				●	●	●	▲
Multiplying larger numbers				●	●	●	▲
Estimating products				●	●	●	●
Checking in multiplication				●	●	●	●
Multiplication expressions and equations						●	●
Exponents and powers							●
Tools for division—models and technology				●	●	●	▲
Dividing by 1-digit numbers with 2-digit quotients				●	●	▲	▲
Dividing by 1-digit numbers with 3-digit quotients					●	●	▲
Zeros in the quotient					●	●	●
Checking division					●	●	▲
Division patterns—multiples of 10, 100, or 1000				●	●	●	▲
Dividing larger numbers by 1-digit numbers					●	●	▲
Estimating quotients				●	●	●	●
Dividing by 2-digit numbers					●	●	●
Dividing by 3-digit numbers							●
Division expressions and equations						●	●

Estimation

ESTIMATING QUANTITIES

	K	1	2	3	4	5	6
Number (whole numbers, decimals, fractions)	●	●	●	●	●	●	●
Money amounts		●	●	●	●	▲	▲
Estimating by grouping tens		●	●	●	▲	▲	▲
Comparing estimates and results			●	●	●	●	●
Estimating from data/real life			▲	▲	▲	▲	▲
Whole number operations			●	●	●	▲	▲
Decimal operations					●	●	●
Operations with fractions and mixed numbers					●	●	●
Estimating with percents							●

STRATEGIES

	K	1	2	3	4	5	6
Benchmarks and referrents	●	●	●	●	●	●	●
Halfway points				●	●	●	●
Rounding				●	●	▲	▲
Front-end with and without adjusting				●	●	▲	▲
Using multiples of 10, 100, or 1000				●	●	●	●
Adjusting estimates—better estimates				●	●	●	●
Substituting compatible numbers					●	●	●

MEASUREMENT

	K	1	2	3	4	5	6
Size of angles—greater than or less than right angle				●	●	▲	▲
Length	●	●	▲	▲	▲	▲	
Capacity	●	●	●	▲	▲	▲	▲
Mass (weight)	●	●	●	▲	▲	▲	▲
Time	●	●	●	▲	▲	▲	▲
Temperature		●	●	●	▲	▲	▲
Perimeter or circumference		●	●	●	●	▲	▲
Area, Surface Area , Volume				●	●	●	▲

KEY Teach and Apply ● Practice and Apply ▲

In Level 3...

Whole Number Computation

USING PLACE–VALUE CONCEPTS

Concrete/pictorial models for multiplication 214, 215, 380–383, 386–389, 392, 393
Tools for multiplication 393, 400, 401
Multiplying 2-digit numbers by 1-digit numbers 380, 381, 386–389
Multiplying 3-digit numbers by 1-digit numbers 394, 395, 398, 399
Multiplying with zeros 398, 399
Multiplication patterns—multiples of 10, 100, or 1000 214, 215, 424–426, 428
Estimating products 382, 383, 386–388, 390, 391, 394, 398–401, 404
Checking in multiplication 398–401
Concrete/pictorial models for division 216, 217, 426, 427
Using a calculator 219
Dividing by 1-digit numbers with 2-digit quotients 424–429
Checking division 424–429
Division patterns—multiples of 10, 100, or 1000 216, 217
Estimating quotients 217, 219, 424–429

Estimation

ESTIMATING QUANTITIES

Number (whole numbers, decimals, fractions) 3, 5, 58, 59, 76, 77, 284, 285, 349, 359
Money amounts 3, 157, 382
Estimating by grouping tens 58, 59
Comparing estimates and results 94, 108, 109, 349, 359, 382, 383, 399
by counting 40, 41
using a calculator 109, 217, 400, 401
Estimating from data/real life 40, 41, 224
Whole number sums 92, 93, 116, 222
Whole number differences 108, 109, 116, 222
Whole number products 175, 203, 382, 383, 386–388, 390, 391, 394, 398–401, 404
Whole number quotients 203, 217, 424–429

STRATEGIES

Benchmarks and referents 284, 285, 349, 359
Halfway points 58, 59
Rounding 58, 59, 92, 93, 108–111, 382, 383
Front-end 92, 93, 108, 109, 382, 383
Using multiples of 10, 100, or 1000 58, 59, 382, 383, 424–429
Estimate or exact? 76, 77, 92, 244, 280, 390
Adjusting estimates—better estimates 92, 93, 108, 109, 424–429

MEASUREMENT

Size of angles—Greater than and less than a right angle 237
Length 11, 304–307, 310, 311, 315, 320, 321
Capacity 39, 312, 313, 324, 325
Mass (weight) 314, 326, 328, 329, 399
Time 40, 41, 203, 224, 225, 333
Temperature 330, 331
Perimeter 308, 309, 319, 321
Area 258–261

In the Program...

Mental Math

	K	1	2	3	4	5	6
Basic facts strategies—addition and subtraction	●	●	●	●	●	▲	▲
Basic facts strategies—multiplication and division		●	●	●	●	▲	▲
Whole number operations							
Sums		●	●	●	●	▲	▲
Differences			●	●	●	▲	▲
Products				●	●	●	●
Quotients				●	●	●	●
STRATEGIES							
Using patterns in addition and subtraction	●	●	●	●	●	●	●
Using properties of whole numbers		●	●	●	●	●	●
Looking for tens and hundreds			●	●	●	▲	▲
Powers and multiples of 10, 100, or 1000—counting zeros				●	●	●	●
Using equivalent forms for numbers				●	●	●	●
Fractions						●	●
Decimals						●	●
Percents							●

Decimals

	K	1	2	3	4	5	6
MODELING, READING, AND WRITING							
Readiness—money amounts with $ and .			●	●	▲	▲	▲
Modeling and writing tenths				●	●	●	●
Modeling and writing hundredths				●	●	●	●
Thousandths and beyond						●	●
Place value with decimals				●	●	●	●
Decimals on the number line					●	●	●
Decimals and the metric system				●	●	▲	▲
NUMBER SENSE							
Decimal sense				▲	▲	▲	▲
Comparing and ordering decimals				●	●	●	●
Estimating decimals				●	●	●	●
Rounding decimals					●	●	●
Equivalent forms—annexing zeros						●	●
Decimals and fractions				●	●	●	●
Decimals and percents						●	●
COMPUTING WITH DECIMALS							
Computing with money amounts			●	●	●	▲	▲
Adding decimals				●	●	●	▲
Subtracting decimals				●	●	●	▲
Multiplying a decimal by a whole number						●	●
Multiplying by multiples of 10, 100, or 1000						●	●
Multiplying a decimal by a decimal						●	●
Dividing a decimal by a whole number						●	●
Expressing remainders						●	●
Dividing by multiples of 10, 100, and 1000						●	●
Dividing decimals by decimals							●
Estimating with decimals						●	●
Expressions and equations with decimals							●

KEY Teach and Apply ● Practice and Apply ▲

In Level 3...

Mental Math

Basic fact strategies—addition and subtraction
- act it out 8, 9, 22, 23
- using order/zero properties 8, 9
- doubles and near doubles 10, 11, 18, 19
- ten frame 16, 17
- counting on or back 16, 20, 21
- making a ten 16–18, 20, 21
- adding and subtracting nine 28, 29

Basic fact strategies—multiplication and division 160, 161, 166, 167, 172–177, 200–203, 206–211
- skip-counting 130, 158–161, 166, 167, 173, 177, 187, 196, 197
- using division rules 195
- using doubles 208, 209
- multiplying and dividing nine 210, 211

Whole number operations
- sums 5, 56, 57, 91, 111
- differences 56, 57, 91, 111
- products 192, 193, 203, 214, 215, 387, 395, 399
- quotients 192, 193, 203, 216, 217, 427, 429

STRATEGIES

Using patterns in addition and subtraction 56, 57
Using properties of whole numbers 8, 9, 18, 19, 180, 181, 194, 195, 388, 389
Looking for tens and hundreds 28, 29, 94
Powers and multiples of 10, 100, or 1000—counting zeros 214–217, 326, 427–429
Using equivalent forms for numbers 210, 211

Decimals

MODELING, READING, AND WRITING

Readiness—money amounts 64–67
Modeling and writing tenths 346–353, 364–367
Modeling and writing hundredths 358, 359
Place value with decimals 352, 353, 366, 367
Using a comma instead of a decimal point 363
Decimals on the number line 356, 357, 362, 364, 365

NUMBER SENSE

Decimal sense 346–349, 351, 355, 362, 363, 371
Comparing and ordering decimals 349, 351, 353, 356, 357, 360, 365, 366
Estimating decimals 349, 359
Decimals and fractions 346–351, 353, 358, 359
Decimals and the metric system 360

COMPUTING WITH DECIMALS

Computing with money amounts 68–71, 91, 95, 105, 111, 113, 165, 176, 177, 182, 183, 201, 244,
Adding decimals 364–367
Subtracting decimals 364–367

In the Program...

Fractions and Mixed Numbers

	K	1	2	3	4	5	6
MODELING, READING, WRITING							
Readiness—parts of figures or groups	●	●	●	▲			
Equal parts		●	●	●	●	●	●
Concrete/pictorial models		●	●	●	●	●	●
Fractional parts of regions		●	●	●	●	▲	▲
Fractional parts of groups or numbers		●	●	●	●	▲	▲
Modeling and writing numerical fractions			●	●	●	●	●
Unit fractions		●	●	▲	▲	▲	▲
Nonunit fractions			●	●	●	▲	▲
Fractions and mixed numbers on the number line				●	●	●	▲
Fractions and division				●	●	●	▲
Fractions and circle graphs				●	●	●	▲
Modeling and writing mixed numbers				●	●	●	●
Mixed numbers and fractions in measurement				●	●	●	●
Mixed numbers as remainders					●	●	●
NUMBER SENSE							
Fraction sense	▲	▲	▲	▲	▲	▲	▲
Comparing and ordering fractions and mixed numbers			●	●	●	●	●
Equivalent fractions				●	●	●	●
Simplest form					●	●	●
Using benchmarks to estimate				●	●	●	●
Least common denominator					●	●	●
Fractions and whole numbers				●	●	▲	▲
Fractions greater than 1 (improper fractions)					●	●	●
Fractions and decimals				●	●	●	●
Fractions and percents						●	●
Reciprocals						●	●
Cross products							●
COMPUTING WITH FRACTIONS AND MIXED NUMBERS							
Adding and subtracting fractions—like denominators				●	●	▲	▲
Fractions with unlike denominators					●	●	●
Mixed numbers—like denominators					●	▲	▲
Mixed numbers—unlike denominators						●	●
Regrouping and renaming in addition and subtraction						●	●
Multiplying with fractions and mixed numbers						●	●
Dividing with fractions and mixed numbers						●	●
Estimating with fractions and mixed numbers						●	●
Expressions and equations with fractions					●	●	●

KEY Teach and Apply ● Practice and Apply ▲

In Level 3...

Fractions and Mixed Numbers

MODELING, READING, WRITING

Readiness—parts of figures or groups 270, 271, 347
Equal parts 272, 273
Pattern block/area models 258–261, 272, 273
Grid or dot paper models 295
Fractional parts of regions 258–261, 272–279, 284, 285
International Alphabet Flags 300, 301
Fractional parts of groups or numbers 275, 414, 415
Modeling and writing numerical fractions 274–277
Unit fractions 272–275
Nonunit fractions 274–277
Ancient Egyptian and Greek fractions 282, 283
Fractions on the number line 277, 287, 289
Fractions and division 166, 167, 414, 415
Modeling and writing mixed numbers 290, 291, 306, 307, 350, 351, 353
Mixed numbers and fractions in measurement 292, 293, 305–307, 321, 325, 339, 345, 385, 402, 403

NUMBER SENSE

Fraction sense 25, 33, 173, 258–261, 270, 271, 280, 282–285, 294, 295, 305, 389, 409
Comparing and ordering fractions and mixed numbers 276, 277, 284, 285, 289, 291
Equivalent fractions 278, 279, 349
Using benchmarks to estimate 284, 285
Fractions and whole numbers 290, 291, 307
Fractions and decimals 346–351, 353, 358, 359
Fractions related to time 292, 293, 335, 337

COMPUTING WITH FRACTIONS AND MIXED NUMBERS

Adding and subtracting fractions—like denominators 286, 287

In the Program...

Integers

MODELING, READING, AND WRITING

	K	1	2	3	4	5	6
Readiness situations—temperatures, money, games	▲	▲	▲	▲	▲	▲	▲
Positive and negative numbers—models							●
The set of integers							●
Integers on the number line							●
Comparing integers							●
Ordering integers							●
Adding integers							●
Subtracting integers							●

Ratios, Proportions, and Percents

MODELING, READING, AND WRITING

	K	1	2	3	4	5	6
Proportional reasoning and relative size	▲	▲	▲	▲	▲	▲	▲
Maps, scale drawings, and models		▲	▲	▲	▲	▲	▲
Speeds and distance				▲	▲	▲	▲
Similar figures					▲	▲	▲
Better buy					●	●	●
Ratio readiness—fractional parts		●	●	●	●	▲	▲
Probability and chance				●	●	●	●
Ratio—meaning of						●	●
Writing ratios—three forms						●	●
Equal ratios						●	●
Using cross products							●
Rates and ratios						●	●
Converting ratios and rates						●	●
Probability ratio						●	●
Pi as a ratio							●
Unit rates/unit prices					●	●	●
Writing and solving proportions							●
Equivalent proportions							●
Drawing scale drawings					●	●	●

PERCENT

	K	1	2	3	4	5	6
Meaning of percent						●	●
Modeling percent						●	●
Writing percents						●	●
Percents and decimals						●	●
Percents and fractions						●	●
Comparing						●	●
Estimating						●	●
Percent of a number						●	●
Percent one number is of another number							●
Finding the whole							●
Using percents in circle graphs						●	●
Using percents in consumer math						●	●

KEY Teach and Apply ● Practice and Apply ▲

In Level 3...

Integers

MODELING, READING, AND WRITING

Readiness situations—temperatures, money, games 30, 31, 42, 43, 86, 87, 99, 100, 101, 136, 137, 145

Ratios, Proportions, and Percents

MODELING, READING, AND WRITING

Proportional reasoning and relative size 32, 33, 38, 39, 63, 67, 70, 71, 201, 237, 242, 360, 409

Maps, scale drawings, and models 32, 33, 94, 110, 113, 121, 129, 137, 167, 179, 183, 199, 213, 218, 254, 255, 262, 263, 321, 339, 369

Speeds and distance 76, 77, 102, 103, 114, 115, 148, 149, 219, 369, 370, 402, 403, 431

Ratio readiness—fractional parts 275, 414, 415

Probability and chance 144–147

In the Program...

Reasoning and Communicating

	K	1	2	3	4	5	6
REASONING							
Critical Thinking	▲	▲	▲	▲	▲	▲	▲
Algebraic Reasoning				▲	▲	▲	▲
Compare and contrast	●	●	●	●	●	▲	▲
Classify and sort	●	●	●	●	●	▲	▲
Order and sequence	●	●	●	●	●	▲	▲
Extend patterns	●	●	●	●	●	●	●
Give It a Try		●	●				
Alternate ways to solve problems	●	●	●	●	●	●	●
Use properties and rules of numbers		●	●	●	●	●	●
Use logical reasoning	●	●	●	●	●	●	●
Make and test predictions from patterns		▲	▲	▲	▲	▲	▲
Visualizations	●	●	●	●	●	●	●
COMMUNICATION/CONNECTIONS							
Cooperative Learning	▲	▲	▲	▲	▲	▲	▲
Write About It		▲	▲	▲	▲	▲	▲
Math Journals				▲	▲	▲	▲
Literature/Magazine connections	▲	▲	▲	▲	▲	▲	▲
Math Power				▲	▲	▲	▲
Investigations		▲	▲	▲	▲	▲	▲
Cultural Diversity/Math World		▲	▲	▲	▲	▲	▲

KEY Teach and Apply ● Practice and Apply ▲

In Level 3...

Reasoning and Communicating

REASONING

Critical thinking 5, 7, 9, 11, 17, 21, 23, 27, 31, 43, 45, 47, 49, 51, 59, 61, 69, 73, 75, 77, 87, 89, 93, 95, 101, 107, 125, 127, 129, 133, 135, 137, 145, 147, 159, 167, 173, 177, 181, 193, 195, 197, 199, 201, 211, 215, 217, 229, 231, 233, 235, 239, 241, 249, 253, 255, 259, 261, 273, 277, 293, 307, 309, 319, 321, 326, 331, 335, 349, 351, 353, 357, 365, 367, 381, 383, 385, 389, 395, 401, 413, 415, 417, 419, 425, 427,

Algebraic Reasoning 11, 21, 29, 47, 57, 67, 91, 131, 137, 143, 165, 173, 209, 259, 279, 287, 293, 309, 313, 319, 367, 389, 425

Compare and contrast 4, 5, 11, 21, 26–28, 60, 61, 65, 67, 90, 92, 93, 94, 96, 105, 108, 109, 125, 133, 135, 137, 143, 160, 175, 181, 217, 219, 227, 229, 231, 233, 236, 237, 239, 243, 249, 250, 251, 257, 273, 276, 277, 287, 289, 310, 321, 325, 326, 328, 329, 347, 349, 357, 360, 365, 366, 381, 394, 400

Classify and sort 52, 66, 67, 229, 231, 234, 235, 237, 239, 243, 248–251, 253, 268, 269, 277, 319, 325, 328, 329

Order and sequence 4, 5, 60, 61, 63, 66, 67, 75, 125, 132–137, 237, 259, 261, 325, 328, 329, 349, 351, 353, 356, 357, 360

Extend patterns 4, 5, 9, 21, 48, 49, 57, 68, 69, 75, 77, 128, 129, 162, 163, 177, 183, 196, 197, 208, 209, 214–217, 219, 229, 231, 233, 235, 237, 253, 256, 257, 259, 323, 333, 335, 339, 353, 355, 357, 378, 379, 429

Alternate ways to solve problems 9, 17, 21, 24, 25, 32, 33, 62, 63, 70, 71, 91, 93, 95, 111–115, 128, 129, 148, 149, 160, 166, 175, 178, 179, 182, 183, 195, 204, 212, 213, 218, 219, 244, 256, 257, 262, 263, 280, 292–295, 336–339, 368–371, 387, 389, 395, 396, 430, 431

Use properties and rules of numbers 8, 9, 18, 19, 180, 181, 194, 195, 398, 399

Use logical reasoning 52, 61, 101, 203, 243, 251, 313

Make and test predictions from patterns 40, 41, 142, 143, 145–147, 195, 231, 328, 329, 379

Visualizations 6, 7, 24, 25, 231, 234, 235, 238, 250, 251

COMMUNICATION/CONNECTIONS

Cooperative Learning 2, 3, 8, 9, 30, 31, 42–45, 58, 59, 74, 75, 86, 87, 100, 101, 124, 125, 142-147, 158, 159, 164, 165, 180, 181, 192-197, 228-233, 236, 237, 240, 241, 248–253, 258, 259, 272, 273, 276–279, 286, 287, 304, 305, 310-313, 320, 321, 328–331, 348-351, 358, 359, 364, 365, 380, 381, 412, 413

Share Your Thinking 7, 25, 27, 33, 49, 63, 71, 107, 113, 115, 127, 129, 149, 163, 179, 183, 199, 213, 219, 235, 244, 257, 263, 280, 289, 293, 295, 323, 327, 339, 355, 361, 369, 371, 385, 390, 397, 403, 420, 431

Write About It 93, 143, 147, 161, 165, 197, 243, 249, 307, 381

Math Journals 19, 21, 31, 43, 47, 95, 101, 131, 135, 167, 195, 215, 229, 243, 273, 287, 311, 335, 353, 389

Literature/Magazine connection 32, 70, 114, 148, 182, 218, 262, 294, 338, 370, 402, 430

Math Power xiv, 40, 84, 122, 156, 190, 226, 270, 302, 346, 378, 410

Investigations 38, 39, 82, 83, 120, 121, 154, 155, 188, 189, 224, 225, 268, 269, 300, 301, 344, 345, 376, 377, 408, 409, 436, 437

Cultural diversity 49, 106, 128, 129, 228, 252, 274, 290, 294, 295, 398, 399

Math World 14, 15, 54, 55, 98, 99, 140, 141, 170, 171, 206, 207, 246, 247, 282, 283, 316, 317, 362, 363, 392, 393, 422, 423

In the Program...

Algebraic Reasoning

	K	1	2	3	4	5	6
READINESS							
Modeling, writing, and completing number sentences	●	●	●	●	●	▲	▲
Addition and subtraction sentences	●	●	●	●	▲	▲	▲
Addition and subtraction are related (inverse operations)		●	●	●	●	●	●
Multiplication and division sentences			●	●	●	●	▲
Multiplication and division are related (inverse operations)				●	●	●	●
Fact families	●	●	●	●	●	▲	▲
Fraction number sentences			●	●	●	●	●
Decimal number sentences						●	●
Equalizing groups—meaning of equality	●	●	●	▲	▲	▲	▲
Using symbols of equality and inequality =, <, and > to write and complete sentences			●	●	●	●	●
Expressions as names for numbers	●	●	●	●	▲	▲	▲
Using properties of addition and multiplication		●	●	●	●	●	●
Comparing numerical expressions			●	▲	▲	▲	▲
Parentheses as grouping symbols					●	●	●
Equivalent forms—decimals, fractions, percents					●	●	●
Ratios and rates						●	●
VARIABLE EXPRESSIONS							
Exploring variables—number sentences and tables with missing parts	●	●	●	●	▲	▲	▲
Sentences with missing addends		●	●	●	▲	▲	▲
Sentences with missing factors				●	●	●	▲
Letter codes		●	●	●	●	▲	▲
Number tables with missing parts			●	●	▲	▲	▲
Writing variable expressions					●	●	●
Evaluating expressions by substituting					●	●	●
Evaluating expressions using order of operations						●	●
Expressions with exponents							●
Pi as a ratio							●
EQUATIONS AND INEQUALITIES							
Using formulas in measurement						●	●
True and false—equations and inequalities						●	●
Modeling equations						●	●
Writing a word equation						●	●
Writing an addition-subtraction equation						●	●
The solution of an equation						●	●
Solving addition-subtraction equations						●	●
Writing a multiplication-division equation						●	●
Solving multiplication-division equations						●	●
Solving equations using inverse operations							●
Writing and solving a proportion							●
Writing and solving percent equations							●

KEY Teach and Apply ● Practice and Apply ▲

In Level 3...

Algebraic Reasoning

READINESS

Modeling, writing, and completing number sentences 8–11, 16–20, 22, 23, 26–31, 158–161, 164–167, 191–195, 200, 202, 203, 208–210, 214–217, 326, 349, 356, 357, 364, 365, 381, 412, 414, 415

Addition–subtraction number sentences 8–11, 16–20, 22, 23, 26–29, 57, 158–161, 200, 364, 365

Addition and subtraction are related 20–23, 27–31, 102, 104, 110

Multiplication–division number sentences 158–161, 164–167, 174, 176, 177, 191–195, 208–210, 214–217, 381, 412, 414, 415

Multiplication and division are related 172–177, 192, 193, 200, 202, 203, 208–211, 413, 424, 426, 428

Fact families 30, 31, 200, 201, 208–210

Fraction number sentences 279, 414, 415

Decimal number sentences 349, 356, 357, 364, 365

Equalizing groups—meaning of equality 11, 218, 328, 329

Using symbols of equality and inequality =, <, and > to write and complete sentences 11, 60, 61, 175, 276, 277, 279, 311, 313, 321, 356–359, 383, 425

Expressions as names for numbers 11, 16, 17, 20, 28, 29, 43, 45–47, 86, 87, 93, 100, 101, 109, 175, 190, 191, 383, 425

Using properties of addition and multiplication 8, 9, 18, 19, 180, 181, 194, 195, 367, 398, 399

Comparing numerical expressions 11, 93, 109, 175, 383, 425

Equivalent forms—decimals and fractions 348–351, 353, 358, 359

VARIABLE EXPRESSIONS

Exploring variables

sentences with missing addends 8, 9, 11, 17, 22, 23, 29

sentences with missing factors 193, 202, 210, 424, 426, 428

Letter codes 300, 301

Number tables with missing parts 21, 47, 51, 91, 156, 157, 162, 177, 203, 209, 311, 313, 321, 325, 333, 367, 389

In the Program...

Patterns and Functions

	K	1	2	3	4	5	6
Color, size, and shape patterns	●	●	▲	▲	▲	▲	▲
Recognizing and extending patterns	●	●	▲	▲	▲	▲	▲
Creating or modeling patterns	●	●	▲	▲	▲	▲	▲
Describing patterns	●	●	●	▲	▲	▲	▲
Counting and number patterns or sequences	●	●	●	●	▲	▲	▲
Make and test predictions from patterns	▲	▲	▲	▲	▲	▲	▲
Calculator patterns			●	●	●	●	●
Figurate numbers			●	●	●	●	●
Special patterns (Doubling, Pascal's triangle, Fibonacci, etc.)		●	●	●	●	●	●
Geometric transformations—slides, flips, and turns	●	●	●	●	●	●	●
Geometry patterns—sides, angles, and diagonals of plane figures						●	●
Geometry patterns—faces, edges, vertices						●	●
Tangrams, pentominoes, and other tessellations						●	●
Patterns in the coordinate plane				●	●	●	●
Patterns and problem solving	●	●	●	●	●	●	●
USING TABLES, GRAPHS, AND DIAGRAMS							
In-out tables		●	●	●	●	●	●
Find rules and patterns for tables		▲	▲	▲	▲	▲	▲
Write expressions for tables						●	●
Line graphs—changes over time					●	●	●
Ordered pairs and coordinate graphs			●	●	●	●	●
Venn or circle diagrams	●	●	●	●	▲	▲	▲

Technology

	K	1	2	3	4	5	6
CALCULATOR							
Counting	●	●	●	●	▲	▲	▲
Whole number operations	●	●	●	●	●	●	●
Money			●	●	●	●	
Decimals				●	●	●	●
Fractions						●	●
Integers							●
Percents							●
As a problem solving tool			●	●	▲	▲	▲
As an investigative tool			●	●	●	●	●
Checking answers or estimates			●	●	▲	▲	▲
In geometry and measurement					●	●	●
In algebra						●	●
COMPUTER							
MathKeys	▲	▲	▲	▲	▲	▲	▲
Internet		▲	▲	▲	▲	▲	▲

KEY Teach and Apply ● Practice and Apply ▲

In Level 3...

Patterns and Functions

Color, size, and shape patterns 6, 7, 24, 49, 63, 128, 129, 183, 212, 226–229, 231–237, 247, 252, 253, 256, 257, 263, 268, 269, 300, 301, 323

Recognizng and extending patterns 5–7, 9, 21, 24, 48, 49, 57, 62–65, 73, 103, 128, 129, 144, 145, 162, 163, 173, 176, 177, 183, 196, 197, 203, 208, 209, 212, 214–217, 219, 226–229, 231–237, 247, 252, 253, 256, 257, 259, 262, 263, 268, 269, 274, 275, 282, 283, 300, 301, 311, 323, 335, 339, 353, 355, 389, 399, 429

Creating or modeling patterns 48, 49, 183, 226, 227, 229, 233, 235, 241, 247, 253, 257, 268, 269, 339

Describing patterns informally 21, 57, 73, 103, 129, 138, 161, 167, 234, 235, 237, 256, 257, 311, 335, 429

Describing patterns with rules 91, 214, 215, 283, 309, 313, 319, 378, 379

Counting and number patterns of sequences 4, 5, 7, 9, 49, 64, 65, 72, 73, 130, 162, 163, 173, 176, 177, 196, 197, 353, 357, 378, 379

Patterns in the Multiplication-Division Table 196, 197, 201, 207, 209

Make and test predictions from patterns 40, 41, 142, 143, 145–147, 195, 226–227, 231, 239, 305, 323 328, 329, 355, 357, 379

Sequencing time 75, 292, 293

Calculator patterns 357, 413

Figurate numbers 49, 158, 159, 172, 173, 200, 259, 323

Special patterns
- doubling patterns 10, 11, 18, 19, 208, 209,

Guatamalan blankets 228
- musical 49
- Native American 49, 228, 247
- tartans 252

Slides, flips, and turns 228–235, 239, 247

Tessellations 226, 227, 238, 239

Patterns in the coordinate plane 263

Patterns and problem solving 24, 48, 49, 62–63, 162–163, 234, 235, 256, 257, 262, 263, 323

USING TABLES, GRAPHS, AND DIAGRAMS

In-out tables 21, 47, 51, 57, 91, 177, 203, 209, 309, 311, 313, 321, 333, 367, 389

Find rules and patterns for tables 57, 91, 161–163, 177, 203, 309, 313, 333

Write expressions for tables 91

Line graphs—changes over time 134–135

Ordered pairs and coordinate graphs 254–256, 263

Venn or circle diagrams (with intersections) 52

Work Backwards diagram 322, 323

Technology

CALCULATOR

Counting 357

Whole number operations 9, 109, 181, 204, 217, 395

Money 400, 401

Decimals 357, 365

As a problem solving tool 51, 106, 107, 113, 175, 181, 204, 280, 395, 400, 401, 431

As an investigative tool 39, 83, 195, 357, 409, 437

Checking answers or estimates 109, 217

Constant function 357

COMPUTER

Internet 15, 39, 55, 83, 99, 121, 141, 155, 171, 189, 207, 225, 247, 269, 283, 301, 317, 345, 363, 377, 393, 409, 423, 437

In the Program...

Probability and Statistics

	K	1	2	3	4	5	6
DATA COLLECTION AND ORGANIZATION							
Experiments and sampling activities	●	●	●	●	●	●	●
Counting	●	●	●				
Surveys and questioning	●	●	●	●	●	●	●
Outside resources				●	●	●	●
Tallies	●	●	●	●	▲	▲	▲
Tables and charts	●	●	●	●	▲	▲	▲
Frequency tables			●	●	●	▲	▲
Systematic counting—tree diagrams or lists					●	●	●
Misleading data						●	●
GRAPHS—READINESS FOR MEDIAN, MODE, AND RANGE							
Pictographs	●	●	●	●	●	▲	▲
Bar graphs	●	●	●	●	▲	▲	▲
Line graphs				●	●	●	●
Circle graphs				●	●	●	●
Selecting appropriate scales/intervals					●	●	●
Double bar graphs					●	●	●
Double line graphs						●	●
Plotting data—line plots, stem and leaf plots, or box and whisker plots					●	●	●
Choosing appropriate graph to make					●	●	●
MEASURING DATA							
Averages or means					●	●	●
Range						●	●
Median and mode						●	●
Clustered and unclustered data						●	●
PROBABILITY							
Concept of chance—games	▲	▲	▲	▲	▲	▲	▲
Combinations			●	●	●	●	●
Likely or unlikely events		●	●	●	●	●	●
Certain and impossible events			●	●	▲	▲	▲
Predicting and guessing		▲	▲	▲	▲	▲	▲
Probability and area—using spinners		▲	▲	▲	▲	▲	▲
Probability and chance				●	●		
Probability ratio						▲	▲
Multiple outcomes				●	●	●	●
Experimental probability						●	●
Theoretical probability						●	●

KEY Teach and Apply ● Practice and Apply ▲

In Level 3...

Probability and Statistics

DATA COLLECTION AND ORGANIZATION

Experiments and sampling situations 8, 9, 30, 31, 38–43, 74, 75, 86, 87, 100, 101, 142–147, 192, 193, 304, 305, 312, 313, 324, 328, 329, 344, 345, 377, 412, 413
Counting 2, 3, 8, 9, 30, 31, 43, 49, 113, 120, 121, 124, 125
Surveys and questioning 39, 122–125, 132, 133, 154, 155
Outside resources 39, 83, 120–125, 147, 225
Tallies 122–125, 130–133, 141–147, 154, 155, 225
Tables and charts 3, 17, 29, 60, 105, 109, 111, 115, 124, 125, 127, 129–138, 143, 146, 147, 149, 182, 201, 225, 304, 305, 307, 312, 313, 325, 328, 329, 345, 363, 383, 385, 397, 400, 401, 403, 412, 413, 415, 437
Frequency tables 123–125, 130–133, 142–147, 225
Systematic counting—tree diagrams or lists 262, 263, 354, 355, 368, 369

GRAPH SENSE—READINESS FOR MEDIAN, MODE, AND RANGE

Pictographs 130, 131, 290, 291
Bar graphs 122, 123, 132, 133, 138, 143, 154, 155
Line graphs 134, 135
Circle graphs 144, 145

PROBABILITY

Concept of chance—games 30, 31, 42, 43, 86, 87, 99, 100, 101, 145, 347
Combinations 262, 263, 354, 355, 368, 369, 371
Likely or unlikely events 144, 145
Certain or impossible events 143–145
Predicting and guessing 40, 41, 142–147, 261, 328, 329, 355
Probability and area—spinners 74, 75, 144, 145, 355
Multiple events—tossing 2 cubes 43, 49, 86, 87, 100, 101, 146, 147

In the Program...

Geometry

	K	1	2	3	4	5	6
SOLID FIGURES							
Basic shapes	●	●	●	▲	▲	▲	▲
Attributes of solid shapes	●	●	●	▲	▲	▲	▲
Classifying and sorting by shape	●	●	●	●	●	●	●
Modeling solids	●	●	●	●	●	●	●
Faces of solids related to plane figures		●	●	●	●	●	●
Prisms and pyramids		●	●	●	●	●	●
Spheres and cylinders		●	●	●	●	●	●
Visualizations		●	●	●	●	●	●
Subdividing and combining			●	●	●	●	●
Faces, edges, and vertices			●	●	●	●	●
BASIC FIGURES							
Exploring paths	●	●	▲	▲	▲	▲	▲
The basic figures—square, rectangle, triangle, and circle	●	●	●	▲	▲	▲	▲
Pattern blocks—triangle, square, rhombus (or diamond), trapezoid, hexagon	●	●	▲	▲			
Attributes of plane figures	●	●	●	●	●	▲	▲
Classifying and sorting	●	●	●	●	●	●	●
Sides, corners, and square corners	●	●	●	●	▲	▲	▲
Parts and wholes	●	●	●	●	●	●	●
Geometric patterns—color and shape	●	●	●	▲	▲	▲	▲
Tessellations, tangrams, and pentominoes		●	●	●	●	●	●
Subdividing and combining		●	●	●	●	●	●
PLANE FIGURES AND SPATIAL SENSE							
Congruence—same size and shape		●	●	●	●	●	●
Line symmetry		●	●	●	●	●	●
Point symmetry						●	●
Orientations	▲	▲	▲	▲	▲	▲	▲
Similarity					●	●	●
Symbols for congruence						●	●
Identify and name polygons					●	●	▲
Classify polygons					●	●	▲
Regular polygons						●	●
Angles as corners				●	●	▲	▲
Drawing angles				●	●	●	●
Rays					●	●	●
Right angles				●	●	●	●
Greater than or less than a right angle (90°)				●	●	▲	▲
Obtuse and acute angles						●	●
Angles greater than a straight angle (180°)						●	●
Estimating angle measures						●	●
Measure angles using a protractor						●	●
Lines and line segments				●	●	●	●
Intersecting or crossing lines				●	●	●	●
Perpendicular lines and segments					●	●	●
Use letters and symbols to name segments, lines, and angles						●	●
Parallel lines and segments				●	●	●	●
Sides, angles, and diagonals of polygons					●	●	●
Circles—radius, diameter, and chord				●	●	●	●
Circumference					●	●	●
TRANSFORMATIONS							
Translations (slides)	●	●	●	●	●	●	●
Reflections (flips)		●	●	●	●	●	●
Rotations (turns)	●	●	●	●	●	●	●
Other transformations		▲	▲	▲	▲	▲	▲
Constructions—using a compass to draw arcs							●

KEY Teach and Apply ● Practice and Apply ▲

In Level 3...

Geometry

SOLID FIGURES

Basic figures—rectangular prism (box), sphere (ball), cube, and cone 248, 249
Classifying and sorting by shape 248, 249, 268, 269
Modeling solids 248, 251
Faces of solids related to plane figures 248, 249
Prisms and pyramids 248, 249
Spheres and cylinders 248, 249
Visualization 250, 251
Views 248–249
Subdividing and combining 250, 251, 294
Faces, edges, and vertices 248, 249
Readiness for volume 250, 251, 294

BASIC FIGURES

Exploring paths 32, 33, 94, 95, 113, 179, 183, 262, 263, 369
The basic figures—square, rectangle, triangle, and circle 7, 107, 226–229, 240–243, 275, 308, 309
Pattern block shapes 235, 272, 273
Classify plane figures 226–229, 240, 241, 268, 269
Attributes of plane figures 228, 229, 242, 243
Modeling on geoboard 238, 239
Modeling on dot paper or grid paper 226, 227, 229, 231–233, 239–241, 259, 269
Sides and corners 229, 238, 239
Square corners 236, 237, 239
Parts and wholes 272, 273
Geometric patterns—color and shape 6, 7, 24, 49, 63, 128, 129, 183, 212, 219, 226–229, 231–235, 237, 247, 253, 256, 257, 259, 268, 269, 300, 301
Tessellations, tangrams, and pentominoes 226, 227, 238, 239
Subdividing and combining 7, 226, 227, 258–261
Readiness for perimeter and area 258–261, 308, 309

PLANE FIGURES AND SPATIAL SENSE

Congruence—same size and shape 238, 239
Line symmetry 240, 241, 243, 246, 247, 257, 263, 268, 269
Orientations 179, 232–235, 237, 238, 263
Angles as corners 236, 237
Drawing angles 236, 237
Right angles 236, 237
Greater than or less than a right angle 237
Lines 246, 252, 253
Intersecting or crossing lines 252, 253
Line segments 252, 253, 305, 307, 319
Parallel lines and segments 252, 253, 255
Circles—radius and diameter 242, 243, 257

TRANSFORMATIONS

Translations (slides) 228–235, 247, 269
Reflections (flips) 230–235, 239, 269
Rotations (turns) 232–235, 269
Half turns 232, 233
Paper folding or cutting 6, 7, 25, 63, 107, 229–233, 240, 241, 247, 257, 289, 339, 423

In the Program...

Measurement

	K	1	2	3	4	5	6
Measurement sense and comparisons	●	●	▲	▲	▲	▲	▲
Fractions and regions		●	●	●	●	●	●
Nonstandard units	●	●	●	●	▲	▲	▲
Selecting appropriate units or tools			●	●	●	●	●
Measuring using grids or squared paper				●	●	●	●
Measuring by computing with denominate numbers					●	●	●
Derived units						●	●
Indirect measurement—experiments			●	●	●	●	●
Scale drawings and maps				●	●	●	●
Similar figures					●	●	●
Relationship among metric units of mass, capacity, and volume				●	●	●	●
Rates—speeds and distances				●	●	●	●
ESTIMATING AND MEASURING LENGTH							
Customary units		●	●	●	●	●	●
Fractional units—precision				●	●	●	●
Metric units		●	●	●	●	▲	▲
Equivalent units			●	●	●	●	●
PERIMETER, AREA, VOLUME							
Perimeter readiness—distance around		●	●	▲			
Perimeter—adding lengths of sides			●	●	●	▲	▲
Formulas for perimeter						●	●
Circumference of a circle					●	●	●
Area readiness—counting squares and pattern blocks	●	●	●	▲	▲		
Finding areas by multiplying				●	●	●	●
Square units				●	●	●	●
Formulas for area						●	●
Estimating area—almost units				●	●	▲	▲
Relating perimeter and area						●	●
Surface area						●	●
Volume readiness—counting cubes				●	●	▲	▲
Cubic units					●	●	●
Using area or volume to compare and order			▲	▲	▲	▲	▲
Formulas for volume						●	●
CAPACITY, WEIGHT, MASS							
Customary units		●	●	●	●	▲	▲
Metric units		●	●	●	●	▲	▲
Equivalent units of capacity		●	●	●	●	▲	▲
Equivalent units of weight or mass				●	●	▲	▲

KEY Teach and Apply ● Practice and Apply ▲

In Level 3...

Measurement

Measurement sense (comparisons) 2, 3, 29, 33, 38, 39, 70, 76, 77, 90, 91, 94, 95, 103, 107, 126, 127, 133, 134–137, 148, 149, 162, 167, 168, 179, 182, 183, 201, 213, 218, 219, 261, 285, 292–295, 302, 303, 310–314, 316–339, 345, 368–371, 394, 395, 397, 398, 402, 403, 409, 427, 429–431
Fractions and regions 272–278, 284, 285
Nonstandard units 302–305, 317, 318
Selecting appropriate units 39, 310, 311, 313, 314, 319, 321, 325, 326
Selecting appropriate tools 303
Measuring using grids 258–261
Indirect measurement—experiments 70, 71, 313, 328, 329
Scale drawings and maps 32, 33, 94, 110, 113, 121, 129, 167, 179, 183, 199, 213, 254, 255, 262, 263, 339, 369
Relationship among metric units of capacity and volume 324, 325
Rates—speeds and distance 76, 77, 102, 103, 115, 148, 149, 219, 369, 370, 402, 403, 431

ESTIMATING AND MEASURING LENGTH

Inch, foot, yard 70, 304, 305, 308–311
Mile 310, 311
Fractional units—$\frac{1}{2}$ inch 306, 307
Centimeter, decimeter, meter 318–321
Kilometer 320, 321
Equivalent units 310, 311, 318–321

PERIMETER, AREA, VOLUME

Perimeter readiness—distance around 308, 309
Perimeter—adding lengths of sides 94, 95, 308, 309, 319, 321, 323
Area readiness—counting squares and pattern blocks 258–261
Square units 258–261
Finding area by multiplying 259
Estimating area—almost units 260, 261
Using area and volume to compare and order 259, 261, 325
Readiness for volume 250, 251

CAPACITY, WEIGHT, MASS

Customary units—cup, pint, quart, gallon 312, 313
Other units—fluid ounce 38, 39
Metric units—liter and milliliter 324, 325
Equivalent units 312, 313
Customary units—pound and ounce 107, 314, 326
Metric units—gram and kilogram 326
Equivalent units 314, 324, 325, 326

In the Program...

Measurement

TEMPERATURE

	K	1	2	3	4	5	6
Readiness—warmer, colder	●	●	●	▲	▲		
Temperature sense—seasons	●	●	▲	▲	▲		
Reading a thermometer			●	●	●	●	●
Degrees Fahrenheit			●	●	●	●	●
Degrees Celsius				●	●	●	●

Time and Money

TIME

	K	1	2	3	4	5	6
Concepts of time	●	●	●	▲	▲	▲	▲
Sequence events—yesterday, today, tomorrow	●		▲	▲	▲	▲	▲
Comparing durations—more time, less time	●	●	●	▲	▲	▲	▲
Calendar concepts and dates	●	●	●	●	●	▲	▲
Analog and digital clocks		●	●	●	●	▲	▲
Reading and writing times		●	●	●	●	▲	▲
Elapsed time			●	●	●	▲	▲
Counting by 5's to tell time		●	●	●	●	▲	▲
A.M. and P.M				●	●	▲	▲
Equivalent units—days, hours, minutes, seconds				●	●	▲	▲
Choosing appropriate unit				●	●	▲	▲
Time zones				●	●	●	●
Schedules			●	●	●	▲	▲
Rates—speeds					●	●	●
Time lines						●	●

MONEY

	K	1	2	3	4	5	6
Coins—penny, nickel, dime	●	●	●	▲	▲	▲	▲
Quarter		●	●	●	▲	▲	▲
Half-dollar and dollar			●	●	▲	▲	▲
Other bills				●	●	▲	▲
Writing amouts for collections of coins							
using cents sign		●	●	▲	▲	▲	▲
using the dollar sign and decimal point			●	●	●		
Modeling amounts	●	●	●	▲	▲	▲	▲
Comparing amounts	●	●	●	▲	▲	▲	▲
Equivalent amounts		●	●	●	●	▲	▲
Making change by counting or subtracting	●		●	●	●	▲	▲
Calculator activities					●	●	●
Estimating amounts—enough money	●	●	●	●	▲	▲	▲
Place value and money			●	●	●	▲	▲
Rounding money amounts					●	●	▲
Adding and subtracting money		●	●	●	●	▲	▲
Multiplying and dividing money				●	●	●	▲
Consumer applications	▲	▲	▲	▲	▲	▲	▲

KEY Teach and Apply ● Practice and Apply ▲

In Level 3...

Measurement

TEMPERATURE

Readiness—warmer, colder 136, 137
Temperature sense—seasons 330, 331, 403
Reading a thermometer—Fahrenheit and Celsius 330, 331

Time and Money

TIME

Concepts of time 2, 3, 12, 15, 21, 33, 40, 41, 54, 55, 63, 72–75, 104, 105, 113, 136, 179, 203, 213, 217, 292, 293, 303, 316, 317, 332–337, 397, 422, 423, 431
Comparing durations 40, 41, 333
Calendar concepts 3, 54, 98, 99, 203, 316, 317, 337
Time line 98, 99
Reading dates 36, 70, 219
Lunar and solar calendars 54
Analog and digital clocks 2, 3, 72–75, 332–335
Reading and writing times 72–75, 332, 333
Elapsed time 40, 41, 63, 113, 334, 335
Counting by 5's to tell time 72–75, 332–335
A.M. and P.M. 74–75, 113, 179, 292, 293, 332, 333, 431
Equivalent units—days, hours, minutes, seconds 203, 332, 333, 402, 403
Choosing appropriate unit 332, 333
Schedules 178, 179, 292, 293, 336
Speeds and distance 76, 77, 102, 103, 115, 148, 149, 219, 369, 370, 402, 403

MONEY

Coins—penny, nickel, dime, quarter, half-dollar 3, 7, 12, 64–67, 70, 71, 346, 347
Dollar and other bills 66, 67
Writing amounts for collections of coins and bills
- using cents sign 64, 65
- using dollar signs and decimal points 66, 67, 346, 347
- using words 66, 67

Modeling amounts 64–67
Comparing amounts 64–67, 255
Equivalent amounts 12, 64–67, 70, 71, 165, 177, 199, 257, 369, 371
Making change by counting or subtracting 19, 68–71, 183, 244, 323
Calculator activities 400, 401
Estimating amounts 3, 12, 64, 93, 383, 390, 400, 401
Place value and money 66, 67
Rounding money amounts 93
Adding and subtracting money 3, 19, 69–71, 91, 93, 95, 105, 111–113, 120, 121, 129, 161, 201
Multiplying money 177, 183, 400, 401
Consumer applications
- budgeting 120, 121
- currency exchange 392
- making purchases 3, 19, 68, 69, 93, 107, 112, 113, 129, 177, 183, 204, 217, 244, 323, 337, 369, 371, 399–401
- raising money 280, 408, 409, 436, 437
- shopping list 83

Pacing

These suggestions help you plan your whole year. They help you make your long-range plans in September — and help you modify them as needed during the year. A complete, practical book, **Daily Lesson Plans,** is available for Grade 3. Included are planning, organization, and additional pacing suggestions for the ***Regular, Multi-Age***, and ***Year-Round*** classroom.

CHAPTER 1 — Addition and Subtraction

Pacing 15 Days

Concepts/Skills	2–5, 8–11, 13A, 16–23, 26–31
Problem Solving/Application	6–7, 12, 12A, 14–15, 24–25, 32–33, 38–39
Assessment	13, 34–37, 35A–35B

CHAPTER 2 — Place Value, Money, and Time

Pacing 15 Days

Concepts/Skills	42–47, 50–51, 53A, 58–61, 64–69, 72–75
Problem Solving/Application	48–49, 52, 52A, 54–55, 62–63, 70–71, 76–77, 82–83
Estimation/Mental Math	56–57
Assessment	53, 78–81, 79A–79B

CHAPTER 3 — Addition and Subtraction

Pacing 14 Days

Concepts/Skills	86–91, 94–95, 97A, 100–105, 110–111
Problem Solving/Application	96, 96A, 98–99, 106–107, 112–115, 120–121
Estimation/Mental Math	92–93, 108–109
Assessment	97, 116–119, 117A–117B

CHAPTER 4 — Collecting and Organizing Data

Pacing 12 Days

Concepts/Skills	124–125, 130–137, 139A, 142–147
Problem Solving/Application	126–129, 138, 138A, 140–141, 148–149, 154–155
Assessment	139, 150–153, 151A–151B

CHAPTER 5 — Multiplication and Division to 5

Pacing 12 Days

Concepts/Skills	158–161, 164–167, 169A, 172–177, 180–181
Problem Solving/Application	162–163, 168, 168A, 170–171, 178–179, 182–183, 188–189
Assessment	169, 184–187, 185A–185B

CHAPTER 6 — Multiplication and Division to 9

Pacing 13 Days

Concepts/Skills	192–197, 200–203, 205A, 208–211, 214–217
Problem Solving/Application	198–199, 204, 204A, 206–207, 212–213, 218–219, 224–225
Assessment	205, 220–223, 221A–221B

CHAPTER 7 — Geometry

Pacing 15 Days

Concepts/Skills	228–233, 236–243, 245A, 248–255, 258–261
Problem Solving/Application	234–235, 244, 246–247, 256–257, 262–263, 268–269
Assessment	245, 264–267, 265A–265B

CHAPTER 8 — Fractions

Pacing 10 Days

Concepts/Skills	272–279, 281A, 284–287, 290–291
Problem Solving/Application	280, 280A, 282–283, 288–289, 292–295, 300–301
Estimation/Mental Math	284–285
Assessment	281, 296–297, 297A–298B, 298–299

CHAPTER 9 — Measurement and Time

Pacing 18 Days

Concepts/Skills	304–315, 315A, 318–321, 324–326, 327A, 328–335
Problem Solving/Application	314A, 316–317, 322–323, 326A, 327, 336–337, 338–339, 344–345
Assessment	315, 340–343, 341A–341B

CHAPTER 10 — Decimals

Pacing 10 Days

Concepts/Skills	348–353, 356–359, 361A, 364–367
Problem Solving/Application	354–355, 360, 360A, 362–363, 368–371, 376–377
Assessment	361, 372–375, 373A–373B

CHAPTER 11 — Multiplying by 1-Digit Numbers

Pacing 10 Days

Concepts/Skills	380–381, 386–387, 388–389, 391A, 394–395, 389–399, 400–401
Problem Solving/Application	384–385, 390, 390A, 392–393, 396–397, 402–403, 408–409
Estimation/Mental Math	382–383
Assessment	391, 404–405, 405A–405B, 406–407

CHAPTER 12 — Dividing by 1-Digit Numbers

Pacing 9 Days

Concepts/Skills	412–413, 414–415, 416–417, 418–419, 421A, 426–427, 428–429
Problem Solving/Application	420, 422–423, 430–431, 436–437
Estimation/Mental Math	424–425
Assessment	421, 432–433, 433A–433B, 434–435

Table of Contents

Volume 1

1 Addition and Subtraction

2 Place Value, Money, and Time

Table of Contents

Place Value, Money, and Time

chapter 2 continued

Addition and Subtraction

Collecting and Organizing Data

Multiplication and Division to 5

Table of Contents

Multiplication and Division to 5

chapter 5 continued

CHAPTER 6 Multiplication and Division to 9

Volume 2

Chapter 7 Geometry

Chapter 8 Fractions

Table of Contents

Fractions

chapter 8 continued

CHAPTER 9 Measurement and Time

Decimals

Multiplying by 1-Digit Numbers

Table of Contents

Multiplying by 1-Digit Numbers

chapter 11 continued

Dividing by 1-Digit Numbers

Geometry

Chapter Overview

Rationale

Chapter Pacing: 15 days

- The focus of this chapter is to help students make observations and discoveries about points, lines, surfaces, and solids.
- By listing, comparing, identifying, classifying, and representing the physical characteristics of geometric attributes, students gain the background for understanding the concepts in this chapter.
- The Math World feature presents geometric lines in architecture.
- In the Investigation, students use lines of symmetery to design a mask.

See **Daily Lesson Plans**, Chapter Management at a Glance, pp. 68–69; Suggested Weekly Plan, pp. 70–71.

Problem Solving

This chapter focuses on the Look for a Pattern strategy for problem solving. It also reinforces strategies students have learned earlier and encourages them to choose and apply their own strategies.

Assessment

- The Chapter Introduction allows you to assess whether students have a firm grasp of geometric shapes and their characteristics.
- Recognize that students' sketches are not expected to be entirely accurate, especially at first, but they should reflect students' understanding that a picture is a model.
- Use the Midchapter Review, the Chapter Test, and the Cumulative Review to assess students' needs for reinforcement or reteaching.

Reading Strategies

- Teach the Self-Question reading strategy minilesson on TAB p. 226J. Then, use the following as opportunities to reinforce the strategy.

  Preparing for Tests, TE pp. 226G–226H

  Problem Solving, Lessons 7.2–7.4, 7.6–7.10, 7.14, 7.16, and 7.17.
- Use the SAE reading support for Lesson 7.4.

Vocabulary

- Introduce students to the chapter with vocabulary minilesson, TAB p. 226J.
- Planning Guide, p. 226C, lists vocabulary for each lesson in the chapter.
- Use the SAE vocabulary support in Lessons 7.1, 7.5–7.8, and 7.10–7.15.

Meeting Individual Needs

Students Acquiring English

Provide practice identifying and classifying geometric figures and concepts.

- Encourage students to keep a notebook containing drawings of geometric vocabulary.
- Use geoboards to construct and classify geometric shapes.
- Help students identify and create patterns; show how to use them to solve problems.

See also **Language Connections** for additional support.

Extra Support

Students may have difficulty representing geometric figures.

- Allow students to explore geometry with manipulatives and concrete objects.
- Encourage students to look back carefully at problems when they are trying to draw a picture.
- To clarify students' understanding of geometry, use the Analyzing Errors strategies on pp. 265A–265B.
- Use the Geometry Workshop's Alternate Approach activity.

Challenge

Students may benefit from this extension activity.

- Ask students, Do all diagonal lines divide a figure into halves?

Multi-Age Classroom

The chart below shows the chapters in books for levels 2 and 4 that can be used in conjunction with this chapter.

2	3	4
Chapter 7 *Geometry and Fractions*	**Chapter 7** *Geometry*	**Chapter 5** *Geometry*

See **Daily Lesson Plans**, Multi-Age Classroom Concept and Skill Development, pp. 4–5.

Chapter Bibliography

Key

Multicultural	★	*Social Studies*	
Science/Health		*Music*	
Literature		*Art*	

Technology

Students can explore geometry with the electronic tools in *Unlocking Geometry 3–6*. The manipulatives provide an enjoyable, flexible environment in which to experiment.

Internet: Education Place
http://www.eduplace.com

Visit the **Mathematics Center** in *Houghton Mifflin Education Place* to find activities, projects, games, and links to other valuable Internet sites.

Ultimate Writing & Creativity Center

Students can use the *Ultimate Writing & Creativity Center*® for all their writing and publishing activities. The software is available from The Learning Company® in Macintosh and Windows formats.

Leapfrog Math includes mathematics skills and concepts for grades 3–6. Each grade is contained on a single CD-ROM. The software is available from Meridian Creative Group, a Division of Larson Texts, Inc.

Test, Practice, Management Program

Use the *Test, Practice, Management Program* to create, administer, and score tests as well as generate practice sets. Questions are correlated to Lesson Objectives.

Graphers Sunburst Communications, Inc.®

Using the friendly tools in *Graphers,* children can easily manipulate data that can be counted or sorted and represent their data in a table or with six types of graphs.

Books for Students

Houghton Mifflin Mathematics Bookshelf

Sam Goes Trucking
Henry Horenstein,
Houghton Mifflin, 1989.
Sam spends the day with his father, a truck driver. A range of activities allows students to explore volume and three-dimensional shapes, and to practice addition, multiplication, and division.

Bedtime for Frances
Russell Hoban,
HarperCollins Publishers, 1996.
Frances is having trouble sleeping because of strange noises and menacing shapes that fill her room after dark. Recommended for introducing visualization.

'Round and Around
James Skofield,
HarperCollins Publishers, 1993.
A little boy and his father go for a walk and find circular shapes in everything they see and do.

★ **Shapes, Shapes, Shapes**
Tana Hoban,
Mulberry Books, 1996.
This vivid collection of urban photographs depicts a wide variety of plane figures in real-life objects. Use as a discussion-starter.

On My Beach There Are Many Pebbles
Leo Lionni,
William Morrow, 1995.
Descriptions of the many different shapes and characteristics of pebbles found at the beach.

Masks
Clare Beaton,
Warwick Press, 1990.
Photographs explain how to make carnival masks, animal masks, and knight masks from simple materials.

First Step Math: Boxes
Gareth Stevens,
Gareth Stevens Publishing, 1994.
Students study three-dimensional objects as they read about collecting, sorting, and measuring in interesting ways. Recommended for connecting mathematics topics.

Books for Families

The World of Shapes: Squares and Cubes
Raintree Steck-Vaughn, 1994.
A part of a series about shapes, this volume includes activities and information to help children connect squares and cubes with everyday objects.

Halloween
Frank Daniel,
Simon and Schuster Children's Books, 1993.
This holiday book shows families how Halloween can take shape with triangles.

Thanksgiving
Frank Daniel,
Aladdin Books: Macmillan, 1993.
Like its Halloween counterpart, this book presents semicircles in a Thanksgiving theme.

Reference Books for Teachers

Teaching Mathematics Through Children's Art
Doug Williams,
Heinemann, 1995.
This fresh approach to mathematics teaching uses creative arts and crafts activities that allow teachers to integrate mathematics and art.

Math by All Means, Geometry, Grade 3
Cheryl Rectanus,
Marilyn Burns Education Associates, 1994.
Using concrete materials and children's literature, this book includes suggestions for providing experiences in logic, numbers, and measurement with two- and three-dimensional figures.

Learning and Teaching Geometry, K–12
Mary Montgomery Lindquist, ed.,
NCTM, 1987.
This reference book provides teachers with perspectives on teaching geometry and continues with the use of geometry in problem solving, applications, activities, and with other areas of mathematics.

Planning Guide

	TE Pages	Lesson Objectives	Lesson Vocabulary	NCTM Standards
7.1 Slides	*228–229*	To identify slides	slide	Geometry and Spatial Sense, Patterns and Functions, Communication, Reasoning
7.2 Flips	*230–231*	To identify flips	flip	Geometry and Spatial Sense, Patterns and Functions, Communication, Reasoning
7.3 Turns	*232–233*	To identify turns	half turn	Geometry and Spatial Sense, Patterns and Functions, Communication, Reasoning
7.4 Look for a Pattern	*234–235*	To use the Look for a Pattern strategy to solve problems		Problem Solving, Communication, Reasoning, Connections, Patterns and Functions
7.5 Angles	*236–237*	To identify angles as greater than, less than, or equal to a right angle	angle square corner right angle	Whole Number Concepts, Geometry and Spatial Sense, Reasoning, Connections
7.6 Congruence	*238–239*	To identify slide, flip, and half turn images as congruent	congruent	Geometry and Spatial Sense, Connections, Communication, Reasoning, Patterns and Functions
7.7 Symmetry	*240–241*	To identify one or more lines of symmetry in plane figures	line of symmetry	Geometry and Spatial Sense, Connections, Problem Solving, Communication, Reasoning
7.8 Circles	*242–243*	To identify the center of a circle and the diameter; to find a line of symmetry	center diameter	Measurement, Geometry and Spatial Sense, Communication, Connections, Reasoning
7.9 Choose a Computation Method	*244*	To decide whether to use mental math or paper and pencil to solve problems		Problem Solving, Reasoning, Whole Number Computation, Communication
7.10 Solids	*248–249*	To identify solids by name; to identify the number of edges, faces, and corners	triangular prism	Whole Number Concepts, Geometry and Spatial Sense, Communication, Reasoning
7.11 Visualization	*250–251*	To decide if solids are the same shape and size; to identify hidden cubes in a drawing of a solid		Whole Number Concepts, Geometry and Spatial Sense, Communication, Reasoning
7.12 Lines and Line Segments	*252–253*	To identify parallel and intersecting lines and line segments	line line segment parallel	Geometry and Spatial Sense, Communication, Connections, Reasoning, Problem Solving
7.13 Ordered Pairs	*254–255*	To use ordered pairs to locate points on a grid	ordered pair	Whole Number Concepts, Connections, Reasoning, Geometry and Spatial Sense
7.14 Using Look for a Pattern and Other Srategies	*256–257*	To use Look for a Pattern and other strategies to solve problems		Problem Solving, Communication, Reasoning, Connections, Patterns and Functions
7.15 Area	*258–259*	To investigate and determine the area of a polygon by counting half and whole square units	area	Geometry and Spatial Sense, Measurement, Communication, Problem Solving
7.16 Area of Irregular Figures	*260–261*	To determine the area of irregular 2-dimensional figures by counting and estimating		Estimation, Geometry and Spatial Sense, Problem Solving, Measurement, Communication
7.17 Using Strategies	*262–263*	To use different strategies to solve problems		Problem Solving, Communication, Reasoning, Connections, Estimation, Measurement

Chapter Objectives

7A To use slides, flips, and half turns to move figures
7B To identify and draw congruent figures
7C To identify and classify angles, lines, and line segments
7D To identify one or more lines of symmetry in plane figures
7E To identify and classify geometric solids
7F To use ordered pairs to locate regions on a grid and on a map
7G To find the area of plane figures by counting
7H To use Look for a Pattern and other strategies to solve problems

Chapter Objectives	math center	State Requirements
7A	• *Slip and Slide,* Activity Card 37	
7A	• *It's a Draw,* Activity Card 38	
7A	• *It's Your Turn,* Activity Card 39; Gameboard 7	
7H	• *Teacher for a Day!,* Project Card 7	
7C	• *Angle Hunt,* How-To Card 22; Gameboard 5	
7A, 7B	• *It's a Draw,* Activity Card 38	
7D	• *Mirror Images,* Activity Card 40	
7D	• *Circle Pictures,* Activity Card 41	
7H	• *Teacher for a Day!,* Project Card 7	
7E	• *Sorting Solids,* How-To Card 23; Workmat 2	
7B	• *Building Blocks,* How-To Card 24; Gameboard 5	
7C	• *Parallel Pick,* Activity Card 42; Gameboard 2	
7F	• *Map It Out,* How-To Card 25; Gameboard 6	
7H	• *Teacher for a Day!,* Project Card 7	
7G	• *Area Antics,* Activity Card 43	
7G	• *Fantastic Areas,* How-To Card 26; Gameboard 7	
7H	• *Teacher for a Day!,* Project Card 7	

Integrating Reading Strategies

- Teach/review the Self-Question strategy using TAB p. 226J.
- Encourage students to practice the strategy in Lessons 7.2–7.4, 7.6–7.10, 7.14, 7.16, and 7.17.

Technology

Unlocking Geometry 3–6

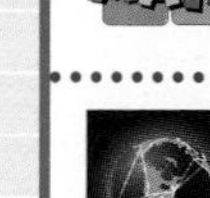
Internet: Education Place
http://www.eduplace.com
Houghton Mifflin Education Place
Mathematics Center

Test, Practice, Management Program

Special Lessons

pp. 226–227
Chapter Introduction
The Introduction links prior knowledge of shapes and solids to geometry.

pp. 262–263

Students apply problem solving strategies in the context of the plan for Lincoln Park.

pp. 246–247
Math World
Geometry Around the World
Use this feature to show students how geometry is used all over the world.

pp. 268–269
Investigation
Mask Task!
Students use their knowledge of geometric shapes and symmetry to make masks for a story they will act out.

Assessment

Use the following assessment tools to help assess individual needs.

- Midchapter Review, p. 245
- Chapter Test, pp. 264–265
- Cumulative Review, pp. 266–267

Geometry Workshop

Patterns and Structures of Geometric Figures

Alternate Approach

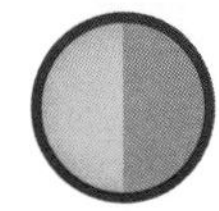

Use with page 250.

30 minutes

Drawing in 3-D

Objective To draw 3-dimensional figures

Management teacher directed; pairs
Materials grid transparency; 1-inch grid paper for each pair of students
Modality *visual*

Activity

- Tell students that by following directions they will draw simple 3-dimensional figures.
- Using an overhead projector, model how to draw a cube. Begin by drawing a square 2″ by 2″on a grid transparency. Demonstrate how to find the center of that square and mark it with a dark dot.

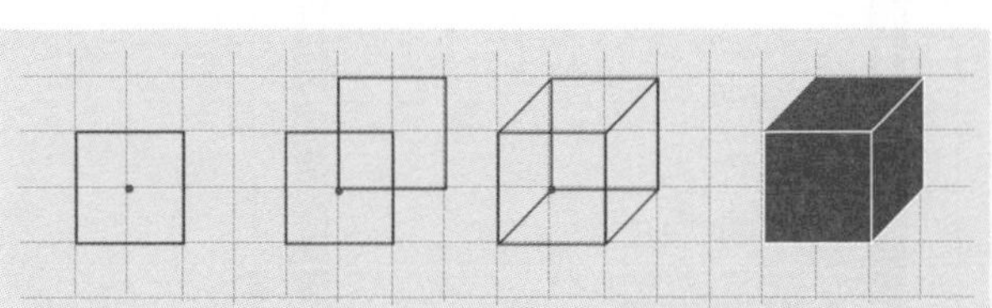

- Use the dark dot as the lower left corner of the next square you draw.
- Connect the congruent corners of the two squares to form a cube. To make it look like a solid cube, erase the lines that would be hidden. Continue similarly until you have drawn a figure that is 1 × 2 × 1.
- Invite pairs of students to draw 3-dimensional rectangular solids using these techniques. They can draw 3 × 2 × 1 and 4 × 5 × 1 figures.

Meeting Individual Needs: *Modify*

Challenge Give students figures formed by connecting cubes and ask them to draw the figures.

Challenge

Use with page 226.

20 minutes

Don't Lift Your Pencil!

Objective To investigate patterns and structures of familiar figures

Management teacher monitored; individuals
Modality *visual*

Activity

- On the board, draw the figure shown, being sure to lift your chalk to connect corners.
- Explain that this figure can be drawn without lifting the chalk from the board and without retracing any lines. Challenge students to find a solution. Answers will vary. One possible answer is shown.

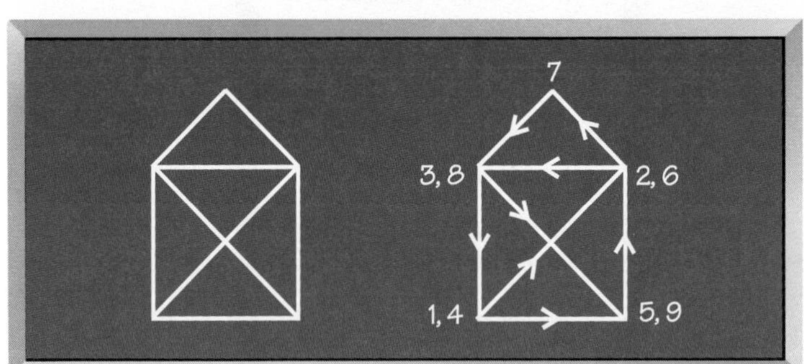

- Let those students who figure out possible answers share them with you. Encourage them not to give away the secret to the other students.

Meeting Individual Needs: *Modify*

Students Acquiring English Some students may not know that *retrace* means "draw over again." Use the term often while demonstrating.

Game

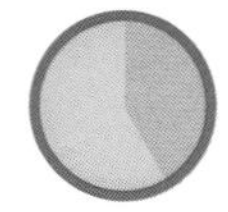

Use with page 240.

25 minutes

Jump to One

Objectives To identify patterns; to use patterns to solve problems

Management teacher monitored; individuals
Materials for each pair: 24 cubes, 1-inch grid paper, and a marker
Modality *visual/kinesthetic*

Activity

- Tell students that the object of this checkers-like game is to jump and remove all the pieces so that only one remains. A player wins by removing the most cubes.
- Distribute grid paper, cubes, and markers. Ask students to create the gameboard shown.
- Have students place a cube in every square except the center. As in checkers, a jump is made by having one piece move over another into an open space. The piece that is jumped is removed from the board.
- Decide in advance if diagonal jumps will be allowed.
- Students should play the game several times so that they develop a strategy for removing the most pieces.
- You may want to set this up as a cooperative game with pairs taking turns and discussing strategies as they play.

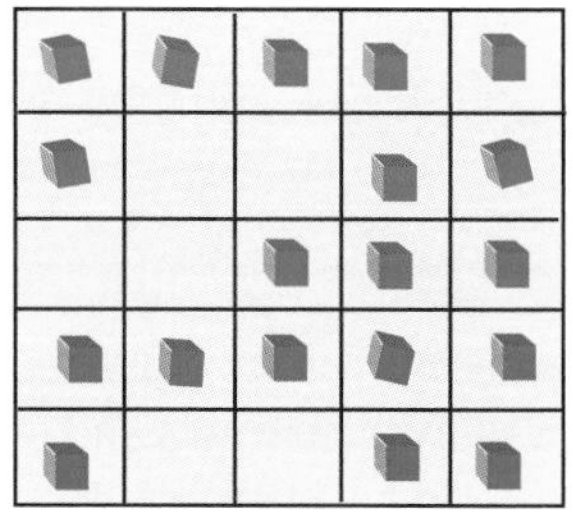

Meeting Individual Needs: *Modify*

Students Acquiring English Some students may not be familiar with the term *jump* as it is used here. Demonstrate the move in several directions including diagonal, repeating the term each time.

Challenge Add a sixth row and column to the gameboard, and have students play with 11 more cubes. Additionally, you can have students try to make their last jump so that the only piece left is in the center square on the gameboard.

Technology

Use with Lesson 7.2

Objective To demonstrate flips, slides, and turns with geometric shapes

Management teacher monitored; pairs
Materials *MathKeys*: *Unlocking Geometry 3–6*, Level 3, Activity 8: Flip, Slide, and Turn; hands-on triangles and grid paper
Modality *visual*

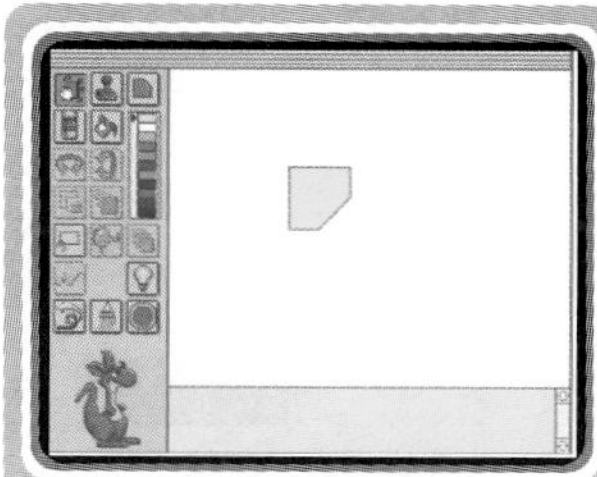

Activity

45 minutes

- Review and practice how to flip, slide, and turn triangles on grid paper. Make sure students can discern the differences among these moves before continuing.
- Distribute copies of Activity 8 Master. Ask students to open *MathKeys*, open the Shape Blocks Nonmagnetic Mat, and select Grid Lines from the Options menu. Then have students open the Shape palette and select the square with the missing corner.
- Invite students to stamp a shape on the mat and to practice flipping the shape using the Vertical Flip and Horizontal Flip buttons.
- Students can begin the activity on their worksheets. They draw a prediction of what the shape will look like when it is flipped, slid, and turned. Then they check their predictions using the electronic mat.
- Encourage students who make incorrect predictions to try the activity again.
- Remind students to print their screens.

Meeting Individual Needs: *Modify*

Extra Support Suggest that students draw arrows to show the directions of their flips, slides, and turns.

Challenge Students can try the activity again using some of the other shapes on the Shape palette.

Preparing for Tests

To develop students' test-taking strategies, model the following types of assessment items found in this program.

Standardized Tests

Draw the following figure on the board. Write the question and answer choices below it.

What does the set of figures show? c

(A) flip
(B) slide
(C) half turn
(D) none of the above

See also Standardized Testing: New Formats, Chapter 7.

Standardized tests usually require that students select the correct answer from a group of possible answers. In this problem, students identify the relationship between two geometric figures.

Strategy

- What do you need to find out? the relationship between the figures
- How do figures look when they show a slide? facing the same way, same size and shape a flip? They are mirror images.
- How about half turns? One seems like an upside-down version of the other.

Open-Ended Questions

Write the following problem on the board.

Make a diagram to help you solve the problem.

You are helping set up for a family party. You place 3 square tables in a row. Each one is 6 feet long. You leave 2 feet between each table. How long is the row of tables from end to end?

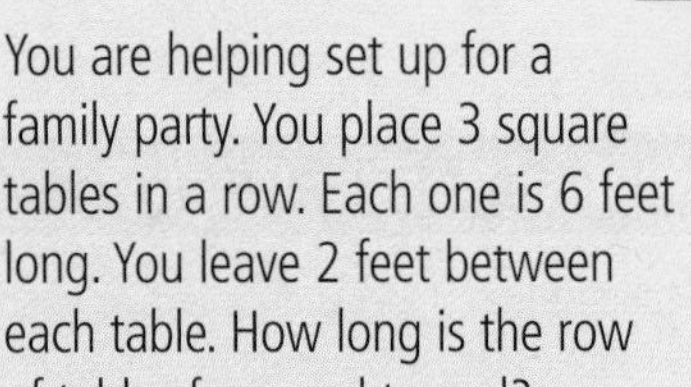

See also Assessments, Chapter 7.

Open-ended questions can be answered in more than one way; they allow students to use a variety of concepts and processes. This problem allows students to draw a diagram to help visualize a problem.

Strategy

- What are you asked to do? find the length of a row of tables
- How can a diagram help you? It makes it easier to see what the numbers mean.
- What addition sentence will solve this problem? 6 + 2 + 6 + 2 + 6
- Why don't you add 2 the last time? 2 stands for feet of space between tables, not space on the ends

Preparing for Tests

Reading Strategies for Test-Taking

Self-Question: As I read, I ask myself questions, then read on or reread to find the answers.

Performance Tasks

Draw the following map and grid on the board.

Use the map and grid to answer the three questions and follow the two directions.

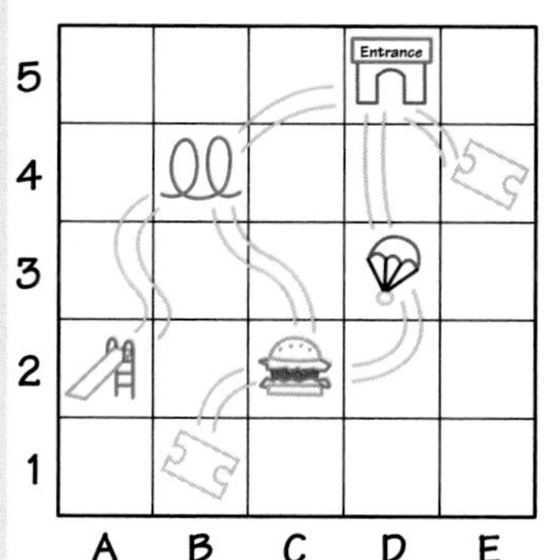

Where is the Parachute Drop?

Which attraction is found in A4?

Where is Loop the Loop?

Add a Carousel in E1.

Copy the map and grid. Add another attraction. Label the attraction. Write a sentence to tell what you added and where it is located.

Performance assessments engage students in meaningful tasks that permit the teacher to observe their working procedures as well as the results they obtain. This problem requires students to make a plan to solve a problem.

Strategy

- What does the problem ask you to do?
  use the grid to answer the questions
- What comes first in the ordered pair?
  the letter

  How do you know?
  because I know to read across the bottom first and then move up the side

Check that students explain directions precisely, and give correct answers, using conventional ordered pairs for map locations.

Test-Taking Tips

- Picture in your mind what is going on in the problem.

See also Performance Assessments, **Chapter 7.**

Additional Assessment Resources

Test, Practice, Management Program

Use the *Test, Practice, Management Program* to create, administer, and score tests as well as generate practice sets. Questions are correlated to the Lesson Objectives.

TAB Chapter 7

Math Center

To meet individual needs, use the following resources from the Math Center. You may first wish to model activities for the whole class in order to demonstrate the rules for games and introduce procedures for independent tasks.

Gameboards

Gameboard 7
Use with Lessons 7.3 and 7.16.

Gameboard 5
Use with Lessons 7.5 and 7.11.

Gameboard 2
Use with Lesson 7.12.

Gameboard 6
Use with Lesson 7.13.

Activity Cards

37 ***Slip and Slide*** Use with Lesson 7.1.

38 ***It's a Draw*** Use with Lessons 7.2 and 7.6.

39 ***It's Your Turn*** Use with Lesson 7.3.

40 ***Mirror Images*** Use with Lesson 7.7.

41 ***Circle Pictures*** Use with Lesson 7.8.

42 ***Parallel Pick*** Use with Lesson 7.12.

43 ***Area Antics*** Use with Lesson 7.15.

Project Card

7 ***Teacher for a Day!*** Use with Lessons 7.4, 7.9, 7.14, and 7.17.

Workmats

Workmat 2
Use with Lesson 7.10.

How-To Cards

22 ***Angle Hunt*** Use with Lesson 7.5.

23 ***Sorting Solids*** Use with Lesson 7.10.

24 ***Building Blocks*** Use with Lesson 7.11.

25 ***Map It Out*** Use with Lesson 7.13.

26 ***Fantastic Areas*** Use with Lesson 7.16.

Managing the Math Center

Selecting group members When assigning groups to work in the Math Center, you must decide whether group members should be randomly chosen or chosen with intention. If you have little information about the class, forming groups at random may be the best approach at first. Then, take note as groups work together to determine which students display behaviors that lead to productive groups.

Vocabulary and Reading Strategies

Use these minilessons to strengthen vocabulary and reading skills.

Vocabulary

- angle
- right angle
- square corner

Linking Prior Knowledge and Vocabulary

Ask students to identify square corners in the classroom. Give each student a color tile or card. Ask students to describe the corners of the tile or card. Explain that these can be called **square corners** or **right angles**. All squares and rectangles have square corners. Encourage students to draw, cut out, or identify shapes (for instance, among pattern clocks) that have right angles.

Graphic Organizer: Diagram

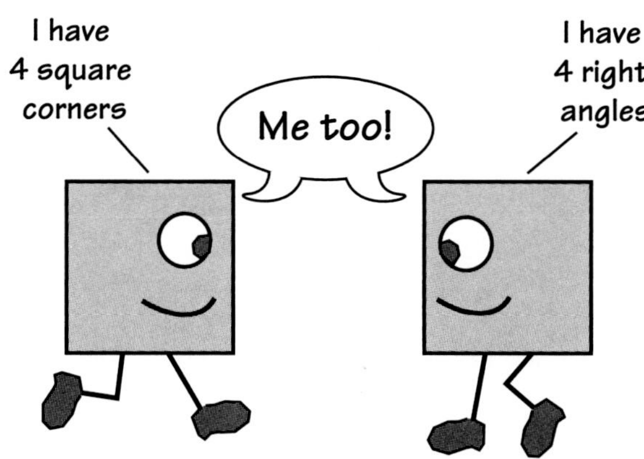

I have 4 square corners
Me too!
I have 4 right angles

Reading Strategies

Strategy: Self-Question

Explain to students that asking questions as they read can help them find important information. Explain that the Self-Question reading strategy can also help them solve problems.

Use the Thinking Aloud box and the graphic organizer to demonstrate how students can use the Self-Question reading strategy with the following example.

How is a circle different from a square, a triangle, and a rectangle?

Lesson 7.8, p. 243, Problem 7

Thinking Aloud

- How can I compare the figures? I need to find similarities and differences.
- The square, triangle, and rectangle have sides and corners. Does the circle have sides or corners? What does a circle have that the other figures don't have?
- I use the answers to my questions to find the answer. Then I check my work to see if my answer is complete.

Graphic Organizer: Diagram

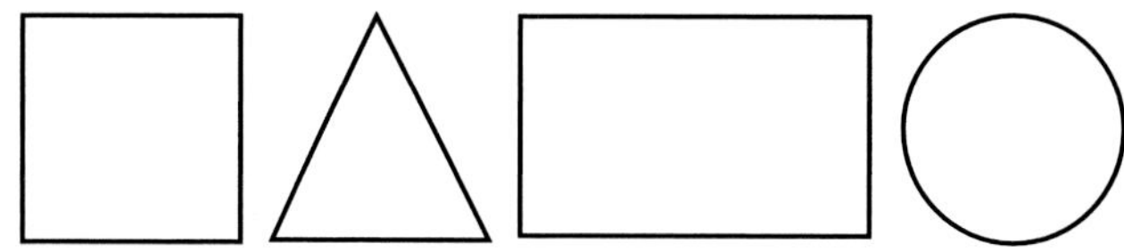

Ask students to share the questions they asked themselves and show how they found the answer.

The reading strategies presented on this page can also apply to Lessons 7.2, 7.3, 7.4, 7.6, 7.7, 7.8, 7.9, 7.10, 7.14, 7.16, and 7.17.

Objective
To use prior knowledge to explore geometry

Lesson Planning

Optional Resources
- Math Language Connections
- MATHKEYS *Unlocking Geometry 3–6*

Every Day Counts Calendar Math
Geometric Patterns
To emphasize the importance of careful observation in learning geometry concepts, use the Every Day Calendar Pattern activities in Every Day Counts, level 3.

Assessing Prior Knowledge

Try This! Use this as a prechapter activity in the classroom or as a homework assignment.

Build confidence in working with geometric figures and recognizing patterns with this construction activity in which children find all the possible ways to connect 3, 4, and 5 squares.

This activity
- assesses prior knowledge of pattern recognition and pattern building.

Geometry

Try This!

Find different ways to connect 3, 4, and 5 squares. Each square needs to share a side with another square.

What You'll Need

color tiles, graph paper, pencil

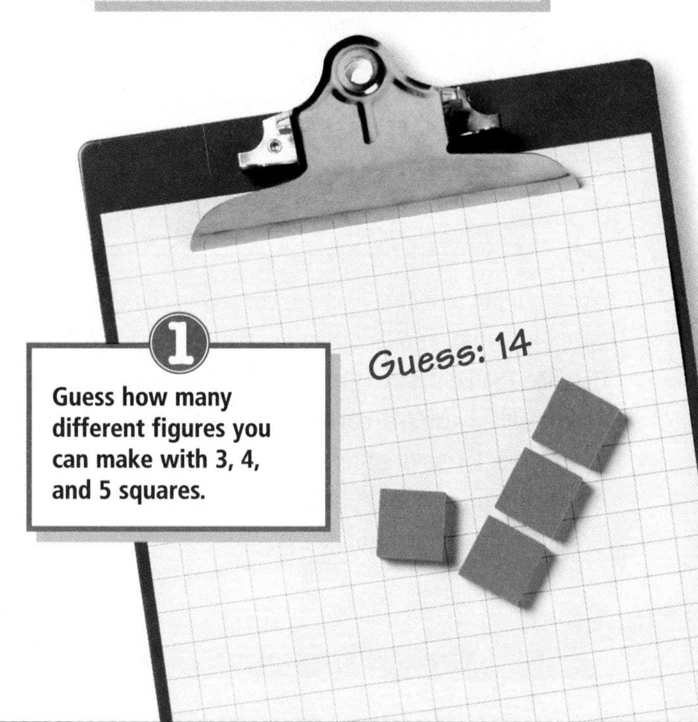

1 **Guess how many different figures you can make with 3, 4, and 5 squares.**

Chapter Connections

Math Links

Throughout this chapter, students will build on prior knowledge as they develop concepts and skills for geometry.

- **Patterns and Relationships** Lessons 7.1, 7.2, 7.3, 7.4, 7.5, 7.6, 7.7, 7.11, 7.12, 7.14, 7.15, 7.17
- **Estimation** Lessons 7.9, 7.16
- **Geometry** Lessons 7.1, 7.2, 7.3, 7.5, 7.6, 7.7, 7.8, 7.10, 7.11, 7.12, 7.13, 7.15, 7.16
- **Measurement** Lessons 7.5, 7.15, 7.16
- **Algebraic Reasoning** Lessons 7.13, 7.15

Real *World*

Social Studies

- **Lesson 7.1, p. 228**
  Guatemalan Designs Students find patterns in Guatemalan designs.
- **Lesson 7.12, p. 252**
  Tartans of Scotland Students examine the tartan plaid patterns of Scotland.
- **Lesson 7.13, p. 254**
  Philadelphia A map of Philadelphia, Pennsylvania, provides practice with ordered pairs.
- **Lesson 7.17, p. 262**
  Lincoln Park Students use problem solving on a plan for a park in Washington, D.C.

Science

- **Lesson 7.16, p. 260**
  Dinosaur Footprints Students estimate the area of dinosaur footprints.

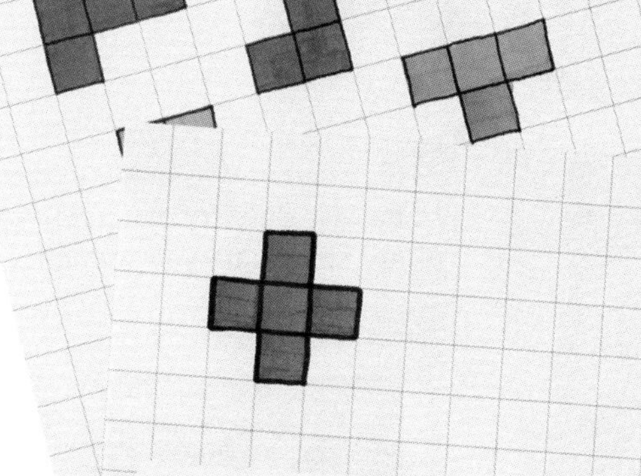

2 Now, model or draw as many different figures as you can. Check to be sure that all the squares share at least one side. Move figures around to be sure they do not match.

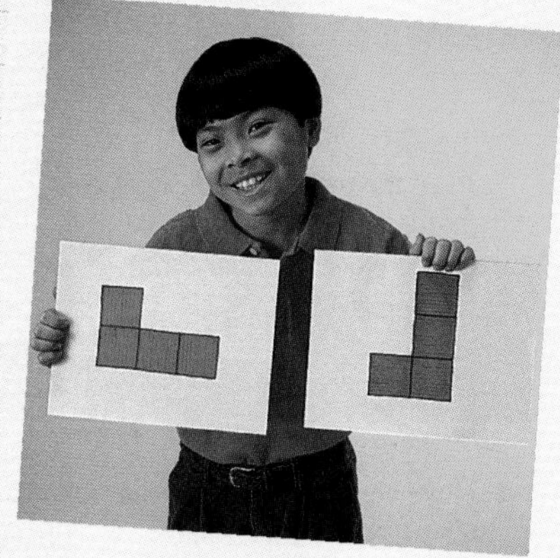

3 How many different figures did you make? Was your guess close? Compare your results with the results of others.

How did you check to see whether your figures were alike or not?

What other shapes do you know besides squares?

Ready to Go!

227

Assessing Prior Knowledge *(continued)*

- acts as a base for a discussion of using patterns as a strategy for finding possibilities.
- provides a foundation for transformational geometry as children move squares in different ways to change a figure.

Meeting Individual Needs

If students have trouble finding patterns or moving shapes to create new figures, start with Quick Help. They may also need a brief teacher-guided review.

Quick Help Explain that in this activity students will use what they already know. Provide graph paper and colored tiles for work with squares. Tangram pieces can be used to practice slides, flips, and turns with other shapes.

Guided Review Refer to:

- **Lesson 2.4** Problem Solving Strategy: Look for a Pattern, Student Book, p. 48
- **Basic Facts** Review Basic Facts, TE p. 245A

Vocabulary Power

Use this graphic organizer to review vocabulary used in geometry.

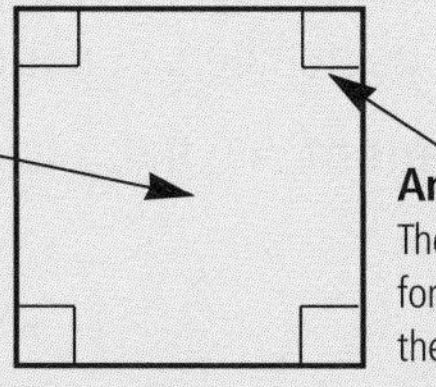
Square
A figure with four equal sides and four equal angles
Angle
The sides of a square form right angles at the corners

Vocabulary One tool for working with figures is a T-square. Have students look up *T-square* in the dictionary. Discuss ways it might be used and why its name contains the word *square*.

Investigation Preview

Mask Task!

Making a mask and working with classmates to create a story for the masks will reinforce students' understanding of symmetry and help them apply flips and turns in a creative art project. See the Investigation, TE pp. 268–269.

What They'll Do

- On graph paper, draw a line of symmetry and use flips and turns to create the pattern for the mask
- Use the pattern to make the actual mask
- Act out a story using the masks

Technology

MATHKEYS

Students will enjoy making patterns with ***MathKeys:*** *Unlocking Geometry 3–6*. Suggest they use either the Pattern Blocks Magnetic Mat or the Shape Blocks Magnetic Mat. Both mats provide square blocks. Students can make and revise many patterns with ease. With the shape blocks, students can paint their blocks different colors. They can also print their work.

Activity

Planning at a Glance

Objective To identify slides

Materials pattern blocks, tracing paper, ruler, scissors, dot paper (TR3), Recording Sheet (Practice 7.1)

Optional Resources

- Reteach 7.1; Enrichment 7.1
- Daily Cumul. Review, p. 84
- Math Center: Act. Card 37
- Every Day Counts
- **TAB**, TE pp. 226E–226F, 226J
- **Problem of the Day**, 84, p. 42; Flip Chart, p. 42b

MATHKEYS *Unlocking Geometry 3–6*, Level 3, Activity 9

Students Acquiring English

Have students tell what a *slide* is. Trace and cut out figures to demonstrate the terms *trace* and *slide*. Help students determine if each mention of the word *slide* or *slides* in this lesson refers to the action or the thing.

Problem of the Day

On the day of her party, Nora's doorbell rang 6 times. One guest was at the door on the first ring. On each ring after that, Nora welcomed two more guests than she did the ring before. How many guests came to Nora's party? 36 guests

Slides

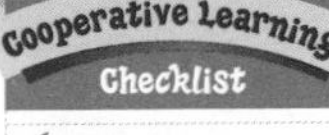

Cooperative Learning Checklist
- ☑ Work alone.
- ☑ Work with a partner.
- ☑ Work with a group.

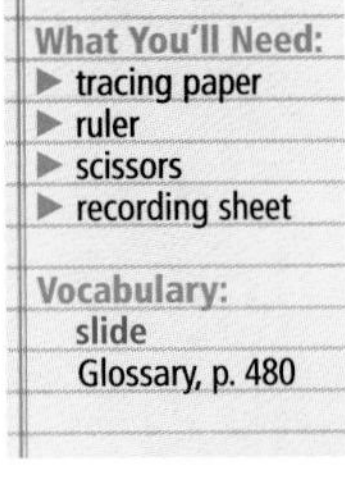

What You'll Need:
- tracing paper
- ruler
- scissors
- recording sheet

Vocabulary:
slide
Glossary, p. 480

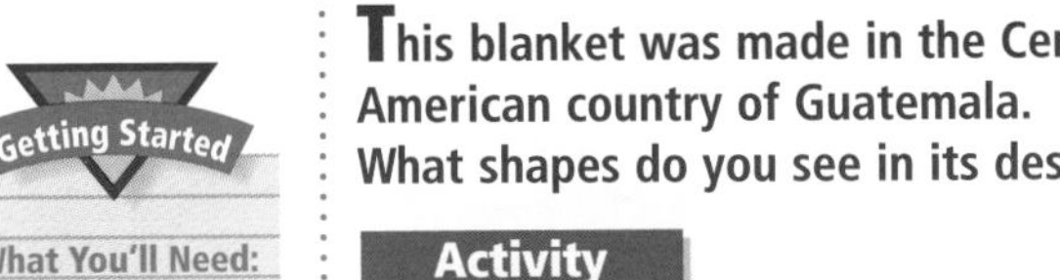

This blanket was made in the Central American country of Guatemala. What shapes do you see in its design?

Activity

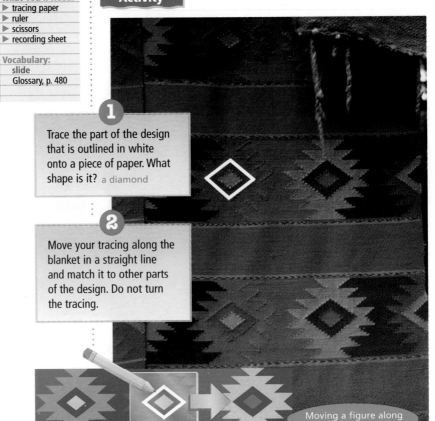

1. Trace the part of the design that is outlined in white onto a piece of paper. What shape is it? a diamond

2. Move your tracing along the blanket in a straight line and match it to other parts of the design. Do not turn the tracing.

Moving a figure along a line is a **slide**.

1 Introduce

Explore **Have students fold a piece of paper into fourths. Have them place a pattern block triangle with one side along one of the creases, trace around it, and then create slides by moving the block along the creases and tracing around it again.**

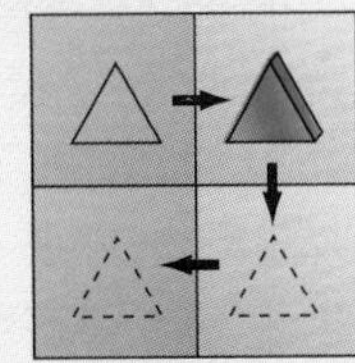

Teach: Activity

Emphasize this point:

- Slides are identical figures in different positions.

2 Develop

Show What You Know!

Have students describe the math meaning of the word *slide* and relate it to slide images.

Common Error Some students may confuse flipped or turned figures with slides. Remind them that slides are identical to the original figures but in different locations. See also Analyzing Errors, TE pp. 265A and 265B.

3 Summarize

- Reemphasize that slides have the same shape and size and face the same direction as the original.
- Point out how figures in geometric patterns follow rules just as numbers in patterns do.

Ongoing Assessment Are these figures slides? Yes.

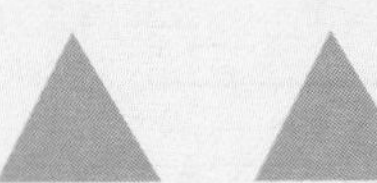

Math Journal: *Communicating*

Students' definitions of slides should describe slide figures as identical in shape, size, and the direction they face, but different in their location.

Draw a line on a piece of paper. Cut a corner off another piece to make a triangle. Put a side of the triangle on the line. Trace the triangle. Move it along the line. Trace it again. Compare the tracings. What do you notice? The triangles are all the same.

Show What You Know!

Answer the question.

1. **Critical Thinking** What happens to a figure in a slide? Tell what changes and what stays the same. The position changes, but size, shape, and direction stay the same.

Does the picture show a slide? Write *yes* or *no*.

2. yes
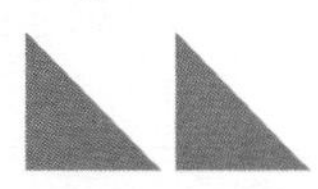

3. no
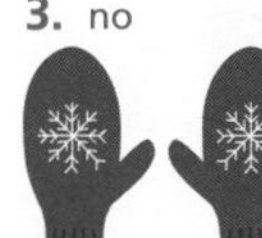

4. yes

5. no

Draw another figure to show a slide. Use your recording sheet or dot paper. Check students' work. See Additional Answers.

6. 7. 8. 9.

10. **Create Your Own** Use your recording sheet or dot paper. Make your own slides. Draw the figures. Check students' work.

Students' definitions should mention that a slide involves a change in position without a change in size, shape, or direction.

Use your own words to tell what a slide is.

Meeting Individual Needs

Extra Support

Drawing Slides ***(visual)*** Have pairs of students work with a drawing program at the computer to create their own slides. Show them how to draw a figure, then copy it and move it to a new location. Discuss the motion of sliding.

Alternate Approach

- Reteach Worksheet 7.1
- **TAB** See TE pp. 226E–226F.

MathZones

Understanding Geometry

Students Acquiring English

See **Language Connections**, Ch. 7.

Challenge

Can slides be on top of each other? Why or why not? No, they must be in different locations.

Practice

Math Center Use Activity Card 37, *Slip and Slide*, to have students practice identifying figures and their congruent slide images.

Challenge Use Activity Card 37 and have students continue as described in Now Try This!

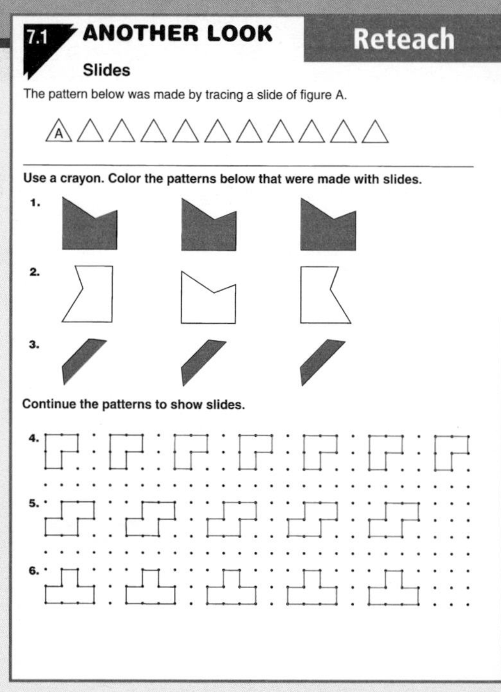

7.1 ANOTHER LOOK — Reteach

Slides

The pattern below was made by tracing a slide of figure A.

Use a crayon. Color the patterns below that were made with slides.

1.

2.

3.

Continue the patterns to show slides.

4.

5.

6.

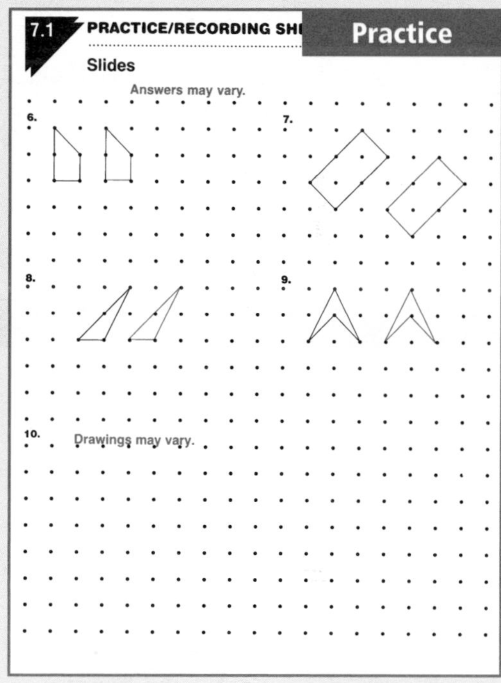

7.1 PRACTICE/RECORDING SHEET — Practice

Slides

Answers may vary.

6. 7.

8. 9.

10. Drawings may vary.

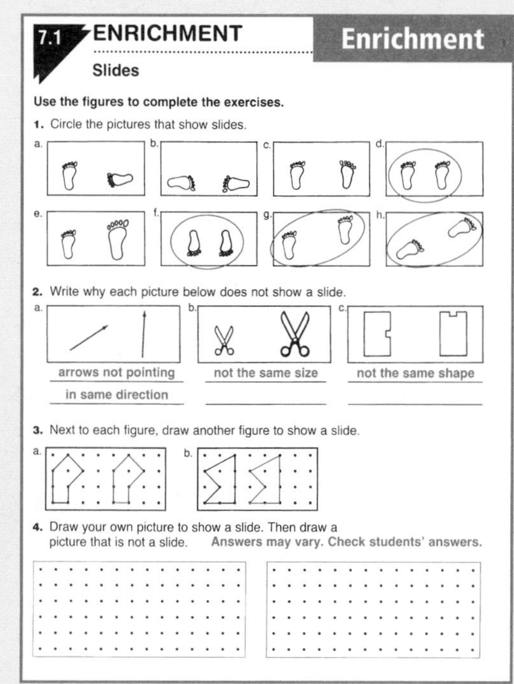

7.1 ENRICHMENT — Enrichment

Slides

Use the figures to complete the exercises.

1. Circle the pictures that show slides.

a. b. c. d. e. f. g. h.

2. Write why each picture below does not show a slide.

a. arrows not pointing in same direction
b. not the same size
c. not the same shape

3. Next to each figure, draw another figure to show a slide.

a. b.

4. Draw your own picture to show a slide. Then draw a picture that is not a slide. Answers may vary. Check students' answers.

Activity

Planning at a Glance

Objective To identify flips

Materials tracing paper, dot paper (TR3), Recording Sheet (Practice 7.2)

Optional Resources

- Reteach 7.2; Enrichment 7.2
- Daily Cumul. Review, p. 85
- Math Center: Act. Card 38
- Every Day Counts
- **TAB**, TE pp. 226E–226F, 226J
- **Problem of the Day**, 85, p. 43; Flip Chart, p. 43a

MATHKEYS *Unlocking Geometry 3–6,* Level 3, Activity 8

Students Acquiring English

Flip a coin to demonstrate the meaning of the verb *flip,* explaining that *flip* can mean an action. Ask students to demonstrate flipping something.

Problem of the Day

Which capital letters look exactly the same in a mirror?
A, H, I, M, O, T, U, V, W, X, Y

Flips

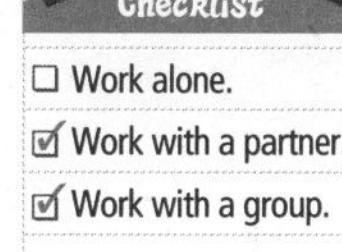

Cooperative Learning Checklist

- ☐ Work alone.
- ☑ Work with a partner.
- ☑ Work with a group.

In this activity you will learn about another way to move a figure.

Getting Started

What You'll Need:
- tracing paper
- recording sheet

Vocabulary:
flip
Glossary, p. 480

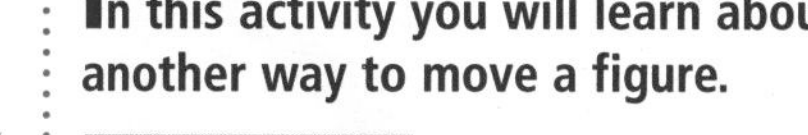

Activity

1 Fold a sheet of tracing paper in half. Then unfold it. Draw around your hand on one side of the paper. Your thumb should be toward the fold.

2 Fold the paper in half again. Make sure that the blank side is on top. Trace your drawing through the paper.

3 Unfold the paper. The two thumbs should face each other. The picture you have made shows a **flip**.

230 Chapter 7

1 Introduce

Prior Knowledge **Ask, How are slide figures the same? How are they different?** Their shape, size, and the direction they are facing are the same; their location is different.

Teach: Activity

Emphasize these points:

- A flip is when figures of the same shape and size face in opposite directions.
- Flip images are usually in different positions.

Modeling Model step 3 of the activity. Ask:

- Are your two hands flip images? Yes.
- How can you tell besides folding the tracings? by placing my hands side by side to show that they match

2 Develop

Show What You Know!
Have students describe the math meaning of the word *flip* and relate it to flip images.

Common Error Some students may confuse slides or turned figures with flips. Using two identical figures, turn one of the figures over to demonstrate that a flip is the back of the original. See also Analyzing Errors, TE pp. 265A and 265B.

Using Reading Strategies Help students to use the Self-Question strategy as they read the Critical Thinking questions. Ask, How can asking questions help you understand the exercises? See TE p. 226J.

3 Summarize

- Reemphasize that flip images have the same shape and size, but face opposite directions.
- Point out that a flip is the original figure turned over.

Ongoing Assessment Do these figures show a flip? No, they show a slide.

Math Journal: *Communicating*

Ask students to compare slides and flips, using drawings to illustrate their description. They should note that both slide and flip images have the same shape and size, but flip images face in different directions.

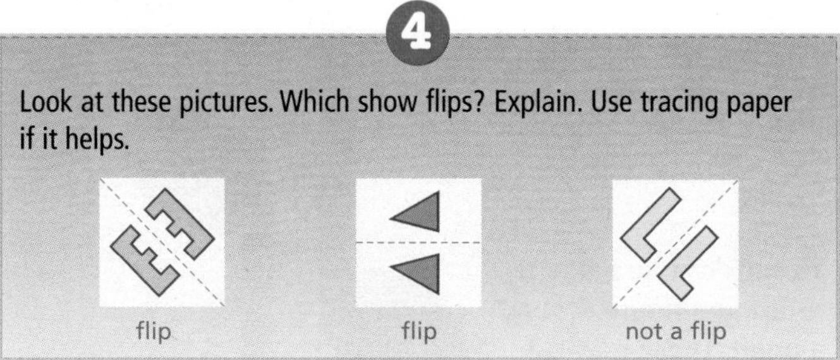

Look at these pictures. Which show flips? Explain. Use tracing paper if it helps.

Show What You Know!

Does the figure show a flip? Write *yes* or *no*.

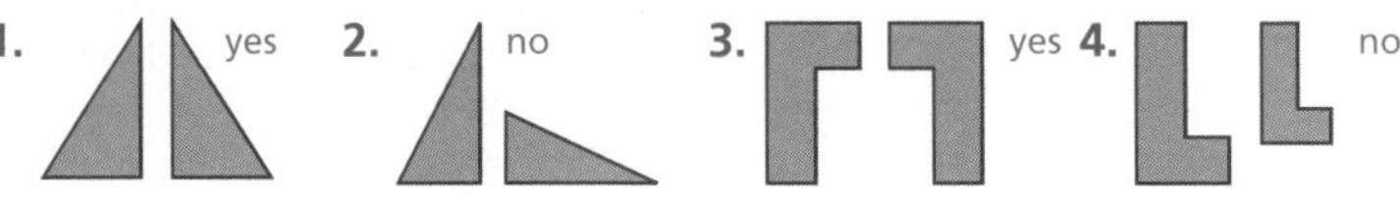

5. **Critical Thinking** What stays the same when you flip a figure? size and shape

Continue the pattern. Use your recording sheet or dot paper.

6.

7.

8.

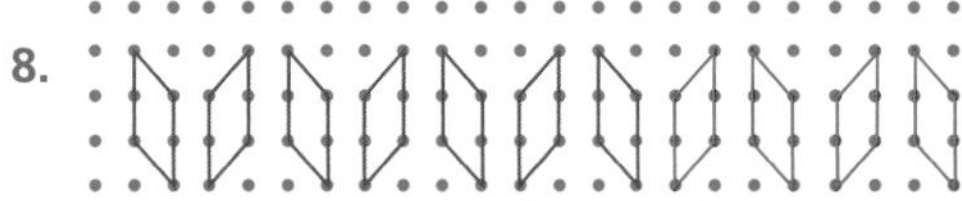

9. **Critical Thinking** If you look at your name in a mirror, will you see a flip or a slide? Try it to check your prediction. flip

Draw another figure to show a flip. Use your recording sheet or dot paper. See Additional Answers.

Meeting Individual Needs

Extra Support

Drawing Flips *(visual)* Have pairs of students work with a drawing program on the computer to create their own flips. Show them how to draw a figure, then flip it and move it to a new location. Discuss the motion of flipping.

Alternate Approach

- Reteach Worksheet 7.2
- **TAB** See TE pp. 226E–226F.
- MATHKEYS Invite students to explore flips and turns on the computer. They move shapes on an electronic mat in *Unlocking Geometry 3–6*, Level 3, Activity 8.

MathZones
Understanding Geometry

Students Acquiring English

See Language Connections, Ch. 7.

Challenge

What numbers from 0 to 9 look the same when flipped? 0 and 8, and possibly 1, depending on how it is written

Practice

Math Center Use Activity Card 38, *It's a Draw*, to have students practice identifying flips.

Challenge Use Activity Card 38 and have students continue as described in Now Try This!

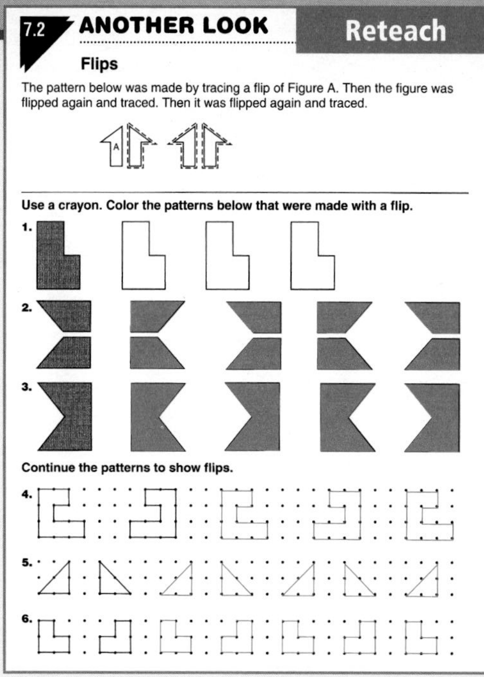

7.2 ANOTHER LOOK — Reteach

Flips

The pattern below was made by tracing a flip of Figure A. Then the figure was flipped again and traced. Then it was flipped again and traced.

Use a crayon. Color the patterns below that were made with a flip.

1.
2.
3.

Continue the patterns to show flips.

4.
5.
6.

7.2 PRACTICE/RECORDING SHEET — Practice

Flips

4. a.
b.
c.

8. a. b. c. d.

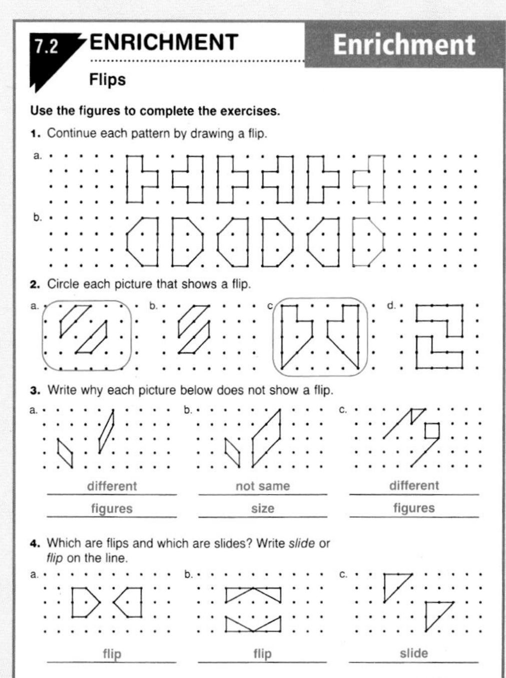

7.2 ENRICHMENT — Enrichment

Flips

Use the figures to complete the exercises.

1. Continue each pattern by drawing a flip.

a.
b.

2. Circle each picture that shows a flip.

a. b. c. d.

3. Write why each picture below does not show a flip.

a. different figures
b. not same size
c. different figures

4. Which are flips and which are slides? Write *slide* or *flip* on the line.

a. flip
b. flip
c. slide

Activity

Planning at a Glance

Objective To identify turns

Materials paper, tracing paper, scissors, crayons, glue, dot paper (TR3), Recording Sheet (Practice 7.3)

Optional Resources

- Reteach 7.3; Enrichment 7.3
- Daily Cumul. Review, p. 86
- Math Center: Act. Card 39
- Every Day Counts
- **TAB**, TE pp. 226E–226F, 226J
- **Problem of the Day**, 86, p. 43; Flip Chart, p. 43b

MATHKEYS *Unlocking Geometry 3–6,* Level 3, Activity 5

Students Acquiring English

Help brainstorm a list of things that turn, such as the hands of a clock or doorknobs. Show how to give an object a half turn, followed by a full turn. Then ask students to tell you when the second hand of a clock has made a half turn and a full turn from a given position.

Problem of the Day

How many triangles can you find in this figure?

8 triangles

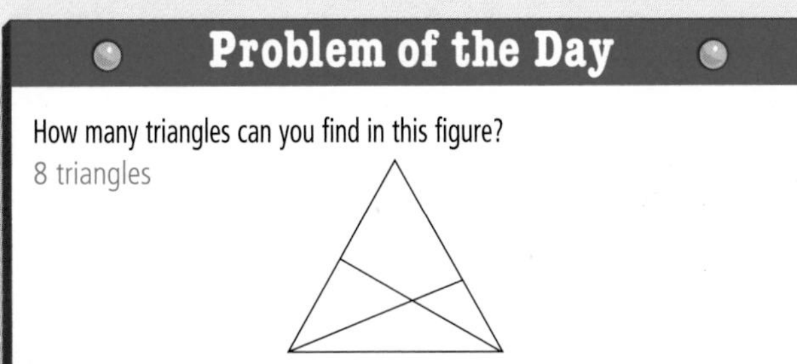

Turns

A turn can be made by rotating a figure around a point. These musical notes show a **half turn**.

Getting Started

What You'll Need:
- paper
- tracing paper
- scissors
- crayons
- glue
- recording sheet

Vocabulary:
half turn
Glossary, p. 480

Cooperative Learning Checklist
- ☑ Work alone.
- ☑ Work with a partner.
- ☑ Work with a group.

Activity

1. Fold a piece of tracing paper in half. Trace the note on the right. Cut out the tracing to make two notes.

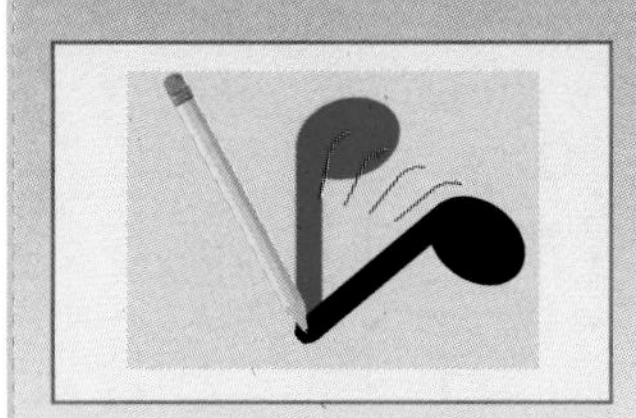

2. Paste one note at the top of a piece of paper with the stem down. Put the other note over the pasted one so it matches.

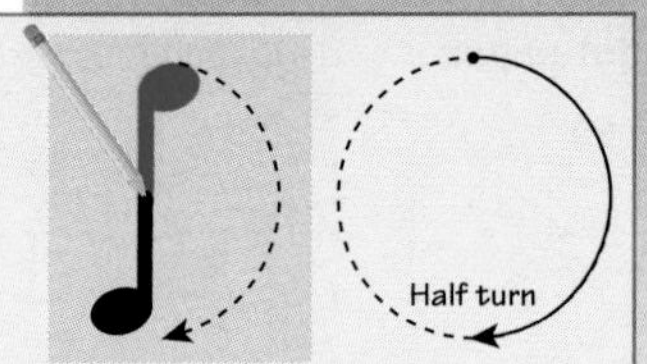

3. Put a pencil point on a corner of the bottom of the stem. With your other hand, turn the note.

4. Turn the note until the stem points up. Paste the note down. Your figure shows a half turn.

Half turn

232 Chapter 7

1 Introduce

Prior Knowledge **Ask, What is the difference between slides and flips?** Slides face the same direction; flips face the opposite direction.

Teach: Activity

Emphasize these points:

- Half turns are figures with the same shape and size as the original, but they are turned halfway around.
- Half turns are identical figures one of which is turned upside down (not *over).*

Modeling Model steps 3 and 4 of the activity. Ask:

- Move the note a half turn. What happens? The note is now upside down.

2 Develop

Show What You Know!
Have students turn the letters in their name by using cutouts.

Common Error Some students may not understand the movement of a half turn. Demonstrate the movement using real objects in the classroom (such as a book or pair of scissors) and ask students to describe what happens. See also Analyzing Errors, TE pp. 265A and 265B.

Using Reading Strategies Encourage students to use the Self-Question strategy as they read direction lines. Ask, How does asking questions help you understand the instructions? See TE p. 226J.

3 Summarize

- Reemphasize that half turns have the same shape and size as the original but have been turned halfway around a circle.
- Point out how turns follow rules just as numbers in patterns follow rules.

Ongoing Assessment Do these figures show a slide or a half turn? Half turn

Math Journal: ***Communicating***

Ask students to compare flips and turns, using drawings to illustrate their descriptions. They should note that both flips and turns have the same shape and size as the original, but flips are "turned over" and half turns are "turned around" or upside down.

Show What You Know!

1. Does the turned note have the same shape and size as the first note? How do you know? Yes. I traced the first note to make the second.
2. How is the turned note different from the first note? The stem faces the opposite direction and the round part is on the other side.
3. Cut six *L*-shaped figures from your recording sheet or trace these. Paste them on a piece of paper to show half turns. Check students' work.

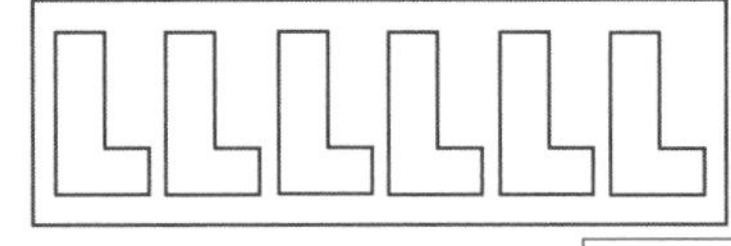

3.

Use your recording sheet or dot paper. Draw one more figure to continue the pattern. See Additional Answers.

4.
5.

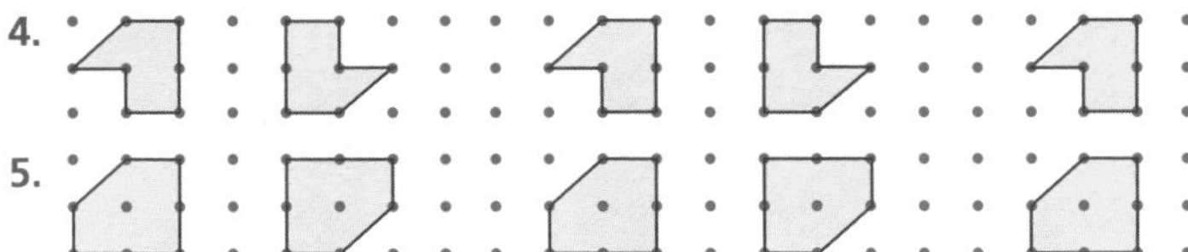

Look at the figure below. On your recording sheet or dot paper, draw another figure that shows a half turn. See Additional Answers.

6. 7. 8. 9.

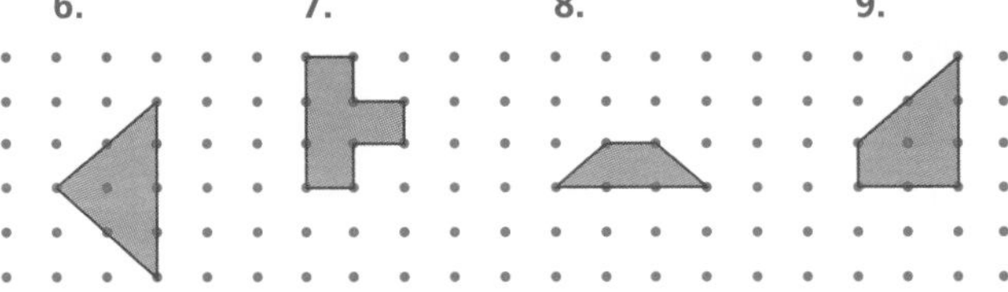

10. **Critical Thinking** How would the note in Step 1 on page 232 look if you made a full turn? Draw a picture. the same as the original

11. **Create Your Own** Create a pattern that shows slides, flips, and turns. Give your pattern to a classmate to continue. Designs will vary but should show slides, flips, and turns.

Mixed Review

Write the answer.

12. 56 ÷ 8 7 13. 4 × 9 36 14. 30 ÷ 6 5 15. 2 × 8 16 16. 5 × 0 0

17. 6 × 4 24 18. 7 ÷ 7 1 19. 72 ÷ 8 9 20. 4 × 4 16 21. 64 ÷ 8 8

Meeting Individual Needs

Extra Support

Repeating Patterns *(kinesthetic)* Invite students to create a repeating pattern using slides, flips, and turns with any shape they like. They may draw their patterns on grid paper using a cutout, or use a drawing program at the computer. Students may trade their designs and challenge classmates to identify the slides, flips, and turns.

Alternate Approach

- Reteach Worksheet 7.3
- **TAB** See TE pp. 226E–226F.

MathZones
Understanding Geometry

Students Acquiring English

See Language Connections, Ch. 7.

Challenge

If a clock shows 3:00, what time would it show if you flipped the hands? 9:00 If you rotated the hands one half turn? about 9:30

Practice

Math Center Use Activity Card 39, *It's Your Turn,* to have students practice identifying figures and their turn images.

Challenge Use Activity Card 39 and have students continue as described in Now Try This!

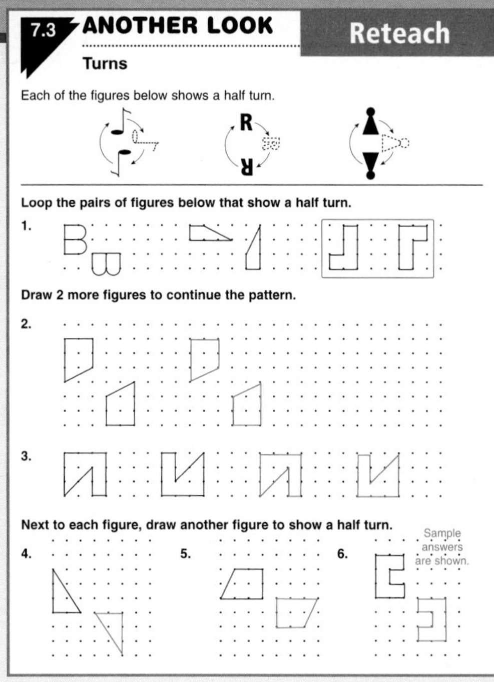

7.3 ANOTHER LOOK — Reteach

Turns

Each of the figures below shows a half turn.

Loop the pairs of figures below that show a half turn.

1.

Draw 2 more figures to continue the pattern.

2.

3.

Next to each figure, draw another figure to show a half turn. Sample answers are shown.

4. 5. 6.

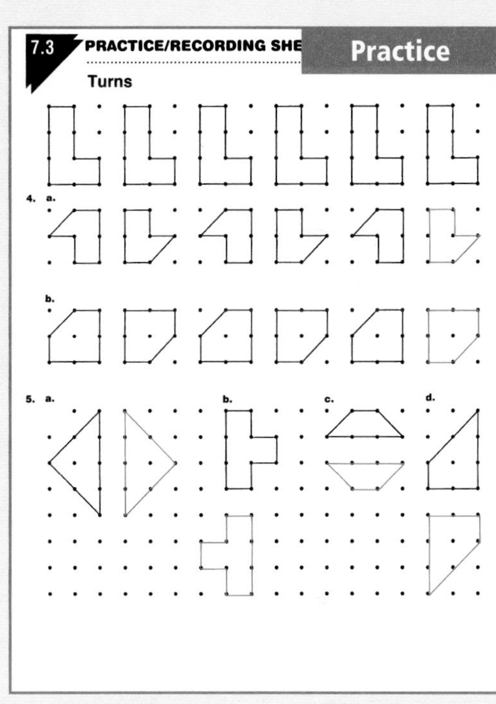

7.3 PRACTICE/RECORDING SHEET — Practice

Turns

4. a.

b.

5. a. b. c. d.

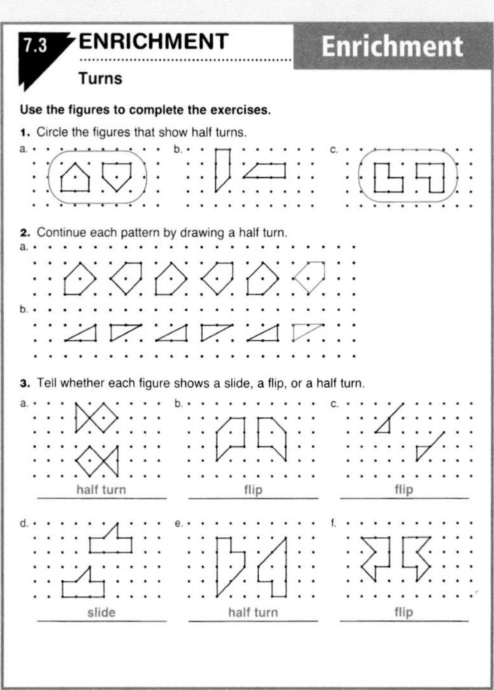

7.3 ENRICHMENT — Enrichment

Turns

Use the figures to complete the exercises.

1. Circle the figures that show half turns.

a. b. c.

2. Continue each pattern by drawing a half turn.

a.

b.

3. Tell whether each figure shows a slide, a flip, or a half turn.

a. half turn b. flip c. flip

d. slide e. half turn f. flip

Problem Solving

Planning at a Glance

Objective To use the Look for a Pattern strategy to solve problems

Materials pattern blocks

Optional Resources

- Reteach 7.4; Practice 7.4; Enrichment 7.4
- Daily Cumul. Review, p. 87
- Math Center: Project Card 7
- Every Day Counts
- **TAB**, TE pp. 226E–226F, 226J
- **Problem of the Day**, 87, p. 44; Flip Chart, p. 44a

MATHKEYS *Unlocking Geometry 3–6,* Level 3, Activity 6

Students Acquiring English

Building Reading Strategies Encourage students to work in pairs to solve problems. Guide them through the following steps: Read the problem; ask about words you don't know; find the question; find the information you need to answer the question; choose a strategy; solve the problem. Have students share strategies and solutions.

Problem of the Day

In a go-cart show, carts roll past the judges along a 65-foot ramp. Rules say that there must be a 10-foot space between go-carts as they pass the judges. If a go-cart is 5 feet long, how many go-carts fit on the ramp at once?

5 go-carts

Problem Solving

Look for a Pattern

Getting Started

What You'll Need:
▶ pattern blocks

You have 5 pieces of wrapping paper. Which 2 could be part of one large sheet of paper?

You can look for a pattern to help you solve some kinds of problems.

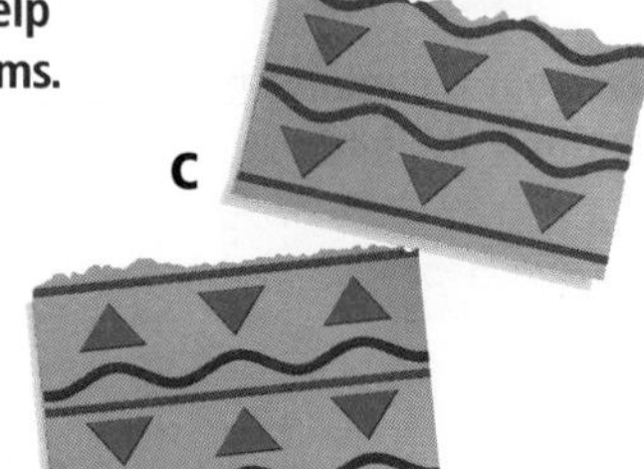

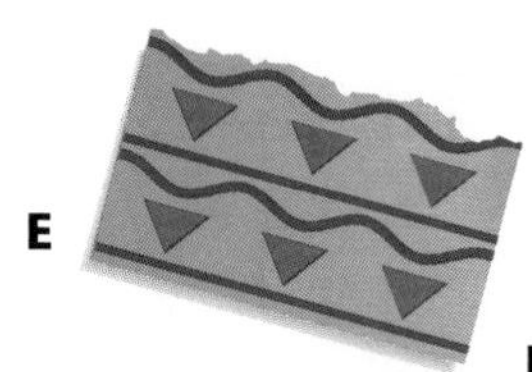

Here's A Way! Use Look for a Pattern to solve.

1. **Understand**
   - What problem are you solving? which 2 sheets could be part of one large sheet of paper
   - Would the larger sheet have many different patterns? No. It would have one design.
2. **Plan**
   - Why would comparing patterns help you to solve this problem? Answers will vary. Possible answer: I can look for a pattern on one piece and see if it occurs on other pieces.
3. **Try It**
   - Do any of the pieces show the same pattern? Yes; pieces C and E.
   - Do you see any slides, flips, or turns? Answers will vary.
4. **Look Back**
   - Pieces C and E are part of the same larger picture. How did looking for a pattern help you to solve this problem? Answers will vary.

1 Introduce

Build Understanding **Draw a pattern of circle, square, circle, square, circle, on the chalkboard. Then ask, what comes next?** a square

Teach: **Here's A Way!**
After working through the problem, ask:

- What pattern did you see?
- How does studying the pattern help solve the problem? You see which pieces fit the pattern and which ones do not.

Modeling Show students how to form patterns by using cutouts.

2 Develop

Show What You Know!
Call on students to discuss the pattern they see in problem 1 and to explain how they recognized the pattern.

Work It Out!

- Discuss with students what strategies they used to solve each problem. For example, they may Draw a Picture to solve problems 3 and 5, and use Make a Table or Guess and Check for problem 4.
- Have students discuss their reasoning for questions 8 and 9.

Using Reading Strategies Guide students to use the Self-Question strategy as they read the problems. Ask, How can asking questions help you find patterns? See TE p. 226J.

3 Summarize

- Discuss situations in which you might make a pattern to solve a problem.

Ongoing Assessment How does a pattern help you solve a problem? Answers will vary. One possible response: If there is a pattern, you can see what you need to do to add to or complete it.

Math Journal: *Communicating*

Why is guessing and checking better than looking for a pattern for problem 4? One possible answer: Because the coins don't necessarily follow a pattern.

Show What You Know!

Use Look for a Pattern to help you finish the problem.

1. Draw the next 3 figures.

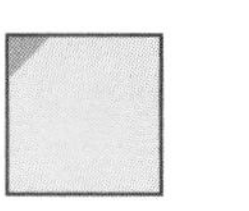
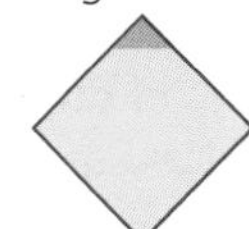

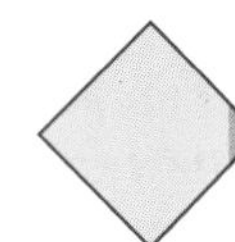

The shape pattern is square–diamond –square–diamond. The orange corner turns clockwise, or to the right.

2. **Critical Thinking** Describe the pattern in problem 1.

Work It Out!

Use Look for a Pattern or any other strategy to solve the problem.

3. A restaurant uses triangular tables. One person can sit at each side of a table. How many people can sit at a row of 7 tables pushed together? 9 people

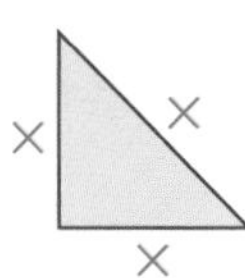
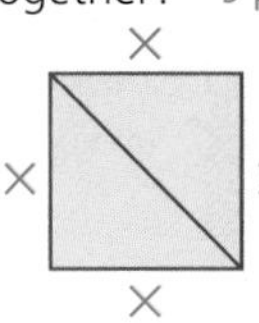
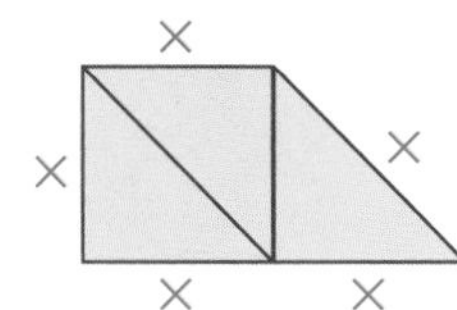

4. What 7 coins equal 25 cents?
2 dimes and 5 pennies
5. Draw a shape that can be covered by 4 green pattern blocks but not by 2 blue pattern blocks.
Check students' work.
6. If you face north and then make a half turn, you will be facing south. What direction will you be facing if you face north and make 4 half turns? 10 half turns? 11 half turns?
north; north; south

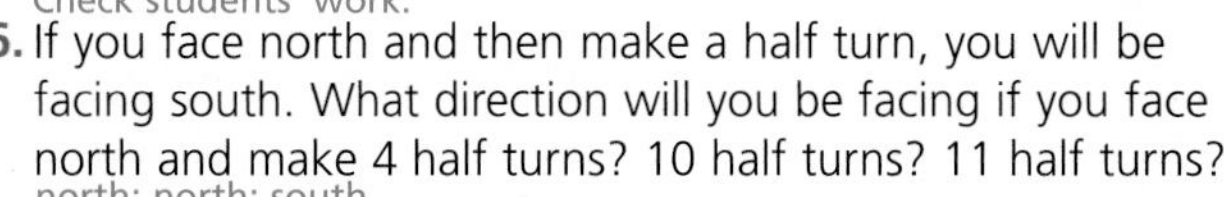

7. On March 1, you save one penny. On March 2, you save 2 pennies. On March 3, you save 3 pennies. At that rate, how many pennies will you save on the last day of March?
31 pennies on March 31

Share Your Thinking

8. What strategy did you use for problem 6? Explain why you chose that strategy. Answers will vary.
9. When can finding a pattern help you to solve problems? Answers will vary but should show students' understanding of the Look for a Pattern strategy.

Meeting Individual Needs

Extra Support

Continue the Pattern *(visual)* Have students draw three or four simple pictures that establish a pattern. (As an example, draw on the chalkboard three arrows, one pointing upward, one to the right, and one downward.) Then, have pairs of students trade pictures and continue each other's patterns.

Alternate Approach

- Reteach Worksheet 7.4
- **TAB** See TE pp. 226E–226F.

MathZones
Understanding Geometry

Students Acquiring English

See **Language Connections**, Ch. 7.

Challenge

Have students solve this problem: Your rich uncle gives you a dollar on May 1. On May 2, he gives you another dollar. On May 3, he gives you $2; on May 4, $3; on May 5, $5; on May 6, $8, on May 7, $13. How much money will he give you on May 8, 9, and 10? $21 $34 $55 What is the pattern? Each number is the sum of the two previous numbers.

Practice

Math Center For more problem solving practice, see Project Card 7, *Teacher for a Day!*

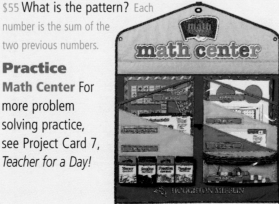

7.4 ANOTHER LOOK — Reteach

Problem Solving Strategy: **Look for a Pattern**

Look at these letters. In which direction should the next letter face? B ꟺ ᗺ B ꟺ ᗺ B ꟺ ᗺ

1. Understand
- You want to add another letter B to the row. You need to figure out which way it will face.

2. Plan
- Look at the row. The direction in which the letter faces changes from one letter to the next. You have to find a pattern.

3. Try It
- Describe the pattern. Each letter faces right, then down, and then to the left.

4. Look Back
- The next letter in the pattern should face right: B.

Solve. Use Look for a Pattern when you can.

1. What letter comes next in this pattern? CEECEECEE
C
2. Suppose you put coins in a row in this order: nickel, penny, nickel, dime, nickel, penny, dime, nickel, penny, nickel, dime. What will the next coin be?
a nickel
3. If you continued the pattern in problem 2 until there were 10 nickels in the row, how much money would you have in all?
$1.05

7.4 PRACTICE — Practice

Problem Solving Strategy: **Look for a Pattern**

Solve. Use Look for a Pattern when you can.

1. Mr. Novak is setting out four rows of chairs for a meeting. The picture shows how many chairs he has set out so far. There will be 5 chairs in each row. How many more chairs does Mr. Novak need to get? 9 chairs
2. Look at the shape at right. How many squares are there? 5 squares
3. Look at the shape below. How many squares are there? 8 squares
4. Kathy lives at 509 Ocean Street. Lee lives next door to Kathy at 507 Ocean Street. Bev lives next door to Lee at 505 Ocean Street. Maria lives 2 doors down from Bev. What is Maria's address? 501 Ocean Street
5. You are putting candles on a birthday cake. You put a candle in each corner of the cake. Then you put candles along the sides. When you are done, each side of the cake has 7 candles. How many candles are on the cake? 24 candles
6. You walk to a nearby store. The store is 10 minutes from your home. You spend 15 minutes in the store and then walk home. You get home at 4:00 P.M. What time did you leave home to go to the store? 3:25 P.M.

7.4 ENRICHMENT — Enrichment

Problem Solving Strategy: **Look for a Pattern**

Solve. Use Look for a Pattern when you can.

1. Carmen is planning a sign for her new restaurant. The sign will show only the name of the restaurant: Pizza Mania! The sign company charges $12.00 for each uppercase letter and $8.00 for each lowercase letter. A punctuation mark costs $3.50. Will she spend more than $100 to buy the sign? Explain.
no; she will spend $24 on uppercase letters, $64 on lowercase letters, and $3.50 on a punctuation mark; the total will be $91.50.
2. The sign company charges Carmen to hang the sign. The charge is $40.00 an hour. Suppose it takes 3 hours to hang the sign. How much will Carmen have spent altogether to buy and hang the sign?
$91.50 to buy it; $120 to hang it; total will be $211.50.
3. One wall of the restaurant is 20 feet long. The tables are 3 feet wide. How many tables will fit along the wall if there are 2 feet between the tables? 4 tables
4. You buy 3 slices of pizza. You pay with a five-dollar bill and get back $2.75. How much did each slice of pizza cost? 75¢
5. There are 12 people waiting in line to buy pizza. Yasmine is second in line, followed by Brad. Behind Brad is Cory. Behind Cory is Otis. How many people are standing in line behind Otis? 7 people
6. Carmen sells 20 pizzas on Monday. Each day after that, she sells 2 more pizzas than the day before. How many pizzas does she sell altogether from Monday to Friday? 120 pizzas

Activity

Planning at a Glance

Objective To identify angles as greater than, less than, or equal to a right angle

Materials oaktag, paper fastener

Optional Resources

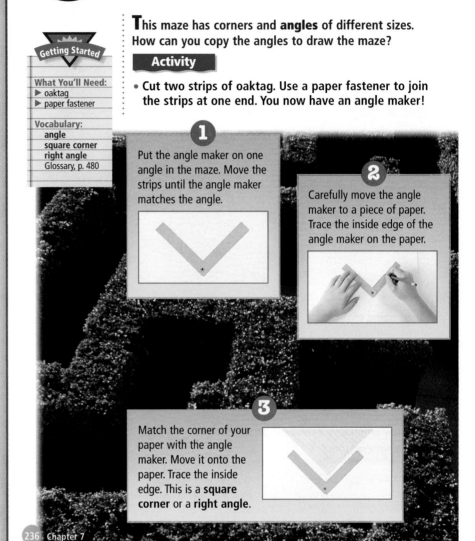

- Reteach 7.5; Practice 7.5; Enrichment 7.5
- Daily Cumul. Review, p. 88
- Math Center: How-To Card 22
- Every Day Counts
- **TAB**, TE pp. 156E–156F, 156J
- **Problem of the Day**, 88, p. 44; Flip Chart, p. 44b

MATHKEYS *Unlocking Geometry 3–6,* Level 3, Activity 2

Students Acquiring English

Draw and identify an angle. Find examples of angles in the classroom. Ask students to identify things they see outside the classroom that form angles. Draw a right angle; explain that it is like the corners of a square. Help students identify right angles.

Problem of the Day

How many red right angles are there on an ordinary checkerboard? You may use a calculator to help you. 32 red squares × 4 right angles in each square = 128 right angles.

Angles

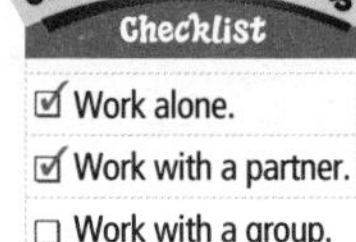

Cooperative Learning Checklist
- ☑ Work alone.
- ☑ Work with a partner.
- ☐ Work with a group.

Getting Started

What You'll Need:
- oaktag
- paper fastener

Vocabulary:
- **angle**
- **square corner**
- **right angle**
- Glossary, p. 480

This maze has corners and angles of different sizes. How can you copy the angles to draw the maze?

Activity

- **Cut two strips of oaktag. Use a paper fastener to join the strips at one end. You now have an angle maker!**

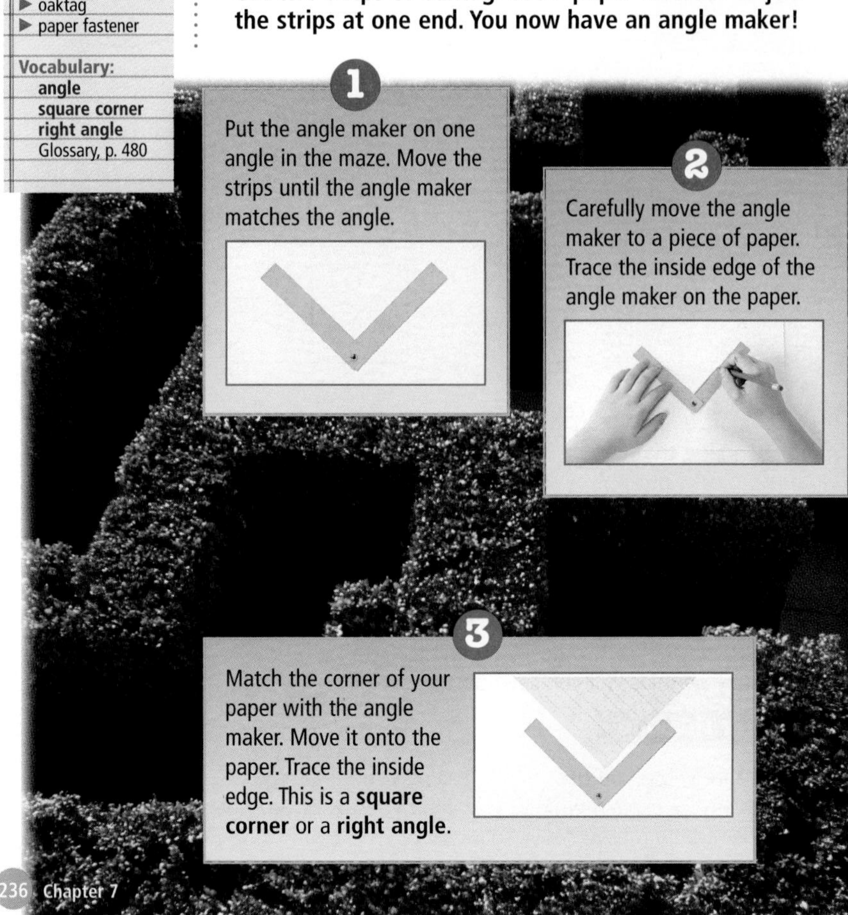

1. Put the angle maker on one angle in the maze. Move the strips until the angle maker matches the angle.
2. Carefully move the angle maker to a piece of paper. Trace the inside edge of the angle maker on the paper.
3. Match the corner of your paper with the angle maker. Move it onto the paper. Trace the inside edge. This is a **square corner** or a **right angle**.

1 Introduce

Prior Knowledge **Describe what a triangle looks like.** It has 3 sides and 3 corners or points.

Teach: Activity

Emphasize these points:

- The two sides that form an angle always begin at the same point.
- The arms of an angle maker can turn in either direction to form an angle.

Modeling Model steps 1–2. Ask:

- Are all the angles in the maze the same? No.
- How can you tell? I would need to move the arms of my angle maker to measure each one, so the angles change.

2 Develop

Show What You Know!

Common Error Some students may not recognize angles that are greater than a right angle. Use two angle makers to show a right angle and an obtuse angle for comparison. See also Analyzing Errors, TE pp. 265A and 265B.

Work It Out!

- Discuss with students how to identify a right angle.
- Ask students to identify objects in the classroom that have right angles.
- Have students look at the nonsquare corners in the figures used for exercises 5–7. Ask, Which are greater than and less than square corners?

3 Summarize

- Remind students that the sides of an angle always begin at the same point.

Ongoing Assessment Which letters have only right angles: E, H, L, M, N, T, V, W, X, or Y? E, H, L, and T

Math Journal: ***Communicating***

Ask students to write a definition of an angle. They should write that an angle has 2 sides joined at the same point. It can be like a square corner, greater than a square corner, or less than a square corner.

Show What You Know!

1. **Critical Thinking** Compare the first angle you made to the right angle. Was the first angle greater than a right angle, less than a right angle, or equal to a right angle? Answers will depend on the angle chosen.

Use the pictures to answer exercises 2–4.

a. 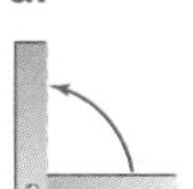  b. 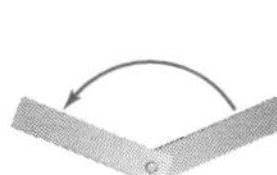  c. 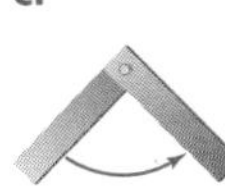 d. 

2. Which angles are right angles? a and c
3. Which angle is greater than a right angle? b
4. Which angle is less than a right angle? d

Use your angle maker to answer exercises 5–7.

a. b. c. d. e.

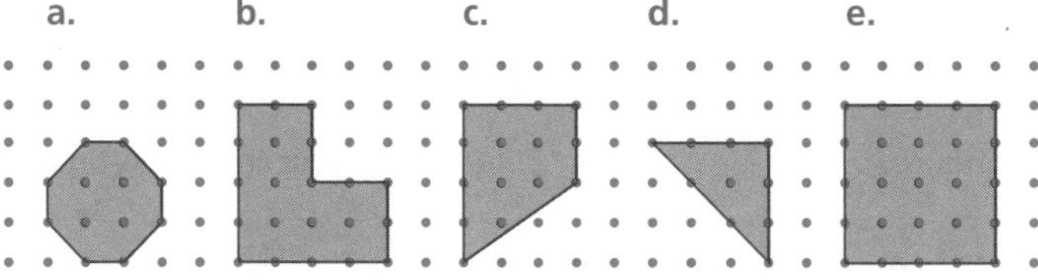

5. How many right angles can you find in each figure? a. 0; b. 6; c. 2; d. 1; e. 4
6. Which figure has the most right angles? The fewest? b; a
7. Which figure has the most angles in all? a
8. **Critical Thinking** Does the angle maker show a right angle? How can you tell? No, because it is bigger than the square corner of the book.

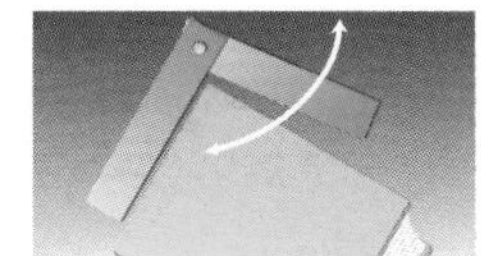

9. **Patterns** Describe this pattern. Then draw the next angle. right angle, less than a right angle, and so on.

More Practice Set 7.5, p. 460

Meeting Individual Needs

Extra Support

Figures with Angles *(kinesthetic)* Challenge students to use their angle makers to draw a figure on square dot paper (TR3) that has at least 1 right angle. Have them share their figures with classmates and compare them in terms of number of sides, number of angles, and number of angles less than and greater than a right angle.

Alternate Approach

- Reteach Worksheet 7.5
- **TAB** See TE pp. 156E–156F.

MathZones
Understanding Geometry

Students Acquiring English

See Language Connections, Ch. 7.

Challenge

How many right angles does a number cube have? 24

Practice

Math Center
Use How-To Card 22, *Angle Hunt,* to have students practice identifying angles.

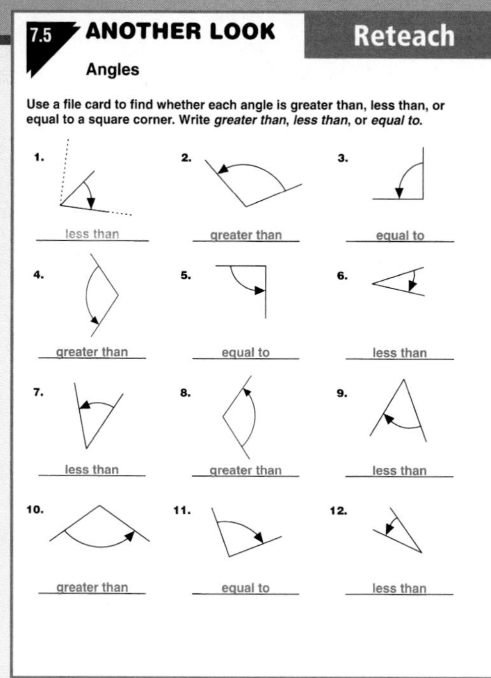

7.5 ANOTHER LOOK — Reteach

Angles

Use a file card to find whether each angle is greater than, less than, or equal to a square corner. Write *greater than, less than,* or *equal to.*

1. less than
2. greater than
3. equal to
4. greater than
5. equal to
6. less than
7. less than
8. greater than
9. less than
10. greater than
11. equal to
12. less than

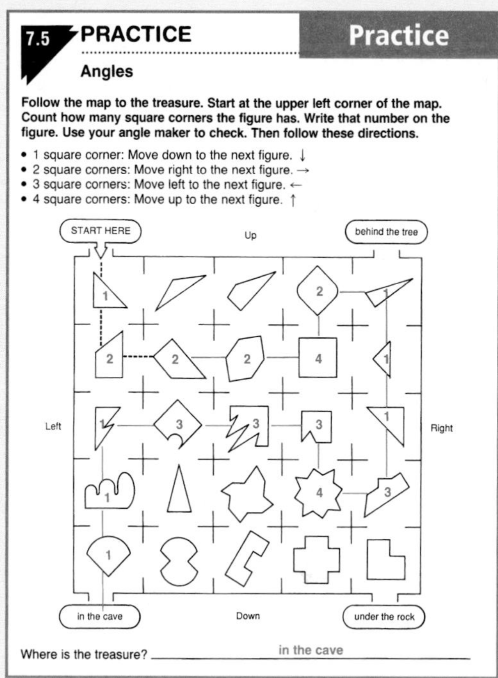

7.5 PRACTICE — Practice

Angles

Follow the map to the treasure. Start at the upper left corner of the map. Count how many square corners the figure has. Write that number on the figure. Use your angle maker to check. Then follow these directions.

- 1 square corner: Move down to the next figure. ↓
- 2 square corners: Move right to the next figure. →
- 3 square corners: Move left to the next figure. ←
- 4 square corners: Move up to the next figure. ↑

Where is the treasure? in the cave

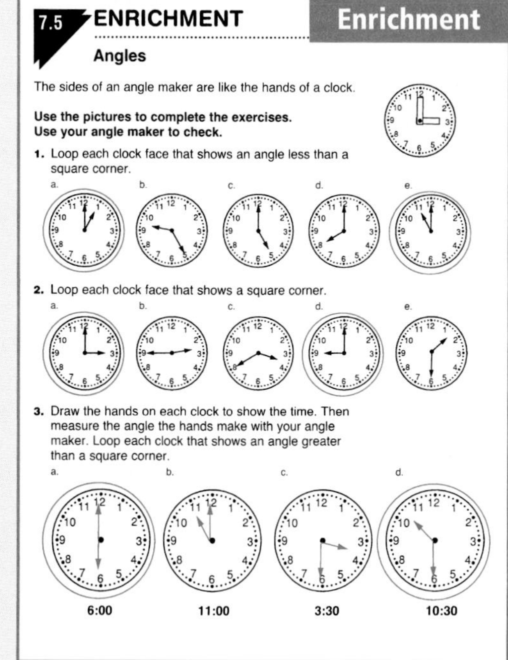

7.5 ENRICHMENT — Enrichment

Angles

The sides of an angle maker are like the hands of a clock.

Use the pictures to complete the exercises.
Use your angle maker to check.

1. Loop each clock face that shows an angle less than a square corner.
a. b. c. d. e.

2. Loop each clock face that shows a square corner.
a. b. c. d. e.

3. Draw the hands on each clock to show the time. Then measure the angle the hands make with your angle maker. Loop each clock that shows an angle greater than a square corner.
a. 6:00 b. 11:00 c. 3:30 d. 10:30

Connecting

Planning at a Glance

Objective To identify slide, flip, and half turn images as congruent

Materials tracing paper, geoboard and geobands, (TR3)

Optional Resources

- Reteach 7.6; Practice 7.6; Enrichment 7.6
- Daily Cumul. Review, p. 89
- Math Center: Act. Card 38
- Every Day Counts
- TAB, TE pp. 226E–226F, 226J
- Problem of the Day, 89, p. 45; Flip Chart, p. 45a

MATHKEYS *Unlocking Geometry 3–6,* Level 3, Activity 12

Students Acquiring English

Be sure students understand the words *size* and *shape.* Draw pairs of figures that are the same size but different shapes, and others whose figures are the same shape but different sizes. Help students label them: same size, different size, same shape, different shape.

Problem of the Day

Along which grid lines could you cut the figure below to form two congruent parts?

One possible answer is shown.

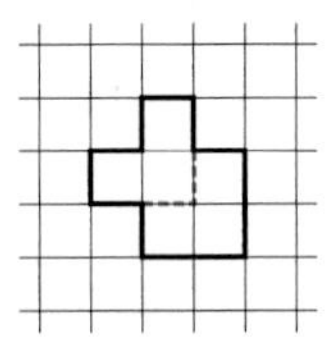

Congruence

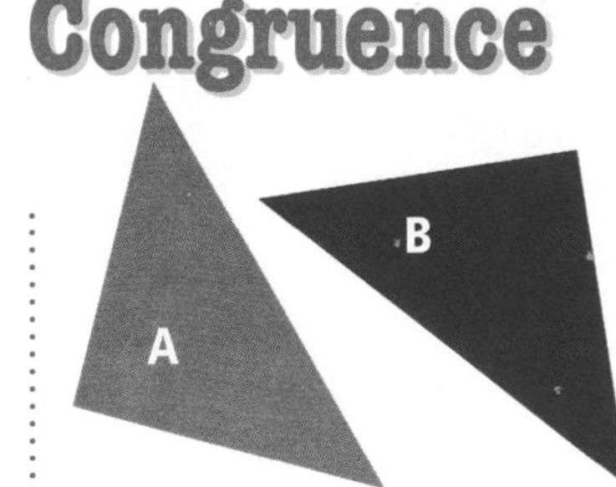

These pieces are congruent.

Getting Started

What You'll Need:
- tracing paper
- geoboard and geobands

Vocabulary:
congruent
Glossary, p. 480

This is a set of tangram pieces. Figures that are the same size and shape are **congruent**.

Are pieces A and B congruent?

Here's A Way! Check for congruence.

Find congruent figures.

1. Trace figure A.

2. Match your tracing to figure B.

Figures A and B are congruent.

Make congruent figures.

You can use a geoboard to make congruent figures.

1. Make a figure on a geoboard.

2. Make a congruent figure. Each side and angle must match the original.

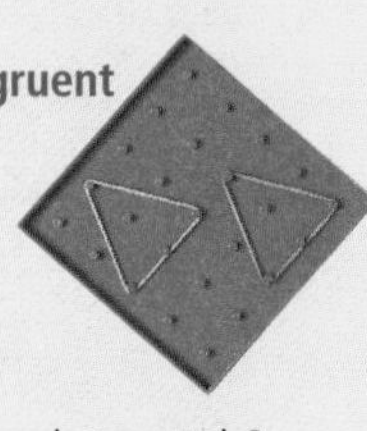

Talk About It! Why did you make the sides and angles match?
in order to make the figures the same size and shape

238 Chapter 7

1 Introduce

Prior Knowledge **Ask, What do slide, flip, and turn images all have in common?** Each has the same shape and size.

Teach: **Here's A Way!**

Emphasize these points:

- A figure and its slide image are congruent. A figure and its flip image are congruent. A figure and its turn image are congruent.
- Congruent figures have the same shape and size.

Modeling Model the second step 2. Ask:

- What makes the 2 figures congruent? They have the same shape and size.
- What can be different about them? They can face different directions

2 Develop

Show What You Know!

You may wish to use exercise 2 to discuss similarity. The triangles are similar figures because they are the same shape but different sizes.

Common Error Some students may not recognize congruent figures that are flipped. Show students that turns keep the figure face-up, but flips show the back. See also Analyzing Errors, TE pp. 265A and 265B.

Work It Out!

- If desired, discuss the similar figures in exercise 12.

Using Reading Strategies Encourage students to use the Self-Question strategy as they read the exercises. Ask them to share their questions with classmates. See TE p. 226J.

3 Summarize

- Remind students that figures in slide, flip, or turn patterns have the same shape and size.
- Reemphasize that figures that have the same shape and size are congruent.

Ongoing Assessment When can an arrow pointing up and an arrow pointing down be congruent? when they are the same shape and size

Math Journal: *Communicating*

Ask students to explain why it may be important to have things made the same size and shape. Answers will vary, but may include: so shoes match, mittens match, socks match.

Show What You Know!

Predict whether the figures are congruent.

1. no
2. no
3. yes

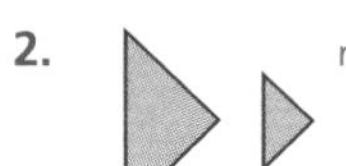

4. Choose one pair of figures from exercises 1–3. Copy one figure and cut it out. Place it on the other figure to check your prediction. Check students' work.
5. **Critical Thinking** If two figures show a flip, are the figures congruent? Explain. Yes. although the figures face different directions, they are the same size and shape.

Work It Out!

Copy each figure. Use square dot paper, a geoboard, or a tracing. Then make a figure that is the same shape and size. Answers will vary. Sample answers shown.

6. 7. 8. 9.

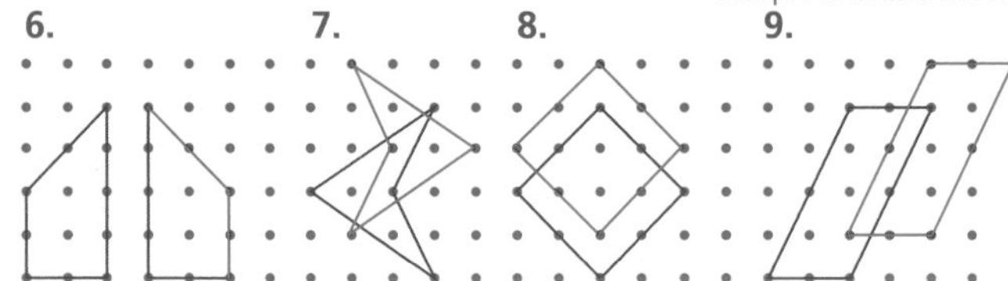

10. **Critical Thinking** Look at your figures from exercise 8. How are they the same? How are they different? They are the same size and shape. They are in different positions.
11. Suppose a figure has exactly 4 right angles. Another figure is congruent to the first figure. How many right angles does the second figure have? 4 right angles
12. **Problem Solving** Which figures in this tangram are congruent? How do you know? (Hint: You can use tracing paper.) The two parallelograms are congruent. Explanations may vary.

More Practice Set 7.6, p. 461

Meeting Individual Needs

Extra Support

Origami Figures *(kinesthetic)* Choose several simple origami designs, and provide students with paper to make one of them. Provide guidance when necessary. When students are finished, have them unfold their figures and find any congruent figures, slides, flips, or turns defined by the folds. They may refold their figures to show family and friends.

Alternate Approach

- Reteach Worksheet 7.6
- **TAB** See TE pp. 226E–226F.

MathZones
Understanding Geometry

Students Acquiring English

See Language Connections, Ch. 7.

Challenge

What machine is probably best at making congruent figures? Possible answers: a computer, a copier

Practice

Math Center Use Activity Card 38, *It's a Draw,* to have students practice identifying slides, flips, and half turns.

Challenge Use Activity Card 38 and have students continue the activity as described in Now Try This!

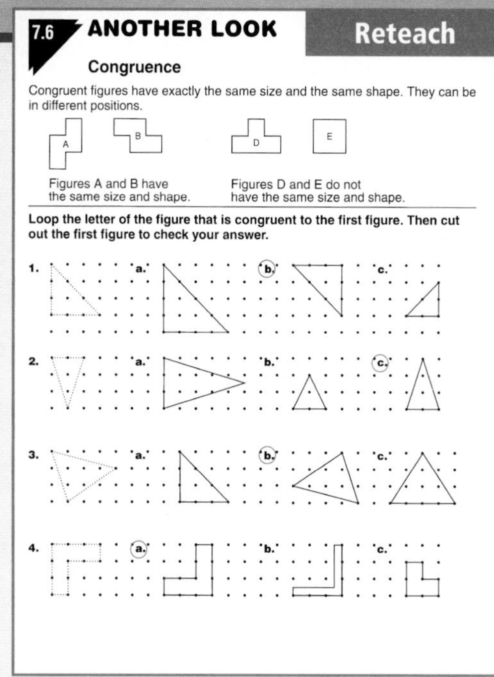

7.6 ANOTHER LOOK — Reteach

Congruence

Congruent figures have exactly the same size and the same shape. They can be in different positions.

Figures A and B have the same size and shape.
Figures D and E do not have the same size and shape.

Loop the letter of the figure that is congruent to the first figure. Then cut out the first figure to check your answer.

1. a. (b.) c.
2. a. b. (c.)
3. a. (b.) c.
4. (a.) b. c.

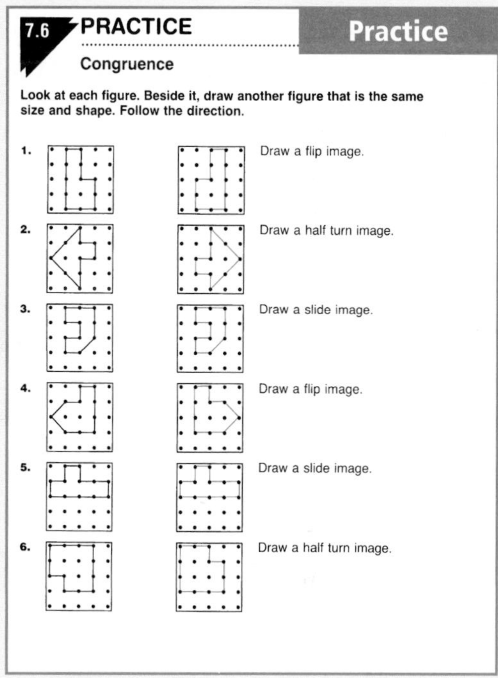

7.6 PRACTICE — Practice

Congruence

Look at each figure. Beside it, draw another figure that is the same size and shape. Follow the direction.

1. Draw a flip image.
2. Draw a half turn image.
3. Draw a slide image.
4. Draw a flip image.
5. Draw a slide image.
6. Draw a half turn image.

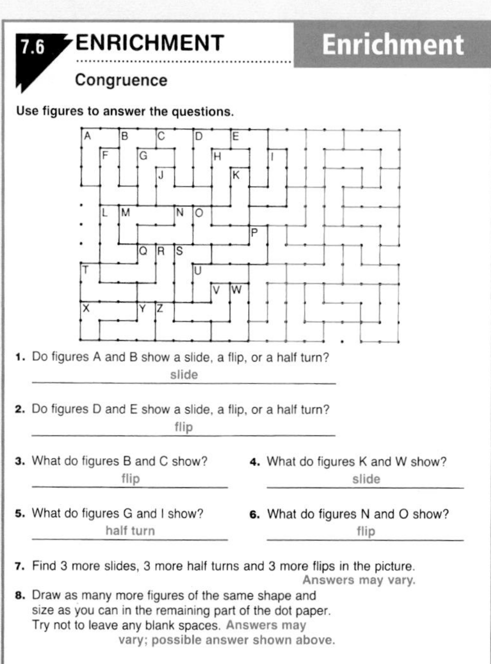

7.6 ENRICHMENT — Enrichment

Congruence

Use figures to answer the questions.

1. Do figures A and B show a slide, a flip, or a half turn? slide
2. Do figures D and E show a slide, a flip, or a half turn? flip
3. What do figures B and C show? flip
4. What do figures K and W show? slide
5. What do figures G and I show? half turn
6. What do figures N and O show? flip
7. Find 3 more slides, 3 more half turns and 3 more flips in the picture. Answers may vary.
8. Draw as many more figures of the same shape and size as you can in the remaining part of the dot paper. Try not to leave any blank spaces. Answers may vary; possible answer shown above.

Activity

Planning at a Glance

Objective To identify one or more lines of symmetry in plane figures

Materials square dot paper (TR3), scissors, tracing paper, Recording Sheet (Practice 7.7)

Optional Resources

- Reteach 7.7; Enrichment 7.7
- Daily Cumul. Review, p. 90
- Math Center: Act. Card 40
- Every Day Counts
- **TAB**, TE pp. 226E–226F, 226J
- **Problem of the Day**, 90, p. 45; Flip Chart, p. 45b

MATHKEYS

Unlocking Whole Numbers 3–5, Level 3, Activity 10

Students Acquiring English

Be sure students understand the meaning of *match*. Show colors, sizes, and shapes that match and do not match, asking students to identify those that match and those that do not. Then have students draw, cut, and fold figures in half, telling if they *match* or not.

Problem of the Day

An ant, a moth, a beetle, a bee, and a fly walked up a log. The bee led the bug parade. The moth was in front of the fly. The ant was three bugs in back of the beetle. In what order did the bugs walk?

bee, beetle, moth, fly, ant

Lesson 7 Symmetry

Cooperative Learning Checklist
- ☑ Work alone.
- ☑ Work with a partner.
- ☑ Work with a group.

Getting Started

What You'll Need:
- square dot paper
- scissors
- tracing paper
- recording sheet

Vocabulary:
- **line of symmetry**
- Glossary, p. 480

Does the left side of the small snowflake below match the right side? If a figure is folded in half and the two parts match, the fold line is called a line of symmetry.

Activity

- **Make a chart like the one below.**

1
- Use dot paper. Draw and cut out a square.
- Fold the square in half so the two sides match.
- Draw a line along the fold to show a line of symmetry.

2
- Find and draw another line of symmetry on the square.
- Find as many lines of symmetry as you can.

3
Make figures with
- 0 lines of symmetry
- 1 line of symmetry
- 2 lines of symmetry
- more than 2 lines of symmetry

Sketch the figures on your chart.

line of symmetry

Number of Lines of Symmetry			
0	1	2	More than 2

1 Introduce

Prior Knowledge **Ask, When are 2 squares congruent?** when they are the same size

Teach: Activity

Emphasize these points:

- If you fold a figure on a line of symmetry, the 2 halves will match.
- Some figures have many lines of symmetry.

Modeling Model step 2 of the activity. Ask:

- How many ways can you fold a square so the 2 halves match? 4
- How many lines of symmetry does a square have? 4
- How many lines of symmetry do you think a heart shape has? 1 Why? A heart can be folded only one way so that the 2 halves match.

2 Develop

Show What You Know!

Ask students to draw buildings they see every day. Then draw a line of symmetry through the outlines of buildings that have them.

- You may wish to have students review the names of the figures in exercise 13.

Common Error Students may not recognize more than 1 line of symmetry without folding cutouts. Encourage these students to try drawing a dotted line through a figure instead. See also Analyzing Errors, TE pp. 265A and 265B.

Using Reading Strategies Help students to use the Self-Question strategy as they read the exercises. Ask them what questions they could ask themselves. See TE p. 226J.

3 Summarize

- Reemphasize that figures that have matching halves have symmetry.
- Remind students that some figures have more than one line of symmetry.

Ongoing Assessment How many lines of symmetry does a rectangle have? 2, unless it's a square

Math Journal: *Communicating*

Have students list objects they see every day. Let them write the number of lines of symmetry they find in each object. Answers will vary.

Show What You Know!

1. Critical Thinking Explain how to find lines of symmetry. Fold a figure in half. If the part on one side of the fold matches the part on the other side, then the fold line is a line of symmetry.

Use your recording sheet or dot paper. Draw the other half of the design. The first one is started for you. Check students' drawings.

2.

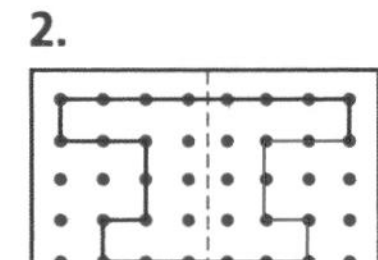

3.

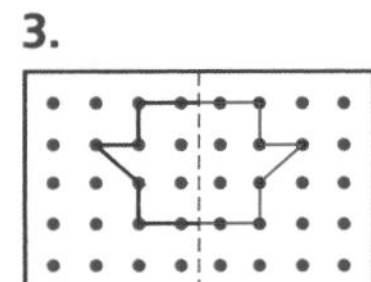

4.

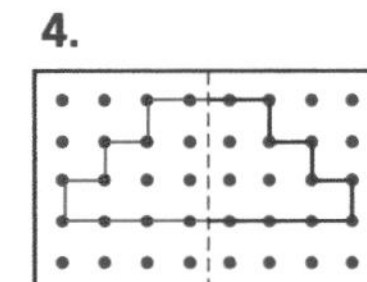

Use your recording sheet or trace the figures. Draw a line of symmetry on the figures that have them.

5. no line of symmetry

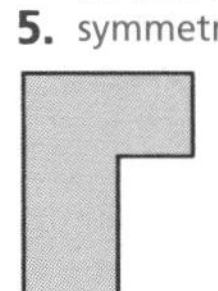

6.

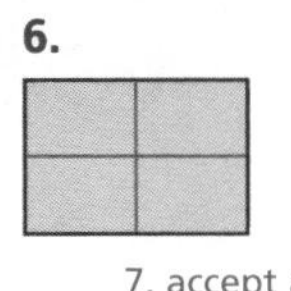

7.

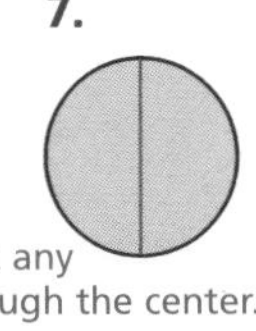

7. accept any line through the center.

8. no line of symmetry **9.**

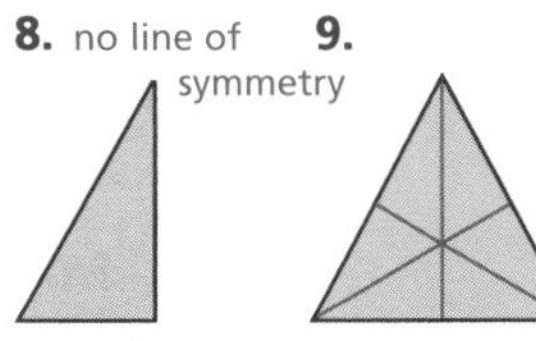

10. Which of the figures in exercises 5–9 could be folded from top to bottom so the two parts match? 6 and 7

11. Use your recording sheet or print the numbers 0–9. Circle the numbers that have a line of symmetry. 0, 3, 8, and possibly 1

12. Critical Thinking How many lines of symmetry does a square have? Would a smaller square have the same number of lines of symmetry? 4 lines of symmetry; yes

13. Trace and cut out each of these figures. Find as many lines of symmetry as you can for each figure. Record the lines of symmetry. The circle has unlimited lines of symmetry. Possible answers shown.

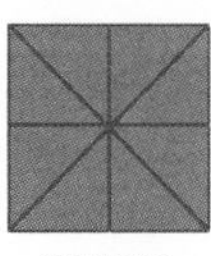

square

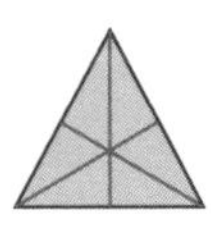

triangle

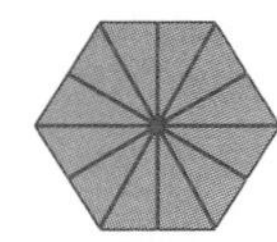

hexagon

circle

14. Create Your Own Draw a figure with exactly two lines of symmetry. Figures will vary but should show only 2 lines of symmetry.

241

Meeting Individual Needs

Extra Support

Symmetry in Nature *(kinesthetic)* Invite students to draw a picture of something in nature that has at least 1 line of symmetry, such as a butterfly, sunflower, rainbow, snowflake, or starfish. Suggest that students color their pictures to help show symmetry. They may cut out their figures and challenge classmates to find all the lines of symmetry.

Alternate Approach

- Reteach Worksheet 7.7
- **TAB** See TE pp. 226E–226F.

MathZones

Understanding Geometry

Students Acquiring English

See **Language Connections**, Ch. 7.

Challenge

How many lines of symmetry does a person's face have? 1

Practice

Math Center Use Activity Card 40, *Mirror Images,* to have students practice identifying lines of symmetry in plane figures.

Challenge Use Activity Card 40 and have students continue the activity as described in Now Try This!

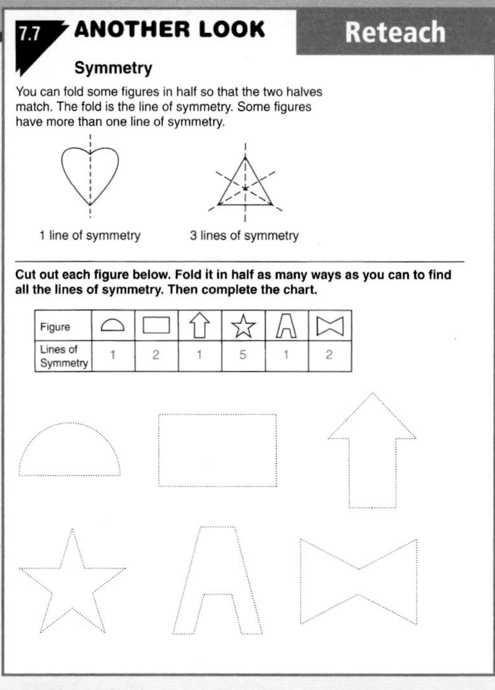

7.7 ANOTHER LOOK — **Reteach**

Symmetry

You can fold some figures in half so that the two halves match. The fold is the line of symmetry. Some figures have more than one line of symmetry.

1 line of symmetry — 3 lines of symmetry

Cut out each figure below. Fold it in half as many ways as you can to find all the lines of symmetry. Then complete the chart.

Figure	half circle	rectangle	arrow	star	A	bow tie
Lines of Symmetry	1	2	1	5	1	2

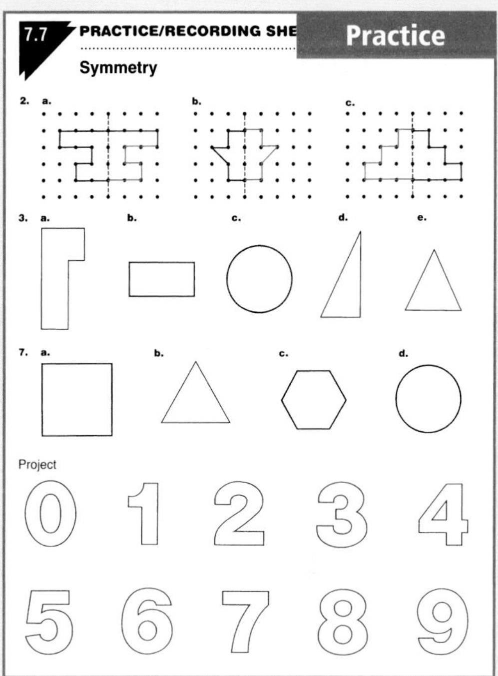

7.7 PRACTICE/RECORDING SHE[ET] — **Practice**

Symmetry

2. a. b. c.

3. a. b. c. d. e.

7. a. b. c. d.

Project

0 1 2 3 4
5 6 7 8 9

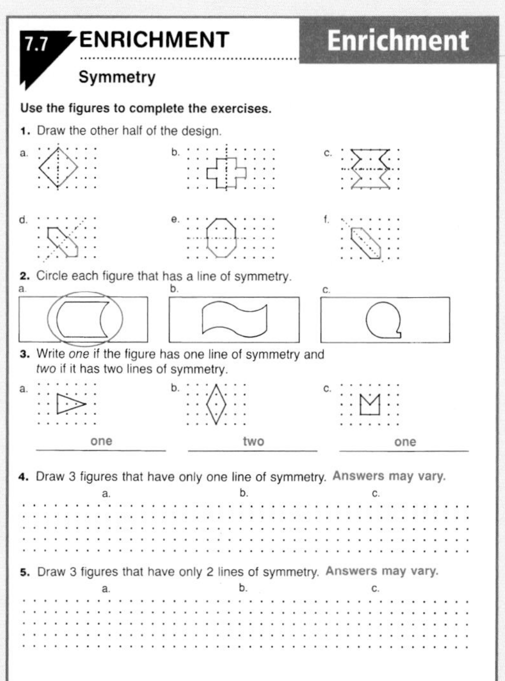

7.7 ENRICHMENT — **Enrichment**

Symmetry

Use the figures to complete the exercises.

1. Draw the other half of the design.

a. b. c.

d. e. f.

2. Circle each figure that has a line of symmetry.

a. b. c.

3. Write *one* if the figure has one line of symmetry and *two* if it has two lines of symmetry.

a. one b. two c. one

4. Draw 3 figures that have only one line of symmetry. Answers may vary.

a. b. c.

5. Draw 3 figures that have only 2 lines of symmetry. Answers may vary.

a. b. c.

Connecting

Planning at a Glance

Objectives To identify the center of a circle and the diameter; to find a line of symmetry

Materials oaktag, 2 pencils, scissors

Optional Resources

- Reteach 7.8; Practice 7.8; Enrichment 7.8
- Daily Cumul. Review, p. 91
- Math Center: Act. Card 41
- Every Day Counts
- **TAB**, TE pp. 226E–226F, 226J
- **Problem of the Day**, 91, p. 46; Flip Chart, p. 46a

Students Acquiring English

Give students practice saying *diameter.* Then invite pairs of students to use two pieces of chalk linked by a string to draw circles on the board. Ask other students to add *diameters*.

Problem of the Day

How can you cut a round pie into 7 pieces with 3 cuts? The pieces do not have to be the same size. One possible answer is shown.

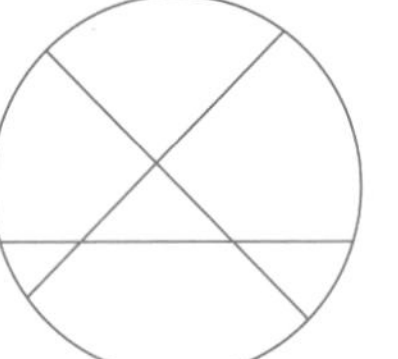

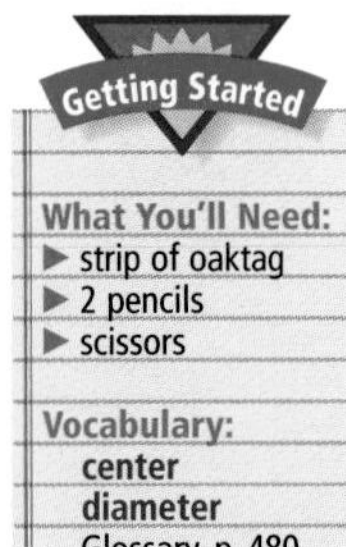

Circles

Getting Started

What You'll Need:
- strip of oaktag
- 2 pencils
- scissors

Vocabulary:
- center
- diameter
- Glossary, p. 480

Circles are everywhere! All these objects you might see every day look like circles. What makes a circle different from other figures? Make circles of your own to find out.

Here's A Way! Make a circle.

1. Use the strip of oaktag. Make a small hole at each end of the strip. Place the strip on a piece of paper. Put one pencil point in one hole. Hold it steady. This will be the **center** of the circle.
2. Put another pencil point in the other hole. With this pencil, turn the strip around. You will draw a circle.
3. Cut out the circle you drew. Fold it in half. Does the fold line pass through the center? A line that passes through the center of a circle is called a **diameter**.

Talk About It!

- How could you change your circle maker to make a smaller circle? Make the holes closer together.
- Think of a way to draw a very large circle. Answers will vary. Possible answer: Use a very long piece of string instead of the oaktag.

1 Introduce

Motivate Have each student draw 2 circles. Let them cut out the circles and connect them with tape to make sunglasses.

Teach: Here's A Way!

Modeling Model step 3. Ask:

- How do you know that you are folding a circle exactly in half? the edges of the circle should align

2 Develop

Show What You Know!

Common Error If students have difficulty identifying basic geometric figures, review the figures. For example, you may review squares, triangles, circles, and rectangles. See also Analyzing Errors, TE pp. 265A and 265B.

Work It Out!

- Have students discuss their reasoning for exercise 13.

Using Reading Strategies Guide students to use the Self-Question strategy as they read the Problem Solving exercise. Ask, How can asking questions help you understand the problem? See TE p. 226J.

3 Summarize

- Ask, How many lines of symmetry does a circle have? an infinite number; accept such answers as "many"

Ongoing Assessment If you cut a round pizza into four slices by making straight cuts through the center, are all the cuts along diameters? yes

Math Journal: *Communicating*

Yes; The diameter is a line through the center of a circle, so the two halves will always match.

Show What You Know!

Write the name of each shape. Is the figure a circle? Write *yes* or *no*.

1. triangle; no
2. circle; yes
3. square; no

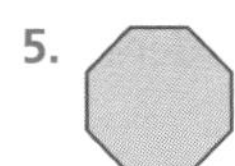

4. rectangle; no
5. hexagon; no
6. circle; yes

7. **Critical Thinking** How is a circle different from a square, a triangle, and a rectangle? no sides, no corners, is a curved line
8. **Write About It** Is every figure that has curves a circle? Draw some figures to support your answer. No. Drawings may include oval or pear-shape.

Work It Out!

Is the line inside the circle a diameter? Write *yes* or *no*, and explain your answer.

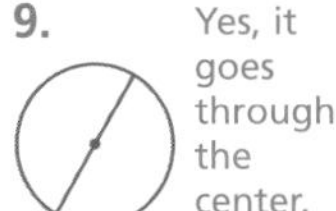

9. Yes, it goes through the center.
10. No, it does not go through the center.
11. No, it does not go through the center.
12. Yes, it goes through the center.

13. **Logical Reasoning** If you make a circle, how can you find the center by folding? (Hint: Start by folding the circle in half.) If you fold a circle in half twice, the fold lines will cross at the center.
14. **Problem Solving** You are setting up chairs for a storytelling performance. How can you make sure that all the chairs are in an exact circle around the storyteller? Have the storyteller sit in the center; make the distance from each chair to the storyteller the same.

Math Journal

Is a diameter of a circle always a line of symmetry? Explain. Yes. The diameter is a line through the center of a circle, so the two halves will always match.

243

Meeting Individual Needs

Extra Support

Circles Everywhere *(visual)* Have students look for circles in the classroom and make a list of circles that they see.

Alternate Approach

- Reteach Worksheet 7.8
- **TAB** See TE pp. 226E–226F.

MathZones

Understanding Geometry

Students Acquiring English

See Language Connections, Ch. 7.

Challenge

Have student pairs experiment with circle designs using jar lids, coins, and other circular objects, and the properties of circles they discovered in this activity. Let them color their designs and share them with the class.

Practice

Math Center Use Activity Card 41, *Circle Pictures*, to have students practice identifying the center of a circle.

Challenge Use Activity Card 41 and have students continue the activity as described in Now Try This!

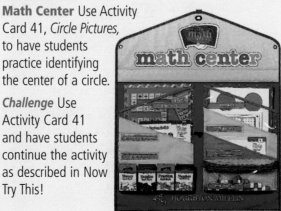

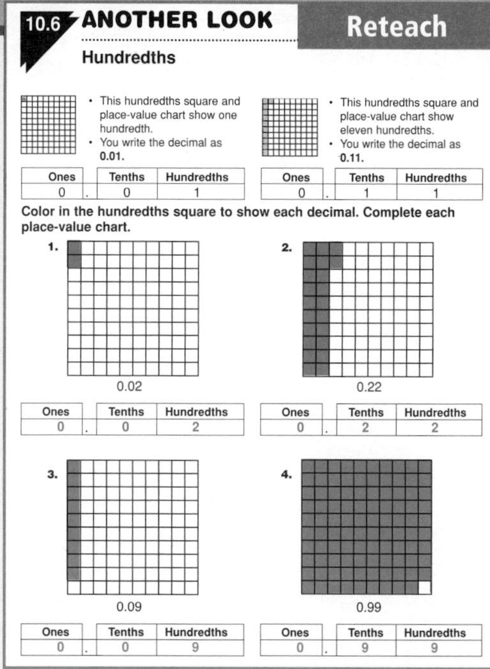

10.6 ANOTHER LOOK — Reteach

Hundredths

- This hundredths square and place-value chart show one hundredth.
- You write the decimal as **0.01**.

Ones	Tenths	Hundredths
0	0	1

- This hundredths square and place-value chart show eleven hundredths.
- You write the decimal as **0.11**.

Ones	Tenths	Hundredths
0	1	1

Color in the hundredths square to show each decimal. Complete each place-value chart.

1. 0.02

Ones	Tenths	Hundredths
0	0	2

2. 0.22

Ones	Tenths	Hundredths
0	2	2

3. 0.09

Ones	Tenths	Hundredths
0	0	9

4. 0.99

Ones	Tenths	Hundredths
0	9	9

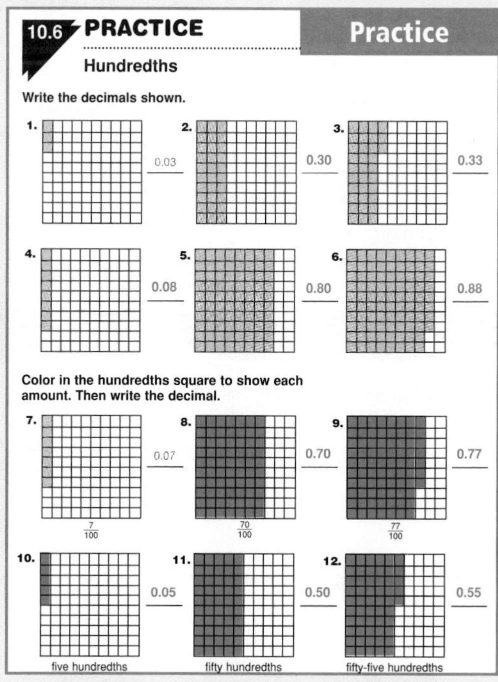

10.6 PRACTICE — Practice

Hundredths

Write the decimals shown.

1. 0.03
2. 0.30
3. 0.33
4. 0.08
5. 0.80
6. 0.88

Color in the hundredths square to show each amount. Then write the decimal.

7. $\frac{7}{100}$ 0.07
8. $\frac{70}{100}$ 0.70
9. $\frac{77}{100}$ 0.77
10. five hundredths 0.05
11. fifty hundredths 0.50
12. fifty-five hundredths 0.55

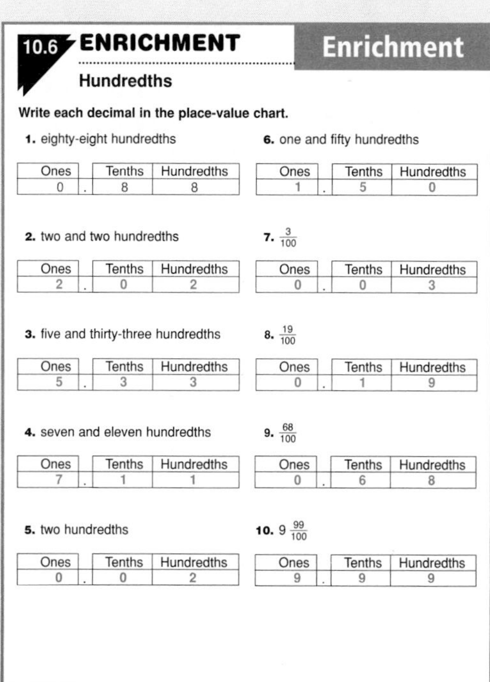

10.6 ENRICHMENT — Enrichment

Hundredths

Write each decimal in the place-value chart.

1. eighty-eight hundredths

Ones	Tenths	Hundredths
0	8	8

2. two and two hundredths

Ones	Tenths	Hundredths
2	0	2

3. five and thirty-three hundredths

Ones	Tenths	Hundredths
5	3	3

4. seven and eleven hundredths

Ones	Tenths	Hundredths
7	1	1

5. two hundredths

Ones	Tenths	Hundredths
0	0	2

6. one and fifty hundredths

Ones	Tenths	Hundredths
1	5	0

7. $\frac{3}{100}$

Ones	Tenths	Hundredths
0	0	3

8. $\frac{19}{100}$

Ones	Tenths	Hundredths
0	1	9

9. $\frac{68}{100}$

Ones	Tenths	Hundredths
0	6	8

10. $9\frac{99}{100}$

Ones	Tenths	Hundredths
9	9	9

Planning at a Glance

Objective To decide whether to use mental math or paper and pencil to solve problems

Materials none

Optional Resources

- Daily Cumul. Review, p. 92
- Math Center: Project Card 7
- Every Day Counts
- **TAB**, TE p. 226E–226F, 226J
- **Problem of the Day**, 92, p. 46; Flip Chart, p. 46b
- **Reteach, Practice, and Enrichment Worksheets for Lesson 7.9**

Unlocking Whole Numbers 3–5, Level 3, Activity 21

Students Acquiring English

Help with *order* and *receive*. Use a familiar context such as a school book club to explain the terms. Discuss how stores have to count what they have so that they will know how much more to order.

Problem of the Day

Each letter stands for a different number. A letter stands for the same number whenever it is used. Find numbers that will make the code work.

AM
+ME
EEL

one possible answer: 38 + 81 = 119

Problem Solving : Decisions

LESSON 9

Problem Solving

Choose a Computation Method

Choose a Computation Method

Ask Yourself:

Do I need an exact answer or an estimate?

Should I use a model, paper and pencil, mental math, or a calculator?

What operation should I use?

Suppose your aunt and uncle work in a bookstore. They ask you to help them find the total number of books to be ordered.

You Decide

- Is it important for you to know the exact number of books you are ordering? Why or why not? Answers will vary. Possible answer: Yes, so you will know the total cost of the order.
- Is there a way to group the numbers to make them easier to work with mentally? Answers will vary.
- Decide whether to use mental math or paper and pencil to find the sum. Explain your decision. Explanations will vary.

Work It Out!

Decide whether to use mental math or paper and pencil. Explain. Explanations will vary. Possible answers shown.

ORDER FORM

James and the Giant Peach	76 books
The Kids' Guide to Money	68 books
Raptors, Fossils, Fins, and Fangs	54 books
Charlotte's Web	82 books

1. You order 216 books and receive 149 books. How many more books should you receive? paper and pencil; regrouping needed
2. The store receives 3 boxes with 25 books in each. How many books are received? mental math; skip-count by 25
3. You order *Jumanji* for $4.99 and 2 copies of *Lyle, Lyle Crocodile* for $4.95 each. What does your order cost? mental math; think of whole dollar amounts to add
4. You buy a copy of *Loo-Loo, Boo, and Art You Can Do* for $8.79 You pay with a $10 bill. What is your change? 4. pencil and paper; need an exact answer

Share Your Thinking

5. How do you know when to use mental math? Answers will vary. Possible answer: when the numbers are easy to work with

244 Chapter 7

---

1 Introduce

Prior Knowledge **Have students solve these problems. Ask, Which one can you solve with mental math?** Answers may vary.

1. 25 X 4 100
2. 3000 + 400 + 90 + 7 3497

Teach: You Decide

Emphasize these points:

- Mental math can be easier and faster than using pencil and paper.
- Students can choose which method to use.

Modeling Model and discuss these examples: 639 – 39 600; 642 – 268 374

- Would you use mental math to solve the first example? Why? Answers will vary.
- What about the second example? Answers will vary.

2 Develop

Work It Out!

- Remind students not to compute before thinking about mental math strategies.
- For exercises 1–4, have students discuss and compare why they chose to use mental math or paper and pencil.
- For exercise 5, have students compare their generalizations about when to use mental math.

Using Reading Strategies Encourage students to use the Self-Question strategy as they read the problems. Ask, How can asking questions help you decide which computation method to use? See TE p. 226J.

Basic Facts Just the Facts Basic Facts Workshop 7, p. 114

3 Summarize

- Have students summarize their decision process for deciding when to use mental math and when to use pencil-and-paper computation.

Ongoing Assessment A team bus travels 4 miles for the first game, 22 miles for the second, 4 for the third, and 19 for the fourth. Which method would you use to find the total miles? Explain why. Answers may vary.

Math Journal: ***Communicating***

Make up a problem that can be solved using mental math. Make up a problem that can be solved using pencil and paper. Answers will vary but should show an understanding of when to use the respective methods.

Problem Solving Workshop

Mental Math or Paper and Pencil?

Review

Use with page 244.

15 minutes

Mental Math or Paper and Pencil?

Management teacher directed; whole class

- Make a chart on the board like the one below.

Which Do You Use?

Paper and Pencil	Mental Math

- Invite students to give examples of expressions that they would solve with mental math, and expressions for which they would use paper and pencil.

Which Do You Use?

Mental Math	Paper and Pencil
5 x 4 =	\$2.46 + \$8.32
16 ÷ 4	900 – 18
40 + 60	4 + 2 + 8 + 9 + 6
600 ÷ 200	
Conclusions: Use mental math for basic operations facts. Use it for operations with tens and hundreds.	Conclusions: Use pencil and paper for expressions that require regroupings or have 3 or more addends.

- When students have entered a variety of expressions in each column on the chart, discuss what they notice about the expressions. Ask, What types of problems do you solve using mental math? Using pencil and paper?
- Write students' conclusions at the bottom of each column.
- Discuss exceptions. For example, 300 –1 requires regrouping but would be easy to do mentally.

Activity

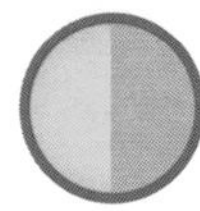

Use with page 244.

30 minutes

Even It Out!

Management groups of 3
Materials pencil and paper

- In this activity, students try to make sure that everyone finishes with the same number of points.
- One student in each group uses pencil and paper. One student uses mental math. The remaining student writes a problem for them to solve.
- The student who solves the problem first gets one point, then players rotate roles.

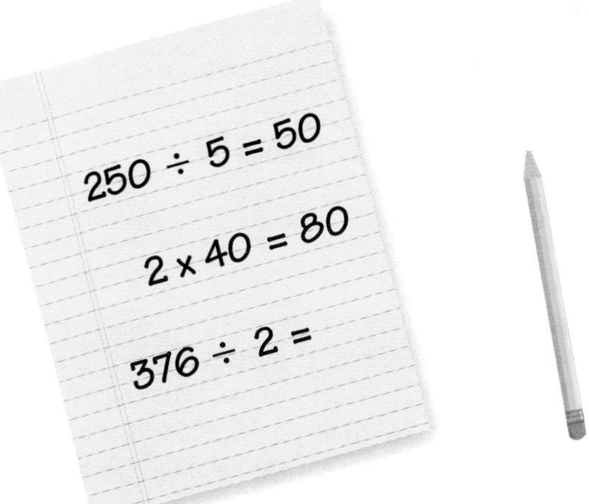

- Play continues in the same way. The student writing the problem should try to "fix" the outcome: problems should have a predictable result, so that the scores of everyone in the group remain as even as possible.
- The game ends when each player in the group has the same number of points over ten.

Basic Facts Workshop

Use with Lesson 7.9

Multiplying by 3

See also *Just the Facts*
- Support Masters
- Practice Worksheets
- Cumulative Practice

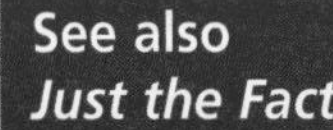
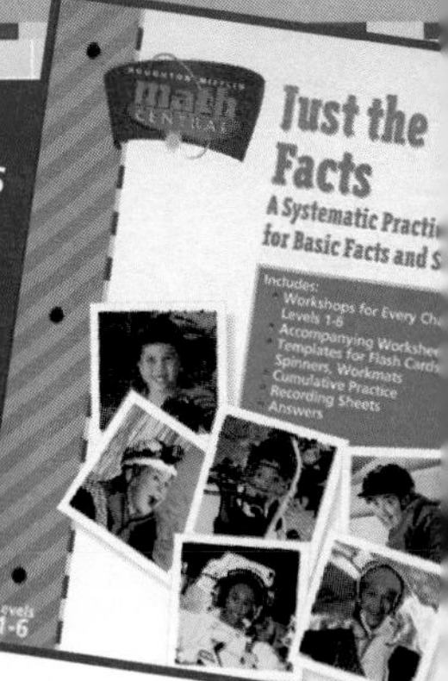

Review

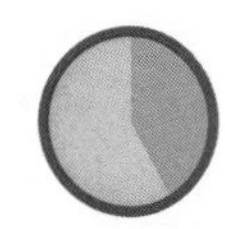

Use 2's to Find 3's

25 minutes

Management whole class
Materials overhead projector; **Just the Facts** Support Master 7 (hundredths square) on p. 288; See also Practice 7A–7B on pp. 132–133 for use with Lessons 7.10–7.11; Cumulative Practice 7 on p. 270 for use with Lesson 7.17.

- Draw a 2 × 5 array on a grid transparency. Ask students to name the array and the multiplication sentence it shows.
  2 × 5, 2 × 5 = 10
- Draw another row on the array to show 3 × 5. Ask students how knowing 2 × 5 = 10 can help them find 3 × 5.
  Another 5 can be added to find the answer to 3 × 5.

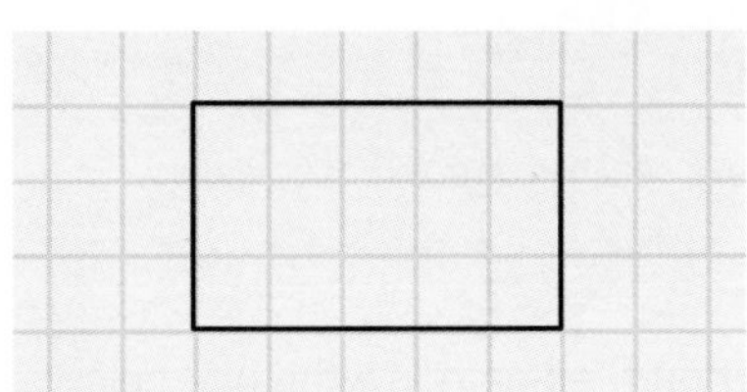

- Repeat the activity, using 2's facts to find 3 × 6, 3 × 4, 3 × 7, 3 × 8, and 3 × 9.
- Remind students that another way to find 3's is to skip-count. Have the class practice skip-counting by 3's to 30. Then ask students how skip-counting could help them figure out 3 × 3, 3 × 6, 3 × 8, and 3 × 9.

Practice

Make ×3 Flash Cards

30 minutes

Management individuals, then pairs
Materials for each student: 11 index cards; **Just the Facts** Support Masters 10, 14 (practice minutes, certificate) on pp. 291, 295; See also Practice 7A–7B on pp. 132–133 for use with Lessons 7.10–7.11; Cumulative Practice 7 on p. 270 for use with Lesson 7.17.

- Distribute index cards to each student and have them make flash cards like the ones shown below for the following facts: 3 × 3, 3 × 5, 3 × 6, 3 × 7, 3 × 8, 3 × 9, 5 × 3, 6 × 3, 7 × 3, 8 × 3, and 9 × 3.

- When students are finished making their cards, they should find partners and use their flash cards to practice multiplying by 3. Remind students to first write their names or initials on the backs of their cards.
- Tell students to add in the flash cards they have already made for 3's facts (3 × 1, 1 × 3, 3 × 2, 2 × 3, 3 × 4, and 4 × 3).
- Encourage students to take all their flash cards home to continue practicing their multiplication facts. Remind students to record the number of minutes they practice at home, and return completed records to school to exchange for a certificate.

Midchapter Review

for Pages 226–244

Problem Solving

Use any strategy to solve. Show your work. (pages 234, 242)

1. You order a cake with a border of frosting roses. The baker makes a blue rose, then a pink rose, then blue, then pink, and so on. Between each rose are 3 leaves. How many roses of each color will there be if there are 24 leaves in all? 4 pink and 5 blue roses
2. There are 4 boys and 4 girls sitting at a rectangular table. One student sits at each short end and 3 students sit at each long side. They sit boy-girl-boy-girl. If a boy sits at one end, is there a boy or a girl at the other end? a boy

Concepts

Write whether each picture shows a slide, a flip, or a half turn. (pages 228, 230, 232)

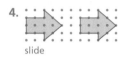

3. 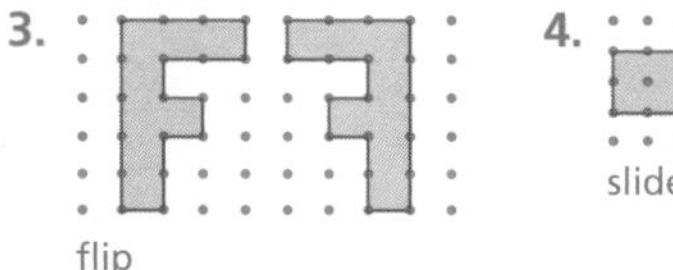 flip
4.  slide
5. half turn

Look at the figure. Draw a congruent figure. Draw the lines of symmetry. (pages 238, 240)

6. 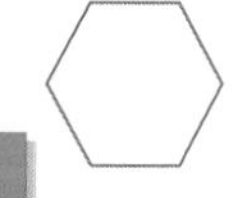 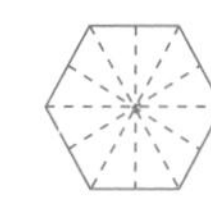
7. 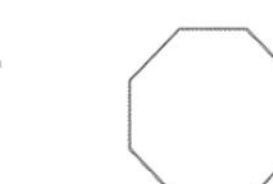 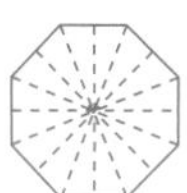

Skills

Compare the figures. (page 236)

8. Which has the most angles? b
9. Which has no angles? a
10. Which has 1 square corner? c

a.  b.  c. 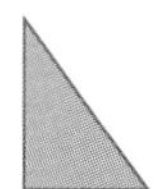

245

Meeting Individual Needs

Students Acquiring English

Some students may need assistance on the Midchapter Review.

- Be prepared to read directions aloud to students.
- Focus special attention on word problems. Expect to paraphrase, diagram, or draw an explanation of the word problem.
- Review important vocabulary words that have been previously introduced.
- Review titles and other elements of graphs and charts.

Additional Assessment Resources

 Test, Practice, Management Program

Use the *Test, Practice, Management Program* to create, administer, and score tests as well as generate practice sets. Questions are correlated to the Lesson Objectives.

Scoring Chart

Item	Points
1–2	16 points each
3–7	10 points each
8–10	6 points each
TOTAL	100 points or 100%

Problem Solving

Give from 0 to 16 points per answer, based on how well students meet the following criteria:

Problem 1

- Answer shows use of a particular strategy carried through to a correct solution.
- Student identifies pattern of roses and leaves.

Problem 2

- Answer shows use of a particular strategy carried through to a correct solution.
- Student identifies pattern of boys and girls alternating around a rectangle.

Concepts and Skills

If students are having difficulty in particular areas, use the appropriate Reteaching Worksheets listed below.

- 48 Slides, p. 140
- 49 Flips, p. 141
- 50 Turns, p. 142
- 51 Angles, p. 143
- 52 Congruence, p. 144
- 53 Symmetry, p. 145

Common Error Alert

If students are making frequent errors, see Analyzing Errors, TE pp. 265A–265B.

Item Analysis

Item	Objectives
1–2	To use Look for a Pattern and other strategies to solve problems (7H)
3–7	To use slides, flips, and half turns to move figures (7A)
8–10	To identify and classify angles, lines, and line segments (7C)

Tasty Symmetry

Background Rosette designs, like those used to make the Mexican pastries called *buñuelos,* may have their source in the Islamic art of medieval Spain, though windows in many Christian churches and cathedrals use similar designs. Complex geometric designs are characteristic of Islamic art, which by custom does not use representational figures.

Activity: Find Rosette Designs

- Ask students to identify and discuss lines of symmetry in the pastry.
- Ask students to look for rosette designs in your community. Where do they see them?
- Have students make card strips out of oaktag or similar material and use them to create their own rosette designs. Another way to create symmetrical designs would be to use a Spirograph or other commercially available kit.
- If there is a Mexican bakery in your community, bring in some *buñuelos* for a class snack. Comment on the lines of symmetry in the designs before eating.

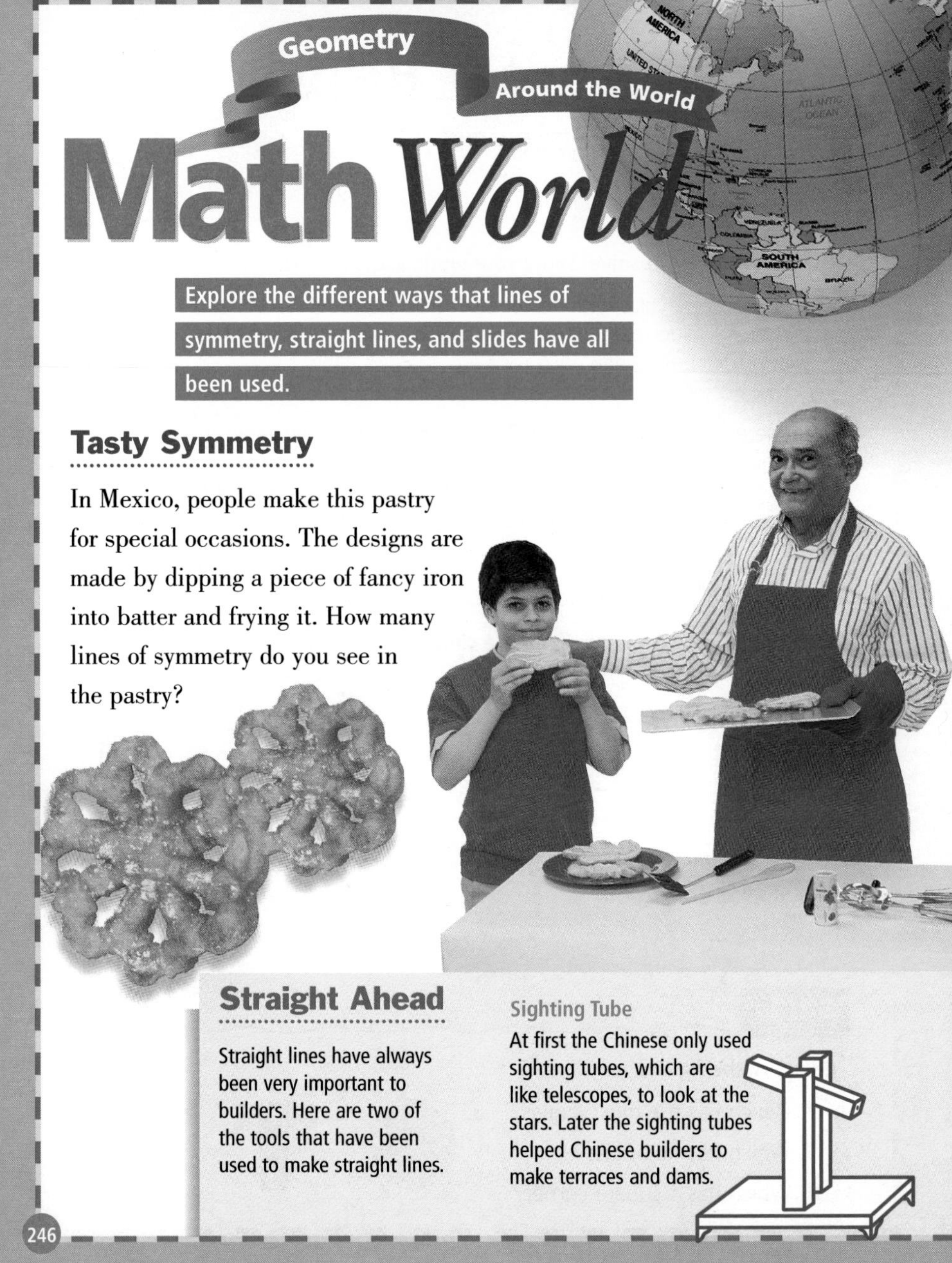
Geometry Around the World

Math World

Explore the different ways that lines of symmetry, straight lines, and slides have all been used.

Tasty Symmetry

In Mexico, people make this pastry for special occasions. The designs are made by dipping a piece of fancy iron into batter and frying it. How many lines of symmetry do you see in the pastry?

Straight Ahead

Straight lines have always been very important to builders. Here are two of the tools that have been used to make straight lines.

Sighting Tube

At first the Chinese only used sighting tubes, which are like telescopes, to look at the stars. Later the sighting tubes helped Chinese builders to make terraces and dams.

246

For More Information

Word Origins

survey

From the Old French *surveeir*, "to survey," from the Latin *super*, meaning "over," and *videre*, "to see."

Among instruments used for surveying are the Chinese sighting tube and the modern laser.

Discuss with students why the word *survey* applies to the art of measuring for size, shape, position, or boundaries.

Literature

Lasers
Marshall Cavendish Corp., 1996
Mary Virginia Fox

Medieval Life
Alfred A. Knopf, Inc., 1996
Andrew Langley

Cultures of the Past: The Ancient Egyptians
Marshall Cavendish Corp., 1996
Elisa Marston

Gordon Gould: Laser Man
Rourke Enterprises, 1993
Scott McPartland

Lasers
Facts on File, 1992
Charlene W. Billings

Janice VanCleave's Geometry for Every Kid: Easy Activities That Make Learning Geometry Fun
John Wiley & Sons Inc., 1994
Janice VanCleave

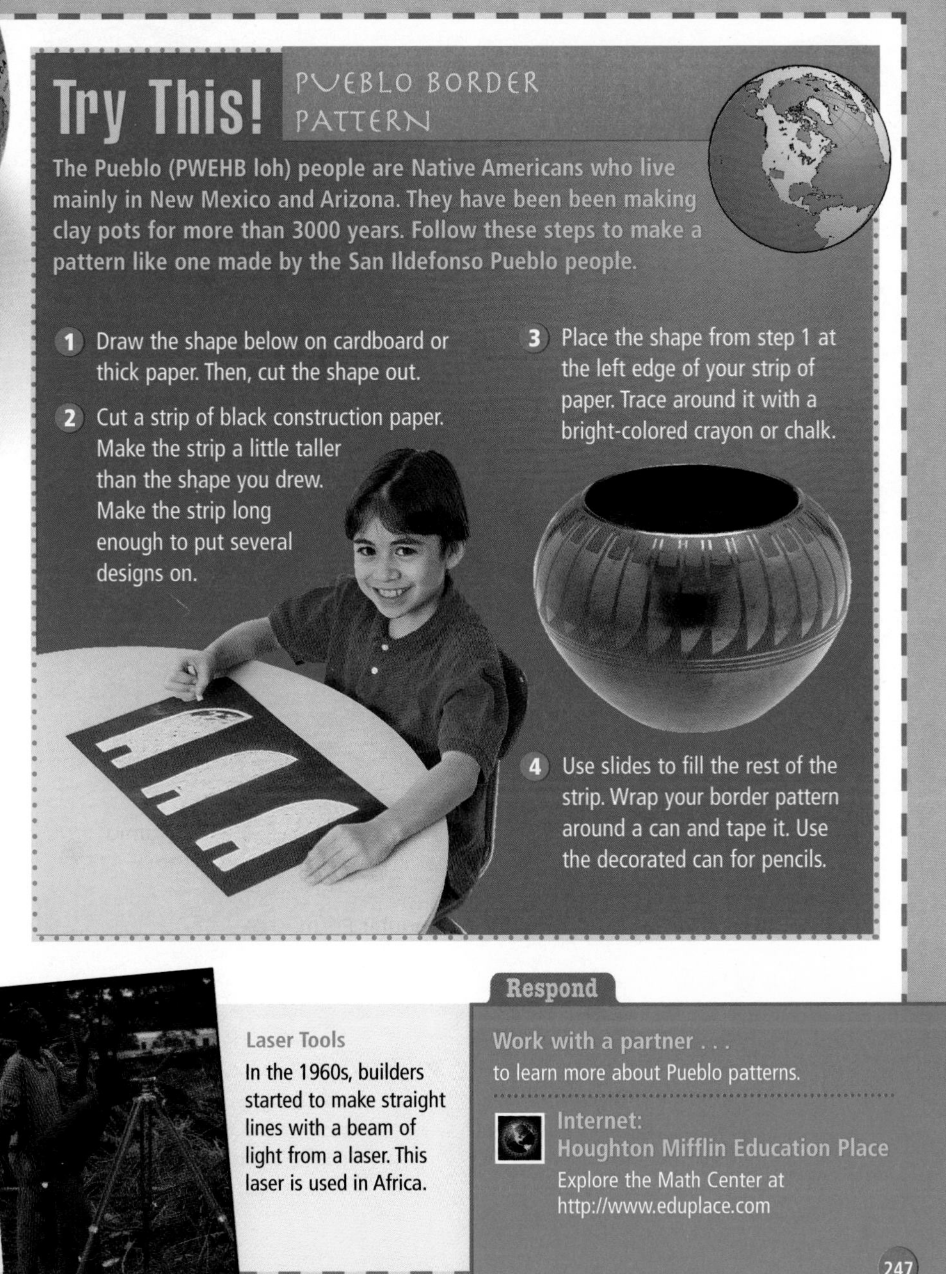

Try This! PUEBLO BORDER PATTERN

The Pueblo (PWEHB loh) people are Native Americans who live mainly in New Mexico and Arizona. They have been been making clay pots for more than 3000 years. Follow these steps to make a pattern like one made by the San Ildefonso Pueblo people.

1. Draw the shape below on cardboard or thick paper. Then, cut the shape out.
2. Cut a strip of black construction paper. Make the strip a little taller than the shape you drew. Make the strip long enough to put several designs on.
3. Place the shape from step 1 at the left edge of your strip of paper. Trace around it with a bright-colored crayon or chalk.
4. Use slides to fill the rest of the strip. Wrap your border pattern around a can and tape it. Use the decorated can for pencils.

Laser Tools
In the 1960s, builders started to make straight lines with a beam of light from a laser. This laser is used in Africa.

Respond

Work with a partner . . .
to learn more about Pueblo patterns.

Internet:
Houghton Mifflin Education Place
Explore the Math Center at http://www.eduplace.com

247

Straight Ahead

Background The Chinese used sighting tubes to lay out terraces and to survey irrigation and flood-control projects. The fact that these early Chinese surveying instruments were originally used for astronomical observation is paralleled by the basic Western surveying tool, the transit, which is essentially a telescope mounted on a tripod. The use of laser tracking levels for projecting straight lines and planes relative to the horizon also has its parallels in astronomy.

Critical Thinking Discuss with students why it is useful for builders to be able to plot straight horizontal and vertical lines.

Pueblo Border Pattern

Background The people of San Idelfonso have occupied their pueblo for more than 700 years. Interest in their pottery and other arts has enhanced the economy of the pueblo since the 1920s. Designs traditionally used by San Idelfonso potters, of which the one used in the activity is among the simplest, include many uses of slides, flips, and turns.

Critical Thinking After completing the activity, ask students to comment on how they used slides, flips, or turns in their design.

Technology

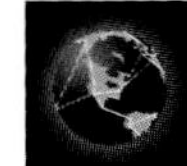

Internet: Education Place
http://www.eduplace.com
Houghton Mifflin Education Place **Mathematics Center** provides teacher and student support, such as links to other Internet sites.

Ultimate Writing & Creativity Center
Students can use the *Ultimate Writing & Creativity Center* for all their writing and publishing activities.

Kid to Kid

Project Ask students what they might ask if they met a student from the San Idelfonso Pueblo.

Suggest:

- *You could ask what they study in school and what they do in their free time.*
- *You could ask if they'd like to trade samples of artwork with you.*

Students could write to the Pueblo Cultural Center, 2401 12th Street NW, Albuquerque, NM 87192 to contact San Idelfonso children.

Activity

Planning at a Glance

Objectives To identify solids by name; to identify the number of edges, faces, and corners

Materials geometric solids, straw, clay, Recording Sheet (Practice 7.10)

Optional Resources
- Reteach 7.10; Enrichment 7.10
- Daily Cumul. Review, p. 93
- Math Center: How-To Card 23
- Every Day Counts
- **TAB**, TE pp. 226E–226F, 226J
- **Problem of the Day**, 93, p. 47; Flip Chart, p. 47a

Students Acquiring English

Hold up cutouts of flat figures as well as solid figures and discuss each one. Point out the corners, edges, and faces of the solid figures, helping students identify each one.

Problem of the Day

Kyra has a wooden box shaped like a pyramid. The top comes off at the heavy line. When the top is off, what shape is the opening?

square or rectangle

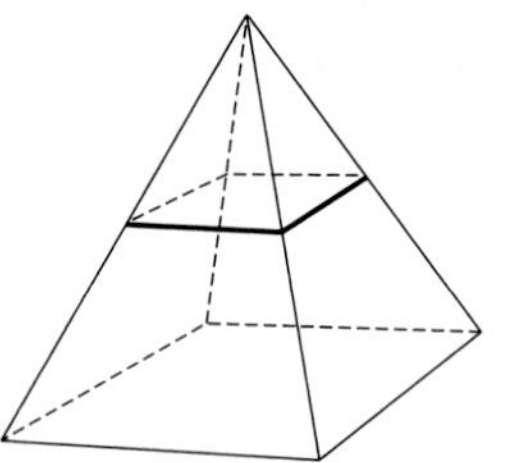

Solids

Cooperative Learning Checklist
- ☐ Work alone.
- ☑ Work with a partner.
- ☑ Work with a group.

Getting Started

What You'll Need:
- straws
- clay
- recording sheet

Vocabulary:
- face
- square pyramid
- triangular prism
- Glossary, p. 480

Solid figures like cubes have flat surfaces. Each flat surface of a solid figure is called a **face**. Try making some solid figures of your own!

Activity

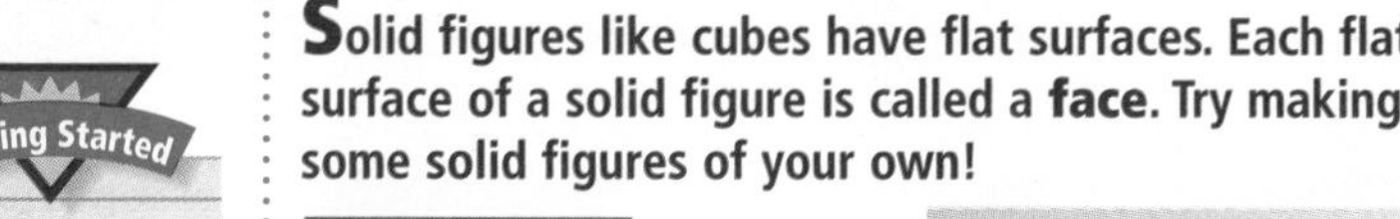

Figures	Corners	Edges	Faces

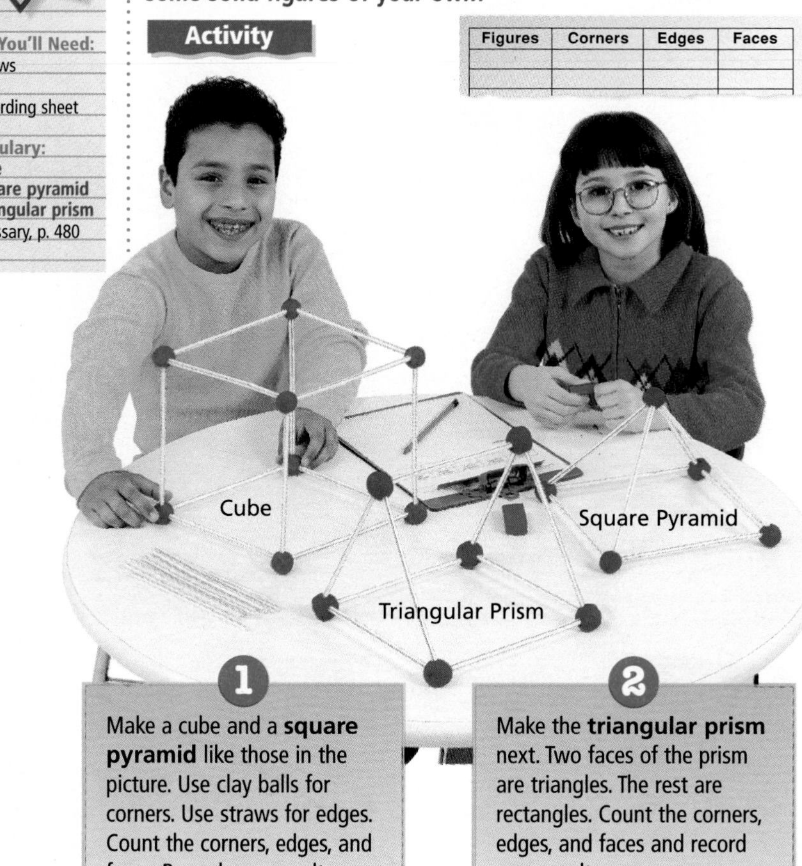

1 Make a cube and a **square pyramid** like those in the picture. Use clay balls for corners. Use straws for edges. Count the corners, edges, and faces. Record your results.
See Additional Answers.

2 Make the **triangular prism** next. Two faces of the prism are triangles. The rest are rectangles. Count the corners, edges, and faces and record your results.
See Additional Answers.

248 Chapter 7

1 Introduce

Build Understanding Provide students with geometric solids. Have students name each solid, count the faces, identify the shapes of the faces, and trace the faces. Sample answer shown.

Square Pyramid
5 faces
1 square face
4 triangle faces
tracings:

Teach: Activity

Emphasize this point:
- Most solids have corners, edges, and faces.

2 Develop

Show What You Know!

Ask students to relate the shape of each solid to a familiar object.

Common Error Some students may use the terms *sides* and *edges* interchangeably. Remind them to use *edges* when referring to where faces meet. See also Analyzing Errors, TE pp. 265A and 265B.

Using Reading Strategies Help students to use the Self-Question strategy as they read the exercises. Ask them to share their questions with a partner. See TE p. 226J.

3 Summarize

- Reemphasize that most solids have corners, edges, and faces.
- Remind students that the flat surfaces of a solid are faces.

Ongoing Assessment How many corners, edges, and faces does a sphere have? none

Math Journal: *Communicating*

Have students look at the shapes of the faces of pyramids and prisms. Then, have students explain the difference between pyramids and prisms. They should write that pyramids have a pointed top and several triangular faces. Prisms have several rectangular faces and matching shapes on 2 ends.

3

Make a rectangular prism with your clay and straws. How many faces does it have? What shape are they? Count the corners and edges. Record your results.

See Additional Answers.

4

Think of a way to sort your figures into 2 different groups.

- Draw a picture of the groups. Write your rule.
- Sort your figures again using a different sorting rule.

Answers will vary. Possible groups: a group with triangular faces, a group without; a group with 5 faces, a group with 6 faces.

Show What You Know!

Name the shape of the red face on each solid.

1. 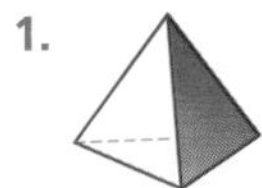 Triangular Pyramid — triangle
2. 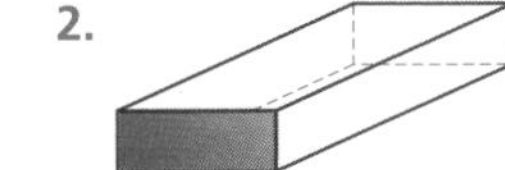 Rectangular Prism — rectangle
3. 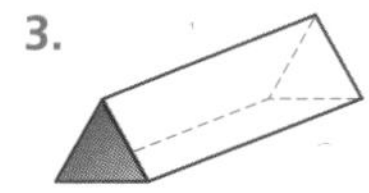 Triangular Prism — triangle
4. The bottom face of a cube and a square pyramid are squares. What shapes are the other faces in each solid? cubes: squares; square pyramid: triangles
5. Look at the triangular pyramid. How is it like a square pyramid? How is it different? Faces other than the base are all triangles; one's base is a triangle and the other's base is a square.
6. You have seen two prisms. What is the same about them? What is different? Both prisms have rectangular faces and 2 congruent, parallel bases. The bases are triangles on one and rectangles on the other.
7. **Critical Thinking** Study these solids. Could you build each solid with your straws and clay? Explain. No. These solids have curved surfaces.

Sphere  Cone   Cylinder 

8. **Write About It** Build a solid with straws and clay. Write a description that tells about the faces, corners, and edges. Give only the description to a friend. Can your friend make the same shape from it? Descriptions will vary but should include the number of faces, edges, and corners.

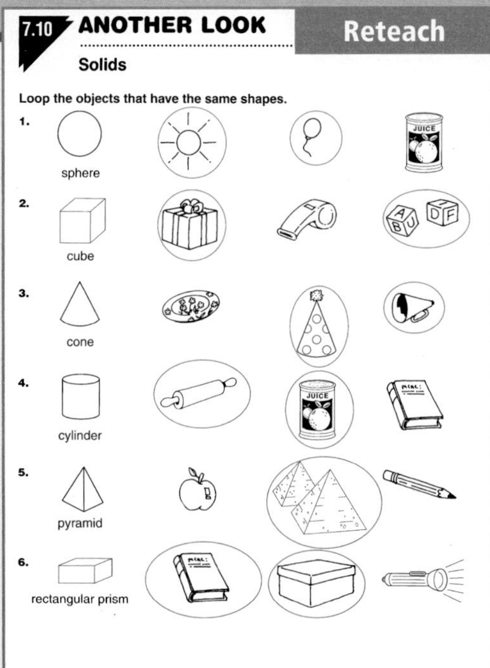

7.10 ANOTHER LOOK — Reteach

Solids

Loop the objects that have the same shapes.

1. sphere
2. cube
3. cone
4. cylinder
5. pyramid
6. rectangular prism

7.10 PRACTICE/RECORDING SHEET — Practice

Solids

	Corners	Edges	Faces
Cube	8	12	6
Square pyramid	5	8	5
Triangular prism	6	9	5
Rectangular prism	8	12	6

Work Space

Meeting Individual Needs

Extra Support

Building Solids *(kinesthetic)* Encourage students to find solids such as milk cartons, cardboard boxes, and blocks. They can use the pictures on Student Book pages 248 and 249 as a guide to help them label each solid as a cube, pyramid, rectangular prism, or triangular prism.

Alternate Approach

- Reteach Worksheet 7.10
- **TAB** See TE pp. 226E–226F.

MathZones

Understanding Geometry

Students Acquiring English

See Language Connections, Ch. 7.

Challenge

If a cone and a cylinder are the same height and their circular surfaces are congruent, which solid could hold more inside it? the cylinder How do you know? The cone will fit inside the cylinder.

Practice

Math Center Use How-To Card 23, *Sorting Solids,* to have students practice identifying solids and counting their edges, faces, and corners.

See **Just the Facts** Practice 7A, p. 132.

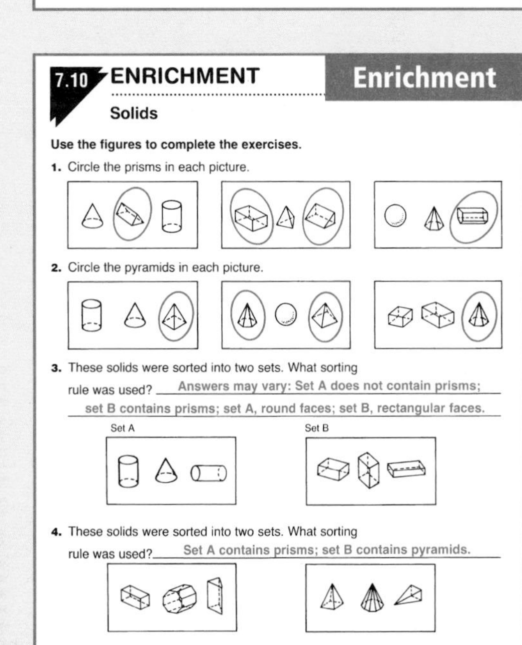

7.10 ENRICHMENT — Enrichment

Solids

Use the figures to complete the exercises.

1. Circle the prisms in each picture.
2. Circle the pyramids in each picture.
3. These solids were sorted into two sets. What sorting rule was used? Answers may vary: Set A does not contain prisms; set B contains prisms; set A, round faces; set B, rectangular faces.

Set A | Set B

4. These solids were sorted into two sets. What sorting rule was used? Set A contains prisms; set B contains pyramids.

Activity

Planning at a Glance

Objectives **To decide if solids are the same shape and size; to identify hidden cubes in a drawing of a solid**

Materials connecting cubes

Optional Resources

- Reteach 7.11; Practice 7.11; Enrichment 7.11
- Daily Cumul. Review, p. 94
- Math Center: How-To Card 24
- Every Day Counts
- **TAB**, TE pp. 226E–226F, 226J
- **Problem of the Day**, 94, p. 47; Flip Chart, p. 47b

MATHKEYS *Unlocking Geometry 3–6*, Level 3, Activity 18

Students Acquiring English

Give students cubes and ask them to make rectangular prisms. Help them identify how many cubes high and wide their prisms are. Then ask them to look at the prisms from one direction only. Ask if there are any cubes they cannot see. Explain that these cubes are *hidden*.

Problem of the Day

Drivers pay 30-cent tolls to cross a bridge. Automatic machines count the coins that drivers drop in as they go by, but the machines will not accept pennies. How many different ways can drivers pay the exact toll without pennies? 5 ways: 1 quarter and 1 nickel, 3 dimes, 2 dimes and 2 nickels, 1 dime and 4 nickels, 6 nickels

Visualization

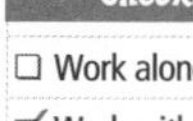

Cooperative Learning Checklist
- ☐ Work alone.
- ☑ Work with a partner.
- ☐ Work with a group.

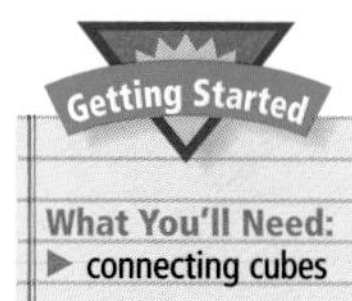

What You'll Need:
- connecting cubes

Are these two figures the same or different? You can find out by making the figures with cubes.

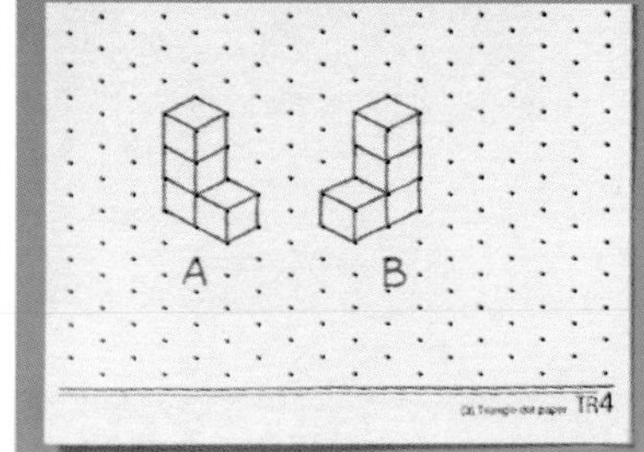

Activity

1 One partner uses the picture to make a stack of cubes that looks like Figure A. The other makes a stack of cubes that looks like Figure B.

2 Count how many cubes are in each model. Do Figure A and Figure B have the same number of cubes? A: 4; B: 4; yes

3 Can you make Figure A look like Figure B? Move Figure A to match Figure B. yes

250 Chapter 7

Prior Knowledge **Ask, How many corners, edges, and faces does a cube have?** 8 corners, 12 edges, 6 faces

Teach: Activity

Emphasize this point:

- The number and position of cubes within the solid determines the size and shape of the solid.

Modeling Model step 4 of the activity. Ask:

- Do the new figures contain the same number of cubes as figures A and B? yes

Show What You Know!
Ask students to identify which solids have the same number of cubes but are different shapes.

Common Error Some students may not recognize that 2 solids are the same when they are in different positions. Remind students that solids in different positions can have the same size and shapes. See also Analyzing Errors, TE pp. 265A and 265B.

- Reemphasize that the number of cubes within a solid contributes to the shape and size.

Ongoing Assessment Have students use cubes to build different figures, each of which contains 8 cubes. They should record their work on triangle dot paper.

Math Journal: *Communicating*

Have students describe how to draw cubes on triangle dot paper. All edges are the same length and each corner of a face is on a dot.

4 Compare Figure A and Figure B. Are they the same shape and the same size? yes

- Make two more figures that are the same shape and size, but in different positions.

Show What You Know!

Use the picture to build each figure. Write the number of cubes. Tell if any figures are the same size and shape. Figures 1 and 3 are the same size and shape.

1. 4 **2.** 6 **3.** 4 **4.** 4

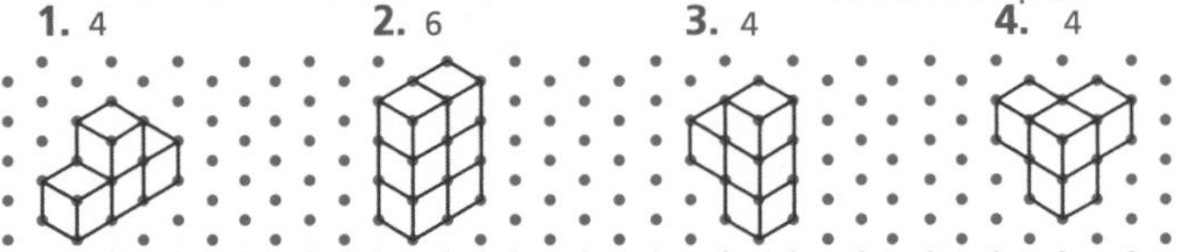

Use the pictures to build the figures. Then fit figures a and b together to make figure c. (Hint: Some cubes may be hidden.) Check students' work.

5. a. b. c.

6. a. b. c.

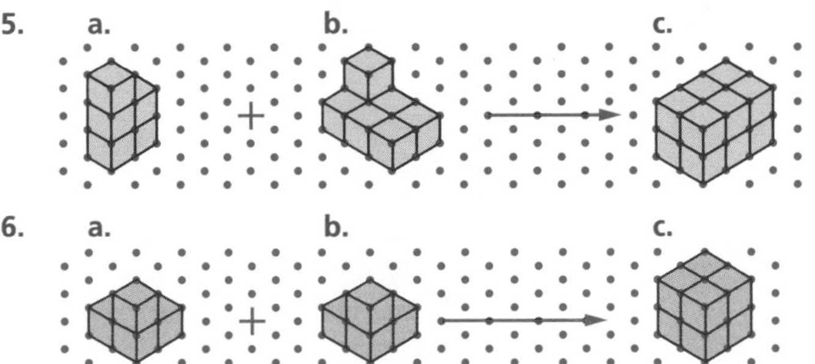

7. **Logical Reasoning** Is there a cube you cannot see in any of the pictures in exercise 5? How do you know? yes, in figure b; it is underneath the cube that sticks up.

Meeting Individual Needs

Extra Support

Solid Puzzles *(kinesthetic)* Ask students to build a rectangular prism with connecting cubes, then break it into 2, 3, or 4 pieces. Have them draw each piece on triangle dot paper (TR4), trade with a classmate, and try to rebuild their classmate's prism using connecting cubes.

Alternate Approach

- Reteach 7.11
- **TAB** See TE pp. 226E–226F.

MathZones

Understanding Geometry

Students Acquiring English

See **Language Connections**, Ch. 7.

Challenge

If a prism has two cubes on each surface, how many cubes would it have altogether if you doubled its length and width? 16 cubes

Practice

Math Center Use How-To Card 24, *Building Blocks,* to have students practice identifying hidden cubes in a solid made with cubes.

See **Just the Facts** Practice 7B, p. 133.

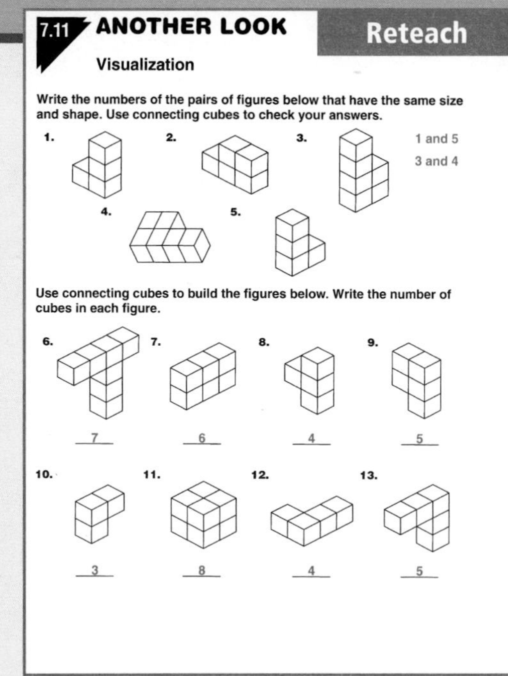

7.11 ANOTHER LOOK — Reteach

Visualization

Write the numbers of the pairs of figures below that have the same size and shape. Use connecting cubes to check your answers.

1. 2. 3. 4. 5. — 1 and 5; 3 and 4

Use connecting cubes to build the figures below. Write the number of cubes in each figure.

6. 7 7. 6 8. 4 9. 5

10. 3 11. 8 12. 4 13. 5

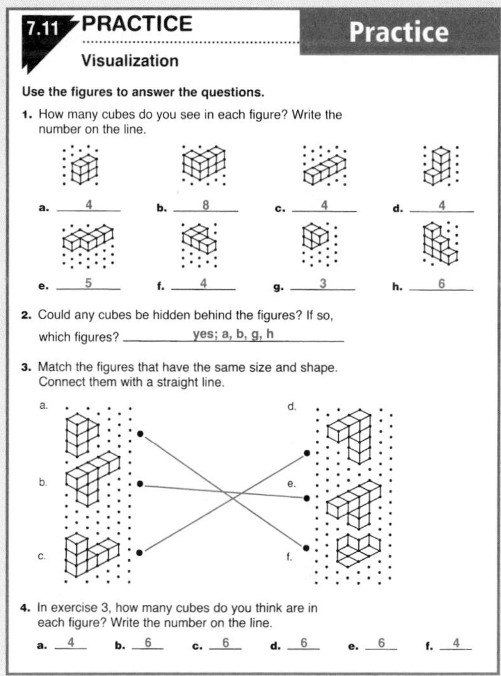

7.11 PRACTICE — Practice

Visualization

Use the figures to answer the questions.

1. How many cubes do you see in each figure? Write the number on the line.

a. 4 b. 8 c. 4 d. 4

e. 5 f. 4 g. 3 h. 6

2. Could any cubes be hidden behind the figures? If so, which figures? yes; a, b, g, h

3. Match the figures that have the same size and shape. Connect them with a straight line.

a. b. c. d. e. f.

4. In exercise 3, how many cubes do you think are in each figure? Write the number on the line.

a. 4 b. 6 c. 6 d. 6 e. 6 f. 4

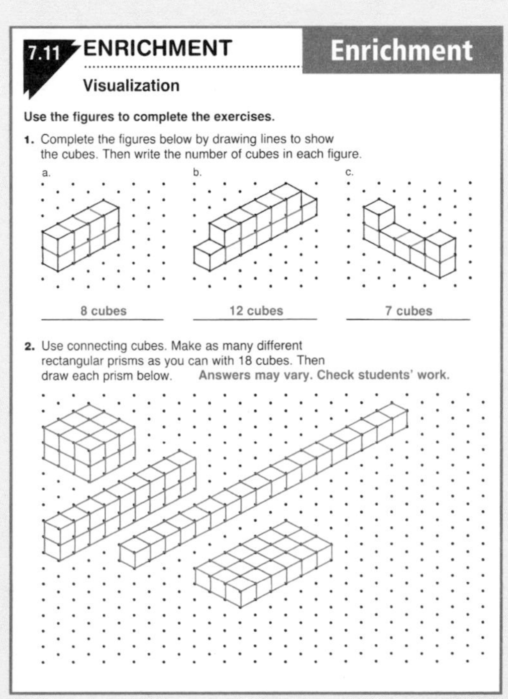

7.11 ENRICHMENT — Enrichment

Visualization

Use the figures to complete the exercises.

1. Complete the figures below by drawing lines to show the cubes. Then write the number of cubes in each figure.

a. 8 cubes b. 12 cubes c. 7 cubes

2. Use connecting cubes. Make as many different rectangular prisms as you can with 18 cubes. Then draw each prism below. Answers may vary. Check students' work.

Activity

Planning at a Glance

Objective To identify parallel and intersecting lines and line segments

Materials markers, ruler, square dot paper (TR3), geoboard, rubber bands

Optional Resources
- Reteach 7.12; Practice 7.12; Enrichment 7.12
- Daily Cumul. Review, p. 95
- Math Center: Act. Card 42
- Every Day Counts
- **TAB**, TE pp. 226E–226F, 226J
- **Problem of the Day**, 95, p. 48; Flip Chart, p. 48a

MATHKEYS *Unlocking Geometry 3–6*, Level 3, Activity 1

Students Acquiring English

Draw a line and a line segment; use them to make sure students understand the vocabulary used in the definitions of line and line segment: *straight, path, extends, directions, arrows, part, points.* Use these words as you give students directions to draw lines and line segments.

Problem of the Day

During a normal school day, when do the minute and hour hands on a clock form a single straight line segment?

One possible answer, with starting and ending times dependent on the school day: 8:11 A.M., 9:16 A.M., 10:22 A.M., 11:27 A.M., 12:33 P.M., 1:38 P.M., 2:44 P.M., 3:49 P.M. Note: these times are to the nearest minute.

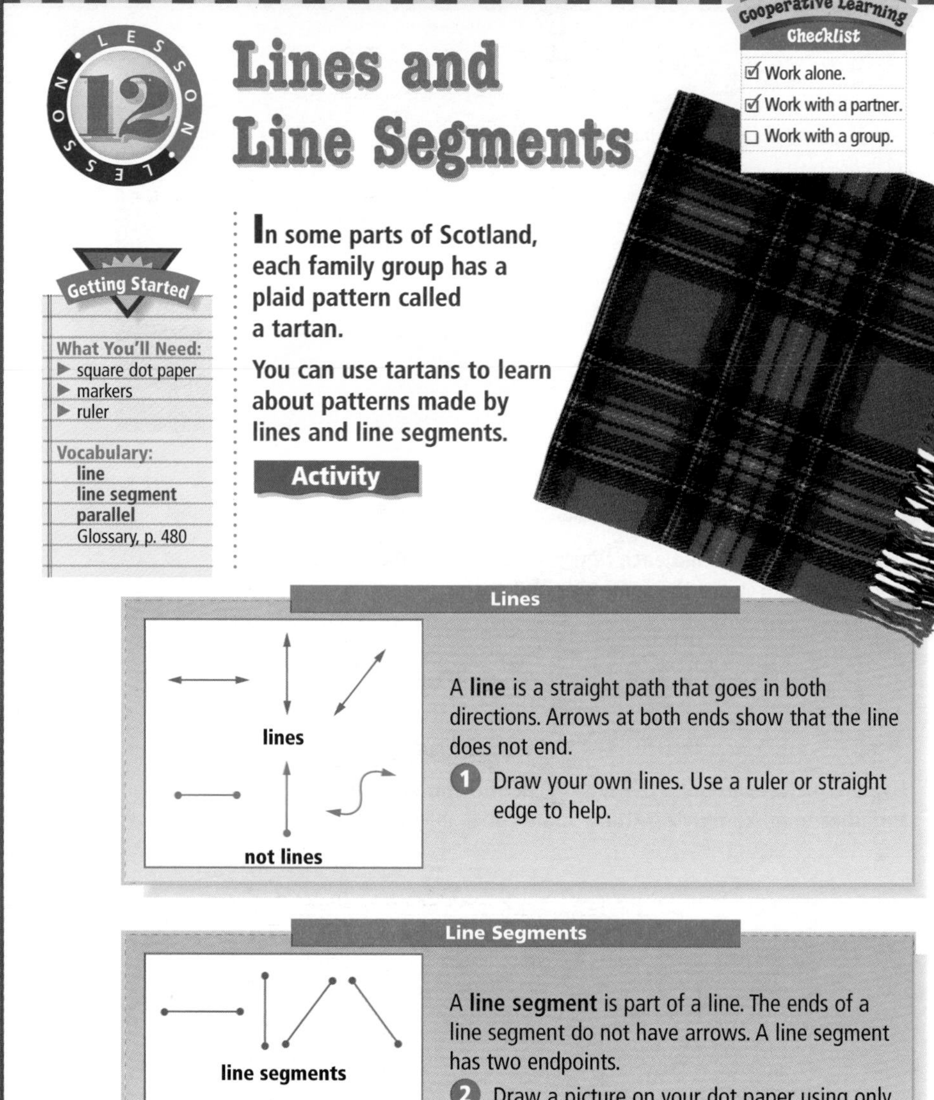

Cooperative Learning Checklist
☑ Work alone.
☑ Work with a partner.
☐ Work with a group.
LESSON 12
Getting Started
What You'll Need:
square dot paper
markers
ruler
Vocabulary:
line
line segment
parallel
Glossary, p. 480

Lines and Line Segments

In some parts of Scotland, each family group has a plaid pattern called a tartan.

You can use tartans to learn about patterns made by lines and line segments.

Activity

Lines

lines

not lines

A **line** is a straight path that goes in both directions. Arrows at both ends show that the line does not end.

1. Draw your own lines. Use a ruler or straight edge to help.

Line Segments

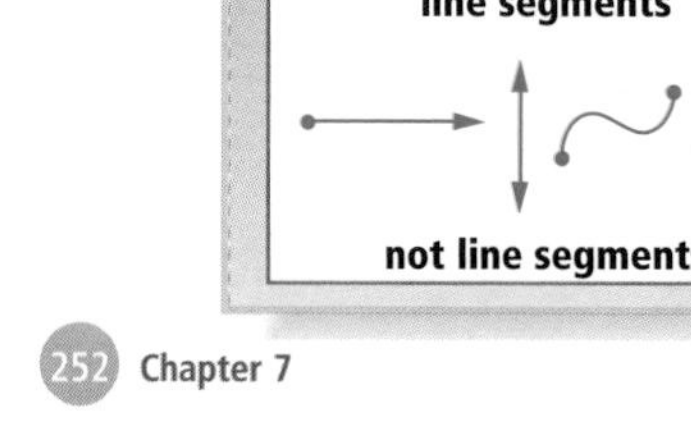

line segments

not line segments

A **line segment** is part of a line. The ends of a line segment do not have arrows. A line segment has two endpoints.

2. Draw a picture on your dot paper using only line segments.

   a. Can you use curves? Why or why not?
   No; Lines and line segments are straight.

252 Chapter 7

1 Introduce

Prior Knowledge **Model this figure on a geoboard.**

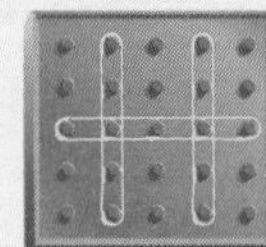

Ask, Which rubber bands cross each other? the horizontal one crosses both vertical ones.
Which rubber bands never touch each other? the vertical ones

Teach: Activity

Emphasize these points:
- Line segments are parts of lines.
- Parallel lines and line segments never cross.

2 Develop

Show What You Know!

Common Error Some students may not understand the difference between lines and line segments. Explain that lines never stop. Line segments stop at a point on each end. See also Analyzing Errors, TE pp. 265A and 265B.

- Discuss with students other fabric patterns besides tartan plaids that use parallel lines.
- Decide on two rules that define parallel line segments.

3 Summarize

- Remind students that lines never end, and line segments stop at a point on each end.
- Point out that lines and line segments are always straight.
- Point out that parallel lines never cross.

Ongoing Assessment If two lines cross, are they parallel? no

Math Journal: *Communicating*

Ask students to describe what their math book would look like without parallel edges. Answers will vary, but may include a description of uneven straight edges or curved edges.

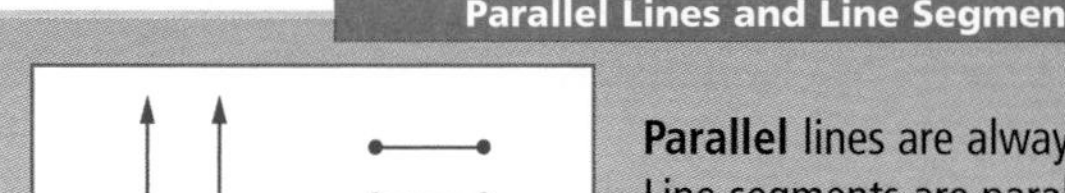

parallel

not parallel

Parallel lines are always the same distance apart. Line segments are parallel when they are part of parallel lines.

3 Draw a square, a rectangle, and a triangle on your paper.

4 Which shapes have sides that are parallel line segments? Mark each pair of parallel line segments with a different color. square and rectangle

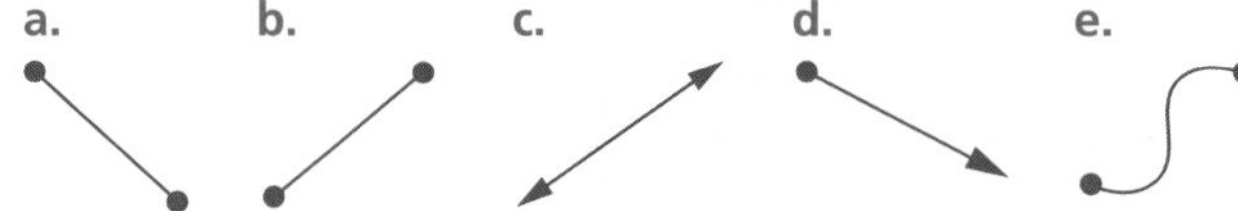

1. **Critical Thinking** Is the design on the blanket on page 252 made of lines or line segments? Explain. line segments, since they end and lines do not end

Use the pictures to answer questions 2 and 3.

a. b. c. d. e.

2. Which pictures show lines? Explain. c; it is straight and has arrows
3. Which pictures show line segments? Explain. a and b; they are straight and have endpoints

Do the colored parts of the drawing show parallel line segments? Explain your answer.

4. 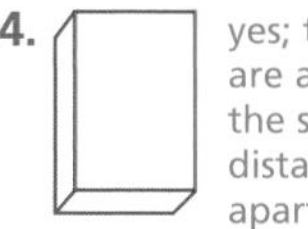 yes; they are always the same distance apart

5.  no; they cross

6. 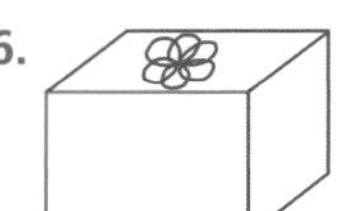 no; they meet at a right angle

7. **Create Your Own** Use a ruler and markers to create your own tartan on dot paper. Use parallel line segments and line segments that cross. Patterns will vary but should show students' understanding of parallel line segments.

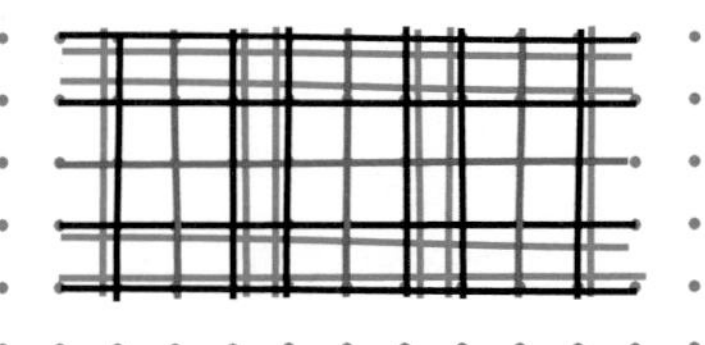

Meeting Individual Needs

Extra Support

Map Making *(visual)* Invite students to include parallel lines on a design of a city map on square dot paper. Suggest that they include a park, school, playground, library, shopping center, homes, and streets. Have them compare their maps with those of their classmates, and discuss the importance of parallel lines in their maps.

Alternate Approach

- Reteach Worksheet 7.12
- **TAB** See TE pp. 226E–226F.

MathZones
Understanding Geometry

Students Acquiring English

See Language Connections, Ch. 7.

Challenge

Name two solids that are made of pairs of parallel line segments. a cube and a rectangular prism Name two solids that have no parallel line segments. a cone and sphere

Practice

Math Center Use Activity Card 42, *Parallel Pick,* to have students practice identifying parallel and intersecting lines.

Challenge Use Activity Card 42 and have students continue as described in Now Try This!

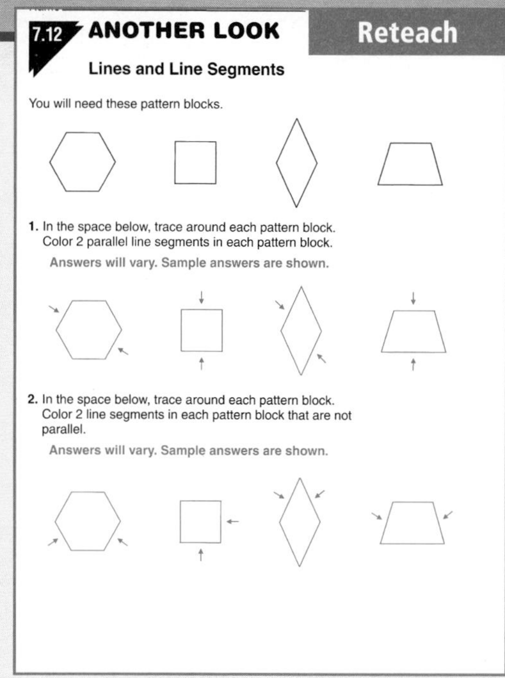

7.12 ANOTHER LOOK — Reteach

Lines and Line Segments

You will need these pattern blocks.

1. In the space below, trace around each pattern block. Color 2 parallel line segments in each pattern block.
Answers will vary. Sample answers are shown.

2. In the space below, trace around each pattern block. Color 2 line segments in each pattern block that are not parallel.
Answers will vary. Sample answers are shown.

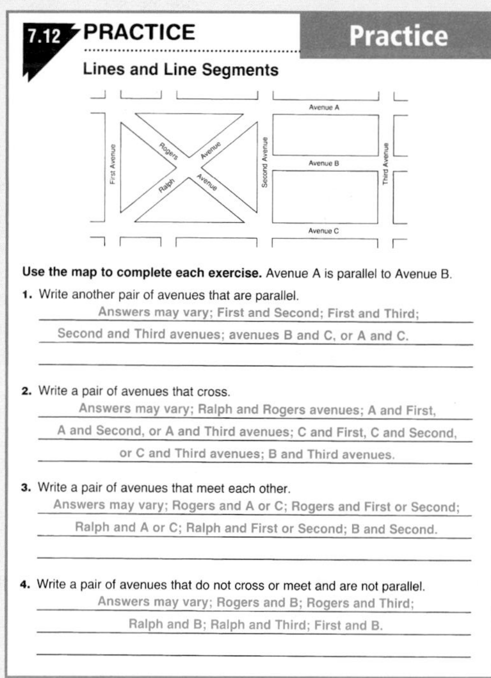

7.12 PRACTICE — Practice

Lines and Line Segments

Avenue A, Avenue B, Avenue C, First Avenue, Second Avenue, Third Avenue, Rogers Avenue, Ralph Avenue

Use the map to complete each exercise. Avenue A is parallel to Avenue B.

1. Write another pair of avenues that are parallel.
Answers may vary; First and Second; First and Third; Second and Third avenues; avenues B and C, or A and C.

2. Write a pair of avenues that cross.
Answers may vary; Ralph and Rogers avenues; A and First, A and Second, or A and Third avenues; C and First, C and Second, or C and Third avenues; B and Third avenues.

3. Write a pair of avenues that meet each other.
Answers may vary; Rogers and A or C; Rogers and First or Second; Ralph and A or C; Ralph and First or Second; B and Second.

4. Write a pair of avenues that do not cross or meet and are not parallel.
Answers may vary; Rogers and B; Rogers and Third; Ralph and B; Ralph and Third; First and B.

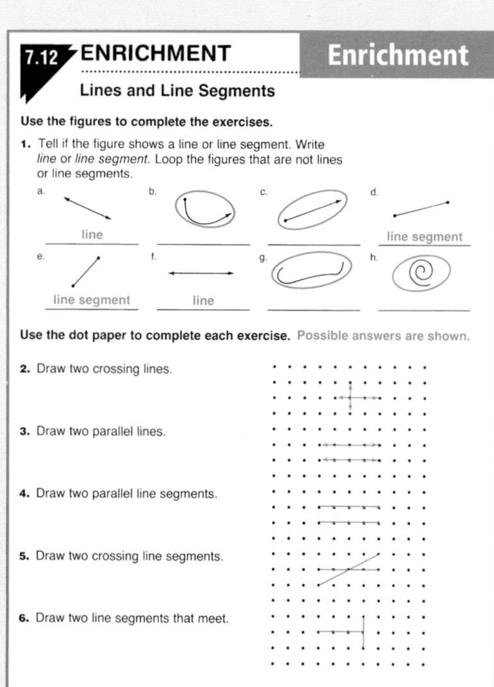

7.12 ENRICHMENT — Enrichment

Lines and Line Segments

Use the figures to complete the exercises.

1. Tell if the figure shows a line or line segment. Write *line* or *line segment*. Loop the figures that are not lines or line segments.
a. line b. c. d. line segment
e. line segment f. line g. h.

Use the dot paper to complete each exercise. Possible answers are shown.

2. Draw two crossing lines.
3. Draw two parallel lines.
4. Draw two parallel line segments.
5. Draw two crossing line segments.
6. Draw two line segments that meet.

Connecting

Planning at a Glance

Objective To use ordered pairs to locate points on a grid

Materials tracing paper, centimeter squared paper (TR2), gram cubes

Optional Resources

- Reteach 7.13; Practice 7.13; Enrichment 7.13
- Daily Cumul. Review, p. 96
- Math Center: How-To Card 25
- Every Day Counts
- TAB, TE pp. 226E–226F, 226J
- **Problem of the Day**, 96, p. 48; Flip Chart, p. 48b

MathKeys *Unlocking Geometry 3–6*, Level 3, Geogrid Mat (Alternate Approach)

Students Acquiring English

Help with the vocabulary of ordered pairs. Draw a numbered grid; label it *grid.* Ask students to point to the numbers on the *bottom* and *side*, and then to move their fingers *up* or *across.* Practice with statements such as: "Start at 0"; "first, move 3 numbers across"; "second, move 2 numbers up."

Problem of the Day

Chet, Maya, Hal, and Willa are the names of Victor's mom, dad, sister, and brother. Victor is older than Maya. Chet's dad has a grandson named Hal. How is each person related to Victor? Willa and Chet are Victor's mom and dad. Maya and Hal are Victor's sister and brother.

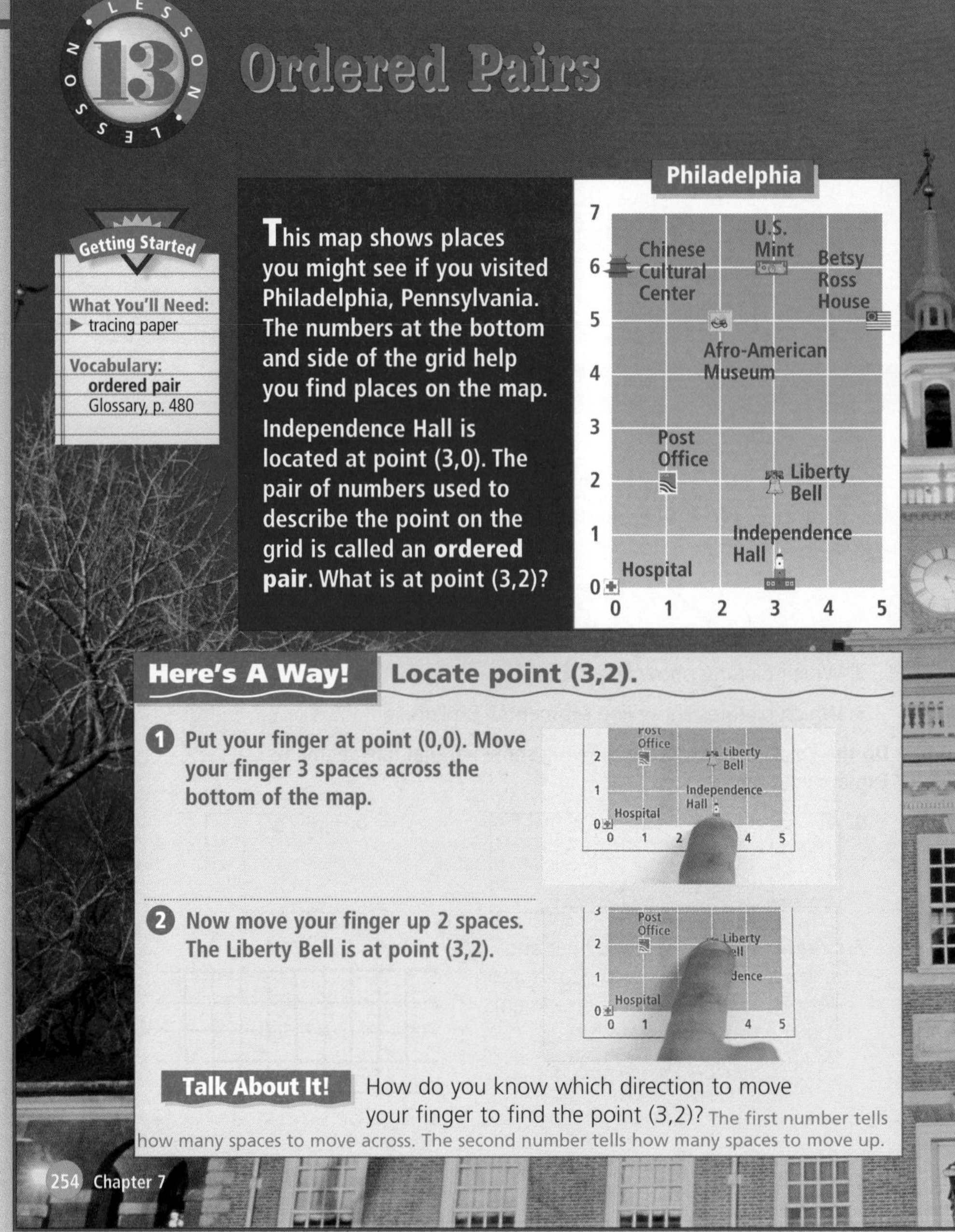

LESSON 13
Ordered Pairs
Getting Started
What You'll Need: tracing paper
Vocabulary: ordered pair Glossary, p. 480
This map shows places you might see if you visited Philadelphia, Pennsylvania. The numbers at the bottom and side of the grid help you find places on the map.
Independence Hall is located at point (3,0). The pair of numbers used to describe the point on the grid is called an ordered pair. What is at point (3,2)?
Philadelphia
Chinese Cultural Center
U.S. Mint
Betsy Ross House
Afro-American Museum
Post Office
Liberty Bell
Independence Hall
Hospital
Here's A Way! Locate point (3,2).
1 Put your finger at point (0,0). Move your finger 3 spaces across the bottom of the map.
2 Now move your finger up 2 spaces. The Liberty Bell is at point (3,2).
Talk About It! How do you know which direction to move your finger to find the point (3,2)? The first number tells how many spaces to move across. The second number tells how many spaces to move up.
254 Chapter 7

1 Introduce

Build Understanding **Have students outline a 10 × 10 square on centimeter squared paper (TR2). Have them place gram cubes in squares as you give these instructions (starting from 0 each time): "4 across, 8 up;" "3 across, 5 up;" "10 across, 1 up;" "2 across, 9 up."**

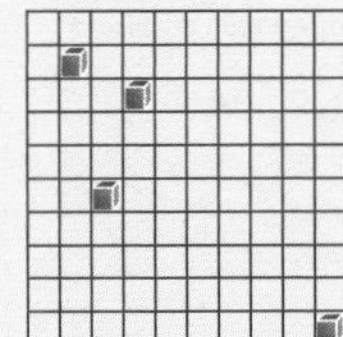

Teach: Here's A Way!

Emphasize this point:

- Move across to the first number in an ordered pair; move up to the second number.

2 Develop

Show What You Know!

Common Error Some students may reverse the numbers in an ordered pair. Point out that when numbers appear on both axes, reversing the numbers describes a different point. See also Analyzing Errors, TE pp. 265A and 265B.

Work It Out!

- Discuss the convenience of using ordered pairs to describe locations on a map.
- Explore other methods of describing points on a map.

Using Reading Strategies Encourage students to use the Self-Question strategy as they read the exercises. Ask them what questions they used. See TE p. 226J.

3 Summarize

- Remind students that an ordered pair describes a point on a grid.
- Reemphasize the importance of number order in an ordered pair.
- Point out that the numbers on both axes begin at the same corner of the map and that an ordered pair defines where two lines cross.

Ongoing Assessment What is located at (0, 0)? the Hospital

Math Journal: *Communicating*

Ask students to describe the location of the Franklin Institute without using ordered pairs. Answers will vary, but should reflect an understanding of the features on the map, including streets and other landmarks.

Show What You Know!

Use the map of Philadelphia on page 254. Find each place. Write the ordered pair of the point it is nearest to.

1. U.S. Mint (3,6)
2. Betsy Ross House (5,5)
3. Independence Hall (3,0)
4. the post office (1,2)
5. **Critical Thinking** Does it matter whether you give the ordered pair of a place as (3,2) or (2,3)? Explain. Yes. They are different locations.

Work It Out!

Use this map of Philadelphia for exercises 6–12. Find the ordered pair for each place.

Philadelphia

Franklin Institute
Hospital
Academy of Natural Sciences
Tourist Info Center
City Hall

6. City Hall (7,0)
7. the Franklin Institute (1,4)
8. the Tourist Information Center (5,1)
9. What is located at (2,3)? Academy of Natural Sciences
10. What is located at (6,4)? Hospital
11. Is (5,7) on the map? Explain. No. Map goes only 5 spaces up and you need to go up 7 spaces.
12. Trace the grid map above. Draw a straight line between the Academy of Natural Sciences and the Franklin Institute. Draw another between the Tourist Information Center and City Hall. Are the lines parallel? Explain. no, they are not parallel; Explanations will vary.
13. **Create Your Own** Trace this grid. Draw your own map. Give a friend the ordered pair for a place. Can your friend find it? Maps will vary but must include numbered grid.

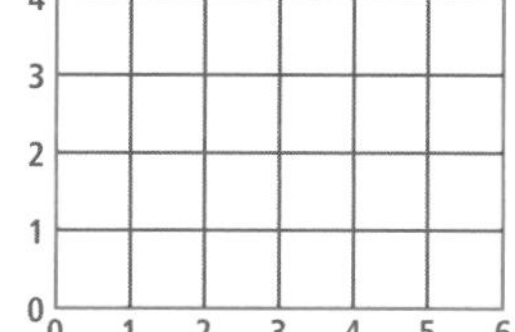

Mixed Review

Write < or >.

14. 741 ● 714 >
15. 2113 ● 987 >
16. $601 ● $599 >
17. 1033 ● 1303 <

More Practice Set 7.13, p. 462

255

Meeting Individual Needs

Extra Support

Bingo (*visual*) Ask students to create their own bingo cards by drawing a 6 by 6 array, and labeling the columns and rows with the numbers 1–6. Have students in small groups take turns rolling two number cubes. The player who rolls writes the product in any available boxes indicated by the two factors. The first player to write all the products in a row, column, or diagonally wins.

Alternate Approach

- Reteach Worksheet 7.13
- **TAB** See TE pp. 226E–226F.

MathZones

Understanding Geometry

Students Acquiring English

See Language Connections, Ch. 7.

Challenge

If a map used letters and numbers, where would 1A be on the map? in the first column, first row; the lower left corner

Practice

Math Center Use How-To Card 25, *Map It Out,* to have students practice using ordered pairs to locate regions on a grid and on a map.

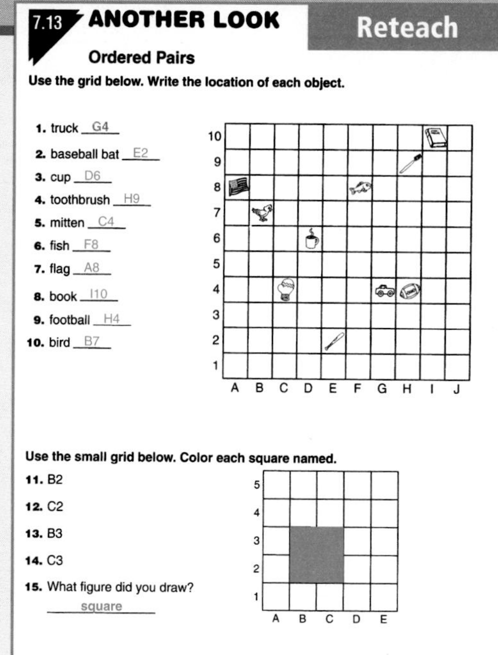

7.13 ANOTHER LOOK — Reteach

Ordered Pairs

Use the grid below. Write the location of each object.

1. truck G4
2. baseball bat E2
3. cup D6
4. toothbrush H9
5. mitten C4
6. fish F8
7. flag A8
8. book I10
9. football H4
10. bird B7

Use the small grid below. Color each square named.

11. B2
12. C2
13. B3
14. C3
15. What figure did you draw? square

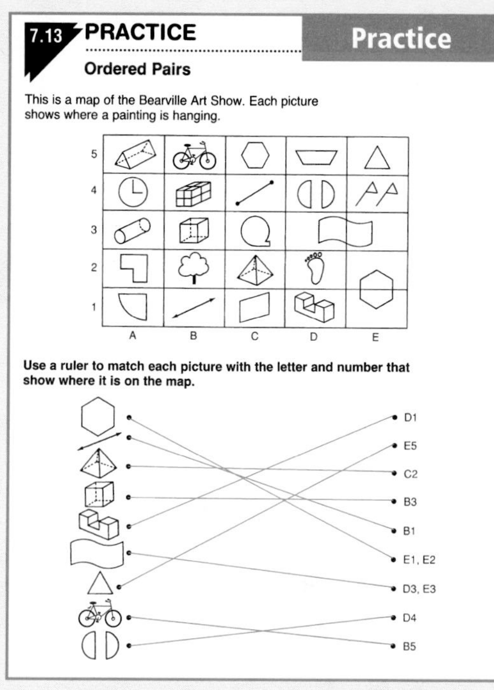

7.13 PRACTICE — Practice

Ordered Pairs

This is a map of the Bearville Art Show. Each picture shows where a painting is hanging.

Use a ruler to match each picture with the letter and number that show where it is on the map.

D1
E5
C2
B3
B1
E1, E2
D3, E3
D4
B5

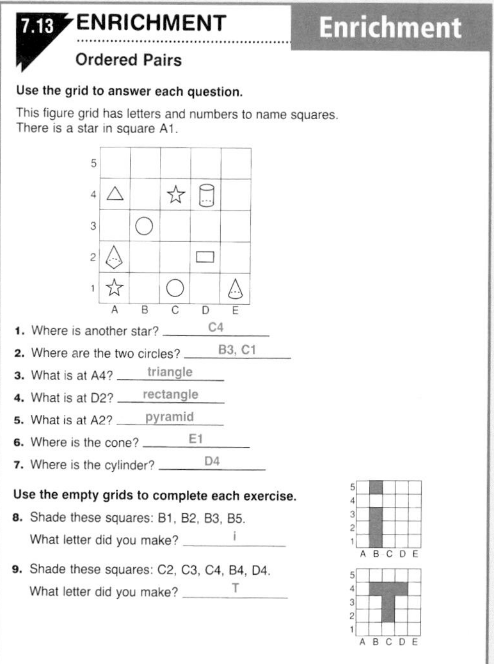

7.13 ENRICHMENT — Enrichment

Ordered Pairs

Use the grid to answer each question.

This figure grid has letters and numbers to name squares. There is a star in square A1.

1. Where is another star? C4
2. Where are the two circles? B3, C1
3. What is at A4? triangle
4. What is at D2? rectangle
5. What is at A2? pyramid
6. Where is the cone? E1
7. Where is the cylinder? D4

Use the empty grids to complete each exercise.

8. Shade these squares: B1, B2, B3, B5. What letter did you make? i
9. Shade these squares: C2, C3, C4, B4, D4. What letter did you make? T

Problem Solving

Planning at a Glance

Objective To use Look for a Pattern and other strategies to solve problems

Materials circular objects (e.g. counters, coins, paper plates), scissors, markers or crayons

Optional Resources

- Reteach 7.14; Practice 7.14; Enrichment 7.14
- Daily Cumul. Review, p. 97
- Math Center: Project Card 7
- Every Day Counts
- **TAB**, TE pp. 226E–226F, 226J
- **Problem of the Day**, 97, p 49; Flip Chart, p. 49a

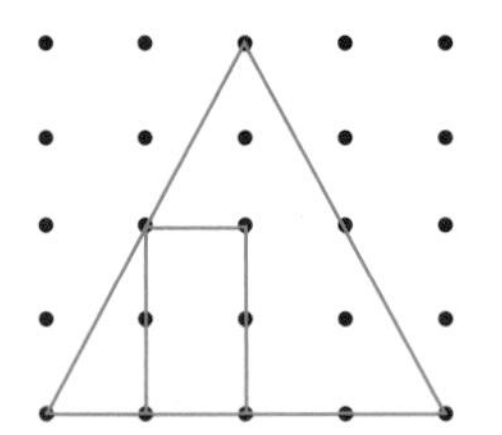

Unlocking Geometry 3–6, Geogrid Mat

Students Acquiring English

Have students acquiring English work in pairs to help each other with problems 1–8.

Problem of the Day

Make a triangle and a rectangle on a geoboard. The triangle must touch 8 pins, the rectangle must touch 6 pins, and both shapes must share 3 pins.

One possible answer is shown.

Problem Solving : Application

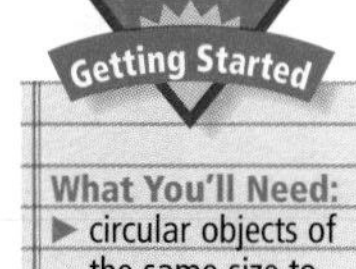

Problem Solving

Using Look for a Pattern and Other Strategies

Getting Started

What You'll Need:
- circular objects of the same size to trace around, such as coins, counters, or paper plates
- scissors
- markers or crayons

Suppose your class is making decorations for your classroom. You want to make a flower with a red center and yellow and orange petals.

Problem Solving Process
- ✓ Understand
- ✓ Plan
- ✓ Try It
- ✓ Look Back

Choose a Strategy You Have Learned
- ✓ Act It Out
- ✓ Look for a Pattern
- ✓ Guess and Check
- ✓ Draw a Picture
- ✓ Make a Table
- Work Backward
- Make a List
- Work a Simpler Problem

You will start with a red plate in the center. You will put 3 rings of plates around the red plate. The first ring will be yellow, the second ring orange, and the third ring yellow. How many plates will you need to make the flower?

- What problem needs to be solved? how many plates you need
- How can you find out how many yellow plates will fit around the red plate? How many orange plates will fit around the ring of yellow plates? Answers will vary. Possible answer: Act It Out
- Do you see a pattern? Describe it. yes; second circle is 6, third is 12, and so on
- Explain a strategy you can use to solve this problem. Then solve it. Strategies will vary. 1 red plate, 12 orange plates, 24 yellow plates; total of 37 plates

256 Chapter 7

---

1 Introduce

Explore **How many coins do you need to make a circle if each coin can only touch two other coins?** at least 5

Teach: *Modeling*

Model the example. Ask:

- How could you find out how many yellow plates you need? act it out with coins or counters
- How many plates will you need for the first ring? The second ring? 6 plates, 12 plates
- What pattern do you notice? each ring has six more plates than the last
- Based on the pattern, how many plates will you need for the third ring? 18 plates

2 Develop

Work It Out!

- Discuss that sometimes students may need to use more than one strategy.
- Have students discuss the strategies they used to solve problems 1–8.
- Ask students to share and discuss the patterns they created for exercise 4.
- Call on students to explain their reasoning for exercises 9 and 10.

Using Reading Strategies Help students to use the Self-Question strategy as they read the problems. Ask, What kinds of questions are most helpful? See TE p. 226J.

3 Summarize

- Have students review the strategies they used to solve each problem.
- Remind students that sometimes they need to use more than one strategy to solve problems.

Ongoing Assessment Ted is putting poles in a triangular garden patch for bean plants to grow on. He puts 1 pole in the first row, 3 in the second, and 5 in the third. If the patch has 7 rows, how many poles will Ted need? 49 poles

Math Journal: *Communicating*

How does looking for a pattern help you solve problems? by letting you see what is going on without having to do complex computations.

Work It Out!

Use any strategy to solve the problem. Show your work.

1. Extend the pattern by drawing the next three circles. See Additional Answers

 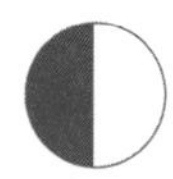 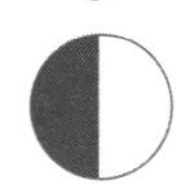 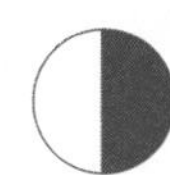 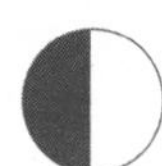

2. If you fold a circle in half, you can see a line of symmetry. How many times would you fold a circle to get exactly 4 lines of symmetry? 3 times

3. You want to make a flower for each person in the class. Eight people want red flowers. The rest want yellow flowers. There are 26 people in the class. How many yellow flowers do you need? 18 yellow flowers

4. **Create Your Own** Create a pattern with circles or figures. See if a classmate can continue your pattern. Check students' work.

5. You buy decorations. Your change is $11. How many different combinations of both $1 and $5 bills can you get? 2 combinations: two $5 bills and 1 $1 bill; one $5 bill and 6 $1 bills

6. Show the next three figures in this pattern. See Additional Answers

7. You need 35 plates for a party. You have 6 packages of 5 plates each. Do you have enough plates? If not, how many more do you need? no; 5 more plates

8. You want to make a border out of 15 plates. Put a red plate first. Then put an orange one, and then a yellow one. Then start over with red. What color will the last plate be? yellow

Share Your Thinking

9. What strategy did you use to solve problem 8? Explain your choice. Strategies will vary. Possible strategy: Draw a Picture.

10. Did you look for patterns to solve any of the problems? Which ones? Choose one problem and explain how you used patterns to help you to solve it. Answers will vary.

257

Meeting Individual Needs

Extra Support

Around in Circles *(kinesthetic)* Have student pairs use counters of uniform size to make concentric rings around a single counter.

Then have them count the counters that are in each ring and record their results. Help them find the difference between the number of counters in each pair of consecutive rings to identify the pattern.

Alternate Approach

- Reteach Worksheet 7.14
- **TAB** See TE pp. 226E–226F.

MathZones

Understanding Geometry

Students Acquiring English

See Language Connections, Ch. 7.

Challenge

A man is laying bricks for a garden wall. He alternates a row of long bricks and a row of short bricks. Three short bricks are the same length as 2 long bricks. The bottom row has 8 long bricks. How many short bricks will be in the second row? 12 short bricks

Practice

Math Center For more problem solving practice, see Project Card 7, *Teacher for a Day!*

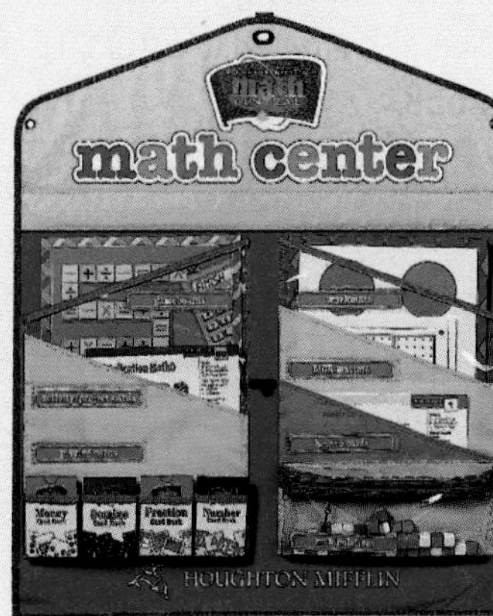

7.14 ANOTHER LOOK — Reteach

Using Look for a Pattern and Other Strategies

Look at these 3 rows of blocks. What pattern do you see? If you continue the pattern, how many blocks would you need to make the top 4 rows?

1. Understand
- You need to find the number of blocks to make the top 4 rows.

2. Plan
- Look at the picture. Find the pattern. There is one fewer block in each row than in the row below it.

3. Try It
- Draw pictures or use squares of paper to model the stack of blocks.
- Look for a way to decide how many blocks go in each row. You need to subtract 1 from the number of blocks in the row below.
- Count to make sure you make the top 4 rows.

4. Look Back
- There are 10 blocks in the top 4 rows. Count the blocks in your model to check your answer.

Solve. Use Look for a Pattern when you can.

1. How many lines would you draw to divide a rectangle into 8 equal sections? Show your work. 4 lines or 7 lines
2. A store display shows cans of different kinds of soup. The cans are in this order: chicken, vegetable, chicken, vegetable, chicken, vegetable. What kind of soup is in the ninth can? chicken soup

7.14 PRACTICE — Practice

Using Look for a Pattern and Other Strategies

Solve. Use Look for a Pattern when you can.

Chores	Minutes
Clean garage	50
Wash dog	40
Weed garden	45
Plant bulbs	30
Wash bikes	10
Clean playroom	25

1. Seth and Li Hua have chores to do. Seth likes washing things. Li Hua likes gardening. How can they divide up the chores so that they each spend the same amount of time on them? Seth—clean garage, wash dog, wash bikes; Li Hua—weed garden, plant bulbs, clean playroom
2. Seth is cleaning out the garage. He packs tools in a rectangular box and a cube-shaped box. The rectangular box holds twice as much as the cube-shaped box. There are 42 tools in all. How many tools are packed into each box? rectangular box—28 tools; cube-shaped box—14 tools
3. Steve is buying his mother a vase for her birthday. The vase costs $9.00. Steve pays with 2 bills and gets back a bill in change. What bills does Steve use to pay for the vase? two five-dollar bills
4. You are making 2 puppets to give to the children's hospital. It takes you 3 hours to make each puppet. You begin at 10:00 A.M. You take a one-hour break after finishing the first puppet. What time do you finish the second puppet? 5:00 P.M.

7.14 ENRICHMENT — Enrichment

Using Look for a Pattern and Other Strategies

Solve. Use Look for a Pattern when you can.

1. The world's largest flower grows in Indonesia. It measures 3 feet across. Suppose 3 of these flowers grow side by side. If there is a space of 6 inches between each flower, how long will the line of flowers be? 10 feet
2. The people of Hawaii make beautiful flower necklaces. Suppose one is made with red, yellow, and pink flowers. The flowers are strung in this pattern: red, yellow, pink, yellow. It takes 60 flowers in all to make the necklace. How many of each color are used? red–15, pink–15, yellow–30
3. The Parade of Roses in Pasadena, California, features floats that are decorated with thousands of flowers. Imagine that 100 people line up along the parade route at 6:00 A.M. Every 10 minutes, 50 more people arrive. How many people are lined up at 7:00 A.M.? 400 people
4. A florist sells carnations for 50¢ each and red roses for $1.00 each. You have $15.00. You want to buy twice as many roses as carnations. How many of each can you buy? 12 roses, 6 carnations
5. A florist is arranging flowers in a vase. It takes her 20 minutes to complete one flower arrangement. The florist will work from 10:30 A.M. until 3:15 P.M. She will take a 30-minute break for lunch and a 15-minute break in the afternoon. How many flower arrangements will the florist be able to make? 12 flower arrangements

Activity

Planning at a Glance

Objective **To investigate and determine the area of a polygon by counting half and whole square units**

Materials ruler, square dot paper (TR3), color tiles

Optional Resources

- Reteach 7.15; Practice 7.15; Enrichment 7.15
- Daily Cumul. Review, p. 98
- Math Center: Act. Card 43
- Every Day Counts
- **TAB**, TE pp. 226E–226F, 226J
- **Problem of the Day**, 98, p. 49; Flip Chart, p. 49b

MATHKEYS *Unlocking Geometry 3–6*, Level 3, Activity 16

Students Acquiring English

To help students with problems 14 and 15, remind them that a pattern is a series of numbers or things that is ordered in a certain way. Show examples with figures and numbers and demonstrate how to figure out what the next items will be. Ask students to work in pairs to draw and complete patterns.

Problem of the Day

Pat, Zed, and Kim are all men. Pat is Zed's father. Zed is Kim's father. How is Pat related to Kim?

Pat is Kim's grandfather.

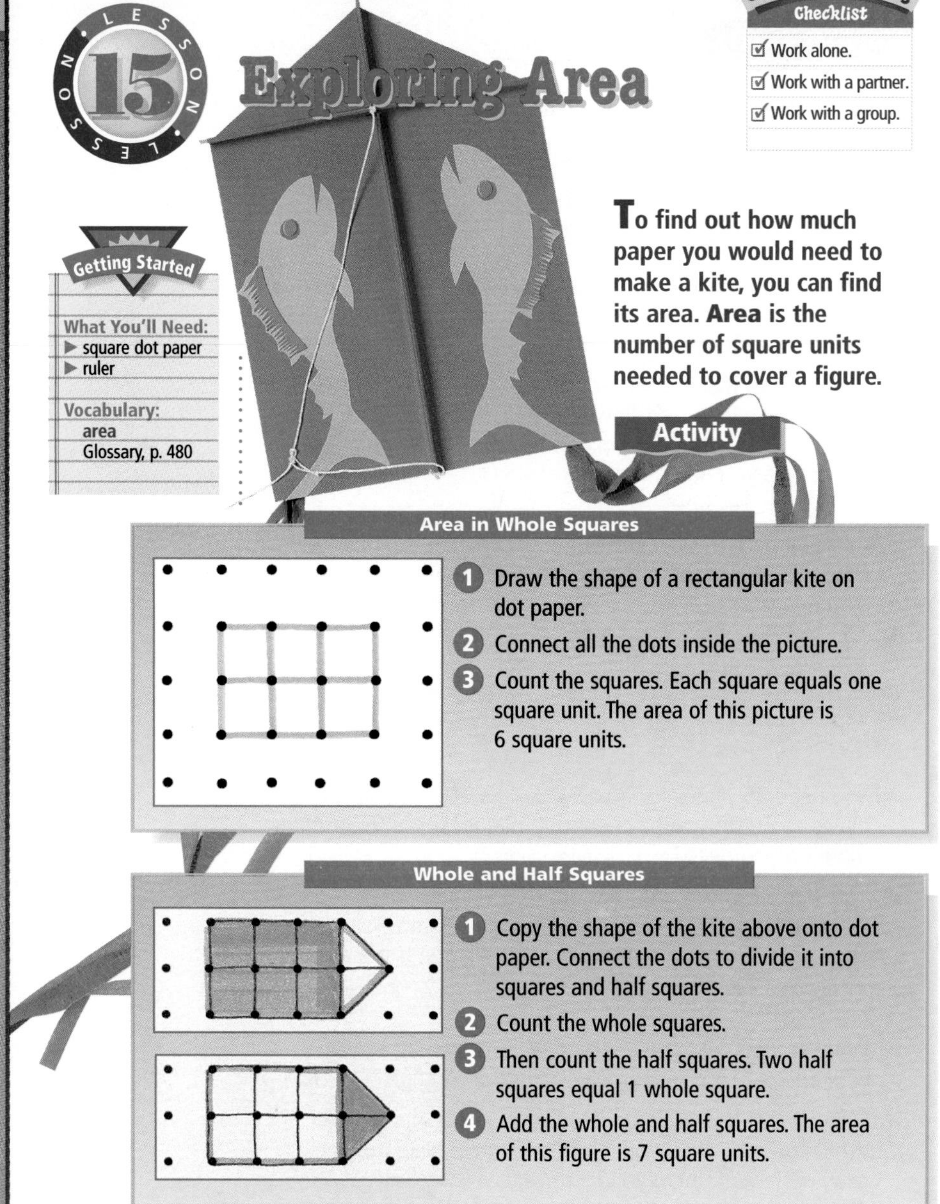

LESSON 15

Exploring Area

Cooperative Learning Checklist
- Work alone.
- Work with a partner.
- Work with a group.

Getting Started

What You'll Need:
- square dot paper
- ruler

Vocabulary:
area
Glossary, p. 480

To find out how much paper you would need to make a kite, you can find its area. Area is the number of square units needed to cover a figure.

Activity

Area in Whole Squares

1. Draw the shape of a rectangular kite on dot paper.
2. Connect all the dots inside the picture.
3. Count the squares. Each square equals one square unit. The area of this picture is 6 square units.

Whole and Half Squares

1. Copy the shape of the kite above onto dot paper. Connect the dots to divide it into squares and half squares.
2. Count the whole squares.
3. Then count the half squares. Two half squares equal 1 whole square.
4. Add the whole and half squares. The area of this figure is 7 square units.

258 Chapter 7

1 Introduce

Prior Knowledge **Have students make rectangles of different shapes and sizes from color tiles. Ask, What is the area of each rectangle?** Answers will vary. Possible answers shown.

6 square units

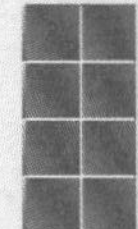

8 square units

Teach: Activity

Emphasize these points:

- Area is the size of a surface.
- Area can be determined by counting the number of squares the surface contains.

2 Develop

Show What You Know!

Common Error Some students may not add the half squares correctly. Demonstrate the concept of one half by drawing a whole square, then bisecting it from corner to corner. Ask students how many halves are in the whole square. See also Analyzing Errors, TE pp. 265A and 265B.

- Ask students to write a number in each square as they count them.
- Discuss with students how the area of the figures in exercise 14 can be found using multiplication.

3 Summarize

- Reemphasize that the area of a figure is the size of its surface.
- Remind students that area can be determined by counting the number of squares it contains.
- Point out that the area of some figures can be found by multiplying.

Ongoing Assessment Draw a figure with an area of 4 whole squares and 2 half squares. Answers will vary.

Math Journal: *Communicating*

Ask students how many different figures could be made that contain 24 squares. Answers should suggest a large number, as there could be many half squares.

Show What You Know!

Copy the figure onto dot paper. Find the area. Show your work. Check students' drawings.

1. 6 square units
2. 7 square units
3. 5 square units
4. 5 square units

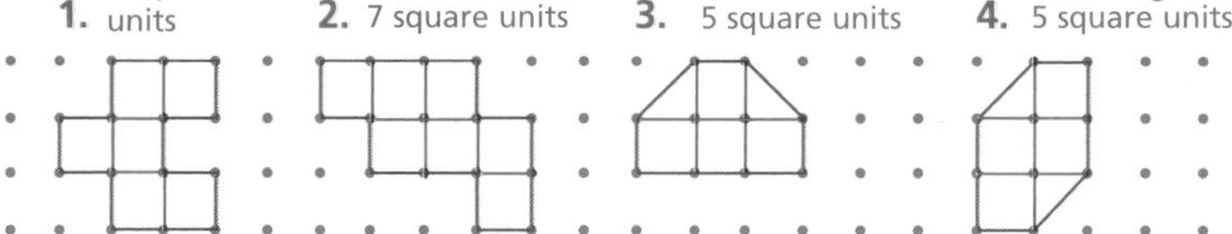

5. **Critical Thinking** Which of the figures above has the greatest area? How do you know? 2; 7 square units is the greatest measurement.

Draw a figure that has the area given. Answers will vary.

6. 6 square units
7. 15 square units
8. 45 square units

Guess which figure below has the largest area. Then count the squares to find the area. Compare the result with your guess. Guesses will vary.

9. 6 square units
10. 7 square units
11. 6 square units
12. 8 square units

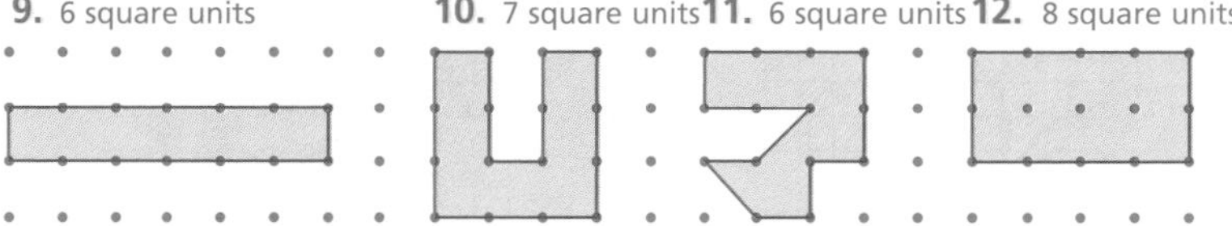

13. **Critical Thinking** How can you use multiplication to find the area of exercise 12? $2 \times 4 = 8$
14. **Patterns** Use color tiles to make this pattern on inch-squared paper. Then make the next two figures in the pattern. See Additional Answers.
15. Copy and complete the chart. Count the number of tiles to find the area of each figure in exercise 14. 4, 6, 8, 10

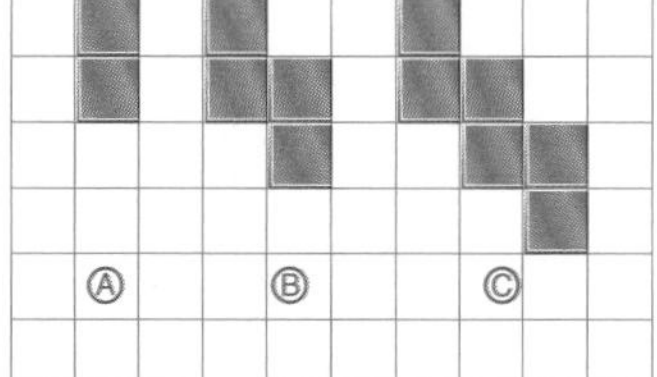

Figure	A	B	C	D	E
Area	2	?	?	?	?

16. **Algebraic Reasoning** How many tiles would there be in the sixth figure? What would the area be? 12; 12 square units

Meeting Individual Needs

Extra Support

Patterns Galore! ***(visual)*** Ask students to create their own patterns by first drawing a figure on square dot paper, using up to 6 squares. Then, they cut out their figures and trace them on dot paper using slides, flips, and turns. Suggest that they each use a repeating pattern, arranging the tracings so that they touch. When they're finished, ask students to predict the number of squares in the area of their pattern, and then find an easy way to figure it out.

Alternate Approach

- Reteach Worksheet 7.15
- **TAB** See TE pp. 226E–226F.

MathZones

Understanding Geometry

Students Acquiring English

See Language Connections, Ch. 7.

Challenge

How many figures like Figure 1 in exercise 14 would it take to make a rectangle 5 squares long and 4 squares wide? 10

Practice

Math Center Use Activity Card 43, *Area Antics*, to have students practice determining the area of a polygon by counting half and whole square units.

Challenge Use Activity Card 43 and have students continue as described in Now Try This!

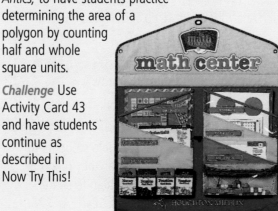

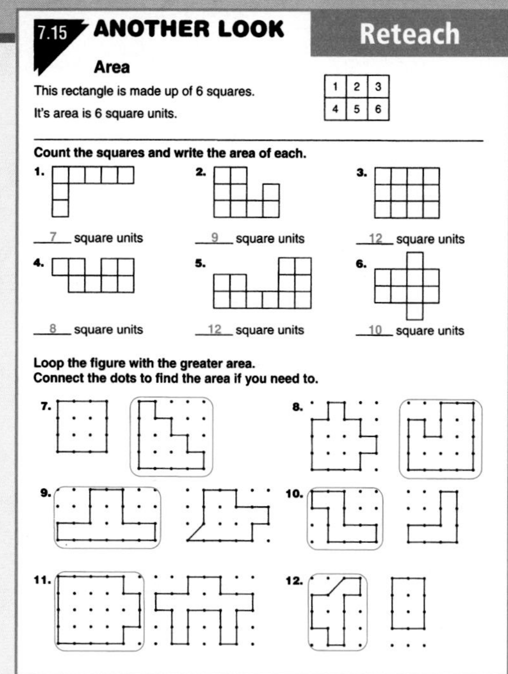

7.15 ANOTHER LOOK — **Reteach**

Area

This rectangle is made up of 6 squares.
It's area is 6 square units.

Count the squares and write the area of each.

1. 7 square units
2. 9 square units
3. 12 square units
4. 8 square units
5. 12 square units
6. 10 square units

Loop the figure with the greater area.
Connect the dots to find the area if you need to.

7. 8. 9. 10. 11. 12.

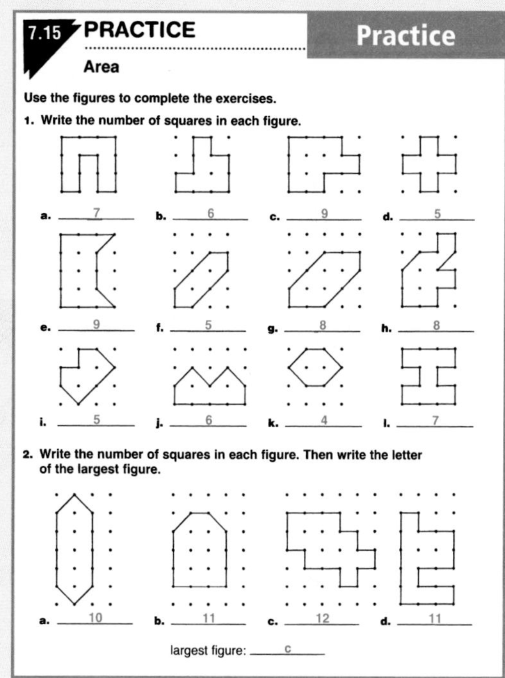

7.15 PRACTICE — **Practice**

Area

Use the figures to complete the exercises.

1. **Write the number of squares in each figure.**

a. 7 b. 6 c. 9 d. 5
e. 9 f. 5 g. 8 h. 8
i. 5 j. 6 k. 4 l. 7

2. **Write the number of squares in each figure. Then write the letter of the largest figure.**

a. 10 b. 11 c. 12 d. 11

largest figure: c

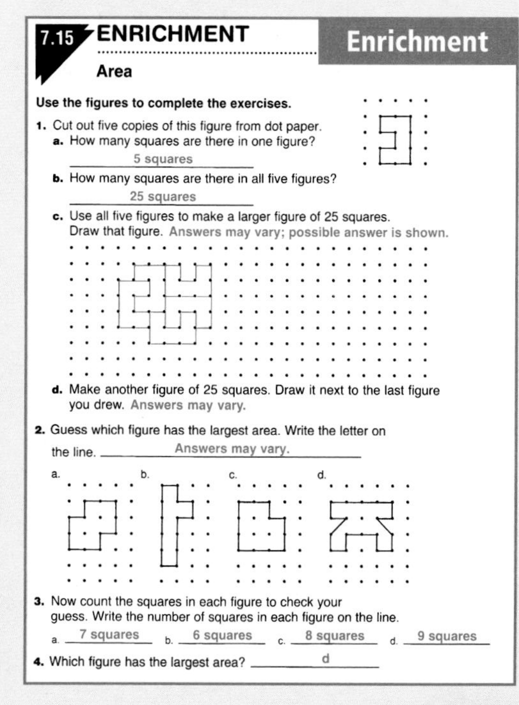

7.15 ENRICHMENT — **Enrichment**

Area

Use the figures to complete the exercises.

1. Cut out five copies of this figure from dot paper.
   a. How many squares are there in one figure? 5 squares
   b. How many squares are there in all five figures? 25 squares
   c. Use all five figures to make a larger figure of 25 squares. Draw that figure. Answers may vary; possible answer is shown.
   d. Make another figure of 25 squares. Draw it next to the last figure you drew. Answers may vary.
2. Guess which figure has the largest area. Write the letter on the line. Answers may vary.

   a. b. c. d.

3. Now count the squares in each figure to check your guess. Write the number of squares in each figure on the line.
   a. 7 squares b. 6 squares c. 8 squares d. 9 squares
4. Which figure has the largest area? d

Connecting

Planning at a Glance

Objective To determine the area of irregular 2-dimensional figures by counting and estimating

Materials grid paper (TR2)

Optional Resources

- Reteach 7.16; Practice 7.16; Enrichment 7.16
- Daily Cumul. Review, p. 99
- Math Center: How-To Card 26
- Every Day Counts
- **TAB**, TE pp. 226E–226F, 226J
- **Problem of the Day**, 99, p. 50; Flip Chart, p. 50a

Unlocking Geometry 3–6, Level 3, Activity 16

Students Acquiring English

Draw a footprint; discuss what it is. Ask students to draw others, including dinosaur fossil footprints. Draw squares over a footprint and show how it is *not regular* (irregular) because it does not fill the squares evenly. Have students identify squares: whole, about half, and almost empty.

Problem of the Day

Betty, Jan, and Fred saved a total of $12. Together, Fred and Betty saved as much as Jan saved by herself. Together, Jan and Betty have $4 more than Fred. How much money did each person save?

Betty saved $2, Fred saved $4, and Jan saved $6.

Area of Irregular Figures

A dinosaur made this footprint millions of years ago.

Getting Started

What You'll Need:
- grid paper

People who study dinosaurs can learn a lot from fossil footprints. How could you estimate the area of a footprint?

Here's A Way! Estimate area by counting squares.

1. Count the whole squares.

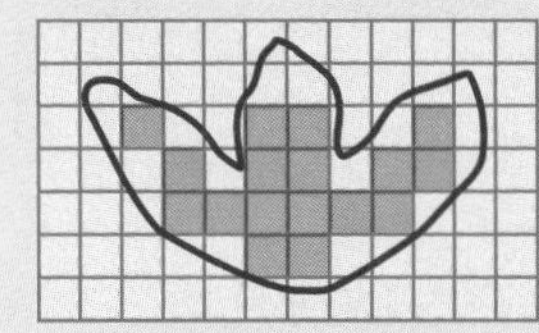

17 whole squares

2. Count the squares that are "almost whole."

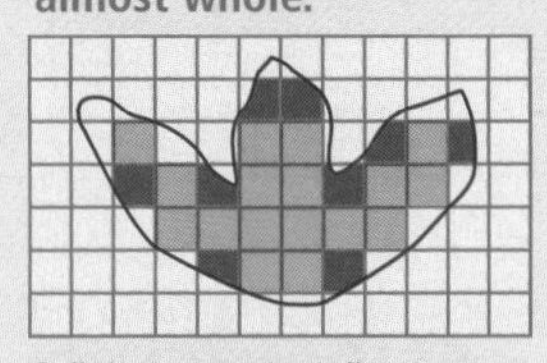

9 "almost whole" squares

3. Count the squares that are "about half." Two of these will equal about one square.

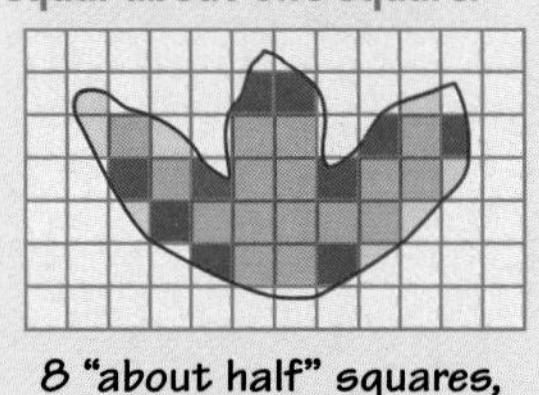

8 "about half" squares, or 4 squares

4. Add to find the total.

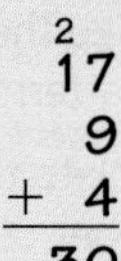

$$\begin{array}{r} \overset{2}{1}7 \\ 9 \\ +\ 4 \\ \hline 30 \end{array}$$

The area of this figure is about 30 square units.

Talk About It! What if a figure has "almost empty" squares? How would you estimate them? If "almost whole" squares were counted as whole squares, ignore "almost empty" squares.

260 Chapter 7

1 Introduce

Prior Knowledge **Ask, What is the area of a figure that has 3 whole squares and 4 half squares?** 5 squares

Teach: Here's A Way!

Emphasize this point:

- Areas of irregular figures can be estimated by counting the number of whole squares, "almost whole" squares, and "about half" squares.

Modeling Model steps 3–4. Ask:

- About how many whole squares can you make with 10 "about half" squares? 5 squares
- Why do you think estimating is a good way to find the area of an irregular figure?

2 Develop

Show What You Know!

Common Error Some students may not be able to distinguish between "almost whole" and "about half" squares. Suggest that these students draw a half square on tracing paper, then use it to measure "almost whole," and "about half" squares. See also Analyzing Errors, TE pp. 265A and 265B.

Work It Out!

- Explore which figure in exercises 6–7 is the most difficult to estimate and why.
- Have students share their work from exercise 10.

Using Reading Strategies Help students to use the Self-Question strategy as they read the Problem Solving exercise. Ask them to share their questions with classmates. See TE p. 226J.

3 Summarize

- Review that the area of irregular figures can be estimated by counting the number of whole, "almost whole," and "about half" squares.
- Remind students to estimate 2 "almost half" squares as 1 whole square.

Ongoing Assessment If a circle has 4 whole squares and 8 "almost half" squares, what is its estimated area? 8 squares

Math Journal: *Communicating*

Ask students how they would estimate the area of all faces of a triangular prism. They may suggest tracing each face on squared paper, counting the area of each face, then estimating the area of the bases.

Show What You Know!

Estimate the area. Count the squares in each footprint drawing. Estimates will vary.

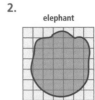

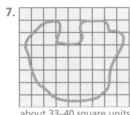

1. deer — about 4 square units
2. elephant — about 25 square units
3. duck — about 2 square units
4. bear — about 13-14 square units

5. **Critical Thinking** What did you do with any "almost empty" squares when you estimated? Explain. Answers will vary. Possible answer: ignored them

Work It Out!

Estimate the area of each figure. Estimates will vary.

6. 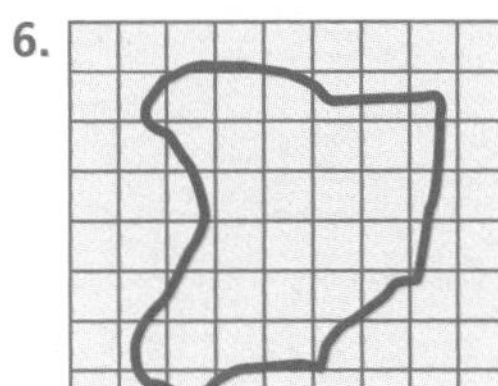
about 25-30 square units

7. about 33–40 square units

8. Trace your shoe on grid paper. Estimate the area of your shoeprint. Estimates will vary.
9. Find something in your classroom that you predict covers a smaller area than your shoeprint. Trace it on grid paper and estimate the area. Compare the area to your shoeprint. Check students' work.
10. **Create Your Own** Use grid paper. Draw a footprint. Estimate the area. Tell how you estimated. Check students' work.
11. **Problem Solving** About how many duck footprints from exercise 3 could fit inside this footprint? Answers will vary. About 7 duck footprints will fit.

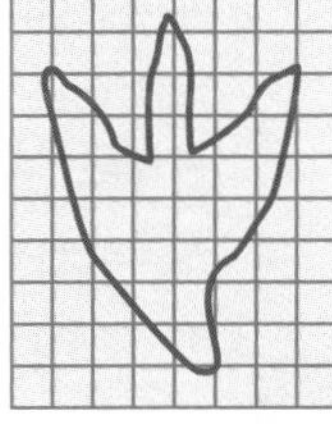

Meeting Individual Needs

Extra Support

Estimating Prints *(visual)* Have students estimate the area of their handprint, shoe print, and thumbprint by tracing them on squared paper, then estimating the number of squares in each. Have them explore the best way to trace their handprint (with fingers close together).

Alternate Approach

- Reteach Worksheet 7.16
- **TAB** See TE pp. 226E–226F.

MathZones
Understanding Geometry

Students Acquiring English

See **Language Connections**, Ch. 7.

Challenge

How could you quickly estimate the area of an irregular figure that has 1 line of symmetry? by estimating the area of half the figure along the line of symmetry, then doubling the estimate

Practice

Math Center Use How-To Card 26, *Fantastic Areas,* to have students practice determining area of irregular 2-dimensional figures by counting and estimating.

7.16 ANOTHER LOOK — **Reteach**

Area of Irregular Figures

Use red, blue, and green crayons.

In each figure below color all the whole squares red.
Color the almost-whole squares blue.
Color the about-half squares green.
Then estimate the total number of squares in each figure. Estimates may vary.

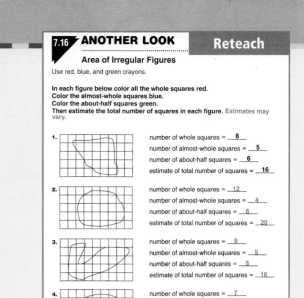

1. number of whole squares = 8
number of almost-whole squares = 5
number of about-half squares = 6
estimate of total number of squares = 16

2. number of whole squares = 12
number of almost-whole squares = 4
number of about-half squares = 6
estimate of total number of squares = 20

3. number of whole squares = 9
number of almost-whole squares = 5
number of about-half squares = 5
estimate of total number of squares = 16

4. number of whole squares = 7
number of almost-whole squares = 1
number of about-half squares = 5
estimate of total number of squares = 10

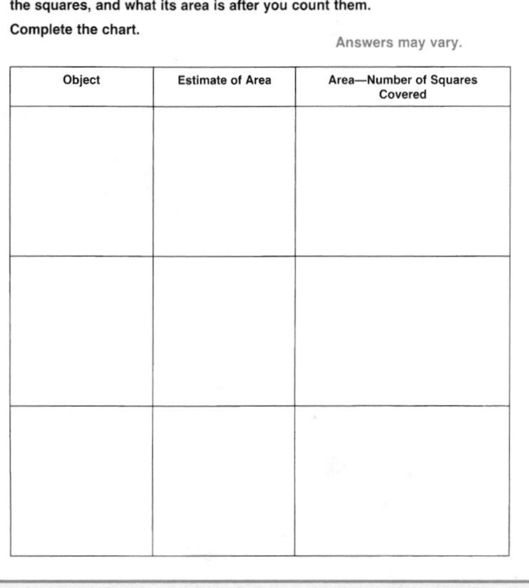

7.16 PRACTICE — **Practice**

Area of Irregular Figures

Look around your classroom and in your desk and choose several objects (pencil, masking-tape holder, chalkboard eraser, ruler, and so on) Trace the outline of each object and copy it on grid paper. Write the object's name, an estimate of its area before you count the squares, and what its area is after you count them.

Complete the chart. Answers may vary.

Object	Estimate of Area	Area—Number of Squares Covered

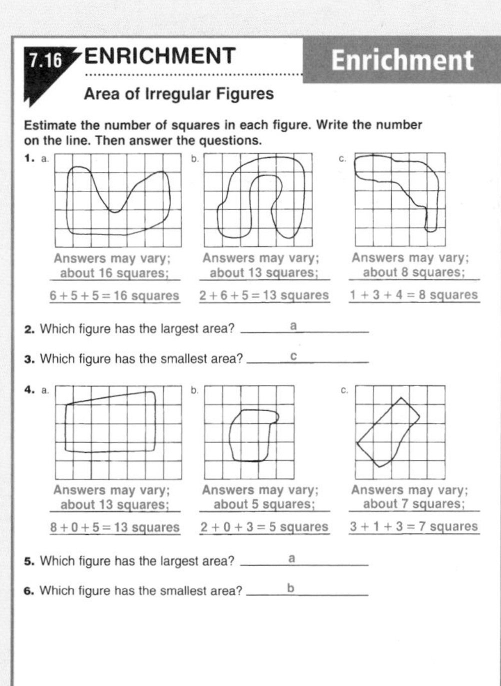

7.16 ENRICHMENT — **Enrichment**

Area of Irregular Figures

Estimate the number of squares in each figure. Write the number on the line. Then answer the questions.

1. a. Answers may vary; about 16 squares; 6 + 5 + 5 = 16 squares
b. Answers may vary; about 13 squares; 2 + 6 + 5 = 13 squares
c. Answers may vary; about 8 squares; 1 + 3 + 4 = 8 squares

2. Which figure has the largest area? a
3. Which figure has the smallest area? c

4. a. Answers may vary; about 13 squares; 8 + 0 + 5 = 13 squares
b. Answers may vary; about 5 squares; 2 + 0 + 3 = 5 squares
c. Answers may vary; about 7 squares; 3 + 1 + 3 = 7 squares

5. Which figure has the largest area? a
6. Which figure has the smallest area? b

LESSON 7.17

Problem Solving

Planning at a Glance

Objective To use different strategies to solve problems

Materials none

Optional Resources

- Reteach 7.17; Practice 7.17; Enrichment 7.17
- Daily Cumul. Review, p. 100
- Math Center: Project Card 7
- Every Day Counts
- TAB, TE pp. 226E–226F, 226J
- Problem of the Day, 100, p. 50; Flip Chart, p. 50b

MATHKEYS *Unlocking Geometry 3–6*, Level 3, Activity 18

Students Acquiring English

Help students with new or confusing vocabulary. For example, if they are not familiar with *plan* as a map or drawing, lead a discussion of the term.

Problem of the Day

It took Isaac the Inchworm 10 minutes to explore one face of a cube. Can Isaac explore all the faces of the cube in an hour? Explain your answer. Yes; a cube has 6 faces, and 6 × 10 = 60 minutes, which is the same as one hour.

Problem Solving : Application

LESSON 17

Problem Solving

Using Strategies

You can read more about Washington, D.C., in the pages of *Cobblestone*.

There are many exciting places to visit in Washington, D.C. This drawing shows the original plan for Lincoln Park, near the Capitol. To make it easier to get across the park quickly, the designers added straight paths.

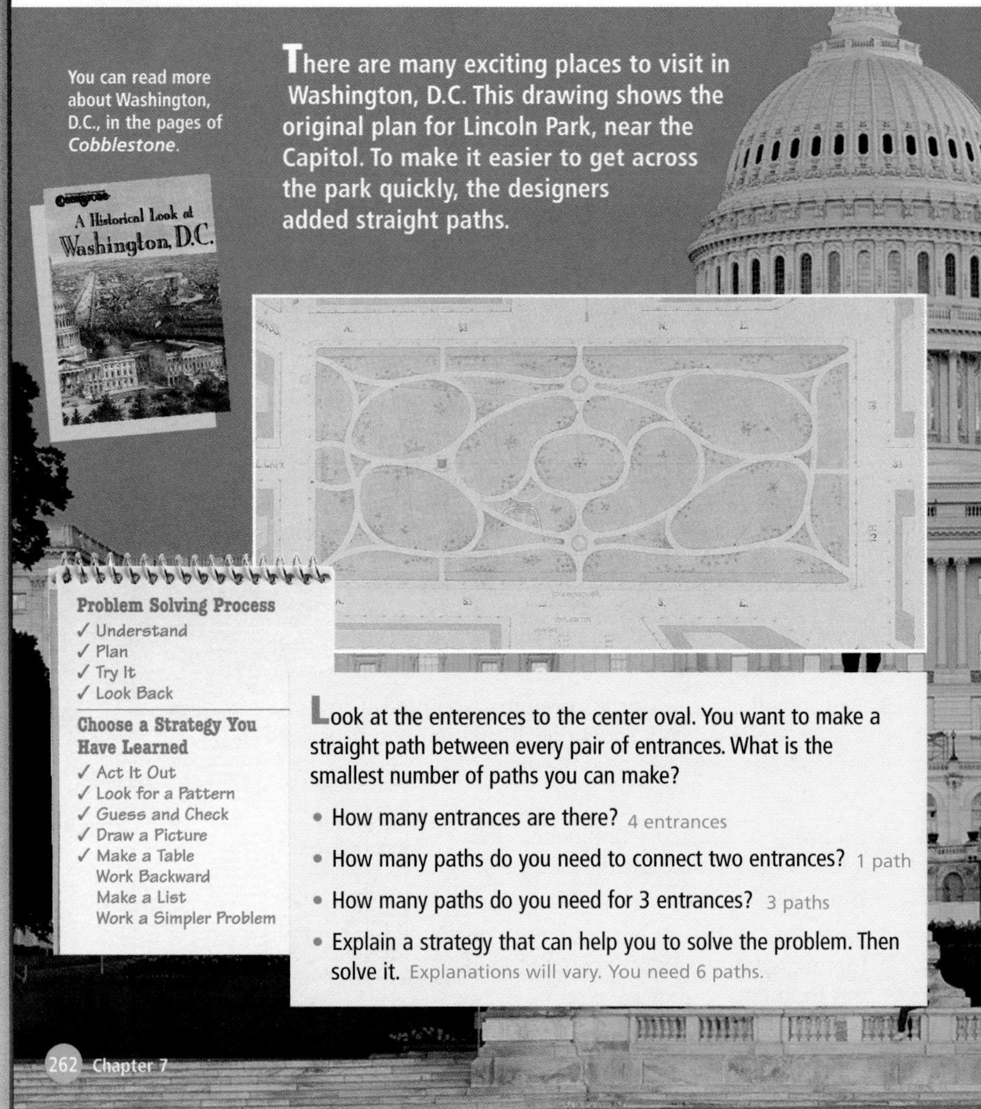

Problem Solving Process
- ✓ Understand
- ✓ Plan
- ✓ Try It
- ✓ Look Back

Choose a Strategy You Have Learned
- ✓ Act It Out
- ✓ Look for a Pattern
- ✓ Guess and Check
- ✓ Draw a Picture
- ✓ Make a Table
- Work Backward
- Make a List
- Work a Simpler Problem

Look at the enterences to the center oval. You want to make a straight path between every pair of entrances. What is the smallest number of paths you can make?

- How many entrances are there? 4 entrances
- How many paths do you need to connect two entrances? 1 path
- How many paths do you need for 3 entrances? 3 paths
- Explain a strategy that can help you to solve the problem. Then solve it. Explanations will vary. You need 6 paths.

262 Chapter 7

1 Introduce

Motivate **Ask, Can you draw an X inside of a square inside of a circle without taking your pencil off of the paper?** Yes; students' drawings will help them solve the introductory problem.

Teach: *Modeling*

Model the introductory problem. Ask:

- What strategy could you use to solve this problem? draw a picture
- How many lines does it take to connect 2 entrances? 1 line To connect 3 entrances? 3 lines To connect 4 entrances? 6 lines
- How could you figure out the number of lines it would take to connect 10 entrances? you could make a table and look for a pattern

2 Develop

Work It Out!

- Have students compare their answers and discuss the strategies they used to solve problems 1–6. Ask why they chose those strategies.
- Discuss whether students used more than one strategy to solve any of the problems. Have them explain why.

Using Reading Strategies Encourage students to use the Self-Question strategy as they read the problems. Ask, How can asking questions help you choose a problem solving strategy? See TE p. 226J.

3 Summarize

- Students can choose the strategy that makes the most sense to solve a problem.
- Sometimes using a combination of strategies is the best way to solve a problem.

Ongoing Assessment Does the park as shown have any lines of symmetry? no How could you change it so it does? Answers will vary. Possible answer: Add paths to one side to make it match the other.

Math Journal: *Communicating*

Have students write about how they choose and use a strategy when they are trying to solve a problem. Answers will vary, but should show that students understand the steps of the problem-solving process.

Work It Out!

Use any strategy to solve the problem. Show your work.

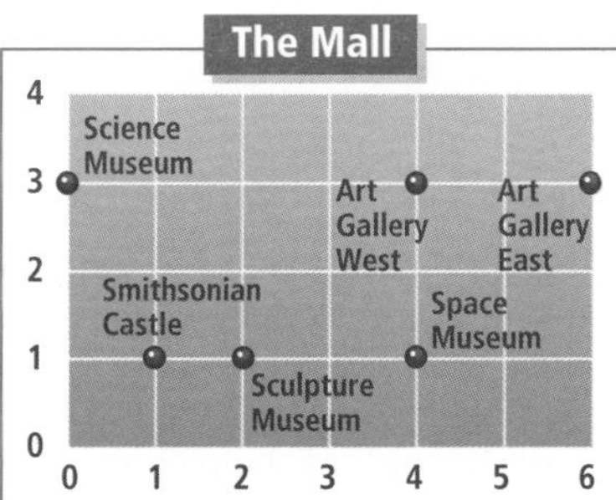

1. Suppose the grid lines are paths and the distance from (0,0) to (0,1) is 1 block. What is the least number of blocks you could walk to go from the Science Museum to the Space Museum? 6 blocks

2. Start at (0,0). Walk 1 block up and 2 blocks to the right. Where will you be if you do this twice more? Art Gallery East

3. This park has a tunnel under it. Suppose the tunnel goes from A to B. Would you go a shorter distance if you drove from A to B around the park or through the tunnel? Explain. through the tunnel; shortest distance between 2 points is always a straight line

4. How could you plant a row of shrubs in this park to show a line of symmetry? in a straight line through the center

5. Your class has volunteered to help repair this wall in a park in Washington. How many square and rectangular bricks do you need to replace all the missing and broken ones? 4 square and 6 rectangular bricks

6. You are planting tulips and irises in Lincoln Park. Each row of tulips has 4 plants. You want 2 iris plants for every tulip plant. You plant 3 rows of tulips. How many iris plants do you need? 24 iris plants

Share Your Thinking

7. What strategy did you use to solve problem 6? Explain why you chose it. Strategies will vary.

8. In which problems did you look for a pattern? Explain how you used this strategy. Answers will vary.

263

Meeting Individual Needs

Extra Support

Problem Solving Process *(auditory)* Have student pairs refer to Student Book p. 262 and review the steps of the problem solving process. Then ask them to work together to read each of the problems on page 263, and choose the strategy or strategies from the checklist that works best to solve the problem.

Alternate Approach

- Reteach Worksheet 7.17
- **TAB** See TE pp. 226E–226F.

MathZones
Understanding Geometry

Students Acquiring English

See **Language Connections**, Ch. 7.

Challenge

Trace a yellow pattern block. What is the greatest number of triangles you can make by drawing 3 straight lines between corners of your tracing? 6 triangles

Practice

Math Center For more problem solving practice, see Project Card 7, *Teacher for a Day!*

See **Just the Facts** Cumulative Practice 7, p. 270.

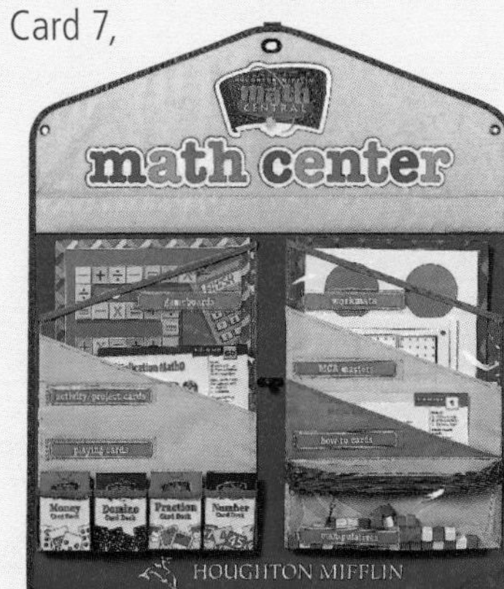

7.17 ANOTHER LOOK — Reteach

Problem Solving: **Using Strategies**

Use any strategy to solve.

1. Suppose you plant tulip bulbs along a fence. You plant 1 bulb where the fence begins. You plant other tulip bulbs 1 foot apart. If the fence is 10 feet long, how many bulbs will you plant? 11 bulbs
2. A gardener is mowing a rectangular lawn. The lawn is 30 feet wide and 60 feet long. The gardener pushes the mower once around the outside edge of the lawn. How far does he push it? 180 feet
3. Two friends are planting a garden. One friend likes roses, daisies, tulips, and clover. The other likes pansies, tulips, sunflowers, and daisies. Which two kinds of flowers should they plant? tulips and daisies
4. Each weekend, Ms. Wong works for 4 hours in her garden. How many hours does she work in the garden in 6 weekends? 24 hours
5. You help your uncle paint a fence around the garden. For every post that you paint, he paints 3. It takes you 1 minute to paint a post. How many posts do you and your uncle paint in 5 minutes? You paint 5; your uncle paints 15.

7.17 PRACTICE — Practice

Problem Solving Applications: **Using Strategies**

Use any strategy to solve.

1. You and your grandfather are planting a garden. There are to be 4 rows of corn each with 6 stalks. The next 3 rows are lettuce. Because lettuce takes less space than corn, you plant twice as many lettuce plants as corn plants in each row. How many lettuce plants will you need? 36 lettuce plants
2. Suppose you are at home. Your friend calls you and invites you over to his house to play video games. Each block in your town is 300 feet long and 200 feet wide. If you stay on the sidewalks, what is the least number of feet you can walk to get to their house? 1300 feet

3. You are helping your aunt remodel the bathroom. You are using square tiles that are 6 inches on each side. You are covering a wall that is 7 feet high and 7 feet long. How many tiles do you need? 196

7.17 ENRICHMENT — Enrichment

Problem Solving: **Using Strategies**

Use any strategy to solve.

1. You just added 12 new stamps to your collection. Half of the stamps are from Italy. One stamp is from Austria. All the other stamps are from Japan. How many stamps are from Japan? 5 stamps
2. You buy a stamp from Brazil to add to your collection. It costs 75¢. You pay with 8 coins. Seven of the coins are the same. You receive no change. What coins do you pay with? 7 dimes, 1 nickel
3. Rosa and her cousin are going to the grocery store. Altogether they have $36.00. Rosa has twice as much money as her cousin. How much money do they each have? Rosa has $24.00; her cousin has $12.00.
4. Three different numbers add up to 35. The numbers are between 1 and 30. Each number ends in either 5 or 0. What are the three numbers? 5, 10, 20
5. The plane can carry 168 passengers. There are 19 children on the flight. Of the adult passengers, 70 are men. How many women passengers are on the flight? 79 women passengers

Chapter Test

Problem Solving

Give 0–5 points per answer based on how well students meet the following criteria:

Problem 1
- Answer shows use of a problem solving strategy
- Strategy is seen through to a correct solution

Problem 2
- Answer shows ability to identify a pattern
- Answer is drawn neatly and clearly
- Student extends pattern correctly as shown

Concepts and Skills

If students need more help with concepts and skills in this chapter, use the following Reteaching Worksheets:

- 48 Slides, p. 140
- 49 Flips, p. 141
- 50 Turns, p. 142
- 51 Angles, p. 143
- 52 Congruence, p. 144
- 53 Symmetry, p. 145
- 54 Congruence, p. 154
- 55 Ordered Pairs, p. 155
- 56 Area of Irregular Shapes, p. 156

Chapter 7 Test

for Pages 226–263

Test-Taking Tips
Be sure to read all of the answer choices before answering a multiple-choice question.

Problem Solving

Solve using any strategy. (pages 234, 256)

1. You are packing lunches for a class picnic. You put a tuna sandwich and an apple in the first bag, a tuna sandwich and an orange in the next, and a cheese sandwich and an orange in the third bag. If you pack 2 more of each kind of lunch, how many more oranges will you use? 4 oranges

2. Extend the pattern. Draw the next 3 figures. See additional answers.

Concepts

Copy the figure on dot paper. Then, show a slide, a flip, or a half turn. (pages 228, 230, 232) See additional answers.

3. Show a slide.
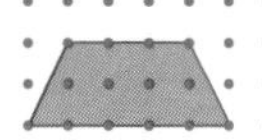

4. Show a flip.
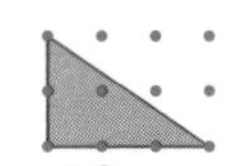

5. Show a half turn.
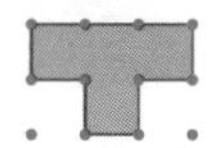

Tell which pairs show congruent figures. Explain. (page 238)

6. a.

b.

c.

a, c

Write the name of each shape. (page 240, 242)

7. a. square b. triangle c. circle d. rectangle e. hexagon

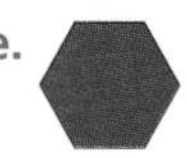

Find the area. Count square units and parts of square units. (page 258)

8. 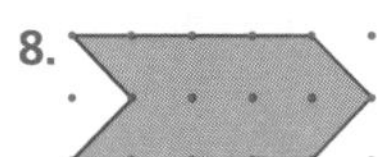 8 square units

9. 8 square units

264

Chapter Correlation to Standardized Tests

Math Central	Standardized Test Objectives						
Chapter Objective	ITBS Form M	CAT/5	CTBS/4	Terra Nova (CTBS/5)	MAT 7th ed.	SAT 9th ed.	State/ Local
A To use slides, flips, and half turns to move figures	•	•	•	•	•	•	
7B To identify and draw congruent figures	•	•	•	•	•	•	
7C To identify and classify angles, lines, and segments	•	•	•	•	•	•	
7D To identify one or more lines of symmetry in plane figures	•	•	•	•	•	•	
7E To identify and classify geometric solids	•	•	•	•	•	•	
7F To use ordered pairs to locate regions on a grid and on a map	•	•	•	•	•	•	
7G To find the area of plane figures by counting	•	•	•	•	•	•	
7H To use Look for a Pattern and other strategies to solve problems	•			•	•	•	

Skills

Choose what the picture shows. Write *a*, *b*, or *c*. (pages 236, 252)

10. c
a. a line
b. a corner
c. a line segment

11. b
a. a square corner
b. an angle
c. a line

12. a
a. a square corner
b. a triangle
c. a line

How many lines of symmetry does the figure have? (page 240)

13. 
2 lines

14. 1 line

15. 1 line

Write the name of each solid figure. (page 248)

16. 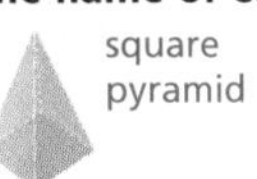
square pyramid

17. triangular pyramid

18. rectangular prism

19. triangular prism

20. cube

21. cylinder

Use the map to find an ordered pair. (page 254)

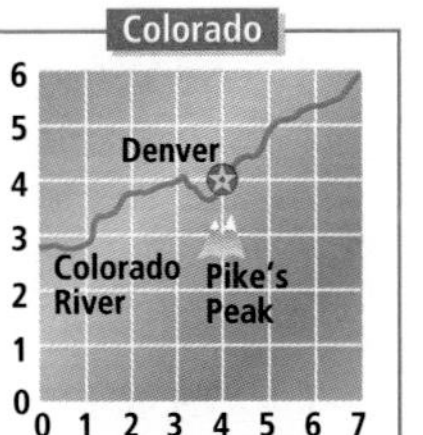

22. Write the ordered pair for Colorado's capital city, Denver. (4,4)

23. Write the ordered pair for the mountain Pike's Peak. (4,3)

24. Which river can be found at (7,6)?
Colorado River

Performance Task

(page 254)

- Copy the grid. Make a map by drawing a house, tree, and pond.
- Write directions that use ordered pairs.

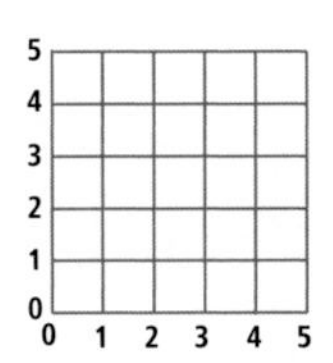

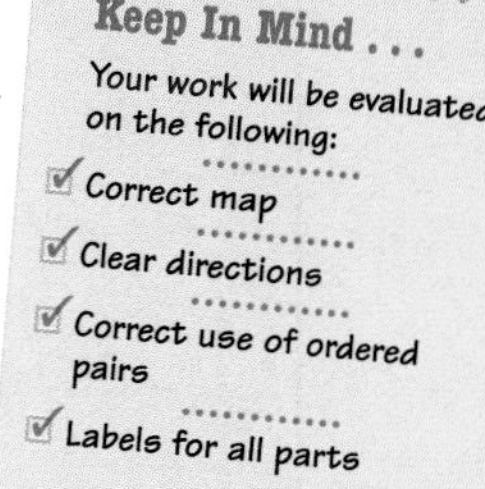

Keep In Mind . . .
Your work will be evaluated on the following:
Correct map
Clear directions
Correct use of ordered pairs
Labels for all parts

265

Performance Tasks

Use the following criteria, each worth 5 points, to evaluate students' responses. These criteria align with *Keep In Mind* in the Pupil Edition on p. 265.

Criteria	
Draws a well-organized grid	Correctly identifies ordered pairs
Writes correct directions using drawings and grid	Labels all parts

Use this 4-level rubric to score students' responses. If you prefer a task with a 6-level rubric, use the Performance Assessment for this chapter.

5 points	Limited Response
10 points	Acceptable
15 points	Capable
20 points	Superior

Common Error Alert

If students are making frequent errors, see Analyzing Errors, TE pp. 265A–265B.

Scoring Chart

Item	Points
1–2	5 points each
3–9	4 points each
10–21	3 points each
22–24	2 points each
Performance Task	20 points
TOTAL	100 points or 100%

Item Analysis

Item	Objectives
1–2	To use Look for a Pattern and other strategies to solve problems (7H)
3–5	To use slides, flips, and half turns to move figures (7A)
6	To identify and draw congruent figures (7B)
8–9	To find the area of plane figures by counting (7G)
10–12	To identify and classify angles, lines, and line segments (7C)
13–15	To identify one or more lines of symmetry in plane figures (7D)
16–21	To identify and classify geometric solids including prisms and pyramids (7E)
22–24	To use ordered pairs to locate regions on a grid and on a map (7F)

Assessment Options

The following materials are found in your **Comprehensive Assessment Package:**

Formal Assessments
- Standardized-Format
- Free-Response Chapter Tests, Forms A and B
- Chapter Tests for Students Acquiring Language Proficiency
- Informal Learning Inventory

Performance Assessments
- Chapter Tasks
- Midyear and Final Project Tasks

Alternative Assessments
- Observation Checklist
- Student Attitude Assessment
- Student Self-Assessment *Individual and Group*

Standardized Testing: New Formats
- Enhanced Multiple-Choice
- Extended-Response
- Short-Response

Management
- Student Record Sheets
- Answer Keys

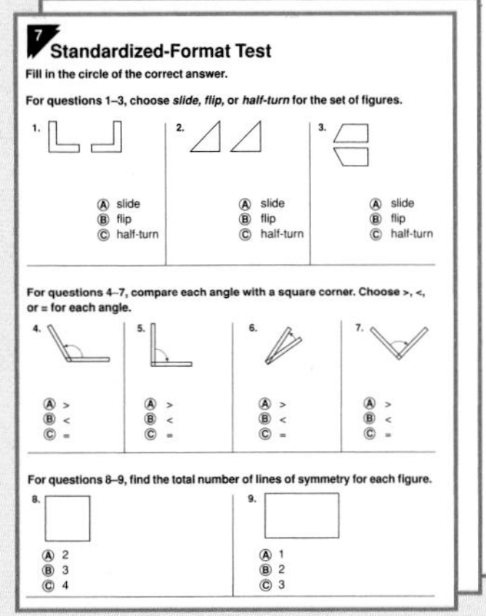
7 Standardized-Format Test

Fill in the circle of the correct answer.

For questions 1–3, choose *slide*, *flip*, or *half-turn* for the set of figures.

1. Ⓐ slide Ⓑ flip Ⓒ half-turn
2. Ⓐ slide Ⓑ flip Ⓒ half-turn
3. Ⓐ slide Ⓑ flip Ⓒ half-turn

For questions 4–7, compare each angle with a square corner. Choose >, <, or = for each angle.

4. Ⓐ > Ⓑ < Ⓒ =
5. Ⓐ > Ⓑ < Ⓒ =
6. Ⓐ > Ⓑ < Ⓒ =
7. Ⓐ > Ⓑ < Ⓒ =

For questions 8–9, find the total number of lines of symmetry for each figure.

8. Ⓐ 2 Ⓑ 3 Ⓒ 4
9. Ⓐ 1 Ⓑ 2 Ⓒ 3

- Standardized-Format Chapter Tests
- Free-Response Chapter Tests, Forms A and B
- Standardized-Format Midyear and Final Tests

Additional Assessment Resources

Test, Practice, Management Program

Use the *Test, Practice, Management Program* to create, administer, and score tests as well as generate practice sets. Questions are correlated to the Lesson Objectives.

Cumulative Test

For a cumulative review in multiple-choice format, see TE pp. T74–T75.

Analyzing Errors

Strategies and Techniques for Reteaching

Errors in Basic Geometric Figures Students who incorrectly identify 2- and 3-dimensional figures may benefit by reviewing figures in the real world. Start with the classroom environment. Guide students to identify any familiar flat figures and solids, such as circles and spheres. Point out any unfamiliar figures, pyramids, cylinders, pentagons, and so on. Use real-world examples or drawings. Students may wish to prepare a geometry scavenger hunt.

Solid Figures

sphere	→	globe, ball
rectangular prism	→	brick, box
triangular prism	→	top of milk carton

Flat Figures

triangle	→	top of envelope
square	→	chessboard
rectangle	→	paper
circle	→	CD, jar top

Using Lines and Angles

Error Involving Lines and Parts of Lines

Error Confuses lines and line segments

Reteaching Show models of line segments such as edges of a door or ruler. Ask students to show the endpoints of each of these segments, and then ask for other examples. Ask them to close their eyes and imagine a line that has no endpoint. Lead students to see that railroad tracks, lines on a highway, or telephone wires seem to go on forever, but a line without end can only be imagined.

Error Involving Angles

Error Judges the size of an angle by the length of its sides

Reteaching Draw two angles on the board. Ask students which is the greater angle and why. Then, use a square corner such as a torn index card to compare the openness of each angle. Help students see that the angle that can contain the greater amount of the square corner is the greater angle.

Error

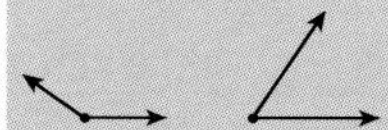

Reteaching

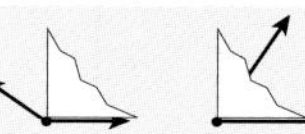

Two-Dimensional Figures

Errors in Repeated Patterns and Symmetry

Error Confuses slides, turns, and flips

Reteaching Students who have difficulty visualizing the motion implied by repeated figures in a pattern may benefit from acting out the three types of motion. Students can practice by drawing block letters or numbers with no symmetry such as: P, F, L, 7, or 2, on tracing paper. Then, have them lay the tracing paper over grid paper and move the figure in either a slide, flip, or half turn. In each case, discuss what has changed and what is the same: The size and shape of the figure does not change. In all cases the location changes. In some cases the direction changes.

Error

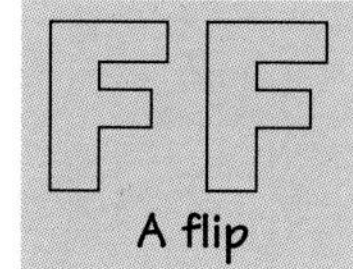

A flip

Reteaching

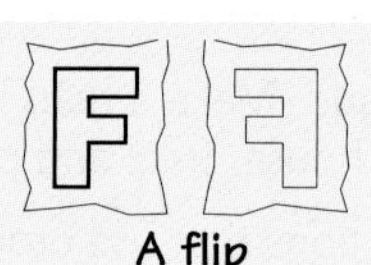

A flip

Error Draws lines of symmetry that do not divide a figure into congruent halves that mirror each other

Reteaching Students may not understand that the two halves in a symmetrical figure must exactly match each other when the figure is folded. Have them draw and cut out a rectangle. Then, ask them to fold opposite corners to meet. Discuss whether the two pieces have the same size and shape. Lead students to see that although they do, the line is not a line of symmetry since the pieces do not overlap when folded.

Error

4 lines of symmetry

Reteaching

2 lines of symmetry

don't match

Three-Dimensional Solid Figures

Errors in Visualizing in 3 Dimensions

Error Confuses two- and three-dimensional figures

Reteaching Display a three-dimensional figure such as a number cube, along with a two-dimensional drawing, such as a cube drawn on the board. Relate corresponding faces of the figure to the faces shown in the linear representation.

Error

1 2 3 4 5 6

hexagon

Reteaching

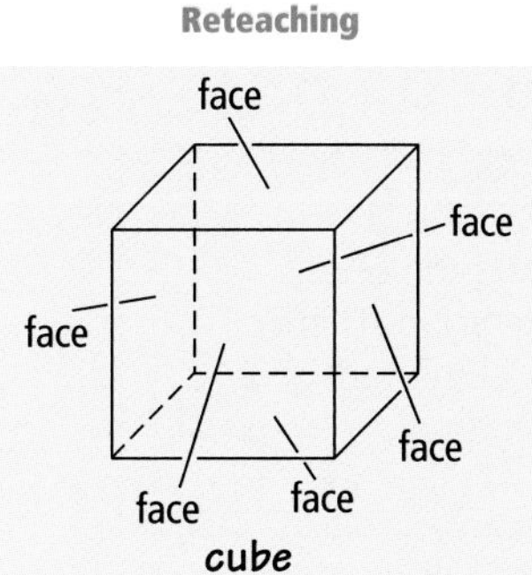

cube

Error Cannot distinguish between prism and pyramid

Reteaching Display a prism. Then, place it behind your back and turn it upside down. Show the class the figure and ask if they can tell whether you turned it upside down. Repeat with a pyramid.

Error

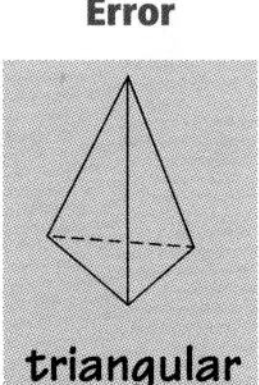

triangular prism

Reteaching

prism

looks the same upside down

Reteaching

pyramid

looks different upside down

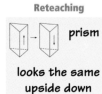

Finding Area and Perimeter

Error in Choosing Units and Operations

Error Chooses linear units, rather than square units when finding an area

Reteaching Stress that area is a measure of a surface. If possible, point out floor or ceiling tiles in the classroom as examples of square units covering a flat surface. Give students geoboards or dot paper and have them draw figures. Provide square cutouts the size of the smallest geoboard square. Have students cover the figure and name the number of square units.

Error | Reteaching

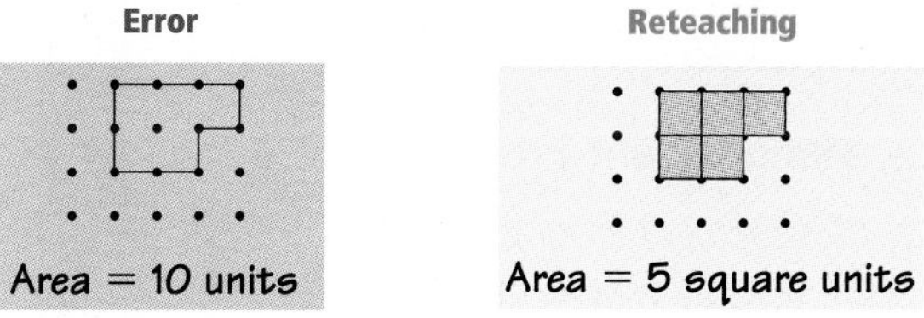

Using Ordered Pairs

Error Involving Ordered Pairs

Error Relates ordered pair to one axis rather than two

Reteaching Help students see that skill with reading a graph can be translated to reading the ordered pair for a point. Have them lay two straightedges across the point, one parallel to the horizontal axis, one parallel to the vertical. Have them read the numbers, first on the horizontal axis, then on the vertical.

Error | Reteaching

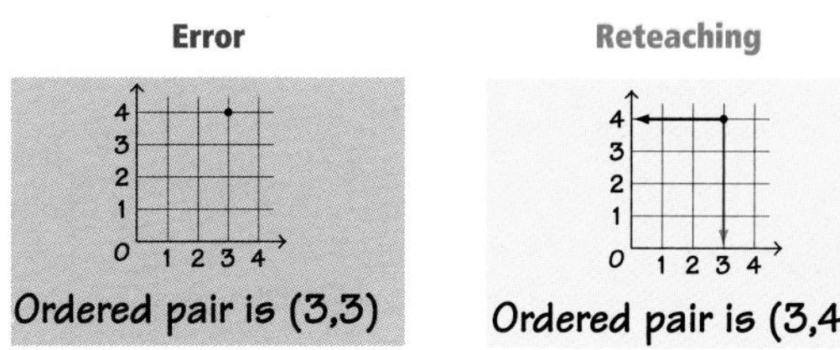

Cumulative Review

Two Ways to Use the Cumulative Review

Maintenance For those students whose results on the current Chapter Test show a good grasp of skills and concepts, you may wish to assign the Cumulative Review as homework. Students may also benefit from the specific review and practice opportunities listed in the Skills Maintenance chart.

Reassessment For those students whose results on the current Chapter Test show only a limited grasp of skills and concepts, you may wish to assign the Cumulative Review as class work. If it then appears that reassessment is needed, the Skills Reteaching chart on the opposite page identifies remedial minilessons in the Teacher's Resource Package.

Additional Assessment Resources

Test, Practice, Management Program

Use the *Test, Practice, Management Program* to create, administer, and score tests as well as generate practice sets. Questions are correlated to the Lesson Objectives.

Cumulative Review

Ordering Numbers (Chapter 1)
What number comes just before 47?

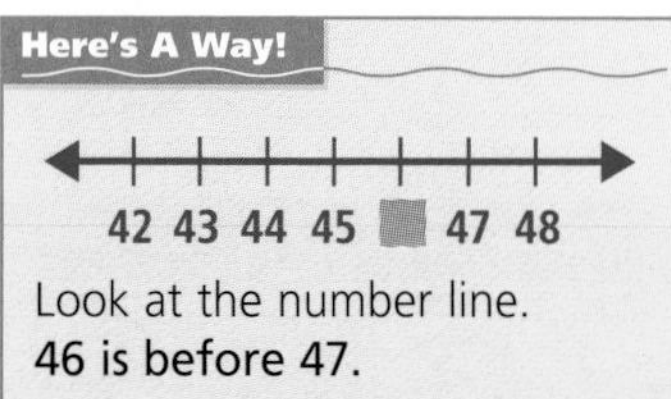

Here's A Way!
42 43 44 45 47 48
Look at the number line.
46 is before 47.

Write the missing number.

1. 56, 57, ■, 59 58
2. 33, ■, 35, 36 34
3. 70, 71, ■, 73 72
4. 18, 19, ■, 21 20
5. 39, 40, ■, 42 41
6. ■, 85, 86, 87 84
7. How does counting backward change the order of numbers? Explain. Answers will vary. Possible answer: You are changing the order by saying the greater number first.

Writing Numbers (Chapter 2)
Write three thousand eight hundred fifty-nine in standard form.

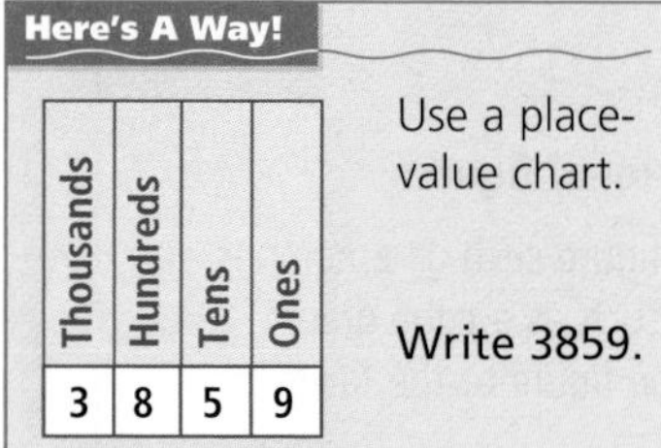

Here's A Way!
Thousands Hundreds Tens Ones
3 8 5 9
Use a place-value chart.
Write 3859.

Write the number in standard form.

8. two thousand thirty-five 2035
9. nine hundred seventy-one 971
10. six thousand four hundred 6400
11. five hundred sixty-eight 568
12. seven hundred five 705
13. one hundred ninety-four 194
14. Look at exercise 13. Does the digit 4 have a greater value than the digit 1? Explain. No; The 4 is in the ones place, and the one is in the hundreds place.

Adding Four Numbers (Chapter 3)
Find 48 + 51 + 13 + 77.

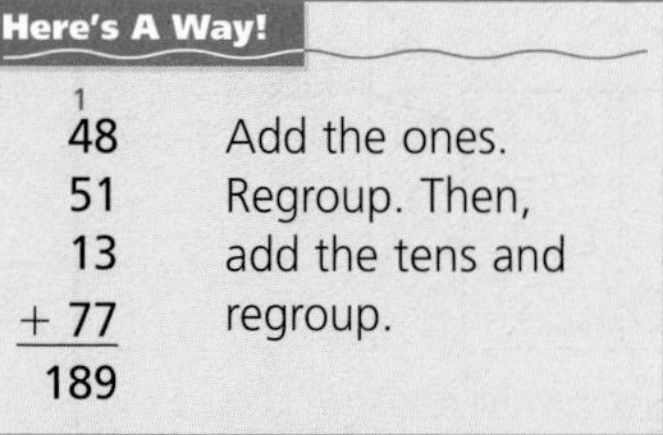

Here's A Way!
1
48
51
13
+ 77
189
Add the ones. Regroup. Then, add the tens and regroup.

Find the sum.

15. 37 + 22 + 90 + 46 = 195
16. 38 + 25 + 75 + 46 = 184
17. 42 + 76 + 20 + 74 = 212
18. How can you use doubles or sums of ten to help you add four numbers? Ten facts and doubles facts are easy to add; then add the rest.

266

Skills Maintenance

Chapter Objectives	Where taught in pupil book	More practice in pupil book
• To compare and order numbers to 100 (1A)	**Chapter 1**, pp. 4–5	More Practice Set 1.2, p. 438
• To model and write numbers through hundred thousands in table, expanded, word, and standard forms (2A)	**Chapter 2**, pp. 50–51	More Practice Set 2.5, p. 444
• To add up to four whole numbers (3B)	**Chapter 3**, pp. 94–95	More Practice Set 3.5, p. 449
• To collect, organize, record, and interpret data (4A)	**Chapter 4**, pp. 124–125	None
• To explore the properties of multiplication (5D)	**Chapter 5**, pp. 180–181	None
• To use Look for a Pattern and other strategies to solve problems (7H)	**Chapter 7**, pp. 234–235	None

Interpreting Data (Chapter 4)
How many students like in-line skating best?

Here's A Way!

Favorite Type of Skating

Activity	Tally	Number
Roller Skating	卌 II	
Ice Hockey	IIII	
Figure Skating	III	
In-Line Skating	卌 卌 卌	15

Skip-count the tally marks by 5's. **15 students like in-line skating best.**

Use the chart to answer the question.

19. What number would you write for roller skating? 7

20. How many students voted for ice hockey? 4 students

21. What number would you write for figure skating? 3

22. How many more students voted for in-line than for roller skating? 8 more students

23. Which kind of skating did the fewest students vote for? figure skating

24. How many students in all voted? 29 students

Properties of Multiplication (Chapter 5)
Find 1496 × 0, 1 × 58, and 7 × 5.

Here's A Way!

Zero Property: **1496 × 0 = 0**
Property of One: **1 × 58 = 58**
Order Property: **7 × 5 = 5 × 7**

Find the product. Use the properties of multiplication.

25. 138 × 1 138 **26.** 1 × 49 49
27. 27 × 0 0 **28.** 0 × 356 0
29. 4 × 10 40 **30.** 4 × 5 20

31. Explain in your own words what the Zero Property means. Any number times zero is zero.

Problem Solving

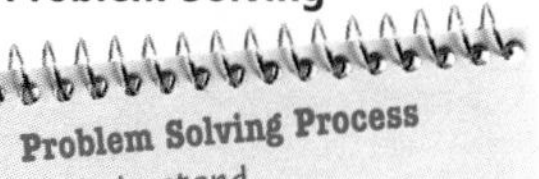

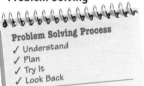

Problem Solving Process
✓ Understand
✓ Plan
✓ Try It
✓ Look Back

Choose a Strategy You Have Learned
✓ Act It Out
✓ Look for a Pattern
✓ Guess and Check
✓ Draw a Picture
✓ Make a Table
Work Backward
Make a List
Work a Simpler Problem

Solve. Show your work.

32. Two numbers have a product of 42. One follows right after the other. What are the two numbers? 6 and 7

33. Suppose there are 180 glue sticks. One teacher takes 25 for her class. Another teacher takes 23. A third teacher takes 24. Are there more than 100 glue sticks left in the art closet? Explain how you can estimate to find out. Yes; Answers will vary. Possible answer: 25 + 23 + 24 is a little less than 75, and 180 − 80 = 100.

Skills Reteaching

Chapter Objectives	Suggested materials for minilessons		
• To compare and order numbers to 100 (1A)	Reteach 1.2	Practice 1.2	Enrichment 1.2
• To model and write numbers through hundred thousands in table, expanded, word, and standard forms (2A)	Reteach 2.5	Practice 2.5	Enrichment 2.5
• To add up to four whole numbers (3B)	Reteach 3.5	Practice 3.5	Enrichment 3.5
• To collect, organize, record, and interpret data (4A)	Reteach 4.1	Practice 4.1	Enrichment 4.1
• To explore the properties of multiplication (5D)	Reteach 5.11	Practice 5.11	Enrichment 5.11
• To use Look for a Pattern and other strategies to solve problems (7H)	Reteach 7.4	Practice 7.4	Enrichment 7.4

Students Acquiring English

Some students may need assistance on the Cumulative Review.

- Be prepared to read directions aloud to students.
- Focus special attention on word problems. Expect to paraphrase, diagram, or draw an explanation of the word problem.
- Review important vocabulary words that have been previously introduced.
- Review titles and other elements of graphs and charts.

INVESTIGATION

Management small groups
Materials graph paper, heavy paper for masks, colored paper for design shapes, markers, crayons

Building Background

Review the concepts of symmetry and geometric shapes with the students. Fold paper in half or use a mirror to demonstrate symmetry.

Management Strategies Cooperative Learning

Introduce

- Meet with the entire class to introduce the activity and assign students to small groups.
- Review the criteria in *Keep In Mind.*

Guide

- Value persistence in thinking and planning, not speed in reaching an outcome.
- Use small-group time to assess math skills.

Summarize

- Discuss the group process: What actions helped your group to work well? Why?
- Challenge students to create a new version of the activity.

CHAPTER 7

INVESTIGATION

Mask Task!

Drama Connection With Your Group

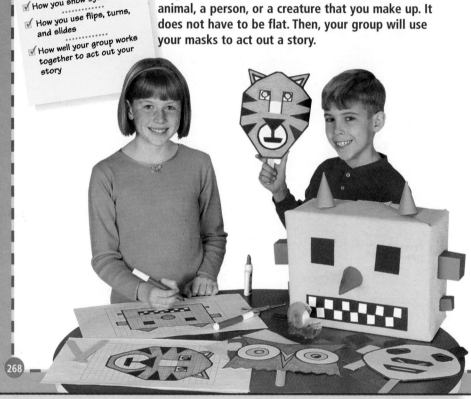

Keep In Mind . . .
Your work will be evaluated on the following:
✓ How you decide what shapes to use in your mask
✓ How you show symmetry
✓ How you use flips, turns, and slides
✓ How well your group works together to act out your story

Wearing a mask is a great way to "put on" the character of a play or a story that you are acting out. Now you are going to use what you know about shapes to make a fun mask! It can be a mask of an animal, a person, or a creature that you make up. It does not have to be flat. Then, your group will use your masks to act out a story.

268

Investigation Support

Technology

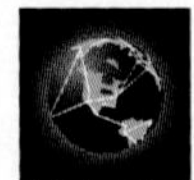
Internet: Education Place
http://www.eduplace.com
Houghton Mifflin Education Place **Mathematics Center** provides teacher and student support, such as links to other Internet sites.

Math Journal: *Communicating*

Ask several people what type of mask they like best: scary, funny, ceremonial, superhero, masquerade, other. Keep track of the results.

Students may record the questions and responses in their math journals.

Portfolio Opportunity

Put masks and stories about masks into individual student portfolios.

1
Plan It
Decide on the story your group would like to act out.
Decide what kind of mask to make and choose some shapes to use.
Plan your mask on graph paper. Begin by folding the paper in half. Draw a dark line on the fold to use as a line of symmetry.
Design half of the mask. Use slides and turns.
Use flips to draw the other half of the design.
2
Put It Together
Cut out your mask. Tape it on construction paper. Cut around the pattern.
Decorate your mask.
Glue your mask to a craft stick to hold it up to your face.
3
Wrap It Up
Find the lines of symmetry in your group's masks.
Act out your story for another group.
4
Discuss Your Results
Did you meet all of the goals in Keep In Mind?
Talk about how the masks were made. How well did the masks fit the characters?
Internet
Visit the Math Center at Houghton Mifflin Education Place. http://www.eduplace.com
269

Problem Solving Tip

Students can make equal size shapes by tracing or folding and cutting.

Completing the Investigation

Step 1 Help students identify shapes that are geometric. Brainstorm ideas for students to use in finding stories to act out.

Step 2 Assist students in drawing lines of symmetry and laying out masks.

Step 3 Suggest that students make pairs of equal size shapes before gluing any shapes to the mask.

Step 4 Encourage students to think of other stories they could tell with their masks.

Extending the Investigation

Groups of students can make up skits about the characters their masks portray.

Assessment Scoring Rubric

These criteria align with *Keep In Mind* in the Pupil Edition on page 268.

Criteria	1 Limited response	2 Acceptable	3 Capable	4 Superior
Accuracy of geometric shapes	Geometric shapes are inaccurate	Some of the geometric shapes are inaccurate	Most of the geometric shapes are accurate	All of the geometric shapes are accurate
Understanding of symmetry and geometric shapes	Lacks understanding of symmetry and geometric shapes	Understands some of the concept of symmetry and geometric shapes	Understands most of the concept of symmetry and geometric shapes	Thoroughly understands symmetry and geometric shapes
Success of the design	Design of the mask is unsuccessful	Design of the mask shows an attempt to be successful	Design of the mask is mostly successful	Design of the mask is successful
Contribution to the group process	Makes no effort to contribute to the group	Makes some effort to contribute to the group	Contributes to the group most of the time	Contributes fully to the group

Use this 4-level rubric to score students' responses. If you prefer a task with a 6-level rubric, use the Performance Assessment for this chapter.

Fractions

Chapter Overview

Vocabulary

- Introduce students to the chapter with vocabulary minilesson, TAB p. 270J.
- Planning Guide, p. 270C, lists vocabulary for each lesson in the chapter.
- Use the SAE vocabulary support in Lessons 8.1, 8.2, 8.4, 8.6, 8.7 and 8.9.

Rationale

Chapter Pacing: 10 days

- This chapter develops the concepts of equivalence and comparison of fractions and provides the necessary framework for students to understand addition and subtraction of simple fractions.
- Students use manipulatives to compare fractions and generate rules about relationships among fractions.
- Creating or coloring drawings further develops students' understanding of fractions.
- Students use these experiences to estimate and do simple computations involving fractions.
- The Math World feature presents Egyptian and Greek fraction symbols.
- In the Investigation, students create message flags, then write and send a message.

See **Daily Lesson Plans**, Chapter Management at a Glance, pp. 78–79; Suggested Weekly Plan, pp. 80–81.

Problem Solving

This chapter focuses on the Draw a Picture strategy for problem solving. It also reinforces strategies students have learned earlier and encourages them to choose and apply their own strategies.

Assessment

- The Chapter Introduction allows you to assess whether students have an understanding of fractions.
- Observe how students relate Fraction Bars and diagrams to writing fractions and solving equations.
- Use the Midchapter Review, the Chapter Test, and the Cumulative Review to assess students' needs for reinforcement or reteaching.

Reading Strategies

- Teach the Summarize reading strategy minilesson on TAB p. 270J. Then, use the following as opportunities to reinforce the strategy.
  - Preparing for Tests, TE pp. 270G–270H
  - Problem Solving Workshop, TE p. 280A
  - Problem Solving, Lessons 8.10, 8.11
- Use the SAE reading support for Lesson 8.3.

Meeting Individual Needs

Students Acquiring English

Help with vocabulary for fractions.

- Practice identifying numerators and denominators.
- Have pairs write, read, compare, estimate, add, and subtract fractions.
- Use models when working with equivalent fractions and mixed numbers.

See also **Language Connections** for additional support.

Extra Support

Students may have difficulty comparing fractions until they can recognize congruent parts of a whole.

- Use models to develop the part-whole theory, and lead students to understand how many parts make a whole in each case.
- To clarify students' understanding of fractions, use the Analyzing Errors strategies, pp. 297A–297B.
- Use the Fraction Workshop's Alternate Approach activity.

Challenge

Many students may benefit from this extension activity.

- Encourage students to identify fractions in everyday life by having them go on a fraction hunt. They can list fractions spotted in newspapers, magazines, catalogs, cookbooks, in advertisements, and so on.

Multi-Age Classroom

The chart below shows the chapters in books for levels 2 and 4 that can be used in conjunction with this chapter.

2	3	4
Chapter 7 *Geometry and Fractions*	**Chapter 8** *Fractions*	**Chapter 9** *Addition and Subtraction of Fractions*

See **Daily Lesson Plans**, Multi-Age Classroom Concept and Skill Development, pp. 4–5.

Chapter Bibliography

Key

Multicultural	★	*Social Studies*	
Science/Health		*Music*	
Literature		*Art*	

Technology

Students can explore fractions with the unique electronic tools in *Unlocking Fractions & Decimals 3–6.* Students can manipulate bar and circle models; the software dynamically reports the fractions they create.

Internet: Education Place

http://www.eduplace.com

Visit the **Mathematics Center** in *Houghton Mifflin Education Place* to find activities, projects, games, and links to other valuable Internet sites.

Ultimate Writing & Creativity Center

Students can use the *Ultimate Writing & Creativity Center®* for all their writing and publishing activities. The software is available from The Learning Company® in Macintosh and Windows formats.

Larson's Leapfrog MATH™

Leapfrog Math includes mathematics skills and concepts for grades 3–6. Each grade is contained on a single CD-ROM. The software is available from Meridian Creative Group, a Division of Larson Texts, Inc.

Test, Practice, Management Program

Use the *Test, Practice, Management Program* to create, administer, and score tests as well as generate practice sets. Questions are correlated to Lesson Objectives.

Graphers Sunburst Communications, Inc.®

Using the friendly tools in *Graphers,* children can easily manipulate data that can be counted or sorted and represent their data in a table or with six types of graphs.

Books for Students

Houghton Mifflin Mathematics Bookshelf

How Many Days to America? A Thanksgiving Story
Eve Bunting,
Clarion Books, 1988.
A refugee family travels to America and arrives on Thanksgiving Day. This book serves as a springboard for activities requiring fractions and division.

Give Me Half!
Stuart J. Murphy,
HarperCollins Publishers, 1996.
This Mathstart book introduces the concept of halves by using a simple rhyming story about a brother and sister who do not want to share their food.

Eating Fractions
Bruce McMillan,
Scholastic, 1991.
Color photographs of different kinds of food demonstrate the number concepts of wholes, halves, thirds, and fourths.

Fractions
David L. Stienecker,
Benchmark Books, 1996.
Activities and illustrations are used to teach the concept of fractions. Good for reinforcing one or more lessons.

How Many Ways Can You Cut a Pie?
Jane Belk Moncure,
Child's World, 1987.
Squirrel promises to divide her pie into sections for her animal friends if she wins the pie contest.

Gator Pie
Louise Mathews,
Dodd, Mead, 1979.
Two alligators consider dividing their pie into halves, thirds, quarters, eighths, and hundredths.

The World of Flags
William Crampton,
Rand McNally, 1994.
The history and construction of flags are discussed in this illustrated guide to flags. The international alphabet flags show different uses of flags for communication.

Books for Families

Elementary School Mathematics: What Parents Should Know about Estimation
Barbara Reys,
NCTM, 1982.
Parents can use helpful techniques and hints for teaching estimation from real-life situations.

Fractions, Decimals, Ratios, and Percents: Hard to Teach and Hard to Learn?
Carne Barnett, et al.,
Heinemann, 1994.
This book may help to change parents' ideas that fractions and decimals are difficult to learn.

Fraction Action
Loreen Leedy,
Holiday House, 1994.
Five humorous mathematics stories include problems to reinforce the fraction concepts introduced in this chapter.

Reference Books for Teachers

Early Fraction Learning
Robert P. Hunting and Gary Davis,
Springer-Verlag, 1991.
This book discusses recent research about teaching and learning fraction concepts.

Maneuvers with Fractions, Teacher Sourcebook
David A. Page and Kathryn Chval,
Dale Seymour Publications, 1995.
Teachers will appreciate the many ideas in this resource book for teaching fractions.

Problem Solving
Lakshmi Hewavisenti,
Gloucester Press, 1991.
This collection of colorful games and puzzles can help develop problem solving skills in several areas of mathematics, including fractions.

Planning Guide

		TE Pages	Lesson Objectives	Lesson Vocabulary	NCTM Standards
8.1	**Exploring Fractions**	*272–273*	To investigate fractions using pattern blocks		Geometry and Spatial Sense, Measurement, Fractions and Decimals, Communication, Connections
8.2	**Writing Fractions**	*274–275*	To use models to identify and write fractions	numerator denominator	Fractions and Decimals, Communication, Connections, Reasoning, Geometry and Spatial Sense
8.3	**Comparing Fractions**	*276–277*	To use concrete models to explore and compare common fractions		Fractions and Decimals, Communication, Connections, Reasoning, Patterns and Functions
8.4	**Equivalent Fractions**	*278–279*	To discover and identify equivalent fractions by using fraction models	equivalent fractions	Fractions and Decimals, Communication, Connections, Reasoning, Patterns and Functions
8.5	**Choose a Computation Method**	*280*	To decide whether to use mental math or a calculator to solve problems		Whole Number Concepts, Problem Solving, Whole Number Computation, Reasoning, Communication
8.6	**Estimating Fractions**	*284–285*	To estimate common fractions of a whole using benchmarks of 0, $\frac{1}{2}$, and 1		Whole Number Concepts, Fractions and Decimals, Estimation, Reasoning
8.7	**Adding and Subtracting Fractions**	*286–287*	To investigate addition and subtraction of fractions with like denominators, using fraction models		Fractions and Decimals, Measurement, Communication, Connections, Reasoning
8.8	**Draw a Picture**	*288–289*	To use the Draw a Picture strategy to solve problems		Problem Solving, Communication, Reasoning, Connections, Fractions and Decimals
8.9	**Mixed Numbers**	*290–291*	To understand and to write mixed numbers	mixed number	Whole Number Computation, Fractions and Decimals, Estimation, Communication, Connections, Reasoning
8.10	**Using Draw a Picture and Other Strategies**	*292–293*	To use Draw a Picture and other strategies to solve problems	quarter	Problem Solving, Communication, Reasoning, Connections, Fractions and Decimals
8.11	**Using Strategies**	*294–295*	To use different strategies to solve problems		Problem Solving, Communication, Reasoning, Connections, Fractions and Decimals

Chapter Objectives

8A To write fractions for fractional parts of regions
8B To compare and order fractions using models
8C To find equivalent fractions using models
8D To estimate fractions using benchmarks of 0, $\frac{1}{2}$, and 1
8E To add and subtract fractions with like denominators
8F To write mixed numbers for fractions greater than 1
8G To use Draw a Picture and other strategies to solve problems

Chapter Objectives	math center	State Requirements
8A	• *The Great Cover-Up,* Activity Card 44	
8A	• *Moving Right Along,* How-To Card 27; Gameboard 5	
8B	• *Who's the Greatest?,* Activity Card 45	
8C	• *Make a Match,* How-To Card 28; Fraction Card Deck	
8G	• *Feeding Fritzy,* Project Card 8	
8D	• *Fraction Flags,* Activity Card 46	
8E	• *Fraction Subtraction Game,* How-To Card 29; Gameboard 2	
8G	• *Feeding Fritzy,* Project Card 8	
8F	• *Mixed Number Challenge,* Activity Card 47; Workmat 1	
8G	• *Feeding Fritzy,* Project Card 8	
8G	• *Feeding Fritzy,* Project Card 8	

Integrating Reading Strategies

- Teach/review the Summarize strategy using TAB p. 270J.
- Encourage students to practice the strategy in Lessons 8.10 and 8.11.

Technology

Unlocking Fractions & Decimals 3–6

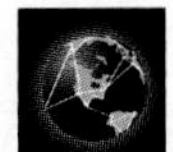
Internet: Education Place
http://www.eduplace.com
Houghton Mifflin Education Place
Mathematics Center

Test, Practice, Management Program

Special Lessons

pp. 270–271

Chapter Introduction

The Introduction shows students how useful fractions are in everyday life.

pp. 294–295

Students apply problem solving strategies in the context of Viking life.

pp. 282–283

Math World

Fractions Around the World

Use this feature to show students how fractions are used all over the world.

pp. 300–301

Investigation

Land Ho!

Students make alphabet flags similar to the signal flags used by ships and use them to send messages to one another.

Assessment

Use the following assessment tools to help assess individual needs.

- Midchapter Review, p. 281
- Chapter Test, pp. 296–297
- Cumulative Review, pp. 298–299

Chapter 8

Fraction Workshop

Use Halves, Thirds, and Fourths

Alternate Approach

Use with page 272.

25 minutes

How Many Halves?

Objective To investigate fractions

Management teacher directed; pairs
Materials dot paper
Modality *visual*

Activity

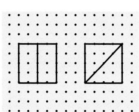

- Draw a 5-dot × 5-dot square on dot paper.
- Ask students how the figure you've drawn can be divided in half, or into two equal parts. Answers will vary. Possible answers shown.
- Give dot paper to student pairs and ask them to draw a 5 × 5 square. Then, ask them to find as many different ways as possible to divide the square in half. Encourage them to explore ways to divide the figure in half other than by a single straight line. Answers will vary. Possible answers shown.

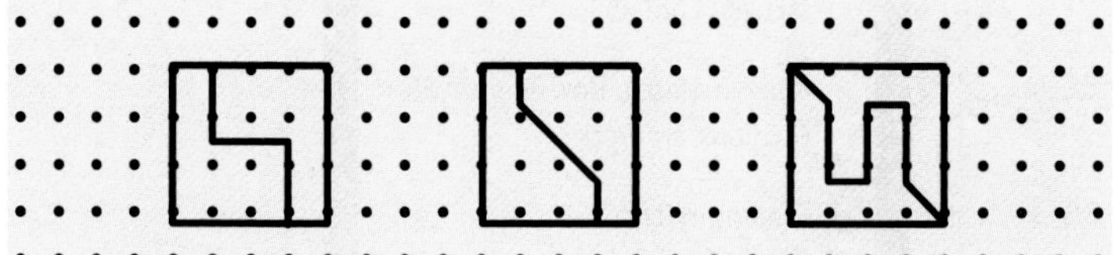

Meeting Individual Needs: *Modify*

Extra Support Have students use geoboards to divide a 5-peg × 5-peg square into halves. They can record their successful divisions on dot paper.

Extra Support

Use with page 286.

20 minutes

Adding Thirds and Fourths

Objective To add fractions with like denominators using a calculator

Management teacher directed; pairs
Modality *visual*

Activity

- Tell students that you are going to add three fractions using a calculator with the fraction keys / and Ab/c. For example, to find $\frac{1}{3} + \frac{1}{3}$, enter 1 / 3 + 1 / 3 =. The display now reads $\frac{2}{3}$. To add another third, enter + 1 / 3 =. The display reads $\frac{3}{3}$.
- Ask students which part of the fraction changes when you press =. the numerator Which part of the fraction stays the same? the denominator
- Then press the Ab/c key to change the fraction to a whole number. The display reads 1 after pressing the Ab/c key. Discuss the relationship of $\frac{3}{3}$ and 1. If necessary, use manipulatives to demonstrate the changes of the fraction into the whole number.

Keystrokes	Display
1 / 3	1/3
+ 1 / 3 =	2/3
+ 1 / 3 =	3/3
Ab/c	1

- Have student pairs work together to follow the same procedure with $\frac{1}{4}$ to prove that $\frac{4}{4} = 1$.

For more practice **Using the Calculator,** see pp. T88–T90.

Meeting Individual Needs: *Modify*

Challenge Invite students to repeat the operation on their own using $\frac{1}{5}$. They can record the display each time they press =. Students may write why $\frac{5}{5} = 1$ in their math journals.

Game

Use with page 278. **30 minutes**

Fraction Relay

Objective To identify equivalent fractions

Management teacher directed; teams of six
Materials one Equivalent Fractions Task Sheet for each team; fraction models for each student or each team
Advance Preparation Create and duplicate an Equivalent Fractions Task Sheet as shown.
Modality *kinesthetic/visual*

Activity

- Divide the class into teams of six players and distribute an Equivalent Fractions Task Sheet to each team.
- Explain that when you tell them to start, the first player on each team completes the first problem in Relay 1 on the task sheet and passes it to the second player, who completes the second problem.
- The third player checks the answers, corrects any mistakes, and hands the paper to the fourth player.
- The fourth and fifth players, in turn, complete the last two problems and pass the paper to the sixth player.
- The sixth player checks all of the work for accuracy and hands it to the teacher. The first team to complete the task sheet correctly wins the relay.
- Rearrange teams, and play again using Relay 2.
- You can replay this game several times to give students the opportunity to take different roles.

Relay 1	Relay 2
$\frac{1}{2} = \frac{\square}{8}$	$\frac{1}{3} = \frac{\square}{6}$
$\frac{1}{2} = \frac{\square}{4}$	$1 = \frac{\square}{3}$
$\frac{1}{4} = \frac{\square}{8}$	$\frac{2}{3} = \frac{\square}{6}$
$\frac{2}{4} = \frac{\square}{8}$	$\frac{2}{6} = \frac{\square}{3}$

Meeting Individual Needs: *Modify*

Extra Support Students who are having difficulty with equivalent fractions should avoid the role of checker.

Technology

MATHKEYS

Use with Lesson 8.4

Objective To explore and find equivalent fractions

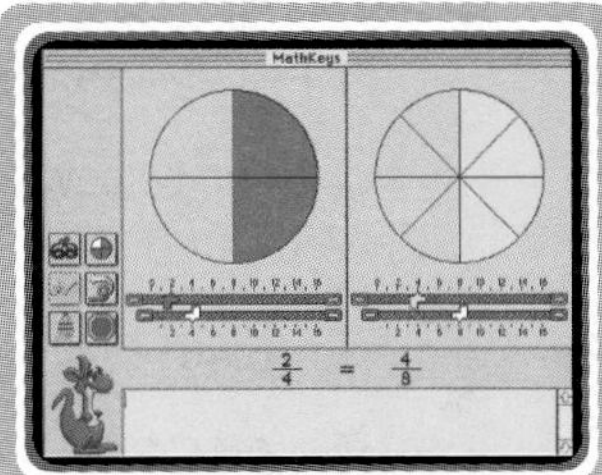

Management teacher monitored; pairs
Materials ***MathKeys****:* *Unlocking Fractions & Decimals 3–6*, Lev. 3, Act. 6: Equivalent Fractions
Modality *visual*

Activity

45 minutes

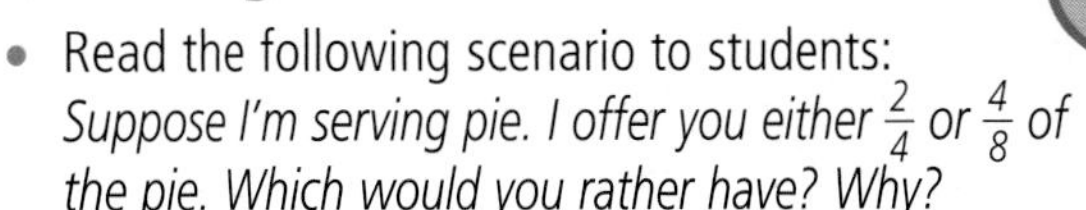

- Read the following scenario to students: *Suppose I'm serving pie. I offer you either $\frac{2}{4}$ or $\frac{4}{8}$ of the pie. Which would you rather have? Why?*
- Open *MathKeys* and open the Circles Models Mat. Create a fraction circle that represents $\frac{2}{4}$. Click on the Compare button and have a student make another fraction equal to $\frac{4}{8}$ on the second circle. Ask students which fraction is bigger. They are the same size. Point out the equal sign that appears on-screen when the fractions shown are equivalent.
- Invite student pairs to open the Circles Models Mat on their computers. Distribute the Activity 6 master and allow them to begin Part 1. Students create the given fraction in one circle and try to find fractional equivalents using the second circle.
- In Part 2, students use the Circles Add/Subtract Mat to find equivalent fractions to fill in a chart. Encourage students to try different strategies for solving the problems in Part 2.

Meeting Individual Needs: *Modify*

Challenge Invite students to play a game. With the Circles Models Mat, one student creates a fraction on the left side of the mat. The partner finds as many equivalent fractions as possible on the right side of the mat, recording the findings in the Notepad. Students switch roles and play again.

Preparing for Tests

To develop students' test-taking strategies, model the following types of assessment items found in this program.

Standardized Tests

Write the following question and answer choices on the board.

Which time shows a quarter to 9?

Ⓐ 8:40

Ⓑ 9:15

Ⓒ 8:50

Ⓓ 8:45 correct

Ⓔ 9:45

See also Standardized Testing: New Formats, **Chapter 8.**

Standardized tests usually require that students select the correct answer from a group of possible answers. In this problem, students must identify a digital time that matches a time expressed with a fraction.

Strategy

- What is another way to say a quarter to nine? Possible answers: 15 minutes before 9; 8:45
- How do you know these times are the same? Possible answer: At 8:45, there are 15 minutes left until 9:00. Since 15 minutes is a quarter of an hour, 8:45 is a quarter to 9.

Open-Ended Questions

Write the following direction and problem on the board.

Decide whether to use a calculator or mental math to solve this problem. Then solve.

About 6000 bats live in a certain cave. If 2000 fly out to feed, how many bats are left in the cave? mental math; about 4000 bats

See also Assessments, **Chapter 8.**

Open-ended questions can be answered in more than one way; they allow students to use a variety of concepts and processes. This problem asks students to choose the best method for solving a word problem.

Strategy

- What are you asked to do? decide whether to use a calculator or mental math to solve a problem, then solve the problem
- How will you make your decision? Possible answer: The numbers are large but not complicated. It may be best not to use a calculator.
- Should you always use a calculator when large numbers are involved? Explain. Possible answer: No; Large numbers are sometimes simple enough to work with mentally.

Preparing for Tests

Reading Strategies for Test-Taking

Summarize: As I read, I summarize the information, noting main ideas and important details.

Performance Tasks

Write the following problem on the board.

Fold a piece of regular writing paper in half. Fold it again. Open the paper. Shade one of the small rectangles. Write the fraction for the shaded part. Write the fraction for the unshaded part.

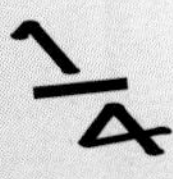

Performance assessments engage students in meaningful tasks that permit the teacher to observe their working procedures as well as the results they obtain. This problem requires students to model and write fractions.

Strategy

- What does the problem ask you to do? fold and shade paper to create fractions, then write the fractions
- What is a fraction? part of a whole
- Which number of the two numbers above or below the line is the numerator? the one above the line
- What does the numerator stand for? how many equal parts you are talking about
- What does the denominator represent? It tells how many equal parts fit into one whole.
- Which of the two numbers is the denominator? the one below the line

Check that students fold paper into even quarters and shade and label the page correctly. $\frac{1}{4}$ and $\frac{3}{4}$

See also Performance Assessments, **Chapter 8.**

Test-Taking Tips

- If one idea you have does not work, try different strategies and methods.

Additional Assessment Resources

Test, Practice, Management Program

Use the *Test, Practice, Management Program* to create, administer, and score tests as well as generate practice sets. Questions are correlated to the Lesson Objectives.

Chapter 8

Math Center

To meet individual needs, use the following resources from the Math Center. You may first wish to model activities for the whole class in order to demonstrate the rules for games and introduce procedures for independent tasks.

Gameboards

Gameboard 5
Use with Lesson 8.2.

Gameboard 2
Use with Lesson 8.7.

Activity Cards

44 ***The Great Cover-Up***
Use with Lesson 8.1.

45 ***Who's the Greatest?***
Use with Lesson 8.3.

46 ***Fraction Flags***
Use with Lesson 8.6.

47 ***Mixed Number Challenge***
Use with Lesson 8.9.

Project Card

8 ***Feeding Fritzy***
Use with Lessons 8.5, 8.8, 8.10, and 8.11.

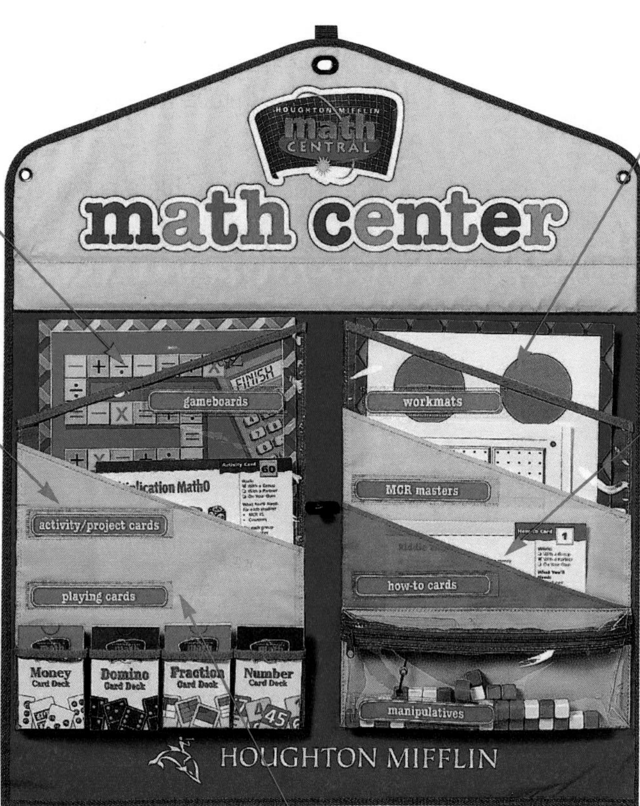

Workmats

Workmat 1
Use with Lesson 8.9.

How-To Cards

27 ***Moving Right Along***
Use with Lesson 8.2.

28 ***Make a Match***
Use with Lesson 8.4.

29 ***Fraction Subtraction Game***
Use with Lesson 8.7.

Card Decks

Fraction Card Deck
Use with Lesson 8.4.

Managing the Math Center

Rearranging groups Deciding how long to keep a given group of students together is based on a number of factors. Group cohesiveness takes time to develop. Students will improve their interpersonal skills if they know their group will be together for some time. But changing groups occasionally is desirable: it gives students the opportunity to share their group experiences in a new setting.

Vocabulary and Reading Strategies

Use these minilessons to strengthen vocabulary and reading skills.

Vocabulary

- fraction
- quarter

Linking Prior Knowledge and Vocabulary

Ask students to share and discuss meanings of the word **quarter.** You may want to list their ideas on the board first, and then work together to create a semantic map such as the one shown below. As you discuss time examples, you might draw simple analog clocks showing 15-minute intervals and explain that each interval is one quarter of an hour, or 15 minutes.

Graphic Organizer: Semantic Map

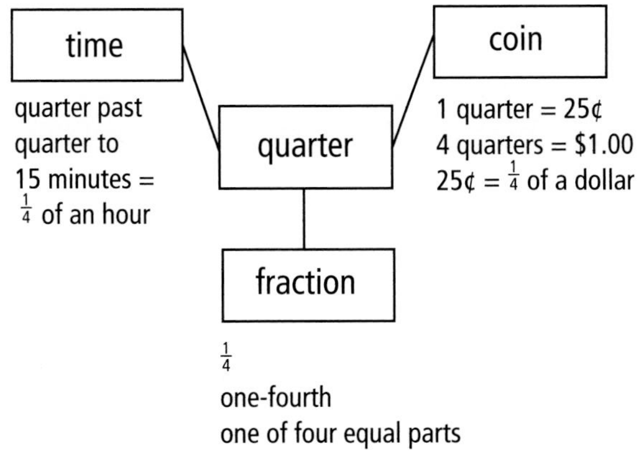

Reading Strategies

Strategy: Summarize

Explain that when an explanation or a problem contains a great deal of information, the Summarize strategy can help students find and remember the most important parts. Suggest that they summarize instructions such as those in Here's A Way! to help them remember the steps.

Then, use the Thinking Aloud box and the graphic organizer to demonstrate the Summarize strategy.

> Plan to make a pizza with different toppings. Your brother likes cheese and beef. Your sister will not eat beef. Your mother likes cheese and beef, but not beans. You like all three. Design a pie so that your brother, your sister, your mother, and you can each have two slices.

Lesson 8.11, p. 295, Problem 1

Thinking Aloud

- I read the problem and look for the main ideas.
- I know that 4 people will share a pizza.
- I know the toppings each person likes. I can summarize that information by making a table.
- I can use the table to design the pizza so everyone gets 2 pieces.

Graphic Organizers: Table, Diagram

brother	cheese, beef
sister	no beef
mother	cheese, beef, no beans
self	cheese, beef, and beans

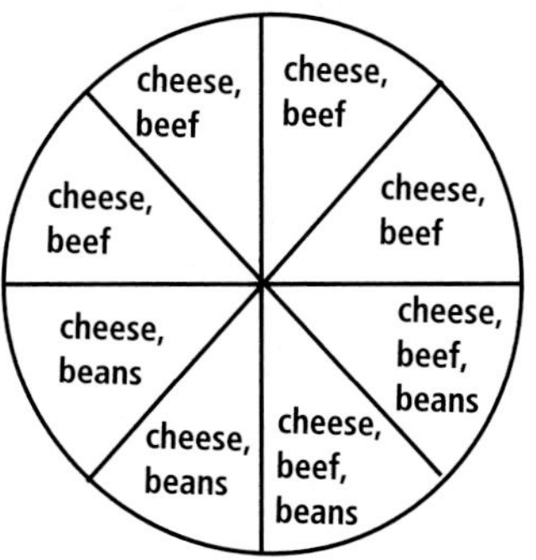

The reading strategies presented on this page can also apply to Lessons 8.10 and 8.11.

Objective
To use prior knowledge to explore fractions

Lesson Planning

Optional Resources
- Math Language Connections
- MATHKEYS *Unlocking Fractions & Decimals 3–6*

Every Day Counts Calendar Math
Fractions
To help students visualize fractions and make comparisons, use the Every Day Calendar activities in Every Day Counts Calendar Math, level 3.

Assessing Prior Knowledge

Try This! Use this as a prechapter activity in the classroom, or as a homework assignment.

Build confidence with this creative writing and art activity in which children create a comic strip showing some ways that fractions can be used.

This activity
- assesses prior knowledge of fractions
- provides a foundation for adding and subtracting fractions and mixed numbers

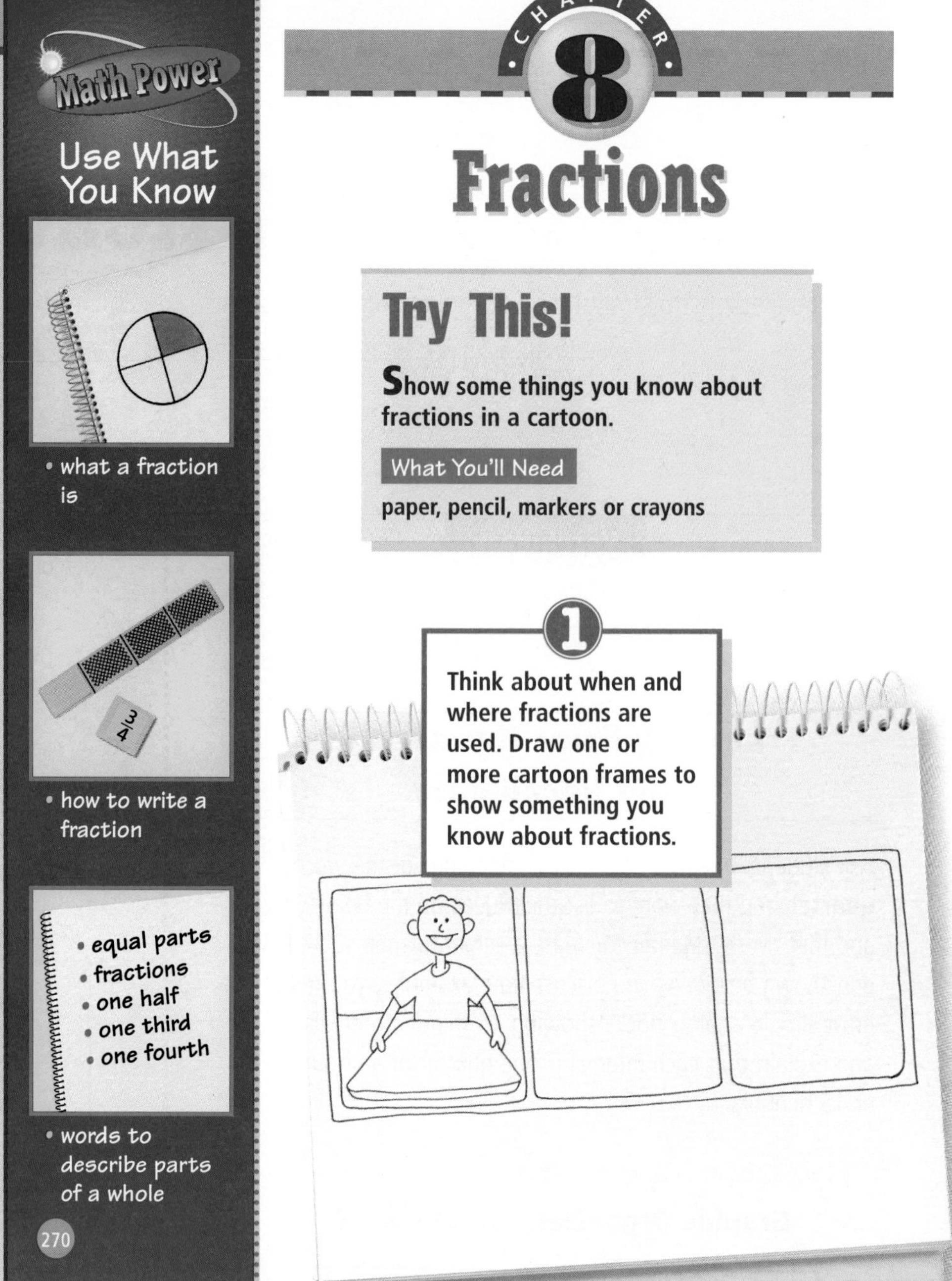

Math Power
Use What You Know
• what a fraction is
3/4
• how to write a fraction
• equal parts
• fractions
• one half
• one third
• one fourth
• words to describe parts of a whole
270
CHAPTER 8
Fractions
Try This!
Show some things you know about fractions in a cartoon.
What You'll Need
paper, pencil, markers or crayons
1
Think about when and where fractions are used. Draw one or more cartoon frames to show something you know about fractions.

Chapter Connections

Math Links

Throughout this chapter, students will build on prior knowledge as they develop concepts and skills for problem solving with fractions.

- **Number Sense** Lessons 8.2, 8.3, 8.6, 8.9
- **Patterns and Relationships** Lessons 8.1, 8.7
- **Estimation** Lessons 8.5, 8.6, 8.9
- **Geometry** Lessons 8.4, 8.11
- **Algebraic Reasoning** Lessons 8.2, 8.3, 8.4, 8.7, 8.9, 8.10
- **Data Analysis** Lessons 8.7, 8.8, 8.9
- **Time** Lesson 8.10

Real *World*

Social Studies

- **Lesson 8.2, p. 274**
  Flags Students use fractions to describe flags from different countries.
- **Lesson 8.5, p. 280**
  Walk for Hunger In a lesson on mental math, students explore the concept of performing service to raise money for those in need.
- **Lesson 8.10, p. 292**
  Martha's Vineyard Students use Draw a Picture and other problem solving strategies to solve problems about the ferryboat schedule at Martha's Vineyard.
- **Lesson 8.8, p. 286**
  Art Show Students add and subtract fractions based on fine art.
- **Lesson 8.11, p. 294**
  Vikings The lifestyle of ancient Viking people in Denmark, Norway, and Sweden becomes the setting for solving problems involving fractions.

2 Write fractions as you need them.

We can each take $\frac{1}{4}$ of the waffle.
I will eat the $\frac{1}{2}$ that is left.

3 Show your cartoon to others to see if they understand the fractions.

Use your cartoon idea with different fractions. How do the pictures and words change?

How does your cartoon help you remember things about fractions?

Ready to Go!

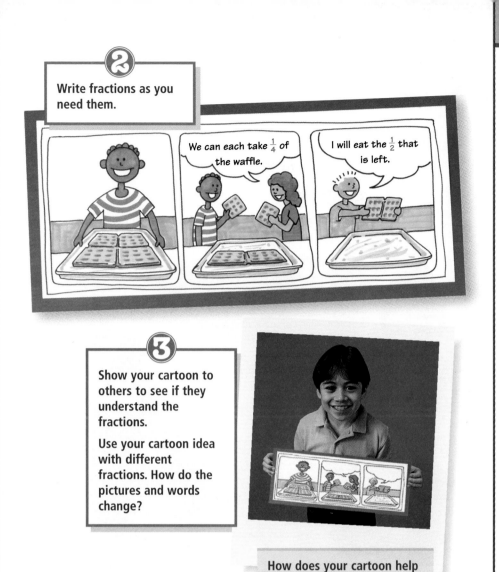

Meeting Individual Needs

If students have trouble writing fractions, start with Quick Help. They may also need a brief teacher-guided review.

Quick Help Explain that in this activity students will use what they already know. Provide pattern blocks and create a shape using only one kind of block. Model how to find the denominator by counting all the equal pieces in the shape. Model how to write the fraction that one block represents. You may also want to model how to find what part one shape is of another using Tangram pieces.

Guided Review Refer to:

- **Lesson 5.5** Dividing by 2, Student Book, p. 166
- **Basic Facts** Review Basic Facts, TE p. 281A

Vocabulary Power

Use this graphic organizer to review vocabulary used in fractions.

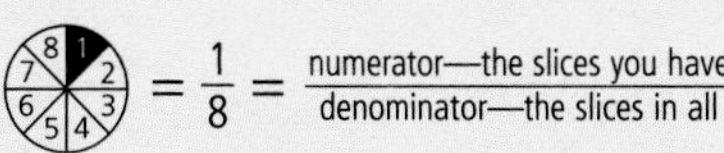

$= \frac{1}{8} = \frac{\text{numerator—the slices you have}}{\text{denominator—the slices in all}}$

Vocabulary Students can look in the dictionary for other words beginning with *frac-*. Discuss which words have a meaning that relates to the word *fraction*. Example: In a *fracture*, a bone is broken into pieces.

Investigation Preview

Land Ho!

Creating signal flags and sending messages will help students apply fractions and geometry in a real-world situation. See the Investigation, TE pp. 300–301.

What They'll Do

- Study examples of signal flags used at sea.
- Choose a message and decide on the number and size of the flags needed.
- Design the flags, using fractions to describe each one.
- Send a message with the flags.

Technology

Suggest the students model their fractions on the computer. Invite them to use the ***MathKeys:*** *Unlocking Fractions & Decimals 3–6* Bars Models Mat or Circles Models Mat. They can type notes in the Notepad and print their screens. Then, they can cut out the fraction models and use them to illustrate or accompany their cartoons.

Activity

Planning at a Glance

Objective To investigate fractions using pattern blocks

Materials pattern blocks, Recording Sheet (Practice 8.1)

Optional Resources

- Reteach 8.1; Enrichment 8.1
- Daily Cumul. Review, p. 101
- Math Center: Act. Card 44
- Every Day Counts
- **TAB**, pp. 270E–270F, 270J
- **Problem of the Day**, 101, p. 51; Flip Chart, p. 51a

MATHKEYS *Unlocking Fractions & Decimals 3–6*, Level 3, Activity 1

Students Acquiring English

Draw two figures, one divided into equal parts and one unequal. Show that the prefix *un-* means "not." Ask students to identify equal and unequal parts. Shade some of the equal parts; help students identify "___ out of ___ parts," with the first number being the shaded parts and the second the total parts.

Problem of the Day

The Magicians' Club bought five new magic wands. The total cost was $12. Club members shared the cost equally. Every member gave at least a quarter but less than $1. What is the greatest number of club members there could have been? The fewest?

most—48 members; fewest—13 members

Exploring Fractions

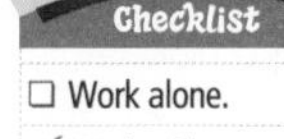

Cooperative Learning Checklist

- ☐ Work alone.
- ☑ Work with a partner.
- ☑ Work with a group.

Getting Started

What You'll Need:
- recording sheet
- pattern blocks

A fraction is a number that names a part of a whole or part of a set. Use pattern blocks and a recording sheet to find out more about fractions.

Activity

- Use pattern blocks to explore figures with equal parts.

1

Figure 1 is divided into 2 parts, or 2 halves. Place a green triangle on Figure 1.

- How many of the equal parts are covered by the triangle?
- One of the halves, or one half, of the whole figure is covered.

272 Chapter 8

1 Introduce

Prior Knowledge Ask students to write the symbol for "less than," "greater than," or "equal to" in each square.

4 □ 3 >; 3 □ 2 >; 2 □ 2 =; 1 □ 3 <

Teach: Activity

Emphasize these points:

- Each figure is divided into equal parts.
- Words such as *one third* name fractional parts of the whole figure.
- Use the notation $\frac{1}{3}$ instead of 1 out of 3.

Modeling Model figures 1 and 2. Ask:

- How many halves are in a whole? 2
- How many blocks would I need to cover more than half of figure 2? 2

2 Develop

Show What You Know!

Common Error Some students may miscount the parts of the more complex figures. Remind them to count carefully. See also Analyzing Errors, TE pp. 297A and 297B.

- Call on students to discuss their reasoning for exercises 1–6.
- Ask students to explain their answer to exercise 7.
- Have students review the meanings of the terms *half, third, fourth, sixth*, and *eighth*.
- Emphasize that a fraction names an equal part of a whole.

3 Summarize

Ongoing Assessment A pizza is cut into 4 equal parts. Alice eats one part. What fractional part of the pizza did Alice eat? one fourth What fractional part of the pizza is left? three fourths

Math Journal: *Communicating*

Answers will vary. Possible answer: Equal parts are the same size parts of a whole figure; unequal parts are not the same size.

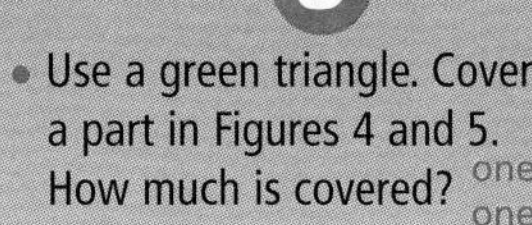

2

Figure 2 is divided into 3 parts or 3 thirds. How many equal parts are in Figure 2?

- Place a green triangle on Figure 2.
- How much of the whole figure is covered? One of the thirds, or one third, is covered.
- Figure 3 is divided into 4 fourths. How much can you cover with a green triangle? one of the fourths, or one fourth

3

- Use a green triangle. Cover a part in Figures 4 and 5. How much is covered? one sixth, one eighth
- Use a blue block. Cover a part in Figures 6 and 7. How much is covered? one half, one third
- Use a red block. Cover a part in Figure 8. How much is covered? one half

Show What You Know!

Discuss each question. Explain your answer.

1. **Critical Thinking** How are Figures 1–5 alike? How are they different? Alike: All the parts are triangles. Different: each has a different number of parts.
2. Would you need more than one green block to cover half of Figure 3? Explain why. Yes; need to cover 2 parts
3. The red block covers half of some figures. Which ones? Figures 4, 7, and 8
4. The blue block covers half of some figures. Which ones? Figures 3 and 6
5. The green block covers five of the eight parts of figure 5. Write this as a fraction. five eighths
6. Place one blue block on Figure 2. How much of the whole figure is covered? two thirds
7. **Critical Thinking** Could you use green blocks to cover exactly half of figure 2? Explain. No, if you cover one third, that's less than one half; if you cover two thirds, that's more than one half.

Math Journal

Use your own words. Explain the difference between equal and unequal parts of a whole figure. Equal parts are the same size. Unequal parts are different sizes.

273

Meeting Individual Needs

Extra Support

Tinted Fractions ***(visual/kinesthetic)*** Have students draw three circles or other shapes on a sheet of paper. Then, have them trade papers with a partner and use crayons to color one half, one third, and one fourth of each shape.

Alternate Approach

- Reteach Worksheet 8.1
- **TAB** See TE pp. 242E–242F.

MathZones

Understanding Fractions

Students Acquiring English

See Language Connections, Ch. 8.

Challenge

Have students show fractions of a whole by folding two square sheets of paper in the following ways:

- Fold sheet 1 into halves and fourths by folding edge to edge. Open and color two fourths red.
- Fold sheet 2 into eighths by folding corner to corner. Color four eighths blue.

Practice

Math Center Use Activity Card 44, *The Great Cover-Up,* to have students practice investigating fractions by using pattern blocks.

Challenge Use Activity Card 44 and have students continue the activity as described in Now Try This!

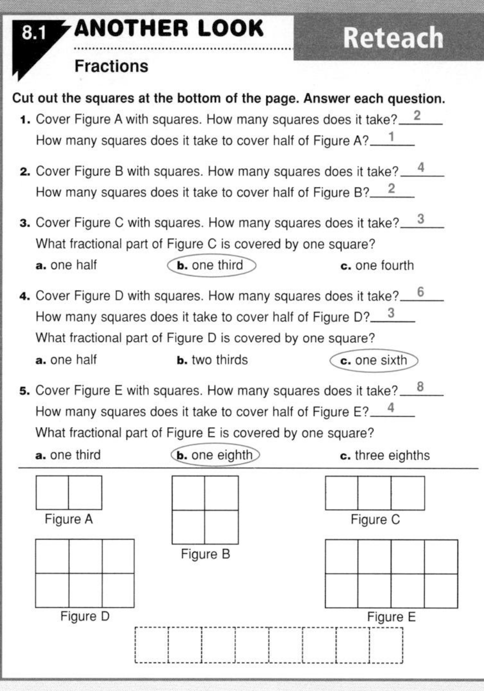

8.1 ANOTHER LOOK — **Reteach**

Fractions

Cut out the squares at the bottom of the page. Answer each question.

1. Cover Figure A with squares. How many squares does it take? 2
   How many squares does it take to cover half of Figure A? 1
2. Cover Figure B with squares. How many squares does it take? 4
   How many squares does it take to cover half of Figure B? 2
3. Cover Figure C with squares. How many squares does it take? 3
   What fractional part of Figure C is covered by one square?
   a. one half (b. one third) c. one fourth
4. Cover Figure D with squares. How many squares does it take? 6
   How many squares does it take to cover half of Figure D? 3
   What fractional part of Figure D is covered by one square?
   a. one half b. two thirds (c. one sixth)
5. Cover Figure E with squares. How many squares does it take? 8
   How many squares does it take to cover half of Figure E? 4
   What fractional part of Figure E is covered by one square?
   a. one third (b. one eighth) c. three eighths

Figure A, Figure B, Figure C, Figure D, Figure E

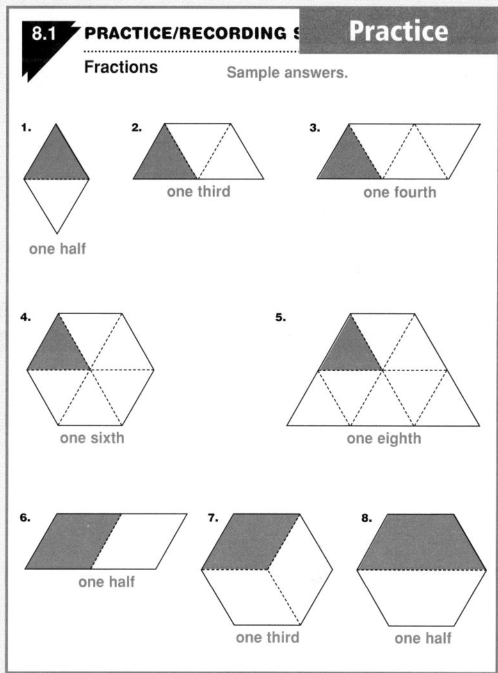

8.1 PRACTICE/RECORDING SHEET — **Practice**

Fractions Sample answers.

1. one half
2. one third
3. one fourth
4. one sixth
5. one eighth
6. one half
7. one third
8. one half

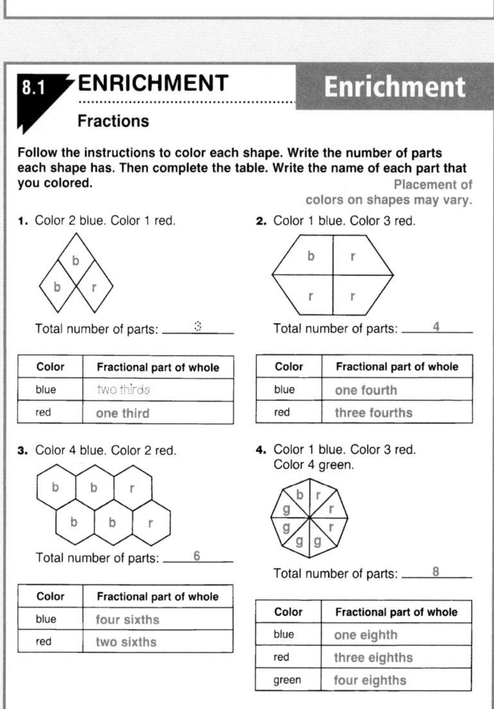

8.1 ENRICHMENT — **Enrichment**

Fractions

Follow the instructions to color each shape. Write the number of parts each shape has. Then complete the table. Write the name of each part that you colored. Placement of colors on shapes may vary.

1. Color 2 blue. Color 1 red.

Total number of parts: 3

Color	Fractional part of whole
blue	two thirds
red	one third

2. Color 1 blue. Color 3 red.

Total number of parts: 4

Color	Fractional part of whole
blue	one fourth
red	three fourths

3. Color 4 blue. Color 2 red.

Total number of parts: 6

Color	Fractional part of whole
blue	four sixths
red	two sixths

4. Color 1 blue. Color 3 red. Color 4 green.

Total number of parts: 8

Color	Fractional part of whole
blue	one eighth
red	three eighths
green	four eighths

Connecting

Planning at a Glance

Objective To use models to identify and write fractions

Materials fraction models (TR28)

Optional Resources

- Reteach 8.2; Practice 8.2; Enrichment 8.2
- Daily Cumul. Review, p. 102
- Math Center: How-To Card 27
- Every Day Counts
- **TAB**, TE pp. 270E–270F, 270J
- **Problem of the Day**, 102, p. 51; Flip Chart p. 51b

MATHKEYS *Unlocking Fractions & Decimals 3–6*, Level 3, Activity 2

Students Acquiring English

Pronounce *numerator* and *denominator*; ask students to repeat them. Ask a student to write a fraction, and a second student to point to the numerator and denominator. Give students practice saying the word forms of different denominators, such as half (2), third (3), fourth (4), and so on.

Problem of the Day

Becky wrote each digit from 1 to 9 on a separate card. Then she made three piles of three cards each. The sums of the digits in the piles were 13, 15, and 17. What cards were in each pile?
one possible answer: $1 + 4 + 8 = 13$, $2 + 6 + 7 = 15$, $3 + 5 + 9 = 17$

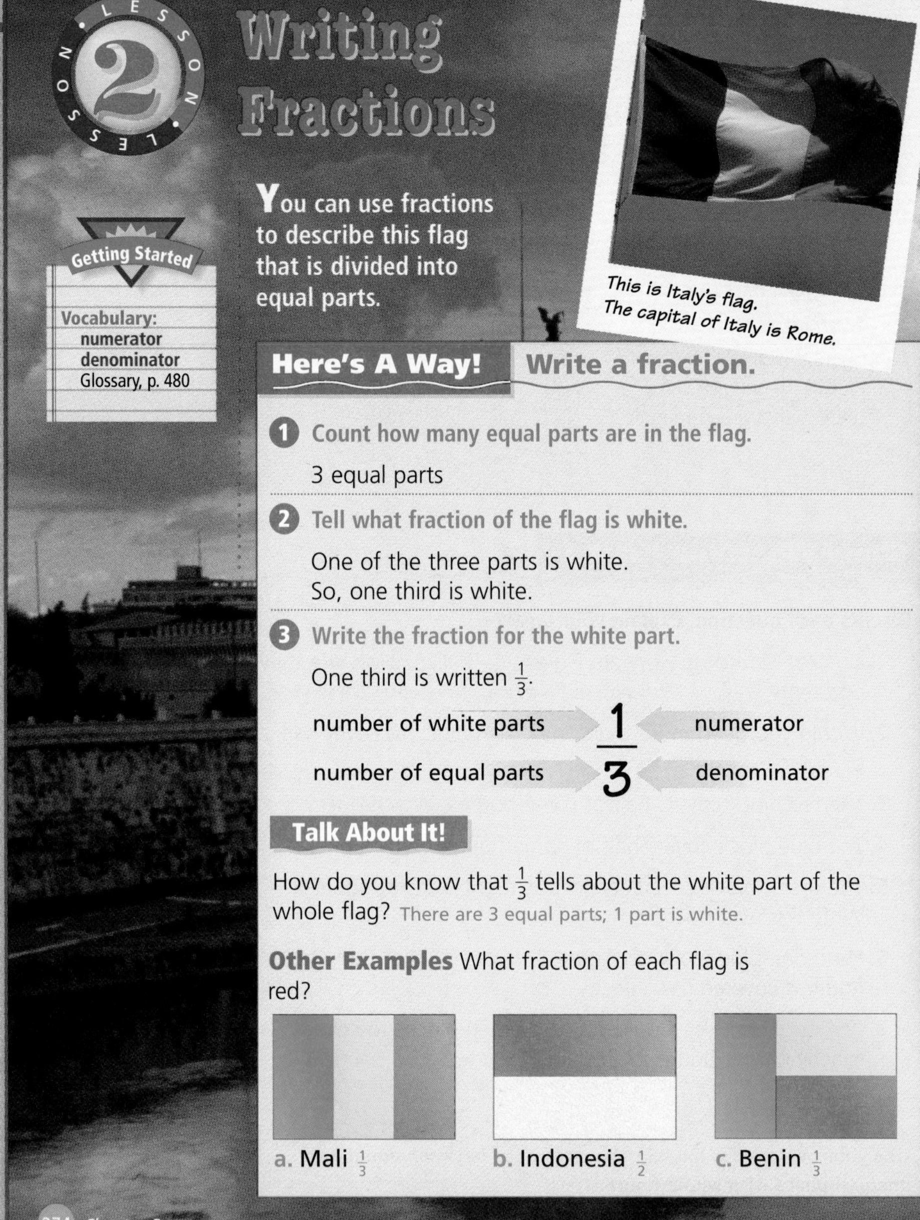
LESSON 2

Writing Fractions

Getting Started

Vocabulary:
numerator
denominator
Glossary, p. 480

You can use fractions to describe this flag that is divided into equal parts.

This is Italy's flag.
The capital of Italy is Rome.

Here's A Way! Write a fraction.

1. Count how many equal parts are in the flag.
   3 equal parts
2. Tell what fraction of the flag is white.
   One of the three parts is white.
   So, one third is white.
3. Write the fraction for the white part.
   One third is written $\frac{1}{3}$.

number of white parts → 1 ← numerator
number of equal parts → 3 ← denominator

Talk About It!

How do you know that $\frac{1}{3}$ tells about the white part of the whole flag? There are 3 equal parts; 1 part is white.

Other Examples What fraction of each flag is red?

a. Mali $\frac{1}{3}$ b. Indonesia $\frac{1}{2}$ c. Benin $\frac{1}{3}$

274 Chapter 8

Build Understanding Have students use or make fraction models (TR28).

Ask, How many equal parts are there? 3 **How many parts are shaded?** 2 out of 3 equal parts **What fraction is shaded?** two thirds

Teach: Here's A Way!

Emphasize this point:

- The numerator of a fraction names the part of the whole. The denominator names the number of equal parts in the whole.

2 Develop

Show What You Know!

- Remind students that a fraction names equal parts of a whole.
- Remind students to think about which number in a fraction is the numerator and which is the denominator.
- Ask students to explain how they calculated the unshaded parts in exercises 1–4.

Work It Out!

- Ask students to discuss their reasoning for exercises 18–19.

- A whole can be divided into any number of equal parts.
- The denominator tells how many equal parts are in a whole, and the numerator names a certain number of those parts.

Ongoing Assessment Bo's spinner has 3 equal parts, 2 red and 1 white. What fraction is red? $\frac{2}{3}$ Which number is the numerator? 2

Math Journal: *Communicating*

A circle is $\frac{5}{6}$ blue and $\frac{1}{6}$ red. How many equal parts is the circle divided into? How do you know? 6 parts; by looking at the denominator, which tells how many parts there are in the whole

Show What You Know!

Write the fraction for the shaded part of the figure.

1. 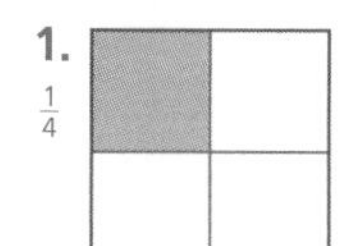 $\frac{1}{4}$
2. 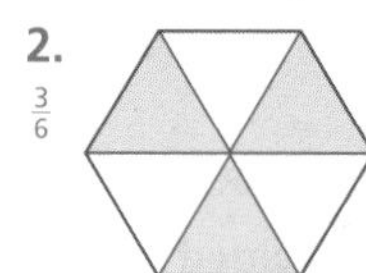 $\frac{3}{6}$
3. 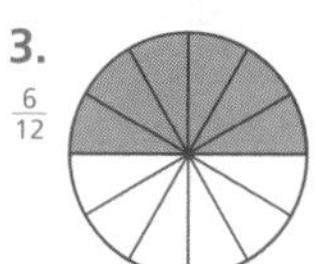 $\frac{6}{12}$
4. 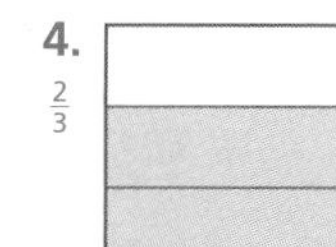 $\frac{2}{3}$
5. **Critical Thinking** Write a fraction for the unshaded part of exercise 4. $\frac{1}{3}$

Work It Out!

Draw a flag. Use the fraction to show the shaded part of the flag.
Check students' work.

6. $\frac{2}{4}$ 7. $\frac{6}{12}$ 8. $\frac{4}{4}$ 9. $\frac{4}{12}$ 10. $\frac{1}{3}$ 11. $\frac{3}{5}$

Look at the chart. Write the missing fractions.

Fraction Name	Fraction	Picture
one half	$\frac{1}{2}$	
one third	12. ? $\frac{1}{3}$	
one fourth	13. ? $\frac{1}{4}$	
14. ? one fifth	15. ? $\frac{1}{5}$	
16. ? one sixth	$\frac{1}{6}$	
one seventh	17. ? $\frac{1}{7}$	
18. ? one eighth	$\frac{1}{8}$	

Look at the set of blocks.

19. How many blocks are in the whole set? six
20. What fraction of the whole set is one block? Two blocks? Three blocks? Four blocks? Five blocks? $\frac{1}{6}, \frac{2}{6}, \frac{3}{6}, \frac{4}{6}, \frac{5}{6}$
21. **Create Your Own** Design a school flag. Divide a rectangle into fourths and color it in. Write fractions for the parts.
Designs will vary but should show fourths.

More Practice Set 8.2, p. 463

275

Meeting Individual Needs

Extra Support

Do I Hear a Fraction? ***(auditory/kinesthetic)***
Student pairs take turns naming fractions aloud and writing their partner's numbers in fractional form. After students check to see whether their partners have written the fractions correctly, let them use dot paper or fraction models to show their fractions.

Alternate Approach

- Reteach Worksheet 8.2
- **TAB** See TE pp. 242E–242F.

MathZones

Understanding Fractions

Students Acquiring English

See **Language Connections**, Ch. 8.

Challenge

On square dot paper, pairs of students draw three different figures with 5, 6, 8, 10, or 12 equal parts, and color a fraction of each figure. Student pairs exchange papers and write the fraction for the shaded part of each figure.

Practice

Math Center Use How-To Card 27, *Moving Right Along,* to have students practice writing fractions from models of fractions.

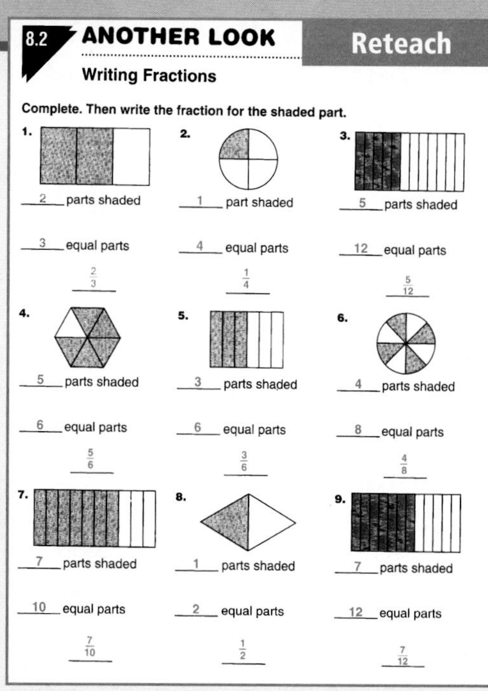

8.2 **ANOTHER LOOK** — **Reteach**

Writing Fractions

Complete. Then write the fraction for the shaded part.

1. 2 parts shaded; 3 equal parts; $\frac{2}{3}$
2. 1 part shaded; 4 equal parts; $\frac{1}{4}$
3. 5 parts shaded; 12 equal parts; $\frac{5}{12}$
4. 5 parts shaded; 6 equal parts; $\frac{5}{6}$
5. 3 parts shaded; 6 equal parts; $\frac{3}{6}$
6. 4 parts shaded; 8 equal parts; $\frac{4}{8}$
7. 7 parts shaded; 10 equal parts; $\frac{7}{10}$
8. 1 parts shaded; 2 equal parts; $\frac{1}{2}$
9. 7 parts shaded; 12 equal parts; $\frac{7}{12}$

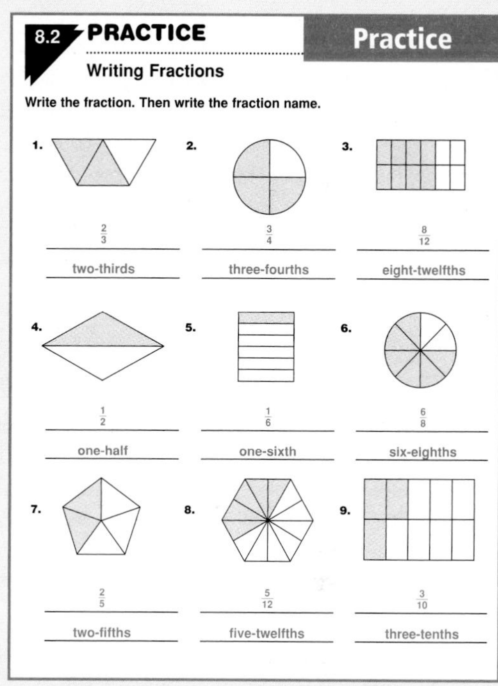

8.2 **PRACTICE** — **Practice**

Writing Fractions

Write the fraction. Then write the fraction name.

1. $\frac{2}{3}$ two-thirds
2. $\frac{3}{4}$ three-fourths
3. $\frac{8}{12}$ eight-twelfths
4. $\frac{1}{2}$ one-half
5. $\frac{1}{6}$ one-sixth
6. $\frac{6}{8}$ six-eighths
7. $\frac{2}{5}$ two-fifths
8. $\frac{5}{12}$ five-twelfths
9. $\frac{3}{10}$ three-tenths

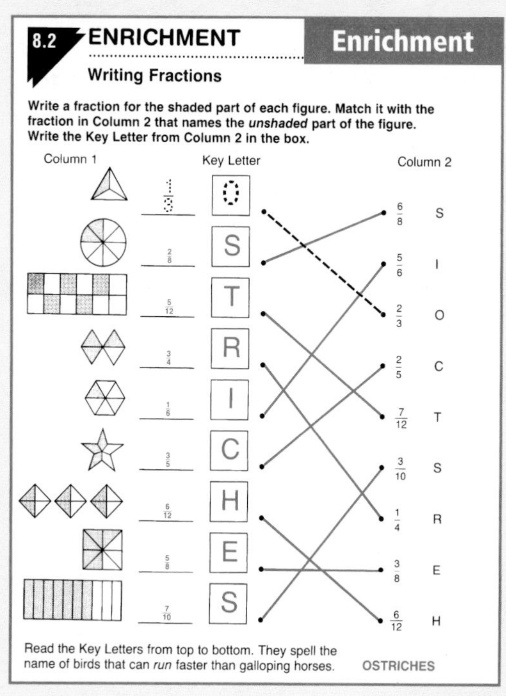

8.2 **ENRICHMENT** — **Enrichment**

Writing Fractions

Write a fraction for the shaded part of each figure. Match it with the fraction in Column 2 that names the *unshaded* part of the figure. Write the Key Letter from Column 2 in the box.

Column 1		Key Letter	Column 2	
	$\frac{1}{3}$	O	$\frac{6}{8}$	S
	$\frac{2}{8}$	S	$\frac{5}{6}$	I
	$\frac{5}{12}$	T	$\frac{2}{3}$	O
	$\frac{3}{4}$	R	$\frac{2}{5}$	C
	$\frac{1}{6}$	I	$\frac{7}{12}$	T
	$\frac{3}{5}$	C	$\frac{3}{10}$	S
	$\frac{6}{12}$	H	$\frac{1}{4}$	R
	$\frac{5}{8}$	E	$\frac{3}{8}$	E
	$\frac{7}{10}$	S	$\frac{6}{12}$	H

Read the Key Letters from top to bottom. They spell the name of birds that can *run* faster than galloping horses. OSTRICHES

Activity

Planning at a Glance

Objective To use concrete models to explore and compare common fractions

Materials fraction models (TR28)

Optional Resources

- Reteach 8.3; Practice 8.3; Enrichment 8.3
- Daily Cumul. Review, p. 103
- Math Center: Act. Card 45
- Every Day Counts
- **TAB**, TE pp. 270E–270F, 270J
- **Problem of the Day**, 103, p. 52; Flip Chart, p. 52a

MATHKEYS

Unlocking Fractions & Decimals 3–6, Level 3, Activity 4

Students Acquiring English

Building Reading Strategies Students may need help expressing themselves when they try to answer questions 11 and 12. Help them simplify the questions by saying: *The denominator is the same, the numerator is greater, is the fraction greater or smaller?* or *The numerator is the same, the denominator is greater, is the fraction greater or smaller?*

Problem of the Day

Davida shared some raisins with her friends. First she gave 6 raisins to Will. Then she gave Patti half of what was left. Next, Bart got half the raisins that were left, plus 1 more. Davida ate the last 5 raisins herself. How many raisins did Davida start with? **Hint:** It is a multiple of 5.
30 raisins

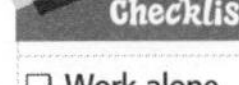

Cooperative Learning Checklist

- ☐ Work alone.
- ☑ Work with a partner.
- ☑ Work with a group.

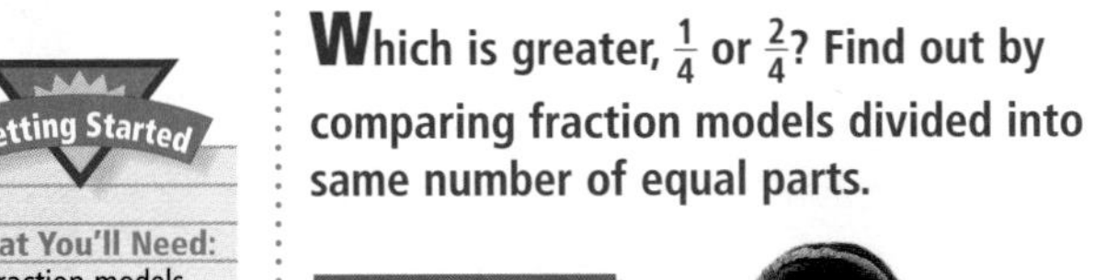

Lesson 3 Comparing Fractions

Getting Started

What You'll Need:
▶ fraction models

Which is greater, $\frac{1}{4}$ or $\frac{2}{4}$? Find out by comparing fraction models divided into the same number of equal parts.

Activity

Compare $\frac{1}{4}$ and $\frac{2}{4}$.

The fractions $\frac{1}{4}$ and $\frac{2}{4}$ have the same denominator but they have different numerators.

1. Use fraction models for $\frac{1}{4}$ and $\frac{2}{4}$. Both fractions have a denominator of 4. Both models show 4 equal parts.
2. Compare the models. Which model shows more shading? $\frac{2}{4}$
3. Write > or < between the fractions to tell which is greater. $\frac{1}{4} < \frac{2}{4}$ or $\frac{2}{4} > \frac{1}{4}$

1 Introduce

Prior Knowledge **Ask students to order these numbers from least to greatest: 5, 6, 4** 4, 5, 6 **2, 6, 3** 2, 3, 6

Teach: Activity

Emphasize these points:

- When fractions have the same denominator, the one with the larger numerator is greater.
- When fractions have the same numerator, the one with the smaller denominator is greater.

Modeling Model comparing the fractions $\frac{1}{4}$ and $\frac{2}{4}$. Ask:

- Which number names the total number of parts? the bottom number or denominator, 4
- Which fraction is greater? $\frac{2}{4}$

2 Develop

Show What You Know!

- Remind students that any fraction names equal parts of a whole.
- Review with students which number in a fraction is the numerator and which is the denominator.
- Call on students to discuss their answers for exercises 11 and 12.
- Have students discuss how they know what fractions to use to complete the number lines in exercises 24 and 25.
- You may wish to have students draw pictures of their models to show how they solved the exercises.

3 Summarize

- Remind students to check both the numerator and the denominator to tell which fraction is greater.

Ongoing Assessment Jan has $\frac{4}{6}$ of a granola bar left. Tim has $\frac{3}{4}$ of an an identical granola bar left. Who has more left? Students may use fraction models to say that Tim has more left; they should see that they cannot simply compare one part of the fractions.

Math Journal: *Communicating*

How can ordering whole numbers help you to order fractions? Answers will vary. Possible answer: The same principles apply to ordering fractions with the same denominator.

Compare $\frac{1}{2}$ and $\frac{1}{6}$.

The fractions $\frac{1}{2}$ and $\frac{1}{6}$ have the same numerator but they have different denominators.

1. Use fraction models for $\frac{1}{2}$ and $\frac{1}{6}$. The denominators are different. Each model is divided into a different number of equal parts.
2. Compare the models. Which model shows more shading? $\frac{1}{2}$
3. Write > or < between the fractions to tell which is greater. $\frac{1}{6} < \frac{1}{2}$ or $\frac{1}{2} > \frac{1}{6}$

Show What You Know!

Use fraction models to compare the pair of fractions. Write > or <.

1. $\frac{3}{6}$ ■ $\frac{5}{6}$ <
2. $\frac{2}{4}$ ■ $\frac{3}{4}$ <
3. $\frac{1}{3}$ ■ $\frac{2}{3}$ <
4. $\frac{1}{2}$ ■ $\frac{2}{2}$ <
5. $\frac{1}{6}$ ■ $\frac{2}{6}$ <
6. $\frac{1}{2}$ ■ $\frac{1}{3}$ >
7. $\frac{1}{6}$ ■ $\frac{1}{4}$ <
8. $\frac{1}{3}$ ■ $\frac{1}{4}$ >
9. $\frac{1}{2}$ ■ $\frac{1}{6}$ >
10. $\frac{1}{4}$ ■ $\frac{1}{2}$ <
11. In exercises 1–5, each pair of fractions has the same denominator. What do you notice about the size of the numerator and the size of the fraction? the greater the numerator, the greater the value of the fraction
12. In exercises 6–10, each pair of fractions has the same numerator. What do you notice about the size of the denominator and the size of the fraction? the greater the denominator, the lesser the value of the fraction
13. The fractions $\frac{2}{3}$ and $\frac{3}{4}$ have different numerators and denominators. Which is greater, $\frac{2}{3}$ or $\frac{3}{4}$? Why? $\frac{3}{4}$; The fraction model shows that $\frac{3}{4}$ is a larger part of the whole than $\frac{2}{3}$.

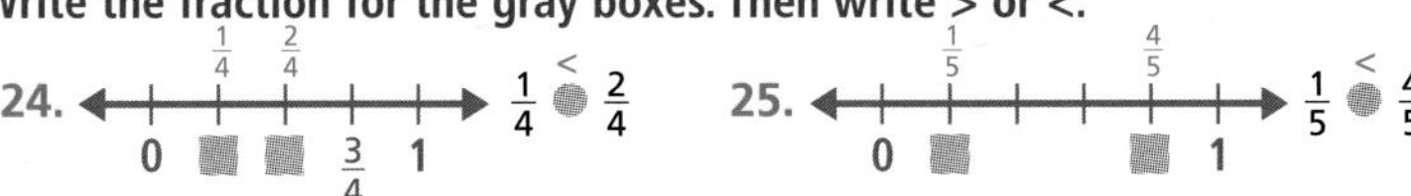

Use fraction models to compare the fractions. Write >, <, or =.

14. $\frac{2}{3}$ ■ $\frac{2}{2}$ <
15. $\frac{2}{4}$ ■ $\frac{2}{6}$ >
16. $\frac{2}{4}$ ■ $\frac{3}{3}$ <
17. $\frac{1}{4}$ ■ $\frac{3}{4}$ <
18. $\frac{2}{5}$ ■ $\frac{4}{5}$ <
19. $\frac{2}{3}$ ■ $\frac{4}{6}$ =
20. $\frac{3}{6}$ ■ $\frac{3}{5}$ <
21. $\frac{3}{6}$ ■ $\frac{1}{2}$ =
22. $\frac{1}{4}$ ■ $\frac{2}{3}$ <
23. $\frac{4}{6}$ ■ $\frac{2}{4}$ >

the greater the numerator, the greater the fraction

Write the fraction for the gray boxes. Then write > or <.

24. Number line: 0 ■ ■ $\frac{3}{4}$ 1 (gray boxes: $\frac{1}{4}$, $\frac{2}{4}$) $\frac{1}{4}$ ● $\frac{2}{4}$ <
25. Number line: 0 ■ ■ 1 (gray boxes: $\frac{1}{5}$, $\frac{4}{5}$) $\frac{1}{5}$ ● $\frac{4}{5}$ <

277

Meeting Individual Needs

Extra Support

Lining Up Fractions *(visual)* Have pairs of students draw a number line from 0 to 1. Then, have them write the following fractions in the correct places on the line: $\frac{1}{4}, \frac{3}{4}, \frac{1}{3}, \frac{2}{3}, \frac{1}{2}$. Invite students to use fraction models or pictures to help them.

Alternate Approach

- Reteach Worksheet 8.3
- **TAB** See TE pp. 242E–242F.

MathZones
Understanding Fractions

Students Acquiring English

See **Language Connections**, Ch. 8.

Challenge

Ask students to work with fraction models or pictures to build equivalent fractions such as $\frac{3}{6}, \frac{1}{2}, \frac{2}{4}, \frac{4}{8}$. Challenge them to define an equivalent fraction. Students in pairs alternate naming three fractions and challenging their partners to order them from least to greatest.

Practice

Math Center Use Activity Card 45, *Who's the Greatest?*, to have students practice comparing common fractions concretely.

Challenge Use Activity Card 45 and have students continue the activity as described in Now Try This!

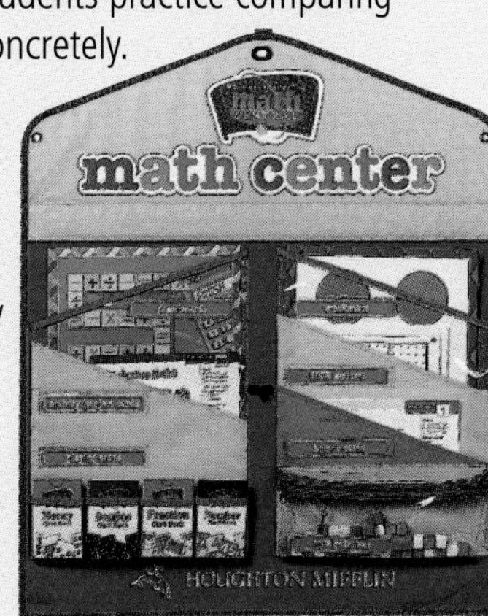

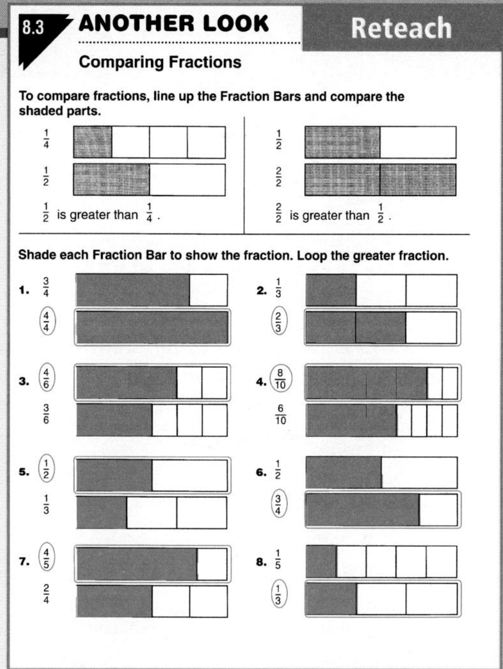

8.3 ANOTHER LOOK — Reteach

Comparing Fractions

To compare fractions, line up the Fraction Bars and compare the shaded parts.

$\frac{1}{4}$, $\frac{1}{2}$ — $\frac{1}{2}$ is greater than $\frac{1}{4}$.

$\frac{1}{2}$, $\frac{2}{2}$ — $\frac{2}{2}$ is greater than $\frac{1}{2}$.

Shade each Fraction Bar to show the fraction. Loop the greater fraction.

1. $\frac{3}{4}$, ($\frac{4}{4}$)
2. $\frac{1}{3}$, ($\frac{2}{3}$)
3. ($\frac{4}{6}$), $\frac{3}{6}$
4. ($\frac{8}{10}$), $\frac{6}{10}$
5. ($\frac{1}{2}$), $\frac{1}{3}$
6. $\frac{1}{2}$, ($\frac{3}{4}$)
7. ($\frac{4}{5}$), $\frac{2}{4}$
8. $\frac{1}{5}$, ($\frac{1}{3}$)

8.3 PRACTICE — Practice

Comparing Fractions

Use Fraction Bars to compare each pair of fractions. Write > or <.

1. $\frac{2}{4} > \frac{3}{8}$
2. $\frac{2}{6} > \frac{1}{4}$
3. $\frac{1}{2} < \frac{5}{8}$
4. $\frac{1}{3} < \frac{2}{4}$
5. $\frac{2}{8} < \frac{1}{3}$
6. $\frac{3}{4} > \frac{4}{6}$
7. $\frac{3}{6} < \frac{3}{4}$
8. $\frac{1}{3} > \frac{1}{5}$
9. $\frac{7}{8} > \frac{3}{4}$
10. $\frac{3}{8} < \frac{2}{3}$
11. $\frac{4}{6} > \frac{2}{5}$
12. $\frac{2}{3} > \frac{1}{2}$
13. $\frac{1}{10} < \frac{1}{5}$
14. $\frac{1}{3} < \frac{2}{5}$
15. $\frac{1}{2} > \frac{2}{8}$

Use Fraction Bars to compare each pair of fractions. Write >, <, or =.

16. $\frac{1}{3} > \frac{1}{4}$
17. $\frac{2}{6} = \frac{1}{3}$
18. $\frac{3}{4} = \frac{9}{12}$
19. $\frac{2}{6} < \frac{2}{4}$
20. $\frac{5}{6} > \frac{8}{12}$
21. $\frac{7}{8} > \frac{3}{6}$
22. $\frac{2}{3} = \frac{8}{12}$
23. $\frac{1}{3} < \frac{3}{6}$
24. $\frac{2}{5} < \frac{5}{10}$
25. $\frac{1}{8} < \frac{2}{4}$
26. $\frac{6}{12} < \frac{2}{3}$
27. $\frac{1}{2} = \frac{2}{4}$
28. $\frac{5}{6} > \frac{4}{5}$
29. $\frac{6}{8} = \frac{3}{4}$
30. $\frac{3}{8} < \frac{3}{5}$

Answer each question.

31. Which fraction is greater, $\frac{2}{3}$ or $\frac{3}{6}$? How do you know? $\frac{2}{3}$; I know by comparing the shaded parts.
32. Which two fractions are equal, $\frac{4}{8}$ and $\frac{2}{3}$ or $\frac{4}{8}$ and $\frac{2}{4}$? $\frac{4}{8}$ and $\frac{2}{4}$

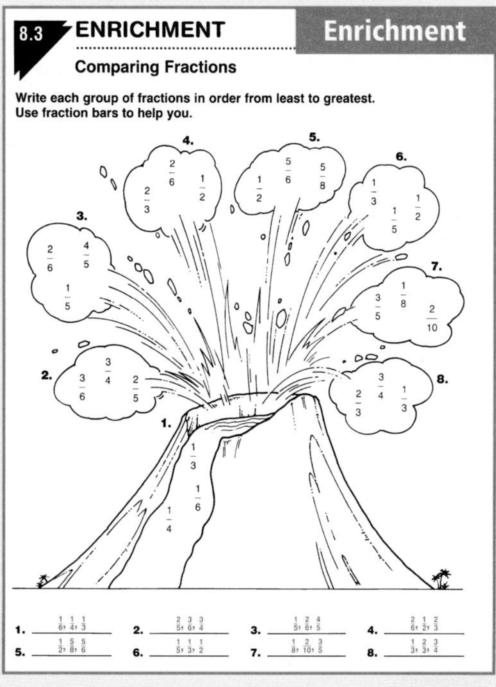

8.3 ENRICHMENT — Enrichment

Comparing Fractions

Write each group of fractions in order from least to greatest. Use fraction bars to help you.

1. $\frac{1}{6}, \frac{1}{4}, \frac{1}{3}$
2. $\frac{2}{5}, \frac{3}{6}, \frac{3}{4}$
3. $\frac{1}{5}, \frac{2}{6}, \frac{4}{5}$
4. $\frac{2}{6}, \frac{1}{2}, \frac{2}{3}$
5. $\frac{1}{2}, \frac{5}{8}, \frac{5}{6}$
6. $\frac{1}{5}, \frac{1}{3}, \frac{1}{2}$
7. $\frac{1}{8}, \frac{2}{10}, \frac{3}{5}$
8. $\frac{1}{3}, \frac{2}{3}, \frac{3}{4}$

Activity

Planning at a Glance

Objective To discover and identify equivalent fractions by using fraction models

Materials drawing paper, scissors, crayons or markers, Fraction Bars (TR28)

Optional Resources

- Reteach 8.4; Practice 8.4; Enrichment 8.4
- Daily Cumul. Review, p. 104
- Math Center: How-To Card 28
- Every Day Counts
- **TAB**, TE pp. 270E–270F, 270J
- **Problem of the Day**, 104, p. 52; Flip Chart, p. 52b

Unlocking Fractions & Decimals 3–6, Level 3, Activity 6

Students Acquiring English

Help with *equal parts* and *equivalent fractions.* Draw identical squares; divide one into two equal parts and the other into four. Shade one part of the first square and two parts of the second. Help students write the fractions. Explain that the shaded parts are *equal*; the fractions are *equivalent*.

Problem of the Day

Find four different ways to divide a square into fourths. Draw your solution. One possible answer is shown.

Equivalent Fractions

Cooperative Learning Checklist
- ☑ Work alone.
- ☑ Work with a partner.
- ☑ Work with a group.

Getting Started

What You'll Need:
- drawing paper
- scissors
- crayons or markers
- fraction models

Vocabulary:
equivalent fractions
Glossary, p. 480

Different fractions can name the same amount. How can that be? Make fraction models to find out.

Activity

- **Cut three strips of paper the same size.**

1. Fold a strip of paper in half so the short ends meet. Draw a dark line along the fold. Shade one part.
   - Write the fraction for the shaded part on the model. $\frac{1}{2}$

2. Fold another strip of paper in half twice to make fourths. Draw a dark line along each fold. Shade two parts.
   - Write a fraction for the shaded parts. $\frac{2}{4}$

278 Chapter 8

1 Introduce

Build Understanding **Name various fractions. Call on students to write them on the board and explain what each fraction means in relation to one whole.**

Teach: Activity

Emphasize these points:

- Different fractions can name the same part of a whole.
- Fractions that name the same part of a whole are called equivalent fractions.

Modeling Model step 3 of the Activity. Ask:

- What fraction names the amount that is shaded? $\frac{4}{8}$
- What are two other fractions that name the same amount? $\frac{1}{2}, \frac{2}{4}$

2 Develop

Show What You Know!

- For exercises 1 and 2, call on students to explain how the fraction models show that the fractions are equivalent. Have student pairs complete exercises 15 to 18 and share their answers with the class.
- Have students discuss their answers for exercise 19.

3 Summarize

- Ask students to use the words *parts* and *whole* to explain the concept of equivalent fractions. Then, ask them to explain the concept using the words *numerator* and *denominator*.

Ongoing Assessment You want to eat half your sandwich for lunch. Your sandwich is cut into four equal parts. How many parts should you eat? 2

Math Journal: *Communicating*

What tenths fraction do you think is equivalent to $\frac{3}{5}$? How can you check your answer? $\frac{6}{10} = \frac{3}{5}$; you could compare paper strips or fraction models for fifths and tenths.

3

Fold another strip into eighths. Darken the fold lines. Shade four parts.

- Write a fraction for the shaded parts. Compare the strips. Are the same amounts shaded? What 3 fractions name this amount? $\frac{4}{8}$, yes; $\frac{1}{2}$, $\frac{2}{4}$, $\frac{4}{8}$

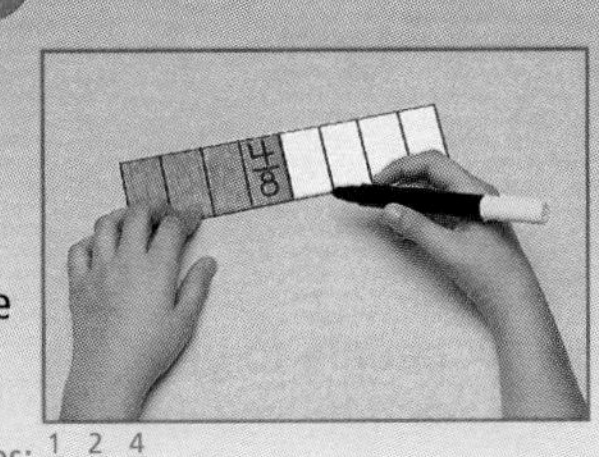

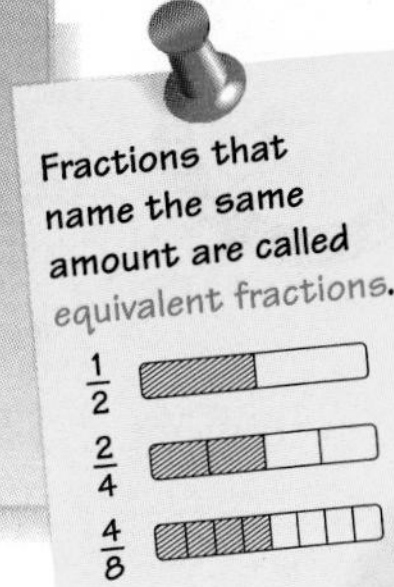

Show What You Know!

Use fraction models to answer the question.

1. Use the $\frac{1}{2}$ model. Find a sixths model that has the same amount shaded as the $\frac{1}{2}$ model. Write the fraction for the sixths model. $\frac{3}{6}$
2. Use the $\frac{1}{2}$ model. Find a tenths model that has the same amount shaded as the $\frac{1}{2}$ model. Write the equivalent fraction. $\frac{5}{10}$

Find a fraction model with the same amount of shading. Write an equivalent fraction. Answers will vary. Possible answers shown.

3. $\frac{1}{3}$ $\frac{2}{6}$ 4. $\frac{1}{4}$ $\frac{2}{8}$ 5. $\frac{4}{6}$ $\frac{2}{3}$ 6. $\frac{2}{5}$ $\frac{4}{10}$ 7. $\frac{2}{3}$ $\frac{8}{12}$ 8. $\frac{3}{4}$ $\frac{9}{12}$

9. $\frac{3}{6}$ $\frac{1}{2}$ 10. $\frac{2}{4}$ $\frac{1}{2}$ 11. $\frac{1}{5}$ $\frac{2}{10}$ 12. $\frac{1}{6}$ $\frac{2}{12}$ 13. $\frac{1}{2}$ $\frac{6}{12}$ 14. $\frac{6}{8}$ $\frac{3}{4}$

Copy and complete the equivalent fractions.

15. 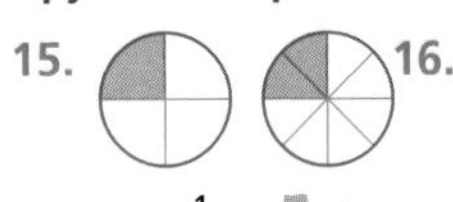 $\frac{1}{4} = \frac{■}{8}$ $\frac{2}{8}$

16. 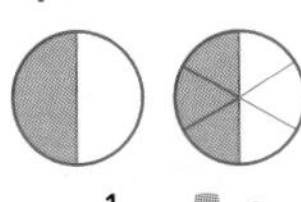 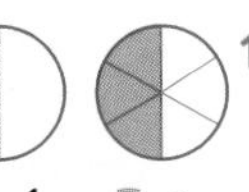 $\frac{1}{2} = \frac{■}{6}$ $\frac{3}{6}$

17. 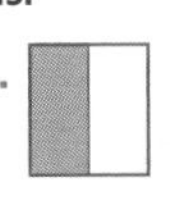 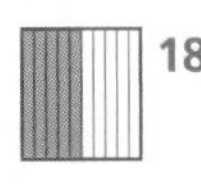 $\frac{1}{2} = \frac{■}{10}$ $\frac{5}{10}$

18. 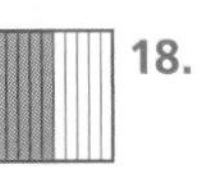 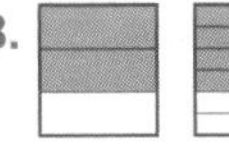 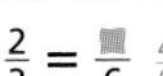 $\frac{2}{3} = \frac{■}{6}$ $\frac{4}{6}$

19. **Algebraic Reasoning** Explain how you know when two fractions are equivalent. When they represent the same part of the whole.

Meeting Individual Needs

Extra Support

Fraction Concentration ***(visual, kinesthetic)***
Distribute fraction models to student pairs. Students place the models facedown and take turns picking two models. If the models show equivalent fractions, the student keeps them and takes another turn. If not, the models are put back, and the next player takes a turn. Play until all models are matched; the player with the most models wins.

Alternate Approach

- Reteach Worksheet 8.4
- MATHKEYS

Encourage students to find equivalent fractions with electronic fraction circles. They model fractions on the computer in *Unlocking Fractions & Decimals* **3–6**, Level 3, Activity 6.

- **TAB** See TE pp. 242E–242F.

MathZones

Understanding Fractions

Students Acquring English

See **Language Connections**, Ch. 8.

Challenge

Have students work in pairs. Each student in turn names a fraction and challenges his or her partner to name three equivalent fractions and to demonstrate how they are equivalent.

Practice

Math Center Use How-To Card 28, *Make a Match,* to have students practice identifying equivalent fractions.

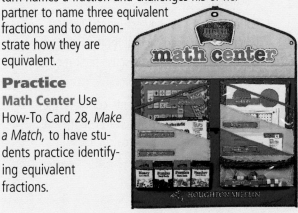

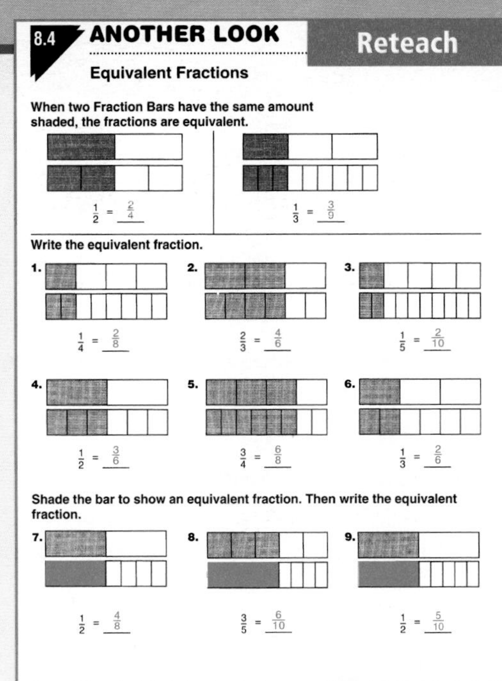

8.4 **ANOTHER LOOK** — Reteach

Equivalent Fractions

When two Fraction Bars have the same amount shaded, the fractions are equivalent.

$\frac{1}{2} = \frac{2}{4}$ $\frac{1}{3} = \frac{3}{9}$

Write the equivalent fraction.

1. $\frac{1}{4} = \frac{2}{8}$ 2. $\frac{2}{3} = \frac{4}{6}$ 3. $\frac{1}{5} = \frac{2}{10}$

4. $\frac{1}{2} = \frac{3}{6}$ 5. $\frac{3}{4} = \frac{6}{8}$ 6. $\frac{1}{3} = \frac{2}{6}$

Shade the bar to show an equivalent fraction. Then write the equivalent fraction.

7. $\frac{1}{2} = \frac{4}{8}$ 8. $\frac{3}{5} = \frac{6}{10}$ 9. $\frac{1}{2} = \frac{5}{10}$

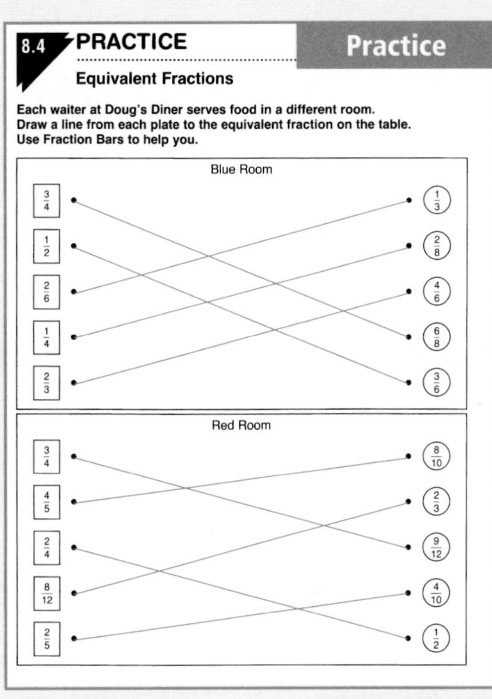

8.4 **PRACTICE** — Practice

Equivalent Fractions

Each waiter at Doug's Diner serves food in a different room. Draw a line from each plate to the equivalent fraction on the table. Use Fraction Bars to help you.

Blue Room

Plate	Table
$\frac{3}{4}$	$\frac{1}{3}$
$\frac{1}{2}$	$\frac{2}{8}$
$\frac{2}{6}$	$\frac{4}{6}$
$\frac{1}{4}$	$\frac{6}{8}$
$\frac{2}{3}$	$\frac{3}{6}$

Red Room

Plate	Table
$\frac{3}{4}$	$\frac{8}{10}$
$\frac{4}{5}$	$\frac{2}{3}$
$\frac{2}{4}$	$\frac{9}{12}$
$\frac{8}{12}$	$\frac{4}{10}$
$\frac{2}{5}$	$\frac{1}{2}$

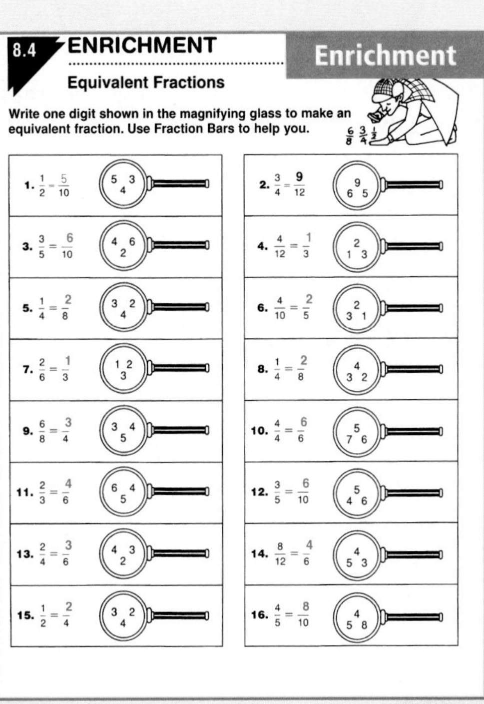

8.4 **ENRICHMENT** — Enrichment

Equivalent Fractions

Write one digit shown in the magnifying glass to make an equivalent fraction. Use Fraction Bars to help you.

Exercise	Digits	Exercise	Digits
1. $\frac{1}{2} = \frac{5}{10}$	5 3 4	2. $\frac{3}{4} = \frac{9}{12}$	9 6 5
3. $\frac{3}{5} = \frac{6}{10}$	4 6 2	4. $\frac{4}{12} = \frac{1}{3}$	2 1 3
5. $\frac{1}{4} = \frac{2}{8}$	3 2 4	6. $\frac{4}{10} = \frac{2}{5}$	2 3 1
7. $\frac{2}{6} = \frac{1}{3}$	1 2 3	8. $\frac{1}{4} = \frac{2}{8}$	4 3 2
9. $\frac{6}{8} = \frac{3}{4}$	3 4 5	10. $\frac{4}{4} = \frac{6}{6}$	5 7 6
11. $\frac{2}{3} = \frac{4}{6}$	6 4 5	12. $\frac{3}{5} = \frac{6}{10}$	5 4 6
13. $\frac{2}{4} = \frac{3}{6}$	4 3 2	14. $\frac{8}{12} = \frac{4}{6}$	4 5 3
15. $\frac{1}{2} = \frac{2}{4}$	3 2 4	16. $\frac{4}{5} = \frac{8}{10}$	4 5 8

Problem Solving

Planning at a Glance

Objective To decide whether to use mental math or a calculator to solve problems

Materials calculator

Optional Resources

- Daily Cumul. Review, p. 105
- Math Center: Project Card 8
- Every Day Counts
- **TAB**, TE pp. 270–270F, 270J
- **Problem of the Day**, 105, p. 53; Flip Chart, p. 53a
- **Reteach, Practice, and Enrichment Worksheets for Lesson 8.5**

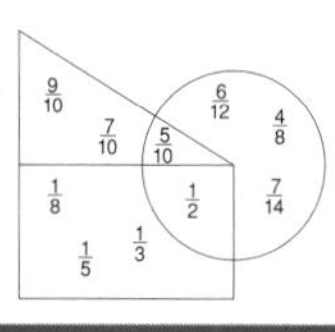

Unlocking Probability 3–6, Level 3, Activity 12

Students Acquiring English

Students may be unfamiliar with the idea of raising money for charity. Discuss a recent school or community event that was held as a fundraiser, and talk about what was done with the money. Look at the chart of ways to raise money on page 280; help students explain how each thing earns money.

Problem of the Day

What is true about all the fractions inside the circle? Inside the triangle? Inside the rectangle? After you find out, write another fraction inside each shape. Circle fractions are equivalent to $\frac{1}{2}$; triangle fractions have a denominator of 10; rectangle fractions have numerators of 1. One possible set of other fractions is $\frac{3}{6}, \frac{3}{10}, \frac{1}{7}$.

$\frac{9}{10}$ $\frac{7}{10}$ $\frac{5}{10}$ $\frac{6}{12}$ $\frac{4}{8}$ $\frac{1}{8}$ $\frac{1}{2}$ $\frac{7}{14}$ $\frac{1}{3}$ $\frac{1}{5}$

Problem Solving : Decisions

LESSON 5

Problem Solving

Choose a Computation Method

Choose a Computation Method

Ask Yourself:

- Do I need an exact answer or an estimate?
- Should I use a model, paper and pencil, mental math, or a calculator?
- What operation should I use?

You ask people to give $2 for each mile you walk for the Walk for Hunger. Five people will pay that. You hope to raise $20. How far do you need to walk?

Walk for Hunger, Boston, Massachusetts

You Decide

- Can you solve the problem in your head? Answers will vary.
- Would using a calculator be quicker? Why? Answers will vary. Possible answer: No, because I know that 2 × 5 = 10 and 20 ÷ 10 = 2, 2 miles.

Work It Out!

Decide whether to use mental math or a calculator. Explain your decision. Then answer the question.
Explanations will vary. Possible answers shown.

1. Would you raise more money washing 12 cars or selling 12 cakes?
2. You earned $16 from the bake sale. How many cakes did you sell?
3. Twelve students danced in the dance-a-thon. Each student danced an hour. How much did they raise? calculator; working with larger numbers; 12 × $2.50 = $30.00

1. mental math; look at the chart; washing 12 cars
2. mental math; use basic facts; 16 ÷ 2 = 8; 8 cakes

Raising Money for a Food Bank

Activity	Amount
Ten-pin Bowling	$5.00 each strike
Car Wash	$3.50 each car
Dance-a-thon	$2.50 each hour
Bake Sale	$2.00 each cake
Recycling Drive	$1.00 each bag

4. **Create Your Own** Look at the chart. Write a problem that you could solve with a calculator rather than with mental math. Explain. Check students' work.

Share Your Thinking

5. How do you decide when to use mental math or a calculator? Answers will vary.

More Practice Set 8.5, p. 463

280 Chapter 8

Build Understanding **Say, Use mental math to add 300 + 450.** 750 **To find the product of 7 X 50.** 350; students should see that mental math strategies work for greater numbers

Teach: You Decide

Emphasize these points:

- You may decide which method to use. Base your decision on whether the numbers are too difficult to compute mentally, or whether there is a mental math strategy you can use.

Modeling Model exercise 4. Ask:

- Can you compute this problem quickly in your head? yes, 100 – 60 = 40
- What mental math strategy did you use? basic facts and knowledge of place value

Work It Out!

- Emphasize that students may decide which computation method to use.
- Encourage students to see if they can use a mental math strategy before they try the calculator.
- For exercises 1–3, have students discuss whether they used mental math or a calculator. Ask them to discuss their mental math strategies.
- For exercise 5, have students compare their generalizations about when to use mental math and when to use a calculator.

Basic Facts Just the Facts Basic Facts Workshop 8, p. 115

- Remind students to try using properties, rules, or mental math strategies before they try the calculator.

Ongoing Assessment You want to collect 350 bottles for recycling. You have already collected 87 bottles. Will you use mental math or a calculator to find how many more bottles you need to collect? Most students will decide that the numbers are fairly difficult and a calculator is the better choice: 263 bottles

Math Journal: *Communicating*

What tasks are easier to do when you have a calculator? Answers will vary. Possible answer: calculations involving very large or difficult numbers

Problem Solving Workshop

Mental Math or Calculator?

Review

Use with page 280.

15 minutes

Sensible Answer?

Management teacher directed; whole class

- Tell students that you are going to read several problems to them. As they listen, ask them to think about whether they would use mental math or a calculator to solve each problem.
- Remind them to ask themselves: What operation should I use? Can I solve the problem faster without a calculator?
- Encourage students to listen carefully as you read the following problems aloud.

1. Your brother weighs 15 pounds more than you. Your brother weighs 84 pounds. How much do you weigh? 69 pounds
2. You are going to visit your cousin who lives 100 miles away. It takes one hour to drive 40 miles. How long will your trip take? $2\frac{1}{2}$ hours
3. You are having your house painted. One gallon covers about 60 square feet of wall. How many gallons will you need to cover 240 square feet? 4 gallons

$$84 - 15 = 69 \qquad 100.0 \div 40 = 2.5 \qquad 240 \div 60 = 4$$

- Discuss the decisions that students made about each of the problems. Did everyone make the same choice?
- Invite students to solve the problems.

Activity

Use with page 280.

15 minutes

Mental Math or Calculator Time?

Management groups of three
Materials four-section spinner (2 for mental math, 2 for calculator math)

Activity

- Divide students into small groups and ask them to make a chart as shown.

Problem	Spinner Landed On	How I Solved the Problem
7 x 8	calculator	mental math

- Provide problems with varying difficulty. Spin the spinner. Students find the answer using the method determined by the spinner.
- If the problem is a basic fact and the spinner lands on calculator, encourage students to use mental math. Have them record their method of calculation on their charts.

Activity

- Ask students to investigate and find numbers around the school. How many classrooms are there? Chairs? Students? Desks?
- Then, have students work in pairs to write several problems with their numbers.
- Invite students to trade their problems with others. Are the numbers too large to use mental math? Do they need a calculator?

classrooms	12
students in school	295

About how many students are in each classroom?

For more practice Using the Calculator, see pp. T88–T90.

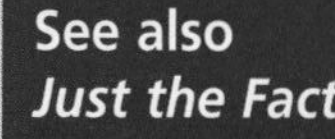

Chapter 8

Basic Facts Workshop

Use with Lesson 8.5

Multiplying by 6

See also *Just the Facts*
- Support Masters
- Practice Worksheets
- Cumulative Practice

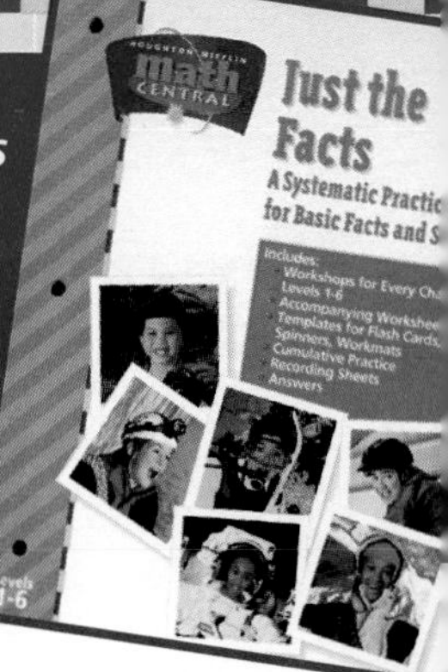

Review

Use 3's to Find 6's

20 minutes

Management whole class
Materials overhead projector; Just the Facts Support Master 7 (hundredths square) p. 228; See also Practice 8A–8B on pp. 134–135 for use with Lessons 8.6–8.7; Cumulative Practice 7 on p. 270 for use with Lesson 8.10.

- Draw a 6 × 4 array on a grid transparency. Then draw a line to divide it into two 3 × 4 arrays.

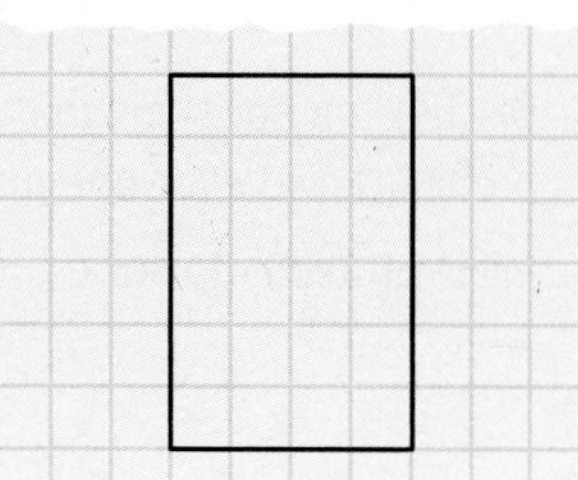

- Cover the bottom array with a piece of paper. Ask students how many squares are in the top 3 × 4 array. 12
- Uncover the bottom array. Ask students how knowing 3 × 4 could help them find 6 × 4. Double the 3 × 4 array to find 24.

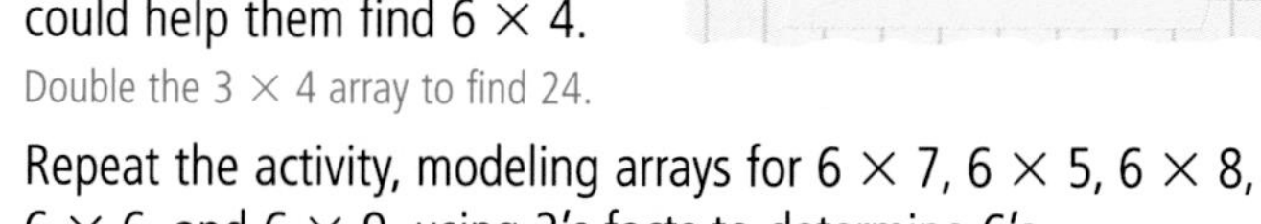

- Repeat the activity, modeling arrays for 6 × 7, 6 × 5, 6 × 8, 6 × 6, and 6 × 9, using 3's facts to determine 6's.

Practice

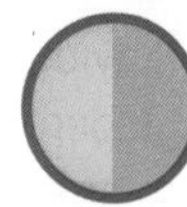

Make ×6 Flash Cards

30 minutes

Management individuals, then pairs
Materials for each student: 9 index cards; Just the Facts Support Masters 10, 14 (practice minutes, certificate) on pp. 291, 295; See also Practice 8A–8B on pp. 134–135 for use with Lessons 8.6–8.7; Cumulative Practice 7 on p. 270 for use with Lesson 8.10.

- Distribute index cards to students and have them make flash cards like those shown for the following facts: 6 × 5, 5 × 6, 6 × 6, 6 × 7, 7 × 6, 6 × 8, 8 × 6, 6 × 9, and 9 × 6.
- Remind students to add the 6's flash cards they have already made (6 × 1, 1 × 6, 6 × 2, 2 × 6, 6 × 3, 3 × 6, 6 × 4, and 4 × 6) to the new set. Also remind them to write their names or initials on the backs of their cards. Then have students find partners. They can use their flash cards to practice their multiplication facts for 6.

- Invite students to take their flash cards home for additional practice. Remind them to keep a record of the minutes practiced. Students may exchange completed records at school for a certificate.

Midchapter Review

for Pages 270–280

Problem Solving

Solve using any strategy. Show your work. (page 280)

1. A recipe for clown cookies says to put 2 nuts for eyes and 5 raisins for a mouth on each cookie. You have 15 nuts and 45 raisins. How many clown cookies can you make? 7 cookies
2. You make a spinner that has 16 equal spaces. You color $\frac{1}{2}$ of the spaces blue. Then you color $\frac{1}{2}$ of the leftover spaces green. How many spaces are green? 4 spaces

Concepts

Use models to compare the fractions. Write > or <. (page 276)

3. $\frac{1}{4}$ ● $\frac{2}{4}$ <
4. $\frac{3}{3}$ ● $\frac{2}{3}$ >
5. $\frac{4}{5}$ ● $\frac{4}{6}$ >
6. $\frac{2}{5}$ ● $\frac{1}{2}$ <
7.   $\frac{2}{4}$ ● $\frac{6}{8}$ <

Skills

Write the fractions for the red and gray parts. (page 274)

8. 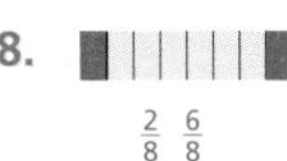 $\frac{2}{8}$ $\frac{6}{8}$
9.  $\frac{1}{3}$ $\frac{2}{3}$
10. 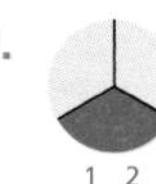 $\frac{3}{5}$ $\frac{2}{5}$
11. 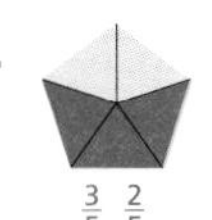 $\frac{4}{6}$ $\frac{2}{6}$

Use fraction models. Write an equivalent fraction. (page 278)
Answers will vary. Possible answers shown.

12. $\frac{2}{4}$ $\frac{1}{2}$
13. $\frac{1}{5}$ $\frac{2}{10}$
14. $\frac{6}{10}$ $\frac{3}{5}$
15. $\frac{2}{6}$ $\frac{1}{3}$

Use the models to write the equivalent fractions. (page 278)

16. $\frac{1}{2} = \frac{■}{8}$ 4
17. $\frac{2}{3} = \frac{■}{6}$ 4
18. $\frac{3}{5} = \frac{■}{10}$ 6

281

Meeting Individual Needs

Students Acquiring English

Some students may need assistance on the Midchapter Review.

- Be prepared to read directions aloud to students.
- Focus special attention on word problems. Expect to paraphrase, diagram, or draw an explanation of the word problem.
- Review important vocabulary words that have been previously introduced.
- Review titles and other elements of graphs and charts.

Additional Assessment Resources

 Test, Practice, Management Program

Use the *Test, Practice, Management Program* to create, administer, and score tests as well as generate practice sets. Questions are correlated to the Lesson Objectives.

Midchapter Review

Scoring Chart

Item	Points
1–2	10 points each
3–18	5 points each
TOTAL	100 points or 100%

Problem Solving

Give from 0 to 10 points per answer, based on how well students meet the following criteria:

Problem 1

- A strategy is seen through to a correct solution.

Problem 2

- Answer shows understanding of the meaning of fractions.
- A strategy is seen through to a correct solution.

Concepts and Skills

If students are having difficulty in particular areas, use the Reteaching Worksheets listed below.

- 57 Writing Fractions, p. 162
- 58 Comparing Fractions with the Same Denominators, p. 163
- 59 Comparing Fractions with Different Denominators, p. 164
- 60 Equivalent Fractions, p. 165

Common Error Alert

If students are making frequent errors, see Analyzing Errors, TE pp. 297A–297B.

Item Analysis

Item	Objectives
1–2	To use Draw a Picture and other strategies to solve problems (8G)
3–7	To compare and order fractions (8B)
8–11	To write fractions for fractional parts (8A)
12–18	To find equivalent fractions (8C)

Math World

Fractions in the Sky

Background The United States was the last country to adopt the international standard of measuring cloud cover in eighths, or "oktas." Before July 1997, American meteorologists used a system based on tenths. The fractions are based on the angle of the cloud cover relative to the horizon and to the weather station. A reading of 3 oktas, for example, means that the advancing or receding edge of the clouds is 69 to 82 degrees above the horizon, or that the edge of the cloud layer around the station is 18 to 24 degrees from the vertical.

Activity: Observe Cloud Cover

- Have students observe the cloud cover. Let them estimate the fraction of the sky that is covered by clouds in eighths. Have students discuss and resolve differences among their estimates.
- Repeat this activity for several days at the same time. Suggest that students graph the changes in cloud cover over time.

Critical Thinking Ask, Why is it important to have world standards for observing and reporting the weather?

Fractions Around the World

Math World

Use fractions to describe the weather and to play a game; then write them the way the Egyptians and Greeks did.

Fractions in the Sky

Scientists watch the sky at weather stations all around the world. They use fractions to describe what they see. They use the same fractions in the United States, in Argentina (AHR juhn TEE nuh), and in Kenya (KEHN yuh). When there aren't any clouds, scientists write $\frac{0}{8}$. If clouds cover half the sky, they write $\frac{4}{8}$. If clouds cover all the sky, they write $\frac{8}{8}$. What fraction would you use to describe the sky where you are?

Egyptian Fraction Symbols

People in ancient Egypt used these special symbols for the $\frac{1}{2}$ and $\frac{1}{4}$ fractions. Use the symbol for $\frac{1}{2}$ to draw a symbol for 1. Then, use the symbol for $\frac{1}{4}$ to make a different symbol for 1.

282

For More Information

Word Origins

fraction

From the Latin *fractio*, a form of *frangere*, "to break."

In mathematics, a fraction is one or more equal parts of a whole number.

Discuss with students how a word that means "breaking" may have come to have the meaning of "equal parts."

Literature

Hurricanes: Earth's Mightiest Storms
Scholastic Press, 1996
Patricia Lauber

Our World: Weather and Climate
Wayland LTD, 1988
John Mason

The Pima-Maricopa
Chelsea House Publications, 1989
Henry F. Dobyns

Fraction Fun
Holiday House, 1996
David Adler

Fractions
Marshall Cavendish Corp., 1996
David Stienecker

Fractions and Decimals
Usborne, 1994
K. Bryant-Mole

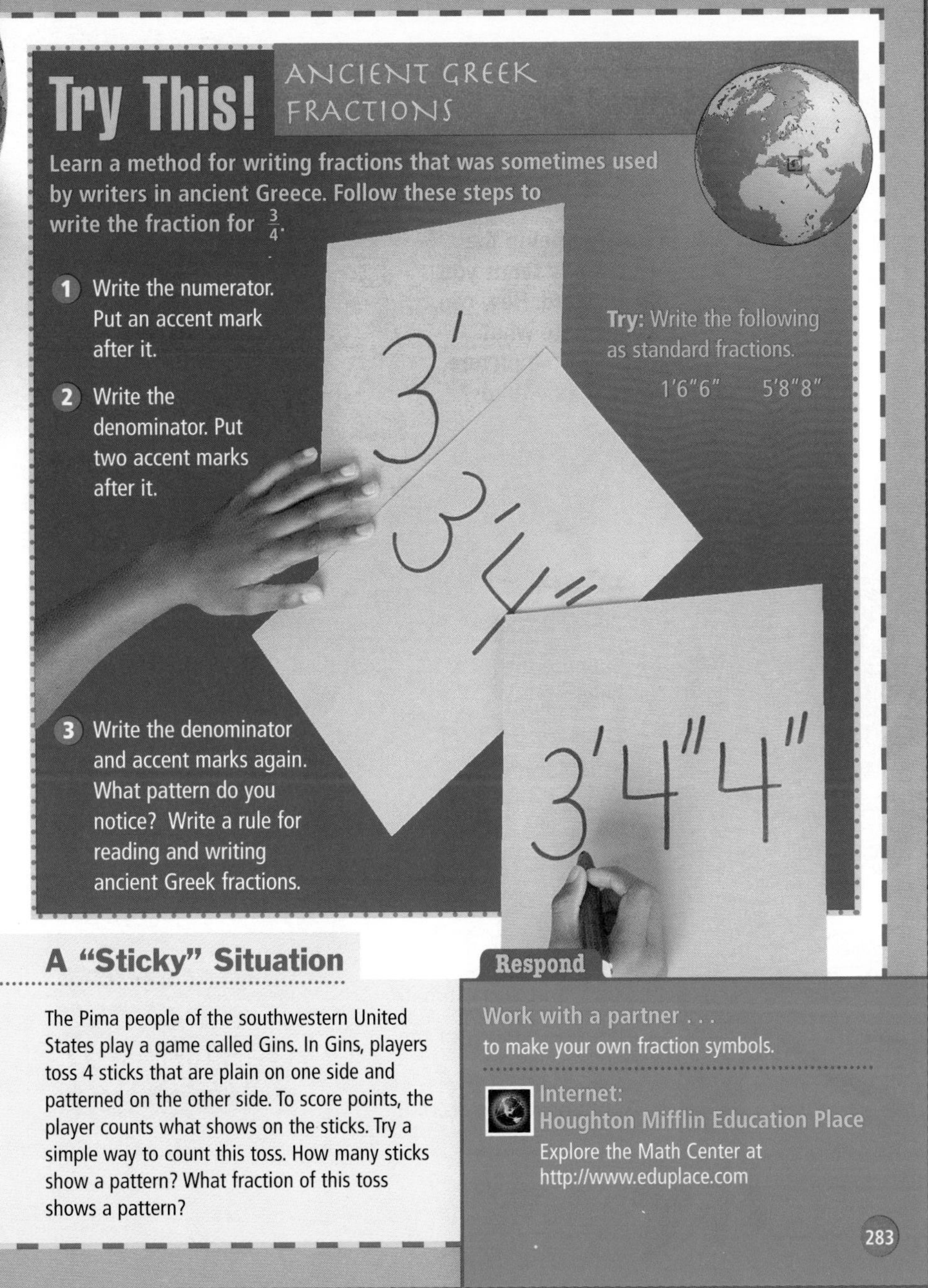

Try This! ANCIENT GREEK FRACTIONS

Learn a method for writing fractions that was sometimes used by writers in ancient Greece. Follow these steps to write the fraction for $\frac{3}{4}$.

1. Write the numerator. Put an accent mark after it.
2. Write the denominator. Put two accent marks after it.
3. Write the denominator and accent marks again. What pattern do you notice? Write a rule for reading and writing ancient Greek fractions.

Try: Write the following as standard fractions.

1'6"6"   5'8"8"

A "Sticky" Situation

The Pima people of the southwestern United States play a game called Gins. In Gins, players toss 4 sticks that are plain on one side and patterned on the other side. To score points, the player counts what shows on the sticks. Try a simple way to count this toss. How many sticks show a pattern? What fraction of this toss shows a pattern?

Respond

Work with a partner . . .
to make your own fraction symbols.

Internet:
Houghton Mifflin Education Place
Explore the Math Center at
http://www.eduplace.com

283

A "Sticky" Situation

Background In *Gins*, each stick has a different point value if it is the only one that falls patterned side up. Points are also scored based on how many sticks fall patterned side up. The game is traditionally played with a large board in which twigs are placed in holes to record players' scores, as in the card game cribbage.

Activity: Make Gins Sticks

Have groups of students use ice-cream sticks or similar objects to make a set of *Gins* sticks. Have each group devise rules for and play a game using the sticks. (Note: the fourth *Gins* stick should have two horizontal lines at each end of its patterned side.)

Ancient Greek Fractions

Background The ancient Greeks often wrote fractions with one number above the other. There was no bar line, however, and the numerator and denominator could be in either position. The way we indicate fractions today, like many other mathematical conventions, was introduced to the West by the Arabs. It did not become standard until the 16th century.

Critical Thinking

- Have students share and discuss the rules they wrote for the activity.
- Ask, How easy do you think it was to calculate with fractions written this way?

Technology

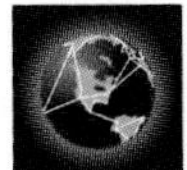

Internet: Education Place
http://www.eduplace.com
Houghton Mifflin Education Place **Mathematics Center** provides teacher and student support, such as links to other Internet sites.

Ultimate Writing & Creativity Center
Students can use the *Ultimate Writing & Creativity Center* for all their writing and publishing activities.

Kid to Kid

Project Ask students what games they play involving materials they make themselves.

Suggest:

- *Could children in other countries easily learn this game and make the materials?*

Students can use the Internet or student networks based in other media to exchange rules of simple games with children around the world.

Connecting

Planning at a Glance

Objective To estimate common fractions of a whole using benchmarks of 0, $\frac{1}{2}$, and 1.

Materials none

Optional Resources

- Reteach 8.6; Practice 8.6; Enrichment 8.6
- Daily Cumul. Review, p. 106
- Math Center: Act. Card 46
- Every Day Counts
- **TAB**, TE pp. 270E–270F, 270J
- **Problem of the Day**, 106, p. 53; Flip Chart. p. 53b

MATHKEYS *Unlocking Fractions & Decimals 3–6*, Level 3, Activity 3

Students Acquiring English

Mark plastic cups to show 4 equal parts. Discuss the marks with students. Then have volunteers partially fill cups with water. Discuss the results, asking questions such as, "Is the cup *exactly* $\frac{1}{2}$ full, or is it *about* $\frac{1}{2}$ full?"

Problem of the Day

Claude and Veronica plan to split a meatball sandwich. "I'm older, so I should get the bigger half," said Claude. "That's impossible," said Veronica. What could Veronica mean? *Half* means two equal parts. If the sandwich is split exactly in half, both parts must be the same size. But in situations like this, we use *half* if the parts are close to the same size.

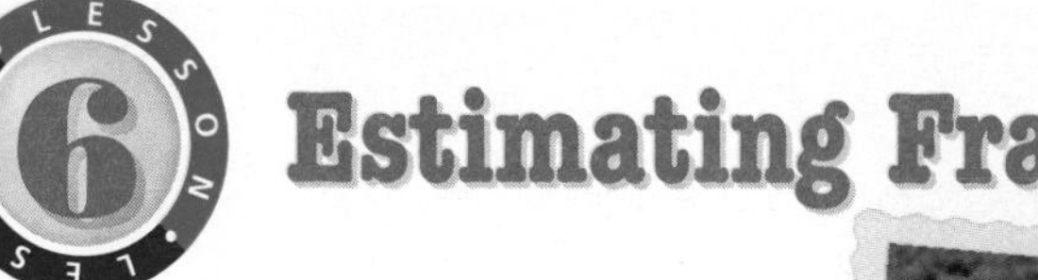

Estimating Fractions

Your pen pal in the Netherlands sends you this postcard. How can you estimate what amount of the picture shows yellow tulips?

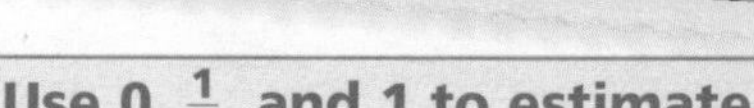

Here's A Way! Use 0, $\frac{1}{2}$, and 1 to estimate.

1. Suppose the picture is divided into 2 equal parts, or halves.
2. Compare. Decide if the amount of the picture that shows yellow flowers is about 0, $\frac{1}{2}$, or 1.

About $\frac{1}{2}$ of the picture shows yellow flowers.

Talk About It!

Is more than or less than $\frac{1}{2}$ of the postcard yellow? Explain.
less; a half is not completely yellow

Other Examples

Use 0, $\frac{1}{2}$, and 1 to estimate.

a. About how much of the row is purple?
almost all of it, or almost 1 row

b. About how much is red?
almost none of it, or about 0 rows

284 Chapter 8

1 Introduce

Prior Knowledge **Have students fold and shade paper strips to show these fractions: $\frac{1}{2}, \frac{1}{4}, \frac{3}{4}, \frac{1}{8}, \frac{5}{8}$.**

Teach: Here's A Way!

Emphasize these points:

- As with whole numbers, estimating fractions tells *about* how much.
- When you estimate, you can compare the fraction to 0, $\frac{1}{2}$, and 1.

Modeling Model Talk About It! example *a*. Ask:

- Where is the halfway mark?

2 Develop

Show What You Know!

- Guide students in recognizing that $\frac{1}{2}$ is exactly halfway between 0 and 1.
- Point out that a fraction such as $\frac{1}{2}$ always represents the same number of equal parts, whether it is part of a set or part of a measurement unit such as area or time.
- Ask students to discuss their reasoning for exercise 4.

Work It Out!

- Have students explain their reasoning for exercise 8.

3 Summarize

- Remind students that estimates tell *about* how much.
- Reiterate that mentally marking off 0, $\frac{1}{2}$, or 1 is a helpful way of estimating fractions.
- **Ongoing Assessment** How can you decide how much $\frac{1}{2}$ of your pencil is? Answers should indicate an understanding of $\frac{1}{2}$ as a halfway mark.

Math Journal: ***Communicating***

How can you tell whether $\frac{1}{3}$ is between 0 and $\frac{1}{2}$ or between $\frac{1}{2}$ and 1? Answers may vary. Possible answer: Use fraction models to compare.

Show What You Know!

Estimate how many acres of the garden are planted. Write 0, $\frac{1}{2}$, or 1.

1. $\frac{1}{2}$ 
2. 1 
3. 0 
4. **Critical Thinking** About how many acres of the garden in exercise 3 are not planted? 1

Work It Out!

Look at the water. About how full is the vase?

5. 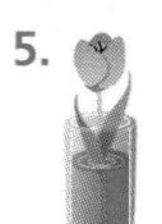 about full
6.  about empty
7.  about $\frac{1}{2}$ full
8. **Number Sense** Look at the vases above. Can you pour all the water from any vase into any other vase? Explain.
yes; you can combine vases 5 and 6, or combine vases 6 and 7

Draw a slice of toast to show how much is eaten.
Check students' drawings.

9. About $\frac{1}{2}$ eaten
10. About 0 eaten
11. About 1 slice eaten
12. Would it be fair to share this slice of toast? Explain.
no; one piece is less than half and the other piece is more than half

Decide whether the fraction is closer to 0 or to 1. Write 0 or 1.

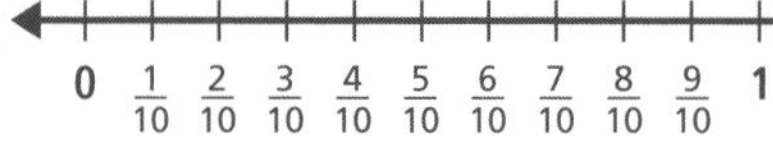

13. $\frac{2}{10}$ 0
14. $\frac{6}{10}$ 1
15. $\frac{9}{10}$ 1
16. $\frac{4}{10}$ 0

Mixed Review Solve.

17. 6 + 6 + 6 + 6 24
18. 5 + 5 + 5 15
19. 4 × 6 24
20. 5 × 9 45
21. 4 × 8 32

More Practice Set 8.6, p. 464

285

Meeting Individual Needs

Extra Support

What Fraction? *(visual)* Have students work in pairs to find things in the classroom that can be described with fractions. For example, students could note that the class is about $\frac{1}{2}$ boys, or that the coatrack is about $\frac{1}{2}$ full.

Alternate Approach

- Reteach Worksheet 8.6
- **TAB** See TE pp. 270E–270F.

MathZones

Understanding Fractions

Students Acquiring English

See **Language Connections**, Ch. 8.

Challenge

Have each student shade one or more sixths of an unsectioned circle. Partners exchange papers and answer these questions:

- About how much is shaded?
- Is the shaded part closest to 0, $\frac{1}{2}$, or 1?

Practice

Math Center Use Activity Card 46, *Fraction Flags,* to have students practice estimating common fractions of a whole, using benchmarks of $\frac{1}{4}$, $\frac{1}{2}$, and $\frac{3}{4}$.

Challenge Use Activity Card 46 and have students continue the activity as described in Now Try This!

See **Just the Facts** Practice 8A, p. 134.

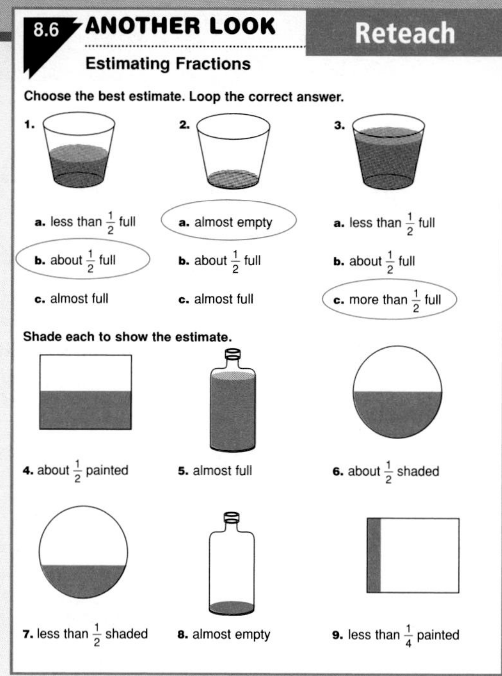

8.6 ANOTHER LOOK — Reteach

Estimating Fractions

Choose the best estimate. Loop the correct answer.

1. a. less than $\frac{1}{2}$ full b. about $\frac{1}{2}$ full c. almost full
2. a. almost empty b. about $\frac{1}{2}$ full c. almost full
3. a. less than $\frac{1}{2}$ full b. about $\frac{1}{2}$ full c. more than $\frac{1}{2}$ full

Shade each to show the estimate.

4. about $\frac{1}{2}$ painted
5. almost full
6. about $\frac{1}{2}$ shaded
7. less than $\frac{1}{2}$ shaded
8. almost empty
9. less than $\frac{1}{4}$ painted

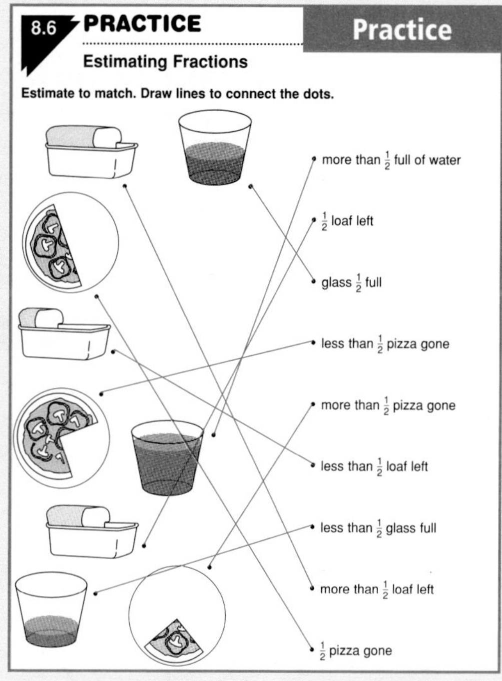

8.6 PRACTICE — Practice

Estimating Fractions

Estimate to match. Draw lines to connect the dots.

- more than $\frac{1}{2}$ full of water
- $\frac{1}{2}$ loaf left
- glass $\frac{1}{2}$ full
- less than $\frac{1}{2}$ pizza gone
- more than $\frac{1}{2}$ pizza gone
- less than $\frac{1}{2}$ loaf left
- less than $\frac{1}{2}$ glass full
- more than $\frac{1}{2}$ loaf left
- $\frac{1}{2}$ pizza gone

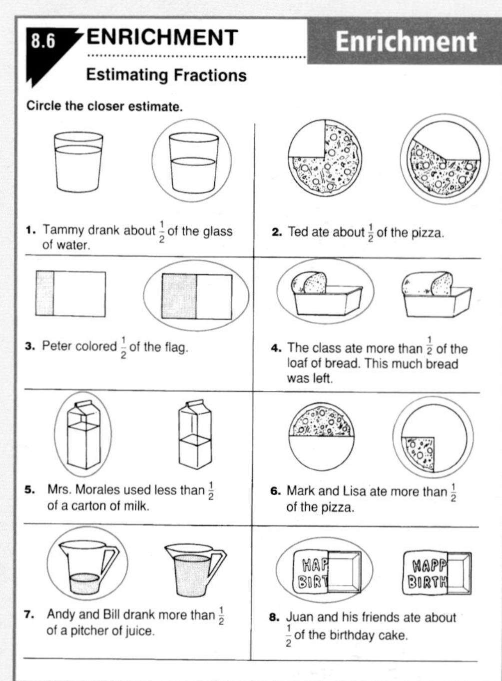

8.6 ENRICHMENT — Enrichment

Estimating Fractions

Circle the closer estimate.

1. Tammy drank about $\frac{1}{2}$ of the glass of water.
2. Ted ate about $\frac{1}{2}$ of the pizza.
3. Peter colored $\frac{1}{2}$ of the flag.
4. The class ate more than $\frac{1}{2}$ of the loaf of bread. This much bread was left.
5. Mrs. Morales used less than $\frac{1}{2}$ of a carton of milk.
6. Mark and Lisa ate more than $\frac{1}{2}$ of the pizza.
7. Andy and Bill drank more than $\frac{1}{2}$ of a pitcher of juice.
8. Juan and his friends ate about $\frac{1}{2}$ of the birthday cake.

Activity

Planning at a Glance

Objective To investigate addition and subtraction of fractions with like denominators, using fraction models

Materials colored markers, fraction models (TR28)

Optional Resources

- Reteach 8.7; Practice 8.7; Enrichment 8.7
- Daily Cumul. Review, p. 107
- Math Center: How-To Card 29
- Every Day Counts
- TAB, TE pp. 270E–270F, 270J
- Problem of the Day, 107, p. 54; Flip Chart, p. 54a
- MATHKEYS *Unlocking Geometry 3–6*, Level 3, Activity 21

Students Acquiring English

Use paper plates divided into equal parts to review vocabulary, such as *fourth, half, third* and so on. Invite groups of students to tell how many slices they would each get if they shared a pizza divided into particular numbers of parts.

Problem of the Day

Use an almanac or atlas to solve the problem. Find the flags of the countries of Bahrain, Cuba, Japan, and Mongolia. Estimate how much of each flag is red.

Estimates may vary; Bahrain: $\frac{3}{4}$, Cuba: $\frac{1}{4}$, Japan: $\frac{1}{3}$, Mongolia: $\frac{2}{3}$

Adding and Subtracting Fractions

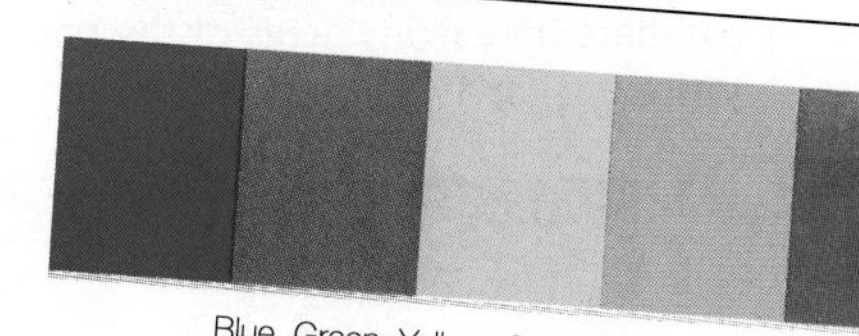

Blue, Green, Yellow, Orange, Red. 1966

Ellsworth Kelly

Solomon R. Guggenheim Museum, New York

What You'll Need:
- fraction models
- colored markers

Cooperative Learning Checklist
- Work alone.
- Work with a partner.
- Work with a group.

You can use fraction models to add and subtract fractions with the same denominator. Look at the way the artist used colors and fractions in this painting.

Activity

Find $\frac{1}{4} + \frac{2}{4}$.

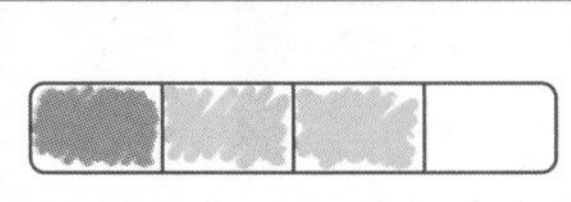

1. Use the fourths fraction model. Shade $\frac{1}{4}$ of the model. Use a different color to shade $\frac{2}{4}$ more.
2. How much is shaded altogether? Write an addition sentence for what you did. $\frac{1}{4} + \frac{2}{4} = \frac{3}{4}$
3. Try these.

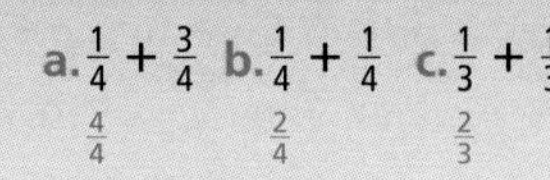

a. $\frac{1}{4} + \frac{3}{4}$ $\frac{4}{4}$ b. $\frac{1}{4} + \frac{1}{4}$ $\frac{2}{4}$ c. $\frac{1}{3} + \frac{1}{3}$ $\frac{2}{3}$

Find $\frac{5}{6} - \frac{2}{6}$.

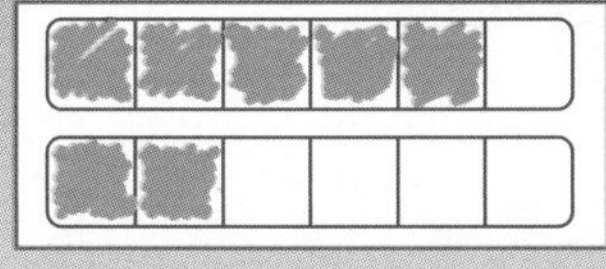

1. Use a sixths fraction model. Shade $\frac{5}{6}$ of the model. Use another sixths fraction model. Shade $\frac{2}{6}$.
2. What is the difference in the number of shaded parts? Write a subtraction sentence using $\frac{5}{6}$ and $\frac{2}{6}$. $\frac{5}{6} - \frac{2}{6} = \frac{3}{6}$
3. Try these.

a. $\frac{5}{6} - \frac{3}{6}$ $\frac{2}{6}$ b. $\frac{4}{6} - \frac{2}{6}$ $\frac{2}{6}$ c. $\frac{3}{4} - \frac{1}{4}$ $\frac{2}{4}$

286 Chapter 8

1 Introduce

Explore **Display a circle with $\frac{1}{4}$ shaded red and $\frac{1}{4}$ shaded green. Ask, What part is red, what part is green, and what part is shaded?** $\frac{1}{4}, \frac{1}{4}, \frac{1}{2}$

Teach: Activity

Emphasize these points:

- When you add or subtract fractions with the same denominator, you are adding and subtracting equal parts of a whole.

Modeling To reinforce students' understanding of adding and subtracting fractions with the same denominator, model the steps of the Activity with fraction bars.

2 Develop

Show What You Know!

- For exercises 1–5, make sure students understand that they are adding equal parts of a whole.
- Help students see that they are subtracting equal parts of a whole in exercises 7–11.
- Emphasize that a fraction that has the same numerator and denominator is equal to the whole, or 1.
- Have students summarize their responses to question 14.
- For exercises 15–18, make sure students know that the number of letters in each word is the number of equal parts.

3 Summarize

- Ask students how they could add and subtract fractions with the same denominator without fraction models.

Ongoing Assessment Jo's recipe calls for $\frac{1}{3}$ cup of white flour and $\frac{1}{3}$ cup of whole wheat flour. How can you find out how much flour that is in all? How much flour is it? Add $\frac{1}{3}$ and $\frac{1}{3}$; $\frac{2}{3}$ cup.

Math Journal: ***Communicating***

Answers may vary. Possible answer: You add and subtract numerators just like whole numbers.

Show What You Know!

Use fraction models to add. Write the sum.

1. $\frac{1}{6}+\frac{1}{6}$ $\frac{2}{6}$ 2. $\frac{2}{3}+\frac{1}{3}$ $\frac{3}{3}$ 3. $\frac{1}{4}+\frac{3}{4}$ $\frac{4}{4}$ 4. $\frac{1}{6}+\frac{2}{6}$ $\frac{3}{6}$ 5. $\frac{1}{4}+\frac{1}{4}$ $\frac{2}{4}$

6. Write whether each sum above is more than, less than, or equal to one half. less than; more than; more than; equal to; equal to

Use fraction models to subtract. Write the difference.

7. $\frac{2}{3}-\frac{1}{3}$ $\frac{1}{3}$ 8. $\frac{5}{6}-\frac{1}{6}$ $\frac{4}{6}$ 9. $\frac{2}{2}-\frac{1}{2}$ $\frac{1}{2}$ 10. $\frac{3}{4}-\frac{2}{4}$ $\frac{1}{4}$ 11. $\frac{4}{6}-\frac{2}{6}$ $\frac{2}{6}$

12. Write whether each difference above is more than, less than, or equal to one half. less than; more than; equal to; less than; less than

13. **Algebraic Reasoning** How is adding and subtracting fractions like adding and subtracting whole numbers? How is it different? You add and subtract the numerator like whole numbers. You have a denominator that you do not add or subtract.

14. **Critical Thinking** How could counting on the number line help you add $\frac{3}{6}$ and $\frac{2}{6}$? Use the numerators. Start with 3 and count on 2 jumps to 5.

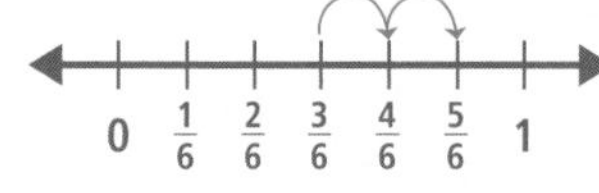

Problem Solving

When red, yellow and blue are mixed, they make all the other colors. Mix these letters to make color words. (Hint: Look at the color wheel.)

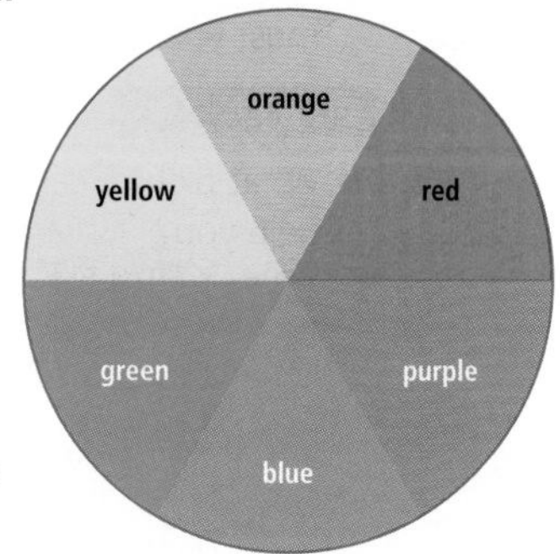

15. Write the first $\frac{2}{5}$ of the letters in *blank* with the last $\frac{1}{2}$ of the letters in *glue*. blue

16. Write the first $\frac{2}{3}$ of the letters in *yes* with the last $\frac{4}{6}$ of the letters in *follow*. yellow

17. Write the first $\frac{1}{4}$ of the letters in *rain* with the last $\frac{1}{2}$ of the letters in *weed*. red

18. **Create Your Own** Use the colors to make up a problem like the one above. Answers will vary.

Math Journal

You know the basic facts for adding and subtracting whole numbers. How can they help you add and subtract fractions?
You use them to add or subtract the numerators.

Meeting Individual Needs

Extra Support

Finding 1 and $\frac{1}{2}$ *(visual/kinesthetic)* Have student pairs use fraction models to find these sums and differences. Ask them to indicate which answers are equal to 1 or $\frac{1}{2}$.

$\frac{1}{4}+\frac{3}{4}$ $\frac{4}{4}=1$ $\frac{1}{4}+\frac{1}{4}$ $\frac{2}{4}=\frac{1}{2}$

$\frac{4}{5}-\frac{3}{5}$ $\frac{1}{5}$ $\frac{4}{4}-\frac{3}{4}$ $\frac{1}{4}$

$\frac{3}{3}-\frac{1}{3}$ $\frac{2}{3}$ $\frac{5}{6}-\frac{3}{6}$ $\frac{2}{6}$

$\frac{1}{6}+\frac{2}{6}$ $\frac{3}{6}=\frac{1}{2}$ $\frac{3}{5}+\frac{2}{5}$ $\frac{5}{5}=1$

Alternate Approach

- Reteach Worksheet 8.7
- **TAB** See TE pp. 270E–270F.

MathZones
Understanding Fractions

Students Acquiring English

See **Language Connections**, Ch. 8.

Challenge

With a partner, students use fraction models to find the sum of $\frac{2}{4}$ and $\frac{4}{8}$. $\frac{8}{8}$

Ask, Is the sum greater than, less than, or equal to 1? equal

Practice

Math Center Use How-To Card 29, *Fraction Subtraction Game,* to have students practice adding and subtracting fractions with like denominators, using fraction bars.

See **Just the Facts** Practice 8B, p. 135.

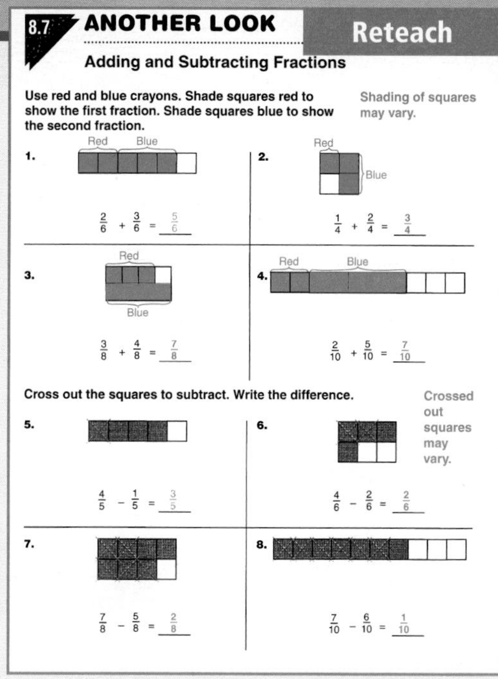

8.7 ANOTHER LOOK **Reteach**

Adding and Subtracting Fractions

Use red and blue crayons. Shade squares red to show the first fraction. Shade squares blue to show the second fraction. Shading of squares may vary.

1. $\frac{2}{6}+\frac{3}{6}=\frac{5}{6}$
2. $\frac{1}{4}+\frac{2}{4}=\frac{3}{4}$
3. $\frac{3}{8}+\frac{4}{8}=\frac{7}{8}$
4. $\frac{2}{10}+\frac{5}{10}=\frac{7}{10}$

Cross out the squares to subtract. Write the difference. Crossed out squares may vary.

5. $\frac{4}{5}-\frac{1}{5}=\frac{3}{5}$
6. $\frac{4}{6}-\frac{2}{6}=\frac{2}{6}$
7. $\frac{7}{8}-\frac{5}{8}=\frac{2}{8}$
8. $\frac{7}{10}-\frac{6}{10}=\frac{1}{10}$

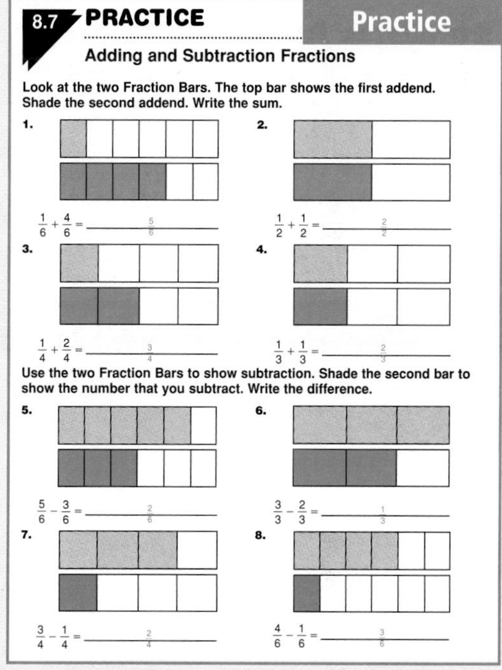

8.7 PRACTICE **Practice**

Adding and Subtraction Fractions

Look at the two Fraction Bars. The top bar shows the first addend. Shade the second addend. Write the sum.

1. $\frac{1}{6}+\frac{4}{6}=\frac{5}{6}$
2. $\frac{1}{2}+\frac{1}{2}=\frac{2}{2}$
3. $\frac{1}{4}+\frac{2}{4}=\frac{3}{4}$
4. $\frac{1}{3}+\frac{1}{3}=\frac{2}{3}$

Use the two Fraction Bars to show subtraction. Shade the second bar to show the number that you subtract. Write the difference.

5. $\frac{5}{6}-\frac{3}{6}=\frac{2}{6}$
6. $\frac{3}{3}-\frac{2}{3}=\frac{1}{3}$
7. $\frac{3}{4}-\frac{1}{4}=\frac{2}{4}$
8. $\frac{4}{6}-\frac{1}{6}=\frac{3}{6}$

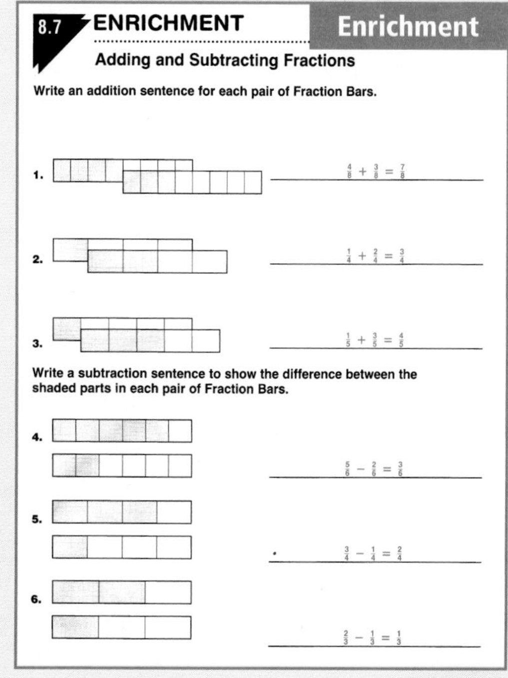

8.7 ENRICHMENT **Enrichment**

Adding and Subtracting Fractions

Write an addition sentence for each pair of Fraction Bars.

1. $\frac{4}{8}+\frac{3}{8}=\frac{7}{8}$
2. $\frac{1}{4}+\frac{2}{4}=\frac{3}{4}$
3. $\frac{1}{5}+\frac{3}{5}=\frac{4}{5}$

Write a subtraction sentence to show the difference between the shaded parts in each pair of Fraction Bars.

4. $\frac{5}{6}-\frac{2}{6}=\frac{3}{6}$
5. $\frac{3}{4}-\frac{1}{4}=\frac{2}{4}$
6. $\frac{2}{3}-\frac{1}{3}=\frac{1}{3}$

Problem Solving

Planning at a Glance

Objective To use the Draw a Picture strategy to solve problems

Materials unlined paper

Optional Resources

- Reteach 8.8; Practice 8.8; Enrichment 8.8
- Daily Cumul. Review, p. 108
- Math Center: Project Card 8
- Every Day Counts
- **TAB**, TE pp. 270E–270F, 270J
- **Problem of the Day**, 108, p. 54; Flip Chart, p. 54b

Unlocking Geometry 3–6, Level 3, Activity 6

Students Acquiring English

Walk students through the process of displaying and labeling class paintings for an exhibit in a school corridor. Help them to see and discuss different ways of arranging the pieces depending upon the space that is available. Suggest that they think of a painting that they have done or would like to do. Have them write a label for their painting.

Problem of the Day

What is the least number of times you could fold a sheet of paper to form 32 equal sections? Make a guess, then experiment to test your guess. 5 times

---

Problem Solving: Strategy

Problem Solving

Draw a Picture

Getting Started

What You'll Need:
- unlined paper

There are 12 paintings on display in your classroom. You write labels for $\frac{1}{3}$ of them. How many paintings do you label? Drawing a picture can help you to solve the problem.

Here's A Way! Use Draw a Picture to solve.

1 Understand

- How many paintings are there? 12
- What fraction of the paintings must you label? $\frac{1}{3}$

2 Plan

- What picture can you draw to help you? Draw 12 squares. Circle $\frac{1}{3}$ of them.

3 Try It

- Draw a picture of the paintings.
- Into how many equal parts should you divide the paintings to show thirds? 3 parts
- How many paintings equal one third? 4 paintings

4 Look Back

- How did drawing a picture help you to find that you need to label 4 paintings? Answers will vary. Possible answer: You could see that 4 paintings were $\frac{1}{3}$ of 12.

288 Chapter 8

---

1 Introduce

Build Understanding **Ask, You and 3 friends want to illustrate a story, each drawing an equal part. What fraction of the story will you illustrate?** $\frac{1}{4}$

Teach: Here's A Way!

Emphasize these points:

- Drawing a picture can help you see how many paintings you need to label.
- Dividing the picture into equal parts shows how many paintings are in each part.

Modeling Model the sample problem. Ask:

- What problem do you have to solve? number of paintings to label
- What can you draw to solve the problem? a model of the wall with squares representing the pictures

2 Develop

Show What You Know!

- Ask students to show the pictures they drew for problem 1. Have volunteers show how they used pictures to solve the problem. Ask students to discuss their reasoning for problem 2.

Work It Out!

- Ask students to discuss which problems they solved by drawing a picture and which they solved by using other strategies.
- Invite students to share the pictures they drew to help them solve the problems.
- Ask students to generalize about when drawing a picture is a useful strategy and when it isn't.

3 Summarize

Ongoing Assessment You have 12 old music tapes. You want to give $\frac{3}{4}$ to your sister and $\frac{1}{4}$ to a friend. How can you draw a picture to show how many tapes to give to each? Answers will vary. Possible answer: Draw 12 tapes in 4 equal rows; shade 3 rows: 9 tapes, 3 tapes

Math Journal: *Communicating*

Could there be more than one way to show $\frac{1}{3}$ of the paintings on the wall? Explain. yes; for example, a vertical row of 4, or any group of 4

Show What You Know!

Draw a picture to finish the problem.

1. The art show is 1 mile from your house. You are $\frac{3}{4}$ of the way there. What part of a mile do you have to go before you get there? $\frac{1}{4}$ mile

0 1

2. **Critical Thinking** Why is the number line divided into four equal parts? to find $\frac{3}{4}$, or three of four parts

Work It Out!

Use Draw a Picture or any other strategy to solve the problem.

3. In another art show, there were 2 rows with 6 paintings in each row. Only $\frac{1}{3}$ of the paintings are left. The rest were sold. How many paintings were sold? 8 paintings
4. One fourth of the 12 paintings were of playgrounds. The remaining paintings were of families. How many paintings were of families? 9 paintings
5. For your artwork you fold a square piece of paper in half 3 times. Then you unfold the paper and paint $\frac{1}{4}$ of the sections green. How many sections are green? 2 sections

These pieces of art are entered in an art show. Look at the chart to solve the problems.

6. Is the number of paintings more than $\frac{1}{2}$ of the art pieces entered? no; exactly $\frac{1}{2}$

Our Art Show

	Class A	Class B	Class C
Paintings	3	1	3
Sculptures	2	2	1
Photos	1	0	1

Share Your Thinking

7. Which problems did you solve by drawing a picture? Why? Answers will vary.
8. What strategies did you use to solve other problems? Answers will vary.

289

Meeting Individual Needs

Extra Support

Sharing a Room *(visual)* Have student pairs solve this problem: Three sisters are going to share a room. Draw two different pictures that show how they can divide up the floor space.

Alternate Approach

- Reteach Worksheet 8.8
- **TAB** See TE pp. 270E–270F.

MathZones

Understanding Fractions

Students Acquiring English

See Language Connections, Ch. 8.

Challenge

Have students set up a video rental store using this floor plan:

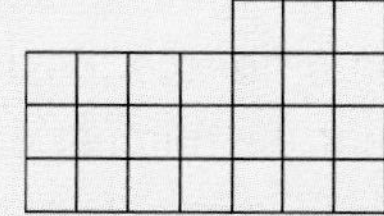

- Half the store will be for movies.
- One fourth will be for games.
- One fourth will be for snacks.

Practice

Math Center For more problem solving practice, see Project Card 8, *Feeding Fritzy.*

Reteach

8.8 **ANOTHER LOOK**

Problem Solving Strategy: Draw a Picture

Ginny is having a party. She has 3 trays with 5 cups on each. Ginny pours apple juice into $\frac{2}{3}$ of the cups. She fills the rest of the cups with lemonade. How many cups have lemonade?

1. Understand
- You need to know the number of cups of lemonade.

2. Plan
- Draw 3 rectangles to stand for the number of trays.
- Draw 5 circles to stand for the cups in each rectangle.

3. Try It
- Divide the circles into 3 equal parts. Color 2 of the parts to show $\frac{2}{3}$. This is the number of cups of apple juice.
- Count the number of circles that are not colored. This is the number of cups Ginny fills with lemonade.

4. Look Back
- Ten cups have apple juice. Five cups have lemonade.

Solve. Use Draw a Picture when you can.

1. Ginny decorates the party room with red, white, and yellow balloons. She has 20 balloons in all. Half of the balloons are red. There is the same number of white balloons as yellow balloons. How many balloons does she have of each color? red–10, white–5, yellow–5
2. What fraction of the balloons is yellow? $\frac{1}{4}$

Practice

8.8 **PRACTICE**

Problem Solving Strategy: Draw a Picture

Mrs. Carter is arranging her classroom. She needs to decide where to put different learning centers for her students. She uses squared paper to make a plan. Each square stands for 1 large floor tile.

Solve. Use Draw a Picture when you can.

1. How many floor tiles are in the classroom? 36 floor tiles
2. Mrs. Carter's desk and her students' desks will take up half the room. How many floor tiles will the desks cover? 18 floor tiles
3. Mrs. Carter will have a math and science center in one corner of the classroom. The center will take up $\frac{1}{4}$ of the room. How many floor tiles will the center cover? 9 floor tiles
4. A reading center will be set up in the space that remains. How many floor tiles will the reading center cover? What fraction of the room will that be? 9 floor tiles, $\frac{1}{4}$
5. Mrs. Carter sets up tables and chairs at her centers. She needs 2 chairs for every small table and 4 chairs for every large table. Mrs. Carter has 3 small tables and 2 large tables. How many chairs does she need? 14 chairs
6. Mrs. Carter has 12 posters. She displays $\frac{1}{2}$ of them on the back wall. She displays $\frac{1}{3}$ of the posters on the front wall. She displays the rest in the reading center. How many are in the reading center? What fraction of the posters is that? 2 posters, $\frac{1}{6}$

Enrichment

8.8 **ENRICHMENT**

Problem Solving Strategy: Draw a Picture

Solve. Use Draw a Picture when you can.

1. You get a piece of rope that is 48 inches long. You cut the rope in half. Next, you cut each of the pieces in half. Then, you cut each of those pieces in half again. How many pieces of rope do you have in all? 8 pieces
2. How long are each of the pieces? 6 inches
3. You and your friend are reading copies of the same book. The book is 42 pages long. You have read $\frac{1}{2}$ of the book. Your friend has read $\frac{1}{3}$ of the book. How many more pages have you read than your friend? 7 pages
4. There are 15 houses on one side of Spruce Street. The first house on one end of the street has neither a dog nor a cat. Every 4th house from that end has a dog. Every 6th house from that end has a cat. How many houses have both a dog and a cat? 1 house
5. The Kato family is having crackers for a snack. There are 24 crackers in all. Mr. Kato eats $\frac{1}{4}$ of the crackers. Mrs. Kato eats $\frac{1}{12}$ of the crackers. Lee eats $\frac{1}{3}$ of the crackers. Minh eats $\frac{1}{6}$ of the crackers. How many crackers does each person eat? Mr. Kato—6 crackers, Mrs. Kato—2 crackers, Lee—8 crackers, Minh—4 crackers
6. Who eats the most crackers? Lee
7. How many crackers are eaten altogether? What fraction of the crackers is that? 20 crackers, $\frac{5}{6}$

Connecting

Planning at a Glance

Objective To understand and to write mixed numbers

Materials none

Optional Resources

- Reteach 8.9; Practice 8.9; Enrichment 8.9
- Daily Cumul. Review, p. 109
- Math Center: Act. Card 47
- Every Day Counts
- **TAB**, TE pp. 270E–270F, 270J
- **Problem of the Day**, 109, p. 55; Flip Chart, p. 55a

MATHKEYS *Unlocking Fractions & Decimals* 3–6, Level 3, Activity 7

Students Acquiring English
Draw simple pictographs of classroom items (books, pencils, etc.) on the board. Next to each pictograph write a numerical equivalent (for example, = 50 books.) Have students use pictographs to show how many of the items are in the classroom.

Problem of the Day

Use the digits 1, 2, 3, and 4. Write all possible true statements that compare fractions in the form shown here.

$\frac{\square}{\square} < \frac{\square}{\square}$

$\frac{1}{2} < \frac{3}{4}, \frac{1}{3} < \frac{2}{4}, \frac{1}{4} < \frac{2}{3}$

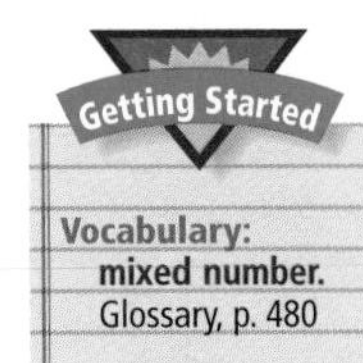

Mixed Numbers

Getting Started

Vocabulary: mixed number. Glossary, p. 480

A new lunch item at school is quesadillas (kehsaDEEyah). The pictograph shows how many quesadillas your classmates ate last week. What mixed number can you use to tell how many quesadillas were eaten on Tuesday?

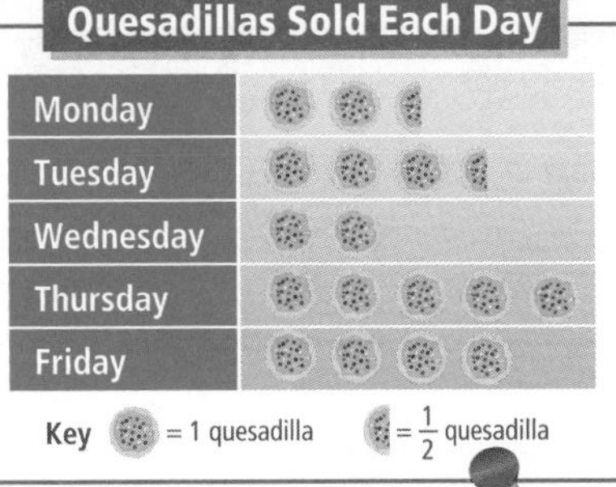

A mixed number has a whole number part and a fraction part.

Here's A Way! Write mixed numbers.

Find the key for the graph. Each stands for a whole quesadilla. Each stands for $\frac{1}{2}$ quesadilla.

1. Find Tuesday on the graph.
   How many are there?
   Write the whole number part of the mixed number. 3

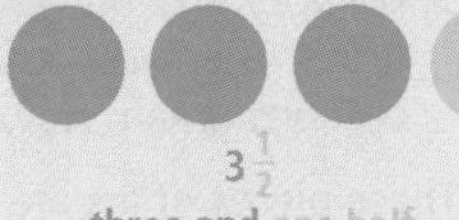
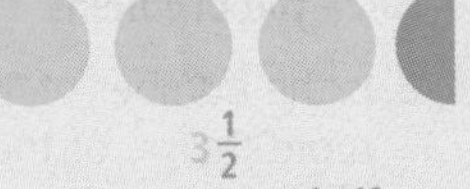

2. How many are there?
   Write the fraction part of the mixed number. $\frac{1}{2}$

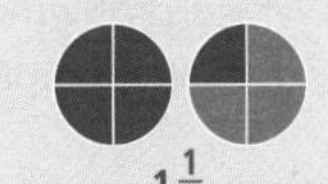
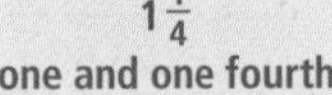

On Tuesday, your class ate $3\frac{1}{2}$ quesadillas.

Talk About It! 3; because each of the 3 pictures stands for a whole quesadilla

How many whole quesadillas were eaten on Tuesday? How do you know?

Other Examples Why does the shading show $1\frac{1}{4}$? It shows 1 whole and 1 part.

$1\frac{1}{4}$
one and one fourth

290 Chapter 8

1 Introduce

Prior Knowledge **Display representations of fraction models on the board with various parts shaded. Call on students to name the shaded fractions.**

Teach: Here's A Way!
Emphasize these points:

- A mixed number has a whole-number part and a fraction part.

Modeling Model the introductory example. Ask:

- How many whole quesadillas are there? 3
- How many half quesadillas are there? 1
- How many quesadillas are there in all? $3\frac{1}{2}$

2 Develop

Show What You Know!
Common Error Some students may write the wrong denominator for the fraction part. Remind them to count the number of equal parts the whole is divided into. See also Analyzing Errors, TE pp. 297A and 297B.

- Call on students to discuss their answers for exercise 7.

Work It Out!

- Have students compare answers to exercises 8 and 13.

3 Summarize

- Remind students that a mixed number has a whole-number part and a fraction part.
- Ask students to name examples of when they use mixed numbers.

Ongoing Assessment You cut out 3 whole circles and 1 half circle. What mixed number can you write for these figures?
$3\frac{1}{2}$ circles

Math Journal: ***Communicating***

What mixed number can you write for $\frac{5}{5}$ and $\frac{1}{5}$? How do you know? $1\frac{1}{5}$, because $\frac{5}{5}$ is the same as 1 whole

Show What You Know!

Write a mixed number for the shaded parts.

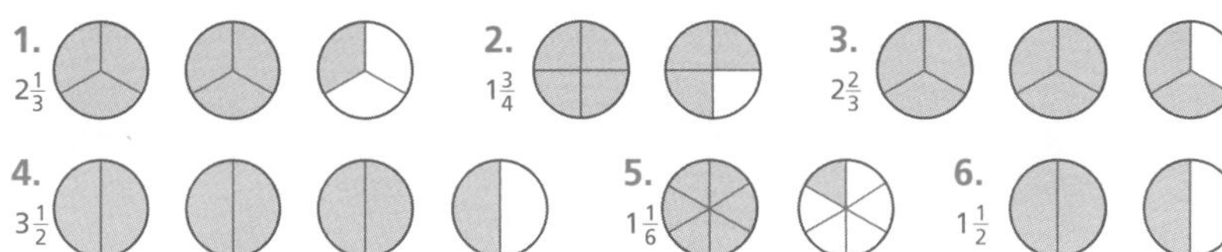

1. $2\frac{1}{3}$ 2. $1\frac{3}{4}$ 3. $2\frac{2}{3}$

4. $3\frac{1}{2}$ 5. $1\frac{1}{6}$ 6. $1\frac{1}{2}$

7. **Critical Thinking** Which picture shows a mixed number that is closest to 4? picture 4

Work It Out!

Write a mixed number for the quesadillas.

8. $1\frac{1}{2}$ 9. $2\frac{1}{2}$ 10. $4\frac{1}{2}$

Write a mixed number for the shaded parts.

11. $1\frac{1}{4}$ 12. $2\frac{1}{2}$ 13. $1\frac{3}{6}$

Write the mixed number.

14. two and two thirds $2\frac{2}{3}$
15. one and one fourth $1\frac{1}{4}$
16. three and two eighths $3\frac{2}{8}$
17. one and one sixth $1\frac{1}{6}$
18. eight and one third $8\frac{1}{3}$
19. four and four sixths $4\frac{4}{6}$

Mixed Review

Write the quotient.

20. $6\overline{)54}$ 9 21. $3\overline{)18}$ 6 22. $7\overline{)49}$ 7 23. $6\overline{)30}$ 5 24. $9\overline{)72}$ 8 25. $8\overline{)72}$ 9

Write the missing factor.

26. 5 × ■ = 40 8 27. ■ × 2 = 18 9 28. ■ × 4 = 24 6 29. 7 × ■ = 21 3

More Practice Set 8.9, p. 464

291

Meeting Individual Needs

Extra Support

Mixed-Number Pizza ***(visual)*** Have small groups work together to figure out how much pizza they could eat. Tell students that each pizza has 6 slices. How many pizzas would they eat if everyone had 1 slice? 2 slices? 3 slices? 4 slices? They can use fraction models to help solve the problem.

Alternate Approach

- Reteach Worksheet 8.9
- **TAB** See TE pp. 270E–270F.

MathZones

Understanding Fractions

Students Acquiring English

See Language Connections, Ch. 8.

Challenge

Have students write their ages as mixed numbers. Point out that one month is $\frac{1}{12}$ year. Ask:

- How old were you on your last birthday?
- How many months ago was your last birthday? What fraction of a year is that?

Practice

Math Center Use Activity Card 47, *Mixed Number Challenge,* to have students practice writing a mixed number as a whole number and a fraction from pictures and models.

Challenge Use Activity Card 47 and have students continue the activity as described in Now Try This!

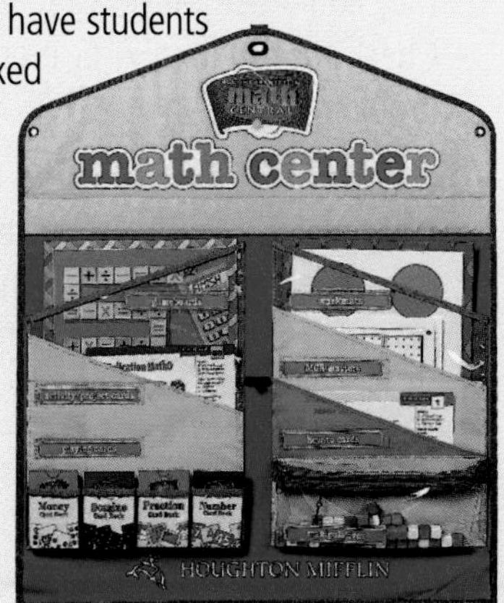

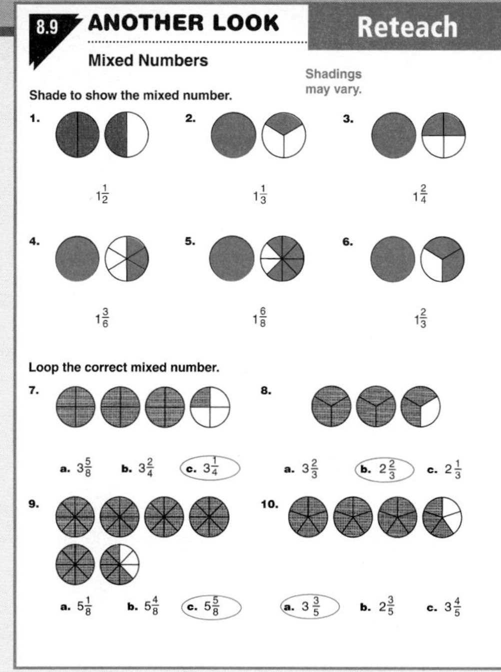

8.9 **ANOTHER LOOK** — Reteach

Mixed Numbers

Shade to show the mixed number. Shadings may vary.

1. $1\frac{1}{2}$ 2. $1\frac{1}{3}$ 3. $1\frac{2}{4}$

4. $1\frac{3}{6}$ 5. $1\frac{6}{8}$ 6. $1\frac{2}{3}$

Loop the correct mixed number.

7. a. $3\frac{5}{8}$ b. $3\frac{2}{4}$ c. $3\frac{1}{4}$ (looped)

8. a. $3\frac{2}{3}$ b. $2\frac{2}{3}$ (looped) c. $2\frac{1}{3}$

9. a. $5\frac{1}{8}$ b. $5\frac{4}{8}$ c. $5\frac{5}{8}$ (looped)

10. a. $3\frac{3}{5}$ (looped) b. $2\frac{3}{5}$ c. $3\frac{4}{5}$

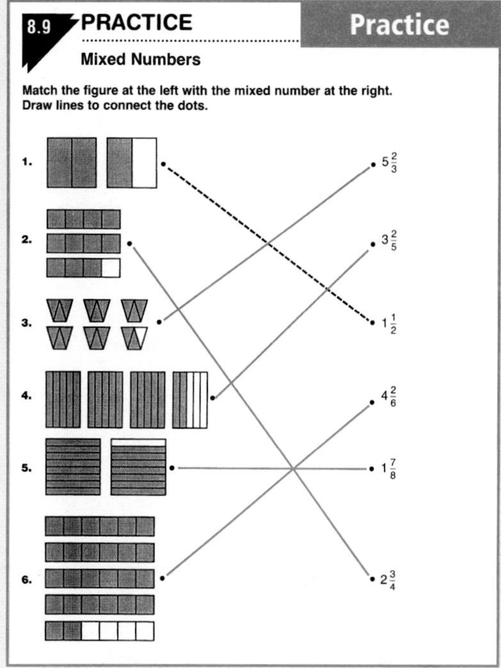

8.9 **PRACTICE** — Practice

Mixed Numbers

Match the figure at the left with the mixed number at the right. Draw lines to connect the dots.

1. • $5\frac{2}{3}$
2. • $3\frac{2}{5}$
3. • $1\frac{1}{2}$
4. • $4\frac{2}{6}$
5. • $1\frac{7}{8}$
6. • $2\frac{3}{4}$

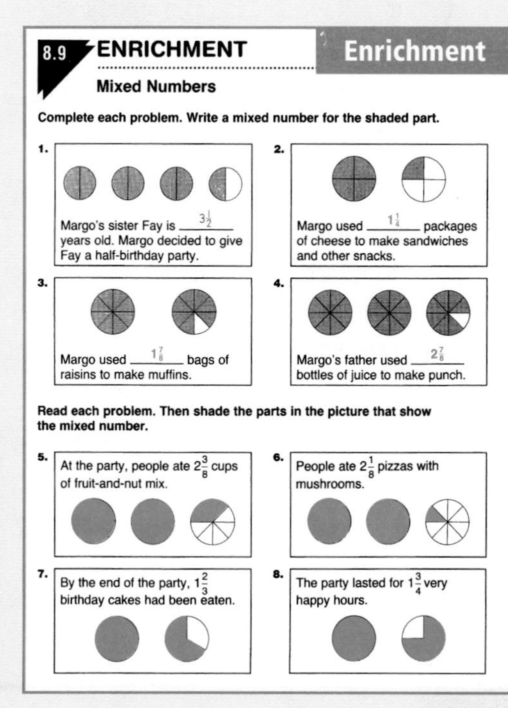

8.9 **ENRICHMENT** — Enrichment

Mixed Numbers

Complete each problem. Write a mixed number for the shaded part.

1. Margo's sister Fay is $3\frac{1}{2}$ years old. Margo decided to give Fay a half-birthday party.

2. Margo used $1\frac{1}{4}$ packages of cheese to make sandwiches and other snacks.

3. Margo used $1\frac{1}{8}$ bags of raisins to make muffins.

4. Margo's father used $2\frac{7}{8}$ bottles of juice to make punch.

Read each problem. Then shade the parts in the picture that show the mixed number.

5. At the party, people ate $2\frac{3}{8}$ cups of fruit-and-nut mix.

6. People ate $2\frac{1}{8}$ pizzas with mushrooms.

7. By the end of the party, $1\frac{2}{3}$ birthday cakes had been eaten.

8. The party lasted for $1\frac{3}{4}$ very happy hours.

LESSON 8.10

Problem Solving

Planning at a Glance

Objective **To use Draw a Picture and other strategies to solve problems**

Materials unlined paper

Optional Resources

- Reteach 8.10; Practice 8.10; Enrichment 8.10
- Daily Cumul. Review, p. 110
- Math Center: Project Card 8
- Every Day Counts
- **TAB**, TE pp. 270E–270F, 270J
- **Problem of the Day**, 110, p. 55; Flip Chart, p. 55b

Unlocking Fractions and Decimals 3–6, Level 3, Activity 11

Students Acquiring English

Point out the picture of the ferryboat and discuss it with students. Be sure students understand that the words *ferryboat, ferry,* and *boat* are all used in the lesson to refer to the same thing. Then point out the ferry schedule. Discuss schedules and invite students to write down their daily schedule.

Problem of the Day

Kendra will turn nine on May 15. If today is March 20, in how many days will she turn nine?
56 days

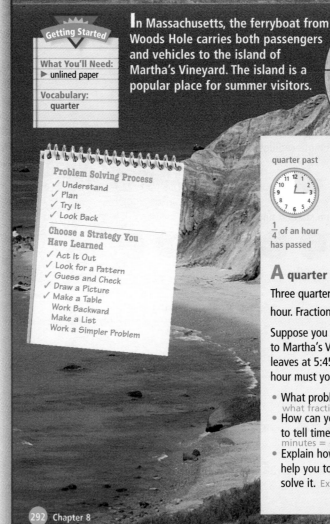

Problem Solving : Application

LESSON 10

Problem Solving

Using Draw a Picture and Other Strategies

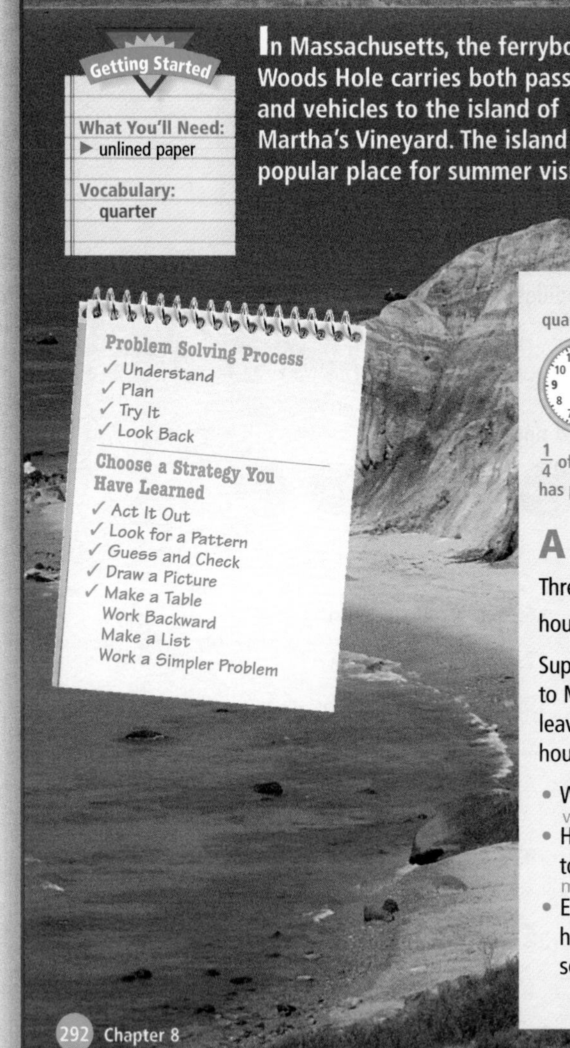

Getting Started
What You'll Need:
▶ unlined paper
Vocabulary:
quarter
ATLANTIC OCEAN
Massachusetts
Woods Hole
Martha's Vineyard
Problem Solving Process
✓ Understand
✓ Plan
✓ Try It
✓ Look Back
Choose a Strategy You Have Learned
✓ Act It Out
✓ Look for a Pattern
✓ Guess and Check
✓ Draw a Picture
✓ Make a Table
Work Backward
Make a List
Work a Simpler Problem

In Massachusetts, the ferryboat from Woods Hole carries both passengers and vehicles to the island of Martha's Vineyard. The island is a popular place for summer visitors.

quarter past	half past	quarter to
$\frac{1}{4}$ of an hour has passed	$\frac{1}{2}$ of an hour has passed	$\frac{3}{4}$ of an hour has passed

A **quarter** of an hour is $\frac{1}{4}$ of an hour. Three quarters of an hour is $\frac{3}{4}$ of an hour. Fractions can help you to tell time.

Suppose you just miss the 5:15 P.M. boat to Martha's Vineyard. The next ferry leaves at 5:45 P.M. What fraction of an hour must you wait for the next ferry?

- What problem needs to be solved? what fraction of an hour you must wait
- How can you use fractions to help you to tell time? 15 minutes = $\frac{1}{4}$ hour; 30 minutes = $\frac{1}{2}$ hour
- Explain how drawing a picture can help you to solve the problem. Then solve it. Explanations will vary. $\frac{1}{2}$ hour

292 Chapter 8

1 Introduce

Prior Knowledge **Ask, What do the long hand and the short hand on a clock show?** The long hand shows minutes; the short hand shows hours.

Teach: *Modeling*

Display a clock face on an overhead projector. Show 12:45 and shade the 45 minutes. Model how to use fractions and time by asking:

- What fraction of an hour is shaded? $\frac{3}{4}$
- How can you say the time in minutes? 45 minutes
- How can you say the time in quarter hours? three quarters of an hour

2 Develop

Work It Out!

- Ask students which problems they used the Draw a Picture strategy to solve. Have them explain why they used this strategy for these problems and not for others. For example, they could use Make a Table or Guess and Check for problem 7, or mental math for problem 5.

Using Reading Strategies Encourage students to use the Summarize strategy as they read the problems. Ask them to restate problems in their own words. See TE p. 270J.

3 Summarize

- Remind students that the Draw a Picture strategy can help them solve problems involving fractions of an hour.
- Have students review and discuss the strategies they used for each problem, and why.

Ongoing Assessment A clock reads 15 minutes past seven when you leave the house. What are two other ways of saying what time it is? seven fifteen; quarter past seven

Math Journal: *Communicating*

How can drawing a picture help you remember the terms *quarter past* and *half past*? The picture can show the quarters and halves of a clock face.

Work It Out!

Look at the ferry schedule to answer the problem. Use any strategy to solve the problem. Show your work.

Leave Woods Hole		
7:15 A.M.	1:15 P.M.	6:15 P.M.
8:00 A.M.	2:45 P.M.	7:45 P.M.
9:45 A.M.	3:45 P.M.	8:45 P.M.
10:45 A.M.	5:15 P.M.	9:45 P.M.
12:15 P.M.	5:45 P.M.	10:45 P.M.

1. The ferryboat ride from Woods Hole to Martha's Vineyard takes $\frac{3}{4}$ of an hour. Is there a boat that will get you there at 1:00 P.M.? Explain.
   Yes. The 12:15 P.M. ferry arrives at 1:00 P.M.
2. Suppose your family wants to go to Martha's Vineyard at night. How many boats leave after 7:00 P.M.? 4 boats
3. Which ferryboats leave Woods Hole $\frac{1}{2}$-hour apart?
   5:15 P.M. and 5:45 P.M. boats; 5:45 P.M. and 6:15 P.M.. boats
4. **Critical Thinking** Is the boat that leaves at 12:15 P.M. more than halfway to Martha's Vineyard at 12:30 P.M.? Explain. No. The trip takes 45 minutes; 15 minutes is less than $\frac{1}{2}$ of 45 minutes.
5. Suppose you get to Martha's Vineyard at 11:30 A.M. That night you leave on a 7:30 P.M. boat. How long did you stay on Martha's Vineyard? 8 hours
6. One-way tickets cost $4.25 for each adult and $2.15 for each child. How much does it cost for a group of two adults and three children to ride one way? $14.95
7. **Algebraic Reasoning** In one group, there are twice as many children as adults. Which costs more, the tickets for all the adults or for all the children? Explain. for the children; 2 children's tickets are $4.30, or 5¢ more than $4.25
8. **Create Your Own** Write a problem about the ferryboats for a friend to solve.
   Check students' work.

Share Your Thinking

9. Choose one of the problems you solved. Talk with a friend about the strategy you used to solve it. Explain how you could solve the problem using another strategy.
   Answers will vary, but should reflect understanding of the problem.

More Practice Set 8.10, p. 465

Meeting Individual Needs

Extra Support

What Time Is It? *(visual/kinesthetic)* On three index cards, write, *quarter past, half past,* and *quarter to*. Have students work in pairs, alternating as A and B:

- Student A names a time to the hour.
- Student B draws a clock face showing that time, and draws one of the cards.
- Student A shades the clock to indicate the fraction of an hour shown on the card.
- Replace the card and mix.

Alternate Approach

- Reteach Worksheet 8.10
- **TAB** See TE pp. 270E–270F.

MathZones

Understanding Fractions

Students Acquiring English

See **Language Connections**, Ch. 8.

Challenge

Distribute sets of pupils' clock faces with three clocks showing 12:25. Have students shade two of the clocks—one to show a quarter hour later and one to show a half-hour later. Students should continue the exercise by challenging each other to use mental math to add one quarter, one half, or three quarters of an hour and tell the new time.

Practice

Math Center For more problem solving practice, see Project Card 8, *Feeding Fritzy.*

See **Just the Facts** Cumulative Practice 7, p. 270.

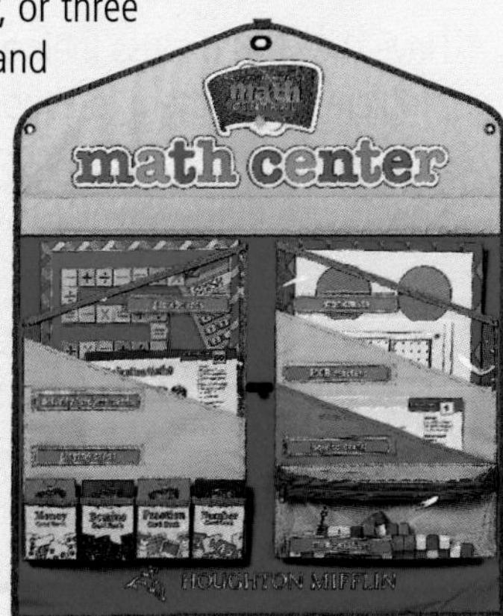

8.10 ANOTHER LOOK — Reteach

Using Draw a Picture and Other Strategies

You and your brother are at the museum. The doors will open in a quarter of an hour. It is 9:15 A.M. now. What time will the museum open?

1. Understand
- You need to figure out what time the museum will open.

2. Plan
- You can use a clock to help you figure out the time.

3. Try It
- Draw a clock as a circle that has been divided into fourths.
- Count the number of minutes in a quarter of an hour.
- Add the number of minutes in a quarter of an hour to 9:15 A.M.

4. Look Back
- The museum will open at 9:30 A.M.

Solve. Use Draw a Picture when you can.

1. You and your friend are examining some rocks. It is 11:30 A.M. You will stop for lunch in half an hour. What time will you stop for lunch? 12:00 P.M.
2. You arrive at the museum at 10:30 A.M. Your friend arrives $\frac{3}{4}$ of an hour later. What time does your friend arrive at the museum? 11:15 A.M.
3. A museum video show begins at 11:00 A.M. A new show begins every half of an hour. What time will the 5th video show of the day begin? 1:00 P.M.

8.10 PRACTICE — Practice

Using Draw a Picture and Other Strategies

Solve. Use Draw a Picture when you can.

1. It is 4:00 P.M. You need to leave for piano practice in a $\frac{1}{2}$ hour. What time will you leave? 4:30 P.M.
2. You have soccer practice at 2:00 P.M. The practice lasts $\frac{3}{4}$ of an hour. What time does your soccer practice end? 2:45 P.M.
3. You arrive at karate practice at 6:30 P.M. You wait $\frac{1}{4}$ of an hour for your class to begin. What time does your class start? 6:45 P.M.
4. Your dance group is going to put on a show. The show starts at 7:00 P.M. You need to be at the theater $\frac{3}{4}$ of an hour before the show begins. What time should you be at the theater? 6:15 P.M.
5. You are going downtown. You miss the 8:15 A.M. bus. The next bus comes at 8:30 A.M. What fraction of an hour do you have to wait? $\frac{1}{4}$ of an hour
6. You arrive at a restaurant for lunch at 12:15 P.M. You leave at 1:00 P.M. What fraction of an hour do you stay at the restaurant? $\frac{3}{4}$ of an hour
7. You board a plane that leaves at 9:00 A.M. for Vancouver. The plane arrives in Vancouver at 11:30 A.M. How long is the flight? $2\frac{1}{2}$ hours
8. You go walking every Saturday. You leave your house at 7:30 A.M. You come back home at 8:45 A.M. How long is your walk? $1\frac{1}{4}$ hours

---

8.10 ENRICHMENT — Enrichment

Using Draw a Picture and Other Strategies

Solve. Use Draw a Picture when you can.

1. You buy a pizza covered half with sausage and half with broccoli. You cut the pizza in half, so the sausage is on one piece and the broccoli is on the other piece. Then you cut the sausage piece in half. Then you cut both of these sausage pieces in half again. How many pieces of pizza do you have? 5 pieces
2. You are stacking blocks in the shape of a triangle. There are 6 blocks in the row at the bottom of the triangle. There are 5 blocks in the second row. There will be 1 block at the top of the triangle. How many blocks will you use altogether? 21 blocks
3. Your mother is driving you to school. The distance from your house to school is 2 miles. You drive halfway there and then realize you forgot your homework. You drive home, get your homework, and drive to school. How many miles have you driven altogether? 4 miles
4. You have $.80. You have 8 coins. None of them are pennies. What 3 combinations of coins might you have? 8 dimes; 1 quarter, 4 dimes, 3 nickels; 2 quarters, 6 nickels
5. A quilt has red, black, and green squares. The quilt repeats the colors in this pattern: red, black, green, red, black, green. What color will the eighth square be? The twelfth square? eighth square will be black; twelfth square will be green

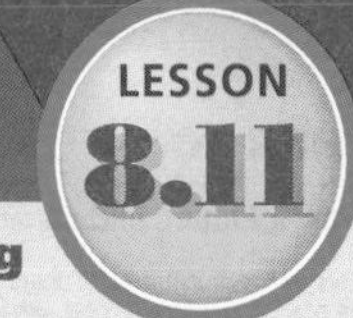

Problem Solving

Planning at a Glance

Objective To use different strategies to solve problems

Materials none

Optional Resources

- Reteach 8.11; Practice 8.11; Enrichment 8.11
- Daily Cumul. Review, p. 111
- Math Center: Project Card 8
- Every Day Counts
- **TAB**, TE pp. 270E–270F, 270J
- **Problem of the Day**, 111, p. 56; Flip Chart, p. 56a

MATHKEYS *Unlocking Fractions and Decimals 3–6*, Level 3, Activity 12

Students Acquiring English

Invite students to draw round shapes. Then ask them what they think a round of cheese is. Explain that it is a large amount of cheese in a round shape. Then discuss the other words for food used in the lesson, inviting students to make a list of three of the foods and draw a picture of each of the three.

Problem of the Day

The square floor in Gino's kitchen is covered with 64 square tiles, all the same size. What fraction of the tiles are along the edges of the square? Hint: Draw a picture.

$\frac{28}{64}$, or $\frac{7}{16}$

Problem Solving : Application

LESSON 11

Problem Solving

Using Strategies

You can read more about the Vikings from the pages of *Kids Discover Vikings.*

The Vikings lived many years ago in what are now Denmark, Norway, and Sweden. Winters were severe. Animals were kept indoors to protect them from the cold weather.

Problem Solving Process
- ✓ Understand
- ✓ Plan
- ✓ Try It
- ✓ Look Back

Choose a Strategy You Have Learned
- ✓ Act It Out
- ✓ Look for a Pattern
- ✓ Guess and Check
- ✓ Draw a Picture
- ✓ Make a Table
- Work Backward
- Make a List
- Work a Simpler Problem

The Vikings ate food from their farms, such as beef, beans, peas, and cheese. Suppose you were a Viking and had to share a round of cheese equally. You slice the cheese so that each piece is $\frac{1}{8}$ of the round. How can you use only 4 straight cuts to slice the cheese?

- Do the parts have to be equal? Why? Yes; to keep the shares equal
- How many cuts can you make? 4 cuts
- Explain a strategy that can help you to solve the problem. Then solve it. Explanations will vary.

294 Chapter 8

---

1 Introduce

Explore **Ask, Do you have a favorite dish that you could write a recipe for? Have students list the ingredients for the recipe and the amount of each ingredient. They should also briefly write how to combine the ingredients. Some students may want to illustrate their recipes. Others may want to prepare them at home and bring them in to share with the class.**

Teach: ***Modeling***

Model the example. Discuss:

- What strategy helped you solve the problem? Explain. Answers will vary.
- Can you think of any other strategies you could have used? Name these strategies. Answers will vary.

2 Develop

Work It Out!

- Have students discuss the strategies they used to solve problems 1–3. For example, students might use Draw a Picture for problems 1 and 3, or Guess and Check for problem 2.
- Have the class discuss their answers for problem 7. Ask them to choose a different strategy than the one they used, and explain how to use that strategy to solve the problem.

Using Reading Strategies Help students to use the Summarize strategy as they read the problems. Have students restate problem 4 to a partner, leaving out any information that is not needed to solve it. See TE p. 270J.

3 Summarize

- Have students review and discuss the different strategies that they used to solve the problems.

Ongoing Assessment You and your best friend have a plot in your neighborhood vegetable garden. You want to grow tomatoes and lettuce to fill $\frac{3}{4}$ of the garden. What fraction will be left for cucumbers? $\frac{1}{4}$

Math Journal: ***Communicating***

For which problems did Draw a Picture help you? Answers may vary but could include any of problems 1–5.

Work It Out!

Use any strategy to solve the problem. Show your work.

1. Plan to make a pizza with different toppings. Your brother likes cheese and beef. Your sister will not eat beef. Your mother likes cheese and beef, but not beans. You like all three. Design a pie so that your brother, your sister, your mother, and you can each have two slices. $\frac{1}{2}$ cheese, beef; $\frac{1}{4}$ cheese, beans; $\frac{1}{4}$ cheese, beef, beans
2. A recipe calls for $\frac{3}{4}$ cup of carrots. You have 1 cup of carrots and a $\frac{1}{4}$ cup measure. How can you measure $\frac{3}{4}$ cup? Is there more than one way? Fill the $\frac{1}{4}$ cup measure 3 times. Or, fill the $\frac{1}{4}$ cup measure once and use the remaining carrots, $\frac{3}{4}$ cup.
3. If you spent $\frac{1}{4}$ of a 24-hour day working on the farm, how many hours did you work? 6 hours
4. Mix $\frac{1}{4}$ cup peas with every 1 cup of beans. If you have 16 cups of beans, how many cups of peas do you need? 4 cups
5. Can you get more peas or more kidney beans into $\frac{1}{2}$ cup? Explain. peas; They are smaller.
6. Look at the Viking alphabet. This alphabet is made up of 16 letters, called runes. The runes were often brightly painted on stones or wood. What fraction of the runes are not painted blue yet? $\frac{1}{4}$
7. The grid paper shows different ways to cut a square piece of cloth in half. Show two other ways you can cut this cloth in half.

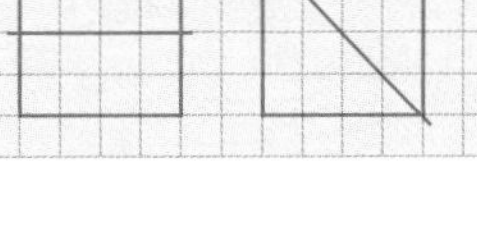

Share Your Thinking

8. What strategy did you use to solve problem 7? What other ways could you have solved it? Answers will vary.
9. Make a list of all the different strategies you used to solve these problems. Compare your list with a classmate's. Answers will vary, but should reflect understanding of the problem.

295

Meeting Individual Needs

Extra Support

Match Pictures *(visual)* Student pairs write on separate cards 3 problems that can each be solved by drawing a picture. On separate cards, they draw the pictures that would help solve each problem. Then students exchange cards with other pairs to match drawings and solve the problems.

Alternate Approach

- Reteach Worksheet 8.11
- **TAB** See TE p. 270E–270F.

MathZones

Understanding Fractions

Students Acquiring English

See **Language Connections**, Ch. 8.

Challenge

Have student pairs solve these problems:

- You are painting 3 rooms of the same size. You use $1\frac{1}{2}$ gallons of paint for the first room. How much more paint will you need? 3 gal
- Another can of paint is $\frac{3}{4}$ full. You use $\frac{1}{2}$ of what is left. Is the can now more than, less than, or exactly half full? less than

Practice

Math Center For more problem solving practice, see Project Card 8, *Feeding Fritzy*.

Reteach

8.11 ANOTHER LOOK

Problem Solving: Using Strategies

Your neighbor is making a brick path to her house. She has used 12 bricks so far. She has only $\frac{1}{4}$ of the path completed. How many more bricks will she need?

1. Understand
- You want to find out how many more bricks your neighbor needs to finish her path.

2. Plan
- Look at the plan. You need to find the number of rows completed. Multiply this number by 4 to find the total number of rows.
- Then you can subtract the number completed from the number of total rows.

3. Try It
- Three rows are completed. $3 \times 4 = 12$. There will be a total of 12 rows.
- $12 - 3 = 9$. She has 9 more rows to make.

4. Look Back
- You know there are 4 bricks in each row, so she will need 36 more bricks.

Use any strategy to solve.

1. Your teacher saws a wooden board that is 60 inches long. She saws the wood into thirds. Then she saws each of those pieces in half. How many pieces of wood does your teacher now have? 6 pieces
2. How long is each piece of wood now? 10 inches
3. What fraction of the whole board is each piece of wood? $\frac{1}{6}$

Practice

8.11 PRACTICE

Problem Solving: Using Strategies

Use any strategy to solve.

1. You are working in the garden this morning. You work from 9:15 A.M. to 11:30 A.M. How many hours is that? $2\frac{1}{4}$ hours
2. You spend 45 minutes weeding $\frac{3}{4}$ of the garden. What fraction of the garden still needs to be weeded? $\frac{1}{4}$
3. You have \$3.00 to buy a hoe and a small shovel. At the hardware store, you see that each item costs a dollar and a half. Do you have enough money? yes
4. You are watering the garden with a sprinkling can. After you water $\frac{1}{2}$ of the garden, $\frac{1}{4}$ of the water is left in the can. Is there enough water left in the sprinkling can to finish watering the garden? How do you know? No. It took $\frac{3}{4}$ of the water in the can to water $\frac{1}{2}$ of the garden, so you will need the same amount to water the other half.
5. You plant 3 rows of flowers in your garden. Each row has 6 flowers. Half of the flowers are red. One-third of the flowers are white. The rest of the flowers are pink. How many flowers of each color are there? red–9 flowers, white–6 flowers, pink–3 flowers

   What fraction of the flowers is pink? $\frac{1}{6}$

Enrichment

8.11 ENRICHMENT

Problem Solving: Using Strategies

Use any strategy to solve.

1. Mrs. Olivia has 24 students in her class. The class is planning a trip to the circus. So far, $\frac{7}{8}$ of the class has decided to go. How many students have not yet decided to go? 3 students
2. Mrs. Olivia, the students, and some parents go to the circus in 4 vans. Each van holds 9 people. In 3 of the vans, there is 1 empty seat. How many people are in the vans? 33 people
3. There are several ways to drive to the circus from the school. Write the letters that show the shortest way. H, J, D
4. Write the letters that show the longest way to the circus. A,B,C,D
5. You want to buy circus T-shirts. Each shirt costs \$5.00. You have \$11.00. How many shirts can you buy? 2 shirts
6. Acrobats perform a stunt, standing on each other's shoulders. There are 5 acrobats in the bottom row, 4 in the second row, and 3 in the third row. There are 5 rows altogether. How many acrobats are performing? 15 acrobats

Chapter Test

Problem Solving

Give 0–6 points per answer based on how well students meet the following criteria:

Problem 1
- A strategy is seen through to a correct solution
- Work is shown clearly

Problem 2
- A strategy is seen through to a correct solution
- Answer shows organization of information

Concepts and Skills

If students need more help with concepts and skills in this chapter, use the following Reteaching Worksheets:

- 57 Writing Fractions, p. 162
- 58 Comparing Fractions with the Same Denominators, p. 163
- 59 Comparing Fractions with Different Denominators, p. 164
- 60 Equivalent Fractions, p. 165
- 61 Estimating Fractions, p. 172
- 62 Adding Fractions, p. 173
- 63 Subtracting Fractions, p. 174
- 64 Writing Mixed Numbers, p. 175
- 65 Fractions and Time, p. 176

Chapter 8 Test

for Pages 270–295

Test-Taking Tips
Decide if you can use models or draw a picture to solve a problem.

Problem Solving

Solve. Show your work. (pages 288, 292)

1. You sew together 36 squares of cloth to create a square quilt. Only the squares along the edges will be red. How many of the squares will be red? 20 squares
2. You have a bookcase with 5 shelves. Tell how you can put books so that:
   - the shelf for spelling is not right above or right below the shelf for math or science.
   - the shelf for math is just above the shelf for science.
   - the shelf for history is not next to reading or science.
   - the shelf for reading is above science but not on the top.

   from top to bottom: history, spelling, reading, math, science

Concepts

Draw fraction models to compare. Write > or <. (page 276)

3. $\frac{5}{10}$ ● $\frac{7}{10}$ <
4. $\frac{2}{8}$ ● $\frac{1}{2}$ <
5. $\frac{2}{2}$ ● $\frac{3}{4}$ >

Which estimate tells about how much of the rectangle is red? (page 284)

6.  a. 0 b. $\frac{1}{2}$ c. 1 — b
7.  a. 0 b. $\frac{1}{2}$ c. 1 — c

Write the missing fraction. Then write the fraction in word form. (page 274)

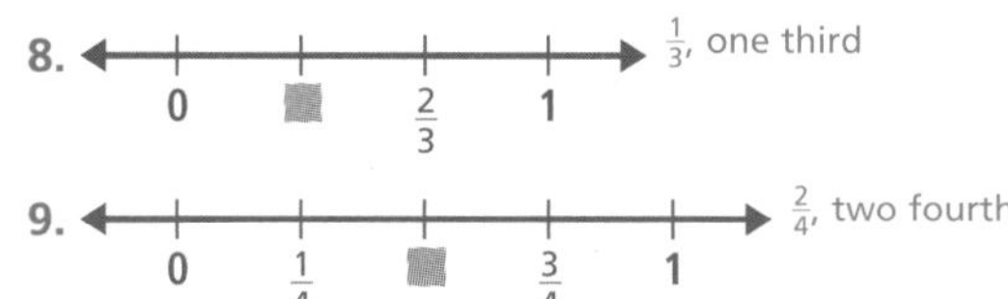

8. $\frac{1}{3}$, one third
9. $\frac{2}{4}$, two fourths

296

Chapter Correlation to Standardized Tests

Math Central	Standardized Test Objectives						
Chapter Objective	**ITBS Form M**	**CAT/5**	**CTBS/4**	**Terra Nova (CTBS/5)**	**MAT 7th ed.**	**SAT 9th ed.**	**State/ Local**
8A To write fractions for fractional parts of regions	•	•	•	•	•	•	
8B To compare and order fractions using models	•	•	•	•	•	•	
8C To find equivalent fractions using models	•	•	•	•	•	•	
8D To estimate fractions using benchmarks of 0, $\frac{1}{2}$, and 1	•	•	•	•	•	•	
8E To add and subtract fractions with like denominators	•	•	•	•	•	•	
8F To write mixed numbers for fractions greater than 1	•	•	•	•	•	•	
8G To use Draw a Picture and other strategies to solve problems	•			•	•	•	

Skills

Write a mixed number for the shaded part. **(page 290)**

10.  $2\frac{1}{2}$

11.  $3\frac{1}{2}$

12. 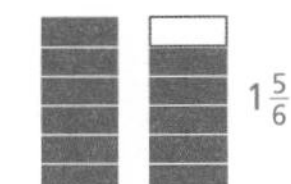 $1\frac{5}{6}$

13. 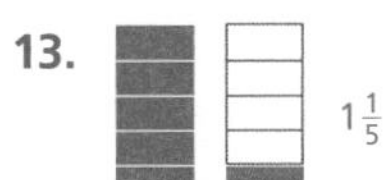 $1\frac{1}{5}$

14. 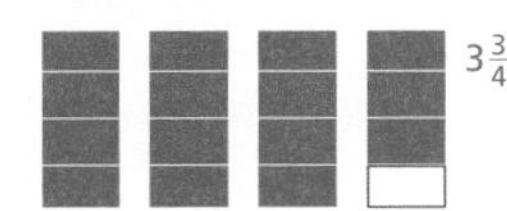 $3\frac{3}{4}$

15.  $1\frac{1}{3}$

Use fraction models. Find an equivalent fraction. **(page 278)**
Answers will vary. Possible answers shown.

16. $\frac{3}{6}$ $\frac{1}{2}$ 17. $\frac{6}{8}$ $\frac{3}{4}$ 18. $\frac{2}{10}$ $\frac{1}{5}$ 19. $\frac{1}{3}$ $\frac{2}{6}$

Use fraction models. Find the answer. **(page 286)**

20. $\frac{3}{4} - \frac{1}{4}$ $\frac{2}{4}$ 21. $\frac{4}{6} - \frac{2}{6}$ $\frac{2}{6}$ 22. $\frac{1}{2} + \frac{1}{2}$ $\frac{2}{2}$ or 1

23. $\frac{3}{6} + \frac{2}{6}$ $\frac{5}{6}$ 24. $\frac{2}{5} + \frac{1}{5}$ $\frac{3}{5}$ 25. $\frac{3}{3} - \frac{2}{3}$ $\frac{1}{3}$

Performance Task

(pages 272, 274)

$\frac{2}{4}$

$\frac{5}{6}$

$\frac{1}{10}$

$\frac{3}{8}$

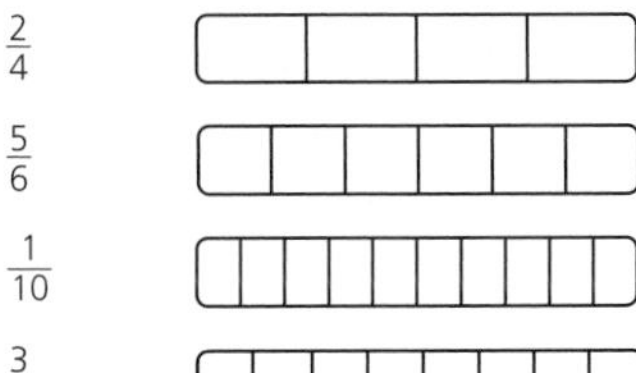

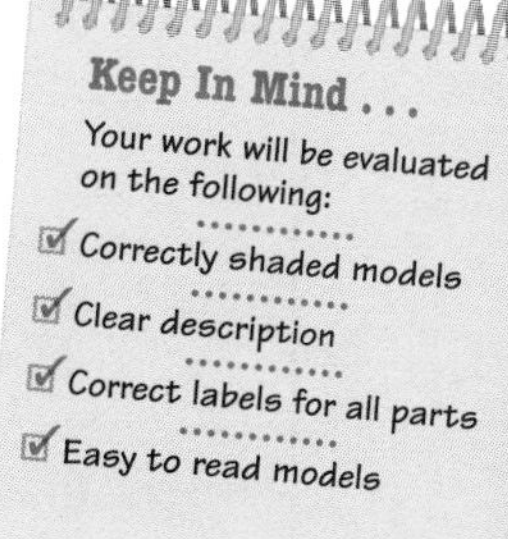

Keep In Mind . . .
Your work will be evaluated on the following:
Correctly shaded models
Clear description
Correct labels for all parts
Easy to read models

- Copy the fraction models and shade to show the fraction named.
- Explain how you decided how many parts to shade.
  Shade 2 parts to show $\frac{2}{4}$ fractions; 5 parts for $\frac{5}{6}$; 1 part for $\frac{1}{10}$; 3 parts for $\frac{3}{8}$.
- What fraction of each model is unshaded? $\frac{2}{4}$, $\frac{1}{6}$, $\frac{9}{10}$, $\frac{5}{8}$

Assessment Options

The following materials are found in your **Comprehensive Assessment Package:**

Formal Assessments
- Standardized-Format
- Free-Response Chapter Tests, Forms A and B

Performance Assessments
- Chapter Tasks
- Midyear and Final Project Tasks

Alternative Assessments
- Observation Checklist
- Student Attitude Assessment
- Student Self-Assessment *Individual and Group*

- Chapter Tests for Students Acquiring Language Proficiency
- Informal Learning Inventory

Standardized Testing: New Formats
- Enhanced Multiple-Choice
- Extended-Response
- Short-Response

Management
- Student Record Sheets
- Answer Keys

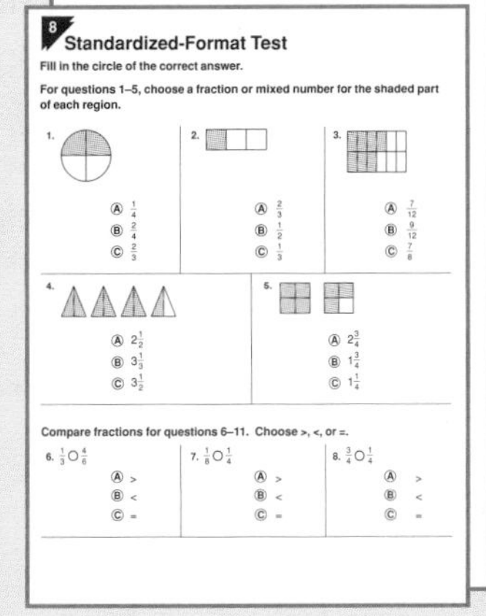

8 Standardized-Format Test
Fill in the circle of the correct answer.
For questions 1–5, choose a fraction or mixed number for the shaded part of each region.

Compare fractions for questions 6–11. Choose >, <, or =.

- Standardized-Format Chapter Tests
- Free-Response Chapter Tests, Forms A and B
- Standardized-Format Midyear and Final Tests

Additional Assessment Resources

Test, Practice, Management Program
Use the *Test, Practice, Management Program* to create, administer, and score tests as well as generate practice sets. Questions are correlated to the Lesson Objectives.

Performance Task

Use the following criteria, each worth 3 points, to evaluate students' responses. These criteria align with *Keep In Mind* in the Pupil Edition on p. 297.

Criteria	
Shows correct models for fractions	Writes a clear description
Labels all parts	Creates easy-to-read models

Use this 4-level rubric to score students' responses. If you prefer a task with a 6-level rubric, use the Performance Assessment for this chapter.

3 points	Limited Response
6 points	Acceptable
9 points	Capable
12 points	Superior

Common Error Alert

If students are making frequent errors, see Analyzing Errors, TE pp. 297A–297B.

Scoring Chart

Item	Points
1–2	6 points each
3–9	4 points each
10–25	3 points each
Performance Task	12 points
TOTAL	100 points, or 100%

Item Analysis

Item	Objectives
1–2	To use Draw a Picture and other strategies to solve problems (8G)
3–5, 8–9	To compare and order fractions (8B)
6–7	To estimate fractions using benchmarks (8D)
10–15	To write mixed numbers (8F)
16–19	To find equivalent fractions using models (8C)
20–25	To add and subtract fractions with like denominators (8E)

Cumulative Test

For a cumulative review in the multiple-choice format, see TE pp. T76 –T77 .

Analyzing Errors

Strategies and Techniques for Reteaching

Errors in Basic Fraction Concepts If students have difficulty in understanding basic fraction concepts, have students share "pizza" circles equally for 4 people. Give them an unmarked paper circle and ask them to show how they would make 4 equal sections. Have students shade the part of the "pizza" one person would have. You may wish to repeat the activity with eighths, asking students to show how eight people could get equal shares. They should continue shading circles, using other numbers.

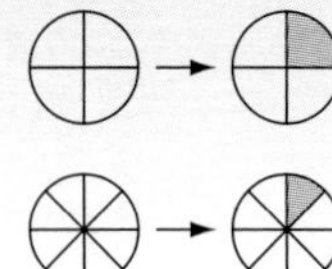

Writing Fractions from Models

Errors in Understanding and Naming Fractions

Error Confuses numerator with denominator

Reteaching Provide students with several concrete or pictorial fraction models. For each model, ask them to describe the fraction by writing "shaded parts" beside the numerator and "parts in all" beside the denominator. Point out that "shaded parts," in this case are the "parts of interest," while at other times the unshaded parts might be the model.

Error

$\frac{3}{1}$

Reteaching

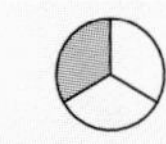

$\frac{\text{1 shaded part}}{\text{3 parts in all}}$

Error Names the unshaded part when asked to name the shaded part

Reteaching Use real world examples such as pieces of cake left in a box, slices of pizza with different toppings, or crossed-out sections of a tic-tac-toe board. Help students see that the numerator of a fraction refers to the part that is of interest. It may be pepperoni or plain, *x's* or *o's*, servings eaten or left, but it is important to know which. Guide students to create their own real contexts for fractions and write fractions with labels telling which real part of a real whole is named.

Error Counts leftover parts to name the denominator rather than counting the number of parts in the whole

Reteaching Guide students to draw figures divided into equal parts with no shading. Ask them to name the total number of parts in a figure. Then, ask them to shade one or more parts of the same figure. Again, ask the total number of parts. Point out that the total number of parts does not change when shading is added. Finally, they can write a fraction for the part they shaded, labeling the numerator "___ parts shaded" and the denominator, "out of ___ parts in all."

Error

$\frac{1}{3}$

Reteaching

$\frac{\text{1 shaded part}}{\text{out of 4 parts in all}}$

Writing Mixed Numbers

Error in Naming the Denominator

Error Counts together all parts of a model to find the denominator for a mixed number

Reteaching Explain to students that only one part of a mixed number is a fraction. Draw two circles, and divide each into fourths. Remind students that the whole and the fraction together form the mixed number. To find the denominator for the fraction in a mixed number, they should only look at the total parts in one circle, the fraction circle.

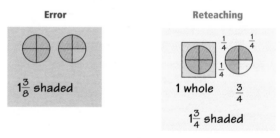

Error

$1\frac{3}{8}$ shaded

Reteaching

$\frac{1}{4}$ $\frac{1}{4}$ $\frac{1}{4}$

1 whole $\frac{3}{4}$

$1\frac{3}{4}$ shaded

Comparing Fractions

Error in Identifying Equivalent Fractions

Error Does not recognize equivalent fractions because they have different denominators

Reteaching Provide students with sheets of paper. Have them fold a sheet in half, open it, and shade $\frac{1}{2}$. Tell them to refold the paper and fold it in half again. When they open it, ask them to name the shaded part, counting the number of shaded sections and the total number of sections. Repeat the steps one or more times.

Error

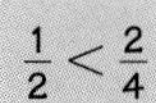

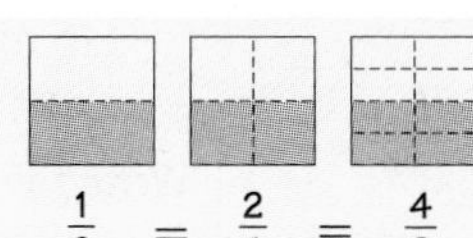

Errors in Comparing and Ordering Fractions

Error Thinks that fractions increase as the denominators increase

Reteaching For students who do not recognize that a fraction decreases as the denominator increases, demonstrate this concept by filling a clear jar $\frac{1}{3}$ full of water. Then, pour out water so the jar is $\frac{1}{4}$ full; then, $\frac{1}{6}$ and $\frac{1}{8}$. Each time write the fraction on the board, and point out that the denominator is greater, but there is a lesser amount of water.

Error

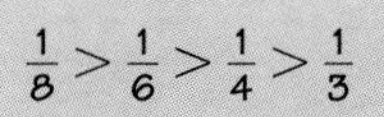

Reteaching

Error Reverses the symbols for greater than (>) and less than (<) when comparing fractions

Reteaching Help students remember that the "open mouth" of the arrow always points to the greater number. Students might try making the shape > with the right hand and < with the left, pretending to be a greedy jaw snapping up food. The written symbols can work the same way. The greedy mouth would want to turn toward $\frac{2}{3}$ of a pie rather than $\frac{1}{3}$.

Error	Reteaching	Reteaching
$\frac{1}{3} > \frac{2}{3}$	$\frac{1}{3}$ (mouth) $\frac{2}{3}$	$\frac{2}{3}$ (mouth) $\frac{1}{3}$

Error Compares the unshaded part of one figure to the shaded part of another

Reteaching Remind students that it is important to define the part of interest before naming a fraction. Before comparing two figures, have students name and write the shaded part of each figure.

Error

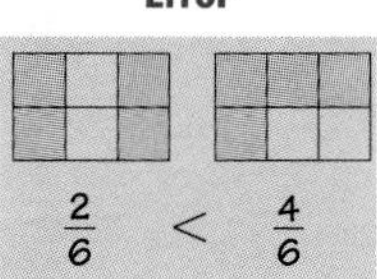

Reteaching

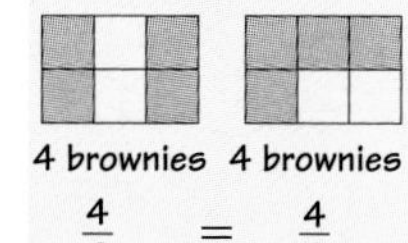

Adding and Subtracting Fractions

Error in adding or subtracting denominators

Error Adds the denominators when giving the sum

Reteaching Use fraction models of fourths. Show students $\frac{2}{4}$ and $\frac{1}{4}$. Combine the models to show $\frac{3}{4}$ and ask students to count what they see. Lead them in counting $\frac{1}{4}, \frac{2}{4}, \frac{3}{4}$. Point out that when you add or subtract same-sized pieces, the size of each piece does not change, only the number of pieces changes.

CHAPTER 8

Cumulative Review

Two Ways to Use the Cumulative Review

Maintenance For those students whose results on the current Chapter Test show a good grasp of skills and concepts, you may wish to assign the Cumulative Review as homework. Students may also benefit from the specific review and practice opportunities listed in the Skills Maintenance chart.

Reassessment For those students whose results on the current Chapter Test show only a limited grasp of skills and concepts, you may wish to assign the Cumulative Review as class work. If it then appears that reassessment is needed, the Skills Reteaching chart on the opposite page identifies remedial minilessons in the Teacher's Resource Package.

Additional Assessment Resources

Test, Practice, Management Program

Use the *Test, Practice, Management Program* to create, administer, and score tests as well as generate practice sets. Questions are correlated to the Lesson Objectives.

Cumulative Review

Rounding (Chapter 2)
Round 57 to the nearest ten, and 219 to the nearest hundred.

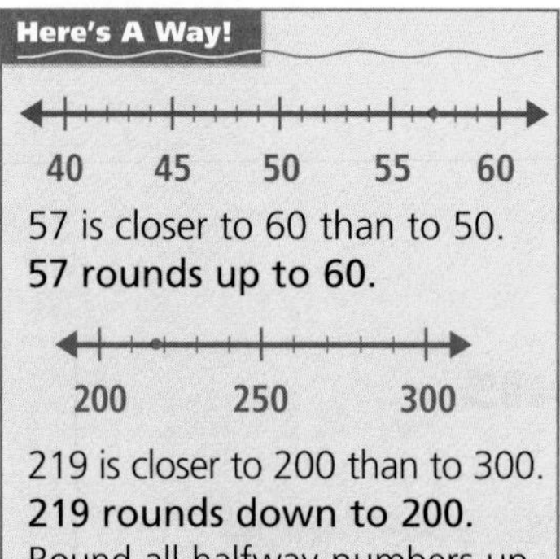

Here's A Way!
40 45 50 55 60
57 is closer to 60 than to 50.
57 rounds up to 60.
200 250 300
219 is closer to 200 than to 300.
219 rounds down to 200.
Round all halfway numbers up.

Round to the nearest ten.

1. 94 90
2. 68 70
3. 25 30

Round to the nearest hundred.

4. 327 300
5. 188 200
6. 854 900
7. Explain how you would round 84 to the nearest ten. Answers will vary. Possible answer: 84 is closer to 80 than to 90, so 84 rounds down to 80.

Subtracting (Chapter 3)
Subtract 28 from 62.

Here's A Way!

$$\begin{array}{r} \overset{5\,12}{\cancel{6}\cancel{2}} \\ -\ 28 \\ \hline 34 \end{array}$$

8 > 2, so regroup 1 ten as 10 ones.
Subtract the ones.
Subtract the tens.

Find the difference.

8. 55 − 17 = 38
9. 21 − 12 = 9
10. 43 − 29 = 14
11. 64 − 9 = 55
12. 85 − 36 = 49
13. 76 − 18 = 58
14. How do you know when you need to regroup the tens? You regroup when there are not enough ones to subtract from.

Multiply by 2 (Chapter 5)
Find 2 × 4.

Here's A Way!

You can use skip-counting.
Skip-count by 4's two times.
Say: **4, 8.**
Write: **2 × 4 = 8.**

Write the product.

15. 2 × 1 2
16. 2 × 2 4
17. 2 × 3 6
18. 2 × 5 10
19. 2 × 6 12
20. 2 × 7 14
21. Draw a picture to show 2 × 8. Answers will vary.

298

Skills Maintenance

Chapter Objectives	Where taught in pupil book	More practice in pupil book
• To round whole numbers to the nearest 10 and 100 (2C)	**Chapter 2**, pp. 58–59	None
• To subtract 2- and 3-digit numbers with regrouping (3C)	**Chapter 3**, pp. 102–103	More Practice Set, 3.8, p. 450
• To use basic multiplication facts to multiply by 1 through 5 (5B)	**Chapter 5**, pp. 160–161	More Practice Set, 5.2, p. 454
• To use properties and rules to complete a multiplication table (6D)	**Chapter 6**, pp. 196–197	None
• To use slides, flips, and half turns to move figures (7A)	**Chapter 7**, pp. 230–231	None

Multiplication Patterns (Chapter 6)
Multiply 3 by 6.

Here's A Way!

×	1	2	3	4	5	6	7	8	9	10
1										
2										
3	3	6	9	12	15	18				

Copy the table. Then, follow the directions.

22. Complete the last row. 21, 24, 27, 30
23. Fill in the first row. What property of multiplication could you use?
property of one
24. Fill in the middle row. What skip-counting pattern could you use?
2, 4, 6, 8, 10, 12, 14, 16, 18, 20; count by two's.

Slides and Flips (Chapter 7)
Which pattern shows a slide?
Which pattern shows a flip?

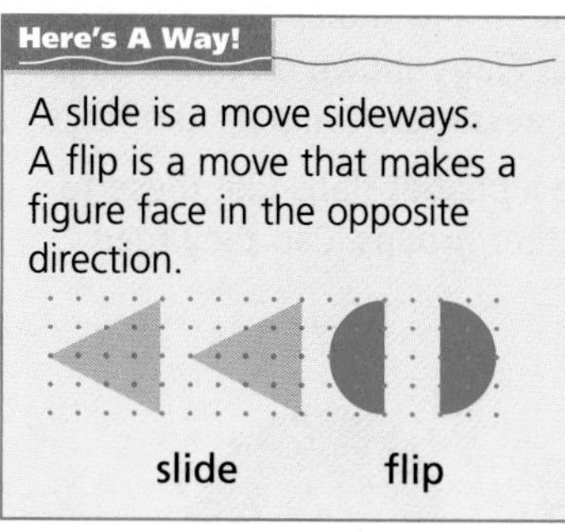

Here's A Way!
A slide is a move sideways.
A flip is a move that makes a figure face in the opposite direction.
slide
flip

Tell if the pattern shows a slide or a flip.

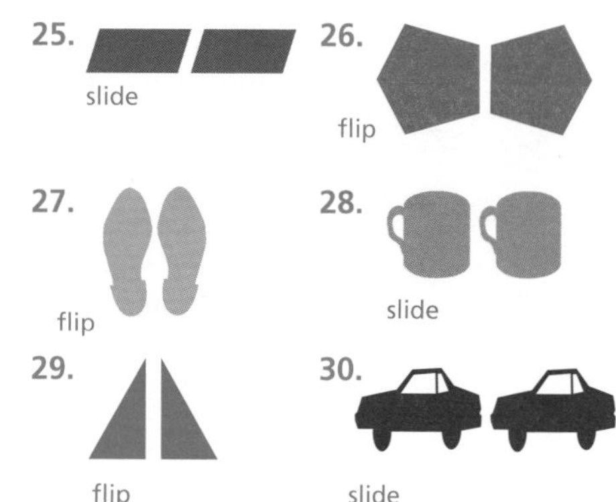

Problem Solving

✓ Understand
✓ Plan
✓ Try It
✓ Look Back

Choose a Strategy You Have Learned
✓ Act It Out
✓ Look for a Pattern
✓ Guess and Check
✓ Draw a Picture
✓ Make a Table
Work Backward
Make a List
Work a Simpler Problem

Use any strategy to help answer the question.

31. Describe the pattern: 8, 12, 16, 20 . . .
Each number is 4 more than the one before it.
32. Suppose you are playing a game at a fair. For every 20 points you score, you earn 3 tickets. How many tickets will you win if you score 160 points?
24 tickets
33. You put toppings on a pizza. You put onions around the outer edge, then a ring of green peppers, then onions, then red peppers. If you can continue the pattern for 5 more rings, what is the last topping you will use? onions

299

Students Acquiring English

Some students may need assistance on the Cumulative Review.

- Be prepared to read directions aloud to students.
- Focus special attention on word problems. Expect to paraphrase, diagram, or draw an explanation of the word problem.
- Review important vocabulary words that have been previously introduced.
- Review titles and other elements of graphs and charts.

Skills Reteaching

Chapter Objectives	Suggested materials for minilessons		
• To round whole numbers to the nearest 10 and 100 (2C)	Reteach 2.8	Practice 2.8	Enrichment 2.8
• To subtract 2- and 3-digit numbers with regrouping (3C)	Reteach 3.8	Practice 3.8	Enrichment 3.8
• To use basic multiplication facts to multiply by 1 through 5 (5B)	Reteach 5.2	Practice 5.2	Enrichment 5.2
• To use properties and rules to complete a multiplication table (6D)	Reteach 6.3	Practice 6.3	Enrichment 6.3
• To use slides, flips, and half turns to move figures (7A)	Reteach 7.2	Practice 7.2	Enrichment 7.2

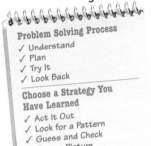

INVESTIGATION

Management small groups
Materials graph paper, markers

Building Background

Discuss the characteristics of the International Alphabet flags. Which flags are divided into two equal parts? What do we call the fraction that represents one part of two equal parts?

Management Strategies Cooperative Learning

Introduce

- Assign students to diverse groups of three to five.
- Review the rules for working in small groups.

Guide

- If students have difficulty, pose a simpler problem for them to solve.
- Leave the group when members can again work independently.

Summarize

- Ask, How did your group check for understanding?
- Challenge students to create a new version of the activity.

INVESTIGATION

Land Ho!

Art Connection **With Your Group**

Keep In Mind . . .
Your work will be evaluated on the following:

- ✓ How you use fractions to make the parts of each flag
- ✓ How you decide the size of the flags
- ✓ How you use fractions to design your own flag
- ✓ How your group shares the work

Did you know that ships at sea often send messages to each other using signal flags? The 26 International Alphabet Flags shown on these pages are used to spell out messages. Compare the flags.

Your group will make alphabet flags like these to send a message to other groups. Can they read your message?

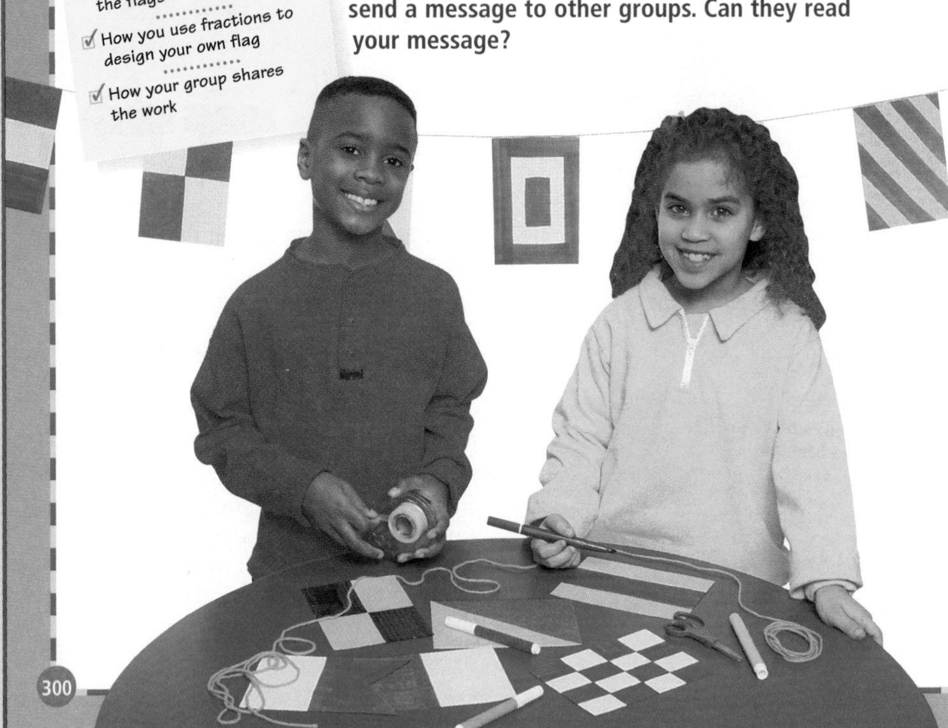

300

Investigation Support

Technology

Internet: Education Place
http://www.eduplace.com
Houghton Mifflin Education Place **Mathematics Center** provides teacher and student support, such as links to other Internet sites.

Math Journal: *Communicating*

Which flag or flags do you think have the most interesting designs?
Students may answer that question by writing a coded message, using the International Alphabet Flags, in their Math Journals.

Portfolio Opportunity

Place coded messages, written by individual students, in their portfolios.

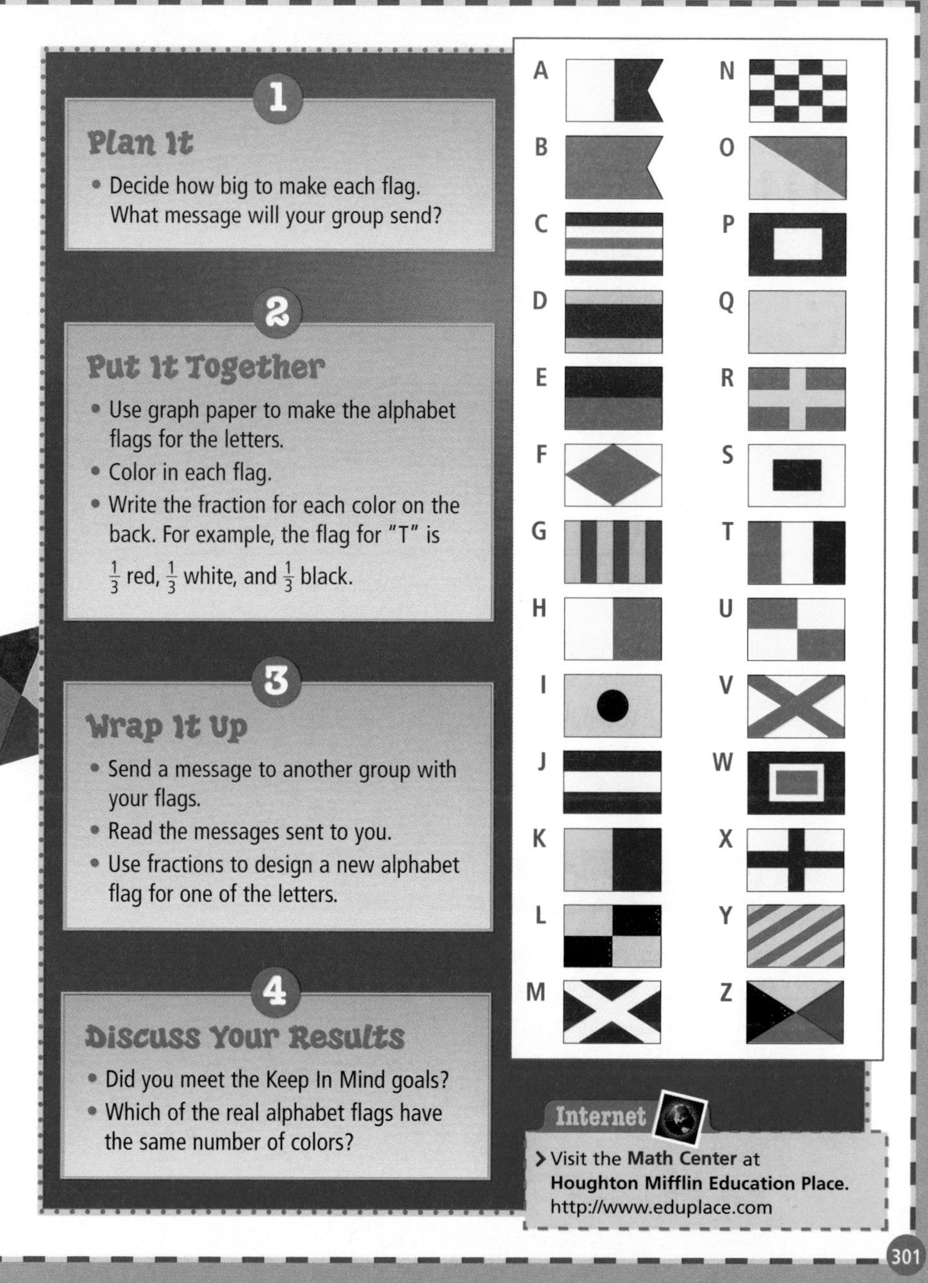

1
Plan It
• Decide how big to make each flag. What message will your group send?
2
Put It Together
• Use graph paper to make the alphabet flags for the letters.
• Color in each flag.
• Write the fraction for each color on the back. For example, the flag for "T" is $\frac{1}{3}$ red, $\frac{1}{3}$ white, and $\frac{1}{3}$ black.
3
Wrap It Up
• Send a message to another group with your flags.
• Read the messages sent to you.
• Use fractions to design a new alphabet flag for one of the letters.
4
Discuss Your Results
• Did you meet the Keep In Mind goals?
• Which of the real alphabet flags have the same number of colors?
A
B
C
D
E
F
G
H
I
J
K
L
M
N
O
P
Q
R
S
T
U
V
W
X
Y
Z
Internet
Visit the Math Center at Houghton Mifflin Education Place. http://www.eduplace.com
301

Problem Solving Tip

Choose a size for the flags that is large enough to make the complex patterns. Practice making the flags for *N* and *Y* to see how large students need their flags to be.

Completing the Investigation

Step 1 Help students decide which flags they need in order to write their messages.

Step 2 Assist them in determining and labeling the fractions for each color on the flags.

Step 3 Assign students to complete their messages and trade with classmates. Students then decode their classmates' messages.

Step 4 Ask students to use fractions to design a new flag for a letter of the alphabet.

Extending the Investigation

Invite students to send a note to a relative or family friend using the International Alphabet Flags as the letters. Enclose the code with the letter. Students can ask the recipient of the letter to respond with a coded reply. Students may bring the replies to class and share.

Assessment Scoring Rubric

These criteria align with *Keep In Mind* in the Pupil Edition on page 300.

Criteria	1 Limited response	2 Acceptable	3 Capable	4 Superior
Accuracy of fractions	Fractions are inaccurate	Some of the fractions are inaccurate	Most of the fractions are accurate	All of the fractions are accurate
Understanding of fractions	Lacks understanding of fractions	Can explain some of the math process	Understands most of the math process	Thoroughly understands the math process
Clarity and completeness of the flags	Design of the flags are unsuccessful	Design of the flags show an attempt to be successful	Design of the flags are mostly successful	Design of the flags are successful
Contribution to the group process	Makes no effort to contribute to the group	Makes some effort to contribute to the group	Contributes to the group most of the time	Contributes fully to the group

Use this 4-level rubric to score students' responses. If you prefer a task with a 6-level rubric, use the Performance Assessment for this chapter.

Measurement and Time

Chapter Overview

Vocabulary

- Introduce students to the chapter with vocabulary minilesson, TAB p. 302J.
- Planning Guide, p. 302C, lists vocabulary for each lesson in the chapter.
- Use the SAE vocabulary support in Lessons 9.1–9.4, 9.6, 9.7, 9.10, and 9.13–9.15.

Rationale

Chapter Pacing: 18 days

- This chapter explores customary and metric units of measure.
- Students develop a sense of size, comparison, and appropriateness of unit by doing a variety of computation and estimation tasks involving measurement.
- The Math World feature presents Arabic numbers and an Egyptian method of measurement.
- In the Investigation, students use their measurement skills to build a model airplane.

See **Daily Lesson Plans**, Chapter Management at a Glance, pp. 86–87; Suggested Weekly Plan, pp. 88–89.

Problem Solving

This chapter emphasizes the Work Backward strategy for problem solving. It also reinforces strategies students learned earlier and encourages them to choose and apply their own strategies.

Assessment

- The Chapter Introduction allows you to assess whether students have a firm grasp of measurement and time.
- Observe students' understanding of measurement as a comparison of an object to an established unit.
- Note students' abilities to choose an appropriate unit of measure.
- Use the Midchapter Review, the Chapter Test, and the Cumulative Review to assess students' needs for reinforcement or reteaching.

Reading Strategies

- Teach the Monitor reading strategy minilesson on TAB p. 302J. Then, use the following as opportunities to reinforce the strategy.
  - Preparing for Tests, TE pp. 302G–302H
  - Problem Solving Workshop, TE p. 327A
  - Problem Solving, Lessons 9.2–9.4, 9.9, and 9.16–9.18
- Use the SAE reading support for Lesson 9.9.

Meeting Individual Needs

Students Acquiring English

Provide extra practice with customary units of measurement.

- Take time to ensure that students know equivalencies for customary units.
- Have pairs estimate and measure using both customary and metric units.
- Help students verbalize what they do as they use strategies to solve problems.

See also **Language Connections** for additional support.

Extra Support

Students may have difficulty comprehending the sizes of various units.

- Help students more directly establish the actual sizes of each unit of measure by having them create their own metric and customary rulers.
- Allow students to handle weights and fill containers to develop a better sense of capacity and weight units.
- Use the Analyzing Errors strategies, pp. 346A–346B.

Challenge

Many students may benefit from this extension activity.

- Have students estimate the perimeter of a classroom object. Then, have them mark their estimate with tape on the floor. Measure the perimeter, and compare the difference in length.

Multi-Age Classroom

The chart below shows the chapters in books for levels 2 and 4 that can be used in conjunction with this chapter.

2	3	4
Chapter 9 *Measurement*	**Chapter 9** *Measurement and Time*	**Chapter 10** *Measurement and Time*

See **Daily Lesson Plans**, Multi-Age Classroom Concept and Skill Development, pp. 4–5.

Chapter Bibliography

Key

Multicultural	★	*Social Studies*	
Science/Health		*Music*	
Literature		*Art*	

Technology

Students can explore geometry with the electronic tools in *Unlocking Geometry 3–6*. The manipulatives provide an enjoyable, flexible environment in which to experiment.

Internet: Education Place
http://www.eduplace.com

Visit the **Mathematics Center** in *Houghton Mifflin Education Place* to find activities, projects, games, and links to other valuable Internet sites.

Ultimate Writing & Creativity Center

Students can use the *Ultimate Writing & Creativity Center*® for all their writing and publishing activities. The software is available from The Learning Company® in Macintosh and Windows formats.

Larson's Leapfrog MATH™

Leapfrog Math includes mathematics skills and concepts for grades 3–6. Each grade is contained on a single CD-ROM. The software is available from Meridian Creative Group, a Division of Larson Texts, Inc.

Test, Practice, Management Program

Use the *Test, Practice, Management Program* to create, administer, and score tests as well as generate practice sets. Questions are correlated to Lesson Objectives.

Graphers Sunburst Communications, Inc.®

Using the friendly tools in *Graphers,* children can easily manipulate data that can be counted or sorted and represent their data in a table or with six types of graphs.

Books for Students

Houghton Mifflin Mathematics Bookshelf

Dragonfly's Tale
Kristina Rodanas,
Clarion Books, 1991.
This story, based on Zuñi legend, explores length, capacity, time, and symmetry.

Anno's Sundial
Mitsumasa Anno,
Philomel Books, 1987.
The earth's movement around the sun results in a movement of shadows that may be used to tell time. Also includes pop-up sundials and instructions of how to make and use them.

Time
Henry Pluckrose,
Children's Press, 1995.
Photographs illustrate the exploration of units of time measurement from seconds to years.

Nine O'Clock Lullaby
Marilyn Singer,
HarperCollins Publishers, 1991.
Readers discover that when it is 9:00 A.M. in New York, people around the world are performing daily tasks that relate to different times of the day.

How Big Is a Foot?
Rolf Myller,
Dell Publishing, 1991.
Children describe the importance of units of measure as they read about a king having trouble determining the size of a bed to buy.

How Big Am I?
Shirley Greenway,
Hambleton-Hill Publishing, 1993.
Readers will see a real-life application of measurement as they learn about size, height, and weight of animals around the world.

Books for Families

The Biggest Fish
Sheila Keenan,
Scholastic, 1996.
Parents and children can discuss mathematics topics while reading this story-centered introduction to nonstandard measurement. The concepts in the book will help prepare children for customary measurement and comparison.

The Time Book
John Cassidy,
Klutz Press, 1991.
A colorful quartz watch is attached to the front of this book, which can be used to answer the questions inside. Parents can help children with such time concepts as estimating, using the minute hand, and telling time to five-minute intervals.

Take Me to Your Liter: Science and Math Jokes
Charles Keller,
Pippin Press, 1991.
Families will get a laugh from these jokes and riddles about science and mathematics, for example, "What does a hungry math teacher like to eat? (a square meal)."

Reference Books for Teachers

Let's Talk Math: Encouraging Children to Explore Ideas
Pat Lilburn and Pam Rawson,
Heinemann, 1994.
This book shows how to encourage students to use everyday language to explore ideas, discuss processes, and describe mathematics experiences. Group activities allow students to communicate in areas related to numbers, space, and measurement.

Mathematics Illustrated Dictionary: Facts, Figures, and People
Jeanne Bendick,
Franklin Watts, 1989.
Teachers can use this dictionary of mathematics terms and concepts to combine study skills with measurement and other areas of math.

Measuring Up! Experiments, Puzzles, and Games Exploring Measurement
Sandra Markle,
Aladdin Paperbacks, 1995.
Students will enjoy these brainteasers and activities that involve measuring distances, size, weight, quantity, and temperature.

Planning Guide

		TE Pages	Lesson Objectives	Lesson Vocabulary	NCTM Standards
9.1	Inch	304–305	To explore measuring to the nearest inch; to estimate length	inch (in) customary system	Whole Number Concepts, Measurement, Estimation, Communication, Connections
9.2	Inch and Half Inch	306–307	To measure to the nearest inch and half inch; to estimate length		Fractions and Decimals, Measurement, Communication, Connections, Estimation
9.3	Perimeter	308–309	To find the perimeters of polygons using standard units (inches and half inches)	perimeter	Whole Number Computation, Fractions and Decimals, Reasoning, Measurement, Estimation
9.4	Foot, Yard, and Mile	310–311	To investigate using foot, yard, and mile to compare lengths; to choose the appropriate linear unit	mile (mi)	Fractions and Decimals, Measurement, Reasoning, Estimation, Patterns and Functions
9.5	Cup, Pint, Quart, and Gallon	312–313	To investigate using cup, pint, quart, and gallon; to rename one customary unit; to estimate capacity	capacity	Measurement, Communication, Connections, Reasoning, Whole Number Computation
9.6	Ounce and Pound	314	To use ounce and pound; to choose the appropriate unit and estimate weight	ounce (oz) pound (lb)	Measurement, Estimation, Reasoning, Connections, Patterns and Functions
9.7	Centimeter	318–319	To measure to the nearest centimeter; to estimate length	decimeter (dm) metric system	Whole Number Concepts, Measurement, Reasoning, Estimation, Patterns and Functions
9.8	Meter and Kilometer	320–321	To investigate using meter and kilometer; to choose the appropriate unit	kilometer (km) meter (m)	Measurement, Estimation, Reasoning, Connections, Communication
9.9	Work Backward	322–323	To use the Work Backward strategy to solve problems		Problem Solving, Communication, Reasoning, Connections, Measurement
9.10	Milliliter and Liter	324–325	To investigate using milliliter and liter to compare and estimate capacities	liter (L) milliliter (mL)	Measurement, Reasoning, Connections, Communication, Problem Solving
9.11	Gram and Kilogram	326	To use gram and kilogram; to choose the appropriate unit of mass; to estimate	gram (g) kilogram (kg)	Whole Number Concepts, Measurement, Estimation, Reasoning, Connections
9.12	Is the Answer Reasonable?	327	To decide and to justify why an answer is reasonable when solving problems		Problem Solving, Communication, Reasoning, Connections, Measurement
9.13	Heavier or Lighter?	328–329	To determine if equal amounts of different materials are equally heavy		Whole Number Concepts, Measurement, Estimation, Reasoning, Communication, Connections
9.14	Measuring Temperature	330–331	To investigate reading Fahrenheit and Celsius thermometers; to choose appropriate temperature	Celsius Fahrenheit temperature	Connections, Reasoning, Measurement, Geometry and Spatial Sense, Fractions and Decimals
9.15	Time	332–333	To use second, minute, hour, and day; to read and write time to the minute	second (s)	Measurement, Estimation, Reasoning, Connections, Communication, Patterns and Functions
9.16	Elapsed Time	334–335	To find elapsed time		Whole Number Concepts, Measurement, Estimation, Reasoning, Connections, Problem Solving
9.17	Using Work Backward and Other Strategies	336–337	To use Work Backward and other strategies to solve problems		Problem Solving, Communication, Reasoning, Connections, Measurement
9.18	Using Strategies	338–339	To use different strategies to solve problems		Problem Solving, Communication, Reasoning, Connections, Whole Number Concepts, Measurement

Chapter Objectives

9A To estimate and measure length using both customary and metric units
9B To find the perimeter of a polygon
9C To estimate and measure capacity, weight, and mass
9D To find simple equivalences for customary and metric units
9E To read Fahrenheit and Celsius thermometers
9F To write time to the minute
9G To use elapsed time to solve problems
9H To use Work Backward and other strategies to solve problems

Chapter Objectives	math center	State Requirements
9A	• *Treasure Hunt*, How-To Card 30; Fraction Card Deck	
9A	• *Measure Up!*, Activity Card 48	
9B	• *Geo-Areas*, Activity Card 49	
9A, 9D	• *What to Measure?*, Activity Card 50	
9C, 9D	• *Fill It Up*, Activity Card 51	
9C	• *Race A-Weigh*, How-To Card 31; Gameboard 2	
9A	• *Ant Kingdom*, How-To Card 32; Fraction Card Deck	
9A	• *String Along*, Activity Card 52	
9H	• *Construction Site*, Project Card 9	
9C	• *More or Less?*, Activity Card 53; Workmat 2	
9C	• *Race A-Weigh*, How-To Card 31; Gameboard 2	
9H	• *Construction Site*, Project Card 9	
9C	• *Weight Detective*, Activity Card 54	
9E	• *Reach the Boiling Point*, How-To Card 33; Workmat 4	
9F	• *Have You Got the Time?*, How-To Card 34; Number Card Deck	
9G	• *Time After Time*, Activity Card 55	
9H	• *Construction Site*, Project Card 9	
9H	• *Construction Site*, Project Card 9	

Integrating Reading Strategies

- Teach/review the Monitor strategy using TAB p. 302J.
- Encourage students to practice the strategy in Lessons 9.2–9.4, 9.9, and 9.16–9.18.

Technology

Unlocking Measurement 3–6

Internet: Education Place
http://www.eduplace.com
Houghton Mifflin Education Place
Mathematics Center

Test, Practice, Management Program

Special Lessons

pp. 302–303

Chapter Introduction

The Introduction shows students how often they use measurement.

pp. 338–339

Students apply problem solving strategies in the context of basketball.

pp. 316–317

Math World
Measurement and Time Around the World

Use this feature to show students how measurement and time are used all over the world.

pp. 344–345

Investigation
Up and Away!

Students build an airplane, fly it, and measure the distance it flies.

Assessment

Use the following assessment tools to help assess individual needs.

- Midchapter Review, p. 315
- Chapter Test, pp. 340–341
- Cumulative Review, pp. 342–343

Chapter 9

Perimeter Workshop

Practice Making Measurements

Alternate Approach

Use with page 308. **40 minutes**

Exploring Perimeter

Objective To explore the perimeters of concrete models using nonstandard measurement

Management teacher monitored; small groups
Materials masking tape
Advance Preparation Use masking tape to lay out rectangles of various sizes on the floor—one per team of students. Identify each rectangle with a letter.
Modality *visual/kinesthetic*

Activity

- Remind students that *perimeter* is the distance around an object.
- Have student groups measure the perimeter of each of the rectangles using one student's foot or shoe length as a unit of measure. Students take turns choosing the unit of measure.
- After all groups measure each of the rectangles, compare their measurements.

A B

	Group 1	Group 2
A	16 Lengths	20 Lengths
B	14 Lengths	18 Lengths

- Discuss why there may be variations from group to group, guiding students to recognize the need for a standard unit of measure.

Meeting Individual Needs: *Modify*

Challenge After students have measured three rectangles, ask them to estimate the perimeter of the last. They can measure to check their estimate.

Challenge

Use with page 308. **20 minutes**

Calculating Perimeter

Objectives To measure to the nearest half inch; to use a calculator to find the perimeters of rectangles

Management teacher directed; pairs
Materials for each pair: ruler or tape measure and rectangular objects, TI-108 calculator
Advance Preparation Collect small rectangular objects with sides that can easily be measured to the nearest half inch.
Modality *visual/kinesthetic*

Activity

- Discuss measurement to the nearest half inch, demonstrating on one of the collected objects.
- Show students how to input a measurement on a calculator that includes a fractional part equal to $\frac{1}{2}$. Then, demonstrate how to add mixed numbers with halves in one or both of the numbers.

keystrokes	display
ON/AC	0
4 Unit 1 / 2 +	4 ᴗ 1/2
2 Unit 1 / 2 =	6 ᴗ 2/2
Ab/c	7

- Have student pairs measure the perimeters of two or three objects to the nearest half inch, using their calculators to add the dimensions. For more practice **Using the Calculator,** see pp. T88– T90.

Meeting Individual Needs: *Modify*

Challenge Ask why the perimeter of a rectangle measured to the nearest half inch will always be a whole number. Since opposite sides are the same length, and $\frac{1}{2} + \frac{1}{2} = 1$

Game

Use with page 326.

40 minutes

Mass Guesstimation

Objective To estimate mass in grams

Management teacher monitored; small groups
Materials balance; 10 g, 25 g, 50 g, 100 g weights
Modality *kinesthetic*

Activity

- Tell students that the object of the game is to accurately estimate the masses of four objects in the classroom.
- On the board, make a chart similar to the one below.
- Place one new pencil on the balance and tell the class the mass of the pencil. This will give them a reference point.
- Invite teams of students to try to find objects in the room that will match the masses you have written on the chart.
- When they decide on an object, ask them to bring it to you and state the target mass they think it will match.
- Help students weigh their object(s) and record the difference between the actual mass and the target mass on the chart next to the team name.
- After all the teams have had a chance to match each mass on the chart, have them add the differences between their actual masses and the target masses. The team with the lowest total is the winner.

Team A

Target Mass	Item	Actual Weight	Difference
10 g	ruler	12 g	2 g
25 g			
50 g			
100 g			

Meeting Individual Needs: *Modify*

Students Acquiring English This is a complex game. Be sure that the goal is clear and that the terms *mass*, *target*, and *difference* are understood.

Challenge Try the game another time using a wider variety of target masses.

Technology

Use with Lesson 9.2

Objective To measure to the nearest half inch

Management teacher monitored; pairs
Materials *MathKeys*: *Unlocking Measurement 3–6*, Lev. 3, Act. 13: Half Lengths
Modality *visual*

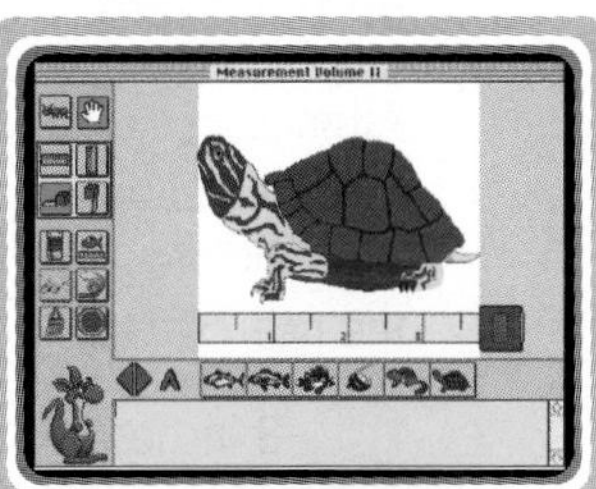

Activity

30 minutes

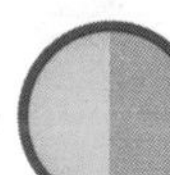

- Review the ruler markings that indicate $\frac{1}{2}$ inch. Ask, If you are measuring an object that is $2\frac{1}{2}$ inches tall, what two whole numbers are on either side of that half-inch mark? 2 and 3 Using examples of objects around the room, clarify the dimensions *length*, *height*, and *width*.
- Distribute copies of the Activity 13 master. Ask students to open *MathKeys* and to open the Length Measure Mat. They should click on the Unit of Measure button and select "half inches" from the Standard Units column.
- Students will search through palettes of objects to find those objects whose measurements round to dimensions given on the worksheet.
- Point out that students can measure with either a tape measure or a ruler. They can highlight the measured area by clicking on the Highlight Zone button.
- When students complete their worksheets, invite volunteers to write the object they found for each target measurement on the board. Discuss whether measuring with quarter inches might make the task easier or harder, and why. Using smaller units can provide greater accuracy.

Meeting Individual Needs: *Modify*

Challenge Students can measure their listed items more exactly, by using the mat's quarter-inch or eighth-inch rulers.

Chapter 9

Preparing for Tests

To develop students' test-taking strategies, model the following types of assessment items found in this program.

Standardized Tests

Write the following problem on the board.

Estimate the width of your math textbook. What is the approximate width, given to the nearest inch?

Ⓐ 8 inches correct

Ⓑ 6 inches

Ⓒ $12\frac{1}{2}$ inches

Ⓓ 21 inches

See also Standardized Testing: New Formats, **Chapter 9.**

Standardized tests usually require that students select the correct answer from a group of possible answers. In this problem, students must use their experience to estimate the width of their math textbooks.

Strategy

- What will you do if you can't estimate by looking at the book? Possible answer: look at or picture similar objects and compare whether the book width is longer or shorter
- How can you make it easier to find the correct answer choice? cross out unreasonable answer choices

Open-Ended Questions

Write the following problem on the board.

You are building a doghouse. To make the sides, you need two pieces of wood. Each piece must be 3 ft long and 3 ft wide. If you have a piece of wood 6 ft by 4 ft, do you need more or less wood to make the two sides? less

See also Assessments, **Chapter 9.**

Open-ended questions can be answered in more than one way; they allow students to use a variety of concepts and processes. This problem allows students to use various strategies to solve a problem.

Strategy

- What are you asked to do? tell whether you need more or less wood for 2 sides of the doghouse
- How could you find out? Possible answer: draw a diagram
- How many 3 ft × 3 ft pieces are needed? 2
- Can you get two 3 ft × 3 ft pieces from the sheet that is 6 feet long and 4 feet wide? yes

Preparing for Tests

Reading Strategies for Test-Taking

Monitor: As I read, I check that what I am reading makes sense to me and try to visualize the situation.

Performance Tasks

Write the following problem and related bus schedule on the board.

You are going on an expedition to dig for ancient artifacts. The ride from your hotel to the Dig Site is $1\frac{1}{2}$ hours. You want to get to the dig by 10:00 A.M. What is the latest bus you can take and still arrive by 10:00 A.M.? Write a question about scheduling your return ride.

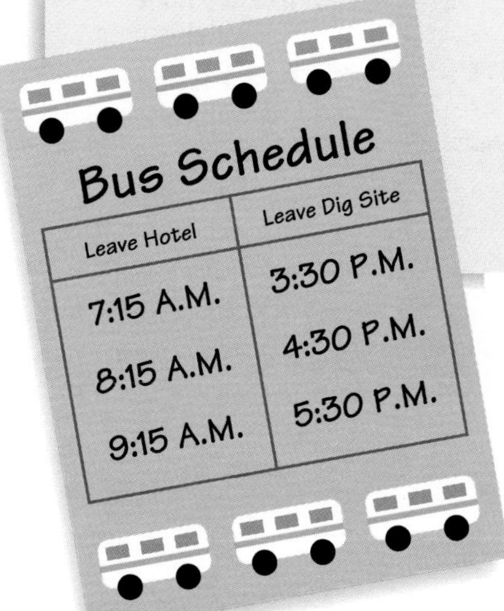

Bus Schedule

Leave Hotel	Leave Dig Site
7:15 A.M.	3:30 P.M.
8:15 A.M.	4:30 P.M.
9:15 A.M.	5:30 P.M.

See also Performance Assessments, Chapter 9.

Performance assessments engage students in meaningful tasks that permit the teacher to observe their working procedures as well as the results they obtain. This problem requires students to interpret information from a schedule to solve a problem and write a new problem.

Strategy

- What does the problem ask you to do?
  tell which is the latest bus that would get me to the Dig Site by 10:00 A.M.
- What could you do to find out?
  Possible answer: try subtracting or draw a clock face and count backward
- What are all the possible buses leaving from the hotel and arriving by 10:00 A.M.?
  7:15, 8:15
- Which is the latest time?
  8:15
- How would you figure what time you would have to leave the Dig Site in order to get back to the hotel at a certain time?
  Possible answer: use addition or draw a clock face and count forward

You can check to see that students correctly interpret information from the schedule, and use it to solve the problem and create a new problem.

Test-Taking Tips

- If you have trouble finding the answer, cross off the answer choices you know are not correct.

Additional Assessment Resources

Test, Practice, Management Program

Use the *Test, Practice, Management Program* to create, administer, and score tests as well as generate practice sets. Questions are correlated to the Lesson Objectives.

Math Center

To meet individual needs, use the following resources from the Math Center. You may first wish to model activities for the whole class in order to demonstrate the rules for games and introduce procedures for independent tasks.

Gameboards

Gameboard 2
Use with Lessons 9.6 and 9.11.

Activity Cards

48 ***Measure Up!*** Use with Lesson 9.2.

49 ***Geo-Areas*** Use with Lesson 9.3.

50 ***What to Measure?*** Use with Lesson 9.4.

51 ***Fill It Up*** Use with Lesson 9.5.

52 ***String Along*** Use with Lesson 9.8.

53 ***More or Less?*** Use with Lesson 9.10.

54 ***Weight Detective*** Use with Lesson 9.13.

55 ***Time After Time*** Use with Lesson 9.16.

Project Card

9 ***Construction Site*** Use with Lessons 9.9, 9.12, 9.17, and 9.18.

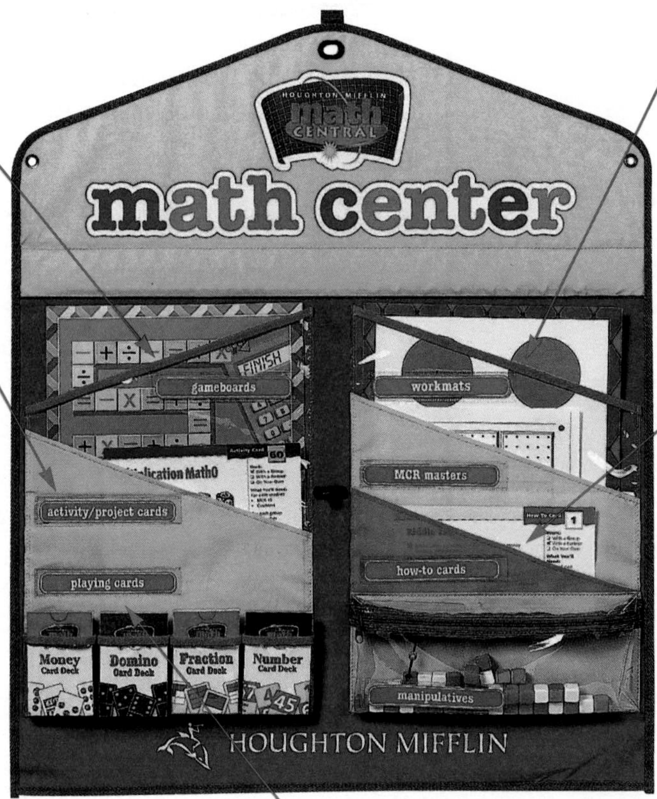

Workmats

Workmat 2
Use with Lesson 9.10.

Workmat 4
Use with Lesson 9.14.

How-To Cards

30 ***Treasure Hunt*** Use with Lesson 9.1.

31 ***Race A-Weigh*** Use with Lessons 9.6 and 9.11.

32 ***Ant Kingdom*** Use with Lesson 9.7.

33 ***Reach the Boiling Point*** Use with Lesson 9.14.

34 ***Have You Got the Time?*** Use with Lesson 9.15.

Card Decks

Fraction Card Deck
Use with Lessons 9.1 and 9.7.

Number Card Deck
Use with Lesson 9.15.

Managing the Math Center

The value of groups Directing students to work in small groups promotes active learning. While working in the Math Center, students should feel free to ask questions, discuss ideas, and make mistakes. They learn to listen to each other and are exposed to different abilities and cultural backgrounds. The entire problem solving process lies open for discussion, and new ideas are often generated.

Vocabulary and Reading Strategies

Use these minilessons to strengthen vocabulary and reading skills.

Vocabulary

- centimeter (cm)
- meter (m)
- decimeter (dm)
- metric system
- kilometer (km)

Linking Prior Knowledge and Vocabulary

Explain that the **meter** is the basic unit of length in the Metric System. Have students note that the word *meter* appears in the units **centimeter, decimeter,** and **kilometer**. The prefixes *cent-, deci-,* and *kilo-* tell how these units relate to a meter.

Use a meter stick to show that a centimeter is $\frac{1}{10}$ of a decimeter and $\frac{1}{100}$ of a meter. A decimeter is $\frac{1}{10}$ of a meter. Explain that 1000 meters make a kilometer.

Graphic Organizer: Chart

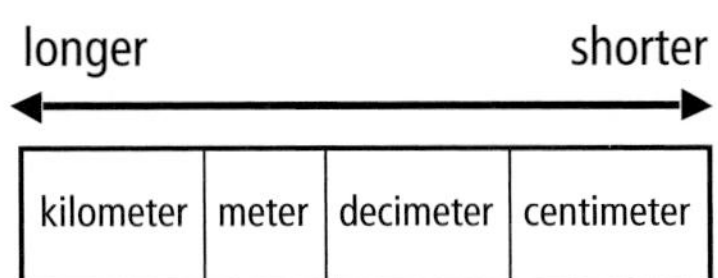

10 cm = 1 dm
10 dm = 1 m
100 cm = 1 m
1000 m = 1 km

Reading Strategies

Strategy: Monitor

Have students read the problem. Explain that using the Monitor strategy here can help them understand how to solve the problem. Suggest that the Monitor strategy can aid their understanding as they work through Math World, the Investigation, and word problems throughout the chapter.

Use the Thinking Aloud box and the graphic organizer to demonstrate how students can use the Monitor reading strategy with the following example.

> Suppose you have a strip of paper. You cut it in half. Then you cut off 6 in. You are left with 8 in. How long was the strip when you started?

Lesson 9.9, p. 323, Problem 1

Model by thinking aloud how to begin solving the problem.

Thinking Aloud

- I reread the problem to see what I know.
- I see that a strip of paper has been cut in half. Then another 6 in. is cut off. There is 8 in. of the strip left.
- I need to find out how long the strip of paper was.
- Since I know what is left, I can work backward.

Graphic Organizer: Diagram

If half the strip was 8 + 6 or 14 in, then the whole strip was 14 + 14 or 28 in.

If a student has solved the problem another way, have him or her explain it to the class.

The reading strategies presented on this page can also apply to Lessons 9.2, 9.3, 9.4, 9.9, 9.16, 9.17, and 9.18.

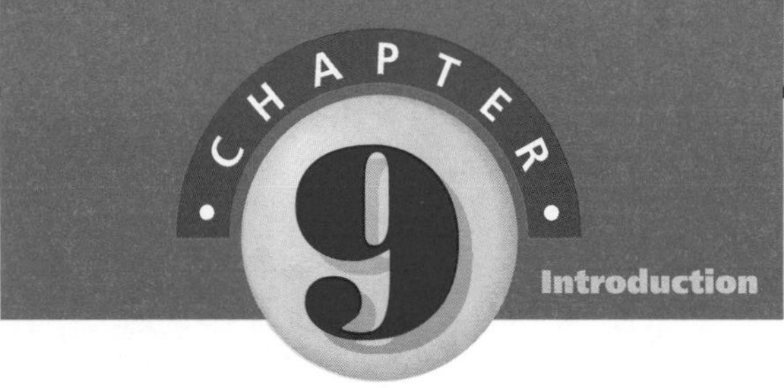

Objective

To use prior knowledge to explore measurement and time

Lesson Planning

Optional Resources

- Math Language Connections
- MATHKEYS *Unlocking Measurement 3–6*

Every Day Counts Calendar Math

Measurement and Time

To actively involve students in measurement and time activities, use the Every Day Clock and Measurement activities from Every Day Counts Calendar Math, level 3.

Assessing Prior Knowledge

Try This! Use this as a prechapter activity in the classroom, or as a homework assignment.

Build confidence with this creative writing activity in which children make an eight-page booklet to show ways they use measurement.

This activity

- assesses prior knowledge of measurement
- provides a foundation for solving problems with length, weight, volume, temperature, and time

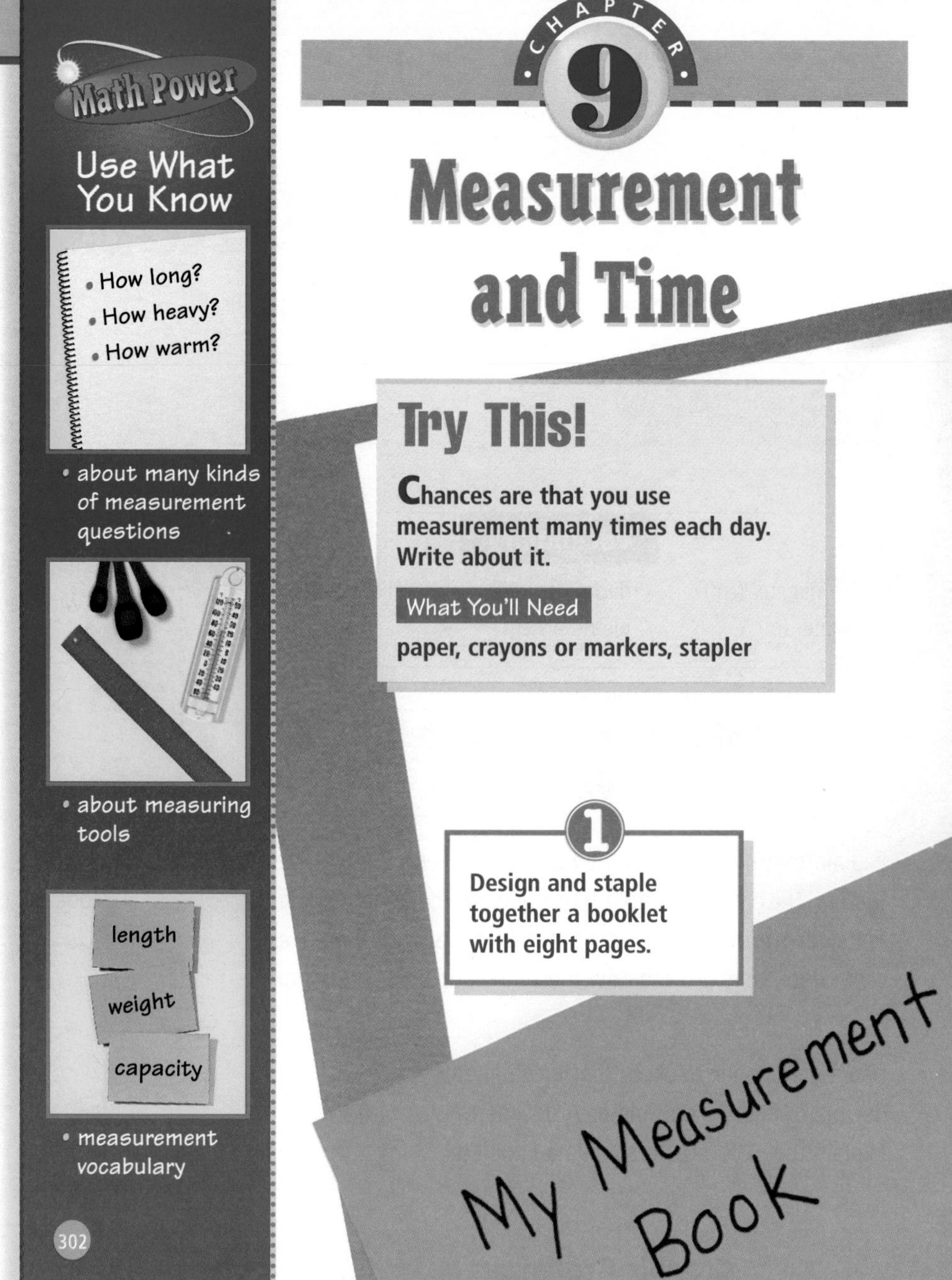

Math Power
Use What You Know
• How long?
• How heavy?
• How warm?
• about many kinds of measurement questions
• about measuring tools
length
weight
capacity
• measurement vocabulary
302
CHAPTER 9
Measurement and Time
Try This!
Chances are that you use measurement many times each day. Write about it.
What You'll Need
paper, crayons or markers, stapler
1
Design and staple together a booklet with eight pages.
My Measurement Book

Chapter Connections

Math Links

Throughout this chapter, students will build on prior knowledge as they develop concepts and skills for solving problems involving measurement and time.

- **Number Sense** Lessons 9.1, 9.3, 9.4, 9.5, 9.10, 9.11, 9.13
- **Rounding** Lesson 9.2
- **Patterns and Relationships** Lessons 9.9, 9.14, 9.15, 9.16, 9.18
- **Estimation** Lessons 9.1, 9.5, 9.8
- **Geometry** Lessons 9.3, 9.18
- **Algebraic Reasoning** Lessons 9.3, 9.4, 9.5, 9.7, 9.8, 9.13

Real *World*

Science

- **Lesson 9.7, p. 318**
  Measuring Plant Growth Students find the approximate growth in centimeters.
- **Lesson 9.13, p. 328**
  Density By comparing relative weight, students explore the concept of density.
- **Lesson 9.14, p. 330**
  Temperature Students learn to read both Fahrenheit and Celsius thermometers.

Art

- **Lesson 9.2, p. 306**
  Decorating with Ribbon By planning the design of a thank-you card, students learn the importance of accurate measurement.

Show different ways of using measurement on six pages.
I use my watch to tell how long it takes to walk to school.
Show ways of measuring time on two pages of your booklet.
Show the booklet to others. Do they measure things in the same way?
How many different kinds of measurement have you shown?
Ready to Go!
303

Meeting Individual Needs

If students have trouble using measurement vocabulary or measuring to the nearest whole unit, start with Quick Help. They may also need a brief teacher-guided review.

Quick Help Explain that in this activity students will use what they already know. Provide number lines showing whole numbers and model how to place marks to indicate half-units between the numbers on the line.

Guided Review Refer to:

- **Lesson 8.6** Estimating Fractions, Student book, p. 284
- **Estimating Fractions** Practice Worksheet 8.6
- **Basic Facts** Review Basic Facts, TE p. 315A

Vocabulary Power

Use a graphic organizer to review vocabulary used in measurement.

What are all the things you can measure about a rocket?

Measurement Vocabulary	Definition
Length	how long it is or how far it travels
Volume	how much it holds
Weight	how heavy it is
Temperature	how hot (or cold) it is
Time	how long it takes to complete its trip

Vocabulary Students can look up the words *meter*, *gram*, and *liter* in the dictionary to find their meanings.

Investigation Preview

Up and Away!

Students will build, fly, and measure the flight length of a paper and straw airplane. Students will also experiment with variations in construction that affect the length of the flight. See the Investigation, TE pp. 344–345.

What They'll Do

- Follow directions to measure and cut materials for a paper and straw airplane.
- Measure and record results of test flights.
- Experiment with various constructions.
- Compare results with their classmates.

Technology

Students can use the tools in *Unlocking Measurement 3–6* to help them show different ways to use measurement. With the Length Measure Mat, students can measure a variety of objects using standard or nonstandard units. The Angles Measure Mat can be used to measure angles. The Shape Measure Mat allows students to create and measure polygons or circles. Students can print out any *MathKeys* screen.

Activity

Planning at a Glance

Objectives To explore measuring to the nearest inch; to estimate length

Materials paper clips, ruler (TR34)

Optional Resources

- Reteach 9.1; Practice 9.1; Enrichment 9.1
- Daily Cumul. Review, p. 112
- Math Center: How-To Card 30
- Every Day Counts
- **TAB**, TE pp. 302E–302F, 302J
- **Problem of the Day**, 112, p. 56; Flip Chart p. 56b
- MATHKEYS *Unlocking Measurement 3–6* Level 3, Activity 5

Students Acquiring English

To build context for the verb *measure*, demonstrate measuring the length of various objects with a ruler. Invite students to do the same. Reinforce the meaning of *length* and the related adjective *long* by asking students to describe the measurements orally.

Problem of the Day

Find the pattern. Then give the three missing numbers. 22, 18, 9

				1				
			3		3			
		5		6		5		
	7		11		11		7	
9		18		___		___		___

Inch

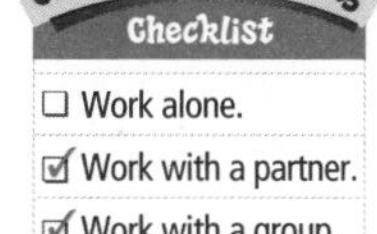

Cooperative Learning
Checklist
☐ Work alone.
☑ Work with a partner.
☑ Work with a group.

Getting Started

What You'll Need:
- paper clips
- ruler

Vocabulary:
- inch (in.)
- customary system
- Glossary, p. 480

Suppose you want to measure something small, like the length of your pencil. You can measure it in inches. How long is one inch?

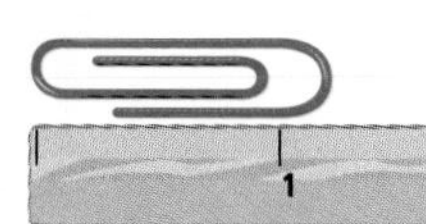

One inch is about the length of a paper clip.

An inch is a unit of length. Inches are part of the customary system of measurement.

Activity

- **Copy the chart.**
- **Try estimating length. Then measure to find the actual length.**

Estimate with Paper Clips

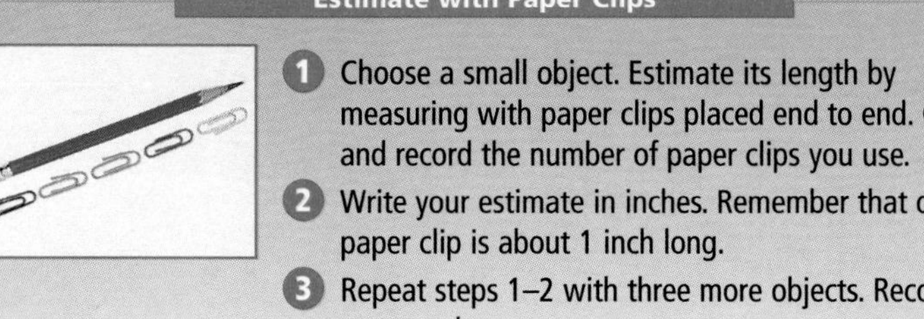

1. Choose a small object. Estimate its length by measuring with paper clips placed end to end. Count and record the number of paper clips you use.
2. Write your estimate in inches. Remember that one paper clip is about 1 inch long.
3. Repeat steps 1–2 with three more objects. Record your results. Answers will vary.

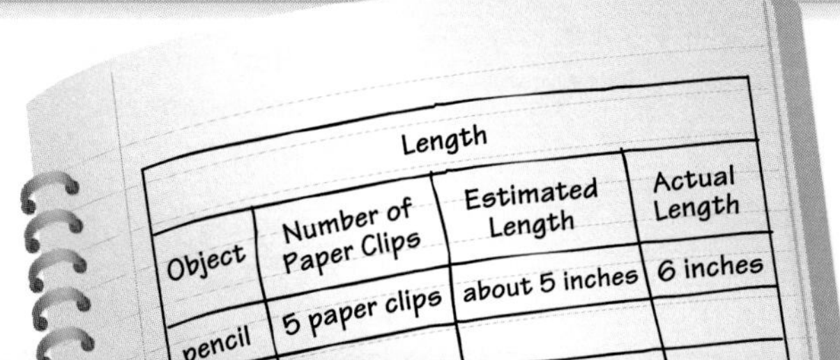

Length			
Object	Number of Paper Clips	Estimated Length	Actual Length
pencil	5 paper clips	about 5 inches	6 inches

304 Chapter 9

1 Introduce

Explore **Have students use their hands to measure their desks. Discuss whether or not the measurements are the same and why.**

Teach: **Activity**

Emphasize these points:

- An inch is a common customary measurement used for small objects.
- The numbers on an inch ruler are the number of inches.
- The abbreviation for *inch* is *in*.

Modeling Model the activity on page 305. Ask:

- Where do I begin measuring an object? at 0
- How can I state the measurement to the nearest inch? round to the closest inch

2 Develop

Show What You Know!

Common Error Some students may not line up their rulers properly before making measurements. Remind them to line up the end of an object with 0. See also Analyzing Errors, TE pp. 341A and 341B.

- Have students discuss their answers to exercise 1. (Some may have measured to the nearest inch, while others may have estimated fractions.)
- Ask students to discuss their strategies for exercise 3.

3 Summarize

- Remind students that they must line up rulers properly in order to measure accurately.
- Review with students how to use a ruler both to read measurements and to draw line segments of specified lengths.

Ongoing Assessment Lila says her book bag is 15 inches long. How can she be sure? Students should suggest measuring the length of the bag with a ruler, beginning by lining up the ruler correctly.

Math Journal: ***Communicating***

How could you measure the distance around a hat or a waste basket? Students should suggest first using a flexible material, such as string or paper, and then measuring the length of the material with a ruler. They may also suggest using a tape measure.

Measure in Inches

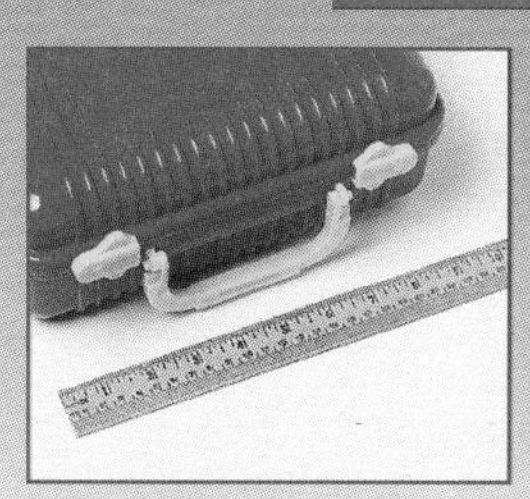

1. Now measure one of your objects with a ruler. Remember to line up the end of the object with the 0 mark on the ruler.
2. Record the number of inches. Compare the actual length to your estimate.
3. Repeat steps 1–2 with the rest of your objects. Record your results. Results will vary.

Show What You Know!

1. **Number Sense** If only half a paper clip fit, how did you write the length? Answers will vary. Possible answer: rounded up or down

Estimate the length of each object in inches. Record your estimate. Then measure the length with a ruler. Estimates will vary.

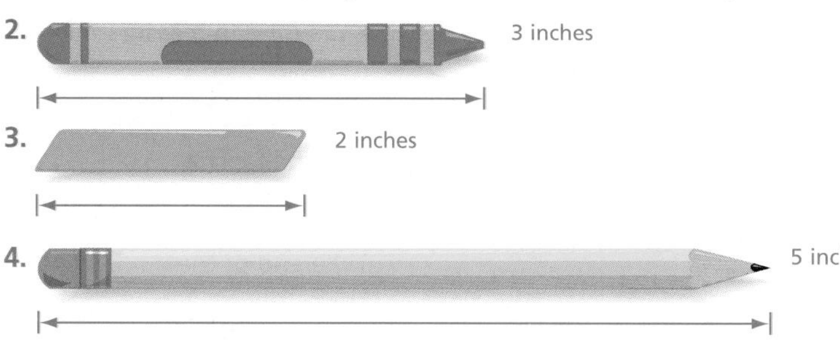

2. 3 inches
3. 2 inches

4. 5 inches

5. **Estimation** In exercises 2–4, how close were your estimates to the actual length? Answers will vary. Estimates may get closer with practice.

Use a ruler to draw the line segment. Check students' drawings.

6. 4 in. 7. 7 in. 8. 10 in. 9. 12 in. 10. 15 in.

Without a ruler, try to draw the line segment. Then measure it. Write the actual length of the line segment. Check students' drawings. Answers will vary. Drawings may get more accurate with practice.

11. 6 in. 12. 11 in. 13. 8 in. 14. 2 in. 15. 5 in.

More Practice Set 9.1, p. 465

Meeting Individual Needs

Extra Support

To the Inch *(visual/kinesthetic)* Have student pairs practice estimating and measuring various classroom items.

First, students agree on five items to be measured. Next, each student records his or her estimate in inches. Finally, pairs measure each item and record the actual measurement.

Alternate Approach

- Reteach Worksheet 9.1
- **TAB** See TE pp. 302E–302F.

Students Acquiring English

See Language Connections, Ch. 9.

Challenge

Have student pairs make up their own measurement system. Pairs decide on a unit of measure, such as the length of a finger, a foot, or a hand span. Then, they use oaktag or cardboard to make a ruler, use it to measure several items, and record results.

Practice

Math Center Use How-To Card 30, *Treasure Hunt*, to have students practice measuring to the nearest inch; to estimate lengths.

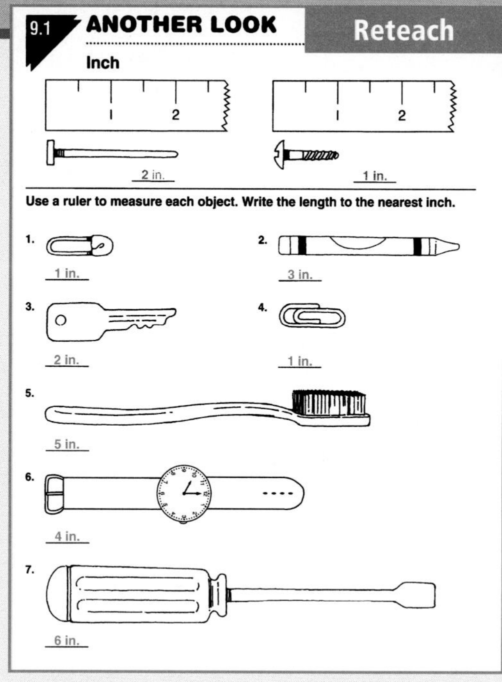

Reteach

9.1 ANOTHER LOOK

Inch

2 in. 1 in.

Use a ruler to measure each object. Write the length to the nearest inch.

1. 1 in.
2. 3 in.
3. 2 in.
4. 1 in.
5. 5 in.
6. 4 in.
7. 6 in.

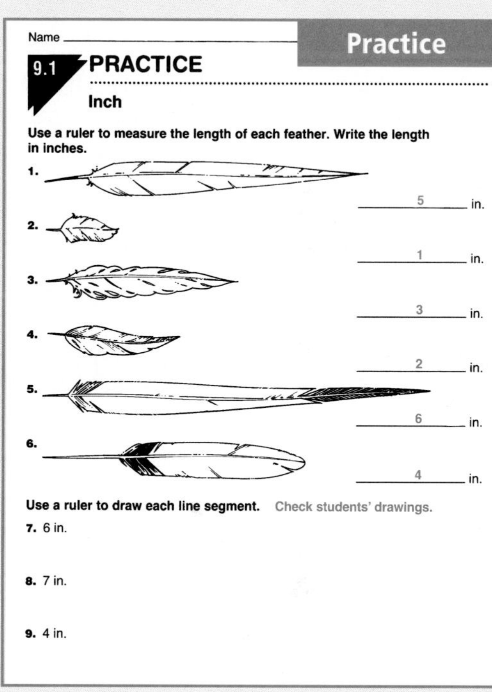

Practice

Name ____

9.1 PRACTICE

Inch

Use a ruler to measure the length of each feather. Write the length in inches.

1. 5 in.
2. 1 in.
3. 3 in.
4. 2 in.
5. 6 in.
6. 4 in.

Use a ruler to draw each line segment. Check students' drawings.

7. 6 in.
8. 7 in.
9. 4 in.

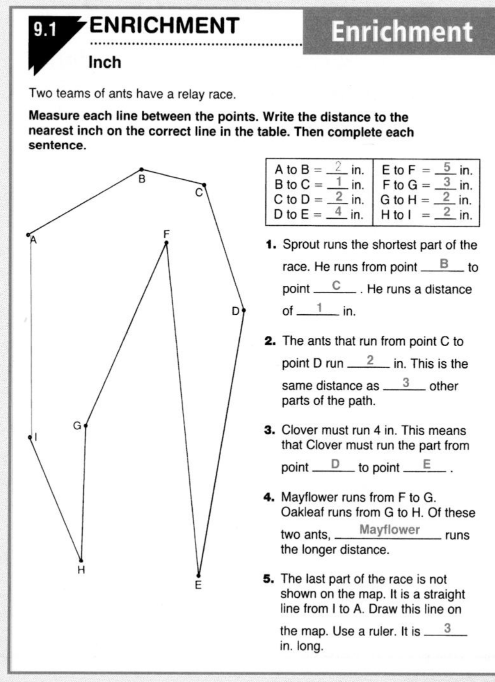

Enrichment

9.1 ENRICHMENT

Inch

Two teams of ants have a relay race.

Measure each line between the points. Write the distance to the nearest inch on the correct line in the table. Then complete each sentence.

A to B = 2 in.	E to F = 5 in.
B to C = 1 in.	F to G = 3 in.
C to D = 2 in.	G to H = 2 in.
D to E = 4 in.	H to I = 2 in.

1. Sprout runs the shortest part of the race. He runs from point B to point C. He runs a distance of 1 in.
2. The ants that run from point C to point D run 2 in. This is the same distance as 3 other parts of the path.
3. Clover must run 4 in. This means that Clover must run the part from point D to point E.
4. Mayflower runs from F to G. Oakleaf runs from G to H. Of these two ants, Mayflower runs the longer distance.
5. The last part of the race is not shown on the map. It is a straight line from I to A. Draw this line on the map. Use a ruler. It is 3 in. long.

Connecting

LESSON 9.2

Planning at a Glance

Objectives To measure to the nearest inch and half inch; to estimate length

Materials half-inch ruler (TR34)

Optional Resources

- Reteach 9.2; Practice 9.2; Enrichment 9.2
- Daily Cumul. Review, p. 113
- Math Center: Act. Card 48
- Every Day Counts
- TAB, TE pp. 302E–302F, 302J
- Problem of the Day, 113, p. 57; Flip Chart, p. 57a

MATHKEYS *Unlocking Measurement 3–6*, Level 3, Activity 13

Students Acquiring English

Help students understand the phrase "to the nearest half inch" by comparing it with rounding to the nearest 10. Use a number line to review rounding. Then draw a line marked in half-inch intervals; point to places on the line and ask students to identify the nearest half inch by rounding up or down.

Problem of the Day

A peach and a pear cost 16¢. A plum and a peach cost 18¢. A plum and a pear cost 20¢. How much does each fruit cost?
pear: 9¢; peach: 7¢; plum: 11¢

Inch and Half Inch

Getting Started

What You'll Need:
▶ half–inch ruler

Suppose you are making a thank-you card for your friend. You want to glue a piece of ribbon across the top of the card. How can you cut the ribbon so it will fit?

You can measure to get the ribbon the right length.

Here's A Way! **Measure to the nearest half inch.**

1. **Look at a ruler with half-inch marks. There are 2 half inches in 1 inch.**
2. **Use the ruler to measure the width of the card.**
   It measures $2\frac{1}{2}$ in. to the nearest half inch.
3. **Measure and cut $2\frac{1}{2}$ in. of ribbon.**
   Put the end of the ribbon at the 0 mark. Cut the ribbon at the $2\frac{1}{2}$ in. mark.

Talk About It! Why do you line up the edge of the card at the 0 mark and not at the 1 mark?
The first inch on a ruler is between the 0 mark and the 1 mark.

Other Examples

Sometimes when you measure to the nearest half inch, you get a whole number.

This piece of yarn measures 2 in. to the nearest half inch and 2 in. to the nearest inch.

306 Chapter 9

1 Introduce

Prior Knowledge **Call on students to estimate the length of classroom items, and then measure.**

Teach: **Here's A Way!**
Emphasize these points:

- Half-inch marks on a ruler are exactly halfway between two inch marks.
- Inch marks also count as half-inch marks.

Modeling Model the activity with ribbon and a card of another size. Ask:

- With what number do I line up the edge of the card? 0
- How wide is the card?
- How long should the ribbon be? same measurement as the width of the card

2 Develop

Show What You Know!

Common Error Some students may make errors reporting the length of an object that is between marks on their rulers. Remind them to look for the nearest inch or half inch. See also Analyzing Errors, TE pp. 341A and 341B.

- Remind students how to correctly place their ruler for taking measurements.

Work It Out!

Using Reading Strategies Help students to use the Monitor strategy as they read the exercises. Ask them to share where they needed to slow down to understand the exercises. See TE p. 302J.

3 Summarize

- Ask students to explain why an inch mark is also a half-inch mark.
- Remind students to record their measurements to the nearest measurement mark.

Ongoing Assessment If you were cutting expensive ribbon, would you measure to the nearest inch or to the nearest half inch?
Students should see that measuring to the nearest half inch would be more economical.

Math Journal: ***Communicating***

When measuring to the nearest half inch, how can you tell whether to round the measurement up or down?
Students should see that a measure that is less than halfway between the half-inch mark and the inch mark rounds down; halfway or more rounds up.

Show What You Know!

Measure the length to the nearest inch. Then measure the length to the nearest half inch. Write each length.

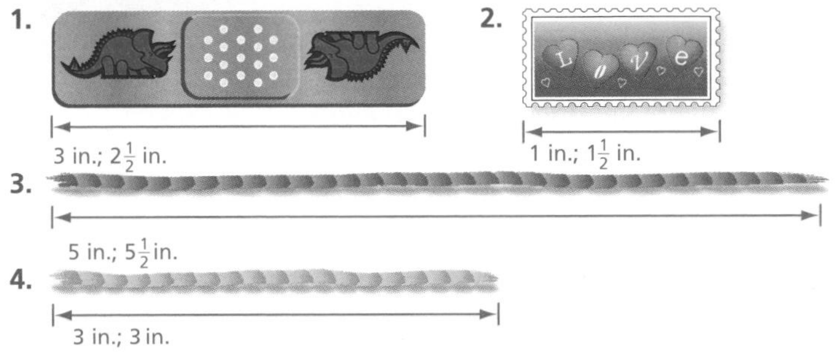

1. 3 in.; $2\frac{1}{2}$ in.
2. 1 in.; $1\frac{1}{2}$ in.
3. 5 in.; $5\frac{1}{2}$ in.
4. 3 in.; 3 in.
5. **Critical Thinking** How many half inches are in 3 inches? Explain your answer. 6; Each inch is made up of 2 half inches.

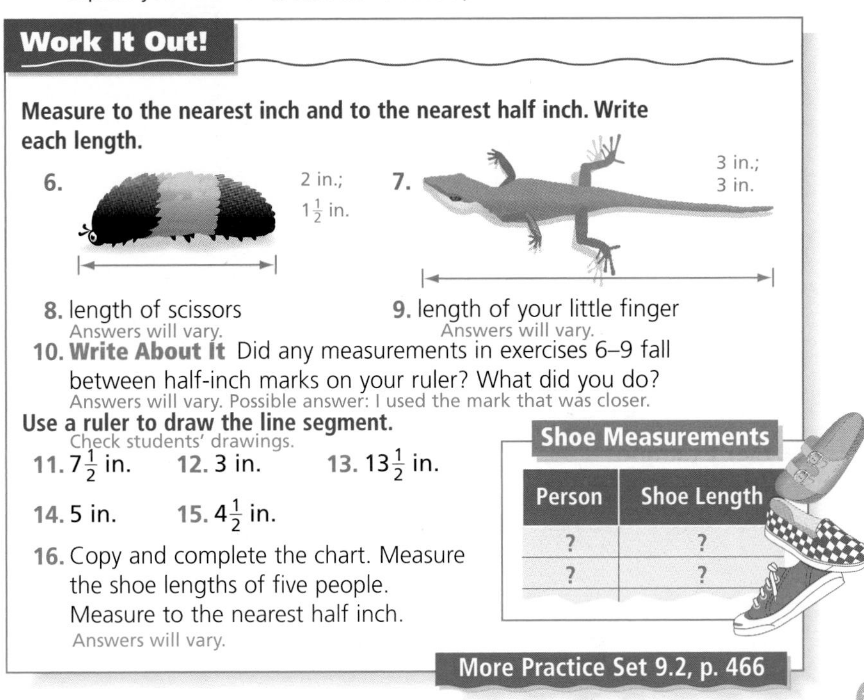

Work It Out!

Measure to the nearest inch and to the nearest half inch. Write each length.

6. 2 in.; $1\frac{1}{2}$ in.
7. 3 in.; 3 in.
8. length of scissors Answers will vary.
9. length of your little finger Answers will vary.
10. **Write About It** Did any measurements in exercises 6–9 fall between half-inch marks on your ruler? What did you do? Answers will vary. Possible answer: I used the mark that was closer.

Use a ruler to draw the line segment. Check students' drawings.

11. $7\frac{1}{2}$ in. 12. 3 in. 13. $13\frac{1}{2}$ in.

14. 5 in. 15. $4\frac{1}{2}$ in.

16. Copy and complete the chart. Measure the shoe lengths of five people. Measure to the nearest half inch. Answers will vary.

Shoe Measurements

Person	Shoe Length
?	?
?	?

More Practice Set 9.2, p. 466

307

Meeting Individual Needs

Extra Support

Half-Inch Measurements ***(visual/kinesthetic)*** Have students work in pairs. Each student traces a ruler and labels one-inch or half-inch intervals. Then they cut their paper ruler into inch or half-inch sections. Have them use their inches and half-inches to measure a few classroom objects. Discuss what they notice about the relationship between the two sets of measuring tools.

Alternate Approach

- Reteach Worksheet 9.2
- **TAB** See TE pp. 302E–302F.
- **MATHKEYS** Invite students to measure objects on the computer with electronic rulers and tape measures. They find objects on-screen that match fractional inch lengths in *Unlocking Measurement 3–6*, Level 3, Activity 13.

Students Acquiring English

See Language Connections, Ch. 9.

Practice

Math Center Use Activity Card 48, *Measure Up!*, to have students practice measuring to the nearest half inch.

Challenge Use Activity Card 48 and have students continue the activity as described in Now Try This!

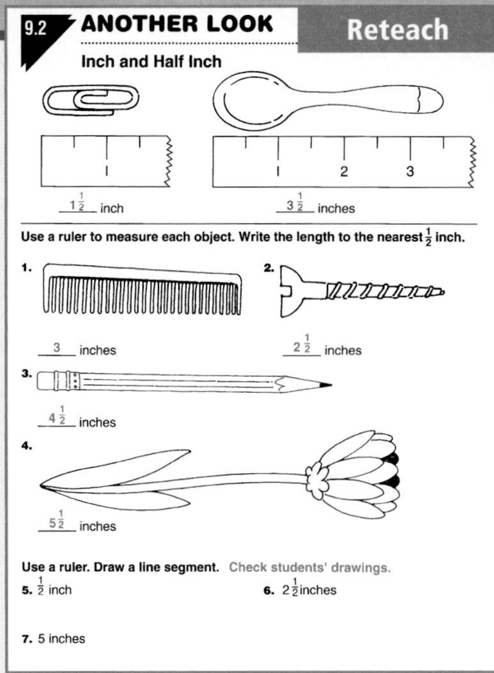

9.2 ANOTHER LOOK — Reteach

Inch and Half Inch

$1\frac{1}{2}$ inch — $3\frac{1}{2}$ inches

Use a ruler to measure each object. Write the length to the nearest $\frac{1}{2}$ inch.

1. 3 inches
2. $2\frac{1}{2}$ inches
3. $4\frac{1}{2}$ inches
4. $5\frac{1}{2}$ inches

Use a ruler. Draw a line segment. Check students' drawings.

5. $\frac{1}{2}$ inch
6. $2\frac{1}{2}$ inches
7. 5 inches

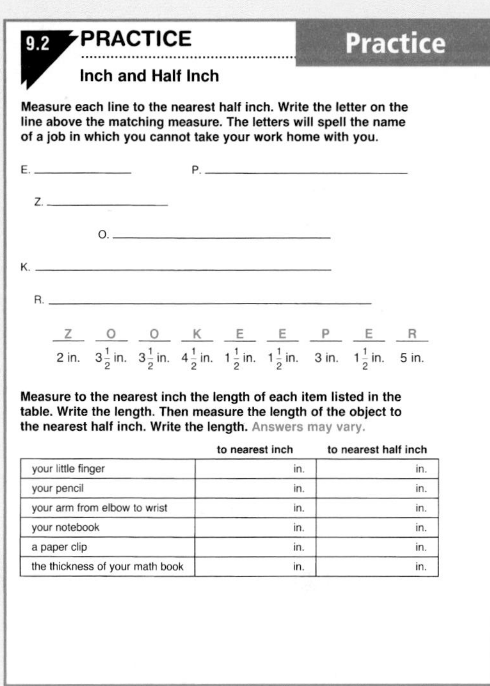

9.2 PRACTICE — Practice

Inch and Half Inch

Measure each line to the nearest half inch. Write the letter on the line above the matching measure. The letters will spell the name of a job in which you cannot take your work home with you.

E. P. Z. O. K. R.

Z	O	O	K	E	E	P	E	R
2 in.	$3\frac{1}{2}$ in.	$3\frac{1}{2}$ in.	$4\frac{1}{2}$ in.	$1\frac{1}{2}$ in.	$1\frac{1}{2}$ in.	3 in.	$1\frac{1}{2}$ in.	5 in.

Measure to the nearest inch the length of each item listed in the table. Write the length. Then measure the length of the object to the nearest half inch. Write the length. Answers may vary.

	to nearest inch	to nearest half inch
your little finger	in.	in.
your pencil	in.	in.
your arm from elbow to wrist	in.	in.
your notebook	in.	in.
a paper clip	in.	in.
the thickness of your math book	in.	in.

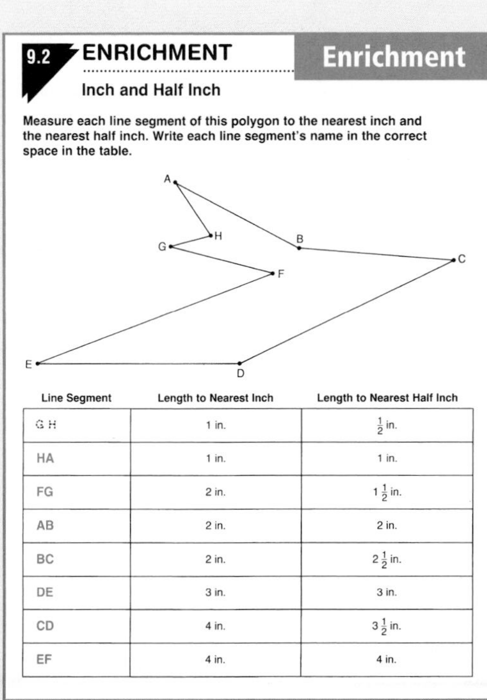

9.2 ENRICHMENT — Enrichment

Inch and Half Inch

Measure each line segment of this polygon to the nearest inch and the nearest half inch. Write each line segment's name in the correct space in the table.

Line Segment	Length to Nearest Inch	Length to Nearest Half Inch
GH	1 in.	$\frac{1}{2}$ in.
HA	1 in.	1 in.
FG	2 in.	$1\frac{1}{2}$ in.
AB	2 in.	2 in.
BC	2 in.	$2\frac{1}{2}$ in.
DE	3 in.	3 in.
CD	4 in.	$3\frac{1}{2}$ in.
EF	4 in.	4 in.

Symbolic

LESSON 9.3

Planning at a Glance

Objective **To find the perimeters of polygons using standard units (inches and half inches)**

Materials tape measure

Optional Resources

- Reteach 9.3; Practice 9.3; Enrichment 9.3
- Daily Cumul. Review, p. 114
- Math Center: Act. Card 49
- Every Day Counts
- **TAB**, TE pp. 302E–302F, 302J
- **Problem of the Day**, 114, p. 57; Flip Chart, p. 57b

MATHKEYS

Unlocking Measurement 3–6, Level 3, Activity 9

Students Acquiring English

Use geometric figures to demonstrate *perimeter* and give students the opportunity to point out the perimeters of various figures. Provide models such as "The perimeter of this rectangle is 12 inches." Pair students so they can work together to write their rules for problem 10.

Problem of the Day

A fence divides a square field in half. If the field is 50 feet long on a side, what is the perimeter of half the field?
150 feet

Perimeter

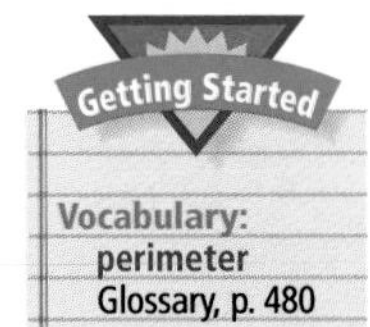

Getting Started

Vocabulary:
perimeter
Glossary, p. 480

Suppose you are making a poster for your class play. You want to put this cloth around the border. How much cloth do you need?

You can measure around the poster. The distance around a figure is called the perimeter.

Here's A Way! **Find the perimeter.**

1. Measure and record the length of each side of the poster.
2. Add the lengths of all the sides.
   $11 + 9 + 11 + 9 = 40$
3. Explain what the sum means.

The perimeter of the poster is 40 in. You need 40 in. of cloth.

Talk About It!

- How many sides does the poster have? How does this help you know how many numbers to add?
  4 sides; You need to add 4 numbers, 1 for each side.
- Could you use mental math to add the lengths? How?
  Yes, add 9 + 11 = 20 and double the answer.

Other Example

$14 + 14 + 9 = 37$
The perimeter is 37 in.

1 Introduce

Build Understanding **Have students use a tape measure to measure the distance around their math book. Then, have them measure each side of the book and add to find the perimeter. Ask, Are the measurements the same? Why or why not?** Answers will vary.

Teach: Here's A Way!

Emphasize this point:

- Add the lengths of all sides, but do not add any side twice.

2 Develop

Show What You Know!

Common Error Some students may not include all the sides of the object being measured. Have them mark each side as they add it and check to be sure they have marked all sides of the figure. See also Analyzing Errors, TE pp. 341A and 341B.

Using Reading Strategies Guide students to use the Monitor strategy as they read the exercises. Ask, How can rereading help you understand the Critical Thinking question? See TE p. 302J

Work It Out!

- Discuss exercise 13 with students.

3 Summarize

- Remind students to measure carefully and add all the sides of a figure to find its perimeter.

Ongoing Assessment You want to frame a rectangular picture that is 9 inches long on two sides and 12 inches long on the other two sides. What is the perimeter of the frame?
9 + 9 + 12 + 12 = 42 inches

Math Journal: ***Communicating***

How could you find the perimeter of a figure that has curved sides? Students may suggest using string to find the distance around the figure and measuring the string to find the perimeter.

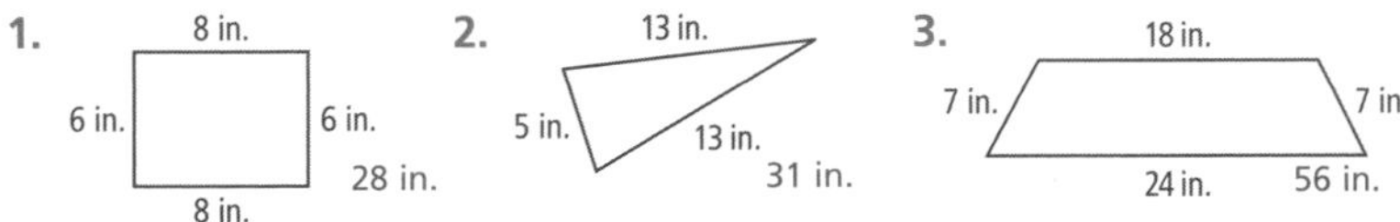

Find the perimeter. The lengths of the sides are labeled.

1. 8 in., 6 in., 6 in., 8 in. — 28 in.
2. 13 in., 5 in., 13 in. — 31 in.
3. 18 in., 7 in., 7 in., 24 in. — 56 in.

4. Draw a figure with a perimeter of 8 in. Label the sides. Check students' drawings. The sum of the sides should equal 8 in.

5. Critical Thinking How could you find the perimeter of a rectangle by measuring only two sides? Answers will vary. Possible answer: Measure one width and double it. Measure one length and double it. Add.

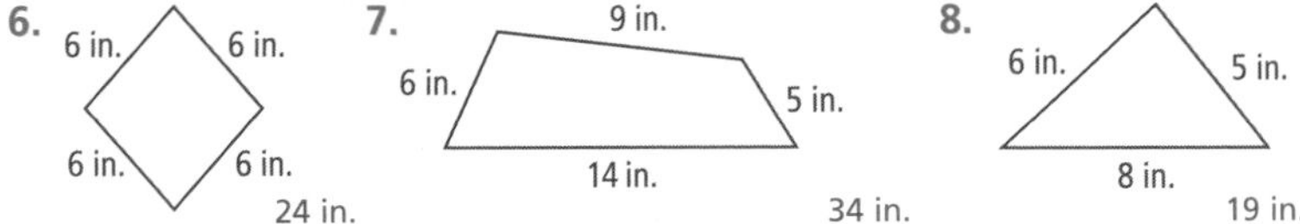

Write the perimeter. The lengths of the sides are labeled.

6. 6 in., 6 in., 6 in., 6 in. — 24 in.
7. 9 in., 6 in., 5 in., 14 in. — 34 in.
8. 6 in., 5 in., 8 in. — 19 in.

9. 10 in., 2 in., 10 in., 2 in. 24 in.
10. 5 in., 5 in., 5 in. 15 in.
11. 6 in., 5 in., 2 in., 4 in. 17 in.
12. 2 in., 9 in., 3 in., 7 in., 2 in 23 in.

13. A square has 4 equal sides. Copy and complete the table to show the perimeters of different squares.

One side of a square	1 in.	2 in.	? 3	4 in.	5 in.	? 6	? 7	8 in.	? 9	? 10
Perimeter of a square	4 in.	8 in.	12 in.	? 16	? 20	24 in.	28 in.	? 32	36 in.	? 40

14. Algebraic Reasoning Look at your table. Write a rule for finding the perimeter of a square. Answers will vary. Possible answer: Multiply the length of 1 side by 4.

**Draw a figure with each perimeter. Label the sides.**

15. 4 in. **16.** 8 in. **17.** 10 in. **18.** 11 in. **19.** 6 in.

Check the perimeters on students' drawings.

More Practice Set 9.3, p. 466

Meeting Individual Needs

Extra Support

All the Way Around *(kinesthetic)* Have students working in pairs take turns suggesting objects and figures found in the classroom with easily measurable perimeters. Let them work together to measure six such items and record their measurements in a chart.

Alternate Approach

- Reteach Worksheet 9.3
- **TAB** See TE pp. 302E–302F.

Students Acquiring English

See **Language Connections**, Ch. 9.

Practice

Math Center Use Activity Card 49, *Geo-Areas*, to have students practice measuring and adding to find the perimeters of polygons using standard units.

Challenge Use Activity Card 49 and have students continue as described in Now Try This!

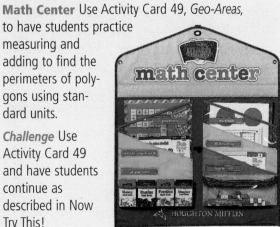

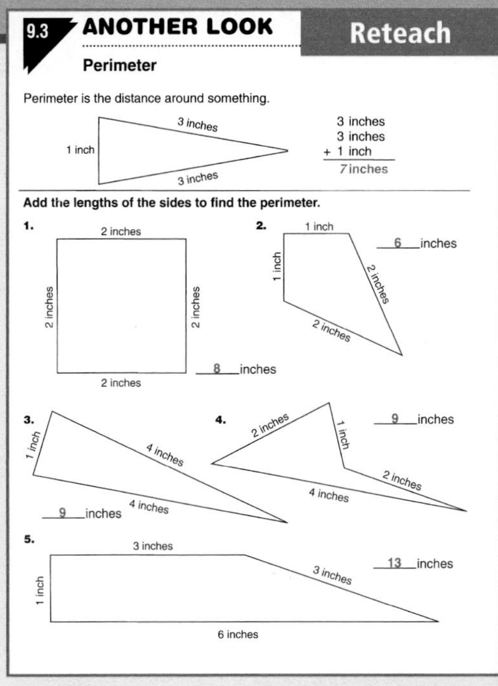

9.3 ANOTHER LOOK — Reteach

Perimeter

Perimeter is the distance around something.

3 inches + 3 inches + 1 inch = 7 inches

Add the lengths of the sides to find the perimeter.

1. 2 inches, 2 inches, 2 inches, 2 inches — 8 inches
2. 1 inch, 1 inch, 2 inches, 2 inches — 6 inches
3. 1 inch, 4 inches, 4 inches — 9 inches
4. 2 inches, 1 inch, 2 inches, 4 inches — 9 inches
5. 3 inches, 1 inch, 3 inches, 6 inches — 13 inches

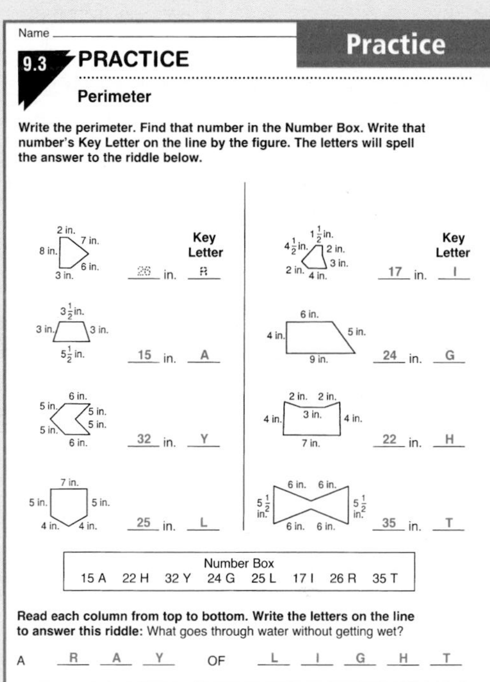

Name ______ — Practice

9.3 PRACTICE

Perimeter

Write the perimeter. Find that number in the Number Box. Write that number's Key Letter on the line by the figure. The letters will spell the answer to the riddle below.

Perimeter	Key Letter	Perimeter	Key Letter
26 in.	R	17 in.	I
15 in.	A	24 in.	G
32 in.	Y	22 in.	H
25 in.	L	35 in.	T

Number Box: 15 A 22 H 32 Y 24 G 25 L 17 I 26 R 35 T

Read each column from top to bottom. Write the letters on the line to answer this riddle: What goes through water without getting wet?

A R A Y OF L I G H T

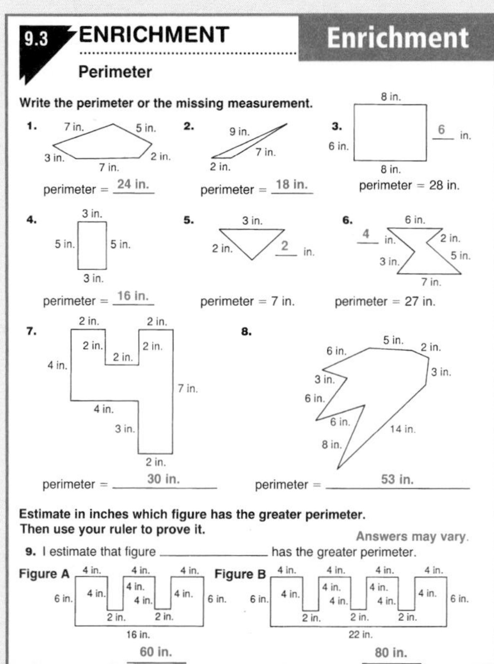

9.3 ENRICHMENT — Enrichment

Perimeter

Write the perimeter or the missing measurement.

1. perimeter = 24 in.
2. perimeter = 18 in.
3. 6 in.; perimeter = 28 in.
4. perimeter = 16 in.
5. 2 in.; perimeter = 7 in.
6. 4 in.; perimeter = 27 in.
7. perimeter = 30 in.
8. perimeter = 53 in.

Estimate in inches which figure has the greater perimeter. Then use your ruler to prove it.

9. I estimate that figure ______ has the greater perimeter. Answers may vary.

Figure A: 60 in. Figure B: 80 in.

LESSON 9.4

Activity

Planning at a Glance

Objectives To investigate using foot, yard, and mile to compare lengths; to choose the appropriate linear unit

Materials none

Optional Resources

- Reteach 9.4; Practice 9.4; Enrichment 9.4
- Daily Cumul. Review, p. 115
- Math Center: Act. Card 50
- Every Day Counts
- **TAB**, TE pp. 302E–302F, 302J
- **Problem of the Day**, 115, p. 58; Flip Chart, p. 58a

MATHKEYS

To meet individual needs, use *Unlocking Measurement 3–6*, Level 3, Activity 6

Students Acquiring English

Use a ruler and yardstick to demonstrate that *foot* and *yard* are units of measurement. Allow students practice writing and saying the singular and plural forms of *inch, foot, yard,* and *mile,* pointing out that the plural of *foot* is *feet.*

Problem of the Day

A kindergarten class did a number parade at the Math Fair. Nine "digit guards" marched in a long row, each holding a giant number card from 1 to 9. Behind each digit guard were the number of marchers marked on the card. How many children were in the parade? How many children were behind the third digit guard, but before the sixth digit guard? 54 children; 14 children: 3 + 4 + 5 marchers, plus digit guards for the numbers 4 and 5

LESSON 4

Foot, Yard, and Mile

Getting Started

Vocabulary:
foot (ft)
mile (mi)
yard (yd)
Glossary, p. 480

Cooperative Learning Checklist

- ☐ Work alone.
- ☑ Work with a partner.
- ☑ Work with a group.

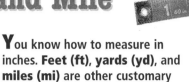

You know how to measure in inches. **Feet (ft), yards (yd),** and **miles (mi)** are other customary units used to measure length.

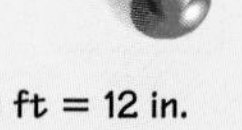

1 ft = 12 in.
1 yd = 3 ft *or* 36 in.
1 mi = 5280 ft

Activity

Measure in Feet, Yards, and Miles

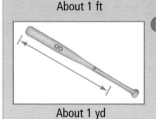

About 1 ft

1. One foot is 12 in. The length of a notebook is about 1 ft.
   - Find something else that is about 1 ft long. Measure and write its length. Answers will vary. Possible answers: computer screen, construction paper

About 1 yd

2. One yard is 3 ft or 36 in. A baseball bat is about 1 yd long.
   - Find something else that is about 1 yd long. Measure and write its length. Answers will vary. Possible answers: gerbil cage, table top

3. One mile is 5280 ft. The street distance shown here is about 1 mi long. Answers will vary. Possible answers: length of a river, distance between two cities, distance across an island
   - List some other things that could be measured in miles.

---

1 Introduce

Prior Knowledge Call on students to name two things each that are typically measured in feet, yards, and miles.

Teach: Activity

Emphasize these points:

- Length can be measured by more than one customary unit.
- It is important to choose the right measure when measuring length.
- The abbreviations for *foot, yard,* and *mile* are *ft, yd,* and *mi.*

Modeling Model Step 3. Ask:

- Which unit would be best to measure the distance you travel to school? Why? miles; inches, feet, yards all are too small

2 Develop

Show What You Know!

Common Error Some students may select inappropriate units of measure. Provide rulers and yardsticks and have students act out the measurements to verify their choices. See also Analyzing Errors, TE pp. 341A and 341B.

- Have students discuss their reasoning for exercises 1–4.
- Remind students that they may need to convert units before comparing amounts in exercises 5–13.

Using Reading Strategies Encourage students to use the Monitor strategy as they read the exercises. Ask them to share their understanding with the class. See TE p. 302J.

3 Summarize

- Remind students that units such as feet, yards, and miles are used to measure greater lengths.
- Discuss the importance of choosing the appropriate unit of measure.

Ongoing Assessment Ed wants to measure the perimeter of his room. What customary unit of measure should he use? feet or yards

- Why wouldn't he use inches or miles? Numbers using inches would be too great; It would only be a small fraction of a mile.

Math Journal: *Communicating*

Answers may vary, but may include that the feet show a pattern of skip-counting by 3's.

Rename Feet as Yards

The curtain on a puppet stage is 12 ft long. How many yards is it?

Feet	3	
Yards	1	

Rename 12 feet as yards.

- Make a table. Show 3 ft = 1 yd.
- Continue the table until you fill in a column for 12 ft.

Feet	3	6	9	(12)
Yards	1	2	3	(4)

- Find the number of yards that equals 12 ft.

12 ft = 4 yd

So, the curtain is 4 yd long.

Show What You Know!

Which unit would you use to measure each? Write *foot, yard,* or *mile.* Explain your choice. Explanations may vary but should show understanding of the relative length of a foot, yard, and mile.

1. distance to the North Pole mile
2. length of a football field yard
3. distance to the lunch room foot or yard
4. length of your desk foot

Complete. Write >, <, or =.

5. 1 mi ■ 2000 ft >
6. 1 ft ■ 29 in. <
7. 2 mi ■ 5000 ft >
8. 1 yd ■ 3 ft =
9. 12 mi ■ 12 yd >
10. 4 yd ■ 13 ft <
11. 6 ft ■ 2 yd =
12. $7\frac{1}{2}$ ft ■ $7\frac{1}{2}$ yd <
13. 2 ft ■ 10 in. >

Mixed Review

Write a fraction for the shaded part.

14.  $\frac{1}{2}$
15. 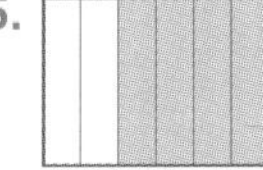 $\frac{4}{6}$
16. 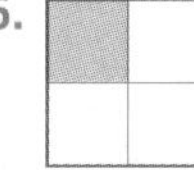 $\frac{1}{4}$
17. 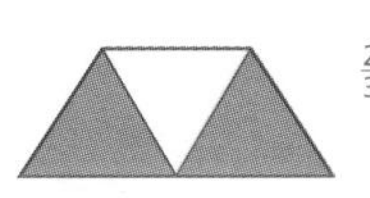 $\frac{2}{3}$

Math Journal

Look at the table at the top of this page. When you rename feet as yards, what pattern do you see?
As the feet increase by 3, the yards increase by 1.

311

Meeting Individual Needs

Extra Support

What Unit? (*auditory*) Students working in pairs take turns naming a unit: inch, foot, yard, or mile. The partner must name an object that can be reasonably measured with that unit. Have students keep a list of the items and units they name and compare them with other pairs.

Alternate Approach

- Reteach Worksheet 9.4
- **TAB** See TE pp. 302E–302F.

Students Acquiring English

See Language Connections, Ch. 9.

Challenge

Have students answer the following, using calculators for exercises *c, d,* and *e:*

a. How many yards are in 15 ft? 5 yd
b. How many inches are in 10 feet? 120 in.
c. How many feet are in 13 yards? 39 ft
d. How many inches are in 1 mile? 63,360 in.
e. How many yards are in 1 mile? 1760 yd

Practice

Math Center Use Activity Card 50, *What to Measure?,* to have students practice choosing the appropriate linear unit.

Challenge Use Activity Card 50 and have students continue as described in Now Try This!

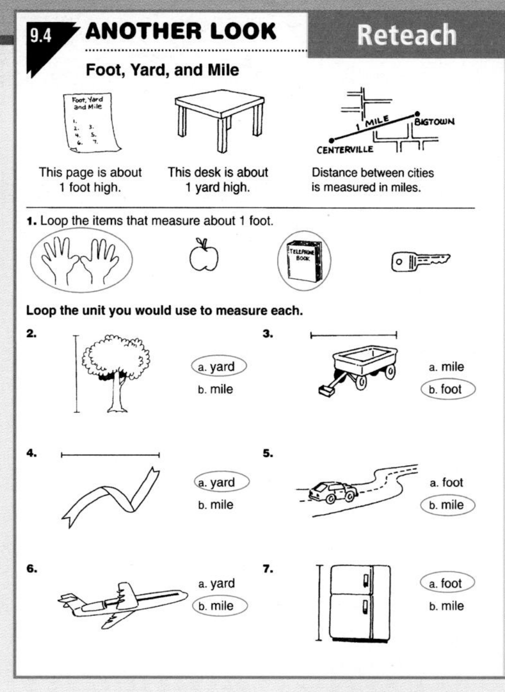

9.4 **ANOTHER LOOK** — Reteach

Foot, Yard, and Mile

This page is about 1 foot high. This desk is about 1 yard high. Distance between cities is measured in miles.

1. Loop the items that measure about 1 foot.

Loop the unit you would use to measure each.

2. a. yard (looped) b. mile
3. a. mile b. foot (looped)
4. a. yard (looped) b. mile
5. a. foot b. mile (looped)
6. a. yard b. mile (looped)
7. a. foot (looped) b. mile

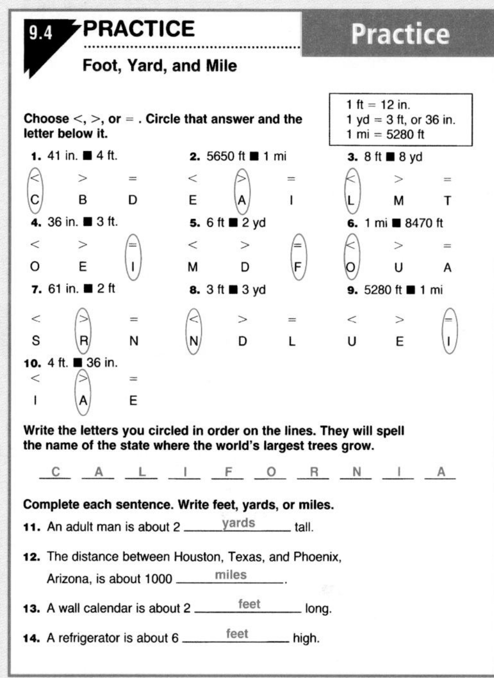

9.4 **PRACTICE** — Practice

Foot, Yard, and Mile

1 ft = 12 in.
1 yd = 3 ft, or 36 in.
1 mi = 5280 ft

Choose <, >, or =. Circle that answer and the letter below it.

1. 41 in. ■ 4 ft. (<) C
2. 5650 ft ■ 1 mi (>) A
3. 8 ft ■ 8 yd (<) L
4. 36 in. ■ 3 ft. (=) I
5. 6 ft ■ 2 yd (=) F
6. 1 mi ■ 8470 ft (<) O
7. 61 in. ■ 2 ft (>) R
8. 3 ft ■ 3 yd (<) N
9. 5280 ft ■ 1 mi (=) I
10. 4 ft. ■ 36 in. (>) A

Write the letters you circled in order on the lines. They will spell the name of the state where the world's largest trees grow.

C A L I F O R N I A

Complete each sentence. Write feet, yards, or miles.

11. An adult man is about 2 yards tall.
12. The distance between Houston, Texas, and Phoenix, Arizona, is about 1000 miles.
13. A wall calendar is about 2 feet long.
14. A refrigerator is about 6 feet high.

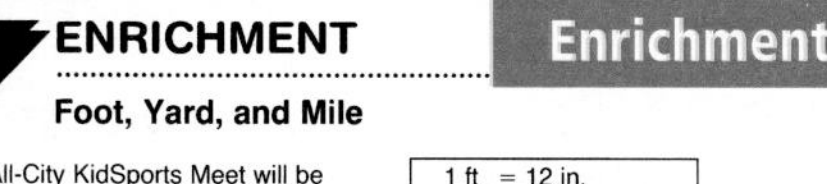

9.4 **ENRICHMENT** — Enrichment

Foot, Yard, and Mile

The All-City KidSports Meet will be held in Albin Park. This diagram shows the layout of the game area.

1 ft = 12 in.
1 yd = 3 ft, or 36 in.
1 mi = 5280 ft

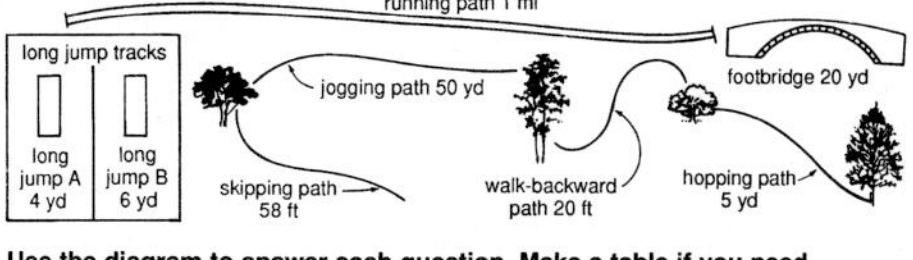

Use the diagram to answer each question. Make a table if you need to. Circle the letter of the best answer.

1. Which path is shorter? **a.** the hopping path (circled) **b.** the jogging path
2. Which distance is longer? **a.** the walk-backward path **b.** the footbridge (circled)
3. The sack race must be run on a course that is exactly 15 ft long. Which path would be the better choice? **a.** the jogging path **b.** the hopping path (circled)
4. The 6000-ft course for the canoe race is on a river in the park. Is this race longer than or shorter than the running path? **a.** longer than (circled) **b.** shorter than
5. For the roller skating race, the finish line will be 1000 ft from the starting line. Where could the race be held? **a.** the jogging path **b.** the running path (circled)
6. The best long jump George has ever done is 9 ft. Which long jump group should he be assigned to? **a.** the group at long jump A (circled) **b.** the group at long jump B
7. In the obstacle race, runners must jump over two fences. One is 10 in. high. One is 1 ft high. Which height is greater? **a.** 10 in. **b.** 1 ft (circled)
8. Sal enters the hopping race. Jo enters the walk-backward race. Which of the two friends must race the greater distance? **a.** Sal **b.** Jo (circled)

Activity

Planning at a Glance

Objectives To investigate using cup, pint, quart, and gallon; to rename one customary unit as another; to estimate capacity

Materials cup, pint, quart, and gallon containers, water

Optional Resources

- Reteach 9.5; Practice 9.5; Enrichment 9.5
- Daily Cumul. Review, p. 116
- Math Center: Act. Card 51
- Every Day Counts
- TAB, TE pp. 302E–302F, 302J
- Problem of the Day, 116, p. 58; Flip Chart, p. 58b

Students Acquiring English

Students will not be able to complete questions 9–15 unless they know the meaning of all the vocabulary. Read the phrases aloud and ask students to draw a picture of the item if they know it. If nobody knows what the phrase means, draw a picture for them and discuss the meaning.

Problem of the Day

Renee bought 4 kinds of drinks in 4 different-sized cartons. She got milk, cider, lemonade, and fruit punch. She got cup, pint, quart, and gallon cartons. Cider came in the largest carton. The lemonade carton was smaller than the punch carton but larger than the milk carton. Match each drink with the size of its carton.
cup of milk, pint of lemonade, quart of punch, gallon of cider

Cup, Pint, Quart, and Gallon

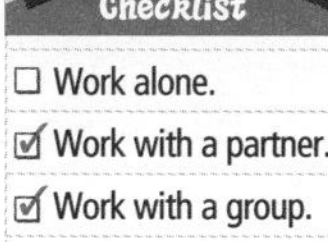

☐ Work alone.
☑ Work with a partner.
☑ Work with a group.

Getting Started

What You'll Need:
- cup, pint, quart, and gallon containers
- water

Vocabulary:
capacity
cup (c)
gallon (gal)
pint (pt)
quart (qt)
Glossary, p. 480

The amount of liquid that a container will hold is its **capacity**. Customary units for measuring capacity are **cup (c)**, **pint (pt)**, **quart (qt)**, and **gallon (gal)**.

Activity

- **Make a chart. Label the columns as shown below.**
- **Use different containers to estimate and measure capacity.**

1 Fill the cup container with water. Estimate how many cups of water you will need to fill the pint container. Record your estimate. Estimates will vary.

2 Empty the cup of water into the pint container. Keep pouring cups of water into the container until it is full. Record your findings. 2 cups

3 Estimate. Then measure.
- the number of pints in 1 quart
- the number of quarts in 1 gallon

Record your results. Estimates will vary; 2 pints; 4 quarts

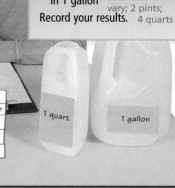

Capacity		
What I'm Finding	Estimate	Exact Number
cups in 1 pint	3 cups	
pints in 1 quart		
quarts in 1 gallon		

312 Chapter 9

1 Introduce

Build Understanding **Invite students to experiment with water and containers that hold cups, pints, quarts, and gallons. They can fill containers, pour contents from one into others, and discuss their observations.**

Teach: Activity

Emphasize this point:

- Recognizing patterns and skip-counting by 2's or 4's can help you rename one unit of capacity as another.

Modeling Model how to find the number of cups in one quart. Ask:

- If there are 2 cups in a pint, and 2 pints in a quart, how many cups are in a quart? 4
- How can I check the answer?

2 Develop

Show What You Know!

- Call on students to explain their reasoning for exercise 1.
- For exercises 2 and 3, remind students to choose carefully whether to multiply or divide to rename one unit of capacity as another.
- Have students explain their reasoning for exercise 4.

3 Summarize

- Remind students that they can use tables for help in renaming one unit as another.
- Invite students to name capacities of containers with which they are familiar.

Ongoing Assessment You want to have enough juice to serve at least 2 cups of juice for 12 people at a party. How much juice should you buy? Students should say at least 6 qt, though 24 cups or 12 pints is also acceptable.

Math Journal: *Communicating*

When you rename a smaller unit as a larger unit, do you have more or fewer of the larger units? Why? fewer; The larger the unit, the fewer it takes to make a given amount.

Show What You Know!

1. **Logical Reasoning** You know there are 2 cups in a pint. You also know there are 2 pints in a quart. How can you find the number of cups in a quart without measuring?
   Answers will vary. Possible answers: by doubling 2; by finding 2×2.

Copy and complete.

2.

Cup	2	4 ?	6	8	10 ?	12 ?	14	16 ?	18 ?
Pint	1	2	3 ?	4 ?	5	6	7 ?	8	9 ?
Quart	$\frac{1}{2}$?	1	$1\frac{1}{2}$	2 ?	$2\frac{1}{2}$?	3	$3\frac{1}{2}$?	4 ?	$4\frac{1}{2}$?

3.

Gallon	1	2	3 ?	4 ?
Quart	4	8 ?	12	16 ?

4. **Algebraic Reasoning** Write a rule for finding the number of quarts when you know the number of gallons.
   Multiply the number of gallons by 4 to find the number of quarts.

Write >, <, or =. You can use the tables you completed.

5. 1 qt ■ 1 pt > 6. 1 gal ■ 4 qt = 7. 8 c ■ 2 pt > 8. 4 c ■ 4 pt <

Estimation **Does the object hold more than or less than 1 quart? Write *more than* or *less than*.**

9. kitchen sink more than 10. baby bottle less than 11. mug less than 12. bathtub more than

Choose the better unit of measure. Write *a* or *b*.

13. glass of milk a
    a. cup b. quart
14. water in a pool b
    a. pint b. gallon
15. water in a fish tank b
    a. cup b. gallon

Mixed Review

Write the answer.

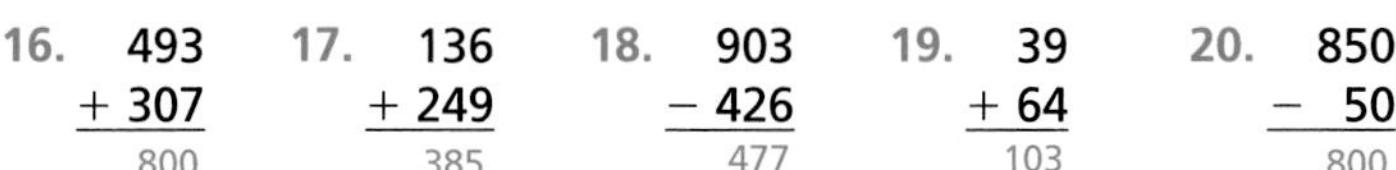

16. 493 + 307 = 800
17. 136 + 249 = 385
18. 903 − 426 = 477
19. 39 + 64 = 103
20. 850 − 50 = 800

313

Meeting Individual Needs

Extra Support

How Much Does It Hold? *(visual)* Ask each student to bring in a clean, empty container. Have student pairs select two containers brought in by other students, estimate their capacity, and check their estimates. Then have them exchange containers with another pair and repeat the procedure.

Alternate Approach

- Reteach Worksheet 9.5
- **TAB** See TE pp. 302E–302F.

Students Acquiring English

See Language Connections, Ch. 9.

Challenge

Have each student bring in a favorite recipe from home. Working in small groups, have students determine how much of each ingredient they would need to double and triple each of their group's recipes.

Practice

Math Center Use Activity Card 51, *Fill It Up,* to have students practice using cup (c), pint (pt), quart (qt), and gallon (gal) to rename one customary unit as another.

Challenge Use Activity Card 51 and have students continue as described in Now Try This!

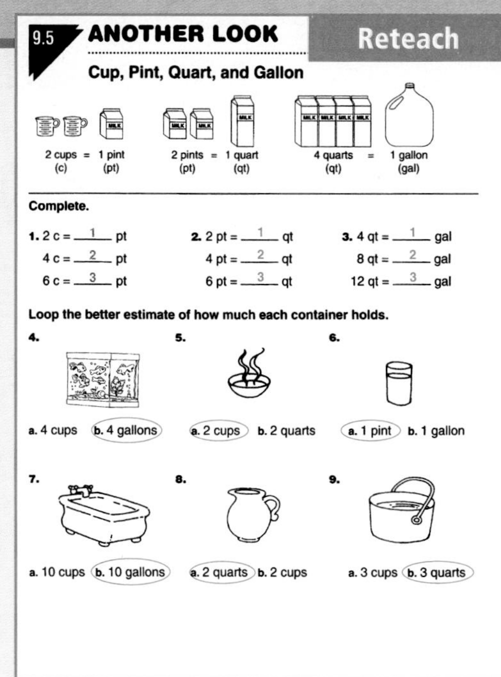

9.5 ANOTHER LOOK — Reteach

Cup, Pint, Quart, and Gallon

2 cups (c) = 1 pint (pt) 2 pints (pt) = 1 quart (qt) 4 quarts (qt) = 1 gallon (gal)

Complete.

1. 2 c = 1 pt; 4 c = 2 pt; 6 c = 3 pt
2. 2 pt = 1 qt; 4 pt = 2 qt; 6 pt = 3 qt
3. 4 qt = 1 gal; 8 qt = 2 gal; 12 qt = 3 gal

Loop the better estimate of how much each container holds.

4. a. 4 cups (b. 4 gallons)
5. (a. 2 cups) b. 2 quarts
6. (a. 1 pint) b. 1 gallon
7. a. 10 cups (b. 10 gallons)
8. (a. 2 quarts) b. 2 cups
9. a. 3 cups (b. 3 quarts)

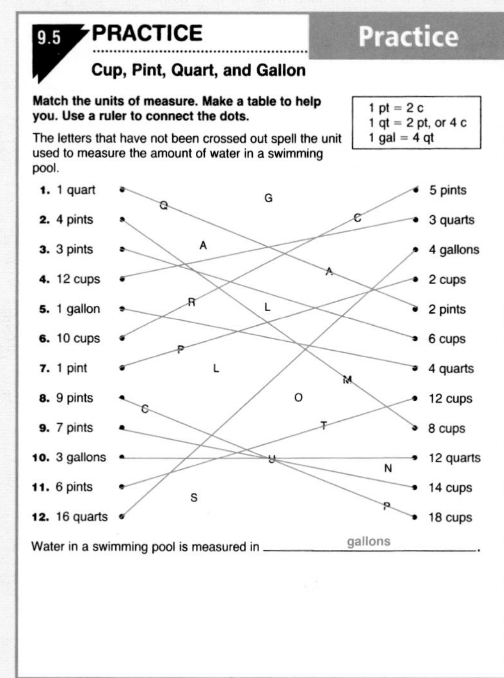

9.5 PRACTICE — Practice

Cup, Pint, Quart, and Gallon

Match the units of measure. Make a table to help you. Use a ruler to connect the dots.

The letters that have not been crossed out spell the unit used to measure the amount of water in a swimming pool.

1 pt = 2 c
1 qt = 2 pt, or 4 c
1 gal = 4 qt

1. 1 quart	5 pints
2. 4 pints	3 quarts
3. 3 pints	4 gallons
4. 12 cups	2 cups
5. 1 gallon	2 pints
6. 10 cups	6 cups
7. 1 pint	4 quarts
8. 9 pints	12 cups
9. 7 pints	8 cups
10. 3 gallons	12 quarts
11. 6 pints	14 cups
12. 16 quarts	18 cups

Water in a swimming pool is measured in gallons.

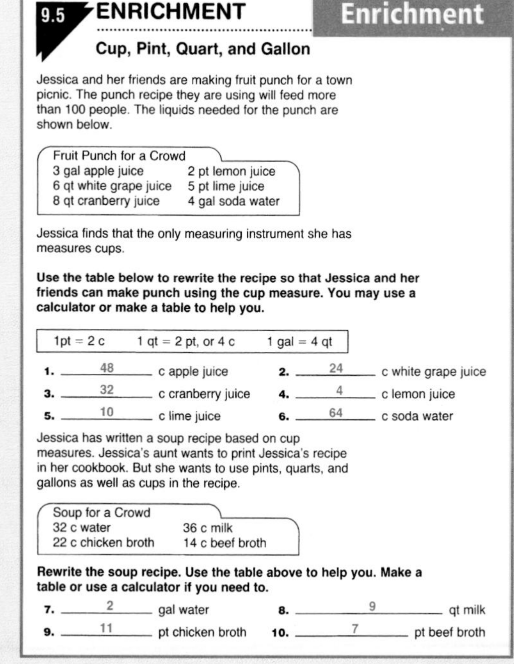

9.5 ENRICHMENT — Enrichment

Cup, Pint, Quart, and Gallon

Jessica and her friends are making fruit punch for a town picnic. The punch recipe they are using will feed more than 100 people. The liquids needed for the punch are shown below.

Fruit Punch for a Crowd
3 gal apple juice 2 pt lemon juice
6 qt white grape juice 5 pt lime juice
8 qt cranberry juice 4 gal soda water

Jessica finds that the only measuring instrument she has measures cups.

Use the table below to rewrite the recipe so that Jessica and her friends can make punch using the cup measure. You may use a calculator or make a table to help you.

1pt = 2 c	1 qt = 2 pt, or 4 c	1 gal = 4 qt

1. 48 c apple juice
2. 24 c white grape juice
3. 32 c cranberry juice
4. 4 c lemon juice
5. 10 c lime juice
6. 64 c soda water

Jessica has written a soup recipe based on cup measures. Jessica's aunt wants to print Jessica's recipe in her cookbook. But she wants to use pints, quarts, and gallons as well as cups in the recipe.

Soup for a Crowd
32 c water 36 c milk
22 c chicken broth 14 c beef broth

Rewrite the soup recipe. Use the table above to help you. Make a table or use a calculator if you need to.

7. 2 gal water
8. 9 qt milk
9. 11 pt chicken broth
10. 7 pt beef broth

Symbolic

Planning at a Glance

Objectives To use ounce and pound; to choose the appropriate unit and estimate weight

Materials none

Optional Resources

- Daily Cumul. Review, p. 117
- Math Center: How-To Card 31
- Every Day Counts
- **TAB**, TE pp. 302E–302F, 302J
- **Reteach, Practice, and Enrichment Worksheets for Lesson 9.6**
- **Problem of the Day**, 117, p. 59; Flip Chart, p. 59a

Students Acquiring English

Help students understand the relative weights of popped and unpopped popcorn by showing both. Weigh out one pound and one ounce of each. To help students with the terms *ounce* and *pound,* let them weigh each in their hands.

Problem of the Day

A Square Dance Club has 5 boys and 4 girls. How many different boy-girl pairs can the dancers make?
20 pairs

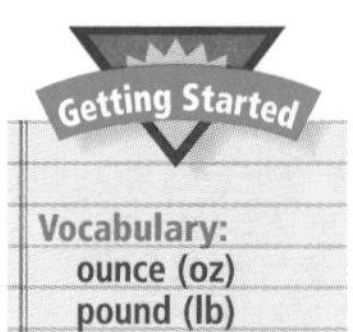

Ounce and Pound

Getting Started

Vocabulary:
ounce (oz)
pound (lb)
Glossary, p. 480

You can measure weight in **ounces (oz)** and **pounds (lb)**. Ounces and pounds are customary units of measure.

1 lb = 16 oz

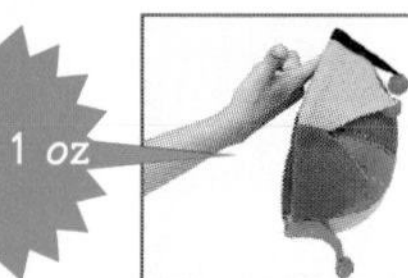

Which bag of popcorn weighs more?

You know that there are 16 oz in 1 lb. How many ounces are in 3 lbs?

16 + 16 + 16 = 48

3 lb = 48 oz

48 oz > 30 oz

So, the unpopped corn weighs more.

Show What You Know!

Which unit would you use to weigh each item? Write *ounce* or *pound*.

1. a box of crayons ounce
2. one apple ounce
3. a large dog pound
4. ten paper clips ounce
5. a full suitcase pound
6. a bicycle pound

Write the missing weight.

7. $\frac{1}{2}$ lb = ■ oz 8
8. 2 lb = ■ oz 32
9. 6 lb = ■ oz 96

More Practice Set 9.6, p. 468

1 Introduce

Build Understanding **Bring a small food scale to class. Invite students to weigh classroom objects and explore whether there are some objects that are too big to be weighed on the scale.**

Teach:

Emphasize these points:

- When measuring weight, it is important to choose the appropriate unit of measure.

Modeling Model the example. Ask:

- How could you find the number of ounces in 2 pounds? find the sum of 16 + 16
- How could you find the number of ounces in three pounds? find the sum of 16 + 16 + 16
- Is 24 ounces more or less than 2 pounds? less

2 Develop

Show What You Know!

Common Error Some students may choose inappropriate customary units for measuring weights. Have students choose ounce or pound as a unit of measurement for the following items: bricks, lb quarters, oz bag of potatoes, lb and a piece of chalk. oz See also Analyzing Errors, TE pp. 341A and 341B.

- Guide students in choosing whether to multiply or divide when converting between ounces and pounds.
- Ask students to state a rule that helps them solve exercise 7.

Basic Facts Just the Facts Basic Facts Workshop 9, p. 116

3 Summarize

- Remind students that ounces and pounds are customary units used to measure weight.
- Ask students to give examples showing why it is important to choose appropriate units of measure.

Ongoing Assessment You buy 17 ounces of grapes. Do the grapes weigh more or less than one pound? more

Math Journal: *Communicating*

Would you rather have 64 ounces of apples or five pounds of apples? Answers may vary, but should reflect the fact that 5 lb is greater than 64 oz.

Ounce & Pound Workshop

Review

Use with page 314.

15 minutes

Pick a Unit

Management teacher directed; whole class
Materials overhead projector or chalkboard

- Write the following list of items on the board or an overhead transparency.

3 crayons	Vacuum cleaner
Delivery truck	Cassette tape
Teacher's desk	Calf
Apple	Empty shoebox

- Ask students whether it would be better to describe each object's weight in ounces or pounds. Discuss their answers. Ask, Why did you choose that unit? Could you use both units for some items? Why or why not?
- If time permits, invite students to create their own lists. Then have them read their lists to a partner and ask, Which unit would you use?

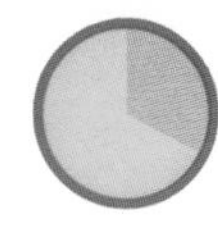

Activity

Use with page 314.

20 minutes

Ounce-Pound Hunt

Management small groups
Materials a variety of classroom objects

- Divide students into small groups. Have each group prepare a chart with two columns labeled "Ounces" and "Pounds." Tell students that they will get 1 point for an object in the Ounces column and 2 for an object in the Pounds column, and that their goal is to get exactly 10 points.
- Allow 5–10 minutes for the groups to look around the classroom. They should choose objects, decide whether the weight of each object should be described in ounces or in pounds, and record the names of the objects in the appropriate columns.
- When time is up, ask students to tally their points. Discuss what strategies they used to make sure they got exactly 10 points.

Basic Facts Workshop

Use with Lesson 9.6

Multiplying by 5

See also *Just the Facts*
- Support Masters
- Practice Worksheets
- Cumulative Practice

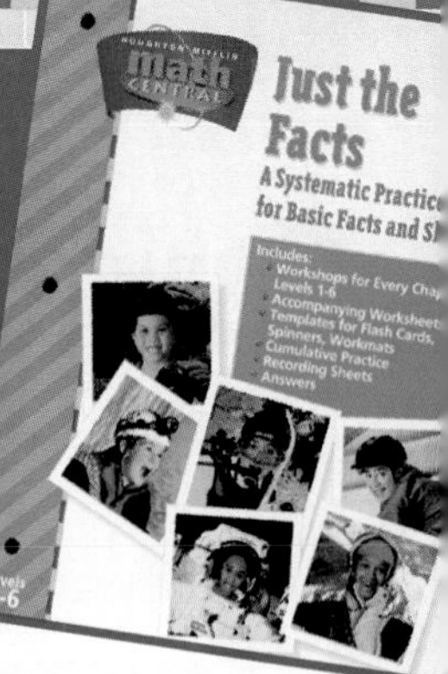

Review

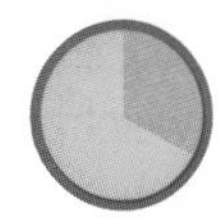

Skip-Count or Use 10's

20 minutes

Management whole class
Materials See also Just the Facts, Practice 9A–9B on pp. 136–137 for use with Lessons 9.10, 9.15; Cumulative Practice 8 on p. 271 for use with Lesson 9.11.

- Ask 5 students to stand in a line and hold up their hands as the class skip-counts by 5's to 50.
- Write 3×5 on the board. Ask students how to model this fact with hands or counters. Holding up three hands or using three rows of five counters shows the fact.
- Ask, If we know that $3 \times 5 = 15$, what other multiplication fact do we know? $5 \times 3 = 15$
- Repeat the activity, asking volunteers to direct students to show 5×5, 7×5, 4×5, 6×5, 9×5, and 8×5.
- Point out that another way to find 5's is to use 10's. Write $4 \times 10 = 40$ on the board. Ask students how knowing $4 \times 10 = 40$ could help them find 4×5.
  4×5 is half of 4×10, or 20.

4 x 10 = 40

4 x 5 = 20

- Have students use 10's to find 6×5, 3×5, 2×5, 8×5, 7×5, and 5×5.
- Ask students whether skip-counting or using a 10 is an easier way to find 5's. Answers will vary.

Practice

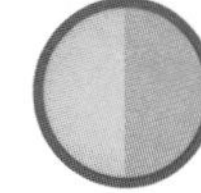

Make ×5 Flash Cards

30 minutes

Management individuals, then pairs
Materials for each student: 7 index cards; Just the Facts Support Masters 10, 14 (practice minutes, certificate) on pp. 291, 295; See also Practice 9A–9B on pp. 136–137 for use with Lessons 9.10, 9.15; Cumulative Practice 8 on p. 271 for use with Lesson 9.11.

- Distribute index cards to each student and have them create flash cards like those shown for the following facts: 5×5, 5×7, 7×5, 5×8, 8×5, 5×9, and 9×5.
- Remind students to write their names or initials on the backs of their cards. Then, have them find partners and review and practice their multiplication facts for 5.
- Remind students that they already know ten of the facts for 5. Have them add their previously made flash cards (5×1, 1×5, 5×2, 2×5, 5×4, 4×5, 5×3, 3×5, 5×6, and 6×5) to the new ones.
- For additional practice, students may want to take their flash cards home. Remind them to keep a record of the minutes they practice. Students may return completed records to school in exchange for a certificate.

Midchapter Review

for Pages 302–314

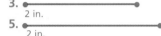

Problem Solving

Solve using any strategy. Show your work. (page 308)

1. You ran 120 laps in 3 days. Each day you ran 10 more than the day before. How many laps did you run on the third day? 50 laps

2. Suppose you glue these two figures together to make a house. You will tape the outside edges. About how many inches of tape do you need?
Estimates may vary. Accept a range from 60 in. to 70 in.

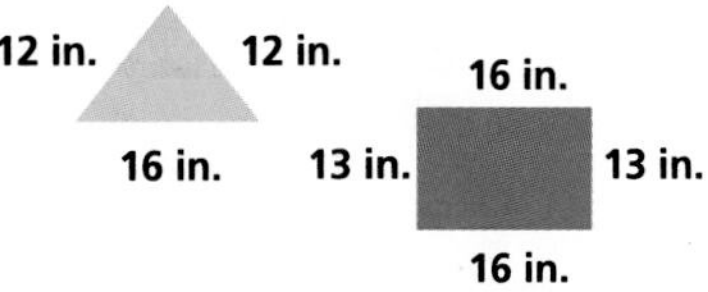

Concepts

Estimate the length. Then, measure to the nearest half inch. (pages 304, 306) Estimates may vary. Nearest half inch shown.

3. 2 in.
4. 3 in.
5. 2 in.
6. $1\frac{1}{2}$ in.

Choose the better unit of measure. Write *a* or *b*. (pages 312, 314)

7. soup in a bowl a
 a. cup
 b. quart

8. a computer b
 a. ounce
 b. pound

9. a calculator a
 a. ounce
 b. pound

Skills

Write the perimeter. (page 308)

10. 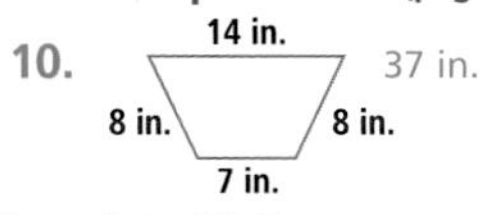

37 in.

11. 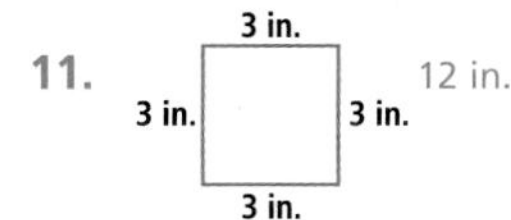

12 in.

Complete. Write >, <, or =. (pages 310, 312)

12. 1 ft ● 12 in. =
13. 1 mi ● 100 ft >
14. 1 qt ● 1 gal <

Complete the number sentence. (page 314)

15. 16 oz = ■ lb 1
16. 8 oz = ■ lb $\frac{1}{2}$
17. 5 lb = ■ oz 80

315

Meeting Individual Needs

Students Acquiring English

Some students may need assistance on the Midchapter Review.

- Be prepared to read directions aloud to students.
- Focus special attention on word problems. Expect to paraphrase, diagram, or draw an explanation of the word problem.
- Review important vocabulary words that have been previously introduced.
- Review titles and other elements of graphs and charts.

Additional Assessment Resources

Test, Practice, Management Program

Use the *Test, Practice, Management Program* to create, administer, and score tests as well as generate practice sets. Questions are correlated to the Lesson Objectives.

Midchapter Review

Scoring Chart

Item	Points
1–2	13 points each
3–9	6 points each
10–17	4 points each
TOTAL	100 points or 100%

Problem Solving

Give from 0 to 13 points per answer, based on how well students meet the following criteria:

Problem 1

- A strategy is seen through to a correct solution.
- Work is shown clearly.

Problem 2

- A strategy is seen through to a correct solution.
- Estimates are reasonable.

Concepts and Skills

If students are having difficulty in particular areas, use the Reteaching Worksheets listed below.

- 66 Measuring and Drawing Lines to the Nearest Inch and Half Inch, p. 183
- 67 Perimeter, p. 184
- 68 Choosing the Appropriate Type of Measure, p. 185
- 69 Choosing the Appropriate Unit of Measure, p. 186
- 70 Comparing Measures, p. 187

Common Error Alert

If students are making frequent errors, see Analyzing Errors, TE pp. 341A–341B.

Item Analysis

Item	Objectives
1–2	To use Work Backwards and other strategies to solve problems (9H)
3–6	To estimate and measure length (9A)
7–9	To measure capacity, weight, and mass (9C)
10–11	To find the perimeter of a polygon (9B)
12–17	To find single equivalencies for customary and metric units (9D)

Math World

Roman Numerals

Background Roman numerals are still used today for numbering things, such as the topics in outlines, the names of kings and queens, and to record dates on some monuments and buildings. Roman use of small numerals in relation to large ones parallels the way we tell time. For example, IX indicates one less than ten, and VI one more than 5, much as we use the expressions "quarter to" and "quarter after" the hour.

Critical Thinking

- Write the numbers 1–20 on the board with their Roman equivalents. Discuss with students how the Roman numbering system worked. Ask, How would the Romans have written 30? XXX 24? XXIV
- Introduce the Roman symbols L (50), C (100), D (500), and M (1000). Ask students to interpret the number MDCCLXXVI, found at the bottom of the pyramid on the back of a $1 bill. 1776
- Ask, How easy would it be to multiply using Roman numerals? Why?
- Have students discuss and compile a list of ways Roman numerals are used today.

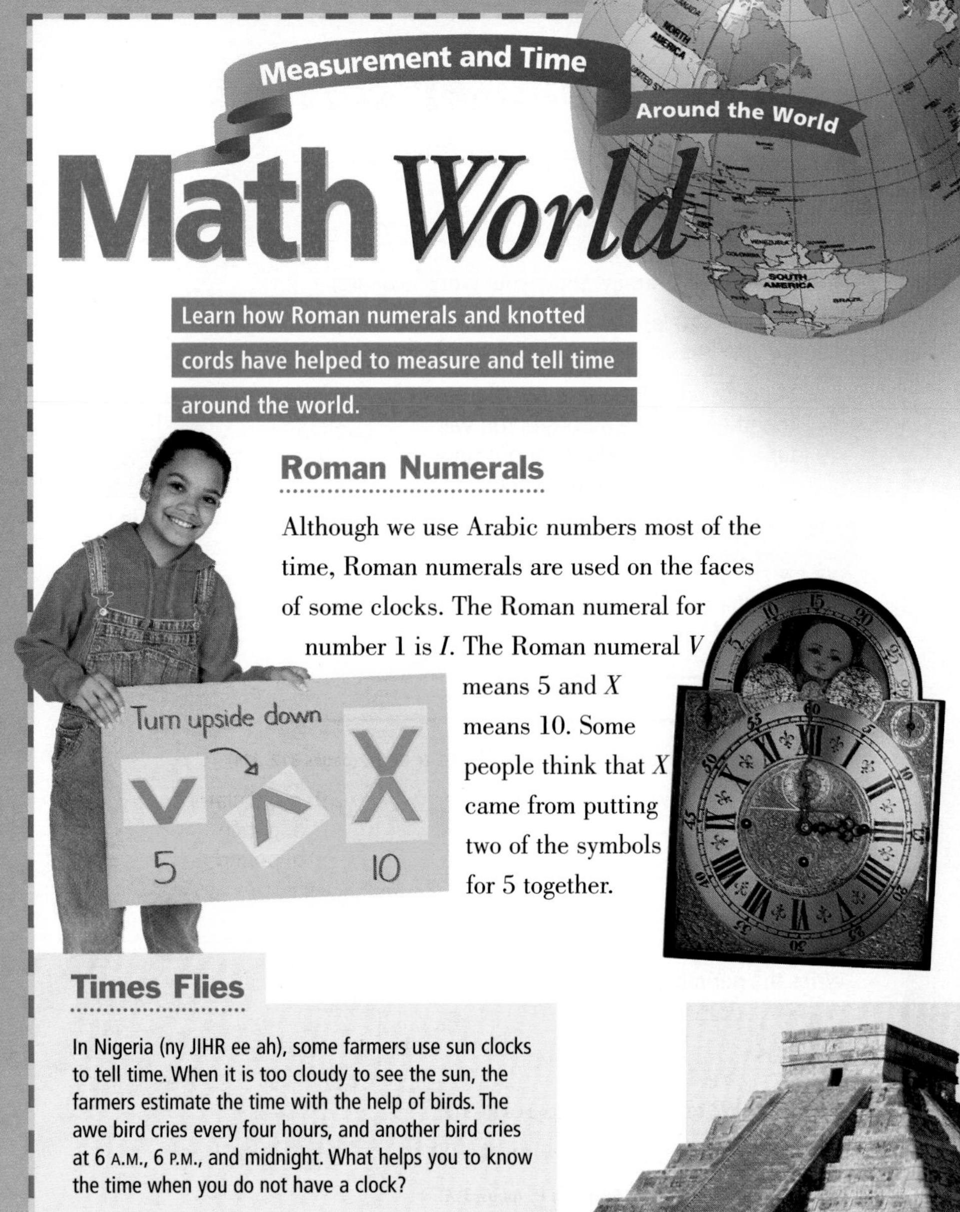

Measurement and Time
Around the World
Math World
Learn how Roman numerals and knotted cords have helped to measure and tell time around the world.
Roman Numerals
Although we use Arabic numbers most of the time, Roman numerals are used on the faces of some clocks. The Roman numeral for number 1 is *I*. The Roman numeral *V* means 5 and *X* means 10. Some people think that *X* came from putting two of the symbols for 5 together.
Turn upside down
V
5
X
10

Times Flies

In Nigeria (ny JIHR ee ah), some farmers use sun clocks to tell time. When it is too cloudy to see the sun, the farmers estimate the time with the help of birds. The awe bird cries every four hours, and another bird cries at 6 A.M., 6 P.M., and midnight. What helps you to know the time when you do not have a clock?

316

For More Information

Word Origins

clock

From old North French *cloque*, in turn from late Latin *clocca*, "bell."

In medieval times, before the invention of the mechanical clock, Europeans noted the time by the ringing of church bells that marked the hours of prayer services.

Discuss with students different ways people used to tell the time before clocks were invented.

Literature

America the Beautiful: New Mexico
Children's Press, 1988
R. Conrad Stein

Enchantment of the World: Mexico
Children's Press, 1984
R. Conrad Stein

Maps & Globes
Thomas Y. Crowell, 1985
Jack Knowlton

Measuring Up: Experiments, Puzzles and Games Exploring Measurement
Maxwell Macmillan 1995
Sandra Markle

Mexico, Giant of the South
Dillon Press, 1983
Eileen Latell Smith

The Sun Rises and Other Questions About Time and Seasons
Kingfisher, 1996
Brenda Walpole

Try This! EGYPTIAN MEASURING CORD

People in ancient Egypt sometimes used knotted cords to measure lengths. Follow these steps to make an Egyptian measuring cord.

1. A *palm* was a unit of length in ancient Egypt. One palm was equal to the width of a person's hand.
2. Tie a knot at the end of a long piece of string. Tie another knot 1 palm away.
3. Keep tying knots that are 1 palm apart. Stop when you have tied 14 knots.
4. Measure at least four objects with your knotted cord. Record the lengths in palms in a chart.

A Step a Day

Thousands of years ago, the Maya built this pyramid in Mexico. All 4 sides of the pyramid have 90 steps, which makes 360 steps in all. The Mayan calendar had 360 regular days. Scientists think that the Maya made a step for every day in their year.

Respond

Work with a partner . . .
to read more Roman numerals.

Internet:
Houghton Mifflin Education Place
Explore the Math Center at
http://www.eduplace.com

317

Egyptian Measuring Cord

Background A standard Egyptian "palm" was equal to about 7.5 centimeters. Each finger in the palm represented the unit. Sticks divided into these units were used to measure the annual rise and fall of the Nile.

Critical Thinking Have students compare the measurements they made using their cords. Discuss: Do you think Egyptian builders used the width of their own hands to measure things? Why, or why not?

A Step a Day

Background The Maya had one of the most sophisticated mathematical systems of any ancient people. They knew the principle of zero as a place holder, and though their calendar year was 360 days long, their understanding of fractions let them compute the actual length of a year with great precision.

Activity

- Tell students that the Mayan number system used base 20, as compared with our base 10. Discuss what this would mean with regard to numerical symbols and place value.

Technology

Internet: Education Place
http://www.eduplace.com
Houghton Mifflin's Education Place **Mathematics Center** provides teacher and student support, such as links to other Internet sites.

Ultimate Writing & Creativity Center
Students can use the *Ultimate Writing & Creativity Center* for all their writing and publishing activities.

Kid to Kid

Project Ask students how they think children in other town or cities might tell time without a clock.

Suggest:

- *What could they know from movements of the sun?*
- *What other ways do people have of telling time?*

Invite students to use the Internet or other student networks to learn about how people tell time when there is no clock handy.

Connecting

Planning at a Glance

Objectives To measure to the nearest centimeter; to estimate length

Materials centimeter ruler (TR34), place-value blocks

Optional Resources

- Reteach 9.7; Practice 9.7; Enrichment 9.7
- Daily Cumul. Review, p. 118
- Math Center: How-To Card 32
- Every Day Counts
- **TAB**, TE pp. 302E–302F, 302J
- **Problem of the Day**, 118, p. 59; Flip Chart, p. 59b

MATHKEYS *Unlocking Measurement* 3–6, Level 3, Activity 2

Students Acquiring English

Write the words *centimeter* and *decimeter.* Help students read the words aloud. Then ask volunteers to show 1 centimeter with ones blocks. Ask another volunteer to put ten ones blocks together to make a decimeter. Ask which one is bigger.

Problem of the Day

A driveway is 50 feet long. The driveway starts and ends with red reflectors. Reflectors also appear every 10 feet along both sides of the driveway. How many reflectors are used in all?
12 reflectors

LESSON 7

Centimeter

See if one of your fingers is 1 cm wide!

Getting Started

What You'll Need:
- centimeter ruler

Vocabulary:
- centimeter (cm)
- decimeter (dm)
- metric system
- Glossary, p. 480

Scientists often measure small things in units of length called **centimeters (cm)**. Centimeters are units in the **metric system** of measurement.

10 centimeters equals 1 decimeter (dm)
10 cm = 1 dm

1 dm

Suppose you planted some seeds one month ago. How tall did your plants grow in one month?

You can measure them to the nearest centimeter.

Here's A Way! Measure in centimeters.

1. This plant is between 10 cm and 11 cm tall.
2. The top of the plant is nearer to the 11-cm mark than to the 10-cm mark.

So, the plant is 11 cm tall to the nearest centimeter.

Talk About It!

- How could you use ones blocks to show the height of the plant? You could stack 11 ones blocks.
- How tall is the plant to the nearest decimeter? 1 decimeter

---

1 Introduce

Building Understanding Have students use tens rods to measure classroom objects.

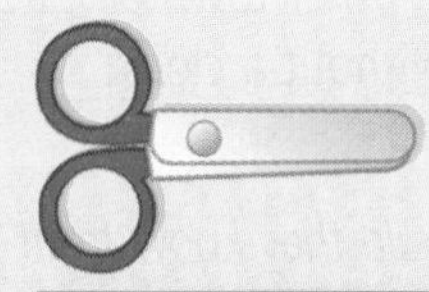

Ask, How many centimeters long is each rod? 10 cm **How long is your object?** Answers will vary.

Teach: Here's A Way!

Emphasize this point:

- A length in decimeters can be renamed in centimeters by multiplying by 10.

2 Develop

Show What You Know!

Common Error If students line up the centimeter ruler incorrectly, remind them that the edge of the object they are measuring should line up with 0 on the ruler. See also Analyzing Errors, TE pp. 341A and 341B.

- Remind students that *cm* is the abbreviation for *centimeters* and *dm* is the abbreviation for *decimeters*.

Work it Out!

- Remind students to make sure they are using the correct units for exercises 13–17.
- Have students explain the reasoning behind their answers to problem 19.

3 Summarize

- Remind students that the method of measuring is the same for metric measures as for customary measures.
- Remind students that a length in decimeters can be converted to centimeters by multiplying by 10.

Ongoing Assessment Choose one of your textbooks. Estimate its length and width in centimeters. Measure to verify. Answers will vary.

Math Journal: *Communicating*

Why do you think there are both metric units, such as the centimeter, and customary units, such as the inch?
Answers will vary; accept reasonable responses.

Show What You Know!

1. Find two objects that are each about 1 cm long.
   Answers will vary. Possible answer: raisin, staple
2. Find two objects that are each about 1 dm long.
   Answers will vary. Possible answer: pencil, computer mouse

First, estimate. Then measure to the nearest centimeter.

3. 
   2 cm

4. 
   5 cm

5. 
   3 cm

6. length of your little finger
   Answers will vary.
7. perimeter of a box of crayons
   Answers will vary.
8. **Critical Thinking** If you wanted to measure something precisely, would it be better to measure in centimeters or decimeters? Explain. centimeters, because they are smaller units

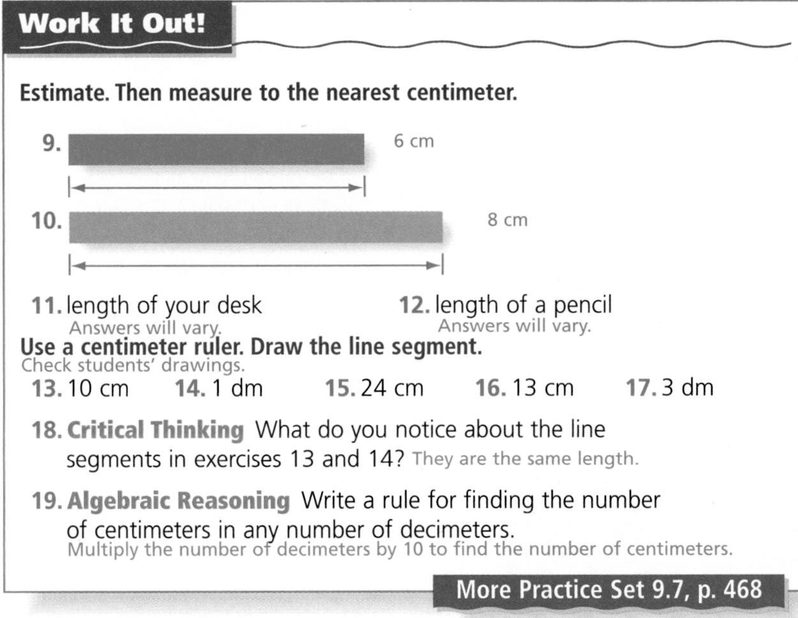

Work It Out!

Estimate. Then measure to the nearest centimeter.

9. 6 cm
10. 8 cm
11. length of your desk
    Answers will vary.
12. length of a pencil
    Answers will vary.

Use a centimeter ruler. Draw the line segment.
Check students' drawings.

13. 10 cm
14. 1 dm
15. 24 cm
16. 13 cm
17. 3 dm
18. **Critical Thinking** What do you notice about the line segments in exercises 13 and 14? They are the same length.
19. **Algebraic Reasoning** Write a rule for finding the number of centimeters in any number of decimeters.
    Multiply the number of decimeters by 10 to find the number of centimeters.

More Practice Set 9.7, p. 468

319

Meeting Individual Needs

Extra Support

To the Centimeter ***(visual, kinesthetic)*** Have student pairs practice measuring classroom items using ones blocks. They should record their results and regroup blocks to record the same measurement to the nearest decimeter.

Alternate Approach

- Reteach Worksheet 9.7
- **TAB** See TE pp. 302E–302F.

Students Acquiring English

See Language Connections, Ch. 9.

Challenge

Have pairs of students use a map with a map scale that is in centimeters. They should choose 5 locations, measure and record in centimeters the distances between the locations, and use the map scale to calculate actual distance.

Practice

Math Center Use How-To Card 32, *Ant Kingdom*, to have students practice measuring to the nearest centimeter.

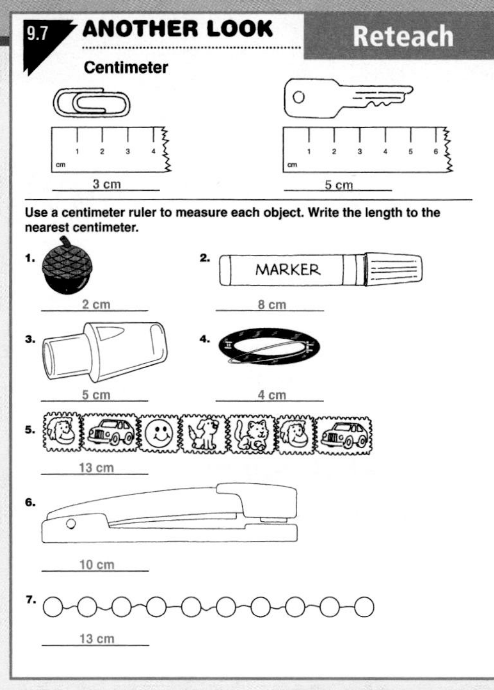

9.7 ANOTHER LOOK — Reteach

Centimeter

3 cm — 5 cm

Use a centimeter ruler to measure each object. Write the length to the nearest centimeter.

1. 2 cm
2. MARKER 8 cm
3. 5 cm
4. 4 cm
5. 13 cm
6. 10 cm
7. 13 cm

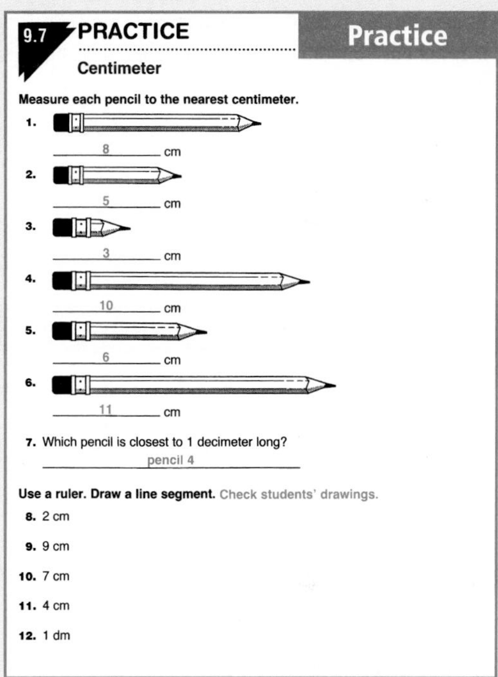

9.7 PRACTICE — Practice

Centimeter

Measure each pencil to the nearest centimeter.

1. 8 cm
2. 5 cm
3. 3 cm
4. 10 cm
5. 6 cm
6. 11 cm
7. Which pencil is closest to 1 decimeter long? pencil 4

Use a ruler. Draw a line segment. Check students' drawings.

8. 2 cm
9. 9 cm
10. 7 cm
11. 4 cm
12. 1 dm

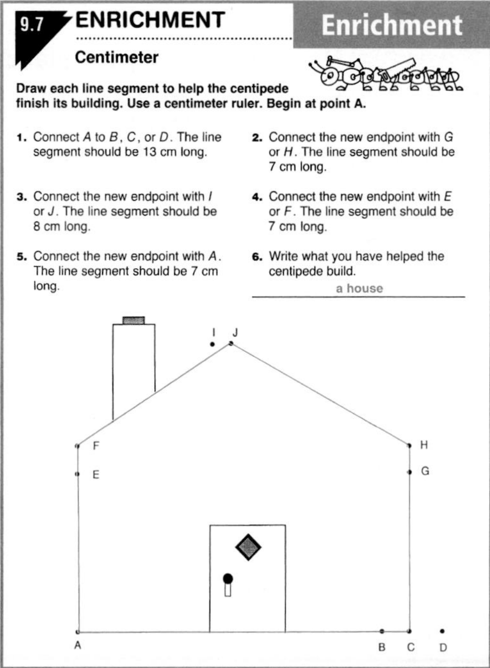

9.7 ENRICHMENT — Enrichment

Centimeter

Draw each line segment to help the centipede finish its building. Use a centimeter ruler. Begin at point A.

1. Connect *A* to *B*, *C*, or *D*. The line segment should be 13 cm long.
2. Connect the new endpoint with *G* or *H*. The line segment should be 7 cm long.
3. Connect the new endpoint with *I* or *J*. The line segment should be 8 cm long.
4. Connect the new endpoint with *E* or *F*. The line segment should be 7 cm long.
5. Connect the new endpoint with *A*. The line segment should be 7 cm long.
6. Write what you have helped the centipede build. a house

LESSON 9.8

Activity

Planning at a Glance

Objectives To investigate using meter and kilometer; to choose the appropriate unit

Materials tens blocks, scissors, tape

Optional Resources

- Reteach 9.8; Practice 9.8; Enrichment 9.8
- Daily Cumul. Review, p. 119
- Math Center: Act. Card 52
- Every Day Counts
- **TAB**, TE pp. 302E–302F, 302J
- **Problem of the Day**, 119, p. 60; Flip Chart, p. 60a

Students Acquiring English

Review the terms used in exercises 10, 11, 13–16. Students may benefit from drawing quick pictures to illustrate each one.

Problem of the Day

Timothy saw two toy dinosaurs he liked at a museum shop. The more expensive dinosaur cost 3 times as much as the other. Together, both dinosaur toys cost $8. Find the price of each dinosaur.
$2 and $6

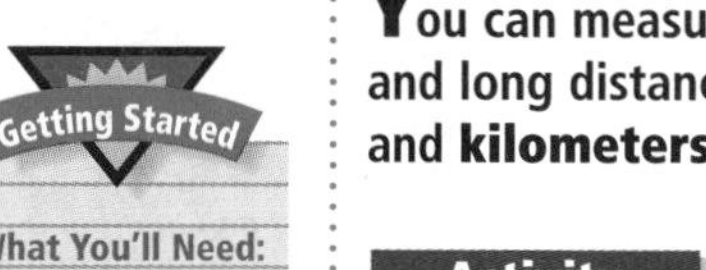

Lesson 8 Meters and Kilometers

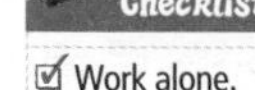

Cooperative Learning Checklist
- ☑ Work alone.
- ☑ Work with a partner.
- ☑ Work with a group.

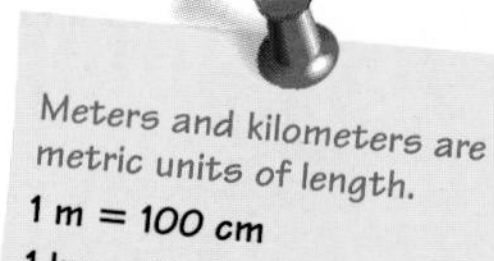

Getting Started

What You'll Need:
- tens blocks
- scissors
- tape

Vocabulary:
- kilometer (km)
- meter (m)
- Glossary, p. 480

You can measure large objects and long distances in **meters (m)** and **kilometers (km)**.

Meters and kilometers are metric units of length.
1 m = 100 cm
1 km = 1000 m

Activity

1 You know 1 m equals 100 cm. A tens block is 10 cm long. Use tens blocks to show how long 1 meter is.
10 tens blocks

2 Make a strip of paper 1 m long. Use your row of tens blocks to measure. You may need to tape several strips together.
- Find some things in your classroom that you think are about 1 m long.
- Use your meter strip to measure them. List the things you measured and their lengths. Answers will vary. Possible answers: teacher's desk, bookshelf

#3. Answers will vary. Possible answer: distance from home to school, distance in a race.

3 This bridge shows about 1 km. You know 1 km equals 1000 m. List five things that could be measured in kilometers.

1 Introduce

Motivate **Have students try the standing long jump, marking off the distances with tape. Tell students that metric units could be used to measure the results.**

Teach: Activity

Emphasize these points:

- The abbreviation for *meter* is *m;* the abbreviation for *kilometer* is *km.*
- When measuring distance, it is important to choose the appropriate unit of measure.

Modeling Model Step 1. Ask:

- How many centimeters are in a tens block? 10 cm
- How many 10-centimeter groups make 100 centimeters? 10

2 Develop

Show What You Know!

- Guide students in choosing the appropriate metric unit for the measurement being made.
- Have students discuss their reasoning for exercise 12.
- Ask students to discuss their answers for exercises 13–16.

3 Summarize

- Remind students they should think about the length or distance that they will measure before choosing centimeters, meters, or kilometers.
- Remind students of the importance of choosing the appropriate unit.

Ongoing Assessment Would you report the distance across our state in meters or kilometers? Explain. in km; they are more appropriate for long distance

Math Journal: *Communicating*

How could you find out how many centimeters there are in 1 kilometer? Multiply 1000 meters by 100 centimeters.

Show What You Know!

1. Copy and complete the table.

m	1000	2000 ?	3000	4000	5000 ?	6000 ?	7000	8000	9000 ?	10,000 ?
km	1	2	3	4 ?	5	6	7 ?	8 ?	9	10 ?

2. **Critical Thinking** How many meters are in half of a kilometer? 500 m
3. How many centimeters are in half of a meter? 50 cm

Write >, <, or =. Use the table that you completed if you need to.

4. 100 cm ■ 1 m =
5. 10 m ■ 10 km <
6. 2500 m ■ 2 km >
7. 10 m ■ 1 km <
8. 2000 m ■ 20 km <
9. 3 km ■ 300 m >

Which unit would you use to measure each? Write *meter* or *kilometer*.

10. length of your classroom meter
11. distance between cities kilometer
12. **Critical Thinking** When is it better to measure in kilometers rather than meters? Answers will vary. Possible answer: when the distance or length is more than can be measured with a meter strip.

Choose the better estimate. Write *a* or *b*.

13. depth of a swimming pool b
    a. 3 cm b. 3 m
14. length of a table a
    a. 1 m b. 1 km
15. length of a ball field a
    a. 100 m b. 100 km
16. length of a skateboard a
    a. 75 cm b. 75 m
17. **Estimation** Estimate the perimeter of your classroom chalkboard in meters. Write your estimate. Then measure the perimeter. How close was your estimate? Answers will vary.
18. **Create Your Own** Measure the perimeter of a room in meters. Draw and label an outline of the room. Check students' drawings.

More Practice Set 9.8, p. 469

Meeting Individual Needs

Extra Support

In Meters and Kilometers *(visual)* Invite students to use their meter strips from step 2 to measure the classroom. Discuss the results. Then have pairs of students estimate the following distances in centimeters, meters, or kilometers, and discuss their estimates with the class:

a. the length of a soccer field
b. the distance from school to the nearest shopping mall
c. the length of the school building
d. the height of a desk

Alternate Approach

- Reteach Worksheet 9.8
- **TAB** See TE pp. 302E–302F.

Students Acquiring English

See **Language Connections**, Ch. 9.

Practice

Math Center Use Activity Card 52, *String Along,* to have students practice using a meter as a unit of measure.

Challenge Use Activity Card 52 and have students continue as described in Now Try This!

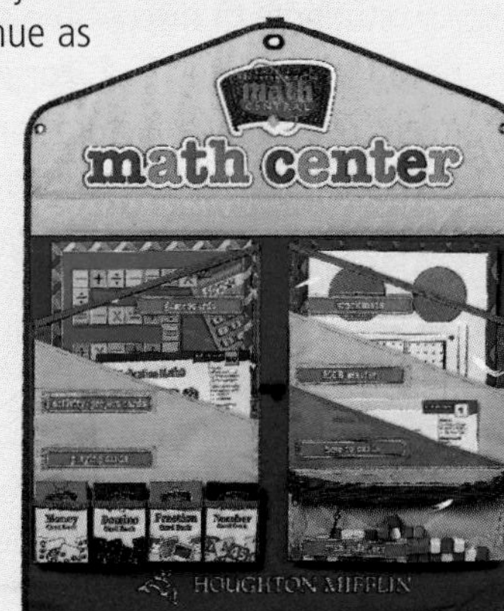

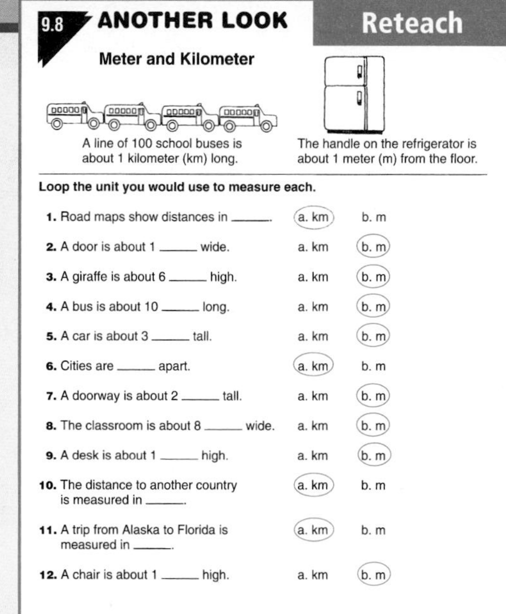

Reteach

9.8 **ANOTHER LOOK**
Meter and Kilometer

A line of 100 school buses is about 1 kilometer (km) long.

The handle on the refrigerator is about 1 meter (m) from the floor.

Loop the unit you would use to measure each.

1. Road maps show distances in ____. (a. km) b. m
2. A door is about 1 ____ wide. a. km (b. m)
3. A giraffe is about 6 ____ high. a. km (b. m)
4. A bus is about 10 ____ long. a. km (b. m)
5. A car is about 3 ____ tall. a. km (b. m)
6. Cities are ____ apart. (a. km) b. m
7. A doorway is about 2 ____ tall. a. km (b. m)
8. The classroom is about 8 ____ wide. a. km (b. m)
9. A desk is about 1 ____ high. a. km (b. m)
10. The distance to another country is measured in ____. (a. km) b. m
11. A trip from Alaska to Florida is measured in ____. (a. km) b. m
12. A chair is about 1 ____ high. a. km (b. m)

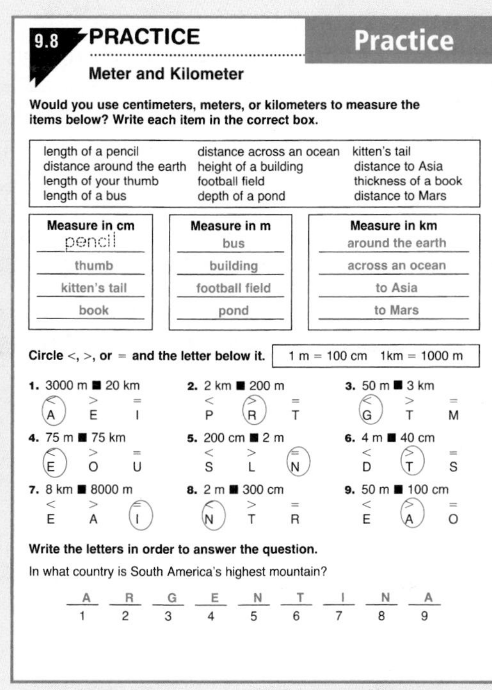

Practice

9.8 **PRACTICE**
Meter and Kilometer

Would you use centimeters, meters, or kilometers to measure the items below? Write each item in the correct box.

length of a pencil
distance around the earth
length of your thumb
length of a bus
distance across an ocean
height of a building
football field
depth of a pond
kitten's tail
distance to Asia
thickness of a book
distance to Mars

Measure in cm	Measure in m	Measure in km
pencil	bus	around the earth
thumb	building	across an ocean
kitten's tail	football field	to Asia
book	pond	to Mars

Circle <, >, or = and the letter below it. 1 m = 100 cm 1km = 1000 m

1. 3000 m ■ 20 km — (< A) > E = I
2. 2 km ■ 200 m — < P (> R) = T
3. 50 m ■ 3 km — (< G) > T = M
4. 75 m ■ 75 km — (< E) > O = U
5. 200 cm ■ 2 m — < S > L (= N)
6. 4 m ■ 40 cm — < D (> T) = S
7. 8 km ■ 8000 m — < E > A (= I)
8. 2 m ■ 300 cm — (< N) > T = R
9. 50 m ■ 100 cm — < E (> A) = O

Write the letters in order to answer the question.

In what country is South America's highest mountain?

A R G E N T I N A
1 2 3 4 5 6 7 8 9

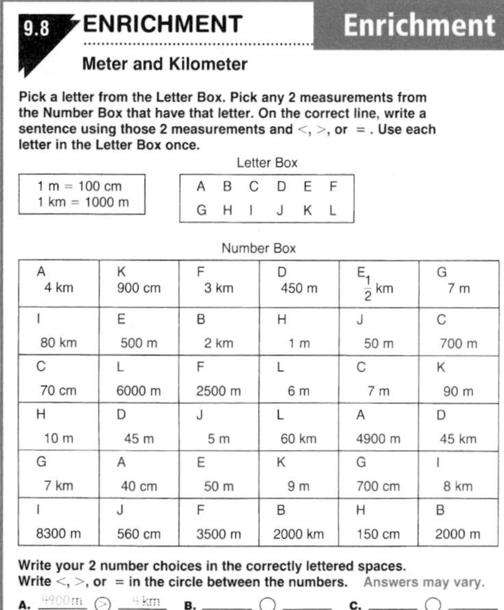

Enrichment

9.8 **ENRICHMENT**
Meter and Kilometer

Pick a letter from the Letter Box. Pick any 2 measurements from the Number Box that have that letter. On the correct line, write a sentence using those 2 measurements and <, >, or =. Use each letter in the Letter Box once.

1 m = 100 cm
1 km = 1000 m

Letter Box

A	B	C	D	E	F
G	H	I	J	K	L

Number Box

A 4 km	K 900 cm	F 3 km	D 450 m	E $\frac{1}{2}$ km	G 7 m
I 80 km	E 500 m	B 2 km	H 1 m	J 50 m	C 700 m
C 70 cm	L 6000 m	F 2500 m	L 6 m	C 7 m	K 90 m
H 10 m	D 45 m	J 5 m	L 60 km	A 4900 m	D 45 km
G 7 km	A 40 cm	E 50 m	K 9 m	G 700 cm	I 8 km
I 8300 m	J 560 cm	F 3500 m	B 2000 km	H 150 cm	B 2000 m

Write your 2 number choices in the correctly lettered spaces. Write <, >, or = in the circle between the numbers. Answers may vary.

A. 4900 m (>) 4 km B. ____ ○ ____ C. ____ ○ ____
D. ____ ○ ____ E. ____ ○ ____ F. ____ ○ ____
G. ____ ○ ____ H. ____ ○ ____ I. ____ ○ ____
J. ____ ○ ____ K. ____ ○ ____ L. ____ ○ ____

LESSON 9.9

Problem Solving

Planning at a Glance

Objective To use the Work Backward strategy to solve problems

Materials none

Optional Resources

- Reteach 9.9; Practice 9.9; Enrichment 9.9
- Daily Cumul. Review, p. 120
- Math Center: Project Card 9
- Every Day Counts
- TAB, TE p. 302E–302F, 302J
- Problem of the Day, 120, p. 60; Flip Chart, p. 60b

MATHKEYS *Unlocking Measurement 3–6*, Level 3, Activity 8

Students Acquiring English

Building Reading Strategies Ask volunteers to do (or act out doing) something backwards, such as walking, writing, or reading a book. Explain that when we solve word problems by working backward, we use what happened at the end to find the answer to something at the beginning or middle.

Problem of the Day

Find the pattern. Then continue it twice more.

Problem Solving : Strategy

Problem Solving
Work Backward

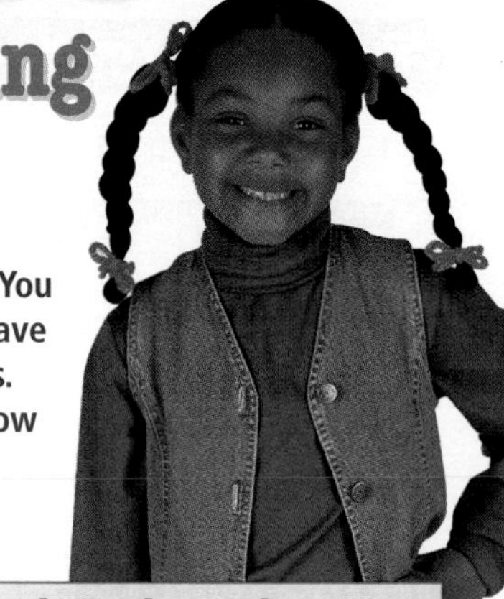

Suppose you bought some yarn. You used half of it to tie boxes. You gave 3 ft of it to a friend for her braids. Now you have 5 ft of yarn left. How much yarn did you buy? You can work backward to find out.

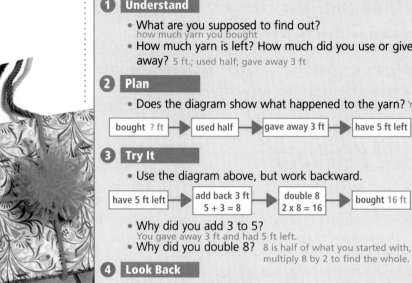

Here's A Way! Use Work Backward.

1 Understand

- What are you supposed to find out? how much yarn you bought
- How much yarn is left? How much did you use or give away? 5 ft.; used half; gave away 3 ft

2 Plan

- Does the diagram show what happened to the yarn? Yes

bought ? ft → used half → gave away 3 ft → have 5 ft left

3 Try It

- Use the diagram above, but work backward.

have 5 ft left → add back 3 ft $5 + 3 = 8$ → double 8 $2 \times 8 = 16$ → bought 16 ft

- Why did you add 3 to 5? You gave away 3 ft and had 5 ft left.
- Why did you double 8? 8 is half of what you started with, multiply 8 by 2 to find the whole.

4 Look Back

- You bought 16 ft of yarn. Check by working forward. $16 \div 2 = 8$; $8 - 3 = 5$; 5 ft left

1 Introduce

Explore **Ask, If you ate 2 cookies, gave away 4, and have 2 left over, how many cookies did you start with?** 8

Teach: Here's A Way!

Emphasize these points:

- Sometimes you can use what you know to work backward and solve a problem.
- Drawing a diagram can help you see what you need to find out.

Modeling Model Step 2. Ask:

- What operation do I use to show that I used half of the yarn for boxes? division by 2
- What operation do I use to show I gave 3 ft of yarn to a friend? subtract 3
- How much yarn was left over? 5 ft

2 Develop

Show What You Know!

Have students compare the steps they followed to solve problem 1, and discuss their answers to the Critical Thinking question.

Work It Out!

- Ask students to discuss the strategies they used for problems 3–7. For example, they might use Draw a Picture for problem 3, Guess and Check for problem 4, Look for a Pattern for problem 6, and Work Backward for problems 5 and 7.

Using Reading Strategies Help students to use the Monitor strategy as they read the Problem Solving exercises. Ask, What should you keep in mind as you reread the problems? See TE p. 302J.

3 Summarize

- Remind students that sometimes they can work backward to solve a problem.
- Point out that if students use Work Backward to solve a problem, they can work forward again to check their work.

Ongoing Assessment To get to school, it takes you 5 minutes to walk to the bus stop. Then it takes you 20 minutes on the bus. If you have to be at school at 8:30 A.M., what time do you need to leave the house? 8:05 A.M.

Math Journal: ***Communicating***

What kinds of problems have you used the Work Backward strategy to solve? Answers will vary.

Show What You Know!

Use Work Backward to solve the problem. Make a diagram if it helps.

1. Suppose you have a strip of paper. You cut it in half. Then you cut off 6 in. You are left with 8 in. How long was the strip when you started? 28 in.

2. **Critical Thinking** How did working backward help you to solve the problem? Answers will vary. Possible answer: Starting with what is left will help you find the original length of the strip.

Work It Out!

Use Work Backward or another strategy to solve the problem.

3. Read the directions from the theater to Joe's Diner. Now write the directions from the diner to the theater. Hint: You can use squared paper to draw a map before you write. See Additional Answers

From the Royal Theater to Joe's Diner

1. Leave the theater, turn right, and walk 3 blocks.
2. Turn left and walk 2 blocks.
3. Turn left and walk half a block. Joe's Diner will be on your right.

From Joe's Diner to the Royal Theater

1. Leave the diner, turn left and

4. Two numbers that come one after the other add up to 35. What are the numbers? 17 and 18

5. At the Craft Shack you bought 2 of the same paintbrushes. You also bought a set of paints for $6.00. You spent $12.00. How much did each paintbrush cost? $3.00

6. **Patterns** Each figure is made from 1-in. squares. Draw Figure 4 and Figure 5. What is the perimeter of each? What would be the perimeter of Figure 9? Figure 4: 16 in.; Figure 5: 20 in. Fig. 9: 36 in. For art, see Additional Answers

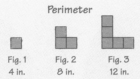

Perimeter

Fig. 1	Fig. 2	Fig. 3
4 in.	8 in.	12 in.

7. The Craft Shack is having a half-price sale on clay. You buy 1 package of clay. You pay with a $10 bill and receive $4.00 change. What is the regular price of the clay? $12.00

Share Your Thinking

8. How could you use Work Backward to solve problem 7? Answers will vary, but should reflect an understanding of the problem

323

Meeting Individual Needs

Extra Support

Start with the Answer *(visual)* Have student pairs choose a number from 1 to 9. Have them create a problem that has their number as the answer. Then, let students trade problems with another pair to solve.

Alternate Approach

- Reteach Worksheet 9.9
- **TAB** See TE pp. 302E–302F.

Students Acquiring English

See **Language Connections**, Ch. 9.

Challenge

You collect $1.00 for recycling cans and bottles. You got 10¢ each for the bottles, and 5¢ each for the cans. $\frac{3}{4}$ of the items you recycled were cans. How many bottles did you recycle? 4 bottles

Practice

Math Center For more problem solving practice, see Project Card 9, *Construction Site.*

9.9 ANOTHER LOOK — Reteach

Problem Solving Strategy: Work Backward

You divide a bag of peanuts into 4 equal piles and give a pile to each of 3 friends. You keep one pile for yourself and eat 5 peanuts. Now you have 4 peanuts left. How many peanuts were in the bag?

1. Understand
- You know how many peanuts you ate and how many you have left. You also know that you and 3 friends each started with the same number of peanuts.

2. Plan
- Work backward. First, find out how many peanuts you had in your pile before you ate any. Then, multiply that number by the number of equal piles you made.

3. Try It
- I have 4 peanuts left. I ate 5 peanuts. $4 + 5 = 9$
  Since my pile had 9 peanuts, all 4 equal piles each had 9 peanuts. $4 \times 9 = 36$

4. Look Back
- The bag had 36 peanuts when I bought it.

Solve. Use Work Backward when you can.

1. Some students from your school are in a parade. Half of them are playing in the band. The other half are marching in 3 rows of 4 as they twirl batons. How many students from your school are in the parade? 24 students
2. The pet store is having a sale on hamster food. You can buy 2 boxes for the price of 1 box. You buy 4 boxes and give the clerk a $5.00 bill. Your change is $1.00. What is the regular price of 1 box of hamster food? $2.00

9.9 PRACTICE — Practice

Problem Solving Strategy: Work Backward

Solve. Use Work Backward when you can.

1. Fill in the blanks. What is the perimeter of the shape? 20 inches 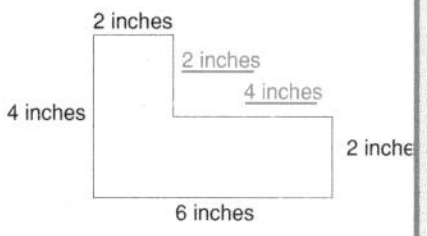
   (Figure labels: 2 inches; 2 inches; 4 inches; 4 inches; 2 inches; 6 inches)
2. You have 8 toothpicks. Each toothpick is 3 inches long. How many 3-inch squares can you make with the toothpicks? 2 squares
3. Discover the magic number using these clues:
   - If you count by 3's you will say the number.
   - It is an even number.
   - It is less than 20.
   - If you count by 4's you will say the number.
   What is the magic number? 12
4. Find the missing number. 10 + 5 − 3 + 4 = 16
5. I am 10 years old and my father is 40. How old was I when my father was 35 years old? 5 years old
6. The chart below shows how fast a bean plant might grow. If the plant grows approximately the same amount each week, how tall was the plant when it was measured the first week? 4 inches tall

Week 1	Week 2	Week 3	Week 4	Week 5
	8 in.	12 in.	16 in.	20 in.

9.9 ENRICHMENT — Enrichment

Problem Solving Strategy: Work Backward

Solve. Use Work Backward when you can.

1. You start with a mystery number. You multiply it by 2. Then you add 6. Then you subtract 4. The answer is 14. What is the mystery number? 6
2. You start with another mystery number. You multiply it by 3. Then you subtract 6. Then you add 12. The answer is 36. What is the mystery number? 10
3. You and a friend are building a clubhouse. You cut off half a board. Your friend cuts 3 feet off the same board. The board that is left is 2 feet long. How long was the original board? 10 feet
4. Two numbers in a row add up to 9. These numbers are 4 and 5. What two numbers in a row add up to 45? 22 and 23
5. The perimeter of a rectangle is 24 inches. The width of the rectangle is 4 inches. What is the length? 8 inches

Activity

Planning at a Glance

Objective To investigate using milliliter and liter to compare and estimate capacities

Materials ones block, thousands block

Optional Resources

- Reteach 9.10; Practice 9.10; Enrichment 9.10
- Daily Cumul. Review,p. 121
- Math Center: Activity Card 53
- Every Day Counts
- **TAB**, TE pp. 270E–270F, 270J
- **Problem of the Day**, 121, p. 61; Flip Chart, p. 61a

Students Acquiring English

Help with container sizes. Show students customary unit containers (pint, quart, or gallon) and ask what amount of liquid they contain. Ask if students have seen a liter container, and how much it holds. Show a container; tell students that it is a liter container because it holds 1 liter. Ask, What would you call a container that holds $\frac{1}{2}$ liter?

Problem of the Day

How many capital letters can you make from 3 toothpicks, using all 3 and not breaking any of them? Which letters can be formed?
15 letters; A, C, D, F, H, I, J, K, L, N, P, T, U, Y, Z—some students may also include S

Milliliter and Liter

Cooperative Learning Checklist
- ☑ Work alone.
- ☑ Work with a partner.
- ☑ Work with a group.

Getting Started

What You'll Need:
- ones block
- thousands block

Vocabulary:
- liter (L)
- milliliter (mL)
- Glossary, p. 480

You know that the amount a container can hold is its capacity. You can measure capacity in **liters (L)** and **milliliters (mL)**.

Milliliters and liters are metric units of capacity.
1 mL = about 5 drops of liquid
1 L = 1000 mL

Activity

1 Look at a ones block. Each side is 1 cm long. If the ones block were hollow, it would hold 1 mL of water.

2 There are 1000 mL in 1 L. Look at a thousands block. If it were hollow, it would hold 1 L of water.

1 Introduce

Prior Knowledge **Display on the board: 1000 meters = 1 kilometer. Ask, How many meters in 2 kilometers? In 7 kilometers?** 2000 m; 7000 m

Teach: **Activity**

Emphasize these points:

- Liters and milliliters are used to measure liquids and liquid capacities.
- You can regroup 1000 mL as 1 L.

Modeling Model Step 3. Ask:

- How can I decide which container has the greater capacity? compare sizes
- How could I check my predictions? by measuring; by pouring a liter of water into each container

2 Develop

Show What You Know!

Common Error If students have trouble completing the table in exercise 1, point out the pattern, and that skip-counting by 1000's can help them complete the table. See also Analyzing Errors, TE pp. 341A and 341B.

- Ask students to explain their reasoning for exercises 6–12.
- Have students explain how they solved problems 13 and 14.

3 Summarize

- Have students review the relationship between liters and milliliters.
- Remind students that liter and milliliter are metric units of capacity.

Ongoing Assessment The label on your juice bottle says the bottle holds 750 mL. Is this more or less than 1 liter? less: 1L = 1000 mL; 750 mL < 1000 mL

Math Journal: ***Communicating***

How much water do you drink in one day? Do you drink more or less than 1 liter? How can you tell? Answers will vary. Accept any reasonable response. One liter holds about the same amount of liquid as 4 large drinking glasses.

3

Look at containers A–F on page 324. Decide if each container holds more than 1 L or less than 1 L.

Copy the chart. Record your results.

See Additional Answers.

Capacity			
Container	About 1 liter	Less than 1 liter	More than 1 liter
A			
B			

Show What You Know!

1. Copy and complete the table.

mL	1000	2000	? 3000	4000	5000	? 6000	? 7000	8000	? 9000	? 10,000
L	1	2	3	4 ?	5 ?	6	7	8 ?	9	9 ?

2. **Critical Thinking** How many milliliters are in half of a liter? Explain. 500 mL; Answers will vary. Possible answer: a liter is 1000 mL and 500 is $\frac{1}{2}$ of 1000.

Write >, <, or = . Use the table you completed if you need to.

3. 1 L ■ 500 mL >
4. 2000 mL ■ 2 L =
5. 50 mL ■ 5 L <

Which unit would you use? Write *liters* or *milliliters*.

6. 
liters

7. 
liters

8. 
milliliter

Does the object hold more than or less than a liter? Write *more than* or *less than*.

9. a sink more than
10. a glass less than
11. a pool more than
12. a soup can less than

Problem Solving

13. For a science project, you need 2 L of water. Your container holds 500 mL. How can you use it to measure 2 L? fill it 4 times

14. Suppose you put 3 spoonfuls of honey on your cereal. A small spoon holds about 5 mL. About how many milliliters of honey will you eat? About 15 mL

More Practice Set 9.10, p. 469

Meeting Individual Needs

Extra Support

Find the Units *(kinesthetic)* Provide ones and thousands blocks. Remind students that a hollow ones block holds 1 mL of water, and a thousands block would hold 1 L. Students group blocks to show 200, 500, and 700 mL, and compare them to the thousands block.

Alternate Approach

- Reteach Worksheet 9.10
- **TAB** See TE pp. 302E–302F.

Students Acquiring English

See Language Connections, Ch. 9.

Challenge

Have students work in pairs to rewrite this fruit punch recipe so that it can be made in a container that holds only 500 mL.

$\frac{1}{2}$ L cranberry juice 50 mL
$1\frac{1}{2}$ L apple juice 150 mL
2 L pineapple juice 200 mL
1 L sparkling water 100 mL

Practice

Math Center Use Activity Card 53, *More or Less?*, to have students practice comparing and estimating capacities.

Challenge Use Activity Card 53 and have students continue as described in Now Try This!

See Just the Facts Practice 9A, p. 136.

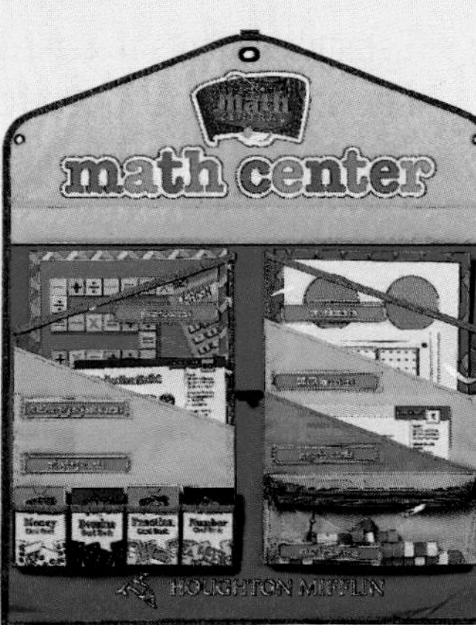

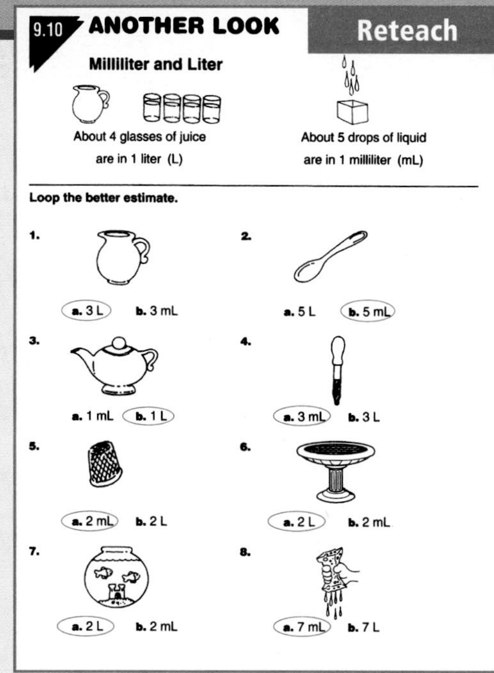

9.10 ANOTHER LOOK — Reteach

Milliliter and Liter

About 4 glasses of juice are in 1 liter (L)

About 5 drops of liquid are in 1 milliliter (mL)

Loop the better estimate.

1. a. 3 L b. 3 mL
2. a. 5 L b. 5 mL
3. a. 1 mL b. 1 L
4. a. 3 mL b. 3 L
5. a. 2 mL b. 2 L
6. a. 2 L b. 2 mL
7. a. 2 L b. 2 mL
8. a. 7 mL b. 7 L

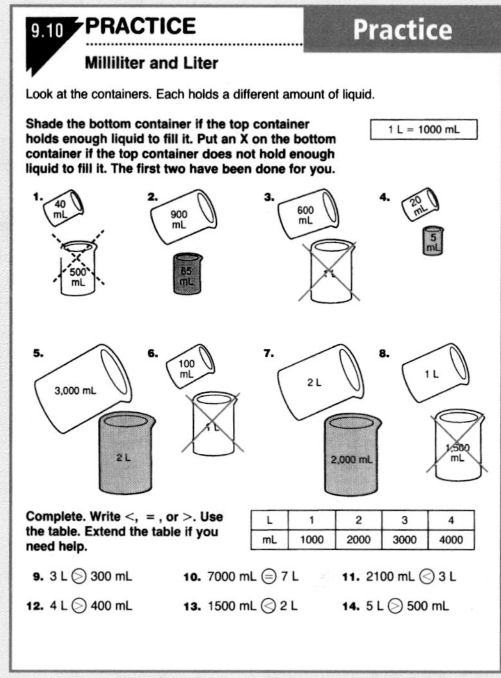

9.10 PRACTICE — Practice

Milliliter and Liter

Look at the containers. Each holds a different amount of liquid.

Shade the bottom container if the top container holds enough liquid to fill it. Put an X on the bottom container if the top container does not hold enough liquid to fill it. The first two have been done for you.

1 L = 1000 mL

1. 40 mL — 500 mL
2. 900 mL — 85 mL
3. 600 mL — 1 L
4. 20 mL — 5 mL
5. 3,000 mL — 2 L
6. 100 mL — 1 L
7. 2 L — 2,000 mL
8. 1 L — 1,500 mL

Complete. Write <, = , or >. Use the table. Extend the table if you need help.

L	1	2	3	4
mL	1000	2000	3000	4000

9. 3 L (>) 300 mL
10. 7000 mL (=) 7 L
11. 2100 mL (<) 3 L
12. 4 L (>) 400 mL
13. 1500 mL (<) 2 L
14. 5 L (>) 500 mL

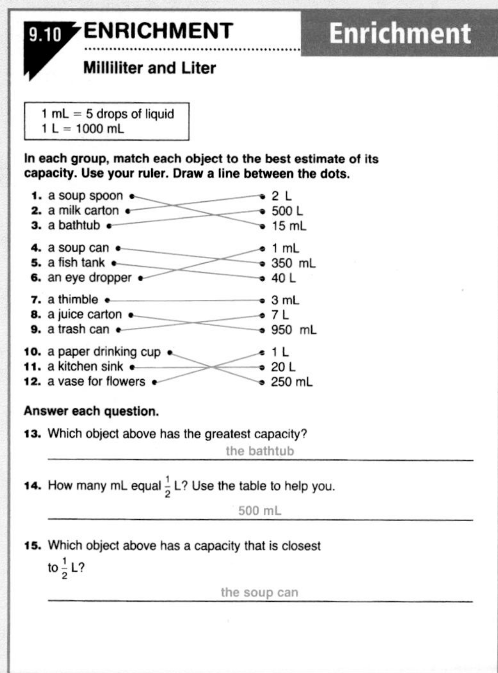

9.10 ENRICHMENT — Enrichment

Milliliter and Liter

1 mL = 5 drops of liquid
1 L = 1000 mL

In each group, match each object to the best estimate of its capacity. Use your ruler. Draw a line between the dots.

1. a soup spoon • • 2 L
2. a milk carton • • 500 L
3. a bathtub • • 15 mL
4. a soup can • • 1 mL
5. a fish tank • • 350 mL
6. an eye dropper • • 40 L
7. a thimble • • 3 mL
8. a juice carton • • 7 L
9. a trash can • • 950 mL
10. a paper drinking cup • • 1 L
11. a kitchen sink • • 20 L
12. a vase for flowers • • 250 mL

Answer each question.

13. Which object above has the greatest capacity? the bathtub
14. How many mL equal $\frac{1}{2}$ L? Use the table to help you. 500 mL
15. Which object above has a capacity that is closest to $\frac{1}{2}$ L? the soup can

Symbolic

Planning at a Glance

Objectives To use gram and kilogram; to choose the appropriate unit of mass; to estimate

Materials none

Optional Resources

- Daily Cumul. Review, p. 122
- Math Center: How-To Card 31
- Every Day Counts
- TAB, TE pp. 302E–302F, 302J
- Reteach, Practice, and Enrichment Worksheets for Lesson 9.11
- Problem of the Day, 122, p. 61; Flip Chart, p. 61b

Students Acquiring English

Invite students to draw each of the items listed in problems 6–10 and to compare their drawings with a partner to be sure that they have understood what each word means.

Problem of the Day

A butcher uses a balance scale. He has only four weights: 1 kg, 2 kg, 4 kg, and 8 kg. What amounts of chopped meat can he measure using combinations of the weights? Explain.

He can measure every whole number weight from 1–15 kg. To weight amounts greater than 15 kg, he can weigh batches of 15 kg, remove the meat from the scale, then measure other batches to add on.

Gram and Kilogram

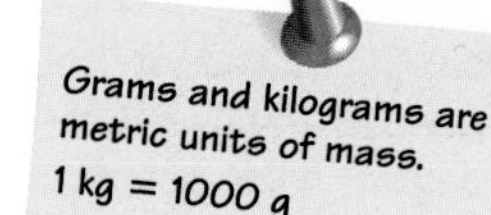

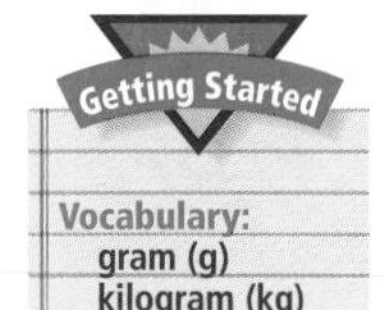

Vocabulary:
gram (g)
kilogram (kg)
Glossary, p. 480

You can use **grams (g)** and **kilograms (kg)** to measure how heavy an object is.

Which is heavier, the watermelon or the basket?

You know that 1 kg = 1000 g.
So, 3 kg = 3000 g.
3000 > 850

The watermelon is heavier.

Show What You Know!

Copy and complete the number sentence.

1. 2 kg = ■ g 2000
2. 4000 g = ■ kg 4
3. $\frac{1}{2}$ kg = ■ g 500
4. 8 kg = ■ g 8000
5. **Critical Thinking** Explain how multiplication patterns can help you find the number of grams in 10 kg. I need to find 10 × 1000. I can use the basic fact 1 × 1 and add 4 zeros.

Which unit would you use to measure how heavy the object is? Write *gram* or *kilogram*.

6. eraser gram
7. pony kilogram
8. carrot gram
9. yourself kilogram
10. car kilogram

Complete the exercise. Write >, <, or =.

11. 3000 g ■ 3 kg =
12. 2 kg ■ 200 g >
13. 7000 g ■ 70 kg <

More Practice Set 9.11, p. 470

1 Introduce

Build Understanding On the board, write: 1000 g = 1 kg. Ask students to decide which measure in the following pairs is greater: 1 kg, 10 g 1 kg **500 g, 1 kg** 1 kg **3000 g, 2 kg** 3000 g **50 g, 500 kg** 500 kg

Teach: *Modeling*

Model the example, Ask:

- How many grams equal 1 kilogram? 1000 g
- How many grams are equal to 3 kg? 3000 g
- Which is greater, 850 g or 3000 g? 3000 g

2 Develop

Show What You Know!

- Point out that *kilo* in *kilogram* or *kilometer* means "one thousand." So, 1 kilogram is 1000 grams. Ask: how many grams are in 5 kilograms? 5000 g
- Remind students to refer to the conversion box on this page for exercises 1–4.
- Have students explain their reasoning for exercise 5.

Basic Facts See **Just the Facts** Cumulative Practice 8, p. 271.

3 Summarize

- Remind students that grams and kilograms are metric units that can be used to measure how heavy an object is.
- Emphasize the importance of choosing the correct unit for the measurement being made.

Ongoing Assessment You buy 1500 grams of cheese. Is this more or less than 2 kilograms? less

Math Journal: *Communicating*

How can you find how many grams are in 6 kilograms?
Answers may vary. Possible answer: skip-count by 1000's six times

Gram and Kilogram Workshop

Review

15 minutes

Use with page 326.

Which Unit?

Management teacher directed; whole class
Materials overhead projector

- Write the conversion rate of *1000 grams = 1 kilogram* on the board.
- Ask students to complete these conversions:

  4 kilograms = _____ grams
  15,000 grams = _____ kilograms
  $\frac{1}{2}$ kilogram = _____ grams
  1500 grams = _____ kilograms
  $5\frac{1}{2}$ kilograms = _____ grams
  17,500 grams = _____ kilograms

- Discuss the two units of measurement. Invite students to give examples of objects measured in both units.
- Then ask students to tell whether they would use grams or kilograms to measure each of the following objects:

Elephant	Computer Disk
Leaf	Wooden Chair
Dictionary	Baseball Bat

- Invite students to list several objects and the metric unit of mass they would use for each. Then, have students read their lists to a partner and ask, Which unit would you use?

Activity

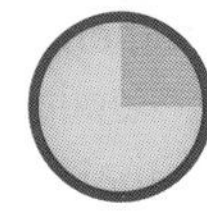

15 minutes

Use with page 326.

Grams and Kilograms

Management pairs
Materials paper or tagboard, scissors, rulers, pencils, paper clips

- To make a spinner, students draw a square with 6-inch sides. Fold the square in half twice to make 4 quarters. Mark the center with a dot. Label two quarters of the spinner *gram*, and two quarters *kilogram*.
- Provide students with a list of items such as the following: horse, crayon, table, apple, wooden chair, wristwatch, bowling ball, baseball, hamster, sheet of paper, airplane, bag of grapefruit.
- The first player spins an open paper clip around a pencil point in the center of the spinner. Then, the player chooses from the list an item that is measured in the unit on which the paper clip end lands. Score 1 point for *gram* and 2 points for *kilogram.*
- Players take turns spinning until all items have been crossed off the list.

Problem Solving Workshop

Measurement Reasonableness

Review

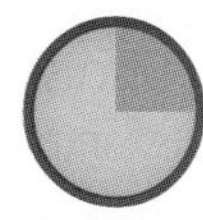

Use with page 327.

15 minutes

Measurement Sense

Management teacher directed; whole class

- Draw the map as shown on the board.
- Tell students to listen carefully and take notes as you read aloud the following story.

  Mary leaves the house and walks along Main Street toward Lisa's house. She checks her watch at the bank and it's 8:00. She picks up Lisa at her house. Mary and Lisa walk together through the park toward school. From the park, they walk along Northern Drive until they get to school. As they are going into school, Mary looks at her watch again, it is 8:30. Mary and Lisa walk at a 3 mile/hour pace.

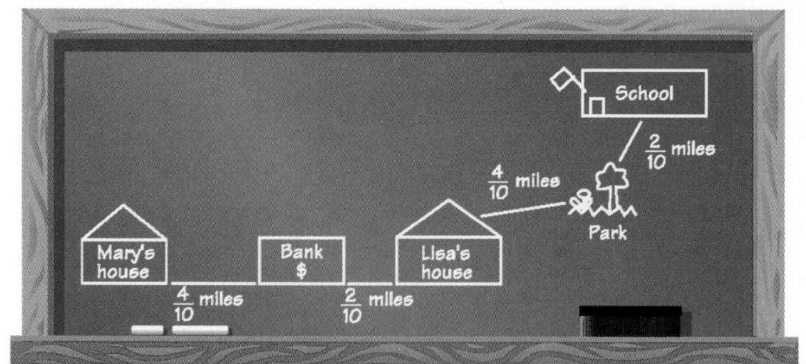

- Ask, Do you think that it is reasonable for Lisa and Mary to have walked all that way in one half-hour? Have students explain their answers.

Activity

Use with page 327.

20 minutes

Create a Map

Management pairs
Materials paper, pencil, ruler

- Ask students to think about the way that they come to school everyday. Do they walk? Take a bus?
- Tell them that they need to draw a map for a new student who will be living in their neighborhood.
- Have students prepare to create their maps by listing the important information necessary to find their way to school. For example, street names, bus changes, left/right turns, and so on.
- Show a map to students. Point out the different characteristics of the map, such as the scale, the title, and the key.
- Then, invite students to draw a map of their route to school. Remind them to think about the items that they saw on the map that you showed to them.

- Maple St.
- walk toward Chestnut Ave.
- take a right onto Chestnut Ave.
- at the Library take a left onto Pine St.
- school is at the end of Pine St.

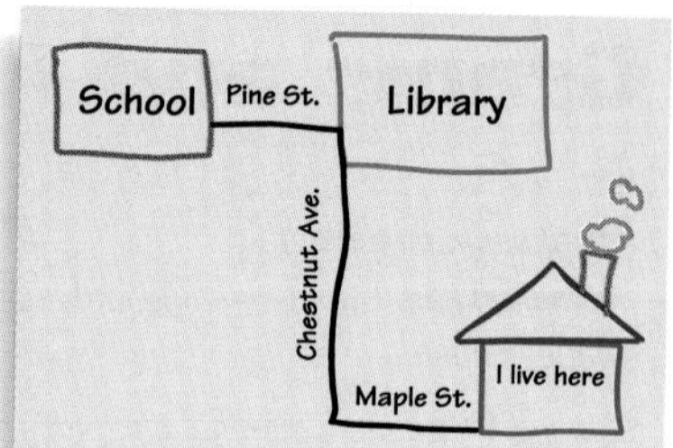

- Some students may have difficulty completing this activity. Ask students to discuss what they found difficult about creating a map. If necessary, discuss how to make the map-making process easier. write out directions before drawing the map; draw a sketch in pencil

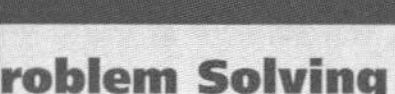

LESSON 9.12

roblem Solving

Planning at a Glance

Objective To decide and to justify why an answer is reasonable when solving problems

Materials none

Optional Resources

- Daily Cumul. Review, p. 123
- Math Center: Project Card 9
- Every Day Counts
- **TAB**, TE p. 302E
- **Problem of the Day**, 123, p. 62; Flip Chart, p. 62a
- **Reteach, Practice, and Enrichment Worksheets for Lesson 9.12**

MATHKEYS

Unlocking Measurements 3–6, Level 3, Activity 8

Students Acquiring English

Use the photos on Student Book p. 327 as the basis for a discussion of the terms *soapbox derby* and *block*. Then have volunteers read aloud problems 1–6. Discuss any unfamiliar vocabulary.

Problem of the Day

Look at the box below. How many different products are there if you can multiply any two numbers? You may repeat factors.

2	4	6	8

10 products: 2 × 2, 2 × 4, 2 × 6, 2 × 8, 4 × 4, 4 × 6, 4 × 8, 6 × 6, 6 × 8, 8 × 8

Problem Solving
Is the Answer Reasonable?

Is the Answer Reasonable?

Ask Yourself:

- Did I answer the question?
- Did I calculate correctly?
- Is the answer labeled with the right units?
- Does my answer need to be rounded to a whole number to make sense?

The soapbox derby starts on your street and ends 2 blocks away. You estimate the race route is 3 meters long. Is your estimate reasonable?

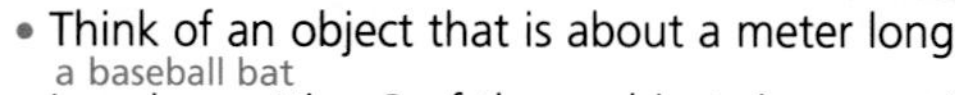

Ready, set, go!

You Decide

- Think of an object that is about a meter long. a baseball bat
- Imagine putting 3 of those objects in a row. Would the row be about 2 blocks long? no
- Decide whether your estimate is reasonable. Explain. no; a meter is a small unit

Work It Out!

Decide whether the measurement makes sense. Explain.

1. A student takes the bus to school. He lives 4 m from the school. no; a meter is about the length of a baseball bat
2. The top of a desk is 22 in. across and 18 in. from front to back. yes; an inch can measure a desk
3. It took two grownups to lift a rock. The rock weighed about 4 oz. no; an ounce measures light objects
4. The principal of a school is between $1\frac{1}{2}$ m and 2 m tall. yes; a meter could measure an adult's height
5. During a soccer game, a player drinks 1 L of juice. yes; a liter can measure a bottle
6. The hallway at school is about 5 cm wide. no; a centimeter is about the width of my finger

Share Your Thinking

7. How did you decide if the measurement in problem 6 is reasonable? by thinking of something that is 1cm and thinking about its size

327

1 Introduce

Prior Knowledge **Ask, Would you measure the length of a street in meters or centimeters?** meters

Teach: You Decide

After working through the problem, discuss:

- How does knowing the length of 1 m help you decide whether 3 m was a reasonable estimate?

Modeling Model the process. Ask:

- If a friend says she drinks 8 gallons of water a day, how can you decide if that is reasonable? think about the size of a gallon; then think of 8 gallons
- Does the measurement seem reasonable? no; it seems too large

2 Develop

Work It Out!

- Remind students that they can use the checklist on Student Book p. 327, to decide if an answer is reasonable.
- Call on students to discuss their answers for problems 1–6.
- Have students explain their reasoning for problem 7.

3 Summarize

- Call on students to describe their procedures for deciding whether a measurement is reasonable.

Ongoing Assessment You read in the newspaper that there will be a 2000 km bike race in the park on Sunday. What conclusion can you draw? The newspaper probably meant 2000 m, because 2000 km is too far for anyone to bike in a day.

Math Journal: *Communicating*

Explain how you decide whether a measurement is reasonable. Answers will vary, but should include thinking about the estimated measurement and comparing it mentally with something you know to measure about the same.

Activity

Planning at a Glance

Objective To determine if equal amounts of different materials are equally heavy

Materials pan balance; 2 small matching containers; materials such as gravel, rice, beans, popcorn, cotton, counters; Recording Sheet (Practice 9.13)

Optional Resources

- Reteach 9.13; Enrichment 9.13
- Daily Cumul. Review, p. 124
- Math Center: Act. Card 54
- Every Day Counts
- **TAB**, TE p. 270E–270F, 270J
- **Problem of the Day**, 124, p. 62; Flip Chart, p. 62b

Students Acquiring English
Display two objects and ask students to *predict* which one is heavier. Repeat several times reinforcing the terms *predict*, and *which is heavier*.

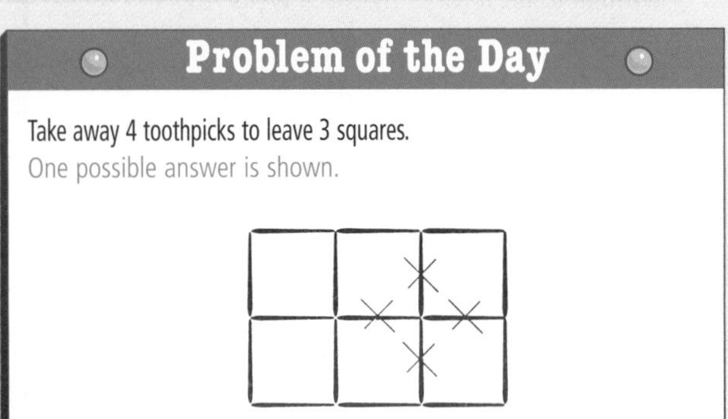

Problem of the Day

Take away 4 toothpicks to leave 3 squares.
One possible answer is shown.

LESSON 13

Heavier or Lighter?

Cooperative Learning Checklist
- ☑ Work alone.
- ☑ Work with a partner.
- ☑ Work with a group.

Getting Started

What You'll Need:
- pan balance
- 2 small containers that match
- materials such as gravel, rice, beans, popcorn, cotton, counters
- recording sheet

You can compare how heavy two things are. First predict which material will be heavier. Then check with a pan balance.

Activity

- Use the recording sheet or make a chart like the one below.

1. Choose two materials to compare, such as counters and cotton. List them.
2. Fill each container with one of the materials. Predict which material will be heavier. Record your prediction.
3. Hold a container in each hand. Compare how heavy they are. Record which material feels heavier.

Name ______ Date ______

Recording Sheet

Which Is Heavier?

Materials		Predict	Compare by holding in your hands	Compare using the pan balance
Cotton	Counters	Cotton	Counters	Counters

328 Chapter 9

1 Introduce

Prior Knowledge **Have students tell which measure in each of the following pairs is greatest:**
17 oz and 2 lb 2 lb, **17 oz and 1 lb** 17 oz
8 oz and $\frac{1}{2}$ lb equal, **32 oz and 3 lb** 3 lb.

Teach: Activity

- Make sure that students fill each container to the same level.
- Encourage students to discuss answers.

Modeling Model any two items on the balance. Ask:

- Which material is heavier?
- How can you tell?

2 Develop

Show What You Know!

- Have students discuss their findings with the rest of the class. Did any of the results surprise them? Why?
- Ask students to compare and discuss their answers for exercises 3–8.

3 Summarize

- Have the class summarize the results of the activity, telling if any of the materials were hard to compare by holding them in their hands, and why.

Ongoing Assessment How can you tell if rice or salt is heavier? Students should explain that they could estimate by holding equal volumes of each material and verify by placing equal amounts on opposite pans of a balance.

Math Journal: ***Communicating***

If you had 1 pound of marbles and 1 pound of popped popcorn, which one would need a bigger container? Why? Answers should show an understanding that the less-dense material, the popcorn, occupies more space.

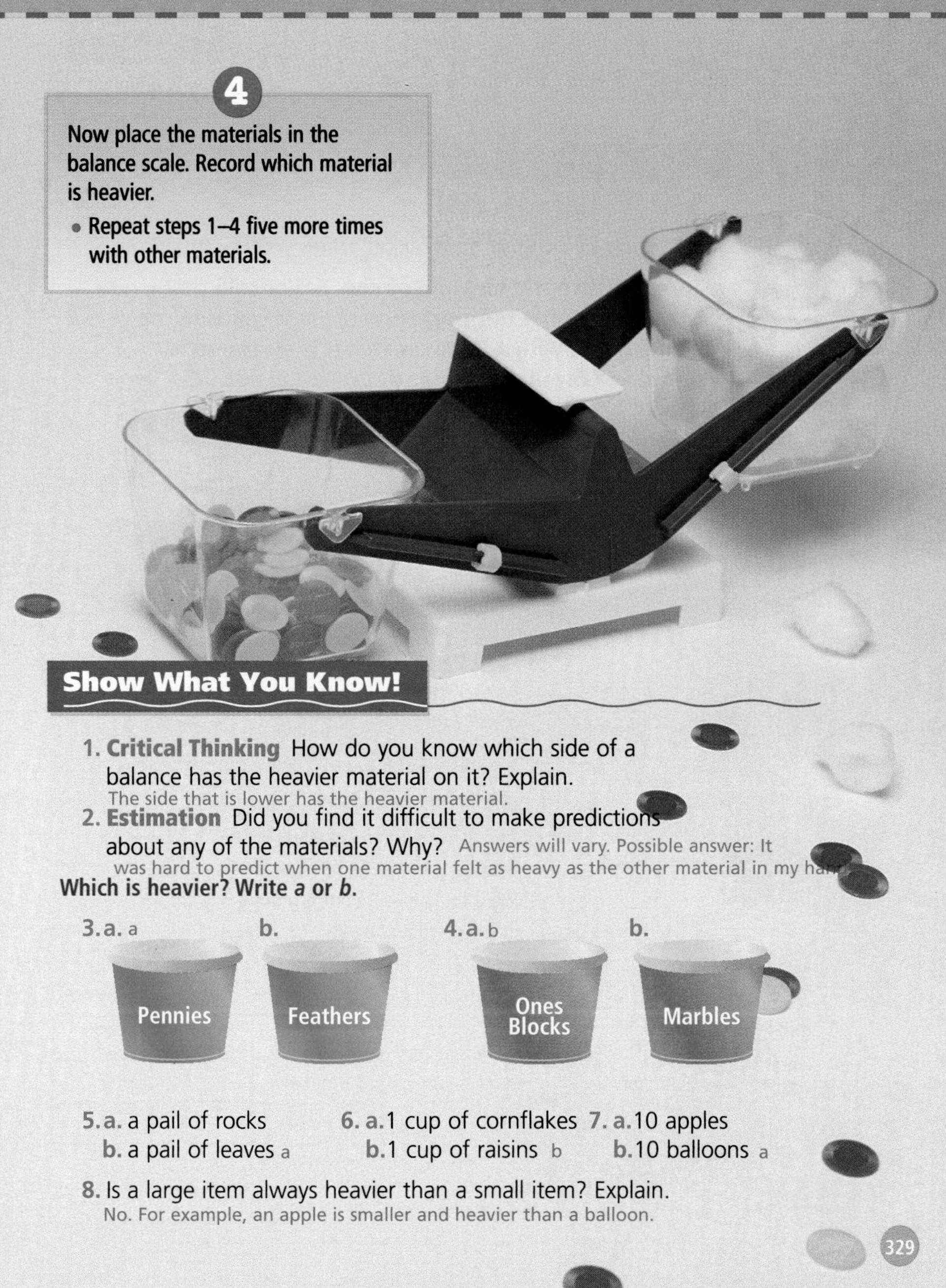

4

Now place the materials in the balance scale. Record which material is heavier.

- Repeat steps 1–4 five more times with other materials.

Show What You Know!

1. **Critical Thinking** How do you know which side of a balance has the heavier material on it? Explain.
   The side that is lower has the heavier material.
2. **Estimation** Did you find it difficult to make predictions about any of the materials? Why? Answers will vary. Possible answer: It was hard to predict when one material felt as heavy as the other material in my hand.

Which is heavier? Write *a* or *b*.

3. a. a — Pennies b. Feathers
4. a. b — Ones Blocks b. Marbles

5. a. a pail of rocks
   b. a pail of leaves a
6. a. 1 cup of cornflakes
   b. 1 cup of raisins b
7. a. 10 apples
   b. 10 balloons a
8. Is a large item always heavier than a small item? Explain.
   No. For example, an apple is smaller and heavier than a balloon.

329

Meeting Individual Needs

Extra Support

Matching Weights *(visual/kinesthetic)* Have students work in pairs. One student places two containers of different materials on a balance scale. That student tells the other what the materials are. The second student then tells which container contains which material.

Alternate Approach

- Reteach Worksheet 9.13
- **TAB** see TE pp. 302E–302F.

Students Acquiring English

See Language Connections, Ch. 9.

Challenge

Have students show how they would make the following weights by combining as few as possible of these weights: 1 oz, 2 oz, 4 oz, 8 oz, and 1 lb.

a. 13 oz 8 oz, 4 oz, 1 oz

b. 20 oz 1 lb, 4 oz

c. 11 oz 8 oz, 2 oz, 1 oz

d. 30 oz 1 lb, 8 oz, 4 oz, 2 oz

Practice

Math Center Use Activity Card 54, *Weight Detective*, to have students practice comparing weights of equal quantities of different materials.

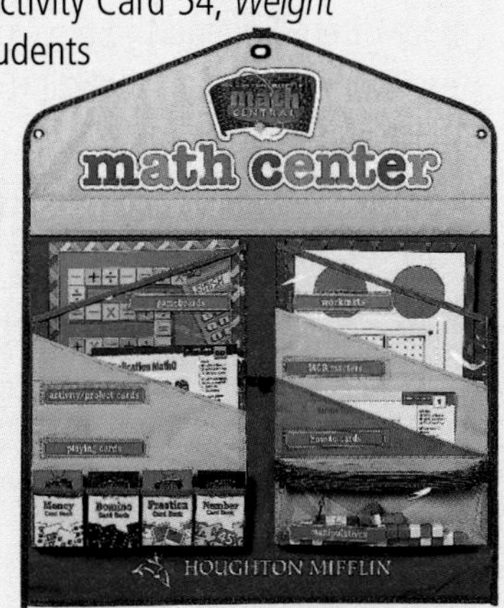

Challenge Use Activity Card 54 and have students continue the activity as described in Now Try This!

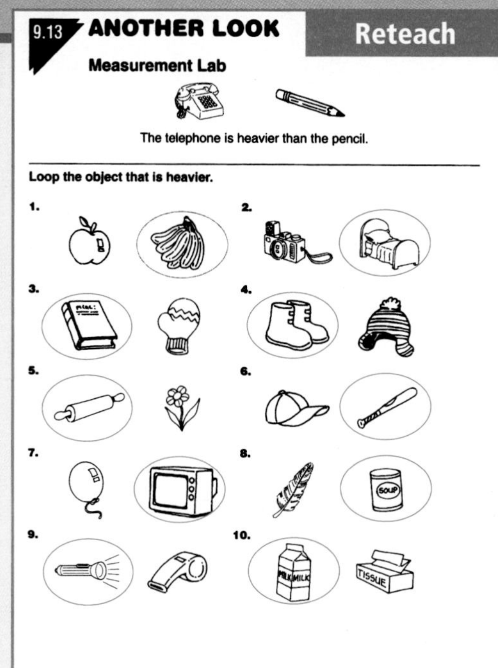

9.13 ANOTHER LOOK — **Reteach**

Measurement Lab

The telephone is heavier than the pencil.

Loop the object that is heavier.

1. 2. 3. 4. 5. 6. 7. 8. 9. 10.

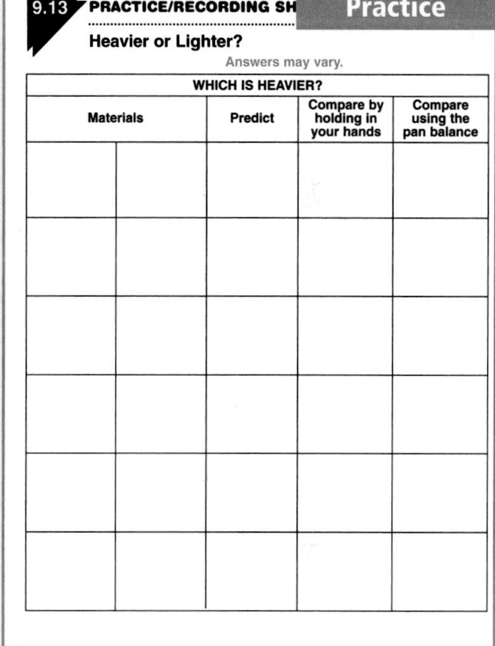

9.13 PRACTICE/RECORDING SHEET — **Practice**

Heavier or Lighter?

Answers may vary.

WHICH IS HEAVIER?

Materials		Predict	Compare by holding in your hands	Compare using the pan balance

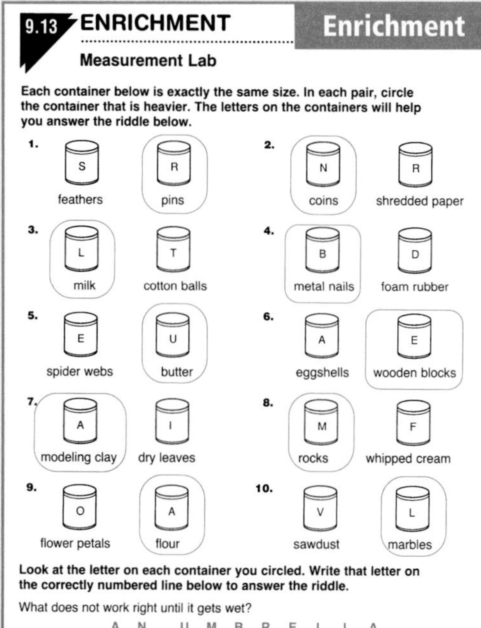

9.13 ENRICHMENT — **Enrichment**

Measurement Lab

Each container below is exactly the same size. In each pair, circle the container that is heavier. The letters on the containers will help you answer the riddle below.

1. S feathers — R pins
2. N coins — R shredded paper
3. L milk — T cotton balls
4. B metal nails — D foam rubber
5. E spider webs — U butter
6. A eggshells — E wooden blocks
7. A modeling clay — I dry leaves
8. M rocks — F whipped cream
9. O flower petals — A flour
10. V sawdust — L marbles

Look at the letter on each container you circled. Write that letter on the correctly numbered line below to answer the riddle.

What does not work right until it gets wet?

A	N		U	M	B	R	E	L	L	A
7	2		5	8	4	1	6	10	3	9

Activity

Planning at a Glance

Objectives To investigate reading Fahrenheit and Celsius thermometers; to choose appropriate temperature

Materials none

Optional Resources

- Reteach 9.14; Practice 9.14; Enrichment 9.14
- Daily Cumul. Review, p. 125
- Math Center: How-To Card 33
- Every Day Counts
- **TAB**, TE p. 302E–302F, 302J
- **Problem of the Day**, 125, p. 63; Flip Chart, p. 63a

Students Acquiring English

Show students pictures of different climates to help stimulate a discussion of temperatures. Elicit examples of temperature words, such as *cold, hot, warm, chilly*, and *freezing*. Display a thermometer and have students show which line on the thermometer would go with each of the words.

Problem of the Day

Find every number between 10 and 100 whose digits add up to 10.
19, 28, 37, 46, 55, 64, 73, 82, 91

Measuring Temperature

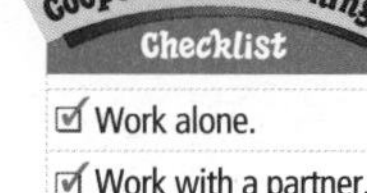

☑ Work alone.
☑ Work with a partner.
☐ Work with a group.

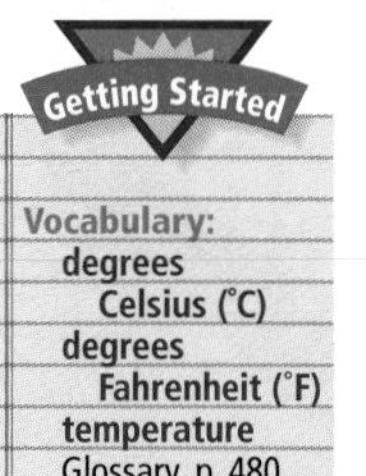

Vocabulary:
degrees Celsius (°C)
degrees Fahrenheit (°F)
temperature
Glossary, p. 480

Do you need to put on a jacket when you go outside?

Temperature is a measure of how hot or cold something is. The temperature of the air outside can be measured with a thermometer. It is measured in **degrees Fahrenheit (°F)** or **degrees Celsius (°C)**.

Degrees Fahrenheit are customary units.
Degrees Celsius are metric units.

Activity

- Copy the chart below.
- Read and record the temperature.

Read a Fahrenheit Thermometer

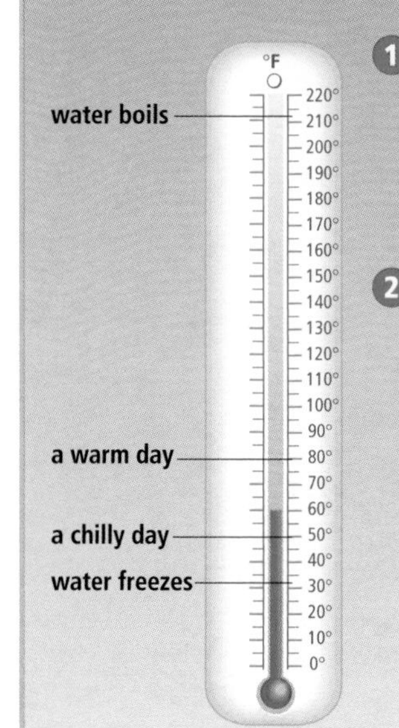

1. What temperature does this Fahrenheit thermometer show?
   - Put your finger on the top of the red line.
   - Move your finger to the right. Read the number.
2. This thermometer shows 60° Fahrenheit, or 60° F. Find each temperature on the thermometer. Read the label. Then write the temperature in the correct place in the chart.
   a. 80°F
   b. 50°F
   c. 32°F
   d. 212°F

What Happens	Temperature of Air: Degrees Fahrenheit	Degrees Celsius
A warm day	80°F ?	27°C ?
A chilly day	50°F ?	10°C ?
Water freezes	32°F ?	0°C ?
Water boils	? 212°F	? 100°C

Chapter 9

1 Introduce

Prior Knowledge Ask, What do we use to measure temperature? a thermometer

Teach: Activity
Emphasize these points:

- Write the degree symbol ° and *C* or *F* after a temperature.
- Numbers indicating temperature increase as temperature gets warmer and decrease as it gets cooler.

Modeling Model Step 2 demonstrating how to read the temperature to the nearest degree.

2 Develop

Show What You Know!

Common Error Some students may have difficulty reading and understanding the Celsius scale because they use Fahrenheit more often. Remind them to look for the letters *C* or *F*. See also Analyzing Errors, TE pp. 341A and 341B.

- Have students explain their reasoning for exercise 5.
- If students have trouble with exercises 9–12, review the Celsius and Fahrenheit scales.

3 Summarize

- Point out that temperature is measured in degrees Fahrenheit (°F) in customary units and degrees Celsius (°C) in metric units.

Ongoing Assessment How should you dress if the temperature is 28°C? If it is 28°F? Answers should reflect that 28°C is a comfortable temperature, while 28°F is very cold.

Math Journal: *Communicating*

Which kind of thermometer is easier to use? Why?
Answers will vary. Possible answers: Celsius thermometer; because the units are larger; or Fahrenheit thermometer; because it is more familiar

Read a Celsius Thermometer

°C
110°
water boils — 100°
80°
90°
70°
60°
50°
40°
a warm day — 30°
20°
a chilly day — 10°
water freezes — 0°

1. What temperature does the Celsius thermometer show?
   The top of the red line is halfway between 10 and 20.
   So, the temperature is 15° Celsius, or 15°C.
2. Find each temperature on the thermometer. Then write the temperature in the correct place in the chart.
   a. 27°C b. 10°C c. 0°C d. 100°C
3. The red line in a thermometer is really a liquid. It can move up or down. What happens to the liquid when the weather gets warmer?
   It rises.

Show What You Know!

Write the temperature that the thermometer shows.

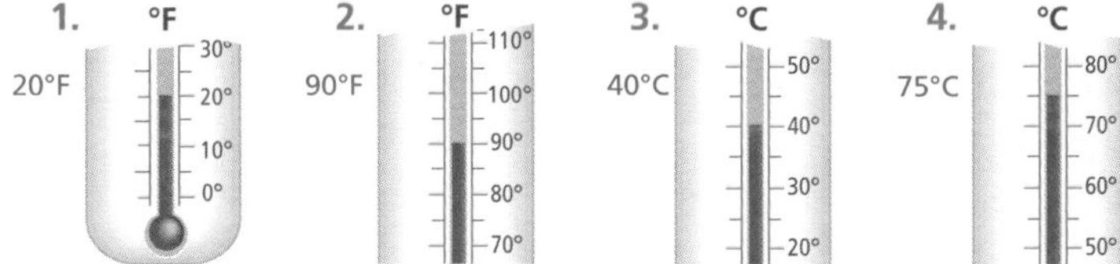

5. **Write About It** Measure the temperature outside for 5 days. Do it at the same time and same place each day. Describe your results. Results will vary.

Use your chart to compare. Write *true* or *not true*.

6. 32°F is the same as 32°C. not true
7. 212°F is the same as 100°C. true
8. 32°F is warmer than 27°C. not true

Tell what you would wear. Write *T-shirt* or *warm jacket*.

9. 0°C warm jacket
10. 30°C T-shirt
11. 85°F T-shirt
12. 30°F warm jacket

More Practice Set 9.14, p. 470

Meeting Individual Needs

Extra Support

What to Wear? ***(kinesthetic)*** Ask students to draw five pictures, showing children dressed appropriately for different temperatures. Have them write a reasonable Fahrenheit or Celsius temperature beside each picture.

Alternate Approach

- Reteach Worksheet 9.14
- **TAB** See TE pp. 302E–302F.

Students Acquiring English

See Language Connections, Ch. 9.

Challenge

Challenge pairs of students to make a line graph on inch squared paper (TR39) using the following information:

Temperatures in Denver at Noon

Monday 20°F	Tuesday 35°F
Wednesday 40°F	Thursday 35°F
Friday 30°F	

- Remind students to title their graphs and write the labels.
- Have students compare and discuss their graphs.

Practice

Math Center Use How-To Card 33, *Reach the Boiling Point,* to have students practice using a Fahrenheit thermometer to determine temperatures above and below freezing.

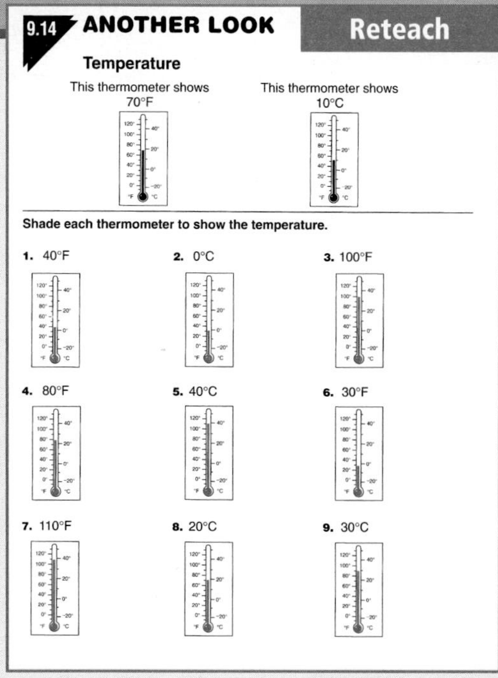

9.14 **ANOTHER LOOK** — Reteach

Temperature

This thermometer shows 70°F This thermometer shows 10°C

Shade each thermometer to show the temperature.

1. 40°F 2. 0°C 3. 100°F
4. 80°F 5. 40°C 6. 30°F
7. 110°F 8. 20°C 9. 30°C

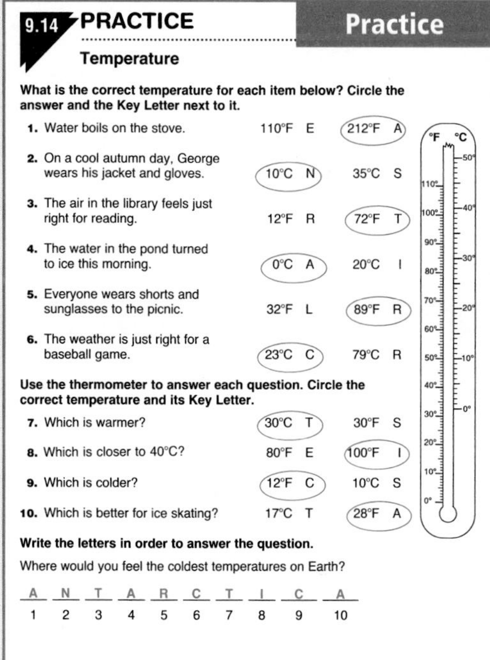

9.14 **PRACTICE** — Practice

Temperature

What is the correct temperature for each item below? Circle the answer and the Key Letter next to it.

1. Water boils on the stove. 110°F E (212°F A)
2. On a cool autumn day, George wears his jacket and gloves. (10°C N) 35°C S
3. The air in the library feels just right for reading. 12°F R (72°F T)
4. The water in the pond turned to ice this morning. (0°C A) 20°C I
5. Everyone wears shorts and sunglasses to the picnic. 32°F L (89°F R)
6. The weather is just right for a baseball game. (23°C C) 79°C R

Use the thermometer to answer each question. Circle the correct temperature and its Key Letter.

7. Which is warmer? (30°C T) 30°F S
8. Which is closer to 40°C? 80°F E (100°F I)
9. Which is colder? (12°F C) 10°C S
10. Which is better for ice skating? 17°C T (28°F A)

Write the letters in order to answer the question.

Where would you feel the coldest temperatures on Earth?

A N T A R C T I C A
1 2 3 4 5 6 7 8 9 10

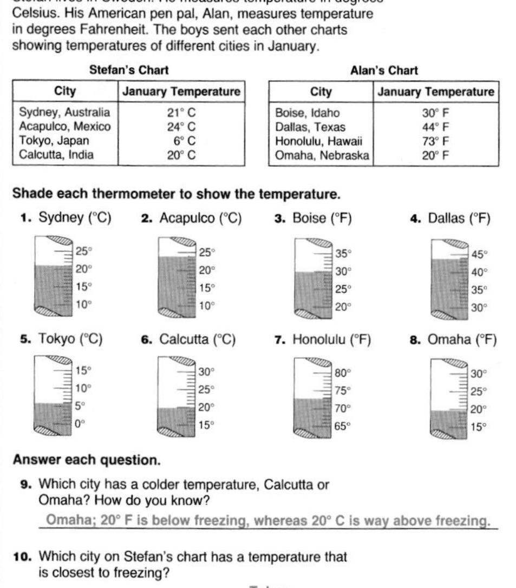

9.14 **ENRICHMENT** — Enrichment

Temperature

Stefan lives in Sweden. He measures temperature in degrees Celsius. His American pen pal, Alan, measures temperature in degrees Fahrenheit. The boys sent each other charts showing temperatures of different cities in January.

Stefan's Chart

City	January Temperature
Sydney, Australia	21° C
Acapulco, Mexico	24° C
Tokyo, Japan	6° C
Calcutta, India	20° C

Alan's Chart

City	January Temperature
Boise, Idaho	30° F
Dallas, Texas	44° F
Honolulu, Hawaii	73° F
Omaha, Nebraska	20° F

Shade each thermometer to show the temperature.

1. Sydney (°C) 2. Acapulco (°C) 3. Boise (°F) 4. Dallas (°F)
5. Tokyo (°C) 6. Calcutta (°C) 7. Honolulu (°F) 8. Omaha (°F)

Answer each question.

9. Which city has a colder temperature, Calcutta or Omaha? How do you know?
   Omaha; 20° F is below freezing, whereas 20° C is way above freezing.
10. Which city on Stefan's chart has a temperature that is closest to freezing?
   Tokyo

Connecting

Planning at a Glance

Objectives To use second, minute, hour, and day; to read and write time to the minute

Materials clock faces

Optional Resources

- Reteach 9.15; Practice 9.15; Enrichment 9.15
- Daily Cumul. Review, p. 126
- Math Center: How-To Card 34
- Every Day Counts
- **TAB**, TE pp. 302E–302F, 302J
- **Problem of the Day**, 126, p. 63; Flip Chart, p. 63b

Students Acquiring English

Help with skip-counting and the multiple meaning of *hands*. Point out that the hour and minute hands of a clock are not the same as people's hands. Then ask students to skip-count by 5's to 10. Explain that in number 2, "the 10" means the numeral 10 written on the clock, not the number they just skip-counted to.

Problem of the Day

Between 1:30 P.M. and 8:20 P.M., how many times does the minute hand move past the 5?

6 times

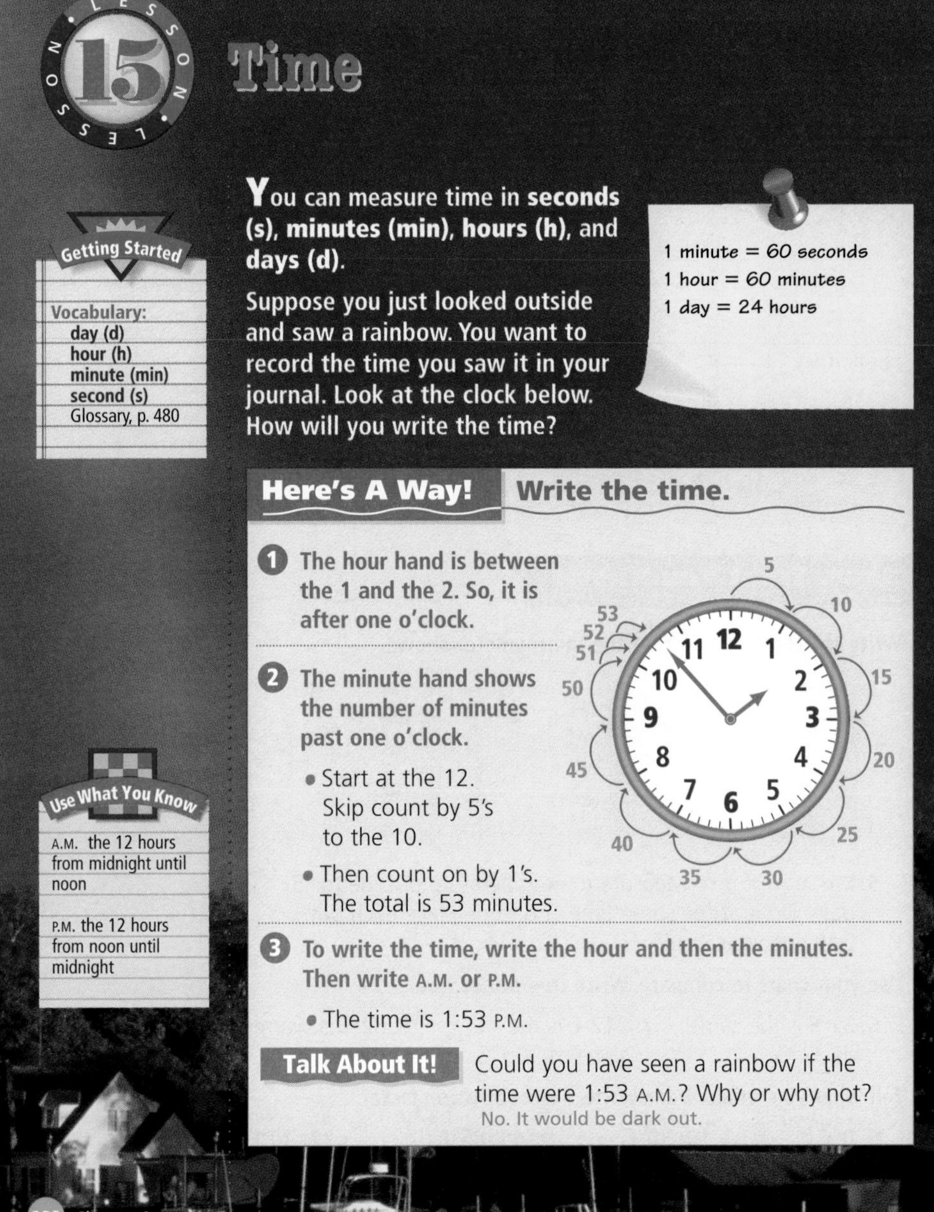

LESSON 15 **Time**

Getting Started

Vocabulary:
day (d)
hour (h)
minute (min)
second (s)
Glossary, p. 480

You can measure time in **seconds (s)**, **minutes (min)**, **hours (h)**, and **days (d)**.

1 minute = 60 seconds
1 hour = 60 minutes
1 day = 24 hours

Suppose you just looked outside and saw a rainbow. You want to record the time you saw it in your journal. Look at the clock below. How will you write the time?

Here's A Way! **Write the time.**

1. The hour hand is between the 1 and the 2. So, it is after one o'clock.
2. The minute hand shows the number of minutes past one o'clock.
   - Start at the 12. Skip count by 5's to the 10.
   - Then count on by 1's. The total is 53 minutes.

3. To write the time, write the hour and then the minutes. Then write A.M. or P.M.
   - The time is 1:53 P.M.

Use What You Know

A.M. the 12 hours from midnight until noon

P.M. the 12 hours from noon until midnight

Talk About It! Could you have seen a rainbow if the time were 1:53 A.M.? Why or why not?
No. It would be dark out.

332 Chapter 9

Prior Knowledge Ask students to show the following times on clock faces.

a. half past 12

b. quarter past 4

c. quarter to 9

Teach: Here's A Way!

- Skip-count by 5's and count by 1's to find the time shown on an analog clock.

2 Develop

Show What You Know!

Common Error Students may forget to begin skip-counting minutes from the 12. Remind them that they should start at the top of the clock face. See also Analyzing Errors, TE pp. 341A and 341B.

Work It Out!

- Remind students that the minute hand should be longer than the hour hand in each clock they draw for exercises 8–17.
- Have students explain their reasoning for exercise 19.

- Remind students to skip-count by 5's and then count by ones to find the correct minute.
- Have students review the conversion note on page 332.
- Point out that there are 5 minute marks from one number to the next on a clock.

Ongoing Assessment You have to leave at 8:25 A.M. to get to school. Where are the hands on the clock when you have to leave? the hour hand is between 8 and 9; the minute hand is on the 5

Math Journal: *Communicating*

If you had one whole day to do whatever you wanted, how would you spend your time? Write down about what time you would begin and end each activity.
Answers will vary.

Show What You Know!

Write the time shown on the clock.

1. 10:41 2. 2:25 3. 8:18

4. **Critical Thinking** Suppose it is the time shown in exercise 3. What might you be doing if the time is labeled A.M.? P.M.?
Answers will vary. Possible answers: getting to school; going to bed.

Work It Out!

Write the time shown on the clock.

5.  7:43 6.  2:03 7.  12:11

Draw a clock to show each time. Check students' drawings.

8. 3:37 9. 9:11 10. 10:41 11. 12:03 12. 2:55

13. 4:59 14. 1:43 15. 6:29 16. 11:21 17. 4:12

18. Copy and complete the table.

min	60	120	180 ?	240	300 ?	360 ?	420	480	540 ?	600 ?
hr	1	2	3	4 ?	5	6	7 ?	8 ?	9	10?

19. How could you multiply to find the number of minutes in 10 hours? How could you find the number by adding?
multiply 10 × 60; skip-count by 60 or add 60 ten times.

20. **Estimation** How many letters of the alphabet can you write in order in 10 seconds? Estimate. Then have a friend time you. Answers will vary.

21. How many letters can you write in 1 minute? Estimate. Then have a friend time you. Repeat the alphabet if you need to. Answers will vary.

More Practice Set 9.15, p. 471

Meeting Individual Needs

Extra Support

Time on the Clock *(visual)* Ask students to list five things they do in a typical day. Have them write the times that they usually do these activities, being sure to include A.M. or P.M. Then, have them work with a partner to draw clock faces that show each of these times.

Alternate Approach

- Reteach Worksheet 9.15
- **TAB** See TE pp. 302E–302F.

Students Acquiring English

See Language Connections, Ch. 9.

Challenge

Have students solve these problems.

a. A movie runs for 120 minutes. How many hours long is it? 2 h

b. A movie runs for 90 minutes. How many hours long is it? $1\frac{1}{2}$ h

Practice

Math Center Use How-To Card 34, *Have You Got the Time?*, to have students practice reading and writing time to the minute.

See **Just the Facts** Practice 9B, p. 137.

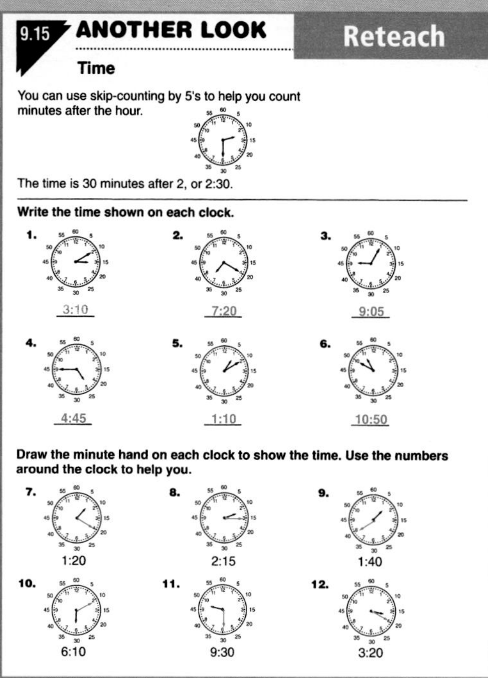

9.15 ANOTHER LOOK — Reteach

Time

You can use skip-counting by 5's to help you count minutes after the hour.

The time is 30 minutes after 2, or 2:30.

Write the time shown on each clock.

1. 3:10 2. 7:20 3. 9:05
4. 4:45 5. 1:10 6. 10:50

Draw the minute hand on each clock to show the time. Use the numbers around the clock to help you.

7. 1:20 8. 2:15 9. 1:40
10. 6:10 11. 9:30 12. 3:20

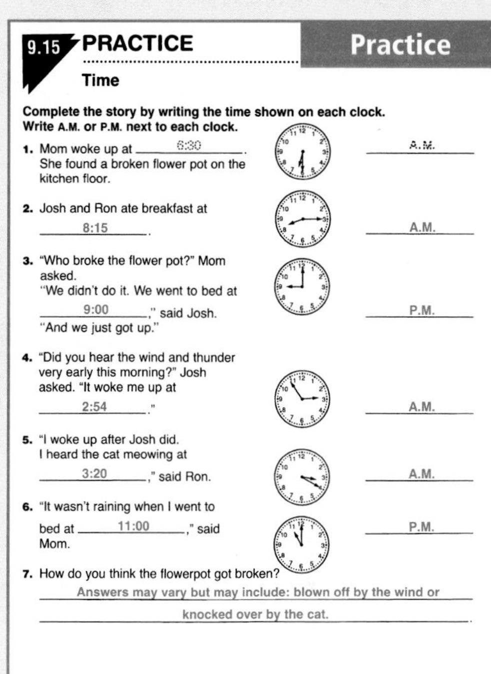

9.15 PRACTICE — Practice

Time

Complete the story by writing the time shown on each clock. Write A.M. or P.M. next to each clock.

1. Mom woke up at 6:30. She found a broken flower pot on the kitchen floor. A.M.
2. Josh and Ron ate breakfast at 8:15. A.M.
3. "Who broke the flower pot?" Mom asked. "We didn't do it. We went to bed at 9:00," said Josh. "And we just got up." P.M.
4. "Did you hear the wind and thunder very early this morning?" Josh asked. "It woke me up at 2:54." A.M.
5. "I woke up after Josh did. I heard the cat meowing at 3:20," said Ron. A.M.
6. "It wasn't raining when I went to bed at 11:00," said Mom. P.M.
7. How do you think the flowerpot got broken? Answers may vary but may include: blown off by the wind or knocked over by the cat.

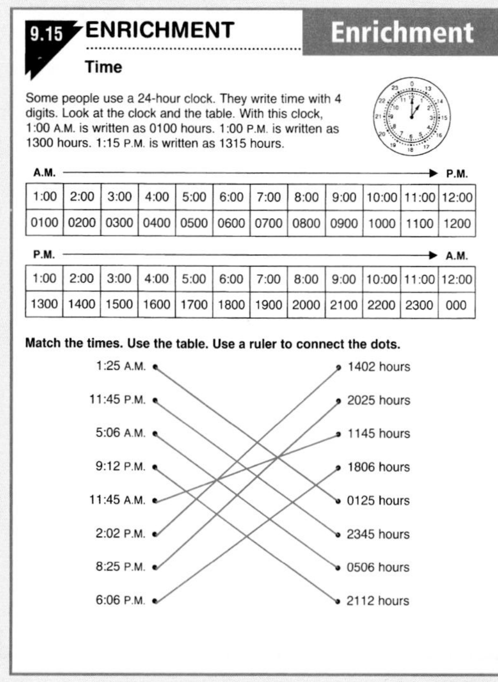

9.15 ENRICHMENT — Enrichment

Time

Some people use a 24-hour clock. They write time with 4 digits. Look at the clock and the table. With this clock, 1:00 A.M. is written as 0100 hours. 1:00 P.M. is written as 1300 hours. 1:15 P.M. is written as 1315 hours.

A.M. → P.M.

1:00	2:00	3:00	4:00	5:00	6:00	7:00	8:00	9:00	10:00	11:00	12:00
0100	0200	0300	0400	0500	0600	0700	0800	0900	1000	1100	1200

P.M. → A.M.

1:00	2:00	3:00	4:00	5:00	6:00	7:00	8:00	9:00	10:00	11:00	12:00
1300	1400	1500	1600	1700	1800	1900	2000	2100	2200	2300	000

Match the times. Use the table. Use a ruler to connect the dots.

1:25 A.M.	1402 hours
11:45 P.M.	2025 hours
5:06 A.M.	1145 hours
9:12 P.M.	1806 hours
11:45 A.M.	0125 hours
2:02 P.M.	2345 hours
8:25 P.M.	0506 hours
6:06 P.M.	2112 hours

Connecting

LESSON 9.16

Planning at a Glance

Objective To find elapsed time

Materials clock face

Optional Resources

- Reteach 9.16; Practice 9.16; Enrichment 9.16
- Daily Cumul. Review, p. 127
- Math Center: Act. Card 55
- Every Day Counts
- **TAB**, TE pp. 270E–270F, 270J
- **Problem of the Day**, 127, p. 64; Flip Chart, p. 64a

Students Acquiring English

Help students with the verb tenses used in this lesson. Ask them to look at a clock. Say *start*; then ask how much time has passed at various points. Help students say, *Ten seconds have passed.* Ask what time it "will be" when ten minutes have passed. Help them answer using the future tense.

Problem of the Day

One afternoon Hector said, "The number of hours that passed since noon are half as many as the number of hours that will pass from now to midnight." What time was it when Hector said this?

4:00 P.M.

LESSON 16

Elapsed Time

Your brother is running a 5-kilometer road race. You are timing him. The race starts at 1:45. Your brother crosses the finish line at 2:13. What was his running time?

Here's A Way!

1:45

2:13

1 Compare the two clocks.

- The first clock shows 1:45. The minute hand points to the 9.
- The second clock shows 2:13. The minute hand is between 2 and 3. The shaded part shows how much time has passed since 1:45.

2 Count the minutes by 5's and 1's.

- Skip-count by 5's to find the number of minutes between 9 and 2.

5, 10, 15, 20, 25 25 minutes

- Then, count on by 1's to find the number of minutes that have passed .

26, 27, 28 28 minutes

Your brother's running time was 28 minutes.

Talk About It! Why did you count by 5's first?

because each number on the clock represents 5 min

1 Introduce

Prior Knowledge **Use a clock face. Ask students the following questions.**

What time will it be in half an hour? 1:30

What time will it be in 1 hour? 4:30

Teach: Here's A Way!

Emphasize this point:

- Skip-counting by 5's and counting by 1's helps you tell elapsed time.

2 Develop

Show What You Know!

- Discuss with students their answers to exercise 4. Answers should show understanding of elapsed time.

Work It Out!

- Have students explain their reasoning, based on the schedule, for problems 11 and 12.

Using Reading Strategies Guide students to use the Monitor strategy as they read the Problem Solving exercises. Ask them to share what parts of the problem they needed to reread to understand. See TE p. 302J.

3 Summarize

- Remind students that they can find elapsed time by skip-counting by 5's from the time of an event, and then counting on by 1's.

Ongoing Assessment You leave at 4:35 to walk to baseball practice. You arrive at the field at 4:50.

- For how many minutes do you walk? 15 min.
- How did you find the answer? skip-counting by 5's

Math Journal: *Communicating*

Students may wish to draw clocks to help them figure out how much time it takes them to get to school.

Show What You Know!

Look at the clocks. Write how much time has passed.

1.   17 minutes

2.   53 minutes

3. Look at the clock in your classroom. Write the time it shows now. What time will it show 15 minutes from now? Answers will vary.

4. **Critical Thinking** You began reading a story at 11:20 A.M. You finished at 11:50 A.M. What fraction of an hour passed between those two times? $\frac{1}{2}$ hour

Work It Out!

Write how much time has passed.

5.   23 minutes

6.   52 minutes

Patterns Copy the times and complete the pattern. Describe each pattern.

7. 9:50, ■, 10:10, 10:20, ■, ■
   10:00; 10:30; 10:40; 10 min apart

8. 3:35, 3:45, 3:55, ■, ■
   4:05; 4:15; 10 min apart

9. 6:20, 6:40, 7:00, ■, ■, ■
   7:20; 7:40; 8:00; 20 min apart

10. 5:15, 5:30, ■, 6:00, ■, ■
    5:45; 6:15; 6:30; 15 min apart

Problem Solving

School Bus Schedule

Leave School	2:25 P.M.
Pine Road	2:35 P.M.
River Road	2:48 P.M.
Woods Street	3:06 P.M.

11. Your friend gets off the bus at Pine Road. You get off at River Road. How much longer will you be on the bus after your friend gets off?
    13 min

12. Four of your classmates get off the bus at Woods Street. How long is their ride from school?
    41 min

More Practice Set 9.16, p. 471

Math Journal

What time do you get up in the morning? What time do you leave for school? How much time passes between these times?
Answers will vary but should include 2 times and the elapsed time.

Meeting Individual Needs

Extra Support

Elapsed Time *(visual)* Students work in pairs. One partner names a starting time. The other names an elapsed time in hours and minutes. Partners then work together to find the ending time, using the classroom clock as a guide.

Alternate Approach

- Reteach Worksheet 9.16
- **TAB** See TE p. 302E–302F.

Students Acquiring English

See Language Connections, Ch. 9.

Practice

Math Center Use Activity Card 55, *Time After Time,* to have students practice finding elapsed time.

Challenge Use Activity Card 55 and have students continue the activity as described in Now Try This!

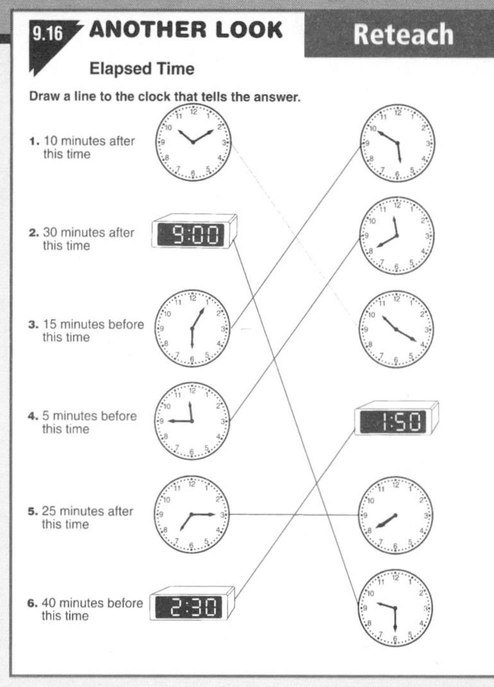

9.16 ANOTHER LOOK — Reteach

Elapsed Time

Draw a line to the clock that tells the answer.

1. 10 minutes after this time
2. 30 minutes after this time (9:00)
3. 15 minutes before this time
4. 5 minutes before this time
5. 25 minutes after this time
6. 40 minutes before this time (2:30)

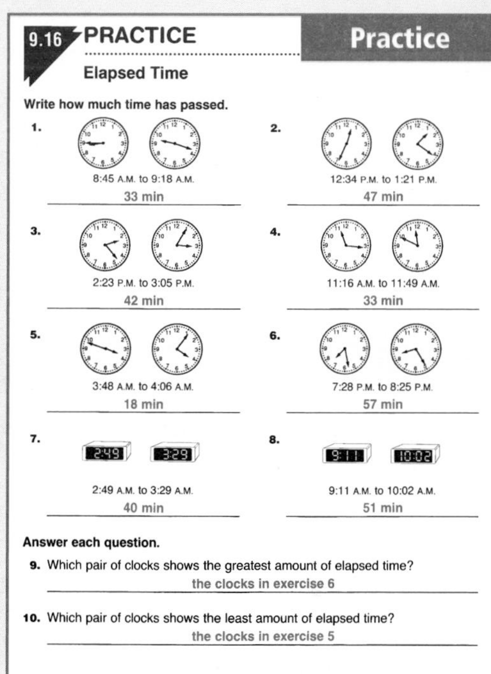

9.16 PRACTICE — Practice

Elapsed Time

Write how much time has passed.

1. 8:45 A.M. to 9:18 A.M. — 33 min
2. 12:34 P.M. to 1:21 P.M. — 47 min
3. 2:23 P.M. to 3:05 P.M. — 42 min
4. 11:16 A.M. to 11:49 A.M. — 33 min
5. 3:48 A.M. to 4:06 A.M. — 18 min
6. 7:28 P.M. to 8:25 P.M. — 57 min
7. 2:49 A.M. to 3:29 A.M. — 40 min
8. 9:11 A.M. to 10:02 A.M. — 51 min

Answer each question.

9. Which pair of clocks shows the greatest amount of elapsed time? the clocks in exercise 6
10. Which pair of clocks shows the least amount of elapsed time? the clocks in exercise 5

9.16 ENRICHMENT — Enrichment

Elapsed Time

Someone dropped a gold pen just inside the door of Varney's Gift Shop. The owner, Mrs. Varney, found the pen when she returned from running an errand. When no one claimed the pen before closing time, she asked Mr. Bell, the salesperson, to try to figure out who had dropped it. From where he had been standing, Mr. Bell had not seen who had dropped the pen. But he knew he had only 3 customers that afternoon. They were a man in a gray suit, a woman in green, and a teenage girl.

Use the clues to figure out who dropped the gold pen.

Clue 1: Mrs. Varney left the store at 2:55 P.M. She returned 20 minutes later. She spotted the pen when she returned.
Clue 2: The woman arrived 6 minutes after Mrs. Varney left to do her errand. The woman left at 3:10 P.M.
Clue 3: The girl arrived 5 minutes before the man.
Clue 4: The man arrived 15 minutes after the woman left the store.

1. At what time did the man arrive? 3:25 P.M.
2. At what time did the girl arrive? 3:20 P.M.
3. At what time did the woman arrive? 3:01 P.M.
4. How long did the woman remain in the store? 9 minutes
5. At what time did Mrs. Varney return? 3:15 P.M.
6. What is the latest time that the pen could have been dropped? 3:10 P.M.
7. Who dropped the gold pen? How do you know? The woman; the other customers got to the store after the pen was found.

LESSON 9.17

Problem Solving

Planning at a Glance

Objective **To use Working Backward and other strategies to solve problems**

Materials none

Optional Resources

- Reteach 9.17; Practice 9.17; Enrichment 9.17
- Daily Cumul. Review, p. 128
- Math Center: Project Card 9
- Every Day Counts
- **TAB**, TE pp. 302E–302F, 302J
- **Problem of the Day**, 128, p. 64; Flip Chart, p. 64b

MATHKEYS *Unlocking Geometry 3–6*, Level 3, Activity 22

Students Acquiring English

Students may have difficulty with the variety of meanings of the word *park*. Ask students to tell what a water park is, and discuss that water parks provide places for swimming and other types of water play. Discuss with students the photo on p. 336.

Problem of the Day

Alana was born on August 23. That year, August had 5 Fridays. How many Tuesdays did that August have? 4 Tuesdays

Problem Solving: Application

LESSON 17

Problem Solving

Using Work Backward and Other Strategies

A new water park is going to open in your town. The owners of the park want to send out flyers about the opening.

Problem Solving Process
✓ Understand
✓ Plan
✓ Try It
✓ Look Back

Choose a Strategy You Have Learned
✓ Act It Out
✓ Look for a Pattern
✓ Guess and Check
✓ Draw a Picture
✓ Make a Table
✓ Work Backward
Make a List
Work a Simpler Problem

It will take 1 week to design, print, and mail the flyers. They must be mailed 2 weeks before the park opens. The park opens on May 30. By what date must the park owners begin designing the flyer?

- What problem needs to be solved? when to begin designing the flyer
- When does the park open? May 30
- How many days before the opening must the flyers be mailed? 21 days
- Explain a strategy you can use to solve the problem. Then solve it. Strategies will vary. May 9

336 Chapter 9

1 Introduce

Prior Knowledge **Ask, When is working backward a good problem solving strategy?** when you know what the outcome is and want to find the starting point

Teach: *Modeling*

Emphasize this point:

- To solve the problem, first find out how long each step will take.

Model the example. Ask:

- Why did I multiply 2 by 7? 2 weeks × 7 days in a week
- Why did I add 7 to the product? 7 days for designing, printing, and mailing
- Why did I subtract 21 from 30? We need to start designing the flyer 21 days before May 30.

2 Develop

Work It Out!

- Have students discuss the strategies they used to solve each problem. For example, they could use Work Backward for problem 6, Draw a Picture for problem 3, and Make a Table for problem 1 and 2.
- Remind students that no single strategy is the only correct one for a problem.
- Ask students to compare and discuss their answers for problem 8.

Using Reading Strategies Encourage students to use the Monitor strategy as they read the Problem Solving exercises. Ask them to work in pairs and discuss the question asked by one problem and how to answer it. See TE p. 302J.

3 Summarize

- Have students review all the strategies they used to solve the problems.
- For each problem, ask students to suggest a different strategy they could have used and to explain how they could have used it.

Ongoing Assessment Your family returned from their vacation on July 31. You spent 7 days camping, 2 days visiting friends, and 4 days driving. What day did you leave? Accept July 17 or 18.

Math Journal: *Communicating*

Write a word problem that a classmate can solve by working backward. Answers will vary.

Work It Out!

Use any strategy to solve the problem. Show your work.

1. You have to wait in line for 8 minutes each time you want to ride the water slide. It takes 2 minutes to slide down and get back in line. How many turns on the slide can you take in $1\frac{1}{2}$ hours? 9 turns
2. Every Wednesday will be half-price day at the water park. Suppose July 1 is a Wednesday. How many half-price days will there be in July and August? (Hint: Both July and August have 31 days.) 9 half-price days

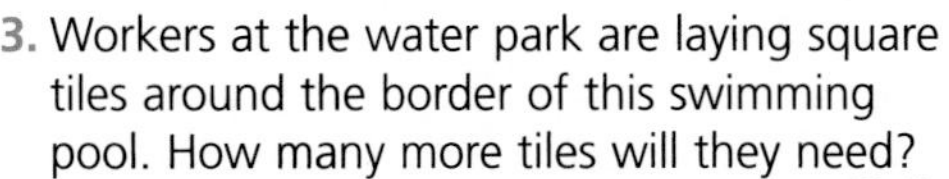

3. Workers at the water park are laying square tiles around the border of this swimming pool. How many more tiles will they need? 47 tiles

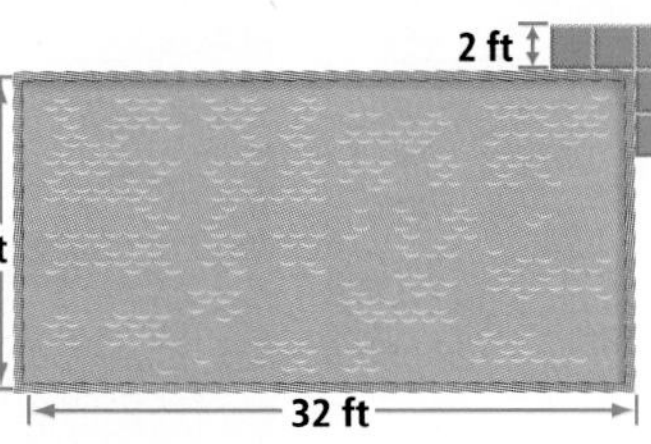

4. You are waiting to go on the water-car ride. Cars leave every 30 seconds. There are 13 people ahead of you in line. If each water-car takes 2 people, how long will you wait in line? 3 min
5. There are 600 inner tubes for the slides at the water park. There are twice as many blue tubes as yellow tubes. How many of each color tubeare at the water park? 200 yellow tubes, 400 blue tubes
6. Suppose you buy a swimming tube, goggles, and a pair of flippers at the water park. You also buy 5 postcards. You receive $1 change. How much money did you give the salesperson? $30.00

Water Park Swim Shop

Item	Cost
Swimming Tube	$8.50
Swim Cap	$3.00
Goggles	$6.00
Flippers	$12.00
Postcards	$5.00 for 10

7. Suppose the Water Park Swim Shop is having a sale. All prices are half off. You buy the same items that are listed in problem 6. Estimate what the total cost will be. about $15.00

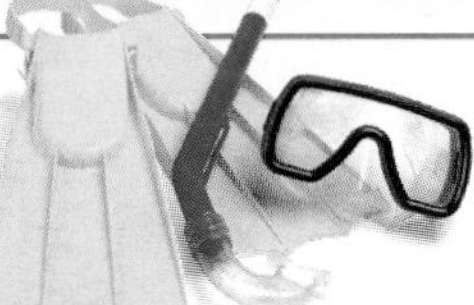

Share Your Thinking

8. What strategy did you use to solve problem 7? Explain. Answers will vary, but should reflect an understanding of the problem.

337

Meeting Individual Needs

Extra Support

Time Travel *(visual)* Distribute calendars to student pairs. Have them find the following dates:

- 22 days before Halloween October 9
- 17 days before July 4 June 17
- 5 weeks before students' birthdays Answers will vary.

Alternate Approach

- Reteach Worksheet 9.17
- **TAB** See TE pp. 302E–302F.

Students Acquiring English

See Language Connections, Ch. 9.

Challenge

You are cooking dinner for a friend who will arrive at 5:30 P.M. The macaroni and cheese needs to bake for 45 minutes. The cake you are making bakes 30 minutes, then needs to chill for $2\frac{1}{2}$ hours. The salad takes 10 minutes to prepare. At what time should you begin baking or preparing each dish? The cake should go in the oven at 3:00 P.M., the macaroni at 4:45 P.M., and the salad can be started at 5:20 P.M.

Practice

Math Center For more problem solving practice, see Project Card 9, *Construction Site.*

Reteach

9.17 ANOTHER LOOK

Using Work Backward and Other Strategies

Your book has 7 chapters. You have time to read 1 chapter each day after school. On Saturday and Sunday, you can read 2 chapters each day. Today is Monday. You must return the book next Monday morning. If you want to finish, on what day must you begin reading?

1. Understand

- You want to know when you must begin reading the book so that you can finish it.
- You know how many chapters the book has and how many chapters you can read each day.

2. Plan

- Work backward. Start with the last day that you can read the book. List the days in reverse order.
- Beside each day, write the number of chapters you can read. Stop when they add up to 7.

3. Try It

- Work backward to solve.

Day	Chapters
Sunday	2
Saturday	2 + 2 = 4
Friday	4 + 1 = 5
Thursday	5 + 1 = 6
Wednesday	6 + 1 = 7

4. Look Back

- You must begin reading the book by Wednesday.

Solve. Use Work Backward when you can.

1. You have $18 in your piggy bank. Several months ago, you began putting $3.00 into your bank every month. Now it is May 31. In what month did you begin saving? December

2. What is the perimeter of this card when opened? 26 inches

Name ______

Practice

9.17 PRACTICE

Using Work Backward and Other Strategies

Solve. Use Work Backward when you can.

November						
S	M	T	W	T	F	S
1	2	3	4	5	6	7
8	9	10	11	12	13	14
15	16	17	18	19	20	21
22	23	24	25	26	27	28
29	30					

1. How many Fridays are there in November? 4
2. Suppose you place 5¢ on every even number of the calendar. How much money will be on the calendar? 75¢
3. Mr. Frank's class has computer lab on Mondays, Wednesdays, and Fridays. How many days will Mr. Frank's class have computer lab during November? 13 times
4. Demetrius and his family will visit relatives for Thanksgiving. They want to arrive the day before Thanksgiving. If the bus ride takes 2 days, when will they have to begin traveling?
HINT: Thanksgiving is the fourth Thursday in November. Monday, November 23
5. Alexei's birthday is November 20. Natasha's birthday is one week before Carol's. Carol's birthday is on Monday during the same week as Alexei's. When is Carol's birthday? November 16
6. When is Natasha's birthday? November 9

Enrichment

9.17 ENRICHMENT

Using Work Backward and Other Strategies

1998

January						
S	M	T	W	T	F	S
				1	2	3
4	5	6	7	8	9	10
11	12	13	14	15	16	17
18	19	20	21	22	23	24
25	26	27	28	29	30	31

February						
S	M	T	W	T	F	S
1	2	3	4	5	6	7
8	9	10	11	12	13	14
15	16	17	18	19	20	21
22	23	24	25	26	27	28

March						
S	M	T	W	T	F	S
1	2	3	4	5	6	7
8	9	10	11	12	13	14
15	16	17	18	19	20	21
22	23	24	25	26	27	28
29	30	31				

April						
S	M	T	W	T	F	S
			1	2	3	4
5	6	7	8	9	10	11
12	13	14	15	16	17	18
19	20	21	22	23	24	25
26	27	28	29	30		

May						
S	M	T	W	T	F	S
					1	2
3	4	5	6	7	8	9
10	11	12	13	14	15	16
17	18	19	20	21	22	23
24	25	26	27	28	29	30
31						

June						
S	M	T	W	T	F	S
	1	2	3	4	5	6
7	8	9	10	11	12	13
14	15	16	17	18	19	20
21	22	23	24	25	26	27
28	29	30				

July						
S	M	T	W	T	F	S
			1	2	3	4
5	6	7	8	9	10	11
12	13	14	15	16	17	18
19	20	21	22	23	24	25
26	27	28	29	30	31	

August						
S	M	T	W	T	F	S
						1
2	3	4	5	6	7	8
9	10	11	12	13	14	15
16	17	18	19	20	21	22
23	24	25	26	27	28	29
30	31					

September						
S	M	T	W	T	F	S
		1	2	3	4	5
6	7	8	9	10	11	12
13	14	15	16	17	18	19
20	21	22	23	24	25	26
27	28	29	30			

October						
S	M	T	W	T	F	S
				1	2	3
4	5	6	7	8	9	10
11	12	13	14	15	16	17
18	19	20	21	22	23	24
25	26	27	28	29	30	31

November						
S	M	T	W	T	F	S
1	2	3	4	5	6	7
8	9	10	11	12	13	14
15	16	17	18	19	20	21
22	23	24	25	26	27	28
29	30					

December						
S	M	T	W	T	F	S
		1	2	3	4	5
6	7	8	9	10	11	12
13	14	15	16	17	18	19
20	21	22	23	24	25	26
27	28	29	30	31		

Solve. Use Work Backward when you can.

1. Mother's Day is celebrated the second Sunday in May. What is the date $1\frac{1}{2}$ weeks after Mother's Day in 1998? May 20
2. Lian's birthday is June 12. Her aunt and uncle are taking her to Disney World for her birthday. The airplane leaves for Disney World on her birthday. They are staying two nights and then returning home. If her birthday is June 12, what day will Lian return home? Sunday, June 14
3. Simon's birthday is on October 15. Cleon's birthday is one week before Missy's. Missy's birthday is on Monday during the same week as Simon's. When is Cleon's birthday? October 5

LESSON 9.18

Problem Solving

Planning at a Glance

Objective To use different strategies to solve problems

Materials none

Optional Resources

- Reteach 9.18; Practice 9.18; Enrichment 9.18
- Daily Cumul. Review, p. 129
- Math Center: Project Card 9
- Every Day Counts
- **TAB**, TE pp. 302E–302F, 302J
- **Problem of the Day**, 129, p. 65; Flip Chart, p. 65a

To meet individual needs, use *Unlocking Measurement 3–6*, Level 3, Activity 7

Students Acquiring English

Point out the words *reaches* and *touch* in the PE. Explain that in the third person, verbs that end in *ch* take the -es ending. Let students write sentences with verbs ending in *ch*.

Problem of the Day

Find the date of the 100th day of a year that is not a leap year.
April 10

Problem Solving : Application

LESSON 18

Problem Solving

Using Strategies

Read more about basketball players in the pages of *Children's Digest.*

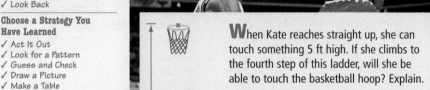

In 1993 Gheorghe Muresan (JAWRJ MYUR uh san) began playing basketball for the Washington Bullets, a team in the National Basketball Association. At 7 ft 7 in. tall, he can almost touch the basketball hoop without jumping!

Problem Solving Process
- ✓ Understand
- ✓ Plan
- ✓ Try It
- ✓ Look Back

Choose a Strategy You Have Learned
- ✓ Act It Out
- ✓ Look for a Pattern
- ✓ Guess and Check
- ✓ Draw a Picture
- ✓ Make a Table
- ✓ Work Backward
- Make a List
- Work a Simpler Problem

When Kate reaches straight up, she can touch something 5 ft high. If she climbs to the fourth step of this ladder, will she be able to touch the basketball hoop? Explain.

10 ft
11 in.
11 in.

- What problem do you have to solve? Can she touch the hoop from the ladder?
- How high is the hoop? 10 ft
- How high can the student reach without a ladder? 5 ft
- How high is each step of the ladder? 11 in.
- Explain a strategy that can help you to solve the problem. Then solve it. Strategies will vary. No. 5ft + 44 in. < 10 ft.

338 Chapter 9

1 Introduce

Build Understanding Have students predict how many of them would have to line up with arms outstretched and fingertips touching to reach across the room. Ask, How can you verify your predictions?

Teach: ***Modeling*** Model the example. Ask:

- Why don't you need to know the height of the ladder to solve this problem? because you know how high each step of the ladder is
- How could you use Draw a Picture to help you solve this problem? by drawing Kate's five-foot reach; it would only be half as high as the hoop

2 Develop

Work It Out!

- Have students discuss the strategies they used to solve problems 1–5. For example, they could use Act It Out for problem 1, Draw a Picture for problems 2–4, Look for a Pattern for problem 6, and Make a Table for problem 8.
- Have students discuss their reasoning for problem 8.

Using Reading Strategies Guide students to use the Monitor strategy as they read the Problem Solving exercises. Ask, How can you keep track of the information you get when you reread a problem? See TE p. 302J.

3 Summarize

- Have students review the strategies they used to solve each problem. Ask them to suggest how they could have used an alternate strategy.

Ongoing Assessment A train reached Oakville at 11:30. It took $\frac{3}{4}$ hour to get from Granby to Oakville, after leaving Colton at 8:45 for its run to Granby. How long did the train take to get from Colton to Granby? 2 hours

Math Journal: ***Communicating***

Write a word problem about how long it takes someone to get somewhere. Answers will vary.

Work It Out!

Use any strategy to solve the problem. Show your work.

1. A basketball coach wants to show her players their positions. She folds a sheet of paper in half 3 times. How many sections will she have on which to draw diagrams? 8 sections

In problems 2–4, player A and player B run to the end of the basketball court and back. The speed of each player does not change. Where is player B when player A finishes if…

2. player A gets to the end of the court when player B is $\frac{3}{4}$ of the way there? $\frac{1}{2}$ of the way back
3. player A gets to the end of the court when player B is $\frac{1}{2}$ of the way there? at the end of the court
4. player A gets to the end of the court when player B is $\frac{1}{4}$ of the way there? $\frac{1}{2}$ of the way across the court for the first time
5. Team A scores 20 points in the first half of the game and 18 points in the second half. If team B scores 32 points during the whole game, who won? By how much? Team A by 6 points
6. Cheerleaders are planning a new cheer to use at a basketball game. They will repeat the same pattern of positions 4 times. Draw pictures to show the next three positions.

7. **Create Your Own** Use stick figures to make up a pattern for a cheer. Repeat the pattern 3 times. Check students' work.
8. Suppose your cousin grew 2 in. each year from his 13th birthday until his 17th birthday. On his 17th birthday he was 5 ft 7 in. tall. How tall was he on his 13th birthday? 4 ft 11 in.

Share Your Thinking

9. What strategy did you use to solve problem 8? Explain. Answers will vary, but should reflect an understanding of the problem.

Meeting Individual Needs

Extra Support

Measuring Reach ***(kinesthetic)*** Have pairs of students take turns marking and labeling each other's reach with arms overhead on a 10 foot length of butcher paper. Then have pairs measure the lengths of their reaches. Ask, How high a ladder would you need to reach 10 ft? Have students answer the question, then measure to check their answers.

Alternate Approach

- Reteach Worksheet 9.18
- **TAB** See TE pp. 302E–302F.

Students Acquiring English

See Language Connections, Ch. 9.

Challenge

Have students solve this problem: Gaia needs $75 for a camping trip. She has two $20 bills in her savings. She earns money cleaning 2 closets at $6 for each closet. She walks a friend's dog for 2 weeks and earns $5 each week. She returns 28 bottles for recycling and receives a nickel a bottle. How much more money must she earn to go on the trip? $11.60

Practice

Math Center For more problem solving practice, see Project Card 9, *Construction Site.*

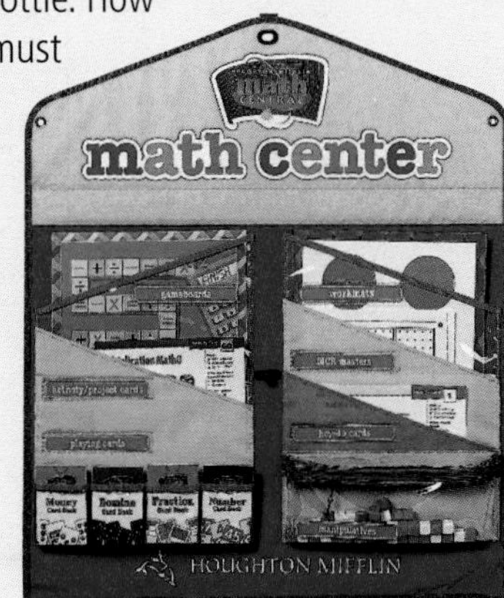

9.18 ANOTHER LOOK — Reteach

Problem Solving: Using Strategies

Frankie is the goalkeeper of his school's soccer team. He must move quickly to all parts of the goal area to stop the ball. What is the perimeter of the goal area?

50 yards
28 yards
44 yards
76 yards
Goal Area
28 yards

1. Understand
- You need to use the drawing of a soccer field to find the perimeter of the goal area.

2. Plan
- The goal area is a rectangle. To find the perimeter of the goal area, you need to find its length and width.
- Decide what operation you will need to use to find the width and length of the goal area.

3. Try It
- To find the length, subtract the other two length measurements from the total length of 76 yards. The length is 20 yards.
- To find the width, subtract 44 from 50. The width is 6 yards.

4. Look Back
- To find the perimeter, find the sum of all 4 sides of the goal area. 20 + 20 + 6 + 6 = 52 yards.

Use any strategy to solve.

1. Frankie can choose 2 different skills to work on during soccer practice. He can choose to practice kicking, passing, heading, or dribbling. How many different combinations can Frankie choose? 6
2. A soccer match is played with 2 teams that each have 10 players and 1 goalie. If there are 3 soccer matches being played, how many people are playing soccer? HINT: Act It Out or Draw a Picture 66 people

9.18 PRACTICE — Practice

Problem Solving: Using Strategies

Use any strategy to solve.

1. What is the perimeter of a rectangle whose length is 12 centimeters and whose width is 9 centimeters. 42 centimeters
2. Using these clues, find out what time school starts at Conway Elementary School: 9:00 A.M.
   - Math, Reading, and Social Studies last 1 hour each.
   - Lunch is $\frac{1}{2}$ hour.
   - Music, art, and library last $\frac{1}{2}$ hour each.
   - There are two 15-minute recesses.
   - School ends at 2:30 P.M.

   HINT: Work Backward
3. Fill in the blanks to continue the pattern.
   a. 3, 6, 9, 12, 15, 18
   b. 4, 8, 16, 32, 64
4. At 8:00 A.M., the thermometer reads 10°C. If the temperature rises 2 degrees every hour, what will the temperature be at 12:00 noon? 18°C
5. Every time you eat 2 dried apples your friend eats 4 peanuts. If you eat 8 dried apples, how many peanuts will your friend eat? 16 peanuts
6. You and a friend share 3 quarters, 3 nickels, and 2 pennies equally. How much could each of you spend? 46¢
7. A pet store owner has 4 aquariums with 4 fish in each aquarium and 3 aquariums with 5 fish in each aquarium. How many fish are in the aquariums? 31 fish

9.18 ENRICHMENT — Enrichment

Problem Solving: Using Strategies

It is field day at Echo Park Elementary School.

Events	
12:15 P.M.	Frisbee Throw
12:30 P.M.	Cartwheel Relay
1:00 P.M.	Egg Toss
1:15 P.M.	Long Jump
1:30 P.M.	Wheelbarrow Run
2:15 P.M.	Relay Race
2:30 P.M.	Sack Race

Use any strategy to solve.

1. All students are told to be on the field 15 minutes before the first event begins. They must remain on the field until 3:00 P.M. How long will the students be on the field? 3 hours
2. The students had math, music, reading, and lunch before the field day started. Each subject was 1 hour long and lunch lasted $\frac{1}{2}$ hour. If lunch ended at 12:00 noon, what time did school begin? 8:30 A.M.
3. You can participate in 3 different events. Each event lasts 20 minutes and you need 5 minutes to move from one event to the next. What 3 events will you participate in? Answers may vary, but the starting time for each event must be at least 25 minutes apart.
4. The relay race is 400 meters long. Each team member runs 100 meters. How many people are on each team? 4 people
5. You and your friend put a rope down to mark the starting line for the sack race. The rope is 10 meters long. You put a post at each end of the rope and at every 2 meters. How many posts did you use? 6 posts
6. Write a question that can be answered by using the data on the chart. Find the answer. Questions and answers will vary.

Chapter Test

Problem Solving

Give 0–7 points per answer based on how well students meet the following criteria:

Problem 1

- A strategy is seen through to a correct solution
- Work is shown clearly

Problem 2

- A strategy is seen through to a correct solution
- Shows understanding of patterns on a calendar

Concepts and Skills

If students need more help with concepts and skills in this chapter, use the following Reteaching Worksheets:

- 66 Measuring and Drawing Lines to the Nearest Inch and Half Inch, p. 183
- 67 Perimeter, p. 184
- 68 Choosing the Appropriate Type of Measure, p. 185
- 69 Choosing the Appropriate Unit of Measure, p. 186
- 70 Comparing Measures, p. 187
- 71 Choosing the Appropriate Type of Measure, p. 200
- 72 Choosing the Appropriate Unit of Measure, p. 201
- 73 Comparing Measures, p. 202
- 74 Telling Time, p. 203
- 75 Elapsed Time, p. 204

Chapter 9 Test

for Pages 302–339

Test-Taking Tips
If you have enough time, always recheck your answers. Ask yourself whether each one makes sense.

Problem Solving

Use any strategy to solve. Show your work. (pages 322, 336)

1. Suppose you have grown 2 in. every year for 4 years. If you are 51 in. now, how tall were you 4 years ago? 43 in.
2. Your class has Show and Tell every other Tuesday. The calendar shows that you had Show and Tell on Tuesday, March 25. When is your next Show and Tell? April 8

Concepts

Use paper clips to estimate the length. Write *a*, *b*, *c*, or *d*. (page 304)

3. a. 1 in. b. 3 in. c. 4 in. d. 2 in. c
4. a. 2 in. b. 4 in. c. 6 in. d. 1 in. d

Which unit would you use to measure? Write *a* or *b*. (pages 310, 312, 314, 320, 324, 326)

5. length of a hammer — a. inches b. yards a
6. distance across a lake — a. kilometers b. decimeters a
7. tea in a teapot — a. cup b. gallon a
8. gas in a gas tank — a. liter b. milliliter a
9. weight of a television set — a. ounce b. pound b
10. a crate of apples — a. ounce b. pound b
11. a slice of bread — a. gram b. kilogram a
12. weight of a comb — a. gram b. kilogram a

340

Chapter Correlation to Standardized Tests

Math Central: Chapter Objective	ITBS Form M	CAT/5	CTBS/4	Terra Nova (CTBS/5)	MAT 7th ed.	SAT 9th ed.	State/ Local
9A To estimate and measure length using both customary and metric units	•	•	•	•	•	•	
9B To find the perimeter of a polygon	•	•	•	•	•	•	
9C To estimate and measure capacity, weight, and mass	•	•	•	•	•	•	
9D To find simple equivalencies for customary and metric units	•	•	•	•	•	•	
9E To read Fahrenheit and Celsius thermometers	•	•	•	•	•	•	
9F To write time to the minute	•	•	•	•	•	•	
9G To use elapsed time to solve problems	•	•	•	•	•	•	
9H To use Work Backward and other strategies to solve problems	•			•	•	•	

Skills

Find the perimeter. (page 308)

13. 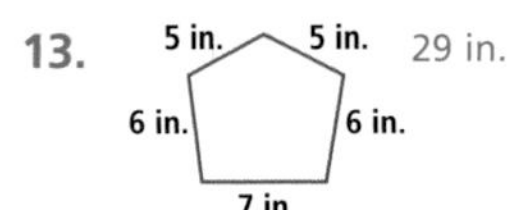 29 in.

14. 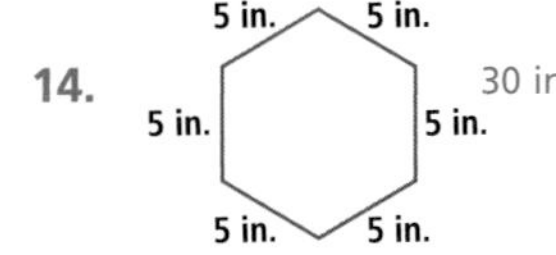 30 in.

Complete. Write >, < , or =. (pages 310, 312, 320, 324)

15. 12 in. ● 1 yd < 16. 10 mi ● 10 ft > 17. 2 c ● 2 pt <

18. 1 km ● 100 cm > 19. 1 m ● 100 cm = 20. 1000 mL ● 1000 L <

Complete the number sentence. (pages 312, 314, 326)

21. 16 oz = ■ lb 1 22. 4 lb = ■ oz 64 23. 5 kg = ■ g 5000

Write the temperature. (page 330)

24. 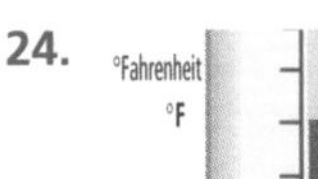 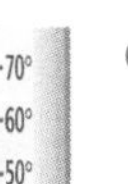 60°F

25. 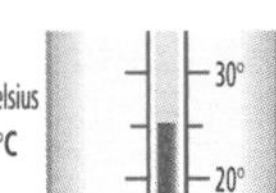 25°C

Write how much time has passed. (page 334)

26.  47 min

27.   31 min

Performance Task

(pages 322, 336, 338)

Students get to choose their own activities for Field Day. Use the schedule to answer the questions.

- The film lasts 1 hour. If you go to the film, what event will you miss? Tour of the gym
- Soccer games will last $1\frac{1}{2}$ hours. If you decide to play, what will be the next activity you can join? Volleyball
- Write a new problem, using the schedule.

Keep In Mind . . .
Your work will be evaluated on the following:
☑ Steps for solving
☑ Method for checking
☑ Written problem
☑ Use of schedule information

FIELD DAY SCHEDULE

Film: *Sports Heros*	8:30 A.M.	Soccer Games	11:00 A.M.
Tour of New Gym	9:00 A.M.	Long Jump	11:30 A.M.
100-Meter Run	9:30 A.M.	Squirt Gun Fun	12:00 P.M.
Snowcone Snack	10:00 A.M.	Volleyball	12:30 P.M.
Team Relays	10:30 A.M.	Picnic Lunch	1:00 P.M.

341

Assessment Options

The following materials are found in your **Comprehensive Assessment Package:**

Formal Assessments
- Standardized-Format
- Free-Response Chapter Tests, Forms A and B

Performance Assessments
- Chapter Tasks
- Midyear and Final Project Tasks

Alternative Assessments
- Observation Checklist
- Student Attitude Assessment
- Student Self-Assessment *Individual and Group*

- Chapter Tests for Students Acquiring Language Proficiency
- Informal Learning Inventory

Standardized Testing: New Formats
- Enhanced Multiple-Choice
- Extended-Response
- Short-Response

Management
- Student Record Sheets
- Answer Keys

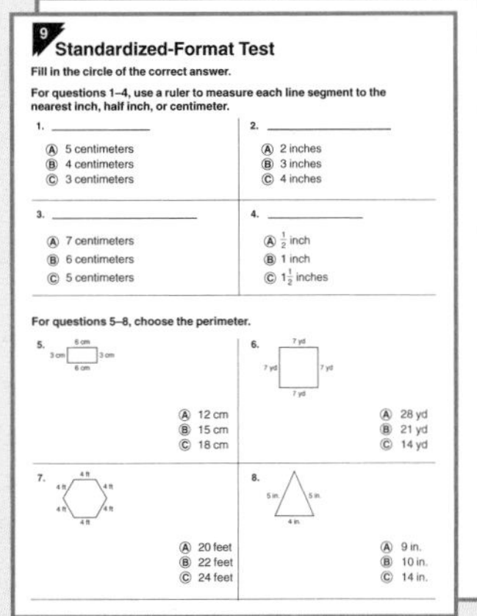

- Standardized-Format Chapter Tests
- Free-Response Chapter Tests, Forms A and B
- Standardized-Format Midyear and Final Tests

Additional Assessment Resources

Test, Practice, Management Program
Use the *Test, Practice, Management Program* to create, administer, and score tests as well as generate practice sets. Questions are correlated to the Lesson Objectives.

Performance Tasks

Use the following criteria, each worth 4 points, to evaluate students' responses. These criteria align with *Keep In Mind* in the Pupil Edition on p. 341.

Criteria	
Shows a step-by-step process	Shows correct anwers and a method for checking
Writes a problem that applies to real world situations	Writes a problem that uses schedule information

Use this 4-level rubric to score students' responses. If you prefer a task with a 6-level rubric, use the Performance Assessment for this chapter.

4 points	Limited Response
8 points	Acceptable
12 points	Capable
16 points	Superior

Common Error Alert

If students are making frequent errors, see Analyzing Errors, TE pp. 341A–341B.

Scoring Chart

Item	Points
1–2	7 points each
3–12	4 points each
13–27	2 points each
Performance Task	16 points
TOTAL	100 points or 100%

Item Analysis

Item	Objectives
1–2	To use Work Backwards and other strategies to solve problems (9H)
3–12	To estimate and measure length, capacity, weight, and mass (9A, 9C)
13–14	To find the perimeter of a polygon (9B)
15–23	To find simple equivalencies for customary and metric units (9D)
24–25	To read Fahrenheit and Celsius thermometers (9E)
26–27	To use elapsed time to solve problems (9G)

Cumulative Test

For a cumulative review in the multiple-choice format, see TE pp. T78–T79.

Analyzing Errors

Strategies and Techniques for Reteaching

Errors in Basic Units of Measure In addition to knowing which units to use, students must become familiar with the relationship between units. Inches and feet, feet and yards, cups and pints, cups and quarts and others can present confusion in labeling. To help students recognize these relationships, provide appropriate skip-counting experiences. For example, use cup-sized containers and have students count the 8 ounces in a cup. Then guide them to count by 8 to 32 to see that there are 4 cups in 1 quart. Similar activities relating inches to feet to yards, and centimeters to meters, can give students the practice they need to become familiar with units of measurement.

Measuring Length, Capacity, and Weight

Errors in Labeling with Units

Error Does not recognize that the smaller the unit, the greater the number needed for a given measurement

Reteaching On the board, list pairs of units, such as feet and inches, yards and feet, miles and feet, pounds and ounces, and so on. For each pair, ask students to name the smaller unit. Circle each unit as it is named. Then, write the number of small units that fit the greater unit in each pair. Lead students to see a pattern: greater numbers of small units equal lesser numbers of big units.

Error

1 foot = 12 inches
3 yards = 1 foot

Reteaching

12 inches = 1 foot
1 yard = 3 feet
5280 feet = 1 mile

Error Confuses ounces and pounds

Reteaching Develop the concept of weighing objects by having students assess an object's heaviness with their hands. They can practice estimating the weight of books, lunches, shoes, and other classroom objects. As they lift each object have them compare it to the weight of a basketball (approximately 1 pound) or the weight of a first class letter (approximately an ounce).

Error

The globe weighs 18 pounds.

Reteaching

basketball → pound
letter → ounce
- lift the globe
- 18 basketballs? no
- 18 letters? yes

The globe weighs 18 oz.

Errors in Measuring to the Nearest Inch

Error Begins at the 1 rather than at the zero end of the ruler when measuring

Reteaching Have students count backward along the edge of a 12 inch ruler beginning with 6. When they get to 1, ask them to name the number that would come next. Point out that when they begin to measure, they must place the zero mark of the ruler at the end of the object they are measuring, even though they do not see the zero written.

Error

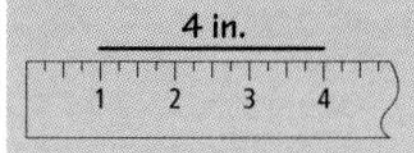

Reteaching

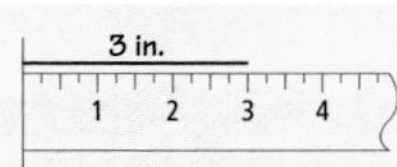

Error Names the next inch when measuring without regard to whether the length should be rounded up or down

Reteaching Have students measure and cut a small length of string and place it alongside a ruler. Ask them to name the two inch marks closest to the end of the string. Then have them place a sheet of paper on the ruler and mark off each of these two inch marks. The mark closer to the end of the string shows which number names the nearest inch.

Error

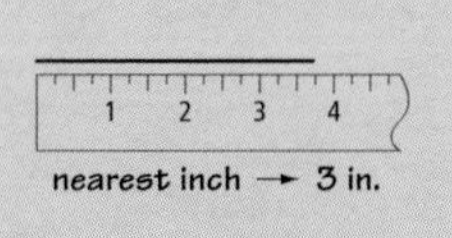

Reteaching

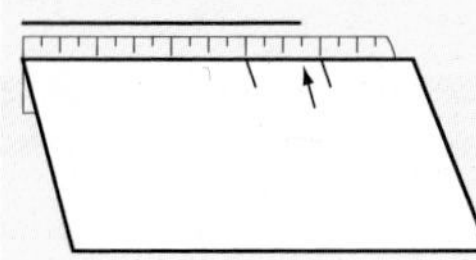

Analyzing Errors

Error Draws a line segment longer or shorter than a specified length

Reteaching Have students use a centimeter or inch ruler to draw a specified length. Remind them that it is just as important to begin at the zero end of the ruler when drawing a length as it is when measuring one that already exists. Suggest that they count each unit, starting with 1 as they draw.

Error

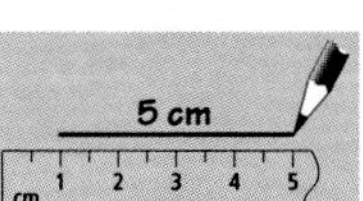

Reteaching

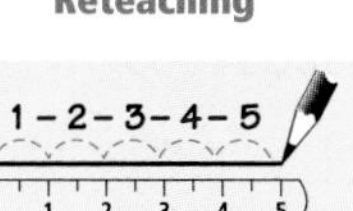

Reading a Thermometer

Error in Reading a Thermometer Scale

Error Cannot read degree markings between those labeled on the thermometer

Reteaching Choose any 10-degree portion of a thermometer to enlarge on the chalkboard. Label only the two multiples of 10. Mark only the labeled points and the midpoint. Then, ask students to name the midpoint. Change the labeled multiples of ten, and again ask for the midpoint. Suggest that students find and name the midpoints for the entire scale on a real thermometer.

Error

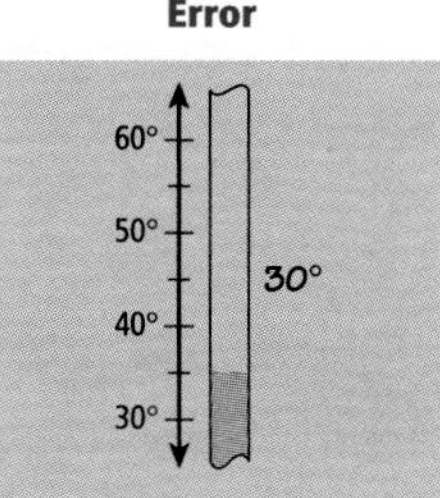

Reteaching

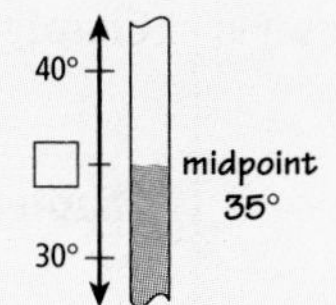

Telling Time

Error in Reading Clocks

Error Cannot read minutes before the hour because of difficulty subtracting from 60

Reteaching Give students varied practice subtracting from 60 and counting backwards from 60 by fives. A numberline marked from 30 to 60 with intervals of 5 may help students practice. Point out that if this numberline curved around, it could show half the clock.

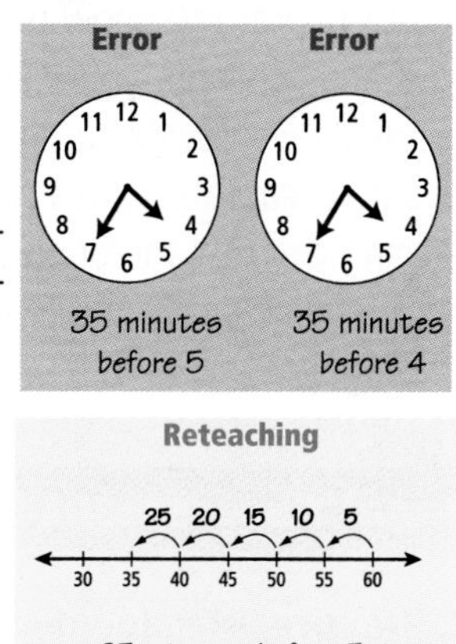

Error in Determining Elapsed Time

Error Incorrectly includes hours when determining elapsed time

Reteaching Students may unnecessarily include an additional hour when calculating the elapsed time. For example, in determining the length of time from 1:49 until 2:15, students may correctly add 11 and 15, but then go on to add the hour, thinking that the elapsed time is 1 hour 26 minutes. When doing elapsed time problems, show a clockface and have students count the minutes. Remind them of the relationship between 1 hour and 60 minutes.

Chapter 9 Cumulative Review

Two Ways to Use the Cumulative Review

Maintenance For those students whose results on the current Chapter Test show a good grasp of skills and concepts, you may wish to assign the Cumulative Review as homework. Students may also benefit from the specific review and practice opportunities listed in the Skills Maintenance chart.

Reassessment For those students whose results on the current Chapter Test show only a limited grasp of skills and concepts, you may wish to assign the Cumulative Review as class work. If it then appears that reassessment is needed, the Skills Reteaching chart on the opposite page identifies remedial minilessons in the Teacher's Resource Package.

Additional Assessment Resources

Test, Practice, Management Program

Use the *Test, Practice, Management Program* to create, administer, and score tests as well as generate practice sets. Questions are correlated to the Lesson Objectives.

Cumulative Review

Coins (Chapter 2)
What is the value of the coins?

Here's A Way!

Skip-count by 10's.
Skip-count by 5's.

10, 20, 30, 40, 45 cents

Write the value of the coins.

1. 50¢

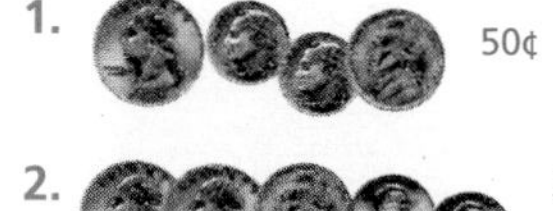

2. 57¢
3. 30¢
4. Write the value in exercise 3 in words. thirty cents

Estimating Sums (Chapter 3)
Estimate 457 + 307.

Here's A Way!

Use front-end estimation.
457 + 307
4 hundreds + 3 hundreds
The sum is about 700.

Use front-end estimation to estimate.
Estimates may vary. Accept adjusted estimates.

5. 321 + 164 400
6. 516 + 373 800
7. 759 + 102 800
8. \$286 + \$367 \$500
9. \$427 + 160 \$500
10. \$785 + 562 \$1200
11. To estimate 89 + 92 using front-end estimation, what would you do?
Look at the digits in the greatest place. 8 tens and nine tens; 80 + 90 = 170.

Division Facts (Chapter 5)
Divide 20 by 5.

Here's A Way!

You can draw a picture.
You can skip-count by 5's:
5, 10, 15, 20;
20 ÷ 5 = 4

Find the quotients.

12. 30 ÷ 5 6
13. 25 ÷ 5 5
14. 15 ÷ 5 3
15. 35 ÷ 5 7
16. 45 ÷ 5 9
17. 40 ÷ 5 8
18. How can you use skip-counting to find out how many nickels are in 40¢? Count by 5's: 5, 10, 15, 20, 25, 30, 35, 40. So, there are 8 nickels.

342

Skills Maintenance

Chapter Objectives	Where taught in pupil book	More practice in pupil book
• To write the value of coins and bills (2D)	**Chapter 2**, pp. 64–65	More Practice Set 2.11, p. 445
• To estimate sums and differences (3E)	**Chapter 3**, pp. 92–93, 108–109	More Practice Sets 3.4, 3.11, pp. 449, 451
• To use basic division facts to divide by 2 through 5 (5C)	**Chapter 5**, pp. 176–177	More Practice Set 5.9, p. 456
• To identify and classify angles, lines, and line segments (7C)	**Chapter 7**, pp. 236–237	More Practice Set 7.5, p. 460
• To write fractions for fractional parts of regions (8A)	**Chapter 8**, pp. 274–275	More Practice Set 8.2, p. 463
• To use Work Backward and other strategies (9H)	**Chapter 9**, pp. 336–337	None

Angles (Chapter 7)
Which figure has a right angle?

Here's A Way!

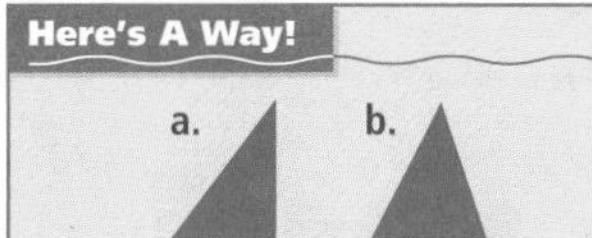

Check each figure to see if any angle is like a corner in a square. **Figure a has a square corner, so it has a right angle.**

Write the number of square corners in each figure.

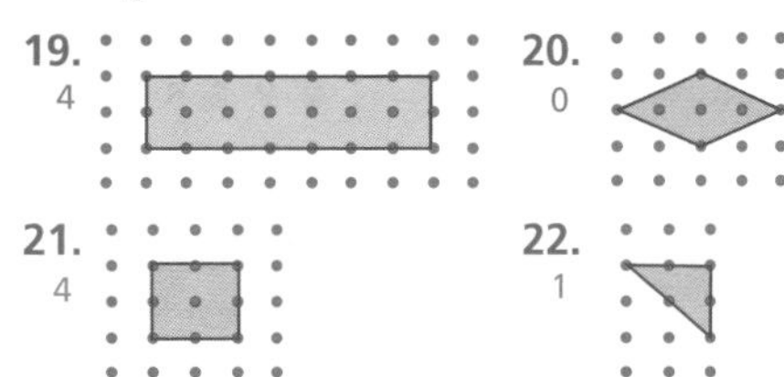

19. 4

20. 0

21. 4

22. 1

23. Look at exercise 21. What is true about the sides and corners of any square? The sides are all the same length. The corners are all square corners.

Writing Fractions (Chapter 8)
What fraction of this figure is shaded?

Here's A Way!

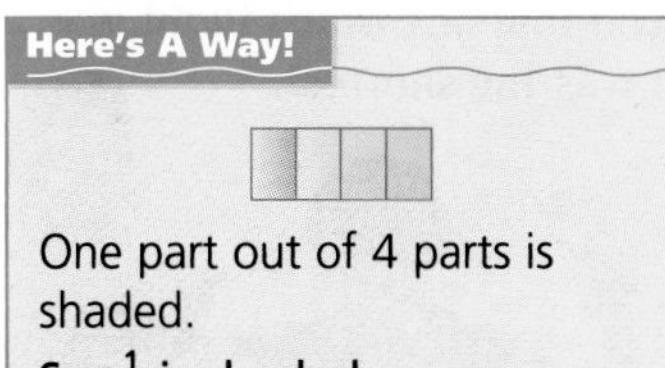

One part out of 4 parts is shaded.
So, $\frac{1}{4}$ is shaded.

What fraction names the shaded part?

24. $\frac{3}{8}$

25.  $\frac{1}{2}$

Write the fraction for the unshaded part.

26.  $\frac{2}{3}$

27. 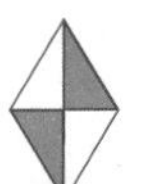 $\frac{2}{4}$

28. What does the top number in a fraction tell? What does the bottom number tell? The top number names how many shaded parts are in the whole. The bottom number tells how many equal parts there are in all.

Problem Solving

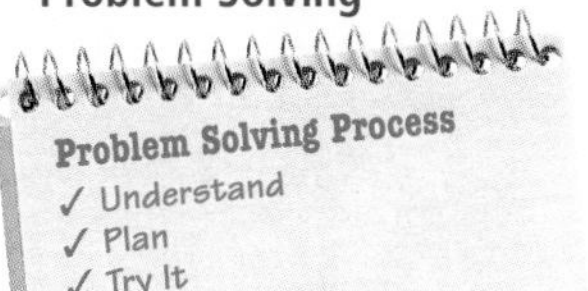

Solve using any strategy. Show your work.

29. You need to plant seeds 2 inches apart in your garden. Your rows are 36 inches long. The first and last seeds must be 2 inches from the edge. How many seeds can you plant in 1 row? 17 seeds

30. You see a blanket that is made with stripes. It has 1 white stripe, 2 blue stripes, 3 red stripes, then 4 white stripes, 5 blue stripes, 6 red stripes. Describe the pattern.
The pattern repeats 3 colors. Each time a color appears it increases one stripe from the color before it.

Students Acquiring English

Some students may need assistance on the Cumulative Review.

- Be prepared to read directions aloud to students.
- Focus special attention on word problems. Expect to paraphrase, diagram, or draw an explanation of the word problem.
- Review important vocabulary words that have been previously introduced.
- Review titles and other elements of graphs and charts.

Skills Reteaching

Chapter Objectives	Suggested materials for minilessons		
• To write the value of coins and bills (2D)	Reteach 2.11	Practice 2.11	Enrichment 2.11
• To estimate sums and differences (3E)	Reteach 3.4 and 3.11	Practice 3.4 and 3.11	Enrichment 3.4 and 3.11
• To use basic division facts to divide by 2 through 5 (5C)	Reteach 5.9	Practice 5.9	Enrichment 5.9
• To identify and classify angles, lines, and line segments (7C)	Reteach 7.5	Practice 7.5	Enrichment 7.5
• To write fractions for parts of regions (8A)	Reteach 8.2	Practice 8.2	Enrichment 8.2
• To use Work Backward and other strategies (9H)	Reteach 9.17	Practice 9.17	Enrichment 9.17

INVESTIGATION

Management small groups
Materials straws, paper, scissors, rulers, tape, measuring tape

Building Background

Students should be familiar with accurately measuring and cutting various materials. Review how to measure to the nearest half inch.

Management Strategies Cooperative Learning

Introduce

- Introduce the activity; assign students to groups.
- Review the criteria in *Keep In Mind.*

Guide

- When a group has difficulty, assess whether the difficulty lies with the activity or with the process.
- If a group is not working well together, review each student's role in the group.

Summarize

- Be sure that all students have completed the activity and are ready for group discussion.
- Record data on the board as it is presented.

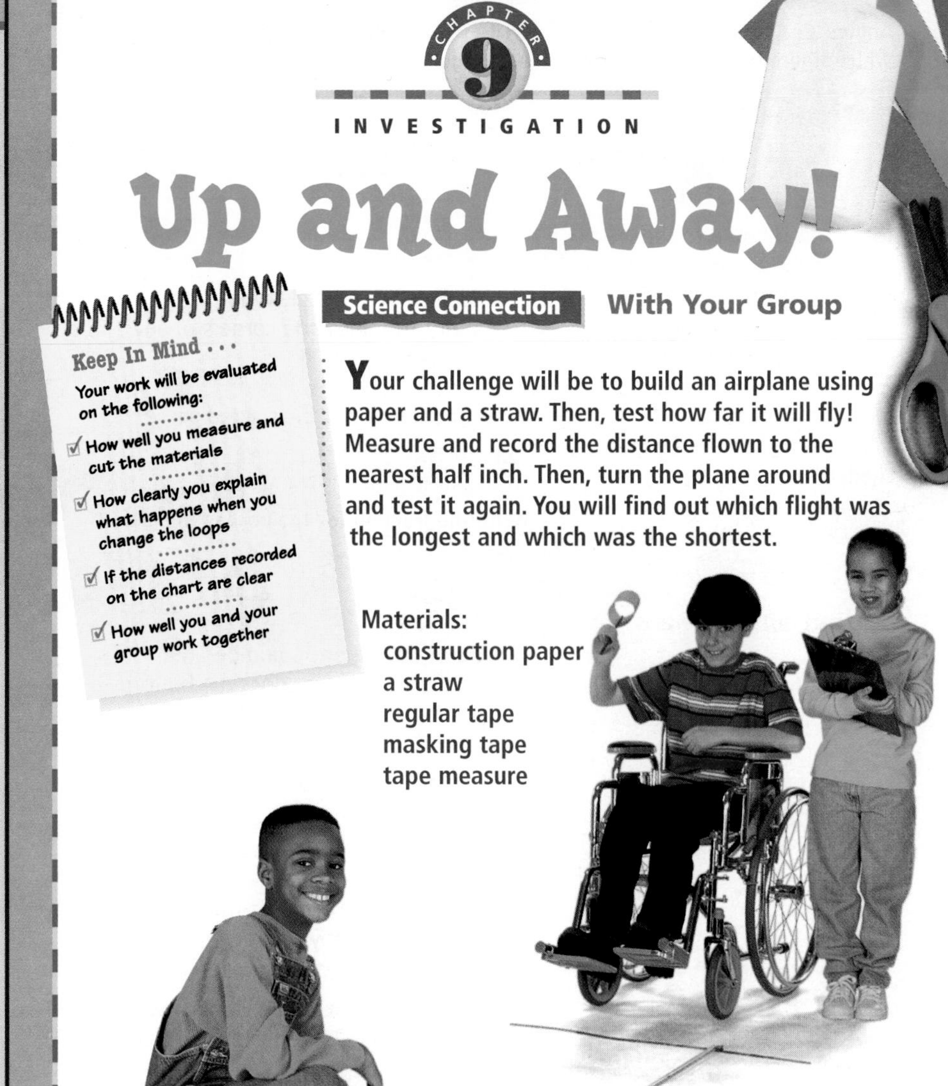
CHAPTER 9

INVESTIGATION

Up and Away!

Science Connection **With Your Group**

Keep In Mind . . .
Your work will be evaluated on the following:
- How well you measure and cut the materials
- How clearly you explain what happens when you change the loops
- If the distances recorded on the chart are clear
- How well you and your group work together

Your challenge will be to build an airplane using paper and a straw. Then, test how far it will fly! Measure and record the distance flown to the nearest half inch. Then, turn the plane around and test it again. You will find out which flight was the longest and which was the shortest.

Materials:
construction paper
a straw
regular tape
masking tape
tape measure

344

Investigation Support

Technology

Internet: Education Place
http://www.eduplace.com
Houghton Mifflin's *Education Place* **Math Center** provides teacher and student support, such as links to other Internet sites.

Math Journal: *Communicating*

Have you ever ridden in an airplane? If not, do you know someone who has? How far did the plane fly? How long did it take to get to its destination? How fast did it fly? How high did it fly? Students can write a response to these questions in their Math Journal.

Portfolio Opportunity

Students can make replicas of their best planes to put in a box in their portfolios. They can also include their records of how far each plane flew.

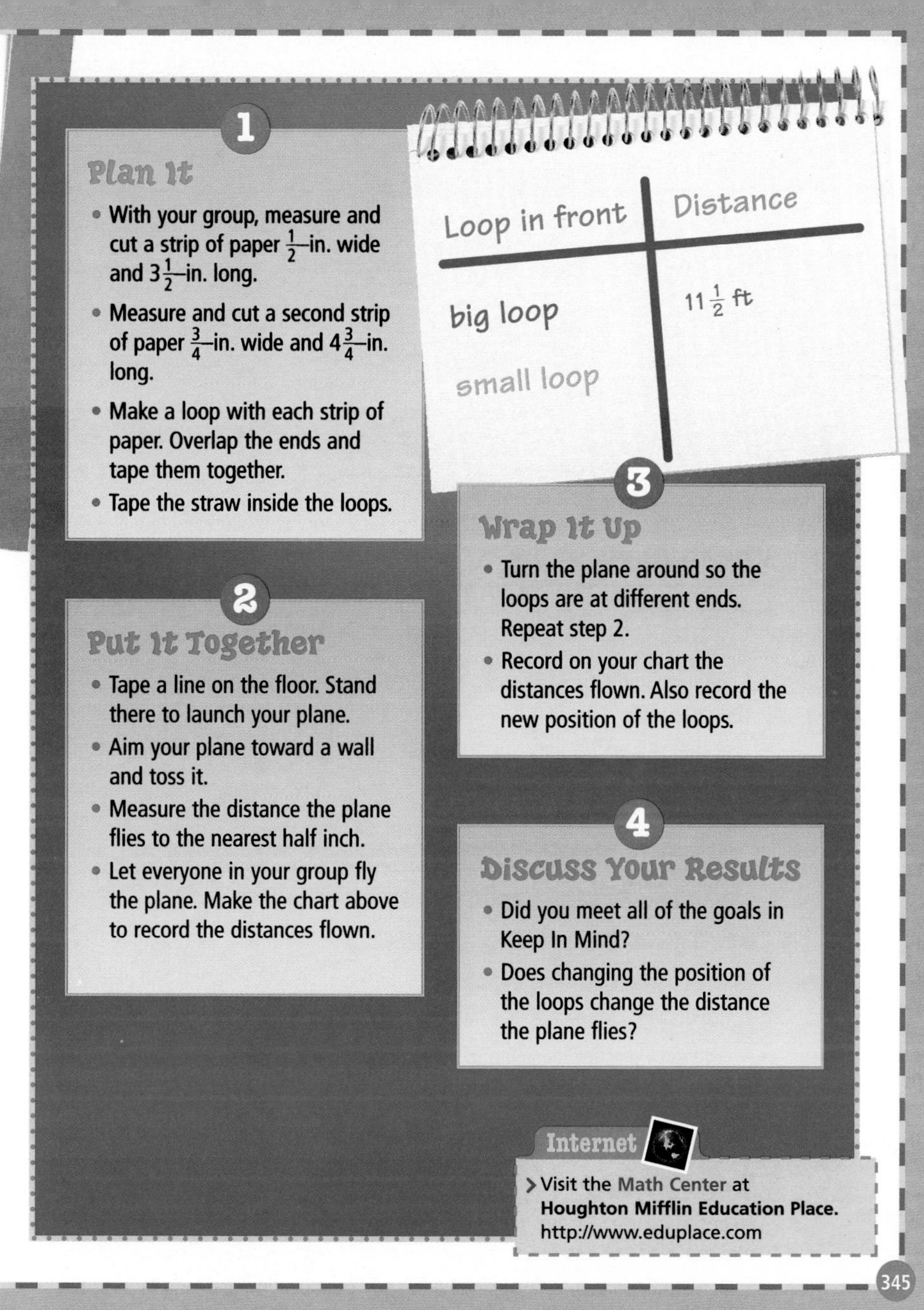

1

Plan It

- With your group, measure and cut a strip of paper $\frac{1}{2}$-in. wide and $3\frac{1}{2}$-in. long.
- Measure and cut a second strip of paper $\frac{3}{4}$-in. wide and $4\frac{3}{4}$-in. long.
- Make a loop with each strip of paper. Overlap the ends and tape them together.
- Tape the straw inside the loops.

Loop in front	Distance
big loop	$11\frac{1}{2}$ ft
small loop	

2

Put It Together

- Tape a line on the floor. Stand there to launch your plane.
- Aim your plane toward a wall and toss it.
- Measure the distance the plane flies to the nearest half inch.
- Let everyone in your group fly the plane. Make the chart above to record the distances flown.

3

Wrap It Up

- Turn the plane around so the loops are at different ends. Repeat step 2.
- Record on your chart the distances flown. Also record the new position of the loops.

4

Discuss Your Results

- Did you meet all of the goals in Keep In Mind?
- Does changing the position of the loops change the distance the plane flies?

Internet

> Visit the Math Center at **Houghton Mifflin Education Place.** http://www.eduplace.com

345

Problem Solving Tip

Suggest that students' charts have columns for Distance, Large Loop, and Small Loop. Students can write *F* or *B* to indicate which loop is in the front and which is in back. They can also measure and record the distance of each loop from the nearest end.

Completing the Investigation

Step 1 Help students measure and cut strips for their loops.

Step 2 Ensure that students understand where to stand and where to measure from.

Step 3 Suggest that students predict whether changing the position of the loops will change the distance.

Step 4 Encourage students to share their observations.

Extending the Investigation

Some planes may not fly far, but can stay airborn for a long period of time. Repeat the investigation using a stop watch to record the time in flight instead of the distance traveled.

Assessment Scoring Rubric

These criteria align with *Keep In Mind* in the Pupil Edition on page 344.

Criteria	1 Limited response	2 Acceptable	3 Capable	4 Superior
Accuracy of measurements	Measurements are inaccurate	Some of the measurements are inaccurate	Most of the measurements are accurate	All of the measurements are accurate
Understanding of the math process	Lacks understanding of the math process	Can explain some the the math process	Understands most of the math process	Thoroughly understands the math process
Clarity and completeness of the chart	Chart is incomplete and disorganized	Chart shows an attempt to organize the information	Chart shows most information clearly	Chart shows all of the information clearly and completely
Contribution to the group process	Makes no effort to contribute to the group	Makes some effort to contribute to the group	Contributes to the group most of the time	Contributes fully to the group

Use this 4-level rubric to score students' responses. If you prefer a task with a 6-level rubric, use the Performance Assessment for this chapter.

Decimals

Chapter Overview

Rationale

Chapter Pacing: 10 days

- This chapter focuses on the development of decimal concepts.
- Students build understanding through visual experiences, for example, shading grid squares or interpreting tenths squares.
- Students use the knowledge derived from visual experiences to undertake symbolic tasks such as reading, writing, and computing with decimals.
- In the Math World feature, students learn about math on the radio, and organize data containing decimals.
- In the Investigation, students use decimals in the context of designing a race.

See **Daily Lesson Plans**, Chapter Management at a Glance, pp. 98–99; Suggested Weekly Plan, pp. 100–101.

Problem Solving

This chapter emphasizes the Make a List strategy for problem solving. It also reinforces strategies students have learned earlier and encourages them to choose and apply their own strategies.

Assessment

- The Chapter Introduction allows you to assess whether students have an understanding of decimal concepts.
- Observe students' understanding of how to use and interpret tenths squares.
- Note students' abilities to represent decimals symbolically.
- Use the Midchapter Review, the Chapter Test, and the Cumulative Review to assess students' needs for reinforcement or reteaching.

Reading Strategies

- Teach the Monitor reading strategy minilesson on TE TAB p. 346J. Then, use the following as opportunities to reinforce the strategy.
  - Preparing for Tests, TE pp. 346G–346H
  - Problem Solving, Lessons 10.3–10.5, 10.7, and 10.9–10.11
- Use the SAE reading support for Lesson 10.1.

Vocabulary

- Introduce children to the chapter with vocabulary minilesson, TAB p. 346J.
- Planning Guide, p. 346C, lists vocabulary for each lesson in the chapter.
- Use the SAE vocabulary support in Lessons 10.1–10.5 and 10.9.

Meeting Individual Needs

Students Acquiring English

Be sure students understand decimals.

- Use drawings to practice matching decimals, fractions, and mixed numbers.
- Give extra practice reading and writing decimals, and focusing on the pronunciation of *tenths.*

See also **Language Connections** for additional support.

Extra Support

Students may need support in moving from the concrete to the symbolic in their understanding of decimals.

- Develop decimal meaning using Tenth Squares and strips, and money.
- Allow students to represent various decimal problems given orally.
- Use the Basic Facts Workshop on p. 361A.
- Use the Analyzing Errors strategies on pp. 373A–373B.

Challenge

Many students may benefit from this extension activity.

- Tell students that car odometers record mileage to the tenth of a mile. Ask them to keep track of the mileage for each car trip they take for one week. Have them find the mileage for each trip and the total mileage for the week.

Multi-Age Classroom

The chart below shows the chapters in books for levels 2 and 4 that can be used in conjunction with this chapter.

2	3	4
Chapter 5 *Time and Money*	**Chapter 10** *Decimals*	**Chapter 11** *Decimals*

See **Daily Lesson Plans**, Multi-Age Classroom Concept and Skill Development, pp. 4–5.

Chapter Bibliography

Key

Multicultural	★	Social Studies	
Science/Health		Music	
Literature		Art	

Technology

Students can explore decimals with electronic manipulatives in *Unlocking Fractions & Decimals 3–6*. The tools allow for different ways of modeling and comparing decimals.

Internet: Education Place

http://www.eduplace.com

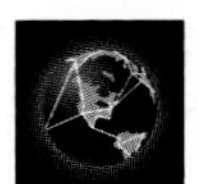

Visit the **Mathematics Center** in *Houghton Mifflin Education Place* to find activities, projects, games, and links to other valuable Internet sites.

Ultimate Writing & Creativity Center

Students can use the *Ultimate Writing & Creativity Center®* for all their writing and publishing activities. The software is available from The Learning Company® in Macintosh and Windows formats.

Larson's Leapfrog MATH™

Leapfrog Math includes mathematics skills and concepts for grades 3–6. Each grade is contained on a single CD-ROM. The software is available from Meridian Creative Group, a Division of Larson Texts, Inc.

Test, Practice, Management Program

Use the *Test, Practice, Management Program* to create, administer, and score tests as well as generate practice sets. Questions are correlated to Lesson Objectives.

Graphers Sunburst Communications, Inc.®

Using the friendly tools in *Graphers,* children can easily manipulate data that can be counted or sorted and represent their data in a table or with six types of graphs.

Books for Students

Houghton Mifflin Mathematics Bookshelf

The Information Please Kid's Almanac
Alice Siegel and
Margo McLoone Basta,
Houghton Mifflin, 1992.
This informative book may be used throughout the grade.

Raceways: Having Fun With Balls and Tracks
Bernie Zubrowski,
William Morrow, 1985.
This Boston Children's Museum Activity Book, with black-and-white illustrations, shows children designing many different raceways with simple materials. Includes a discussion of what happens to the velocity of the objects used.

Fractals, Googols, and Other Mathematical Tales
Theoni Pappas,
Wide World Publishing/Tetra House, 1993.
A collection of short stories presents a variety of mathematical topics, including decimals and number lines.

Sometimes I Don't Like School
Paula Z. Hogan,
Raintree Children's Books, 1980.
Students can relate to George, who after trying everything to avoid his dreaded mathematics class, decides to face the situation head on.

How Much and How Many? The Story of Weights and Measures
Jeanne Bendick,
Franklin Watts, 1989.
Readers discover that decimals frequently appear in weights and measures.

Making Cents: Every Kid's Guide to Money
Elizabeth Wilkinson,
Little Brown, 1989.
Students learn about money and how decimals represent cents.

Books for Families

Exploring Everyday Math: Ideas for Students, Teachers, and Parents
Maja Apelman and Julie King,
Heinemann, 1993.
These practical ideas provide plans for activities centered on family life. Included are several opportunities for relating decimals and money.

Decimals and Fractions
Mary S. Charuhas, et. al.,
Glencoe, 1995.
This book provides real-life applications for decimals and fractions.

The Search for the Mystery Planet
edited by Jean B. Crawford,
Time-Life, 1993.
Families read, solve riddles, and play games while learning about mathematics as it relates to astronomy and other aspects of space.

Reference Books for Teachers

A Collection of Math Lessons: From Grades 1 Through 3 and From Grades 3 Through 8
Marilyn Burns,
Heinemann, 1987 and 1988.
These books contain a variety of classroom-tested ideas for teaching mathematics through problem solving.

Decimals, Fractions, Ratios, and Percents
Ellen Carley Frechette,
New Readers Press, 1995.
Many practical activities involving fractions and decimals are included in this teacher guide from the Math Solutions series.

Fractions and Decimals
Karen Bryant-Mole,
EDC Publishing, 1994.
Students can complete these problems and exercises to practice decimal concepts.

Planning Guide

	TE Pages	Lesson Objectives	Lesson Vocabulary	NCTM Standards
10.1 Exploring Tenths	*348–349*	To explore tenths	tenth decimal	Fractions and Decimals, Measurement, Reasoning, Connections, Communication
10.2 Decimals Greater Than 1	*350–351*	To investigate decimals greater than 1 using tenths squares		Whole Numbers Concepts, Fractions and Decimals, Reasoning, Connections, Communication
10.3 Tenths	*352–353*	To read and write decimals to tenths; to use word names, models, and fractions for decimals		Fractions and Decimals, Measurement, Connections, Patterns and Functions
10.4 Make a List	*354–355*	To use the Make a List strategy to solve problems		Problem Solving, Reasoning, Connections, Communication, Fractions and Decimals
10.5 Comparing and Ordering Decimals	*356–357*	To compare decimals greater and less than 1 using a number line		Whole Number Concepts, Fractions and Decimals, Measurement, Reasoning, Connections
10.6 Hundredths	*358–359*	To explore and write decimals to hundredths using hundredths squares		Fractions and Decimals, Measurement, Reasoning, Connections, Communication
10.7 Is the Answer Reasonable?	*360*	To decide and to justify why an answer is reasonable		Problem Solving, Connections, Reasoning, Communication, Measurement
10.8 Adding and Subtracting Tenths	*364–365*	To use tenths models to investigate how to add and subtract decimals in tenths		Fractions and Decimals, Measurement, Reasoning, Connections, Communication
10.9 Adding and Subtracting Decimals	*366–367*	To add and subtract tenths		Fractions and Decimals, Problem Solving, Measurement, Patterns and Functions
10.10 Using Make a List and Other Strategies	*368–369*	To use Make a List and other strategies to solve problems		Problem Solving, Connections, Measurement, Geometry and Spatial Sense
10.11 Using Strategies	*370–371*	To use different strategies to solve problems		Problem Solving, Connections, Reasoning, Whole Number Computation

Chapter Objectives

10A To explore and model decimals in tenths and hundredths
10B To relate decimals in tenths to fractions and mixed numbers in tenths
10C To read and write a decimal in word, table, and standard forms
10D To compare and order decimals using models
10E To add and subtract decimals with and without models
10F To use Make a List and other strategies to solve problems

Chapter Objectives	math center	State Requirements
10A, 10B	• *Decimal Match*, How-To Card 35; Fraction Card Deck	
10A, 10B	• *Snail's Pace!*, How-To Card 36; Gameboard 3	
10C	• *Decimal MathO*, Activity Card 56	
10F	• *Newspaper Numbers*, Project Card 10	
10D	• *Dueling Decimals*, Activity Card 57; Workmat 3	
10A, 10B, 10C	• *Decimal Lineup*, Activity Card 58	
10F	• *Newspaper Numbers*, Project Card 10	
10E	• *Decimal Star*, How-To Card 37; Gameboard 4	
10E	• *Magic Tenths Squares*, Activity Card 59	
10F	• *Newspaper Numbers*, Project Card 10	
10F	• *Newspaper Numbers*, Project Card 10	

Integrating Reading Strategies

- Teach/review the Monitor strategy using TAB p. 346J.
- Encourage students to practice the strategy in Lessons 10.3–10.5, 10.7, and 10.9–10.11.

Technology

Unlocking Fractions & Decimals 3–6

Internet: Education Place
http://www.eduplace.com
Houghton Mifflin Education Place
Mathematics Center

Test, Practice, Management Program

Special Lessons

pp. 346–347
Chapter Introduction
The Introduction shows students that there are many ways to represent part of a group.

pp. 370–371

Students apply problem solving strategies in the context of baseball.

pp. 362–363
Math World
Decimals Around the World
Use this feature to show students how decimals are used all over the world.

pp. 376–377
Investigation
Lickety-Split!
Students form teams and compete in a relay race of their own design, timing each leg and recording the results.

Assessment

Use the following assessment tools to help assess individual needs.

- Midchapter Review, p. 361
- Chapter Test, pp. 372–373
- Cumulative Review, pp. 374–375

Chapter 10

Place-Value Workshop

Using Decimals

Alternate Approach

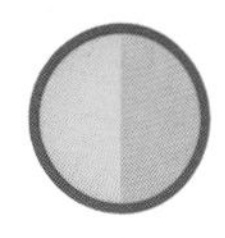

Use with page 352. 30 minutes

Modeling Tenths

Objective To model decimal numbers using place-value blocks

Management teacher directed; pairs
Materials overhead projector; place-value blocks for each pair
Modality *visual/kinesthetic/verbal*

Activity

- Explain to students that in this activity, a tens rod equals one whole, and a unit cube equals one tenth.
- Using the overhead projector, model 3.4.
- Ask students to identify the number that the cubes represent. three and four tenths

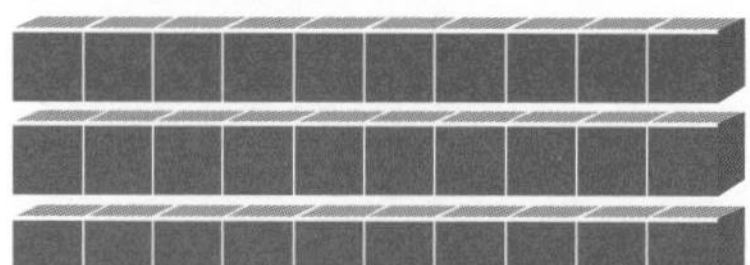

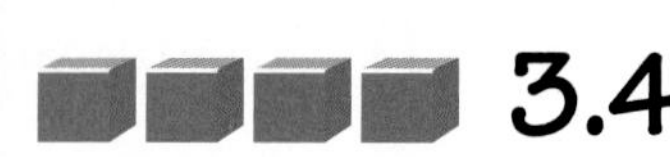

- Model several other decimal numbers such as 0.8, 5.6, and so on, inviting students to identify each number as it is modeled.
- Write a list of numbers on the board. Invite pairs to model each of the numbers. Include numbers written in several different forms (word, fraction, and decimal), such as: four and two tenths, 0.9, $6\frac{2}{10}$, and so on.

Two and three tenths
6.4
$5\frac{1}{2}$
7.8

Meeting Individual Needs: *Modify*

Students Acquiring English Some students may not understand, hear, and pronounce the differences among the words *tenths*, *tens*, and *tense*. Write the words on the board, discuss their meanings and have students practice hearing and reciting the words.

Challenge

Use with page 364. 30 minutes

Decimal Calculations

Objective To add decimals using a calculator

Management teacher monitored; pairs
Modality *visual/verbal*

Activity

- Invite students to watch and mimic what you do as you demonstrate. Enter 5.6 into the calculator.
- Add 3.1 to 5.6 by pressing + 3.1 =. Ask a student to read aloud the number in the display. 8.7
- Clear the calculator. Enter 5.6 again, and have students follow along. Add 3.4 by pressing + 3.4 =. Have students read the sum in the display. 9 Ask, What happened to the decimal point? It disappears because when .4 is added to .6, the sum is 1.0; the 1 is regrouped; and when there are 0 tenths, the decimal is not shown.
- Have students continue with the following problems, predicting and then verifying which will show a decimal point in the answer.

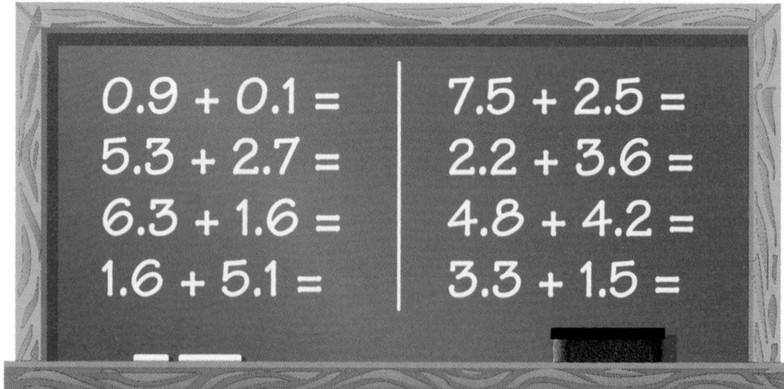

For more practice Using the Calculator, see pp. T88–T90.

Meeting Individual Needs: *Modify*

Challenge You can modify this activity to include subtraction of decimals.

Game

Use with page 356. 25 minutes

Guess My Decimal

Objective To order decimals

Management teacher directed; groups of 4–6 students
Modality *visual/verbal*

Activity

- Tell students that they are going to play a game in which the object is to guess a secret decimal number.
- Explain that one student, who acts as game master, selects a secret decimal number between 0.1 and 9.9 and writes it on a piece of paper. The other group members take turns writing down guesses on a recording sheet.
- After each student guesses, the game master writes < if the number guessed is less than the secret number, or > if the number guessed is greater than the secret number. Play continues until one of the students guesses the secret number; students take turns being the game master.

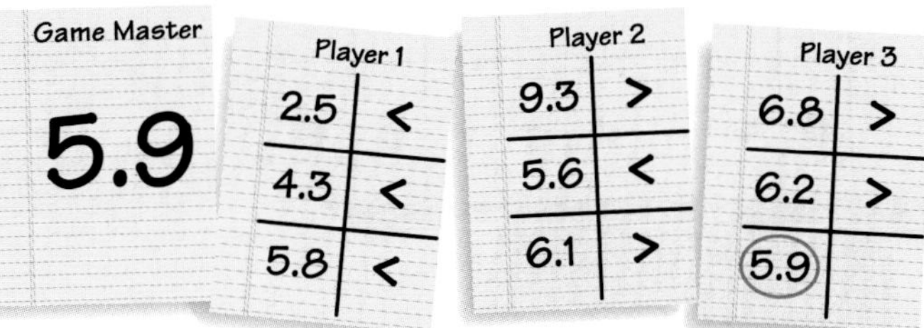

Game Master
5.9
Player 1
2.5 <
4.3 <
5.8 <
Player 2
9.3 >
5.6 <
6.1 >
Player 3
6.8 >
6.2 >
5.9

Meeting Individual Needs: *Modify*

Students Acquiring English This is a good time for students to practice saying decimal numbers correctly. Encourage them to read aloud the numbers instead of just writing down their guesses.

Extra Support Using a decimal number line to bracket guesses might help some students. You may want to provide a model for students to use to keep track of numbers guessed and to help them close in on the secret numbers.

Challenge Suggest that students widen the range of secret numbers into the teens or include decimals into the hundredths.

Technology

Use with Lesson 10.1

Objective To represent and order decimals in tenths

Management teacher monitored; pairs
Materials ***MathKeys:*** *Unlocking Fractions & Decimals 3–6*, Lev. 3, Act. 15: Tenths
Modality *visual*

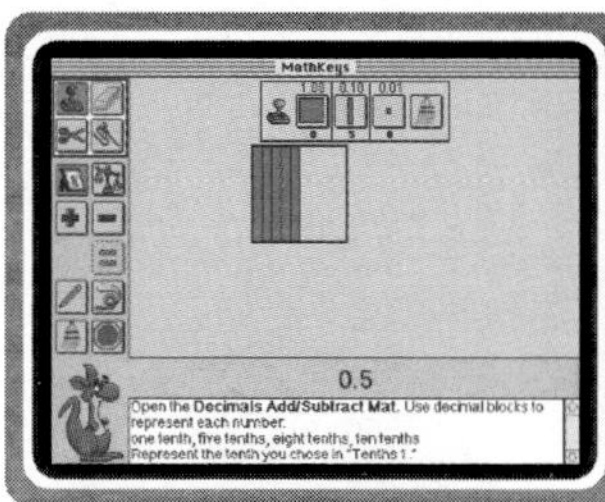

Activity

30 minutes

- Ask students what a tenth is. Allow them to describe and model a tenth in as many ways as they can, including using classroom manipulatives. Responses may include that a dime is one tenth of a dollar, or a finger is one tenth of a set of fingers.
- Open the *MathKeys* Decimals Add/Subtract Mat and demonstrate how one tenth can be shown with decimal blocks. Ask students to model $\frac{3}{10}$, $\frac{4}{10}$, $\frac{5}{10}$ and so on.
- Invite student pairs to select Tenths 1 from the Activities option on the Main menu. Students will represent numbers with counters in Tenths 1. In Tenths 2, they will use fraction models or circles, and in Tenths 3 they will use decimal blocks.
- In Tenths 4, students will be asked to order seven numbers between $\frac{1}{10}$ and 3 from least to greatest using the computer tool of their choice.

Meeting Individual Needs: *Modify*

Extra Support Have students work with hands-on decimal blocks to represent $\frac{1}{10}$, $\frac{5}{10}$, $\frac{8}{10}$, $\frac{10}{10}$, and a number of tenths of their choosing.

Challenge Invite students to choose their own sets of tenths to represent in different ways, ordering their sets from least to greatest.

Chapter 10

Preparing for Tests

To develop students' test-taking strategies, model the following types of assessment items found in this program.

Standardized Tests

Write the following question on the board.

How is $1\frac{8}{10}$ written as a decimal?

(A) 1.8 correct

(B) 0.18

(C) 1.08

(D) 1.810

Standardized tests usually require that students select the correct answer from a group of possible answers. In this test item, students must choose how to express a fraction as a decimal.

Strategy

- What does the question ask you to do? tell which decimal shows $1\frac{8}{10}$
- How are fractions and decimals alike? They both name parts of a whole.
- How would $1\frac{8}{10}$ be written in a place-value chart? 1 one, 8 tenths

See also Standardized Testing: New Formats, **Chapter 10.**

Open-Ended Questions

Write the following problem on the board.

You want to sew pillows that have a different color on each side. You have red, purple, yellow, green, and blue cloth. How many different color combinations can you make? 10 combinations

Open-ended questions can be answered in more than one way; they allow students to use a variety of concepts and processes. This problem requires that students use a strategy such as Make a List to solve a problem.

Strategy

- What are you asked to do? tell how many different color pairs can be made
- What pattern can help you find all possible combinations? begin with one color, list all possible combinations with that color, then go on to the next color
- Would purple and red be different from red and purple? Explain. No, the pillow would look the same both ways.

See also Assessments, **Chapter 10.**

Preparing for Tests

Reading Strategies for Test-Taking

Monitor As I read, I check that what I am reading makes sense to me and try to visualize the situation.

Performance Tasks

On the board, write the following direction.

Draw a number line to show these decimals in order from least to greatest.

1.5, 0.6, 0.8

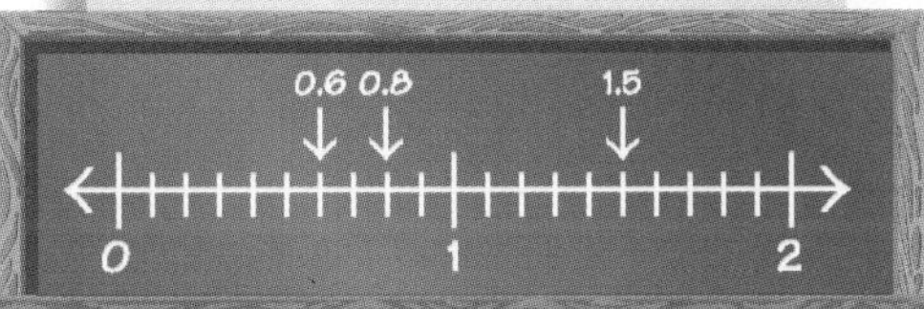

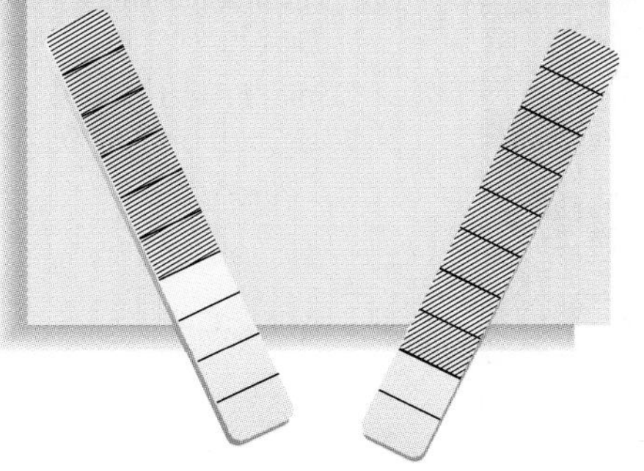

Performance assessments engage students in meaningful tasks that permit the teacher to observe their working procedures as well as the results they obtain. This task requires students to draw a number line and use it to order three decimal numbers from least to greatest.

Strategy

- What does the problem ask you to do? draw a number line that shows the decimal numbers in order from least to greatest
- How will you decide which decimal is the least? Answers will vary. Possible answer: find the number with the lowest digit to the left of the decimal point; if two are the same, compare the digits in the tenths place
- How could shaded tenths squares help you? They give a way to see which decimal has a bigger part shaded.
- How will you draw your number line? Answers will vary. Possible answer: start with 0 and end with 2; make spaces showing tenths across the line
- Which way do you move across the number line to find greater numbers? Numbers increase as you move from left to right.

You can check that students draw number lines and order decimals correctly from least to greatest.

See also Performance Assessments, **Chapter 10.**

Test-Taking Tips

- If you have trouble finding the answer, make your best guess.

Additional Assessment Resources

Test, Practice, Management Program

Use the *Test, Practice, Management Program* to create, administer, and score tests as well as generate practice sets. Questions are correlated to the Lesson Objectives.

Chapter 10

Math Center

To meet individual needs, use the following resources from the Math Center. You may first wish to model activities for the whole class in order to demonstrate the rules for games and introduce procedures for independent tasks.

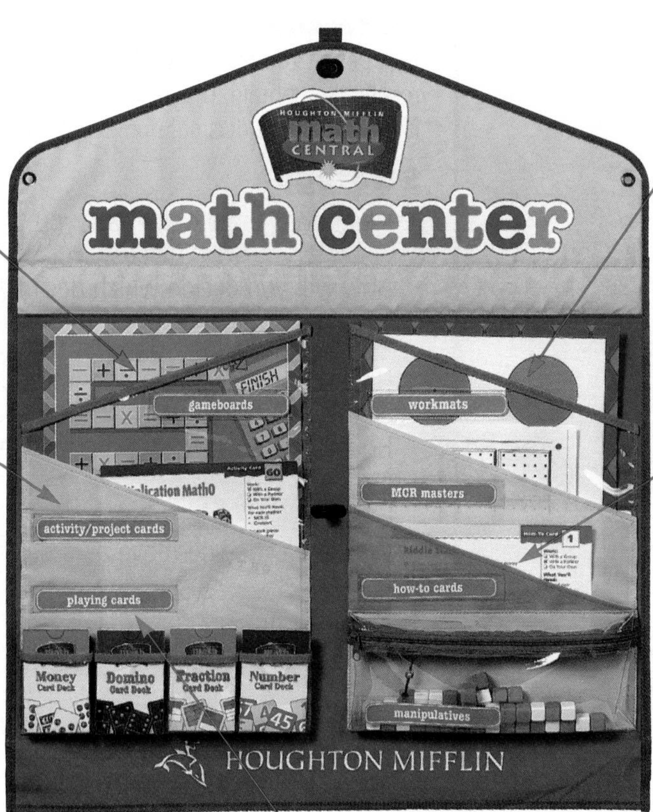

Gameboards

Gameboard 3
Use with Lesson 10.2.

Gameboard 4
Use with Lesson 10.8.

Activity Cards

56 ***Decimal MathO*** Use with Lesson 10.3.

57 ***Dueling Decimals*** Use with Lesson 10.5.

58 ***Decimal Lineup*** Use with Lesson 10.6.

59 ***Magic Tenths Squares*** Use with Lesson 10.9.

Project Card

10 ***Newspaper Numbers*** Use with Lessons 10.4, 10.7, 10.10, and 10.11.

Workmats

Workmat 3
Use with Lesson 10.5.

How-To Cards

35 ***Decimal Match*** Use with Lesson 10.1.

36 ***Snail's Pace!*** Use with Lesson 10.2.

37 ***Decimal Star*** Use with Lesson 10.8.

Card Decks

Fraction Card Deck
Use with Lesson 10.1.

Managing the Math Center

Managing materials Before assigning an activity, provide time for students to freely explore the materials. Then, make sure they know what they are supposed to do with them. Let students take responsibility for maintaining the materials. They might label shelves or drawers or prepare individual bags of materials. Be sure to clearly mark any storage containers, perhaps in more than one language.

Vocabulary and Reading Strategies

Use these minilessons to strengthen vocabulary and reading skills.

Vocabulary

- decimal
- tenths

Linking Prior Knowledge and Vocabulary

Use tenths squares to demonstrate the meaning of **tenths**. Explain that the tenths square shows 10 equal parts. Show how the parts can be expressed as a fraction or a **decimal.** If you shade 2 of the 10 equal parts, you have shaded $\frac{2}{10}$ or 0.2 of the square. Have students show 0.3, 0.5, and 0.9. Ask what happens when they shade ten tenths of the tenths square. They may recognize that they have shaded the whole square. The decimal 1.0 is used to show the whole.

Graphic Organizer: Diagram

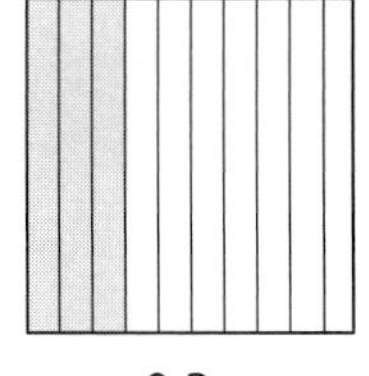
0.3

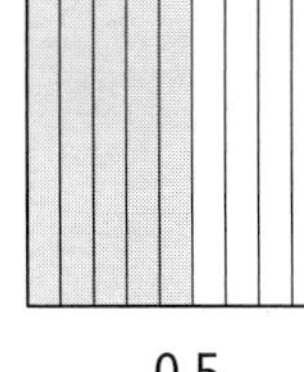
0.5

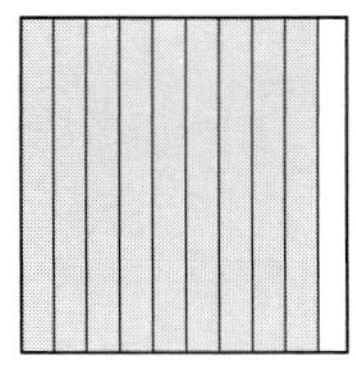
0.9

Reading Strategies

Strategy: Monitor

Help students use the Monitor reading strategy to check their understanding. Encourage them to monitor their reading of steps in Here's A Way.

As students read the problem below, ask them to think about how they can use monitoring to help them make sense of the problem. Encourage students to think of a way to help them organize what they know.

Use the Thinking Aloud box and the graphic organizer to demonstrate how students can use the Monitor reading strategy with the following example:

> You and 3 classmates form pairs to do a class project. How many different pairs of partners can the four of you make?

Lesson 10.4, p. 355, Problem 5

Model by thinking aloud how to begin solving the problem.

Thinking Aloud

- I can reread the problem to make sure I understand what it says.
- I know there are 4 students. I need to find out how many different pairs I can make with 4 students.
- A list can help me keep track of the pairs I make.
- I will check the list to be sure I have found all the possible pairs and that the pairs are different.

Graphic Organizer: List

Kate Mary Barbara Ed

Kate and Mary
Kate and Barbara
Kate and Ed
Mary and Barbara
Mary and Ed
Barbara and Ed

The reading strategies presented on this page can also apply to Lessons 10.3, 10.4, 10.5, 10.7, 10.9, 10.10, and 10.11.

Objective
To use prior knowledge to explore decimals

Lesson Planning

Optional Resources
- Math Language Connections
- MATHKEYS *Unlocking Fractions & Decimals 3–6*

Every Day Counts Calendar Math

Decimals

To reinforce decimal concepts, use the Coin Counter activities in Every Day Counts, level 3.

Assessing Prior Knowledge

Try This! Use this as a prechapter activity in the classroom or as a homework assignment.

Build confidence in using money by asking students to tell how many dimes are in various amounts up to one dollar. In this activity, students subtract different dime combinations from one dollar to explore fractions and decimals.

This activity
- assesses prior knowledge of fractions and decimal points
- acts as a base of discussion for making change

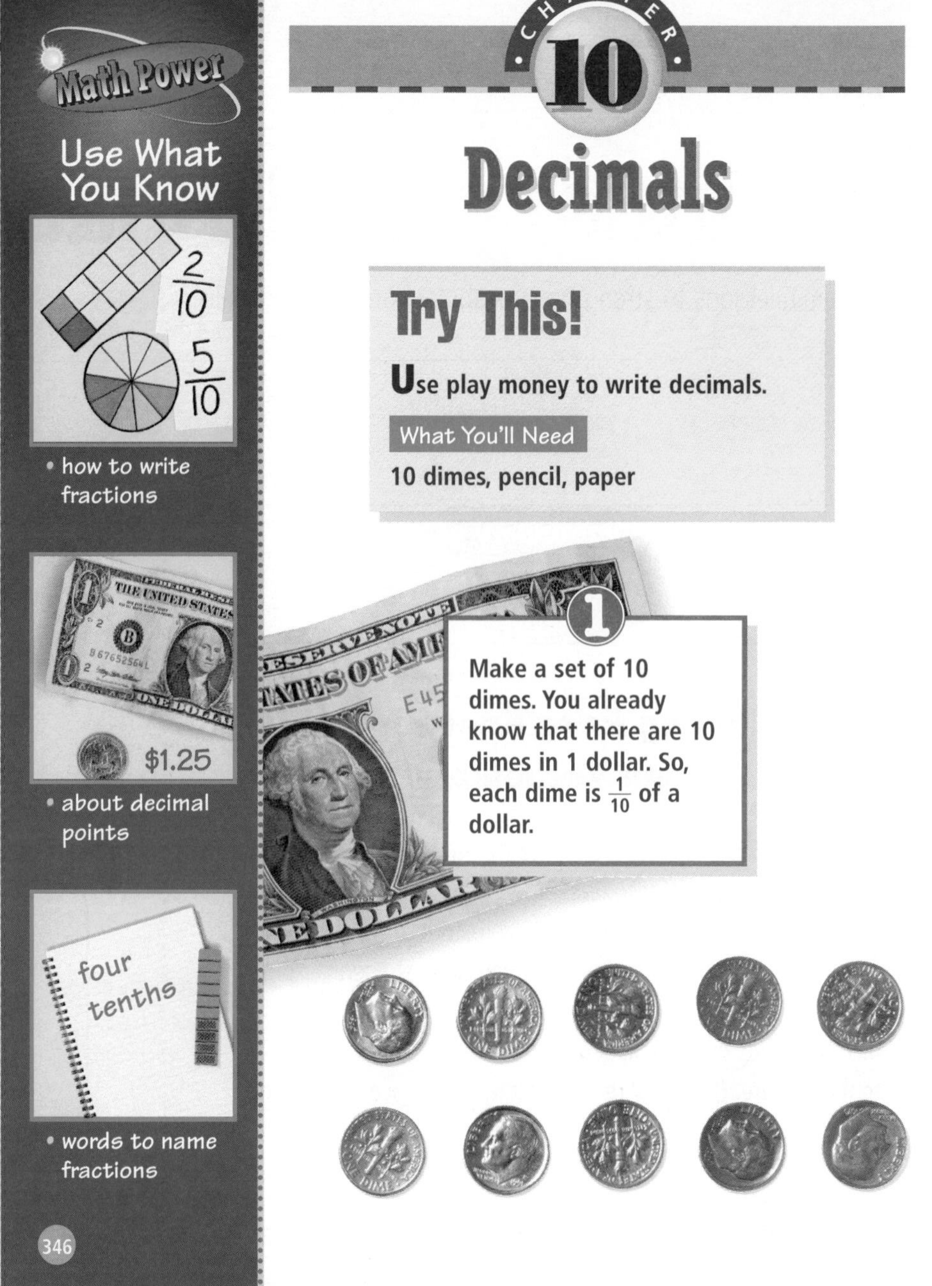

Math Power
Use What You Know
2/10
5/10
• how to write fractions
$1.25
• about decimal points
four tenths
• words to name fractions
346
CHAPTER
10
Decimals
Try This!
Use play money to write decimals.
What You'll Need
10 dimes, pencil, paper
1
Make a set of 10 dimes. You already know that there are 10 dimes in 1 dollar. So, each dime is 1/10 of a dollar.

Chapter Connections

Math Links

Throughout this chapter, students will build on prior knowledge as they develop concepts and skills for problem solving with decimals.

- **Number Sense** Lessons 10.1, 10.2, 10.3, 10.4, 10.6, 10.7, 10.8
- **Patterns and Relationships** Lessons 10.3, 10.4, 10.5, 10.6
- **Estimation** Lessons 10.1, 10.6
- **Measurement** Lessons 10.5, 10.9, 10.10, 10.11
- **Probability** Lesson 10.4
- **Algebraic Reasoning** Lessons 10.1, 10.2, 10.5, 10.6, 10.9

Real *World*

Social Studies

- **Lesson 10.10, p. 368**

  Pioneer Houses The construction of sod houses provides the context for solving problems using Make a List and other problem solving strategies.

Science

- **Lesson 10.3, p. 352**

  Blood Students explore the meaning of tenths using amounts of blood in liters found in the circulatory systems of infants and adults.
- **Lesson 10.5, p. 356**

  Animal Weights Students use the weights of pets to compare and order decimals.

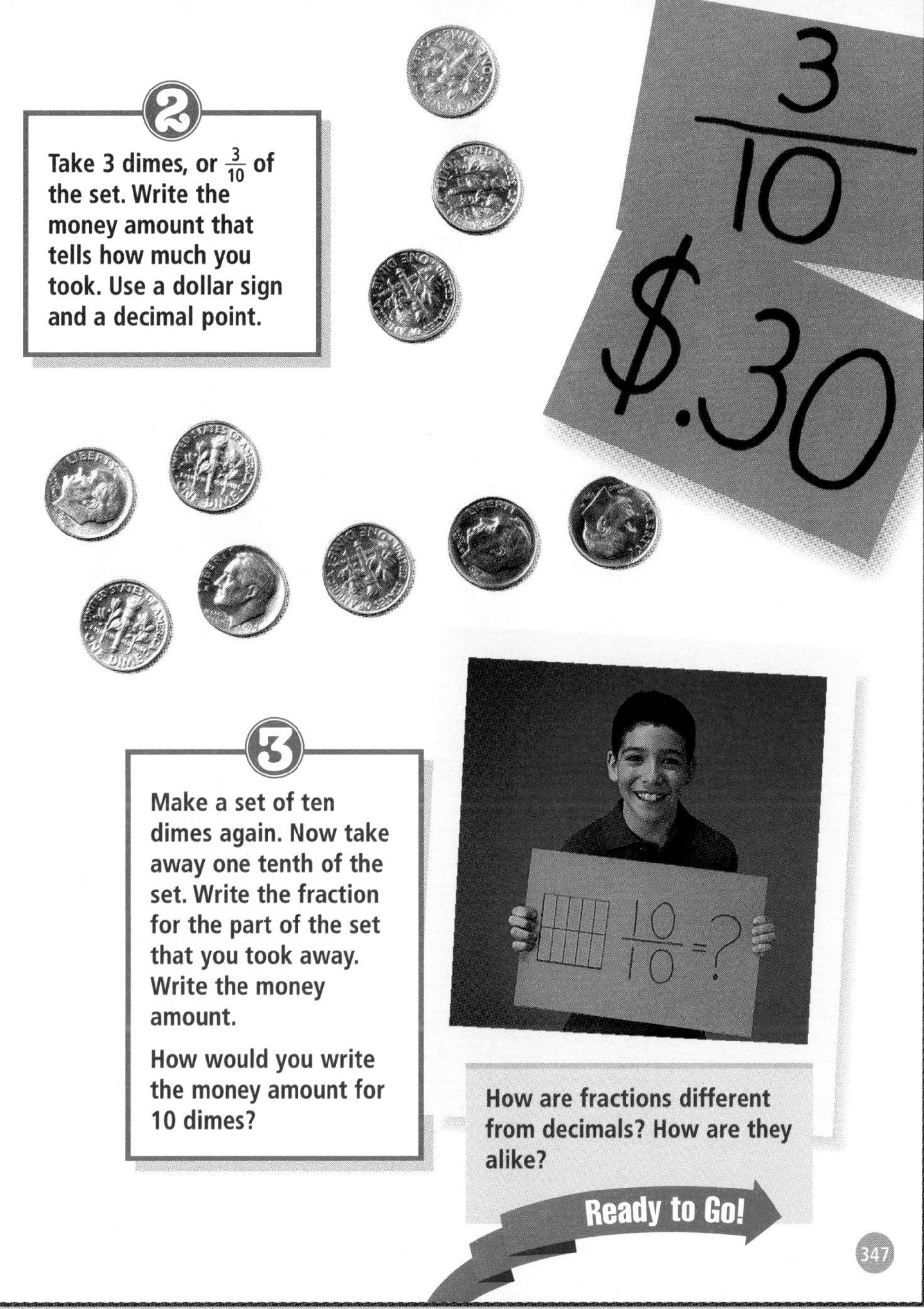

2

Take 3 dimes, or $\frac{3}{10}$ of the set. Write the money amount that tells how much you took. Use a dollar sign and a decimal point.

$\frac{3}{10}$

$.30

3

Make a set of ten dimes again. Now take away one tenth of the set. Write the fraction for the part of the set that you took away. Write the money amount.

How would you write the money amount for 10 dimes?

$\frac{10}{10}$ = ?

How are fractions different from decimals? How are they alike?

Ready to Go!

347

Assessing Prior Knowledge *(continued)*

- provides a foundation for understanding decimals

Meeting Individual Needs

If students have trouble writing tenths or hundredths correctly, start with Quick Help. They may also need a brief teacher-guided review.

Quick Help Explain that in this activity students will use what they know to create sets of numbers. Provide base ten blocks or coins to create each number before recording it on the cards.

Guided Review Refer to:

- **Lesson 2.12** Dollars and Cents, Student Book p. 66
- **Dollars and Cents** Practice Worksheet 2.12
- **Basic Facts** Review Basic Facts TE p. 361A

Vocabulary Power

Use these graphic organizers to review vocabulary used in decimals.

Tenth: One out of ten equal parts

0.1 = [model] = $\frac{1}{10}$ =

Hundredth: One out of 100 equal parts

0.01 = [model] = $\frac{1}{100}$ =

Vocabulary Students can look in a newspaper for numbers that have a decimal point. Make a table on the board to categorize their findings. Discuss what numbers with a decimal point have in common.

Investigation Preview

Lickety-Split!

Planning a race course, forming teams, and timing each leg of the race with a digital stopwatch will reinforce understanding of decimals as children add and compare total times. See the Investigation, TE pp. 376–377.

What They'll Do

- Decide what the participants will do.
- Make a chart to record times for each leg.
- Run the race and time each leg with a digital stopwatch.
- Find the total time for each team.

Technology

Invite students to model tenths in several ways using ***MathKeys***: *Unlocking Fractions & Decimals 3–6*. They can model tenths of a set using the Counters Mat, fractions in tenths using the Bars Models Mat or the Circles Models Mat, and decimals in tenths using the Decimals Add/Subtract Mat. Challenge students to make up rules for a game in which one player models a number on one mat, and other players must model the same number on different mats.

Activity

Planning at a Glance

Objective To explore tenths

Materials paper, tenths squares (TR19)

Optional Resources

- Reteach 10.1; Practice 10.1; Enrichment 10.1
- Daily Cumul. Review, p. 130
- Math Center: How-To Card 35
- Every Day Counts
- **TAB**, TE pp. 346E–346F, 346J
- **Problem of the Day**, 130, p. 65; Flip Chart, p. 65b

MATHKEYS
Unlocking Fractions and Decimals 3–6, Level 3, Activity 15

Students Acquiring English

Building Reading Strategies Help students with the expression "1 of 10." Draw ten circles; shade one of them. Say "1 of 10 circles is shaded." Draw other sets with various total numbers and shaded numbers and help students use "of" to describe them. Follow the same procedure with fractional parts of figures and with tenths squares.

Problem of the Day

Each letter in the subtraction exercise stands for a different digit. A letter stands for the same digit every time it repeats. Can you crack the code? FIVE – FOUR = ONE

One possible answer: 9856 – 9430 = 426

Exploring Tenths

Cooperative Learning Checklist
- ☑ Work alone.
- ☑ Work with a partner.
- ☑ Work with a group.

In this lesson, you will explore a new way to write tenths.

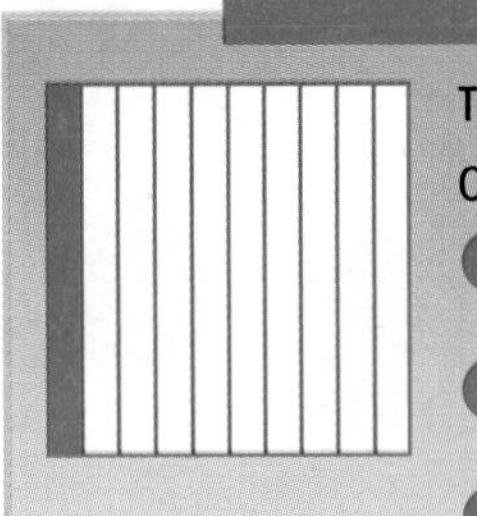

What You'll Need:
- 10 tenths squares
- paper
- recording sheet

Vocabulary:
tenths
decimal
Glossary, p. 480

Activity

Using Tenths

This square is divided into 10 equal parts. One of 10 parts is red. So, $\frac{1}{10}$ is red.

1. You can say: One tenth of the square is red.
2. You can write a fraction: $\frac{1}{10}$ of the square is red.
3. You can write a decimal: 0.1 of the square is red.

Making a Decimal Chart

Shade	Fraction	Decimal
1 of 10	$\frac{1}{10}$	0.1
2 of 10		
3 of 10		
4 of 10		
5 of 10		
6 of 10		
7 of 10		
8 of 10		
9 of 10		
10 of 10		

1.0

1. Use tenths squares to make 9 decimal cards. Shade 1 part on the first square, 2 parts on the second, and so on, up to 9 parts.
2. Copy this chart onto paper. Fill in the spaces with information about your decimal cards.
3. Now shade all of the parts on another card. To show this number, you can write the whole number 1, a fraction $\frac{10}{10}$, or the decimal 1.0.

348 Chapter 10

1 Introduce

Prior Knowledge **Ask students where they might see numbers such as 9.1 and 22.5 oz.** gymnastics scores; food cans

Teach: Activity

Emphasize these points:

- A decimal is a fraction written using place value.
- 0.5 equals five tenths, or one half; 1.0 equals $\frac{10}{10}$ or one whole.

Modeling Model a circle divided into 10 equal segments, with 7 shaded. Tell students that the circle represents a pizza, and the shaded parts have been eaten. Ask:

- What part of the whole has been eaten?
- Write *seven tenths*, $\frac{7}{10}$, and 0.7 on the board.

2 Develop

Show What You Know!

Common Error Students may need to be reminded always to write the zero before the decimal point. See also Analyzing Errors, TE pp. 373A and 373B.

- Have students discuss their answer to exercise 2. Point out that if they have read the question carefully, their order will be from least to greatest.
- Ask students to discuss how they arrived at their answers for exercises 7–9.
- Have the class share their answers to exercises 10 and 11.

3 Summarize

- Have the class review similarities and differences between fractions and decimals.
- Ask: What decimal would describe a decimal card with no sections shaded? With all sections shaded? 0.0; 1.0

Ongoing Assessment Suppose you paint $\frac{5}{10}$ of a fence green. What decimal can you write to show how much of the fence you painted? 0.5

Math Journal: *Communicating*

What does the 6 in the decimal 0.6 tell you? It shows six parts out of ten equal parts, or six tenths.

Show What You Know!

Use the tenths squares you made.

2. $\frac{1}{10}, \frac{2}{10}, \frac{3}{10}, \frac{4}{10}, \frac{5}{10}, \frac{6}{10}, \frac{7}{10}, \frac{8}{10}, \frac{9}{10}, \frac{10}{10}$
0.1, 0.2, 0.3, 0.4, 0.5, 0.6, 0.7, 0.8, 0.9, 1.0

1. On the back of each tenths square you shaded, write the fraction and the decimal it shows. Check students' work.
2. Put your tenths squares in order from least to greatest. Write the fractions and decimals in order on a sheet of paper. See above.

Estimation Is the decimal closer to 0 or to 1.0? Write *0* or *1*.

3. 0.3 0   4. 0.6 1   5. 0.1 0

6. You know that $\frac{1}{2}$ and $\frac{5}{10}$ are equivalent fractions. Find the decimal card that shows half of the tenths shaded. What do you notice? If $\frac{1}{2}$ of the tenths are shaded, you can write $\frac{5}{10}$ or 0.5.

Shade parts to show each decimal. Use a tenths square or the recording sheet.

7. 0.3   8. 0.9   9. 0.6

10. **Critical Thinking** How are decimals and fractions alike?
Answers may vary. Possible answer: Both describe parts of a whole.
11. **Critical Thinking** How do decimals and fractions differ?
Answers may vary. Possible answer: They are written differently.

Copy the chart or use the recording sheet. Use your decimal cards to complete the chart. See Additional Answers.

Decimal	Words	Greater Than, Less Than, or Equal to $\frac{1}{2}$
12. 0.2	two tenths	?
13. 0.7	seven tenths	?
14. 0.5	?	?
15. ?	four tenths	?
16. 0.6	?	?

Copy the chart or use your recording sheet.
Use your decimal models to find the greater decimal.

	Find These Decimal Squares	Compare
	0.6 and 0.3	0.6 > 0.3
17.	0.6 and 0.7	0.6 < 0.7
18.	0.1 and 0.4	0.1 < 0.4
19.	0.9 and 0.8	0.9 < 0.8

349

Meeting Individual Needs

Extra Support

How Many Tenths? *(visual/kinesthetic)* Have students make 10-link paper chains using two different colors of construction paper. Ask them to join all the links of one color, then attach the links of the second color. Then, have pairs compare chains and discuss how many tenths are in each color.

Alternate Approach

- Reteach Worksheet 10.1
- **TAB** See TE pp. 346E–346F.
- MATHKEYS Encourage students to model decimals on the computer. They use counters, bars, circles, and decimal blocks to represent and order tenths in *Unlocking Fractions and Decimals 3–6*, Level 3, Activity 15.

Students Acquiring English

See Language Connections, Ch. 10.

Challenge

Have students make two sets of 10 index cards. On one set, they write fractions in tenths, from $\frac{1}{10}$ to $\frac{10}{10}$. On the other, they write decimals from 0.1 to 1.0. Student pairs can use the cards to play a form of Concentration.

Practice

Math Center Use How-To Card 35, *Decimal Match*, to have students practice exploring tenths.

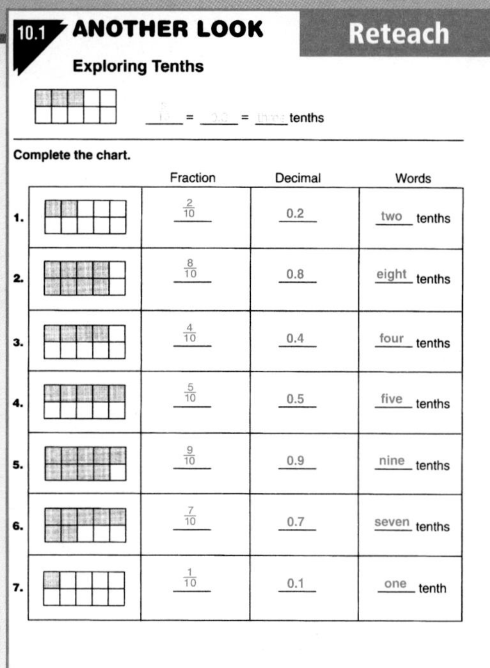

10.1 ANOTHER LOOK — Reteach

Exploring Tenths

___ = ___ = ___ tenths

Complete the chart.

	Fraction	Decimal	Words
1.	$\frac{2}{10}$	0.2	two tenths
2.	$\frac{8}{10}$	0.8	eight tenths
3.	$\frac{4}{10}$	0.4	four tenths
4.	$\frac{5}{10}$	0.5	five tenths
5.	$\frac{9}{10}$	0.9	nine tenths
6.	$\frac{7}{10}$	0.7	seven tenths
7.	$\frac{1}{10}$	0.1	one tenth

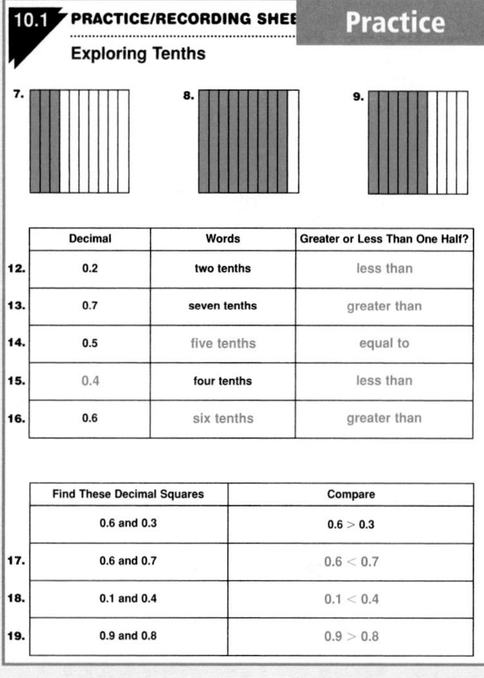

10.1 PRACTICE/RECORDING SHEET — Practice

Exploring Tenths

7.   8.   9.

	Decimal	Words	Greater or Less Than One Half?
12.	0.2	two tenths	less than
13.	0.7	seven tenths	greater than
14.	0.5	five tenths	equal to
15.	0.4	four tenths	less than
16.	0.6	six tenths	greater than

	Find These Decimal Squares	Compare
	0.6 and 0.3	0.6 > 0.3
17.	0.6 and 0.7	0.6 < 0.7
18.	0.1 and 0.4	0.1 < 0.4
19.	0.9 and 0.8	0.9 > 0.8

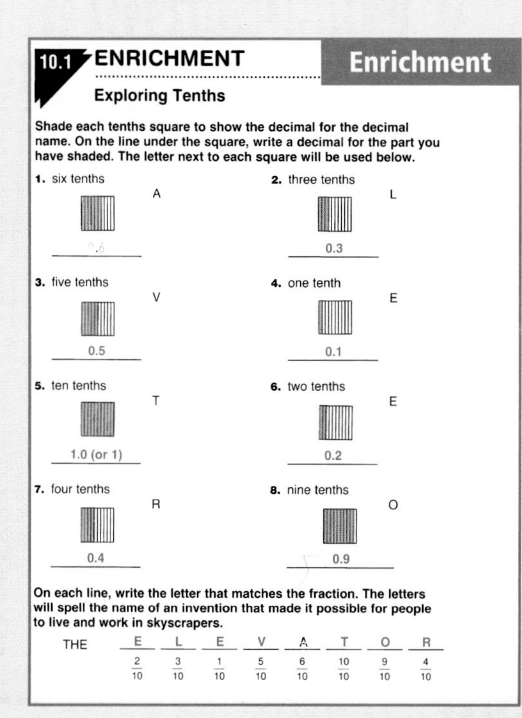

10.1 ENRICHMENT — Enrichment

Exploring Tenths

Shade each tenths square to show the decimal for the decimal name. On the line under the square, write a decimal for the part you have shaded. The letter next to each square will be used below.

1. six tenths A — 0.6
2. three tenths L — 0.3
3. five tenths V — 0.5
4. one tenth E — 0.1
5. ten tenths T — 1.0 (or 1)
6. two tenths E — 0.2
7. four tenths R — 0.4
8. nine tenths O — 0.9

On each line, write the letter that matches the fraction. The letters will spell the name of an invention that made it possible for people to live and work in skyscrapers.

THE E L E V A T O R
$\frac{2}{10}$ $\frac{3}{10}$ $\frac{1}{10}$ $\frac{5}{10}$ $\frac{6}{10}$ $\frac{10}{10}$ $\frac{9}{10}$ $\frac{4}{10}$

LESSON 10.2

Activity

Planning at a Glance

Objective To investigate decimals greater than 1 using tenths squares

Materials Recording Sheet (Practice 10.2)

Optional Resources

- Reteach 10.2; Enrichment 10.2
- Daily Cumul. Review, p. 131
- Math Center: How-To Card 36
- Every Day Counts
- **TAB**, TE pp. 346E–346F, 346J
- **Problem of the Day**, 131, p. 66; Flip Chart, p. 66a

MATHKEYS

Unlocking Fractions and Decimals 3–6, Level 3, Activity 16

Students Acquiring English

Give students practice with oral and written forms of decimals and fractions. First, have them write down numbers you say in decimal and fraction form (use only numbers with tenths). Then write several fractions and decimals on the board and invite students to read them aloud.

Problem of the Day

Find two numbers whose sum is half their product.

Possible answers include: $3 + 6 = 9$ and $3 \times 6 = 18$; $4 + 4 = 8$ and $4 \times 4 = 16$.

Decimals Greater Than 1

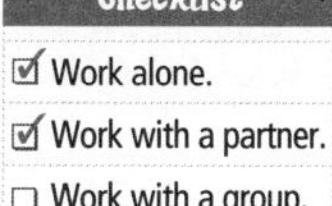

Cooperative Learning Checklist

- ☑ Work alone.
- ☑ Work with a partner.
- ☐ Work with a group.

Getting Started

What You'll Need:
▶ recording sheet

This comic book shows more than one page filled in. Use what you know about decimal models to write the amount in the decimal form.

Activity

Use What You Know

$1\frac{3}{10}$

A mixed number has a whole number and a fraction.

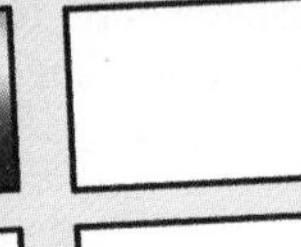

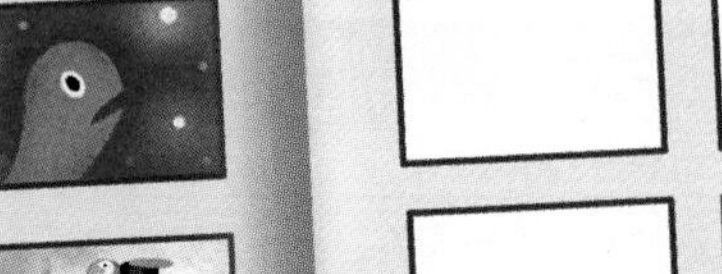
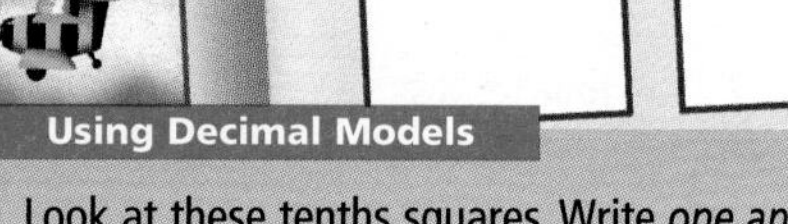

Using Decimal Models

1. Look at these tenths squares. Write *one and three tenths* to tell how many squares are shaded.
2. You can use the tenths squares and the words to help you write the decimal.

one and three tenths ⟶ 1.3

350 Chapter 10

1 Introduce

Build Understanding Write 0.9 and \$.90 on the board and invite students to read them aloud. Ask; What is ninety cents $\frac{9}{10}$ of? a dollar

Teach: Activity

Emphasize these points:

- A decimal greater than 1 is like a mixed number. It has a whole number to the left of the decimal point and a fraction to the right.
- Numbers such as $1\frac{3}{10}$ and 1.3 have the same value.

Modeling Model 1.7. Ask:

- How can I tell that this number is greater than 1? by the whole number on the left
- How can I write it as a mixed number? $1\frac{7}{10}$

2 Develop

Show What You Know!

- For exercises 1–3 and 6–8, guide students in recognizing the relationships among tenths squares, decimals, and word names for fractions.
- Have students share their answers to exercise 5. Some may mention distances on maps and odometer readings as well as package weights, sports statistics, and money amounts.
- Have students discuss their answers for exercise 11.

3 Summarize

- Call on students to explain why 1.4 is not the same as $\frac{1}{4}$ even though they have the same digits.

Ongoing Assessment Jim scored 4.4 in the brain-twister contest. Amy scored $4\frac{4}{10}$. Whose score was higher? Neither; students should see that 4.4 and $4\frac{4}{10}$ are both equal to four and four tenths.

Math Journal: *Communicating*

How are one dollar and three dimes like the decimal 1.3? Both show a whole number part (one dollar and one), and both show three parts of a whole (three tenths of one dollar, and three tenths).

Writing Numbers Greater Than 1

1. On your recording sheet, shade the tenths squares to show two and five tenths.

   You can write a mixed number to help you : $2\frac{5}{10}$.
   Then you can write a decimal: 2.5

2. Shade three and three tenths. Write the mixed number. Write the decimal. $3\frac{3}{10}$;3.3

   a. How do you know the decimal and the mixed number name the same amount?
   They both describe the same model; they both tell how many squares are shaded.

2. 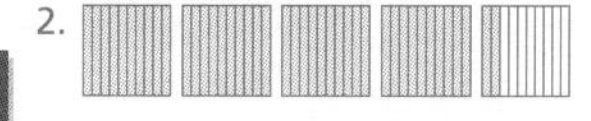

Show What You Know!

On your recording sheet, use shading to show the decimal.

1. 1.9   2. 4.2 see above   3. 2.4

4. **Number Sense** Look at your shaded squares. Which is greater, 1.9 or 4.2? How do you know?
4.2; More squares are shaded.
5. **Critical Thinking** Where else have you seen decimals used besides in your math book? Answers will vary.
Possible answers: cans of food; money amounts; social studies book

Write the decimal.

6. 6 and 1 tenth 6.1   7. 1 and 5 tenths 1.5   8. 3 and 0 tenths 3.0

Write the words, mixed number, and decimal that names how many squares are shaded.

9. 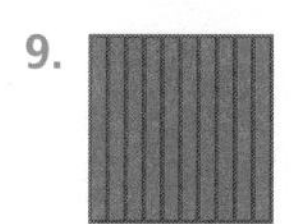 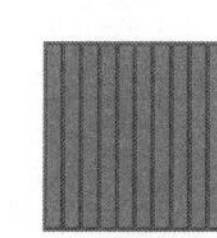   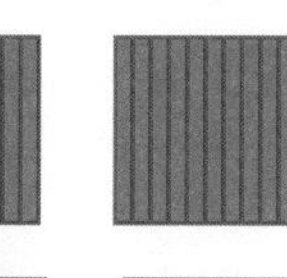 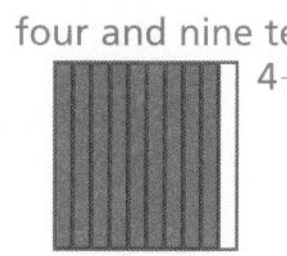
four and nine tenths; $4\frac{9}{10}$; 4.9

10.    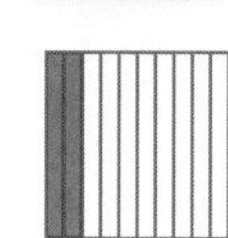
three and two tenths; $3\frac{2}{10}$; 3.2

11. **Write About It** Without drawing pictures, explain how you can tell that 1.2 is greater than 0.9. 1.2 is more than 1 and 0.9 is less than 1.

Meeting Individual Needs

Extra Support

Fractions and Decimals *(visual/kinesthetic)*
Have pairs use graphic aids to show that:

- $\frac{10}{10}$ is the same as 1.0
- 1.7 is the same as $1\frac{7}{10}$
- 1.5 is greater than $\frac{1}{5}$
- 0.8 is less than $1\frac{1}{10}$

Alternate Approach

- Reteach Worksheet 10.2
- **TAB** See TE p. 346E–346F

Students Acquiring English

See Language Connections, Ch. 10.

Challenge

Have pairs draw pictures to solve the following:

- Your new stamps can fill 0.9 pages in your stamp album. You already have 0.3 pages filled. Can you fill that page? yes
- After you fill in your first page, you place the rest of the new stamps on the next page. How much of this page do they fill? 0.2 pages
- What decimal tells how many pages are now filled? 1.2 pages

Practice

Math Center Use How-To Card 36, *Snail's Pace!*, to have students practice investigating decimals greater than 1 using tenths squares.

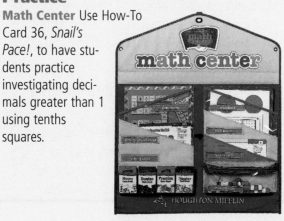

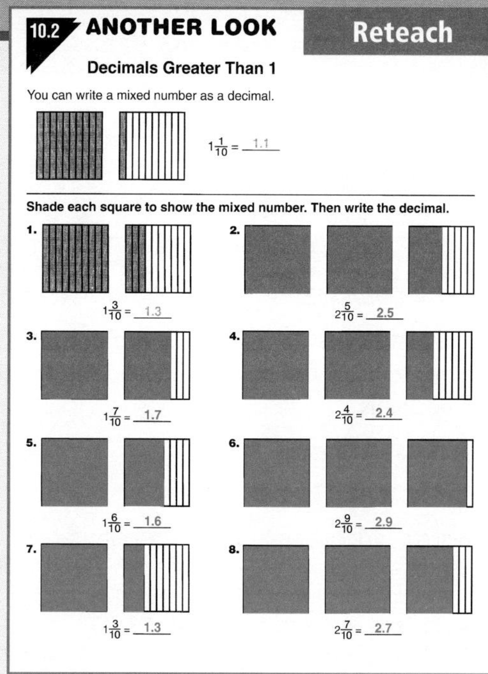

Reteach

10.2 ANOTHER LOOK

Decimals Greater Than 1

You can write a mixed number as a decimal.

$1\frac{1}{10}$ = 1.1

Shade each square to show the mixed number. Then write the decimal.

1. $1\frac{3}{10}$ = 1.3
2. $2\frac{5}{10}$ = 2.5
3. $1\frac{7}{10}$ = 1.7
4. $2\frac{4}{10}$ = 2.4
5. $1\frac{6}{10}$ = 1.6
6. $2\frac{9}{10}$ = 2.9
7. $1\frac{3}{10}$ = 1.3
8. $2\frac{7}{10}$ = 2.7

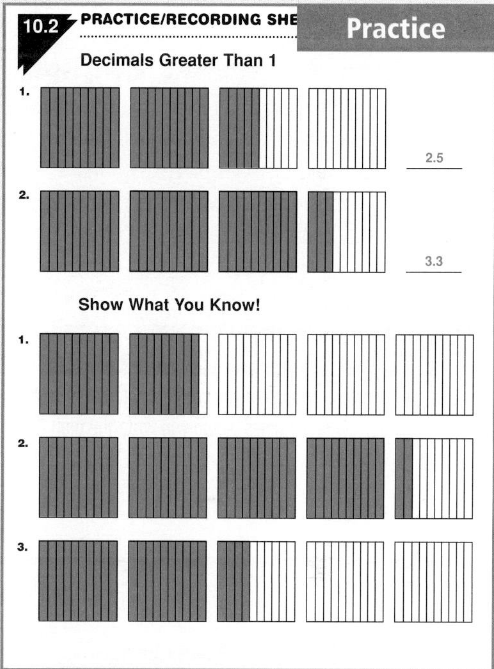

Practice

10.2 PRACTICE/RECORDING SHE

Decimals Greater Than 1

1. 2.5
2. 3.3

Show What You Know!

1.
2.
3.

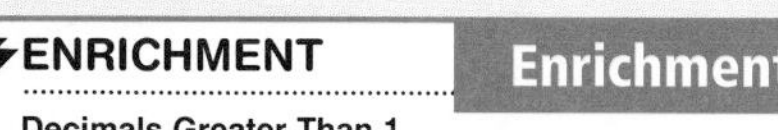

Enrichment

10.2 ENRICHMENT

Decimals Greater Than 1

Alba City held a walkathon to raise money for an arts center. Teams kept track of how far members walked.

Read the numbered items. Write the correct decimal next to each name on the list of results.

1. Alison walked two and one tenths kilometers.
2. Mr. Evans walked three and six tenths kilometers.
3. Mrs. Gomez walked four and eight tenths kilometers.
4. Peter walked two and nine tenths kilometers.
5. Julia walked three and five tenths kilometers.
6. Rachel walked three and two tenths kilometers.

Team Results					
1. Alison:	2.1	km	4. Peter:	2.9	km
2. Mr. Evans:	3.6	km	5. Julia:	3.5	km
3. Mrs. Gomez:	4.8	km	6. Rachel:	3.2	km

Answer each question. You can use tenths squares or a calculator.

7. Bailey's Supermarket gave $10 in the name of every person who walked 3.5 kilometers or more. For which team members did Bailey's give money?
Mr. Evans, Mrs. Gomez, and Julia
8. George Chee walked exactly 3 kilometers. Which of the team members finished closest to George's distance?
Peter

Connecting

Planning at a Glance

Objectives To read and write decimals to tenths; to use word names, models, and fractions for decimals

Materials none

Optional Resources

- Reteach 10.3; Practice 10.3; Enrichment 10.3
- Daily Cumul. Review, p. 132
- Math Center: Act. Card 56
- Every Day Counts
- **TAB**, TE pp. 346E–346F, 346J
- **Problem of the Day**, 132, p. 66; Flip Chart, p. 66b

MATHKEYS

Unlocking Fractions and Decimals 3–6, Level 3, Activity 19

Students Acquiring English

Draw a place-value chart and review its use with whole numbers. Say two-digit numbers and have students write the digits in the tens place and the ones place. Then make a chart showing ones and tenths. Practice with mixed numbers such as 1.3. Be sure students can distinguish *tens* and *tenths*.

Problem of the Day

Suppose you wrote each decimal you would say to count by tenths from 0.4 to 3.5. How many times would you write the digit 2?
13 times

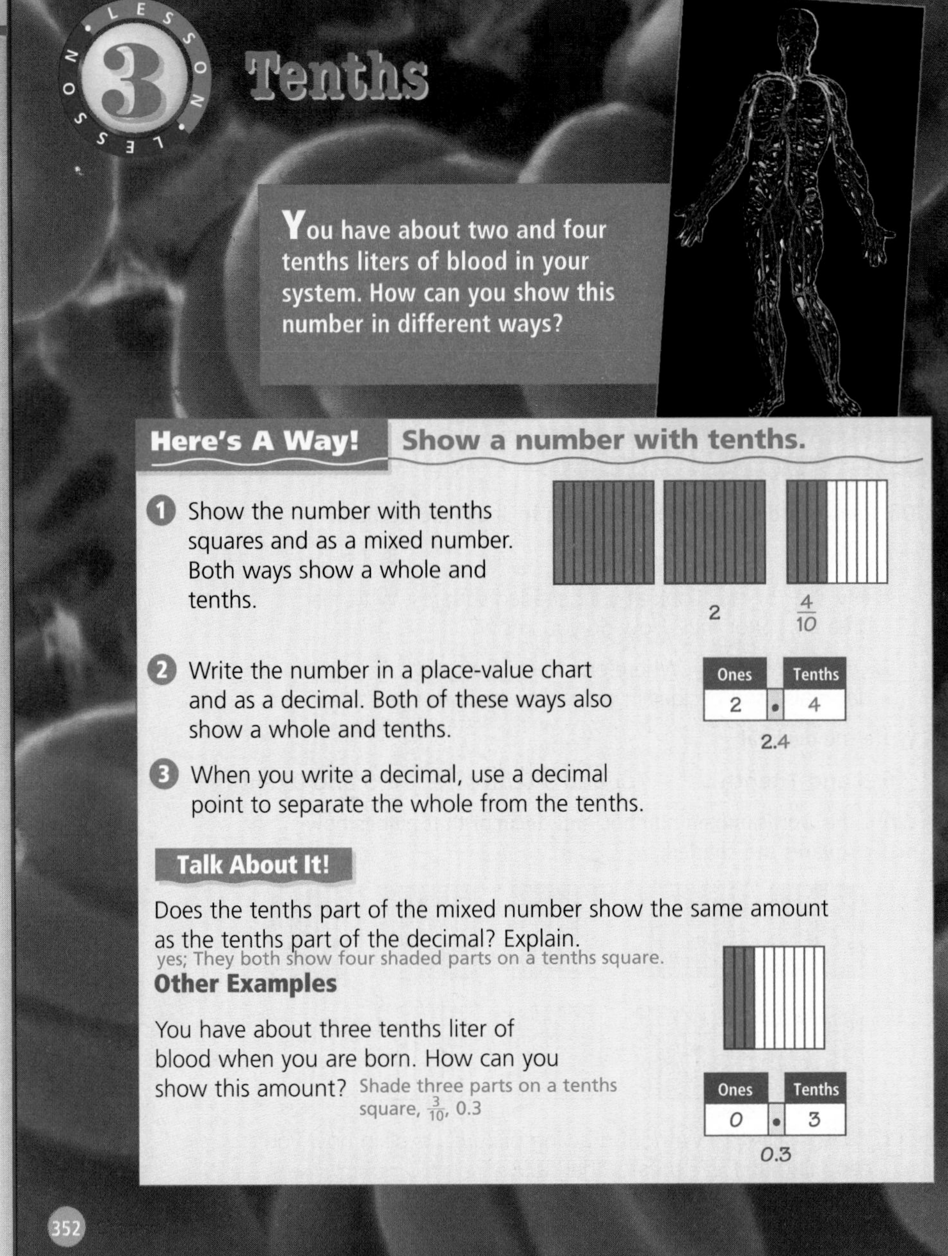

LESSON 3 LESSON
Tenths
You have about two and four tenths liters of blood in your system. How can you show this number in different ways?
Here's A Way! Show a number with tenths.
1 Show the number with tenths squares and as a mixed number. Both ways show a whole and tenths.
2
4/10
2 Write the number in a place-value chart and as a decimal. Both of these ways also show a whole and tenths.
Ones Tenths
2 . 4
2.4
3 When you write a decimal, use a decimal point to separate the whole from the tenths.
Talk About It!
Does the tenths part of the mixed number show the same amount as the tenths part of the decimal? Explain.
yes; They both show four shaded parts on a tenths square.
Other Examples
You have about three tenths liter of blood when you are born. How can you show this amount? Shade three parts on a tenths square, 3/10, 0.3
Ones Tenths
0 . 3
0.3
352

1 Introduce

Prior Knowledge Have students write each number as a decimal: three and two tenths 3.2, two and nine tenths 2.9, six tenths 0.6.

Teach: Here's A Way!

Emphasize these points:

- Any fraction with a denominator of 10 can be written as a decimal.
- Ten tenths is equal to one whole.

Modeling Model the second example on p. 352. Ask:

- Is three tenths greater than or less than 1? less than
- How would I write that number as a fraction? How would I write it as a decimal? $\frac{3}{10}$; 0.3

Show What You Know!

Common Error Some students may incorrectly name the number of tenths from the model. Remind them to count carefully. See also Analyzing Errors, TE pp. 373A and 373B.

- Remind students always to show the zero to the left of the decimal *except* when writing money amounts less than a dollar.

Work It Out!

- Call on students to explain their reasoning for exercises 21 and 23.

Using Reading Strategies Help students to use the Monitor strategy as they read the problem solving exercises. Ask, what should you keep in mind as you reread a problem? See TE p. 346J.

- Remind students that the digit to the right of the decimal point shows the number of tenths, and the digit to the left of the decimal point shows the number of ones.
- Have students summarize how place value and fractions can help in writing decimals.

Ongoing Assessment Your sister rode her bike $4\frac{2}{10}$ miles last week. What decimal can she write to show this amount? 4.2

Math Journal: *Communicating*

One possible answer: since the place values of the two digits are the same and 7 is greater than 4, 0.7 is greater than 0.4.

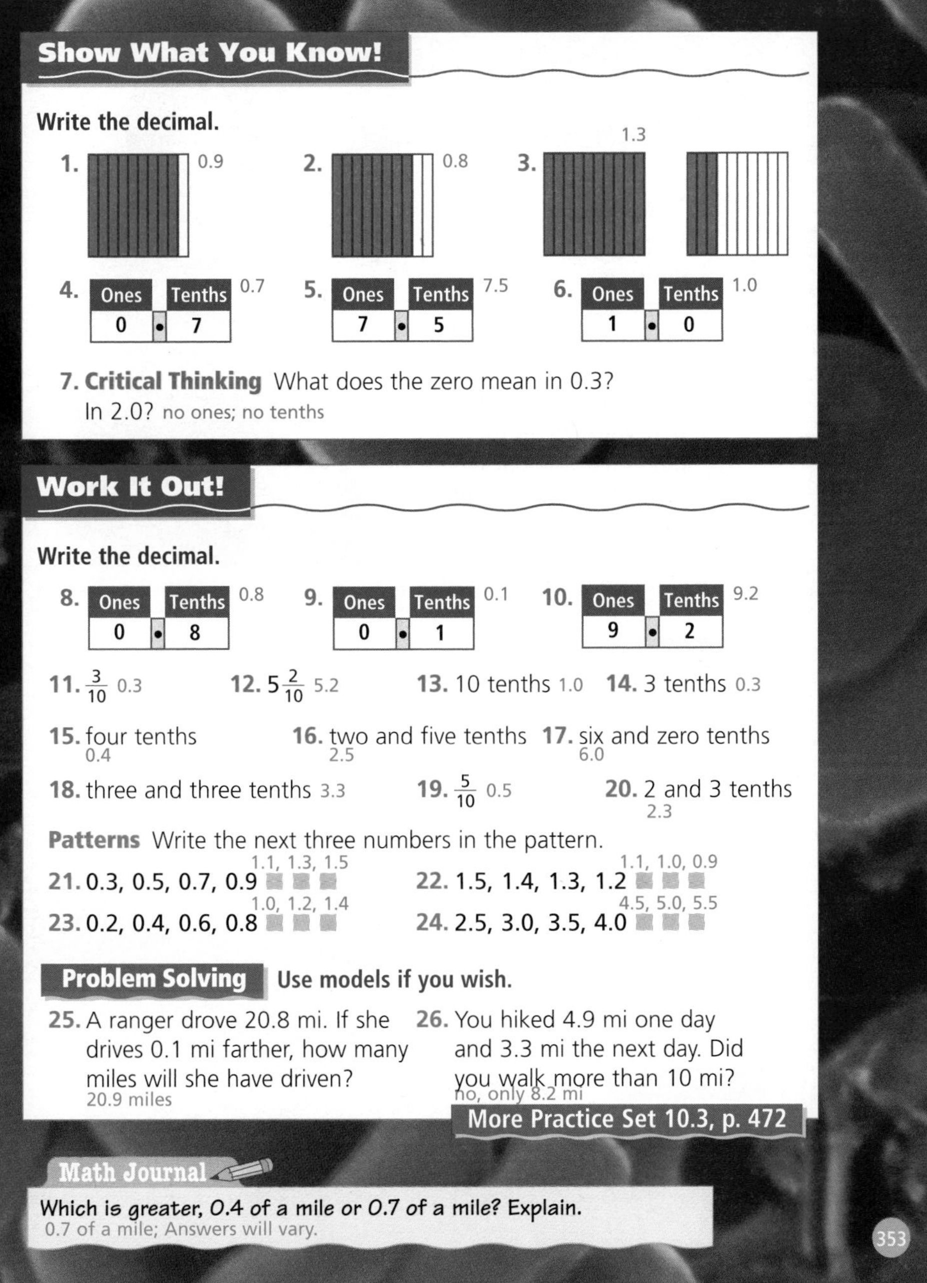

Show What You Know!

Write the decimal.

1. [tenths model] 0.9
2. [tenths model] 0.8
3. [tenths models] 1.3

4. | Ones | Tenths |
|---|---|
| 0 | 7 |

0.7

5. | Ones | Tenths |
|---|---|
| 7 | 5 |

7.5

6. | Ones | Tenths |
|---|---|
| 1 | 0 |

1.0

7. **Critical Thinking** What does the zero mean in 0.3? In 2.0? no ones; no tenths

Work It Out!

Write the decimal.

8. | Ones | Tenths |
|---|---|
| 0 | 8 |

0.8

9. | Ones | Tenths |
|---|---|
| 0 | 1 |

0.1

10. | Ones | Tenths |
|---|---|
| 9 | 2 |

9.2

11. $\frac{3}{10}$ 0.3
12. $5\frac{2}{10}$ 5.2
13. 10 tenths 1.0
14. 3 tenths 0.3
15. four tenths 0.4
16. two and five tenths 2.5
17. six and zero tenths 6.0
18. three and three tenths 3.3
19. $\frac{5}{10}$ 0.5
20. 2 and 3 tenths 2.3

Patterns Write the next three numbers in the pattern.

21. 0.3, 0.5, 0.7, 0.9 ■ ■ ■ 1.1, 1.3, 1.5
22. 1.5, 1.4, 1.3, 1.2 ■ ■ ■ 1.1, 1.0, 0.9
23. 0.2, 0.4, 0.6, 0.8 ■ ■ ■ 1.0, 1.2, 1.4
24. 2.5, 3.0, 3.5, 4.0 ■ ■ ■ 4.5, 5.0, 5.5

Problem Solving Use models if you wish.

25. A ranger drove 20.8 mi. If she drives 0.1 mi farther, how many miles will she have driven? 20.9 miles
26. You hiked 4.9 mi one day and 3.3 mi the next day. Did you walk more than 10 mi? no, only 8.2 mi

More Practice Set 10.3, p. 472

Math Journal

Which is greater, 0.4 of a mile or 0.7 of a mile? Explain.
0.7 of a mile; Answers will vary.

353

Meeting Individual Needs

Extra Support

Ones and Tenths ***(visual)*** Write the digits 0 through 9 on a set of 10 index cards. Have student pairs draw two cards randomly. One partner writes the two digits with a decimal point between them and uses tenths squares to show the value of the decimal. The other partner reverses the place value of the two digits and follows the same procedure. Students then compare their numbers. Repeat for three pairs of numbers.

Alternate Approach

- Reteach Worksheet 10.3
- **TAB** See TE pp. 346E–346F.

Students Acquiring English

See Language Connections, Ch. 10.

Challenge

Invite students to write the next three numbers in this pattern: 1.0, 2.3, 3.6, 4.9, □□□
6.2, 7.5, 8.8

Practice

Math Center Use Activity Card 56, *Decimal MathO,* to have students practice reading and writing decimals to tenths, using word names, models, and fractions for decimals.

Challenge Use Activity Card 56, and have students continue as described in Now Try This!

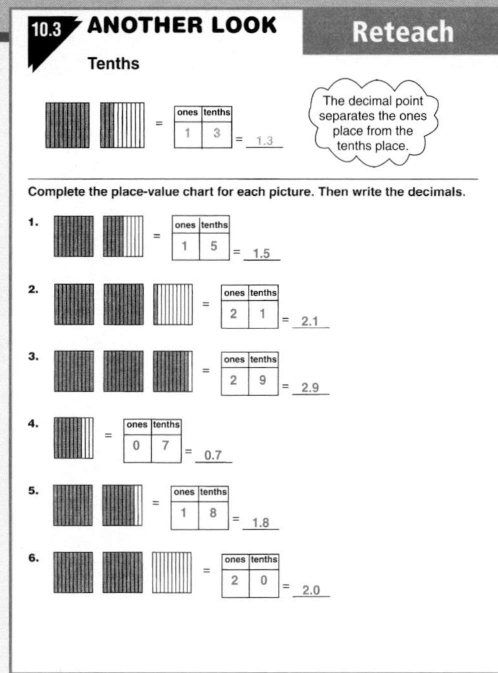

10.3 ANOTHER LOOK — Reteach

Tenths

The decimal point separates the ones place from the tenths place.

Example: ones 1, tenths 3 = 1.3

Complete the place-value chart for each picture. Then write the decimals.

	ones	tenths	decimal
1.	1	5	1.5
2.	2	1	2.1
3.	2	9	2.9
4.	0	7	0.7
5.	1	8	1.8
6.	2	0	2.0

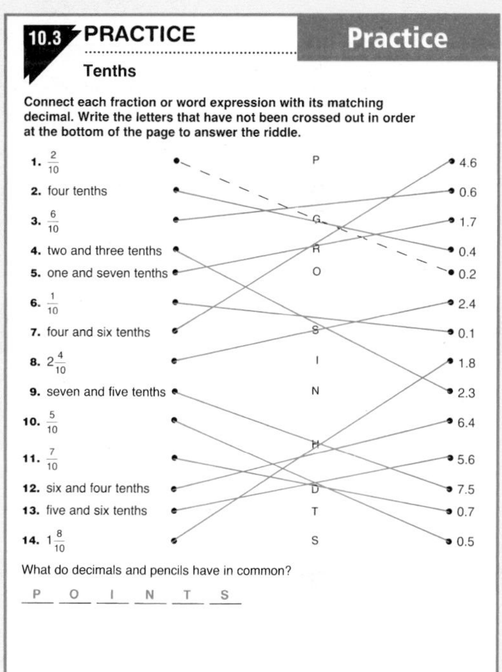

10.3 PRACTICE — Practice

Tenths

Connect each fraction or word expression with its matching decimal. Write the letters that have not been crossed out in order at the bottom of the page to answer the riddle.

1. $\frac{2}{10}$ — P — 4.6
2. four tenths — 0.6
3. $\frac{6}{10}$ — G — 1.7
4. two and three tenths — R — 0.4
5. one and seven tenths — O — 0.2
6. $\frac{1}{10}$ — 2.4
7. four and six tenths — S — 0.1
8. $2\frac{4}{10}$ — I — 1.8
9. seven and five tenths — N — 2.3
10. $\frac{5}{10}$ — 6.4
11. $\frac{7}{10}$ — H — 5.6
12. six and four tenths — 7.5
13. five and six tenths — D — T — 0.7
14. $1\frac{8}{10}$ — S — 0.5

What do decimals and pencils have in common?
P O I N T S

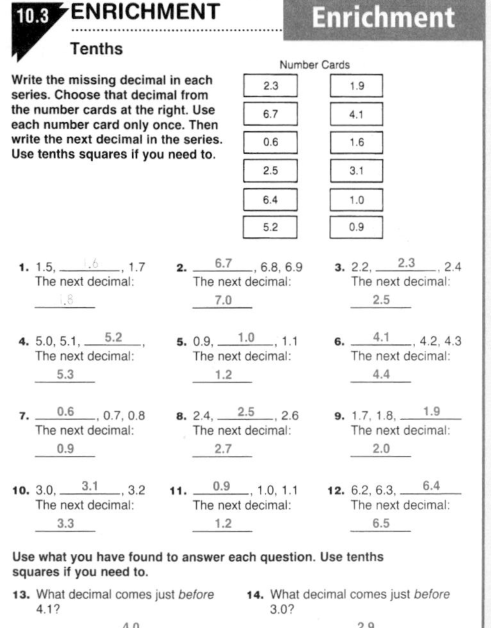

10.3 ENRICHMENT — Enrichment

Tenths

Write the missing decimal in each series. Choose that decimal from the number cards at the right. Use each number card only once. Then write the next decimal in the series. Use tenths squares if you need to.

Number Cards: 2.3, 1.9, 6.7, 4.1, 0.6, 1.6, 2.5, 3.1, 6.4, 1.0, 5.2, 0.9

1. 1.5, 1.6, 1.7 The next decimal: 1.8
2. 6.7, 6.8, 6.9 The next decimal: 7.0
3. 2.2, 2.3, 2.4 The next decimal: 2.5
4. 5.0, 5.1, 5.2 The next decimal: 5.3
5. 0.9, 1.0, 1.1 The next decimal: 1.2
6. 4.1, 4.2, 4.3 The next decimal: 4.4
7. 0.6, 0.7, 0.8 The next decimal: 0.9
8. 2.4, 2.5, 2.6 The next decimal: 2.7
9. 1.7, 1.8, 1.9 The next decimal: 2.0
10. 3.0, 3.1, 3.2 The next decimal: 3.3
11. 0.9, 1.0, 1.1 The next decimal: 1.2
12. 6.2, 6.3, 6.4 The next decimal: 6.5

Use what you have found to answer each question. Use tenths squares if you need to.

13. What decimal comes just *before* 4.1? 4.0
14. What decimal comes just *before* 3.0? 2.9

Planning at a Glance

Objective To use the Make a List strategy to solve problems

Materials index cards or slips of paper

Optional Resources

- Reteach 10.4; Practice 10.4; Enrichment 10.4
- Daily Cumul. Review, p. 133
- Math Center: Project Card
- Every Day Counts
- **TAB**, TE p. 346E–346F, 346J
- **Problem of the Day**, 133, p. 67; Flip Chart, p. 67a

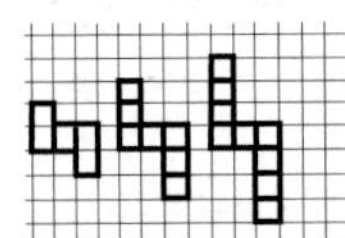

Unlocking Whole Numbers 3–5, Level 3, Activity 17

Students Acquiring English

Showing different combinations of a group of objects, help students pronounce the words *combination* and *groups.* Give students groups of objects and ask them to make different combinations of things.

Problem of the Day

Look at the picture pattern. Draw the next figure. How many boxes would be in the next figure after that? 13 boxes

Problem Solving
Make a List

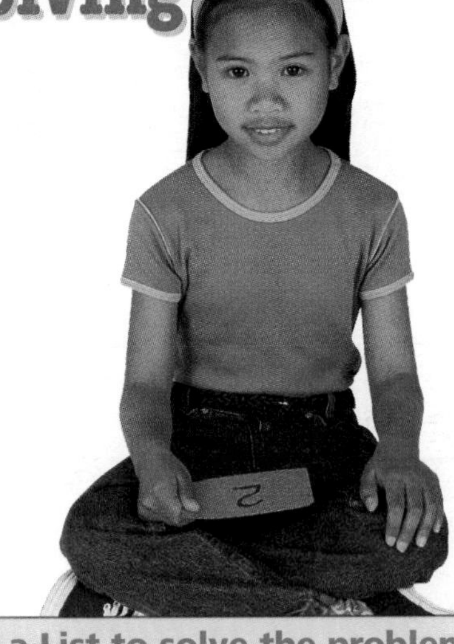

Getting Started

What You'll Need:
▶ 4 index cards or slips of paper

Your class is playing a sorting game. Using two digits, you must make as many decimals greater than 1 as possible using the digits 2, 3, and 5. How can you be sure that you find all the possible combinations? You can make a list of the numbers.

Here's A Way! Use Make a List to solve the problem.

1 Understand
- You can make a list to help you find the decimals.

2 Plan
- Use cards to make decimals.
- List the decimals that you make.

3 Try It
- Write one digit on each of 3 cards. Use a fourth card to show a decimal point.
- List all the decimals you make.

4 Look Back
- There are 6 decimals greater than 1: 2.3, 2.5, 3.2, 3.5, 5.2, 5.3. How did making a list help you to solve the problem? Answers will vary. Possible answer: It showed all the combinations so you knew you got them all and did not repeat any.

354 Chapter 10

1 Introduce

Prior Knowledge **Ask, How would you order these numbers from least to greatest—0.4, 1.2, 0.7?** 0.4, 0.7, 1.2

Teach: Here's A Way!

After solving the problem, ask:

- Why make a list? to keep track of all possible numbers
- How can you be sure that all possible decimal numbers have been listed? Include all numbers that begin with 2, with 3, and with 5.

Modeling Model finding all possible orders for doing these pet-care tasks: feeding, exercising, cleaning. Ask:

- How can you be sure you find all possible orders? You can make a list.

2 Develop

Show What You Know!

Suggest that students make lists to help them solve exercises 1 and 2. Then ask them to discuss and compare the strategies they used.

Work It Out!

- Ask students to suggest other strategies for solving each problem.
- Have students discuss their answers for exercises 7 and 8.

Using Reading Strategies Guide students to use the Monitor strategy as they read the Problem Solving exercises. Ask them to share where they needed to slow down to understand the problems. See TE p.346J.

3 Summarize

- Have students summarize the strategies they used.
- Ask students to discuss how they can tell when making a list could help them solve a problem.

Ongoing Assessment Four friends are playing a game. How many different ways can they order their turns? Explain your strategy. 12 ways; strategy may combine making a list and finding a pattern

Math Journal: *Communicating*

Make a list of 3 chores you might have to do. Write all the different orders in which you can do them. Answers will vary but should show six different orders of doing the chores.

Show What You Know!

Use Make a List to solve this problem.

1. Using two digits, how many decimals greater than 1 can you make with the digits 1, 6, 8, and 3? 12 decimals using index cards; with pencil and paper, can also make 1.1, 3.3, 6.6, and 8.8
2. **Critical Thinking** Once your list is complete, predict how many 2-digit decimals you can make with a fifth card. 20 decimals with index cards; 21 decimals with paper and pencil

Work It Out!

Use Make a List or any other strategy to solve the problem.

3. How many different ways can you shade 0.1 of a tenths square? This picture shows one way. 10 ways

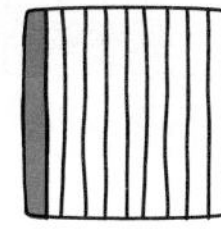

4. How many different ways can you shade 0.9 of a tenths square? This picture shows one way. 10 ways

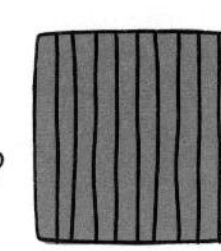

5. You and 3 classmates form pairs to do a class project. How many different pairs of partners can the four of you make? 6 pairs
6. You and a friend each choose a tenths square. Yours shows 0.8. Your friend's shows 0.4. Count up from your partner's number to your number. You get 1 point for each tenth. How many points do you get? 4 points
7. You have a spinner that is divided into tenths. You want to color 0.2 of the spinner blue and the rest of it red. Show 5 different ways to do it. See Additional Answers

8. You have 2 equal piles of pennies. To buy a cookie, you use one of your piles plus 1 penny more. After you buy the cookie, you have 4 pennies left. How much money did you have before you bought the cookie? 10¢

Share Your Thinking

9. Which problems did you solve by making a list? Answers will vary. Possible answer: 3, 4, 5, 7

355

Meeting Individual Needs

Extra Support

Two out of Three *(visual)* Have student pairs solve this problem: A penny, a nickel, and a dime are in a jar. If you pick out 2 coins, how many different amounts of money might you get? 3 different amounts: 6¢, 11¢, or 15¢

Alternate Approach

- Reteach Worksheet 10.4
- **TAB** See TE pp. 346E–346F.

Students Acquiring English

See Language Connections, Ch. 10.

Challenge

Have students write problems that can be solved by making an organized list. Then have them exchange problems with a partner and solve.

Practice

Math Center For more problem solving practice, see Project Card 10, *Newspaper Numbers.*

Reteach

10.4 ANOTHER LOOK

Problem Solving Strategy: Make a List

You have three digit cards and one symbol card. The digits are 2, 3, 4. The symbol is a decimal point. Find all the ways to make decimals with the cards. The decimals should have digits in the ones place and the tenths place.

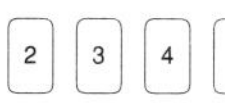

1. Understand
- Put the digits in different places to make decimals.
- Put one digit to the left of the decimal point and one digit to the right of the decimal point.

2. Plan
- Make a list. Record each decimal you create.
- Use the list to check the decimals. Make sure they are all different.
- Count the list to find out how many you made.

3. Try It
- List all the decimals you made with 2 in the ones place.
- List all the decimals with 3 in the ones place.
- List all the decimals with 4 in the ones place.

4. Look Back
- Count the decimals on your list. You should have 6 decimals: 2.3, 2.4, 3.2, 3.4, 4.2, and 4.3.

Solve. Use Make a List when you can.

1. Suppose your teacher also gives you a digit card for 5. Find all the ways to make decimals. Put a digit in the ones place and the tenths place. 12 decimals: 2.3, 2.4, 2.5, 3.2, 3.4, 3.5, 4.2, 4.3, 4.5, 5.2, 5.3, 5.4

Practice

10.4 PRACTICE

Problem Solving Strategy: Make a List

Solve. Use Make a List when you can.

1. Suppose you have four number cards: 4, 8, 5, 3. You also have a decimal point card. How many 2-digit decimals can you make with these cards? What are the combinations? 12 combinations: 4.8, 4.5, 4.3, 8.4, 8.5, 8.3, 5.4, 5.8, 5.3, 3.4, 3.8, 3.5
2. Suppose you have three coins: a dime, a nickel, and a quarter. You put these coins into a bag and pick out two at a time without looking. What are the different coin combinations you might pick? Dime, quarter; dime, nickel; nickel, quarter
3. What is the largest amount of money you could pick from the bag? 35¢.
4. What is the least amount of money you could pick from the bag? 15¢
5. Find the secret number. It is greater than 1.1. It is less than 2. If you add the number to itself, you get 3. What is the secret number? 1.5
6. A train travels daily to Portland, Oregon. The train includes a dining car, a sleeping car, and a lounging car. How many different ways can the passenger cars be arranged behind the engine? 6 ways

Enrichment

10.4 ENRICHMENT

Problem Solving Strategy: Make a List

Solve. Use Make a List when you can.

1. You have 5 cards numbered 1–5. How many 2-digit numbers can you make with these cards? 20 numbers
2. Three friends go to the movies. There are 4 seats in a row. How many different ways can the friends sit in a row? Remember, there are 4 seats and 3 friends. 24 ways
3. Your cousin likes to go jogging. On Monday, she ran 1.2 miles; on Tuesday, she ran 1.5 miles. How many miles did she run in the two days? 2.7 miles
4. Your cousin always jogs 0.3 miles more than the previous day. How many miles will she jog on Friday? 2.4 miles
5. You have 4 number cards: 5, 2, 6, and 7. What is the largest number you can make with the digits? What is the smallest number you can make using all the digits? 7652; 2567
6. Your friend has a mystery number. It is greater than 2. It is less than 3. If you multiply it by 2 you get 5. What is the mystery number? 2.5

Connecting

Planning at a Glance

Objective To compare decimals greater than and less than 1 using a number line

Materials tenths squares (TR19)

Optional Resources

- Reteach 10.5; Practice 10.5; Enrichment 10.5
- Daily Cumul. Review, p. 134
- Math Center: Act. Card 57
- Every Day Counts
- TAB, TE pp. 346E–346F, 346J
- Problem of the Day, 134, p. 67; Flip Chart, p. 67b

Unlocking Fractions and Decimals 3–6, Level 3, Activity 15

Students Acquiring English

Give students practice with oral and written forms of tenths. First, have them write down numbers you say in decimal and fraction form. Then write several fractions and decimals on the board and invite students to read them aloud.

Problem of the Day

Len, Kay, Max, and Sara went to the zoo. They all drew pictures of their favorite animals. No one's favorite animal began with the same letter as his or her name. Sara drew a kangaroo. The others drew a lion, a monkey, or a seal when it was feeding time. Kay got wet when her favorite animal splashed too hard. Who drew which animal? Len drew a monkey; Max drew a lion; Kay drew a seal; Sara drew a kangaroo.

Comparing and Ordering Decimals

You help your neighbors take their pets to the veterinarian. You learn that the hamster is 0.3 kg, the kitten is 0.9 kg, and the puppy is 1.2 kg. You can use a number line to compare the decimals.

Here's A Way! Use a number line.

0 0.1 0.2 0.3 0.4 0.5 0.6 0.7 0.8 0.9 1.0 1.1 1.2 1.3 1.4

1. **Put your finger at 0 on the number line.**

   As you move your finger to the right, the decimals are greater.

2. **Compare the decimals on the number line.**

   0.9 is to the right of 0.3 → 0.9 > 0.3
   1.2 is to the right of 0.9 → 1.2 > 0.9

   The kitten is heavier than the hamster.
   The puppy is heavier than the kitten.

3. **Write the decimals in order from least to greatest.**

   0.3, 0.9, 1.2

   The hamster is lightest, the kitten is heavier, and the puppy is heaviest.

Talk About It! Answers will vary. Possible answer: 1.3; It is to the right of 1.2 on the number line.

Name a decimal greater than 1.2. Explain how you know.

 Chapter 10

1 Introduce

Build Understanding **Have students find tenths squares for 3 tenths, 7 tenths, and 1 tenth, or make them using TR19. Ask them to put the squares in order from least to greatest.**

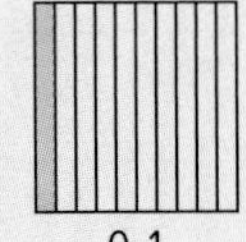
0.1

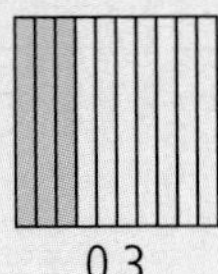
0.3

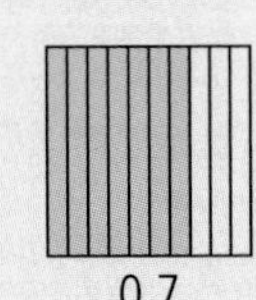
0.7

Teach: Here's A Way!

Emphasize these points:

- Compare whole numbers first, then tenths.
- Use >, <, and = when comparing numbers.

2 Develop

Show What You Know!

- Remind students that if they remember to compare the whole numbers first, they may not have to compare the decimals.

Work It Out!

- Have students compare and discuss their answers to exercise 18.
- Encourage students to compare their results for the calculator activity, exercise 20.

Using Reading Strategies Help students to use the Monitor strategy as they read the exercises. Ask them to share what parts of the Problem Solving exercise they needed to reread to understand. See TE p. 346J

3 Summarize

- Remind students that they can compare decimals by comparing the whole number amounts first and then comparing the tenths.

Ongoing Assessment Julia walks 2.1 miles. Mia walks 2.6 miles. Who walks farther? Mia

- Discuss with students how they found the answer. by comparing

Math Journal: *Communicating*

Which is greater, 1.0 or 0.9? How can you tell? The number 1.0 is greater, since it has 1 one and 0.9 has no ones, and 1 is greater than 0.

Show What You Know!

Write <, >, or =. Use a number line.

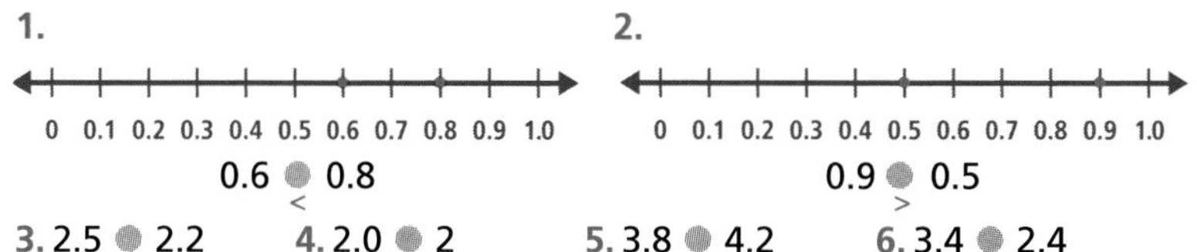

1. 0.6 ● 0.8 <
2. 0.9 ● 0.5 >
3. 2.5 ● 2.2 >
4. 2.0 ● 2 =
5. 3.8 ● 4.2 <
6. 3.4 ● 2.4 >
7. **Critical Thinking** For exercise 6, how did you decide which decimal was greater? 3.4 is to the right of 2.4 on the number line, so it is greater.

Work It Out!

Write <, >, or =. Use a number line if you wish.

8. 1.7 ● 2.3 <
9. 0.6 ● 0.2 >
10. 1.3 ● 1.4 <
11. 3.7 ● 3.5 >
12. 3 ● 3.0 =
13. 7.0 ● 0.7 >

Write the decimals in order from least to greatest.

14. 0.5, 0.2, 0.7 0.2, 0.5, 0.7
15. 2.0, 2.2, 0.2 0.2, 2.0, 2.2
16. 2.3, 2.8, 2.4 2.3, 2.4, 2.8
17. 8.2, 5.2, 3.2 3.2, 5.2, 8.2

Use the pictures to write your answer.

18. Order the weights of the pets from least to greatest. 3.2 kg, 7.9 kg, 9.9 kg
19. Which animals are less than 3.5 kg? Explain. turtle is less; 3.2 is to the left of 3.5 on a number line

Problem Solving

20. **Calculator** Make your calculator count by tenths. Press 0 + 0 . 1 =. Keep pressing = and see what happens. Use your calculator to find the missing numbers. 1.5, 1.6, ■, 1.8, ■, 2.0, ■. 1.7, 1.9, 2.1

More Practice Set 10.5, p. 472

357

Extra Support

Do I Hear a Decimal? *(auditory)* Students work in pairs. Each student writes a decimal number in tenths, with the whole number part no greater than 3. Each reads his or her decimal aloud, and the partner writes it down. Then they compare what they have written, discussing any differences. Repeat 5 times.

Alternate Approach

- Reteach Worksheet 10.5
- **TAB** See TE pp. 346E–346F.

Students Acquiring English

See Language Connections, Ch. 10.

Challenge

Players each toss a standard 1–6 number cube twice to create a decimal. Before making the second toss, the player must decide whether the first toss will represent the whole number or the tenth. In each round, the greater decimal wins.

Practice

Math Center Use Activity Card 57, *Dueling Decimals*, to have students practice comparing decimals greater than and less than 1.

Challenge Use Activity Card 57 and have students continue as described in Now Try This!

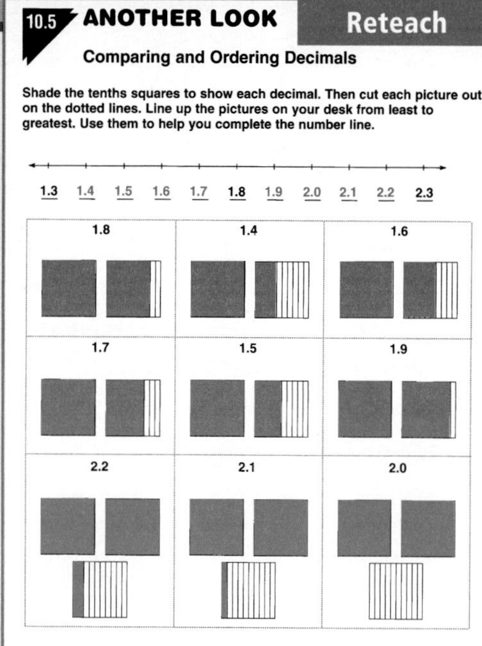

10.5 ANOTHER LOOK — Reteach

Comparing and Ordering Decimals

Shade the tenths squares to show each decimal. Then cut each picture out on the dotted lines. Line up the pictures on your desk from least to greatest. Use them to help you complete the number line.

1.3 1.4 1.5 1.6 1.7 1.8 1.9 2.0 2.1 2.2 2.3

1.8	1.4	1.6
1.7	1.5	1.9
2.2	2.1	2.0

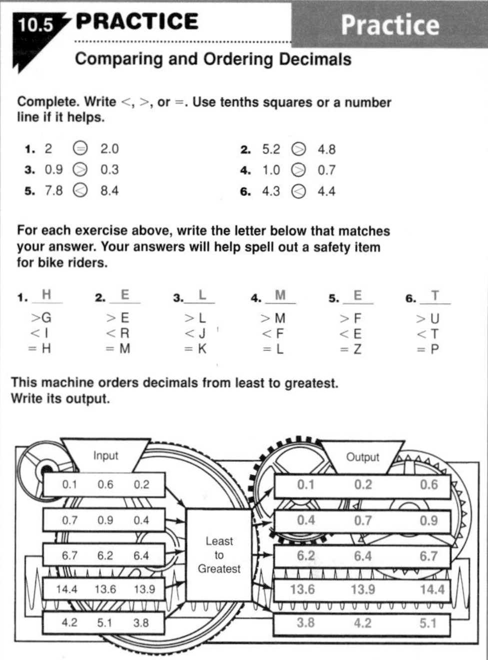

10.5 PRACTICE — Practice

Comparing and Ordering Decimals

Complete. Write <, >, or =. Use tenths squares or a number line if it helps.

1. 2 (=) 2.0
2. 5.2 (>) 4.8
3. 0.9 (>) 0.3
4. 1.0 (>) 0.7
5. 7.8 (<) 8.4
6. 4.3 (<) 4.4

For each exercise above, write the letter below that matches your answer. Your answers will help spell out a safety item for bike riders.

1. H	2. E	3. L	4. M	5. E	6. T
>G	>E	>L	>M	>F	>U
<I	<R	<J	<F	<E	<T
=H	=M	=K	=L	=Z	=P

This machine orders decimals from least to greatest. Write its output.

Input			Output		
0.1	0.6	0.2	0.1	0.2	0.6
0.7	0.9	0.4	0.4	0.7	0.9
6.7	6.2	6.4	6.2	6.4	6.7
14.4	13.6	13.9	13.6	13.9	14.4
4.2	5.1	3.8	3.8	4.2	5.1

Least to Greatest

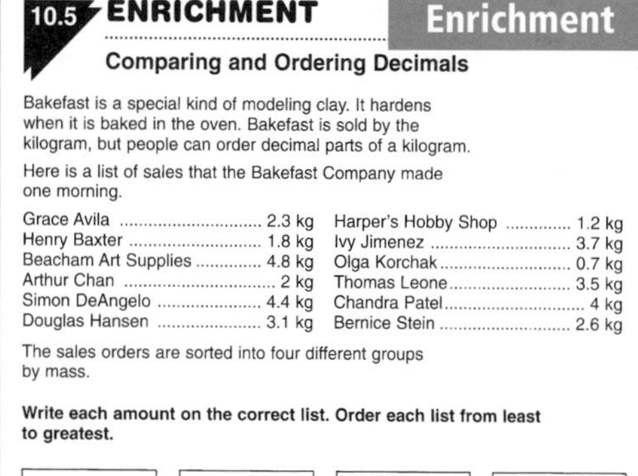

10.5 ENRICHMENT — Enrichment

Comparing and Ordering Decimals

Bakefast is a special kind of modeling clay. It hardens when it is baked in the oven. Bakefast is sold by the kilogram, but people can order decimal parts of a kilogram.

Here is a list of sales that the Bakefast Company made one morning.

Grace Avila	2.3 kg	Harper's Hobby Shop	1.2 kg
Henry Baxter	1.8 kg	Ivy Jimenez	3.7 kg
Beacham Art Supplies	4.8 kg	Olga Korchak	0.7 kg
Arthur Chan	2 kg	Thomas Leone	3.5 kg
Simon DeAngelo	4.4 kg	Chandra Patel	4 kg
Douglas Hansen	3.1 kg	Bernice Stein	2.6 kg

The sales orders are sorted into four different groups by mass.

Write each amount on the correct list. Order each list from least to greatest.

Up to 1.9 kg	From 2.0 kg to 2.9 kg	From 3.0 kg to 3.9 kg	From 4.0 kg to 4.9 kg
0.7 kg	2 kg	3.1 kg	4 kg
1.2 kg	2.3 kg	3.5 kg	4.4 kg
1.8 kg	2.6 kg	3.7 kg	4.8 kg

Use what you have learned to answer each question.

1. The company charges $1.50 for postage for all amounts from 1.5 kg up to 2.5 kg. Which amounts from the list can be mailed for $1.50? Write them in order from *greatest to least*. 2.3 kg, 2 kg, and 1.8 kg
2. What is the greatest amount that is less than 4.5 kg? 4.4 kg

Activity

Planning at a Glance

Objective To explore and write decimals to hundredths using hundredths squares

Materials hundredths squares (TR20)

Optional Resources

- Reteach 10.6; Practice 10.6; Enrichment 10.6
- Daily Cumul. Review, p. 135
- Math Center: Act. Card 58
- Every Day Counts
- TAB, TE pp. 346E–346F, 346J
- Problem of the Day, 135, p. 68; Flip Chart, p. 68a

MATHKEYS *Unlocking Fractions and Decimals 3–6*, Level 3, Activity 16

Students Acquiring English

Explain that a quilt is a kind of blanket made by sewing layers of fabric together. Point out that *quilt* can be used as a verb; in its *-ed* form it can be used as an adjective. Let students make up sentences using *quilt* as a noun and an adjective.

Problem of the Day

Use the digits 0, 2, 4, 6, and 8. You may repeat digits. You do not have to use all the digits. Write the following decimals: a decimal less than half, a decimal between 0.4 and 1, a decimal less than 3, and a decimal close to 5.

one possible set of answers: 0.2, 0.6, 2.6, 4.8

Cooperative Learning Checklist

- ☑ Work alone.
- ☑ Work with a partner.
- ☐ Work with a group.

LESSON 6

Hundredths

Getting Started

What You'll Need:
- hundredths squares

Quilting is a popular tradition in many parts of the world. Skilled quilters, like the women in the picture, make these large covers for the cold winters.

Activity

Make a Decimal Model

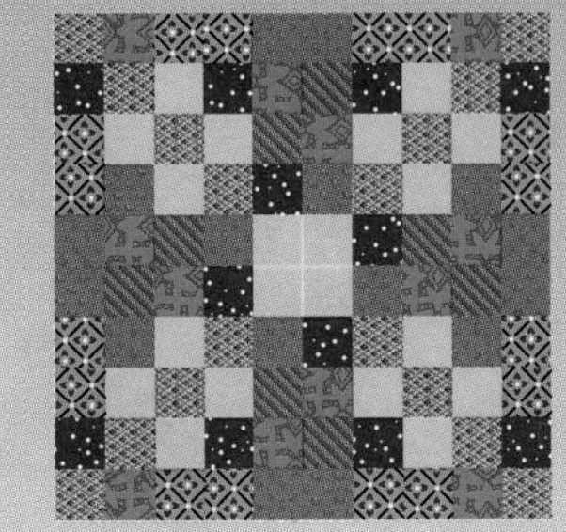

- This quilt is divided into 100 equal parts
- Of the 100 parts, only 20 parts are yellow. So, $\frac{20}{100}$ of the quilt is yellow.
- You can write this fraction as a decimal.

$\frac{20}{100} = 0.20$

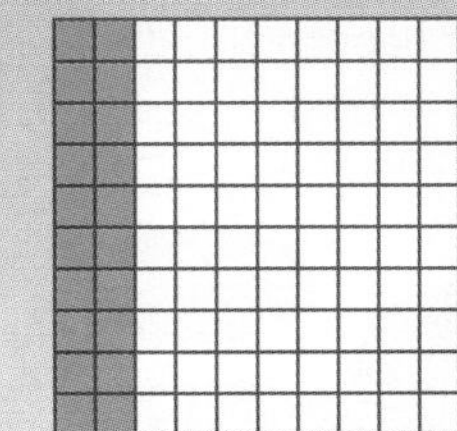

- Read this decimal as twenty hundredths.
- Color in a hundredths square to show 0.20. Shade 20 parts.

358 Chapter 10

1 Introduce

Explore **Use a penny, a dime, and a dollar to explore place value. Lead up to such questions as: What is a penny a tenth part of? What is it a hundredth part of?**

Teach: Activity

Emphasize these points:

- A decimal in hundredths is like a fraction with 100 in the denominator.
- You write hundredths in two places to the right of a decimal point.
- To order hundredths, first compare the tenths, then the hundredths.

Modeling Model money amounts. Ask:

- How many hundredths of a dollar is 20¢? 20 hundredths How many is 37¢? 37 hundredths

2 Develop

Common Error Students may confuse tens and tenths, hundreds and hundredths. Emphasize the *-th* spelling for places to the right of the decimal point. See also Analyzing Errors, TE pp. 373A and 373B.

Show What You Know!

- For exercises 5–10, allow students to use a number line if it helps.
- Call on students to show and explain their answers for exercises 11–14.
- Ask students to discuss their reasoning for estimation exercises 17–20. Point out that 0.01 is very close to 0, and that 0.99 is very close to 1. Did they need to use a number line?

3 Summarize

- Remind students that the first digit to the right of a decimal point shows tenths and the second digit shows hundredths.
- Ask students to explain the relationship between decimal hundredths and fractions with 100 in the denominator.

Ongoing Assessment Kim swam 0.19 km, Yuri swam 0.45 km, and Carin swam 0.42 km. Who swam the farthest? Yuri

Math Journal: ***Communicating***

Is 0.14 closer to 0.1 or 0.2? How do you know? It is closer to 0.1, because it is less than halfway between 0.1 and 0.2.

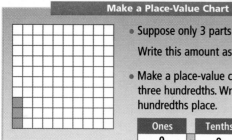

Make a Place-Value Chart

- Suppose only 3 parts are yellow. Write this amount as $\frac{3}{100}$ or 0.03.
- Make a place-value chart to show three hundredths. Write 3 in the hundredths place.

Ones		Tenths	Hundredths
0	•	0	3

Show What You Know!

Write the decimal.

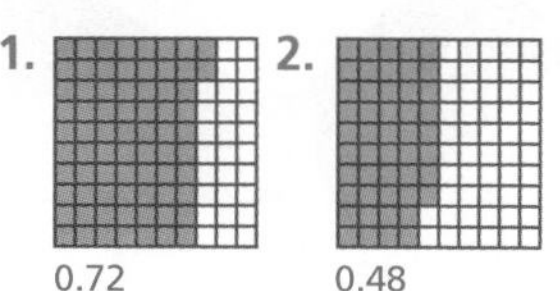

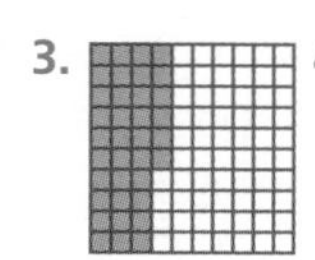

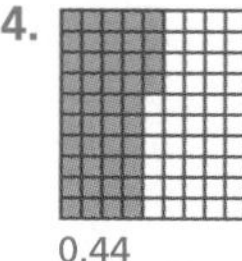

1. 0.72 2. 0.48 3. 0.36 4. 0.44

5. $\frac{70}{100}$ 0.70 6. $\frac{12}{100}$ 0.12 7. $\frac{56}{100}$ 0.56 8. $\frac{5}{100}$ 0.05

9. four hundredths 0.04 10. fifty hundredths 0.50

Color in a hundredths square to show each decimal. See Additional Answers.

11. 0.12 12. 0.32 13. 0.67 14. 0.06

15. Suppose you shaded 24 parts of a hundredths square. Write a decimal for the number of parts you shaded. 0.24

16. **Critical Thinking** Suppose you shaded 5 columns of a hundredths square. How many hundredths of the whole did you shade? 50 hundredths

Estimation Is the number closer to 0.01 or to 0.99? How do you know? Explanations will vary.

17. 0.03 0.01 18. 0.87 0.99 19. 0.12 0.01 20. 0.45 0.01

Mixed Review **Write the fraction or mixed number.**

21. seven tenths $\frac{7}{10}$ 22. five eighths $\frac{5}{8}$ 23. one and three fourths $1\frac{3}{4}$

More Practice Set 10.6, p. 473

Meeting Individual Needs

Extra Support

Decimal Spotting *(visual)* Ask students to find and cut out from newspapers or magazines two examples of decimals to hundredths, only one of which can be a money amount. Have pairs of students show their numbers using a number line and hundredths squares.

Alternate Approach

- Reteach Worksheet 10.6
- **TAB** See TE pp. 346E–346F.
- **TAB** See TE p. 346J, "Order, Order."

Students Acquiring English

See Language Connections, Ch. 10.

Challenge

Have each student write a word problem using the following information. Then have them trade problems and solve.

- 0.35 kg of apples
- 0.42 kg of pears
- 0.13 kg of plums

Practice

Math Center Use Activity Card 58, *Decimal Lineup*, to practice comparing decimals.

Challenge Use Activity Card 58 and have students continue as described in Now Try This!

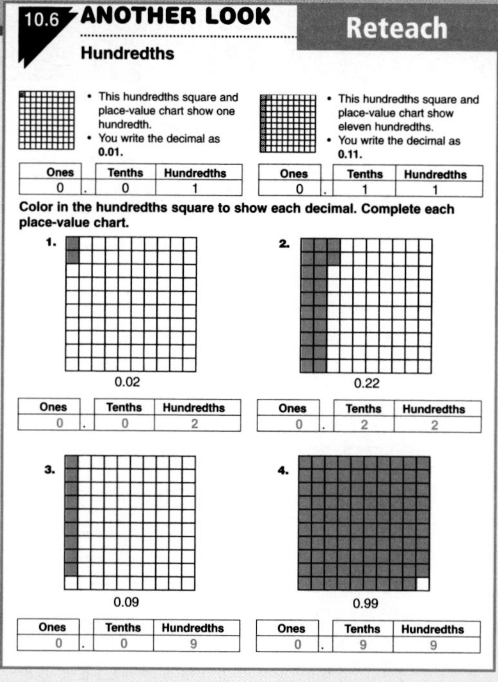

10.6 ANOTHER LOOK — **Reteach**

Hundredths

- This hundredths square and place-value chart show one hundredth.
- You write the decimal as **0.01.**

Ones		Tenths	Hundredths
0	.	0	1

- This hundredths square and place-value chart show eleven hundredths.
- You write the decimal as **0.11.**

Ones		Tenths	Hundredths
0	.	1	1

Color in the hundredths square to show each decimal. Complete each place-value chart.

1. 0.02

Ones		Tenths	Hundredths
0	.	0	2

2. 0.22

Ones		Tenths	Hundredths
0	.	2	2

3. 0.09

Ones		Tenths	Hundredths
0	.	0	9

4. 0.99

Ones		Tenths	Hundredths
0	.	9	9

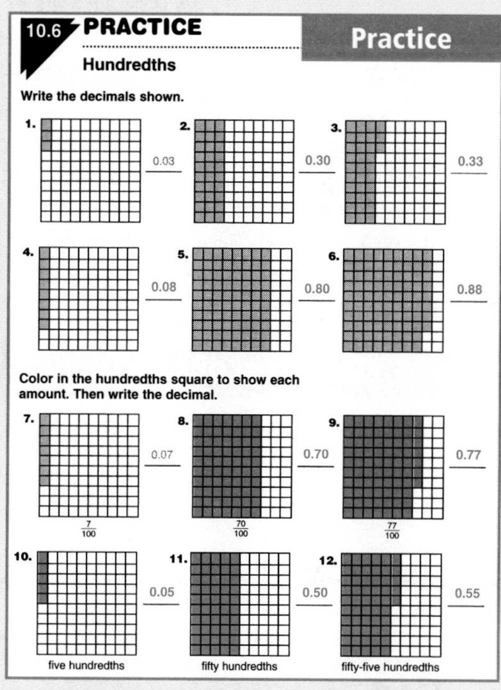

10.6 PRACTICE — **Practice**

Hundredths

Write the decimals shown.

1. 0.03 2. 0.30 3. 0.33

4. 0.08 5. 0.80 6. 0.88

Color in the hundredths square to show each amount. Then write the decimal.

7. $\frac{7}{100}$ 0.07 8. $\frac{70}{100}$ 0.70 9. $\frac{77}{100}$ 0.77

10. five hundredths 0.05 11. fifty hundredths 0.50 12. fifty-five hundredths 0.55

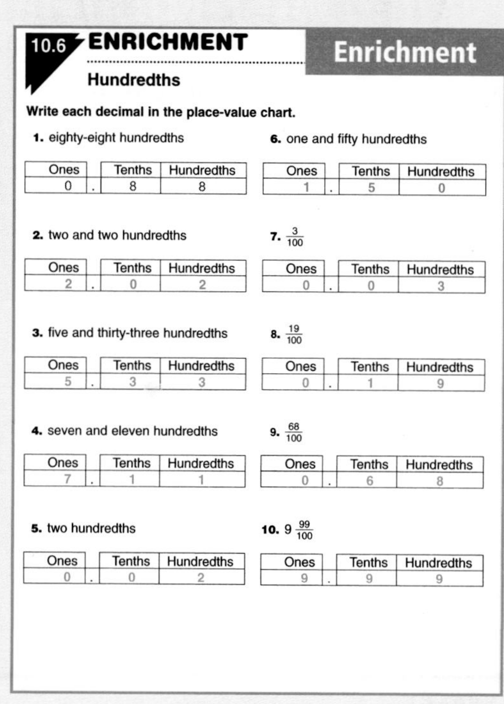

10.6 ENRICHMENT — **Enrichment**

Hundredths

Write each decimal in the place-value chart.

1. eighty-eight hundredths

Ones		Tenths	Hundredths
0	.	8	8

2. two and two hundredths

Ones		Tenths	Hundredths
2	.	0	2

3. five and thirty-three hundredths

Ones		Tenths	Hundredths
5	.	3	3

4. seven and eleven hundredths

Ones		Tenths	Hundredths
7	.	1	1

5. two hundredths

Ones		Tenths	Hundredths
0	.	0	2

6. one and fifty hundredths

Ones		Tenths	Hundredths
1	.	5	0

7. $\frac{3}{100}$

Ones		Tenths	Hundredths
0	.	0	3

8. $\frac{19}{100}$

Ones		Tenths	Hundredths
0	.	1	9

9. $\frac{68}{100}$

Ones		Tenths	Hundredths
0	.	6	8

10. $9\frac{99}{100}$

Ones		Tenths	Hundredths
9	.	9	9

Problem Solving

Planning at a Glance

Objective To decide and to justify why an answer is reasonable

Materials none

Optional Resources

- Daily Cumul. Review, p. 136
- Math Center: Project Card
- Every Day Counts
- TAB, TE p. 346E–346F, 436J
- Problem of the Day, 136, p. 68; Flip Chart, p. 68b
- Reteach, Practice, and Enrichment Worksheets for Lesson 10.7

Unlocking Fractions and Decimals 3–6, Level 3, Activity 16

Students Acquiring English

Point out the wingspan of an airplane in a picture. Then invite a volunteer to point out the wingspan of a bird in a picture. Explain that *wingspan* is a word made up of two words: *wing* and *span*, which means the space between two points. Point out that *span* is also a verb. Have students use span in a sentence, such as *The bridge spans the river.*

Problem of the Day

If you only move to the right and up, how many different paths can you find that join points A and B?
10 paths

LESSON 7

Problem Solving

Is the Answer Reasonable?

Is the Answer Reasonable

Ask Yourself:

- Did I answer the question?
- Did I calculate correctly?
- Is the answer labeled with the right units?
- Does my answer need to be rounded to a whole number to make sense?

You want to compare the wingspans of the airplane and the stork. Which wingspan is greater?

You Decide

- There are more digits in the airplane's measurement than in the stork's. Does that mean the airplane's wingspan is greater? Why or why not? no; The second digit is tenths.
- Can you use what you know about comparing decimals to help answer the question? Explain. yes; 4 m > 1.7 m, so the stork's wingspan is larger.

Work It Out!

Decide if the answer is reasonable. Explain.

1. *Silver Bullet*, the world's smallest jet, has a wing span of 5.2 m. The large albatross has a wingspan of 3.7 m. Which has the greater wingspan? (Answer: The jet has the greater wingspan.) reasonable; 5.2 > 3.7
2. *Baby Bird* is a small airplane with a wingspan of about 190 cm. Is it greater than or less than the 1.7-m wingspan of *Bumble Bee Two*? (Answer: Baby Bird's wingspan is greater than Bumblebee Two's.) not reasonable; 2 > 1.7

Share Your Thinking

3. What can you do to make sure that your answers are reasonable? Answers will vary. Possible answer: think about tenths squares or a number line

360 Chapter 10

---

1 Introduce

Prior Knowledge **Ask, Which is greater, 1.9 or 3?** 3

Teach: You Decide

Emphasize this point:

- Think about the things you are comparing when deciding whether the numbers used to describe them make sense.

Modeling Model this example: In a restaurant, you order a hamburger for $4.50, french fries for $1.75, and a drink for $1. Your bill comes to $13.25.

Ask:

- Does the bill make sense?
- How can you tell without adding the numbers?

2 Develop

Work It Out!

- Have students discuss their answers to exercises 1–2. Ask them to describe the strategies they used to determine whether numbers made sense.
- Discuss students' answers to exercise 3.

Basic Facts Just the Facts, Basic Facts Workshop 10, p. 117

Using Reading Strategies Encourage students to use the Monitor strategy as they read the Problem Solving exercises. Ask them to share their understanding with the class. See TE p. 346J.

3 Summarize

- Have students summarize ways they can tell whether their answers make sense.

Ongoing Assessment You travel 3 miles each day to get to school. Your friend travels 1.9 miles each day. She remarks that she has to go farther than you do to get to school. Is she right? No; 1.9 is less than 3.

Math Journal: *Communicating*

Why is it important to decide whether numbers make sense? Answers will vary; students should indicate that deciding whether a number makes sense is a way to check whether they have solved a problem correctly.

Problem Solving Workshop

Does It Make Sense?

Review

30 minutes

Use with page 360.

Does the Answer Make Sense?

Management teacher directed; partners and whole class

- Have students predict whether their "wingspan"—the width of their reach when they spread their arms—is greater than, equal to, or less than their height.
- Invite partners to measure each other's "wingspan." Students record measurements to the nearest 0.01 meter on a chart on the board.
- Share some true and false statements about the measurements, such as "Jessica's reach is the longest in the class." Ask the class to decide whether your statements make sense and why.
- Discuss how students' knowledge about numbers, decimals, and units of measure helps them decide if the statements make sense.
- Encourage volunteers to use the information on the board to make more true or false statements for the class to evaluate.

Activity

20 minutes

Use with page 360.

Does the Answer Make Cents?

Management small groups
Materials play money and store catalogs for each group

- One student from each group chooses some bills and coins from the play money, then displays them on the desk.
- The student then thinks of a true or false statement about the play money and something they would like to purchase from the catalog, and shares the statement with the group. One example might be, "I have $5.62. I don't have enough money to buy a video game."

- Other students in the group decide if the statement makes sense or not.
- Students take turns choosing money and making statements to be assessed by the group.

Chapter 10

Basic Facts Workshop

Use with Lesson 10.7

Multiplying by 9

See also *Just the Facts*
- Support Masters
- Practice Worksheets
- Cumulative Practice

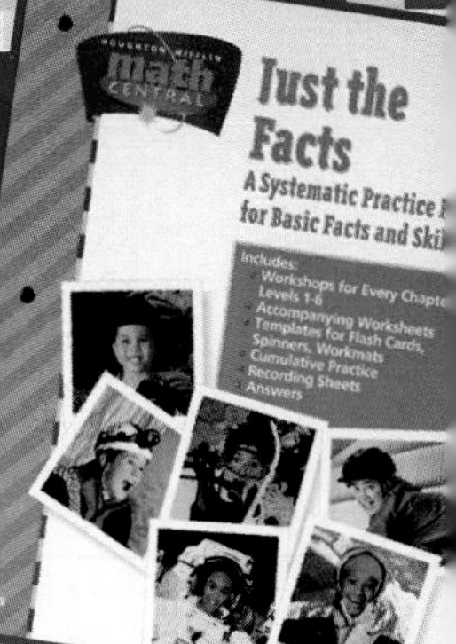

Review

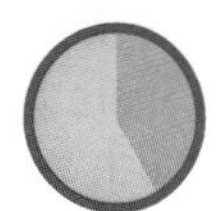

25 minutes

Think Ten to Learn Nines

Management whole class
Materials overhead projector; **Just the Facts** Support Master 7 (hundredths square) on p. 288; See also Practice 10A–10B on pp. 138–139 for use with Lessons 10.9, 10.11.

- Draw four 2 × 5 rectangles on a grid transparency to make ten-frames. Ask students how many squares are in 4 tens. 40
- Draw 9 dots in each ten-frame to model the multiplication fact 4 × 9. Ask the class how much less 4 × 9 is than 40. It is 4 less Then, ask students for the answer to 4 × 9. 4 less than 40, or 36

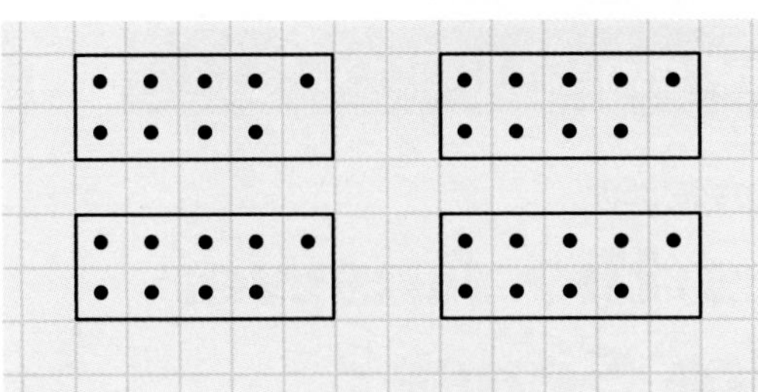

- Ask students why using the strategy of thinking about tens is a good way to help with 9's facts. It's easy to multiply by 10 and then subtract.
- Repeat the activity, modeling 3 × 9, 6 × 9, 5 × 9, and 2 × 9.
- Turn off the projector, and ask students to visualize ten-frames. Have them use tens to find the products for these multiplication facts: 7 × 9, 8 × 9, and 9 × 9.

Practice

30 minutes

Make ×9 Flash Cards

Management individuals, then pairs
Materials for each student: 6 index cards; **Just the Facts** Support Masters 10, 14 (practice minutes, certificate) on pp. 291, 295; See also Practice 10A–10B on pp. 138–139 for use with Lessons 10.9, 10.11.

- Distribute index cards and have students make flash cards like the ones shown for the following facts: 7 × 9, 9 × 7, 8 × 9, 9 × 8, 9 × 9, and 9 × 5.
- When students complete their flash cards, have them add in the 9's cards they have already made. Then, have them practice multiplying by 9 with partners.
- Encourage students to take all of their flash cards home for additional practice. Remind them to keep a record of the number of minutes they work at home. Students may return completed records to school in exchange for a certificate.

Midchapter Review

for Pages 346–360

Problem Solving

Use any strategy to solve the problem. Show your work. (page 354)

1. For a trip, you pack a red shirt, a blue shirt, jeans, tan pants, a black hat, and a white hat. How many outfits can you make? 8 outfits
2. You have grape juice, apple juice, cherry, and peach. If you mix 3 juices in equal amounts, how many combinations can you make? 4 combinations

Concepts

Fill in the chart. Use tenths squares to help you. (page 348)

	Fraction	Decimal	Word Form	Is it closer to 0 or 1?	
3.	?	?	four tenths	0	$\frac{4}{10}$, 0.4
4.	?	0.8	?	?	$\frac{8}{10}$, eight tenths, 1
5.	?	?	one tenth	?	$\frac{1}{10}$, 0.1, 0

Write the decimal. (page 350)

6. $4\frac{9}{10}$ 4.9
7.  1.7
8. 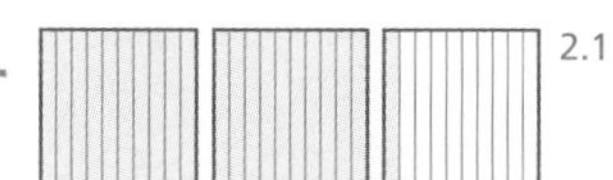 2.1

Skills

Write the decimal. (page 352)

9.

Ones		Tenths
2	•	9

2.9

10.

Ones		Tenths
0	•	4

0.4

11. five and six tenths 5.6
12. 7 tenths 0.7
13. $\frac{9}{10}$ 0.9
14. $\frac{6}{10}$ 0.6

Write >, <, or =. (page 356)

15. 0.8 ● 0.3 >
16. 6.1 ● 6.2 <
17. 0.2 ● 0.9 <
18. 0.4 ● 0.2 >

Write the decimals in order from least to greatest. (page 356)

19. 1.5, 1.0, 1.1 1.0, 1.1, 1.5
20. 6.5, 5.6, 0.6 0.6, 5.6, 6.5

361

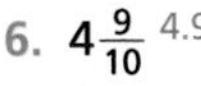

Meeting Individual Needs

Students Acquiring English

Some students may need assistance on the Midchapter Review.

- Be prepared to read directions aloud to students.
- Focus special attention on word problems. Expect to paraphrase, diagram, or draw an explanation of the word problem.
- Review important vocabulary words that have been previously introduced.

Additional Assessment Resources

Test, Practice, Management Program

Use the *Test, Practice, Management Program* to create, administer, and score tests as well as generate practice sets. Questions are correlated to the Lesson Objectives.

Chapter 10 Midchapter Review

Scoring Chart

Item	Points
1–2	8 points each
3–8	6 points each
9–20	4 points each
TOTAL	100 points or 100%

Problem Solving

Give from 0 to 8 points per answer, based on how well students meet the following criteria:

Problem 1

- Information is organized to show that 8 different outfits can be made.

Problem 2

- Information is organized to show that 4 different juice combinations can be made.

Concepts and Skills

If students are having difficulty in particular areas, use the appropriate Reteaching Worksheets listed below.

- 76 Writing Decimals from Tenths Squares, p. 212
- 77 Writing Decimals from Words and Fractions, p. 213
- 78 Counting with Decimals, p. 214
- 79 Comparing Decimals, p. 215
- 80 Ordering Decimals, p. 216

Common Error Alert

If students are making frequent errors, see Analyzing Errors, TE pp. 373A–373B.

Item Analysis

Item	Objectives
1–2	To use Make a List and other strategies to solve problems (10F)
3–5	To explore and model decimals in tenths (10A)
6–8	To relate decimals in tenths to fractions and mixed numbers in tenths (10B)
9–14	To read and write a decimal in word, table, and standard forms (10C)
15–20	To compare and order decimals using models (10D)

Math World

Why 10?

Background Even into the 20th century, some cultures had words for only three counting concepts: one, two, and "many." Counting beyond two was an abstract idea, done by matching sets of objects. This concept, of course, is quite different from binary arithmetic, the base-2 system used in computers.

Critical Thinking Ask:

- Why do you think we ended up with a number system based on 10? Why does it work so well?

Decimals Around the World

Math World

Learn about early number systems, math on the radio, and how decimals can be used to organize information.

Why 10?

We use a number system with 10 digits. All of our numbers are made from 0, 1, 2, 3, 4, 5, 6, 7, 8, and 9. The first number systems only had two digits. Later systems had 5, 12, and 20 digits. The Babylonians used a system with 60 symbols! But, a system with 10 digits seems best for counting. Why do you think this is true?

Tune In to Decimals

People all over the world use decimals every time they turn on the radio. In most countries, the radio dial for FM stations uses numbers with tenths. Does this radio dial use decimals? Are they in order on the number line?

88.1 91.3 94 103 104.5 108 FM
1000 1020.2 1100 1250 1300 AM

362

For More Information

Word Origins

binary

From the Late Latin *binarius*, "made up of two," from the Latin *bini*, "two at a time."

We use binary numbers for coding computers because the tiny switches inside computers can be in only two positions: on or off.

Discuss with students the different jobs for which we use computers.

Literature

Make It Graphic!: Drawing Graphs for Science and Social Studies Projects
J. Messner, 1985
Eve Stwertka

Mapping a Changing World
Thomasson-Grant, 1995
Yvette LaPierre

Marvelously Meaningful Maps
Barrons, 1992
Madilyn Carlisle

The Raintree Illustrated Science Encyclopedia
Raintree Steck-Vaughn Library, 1991

Turning in the Sounds of Radio
Silver Burdett, 1993
Eve Stwertka

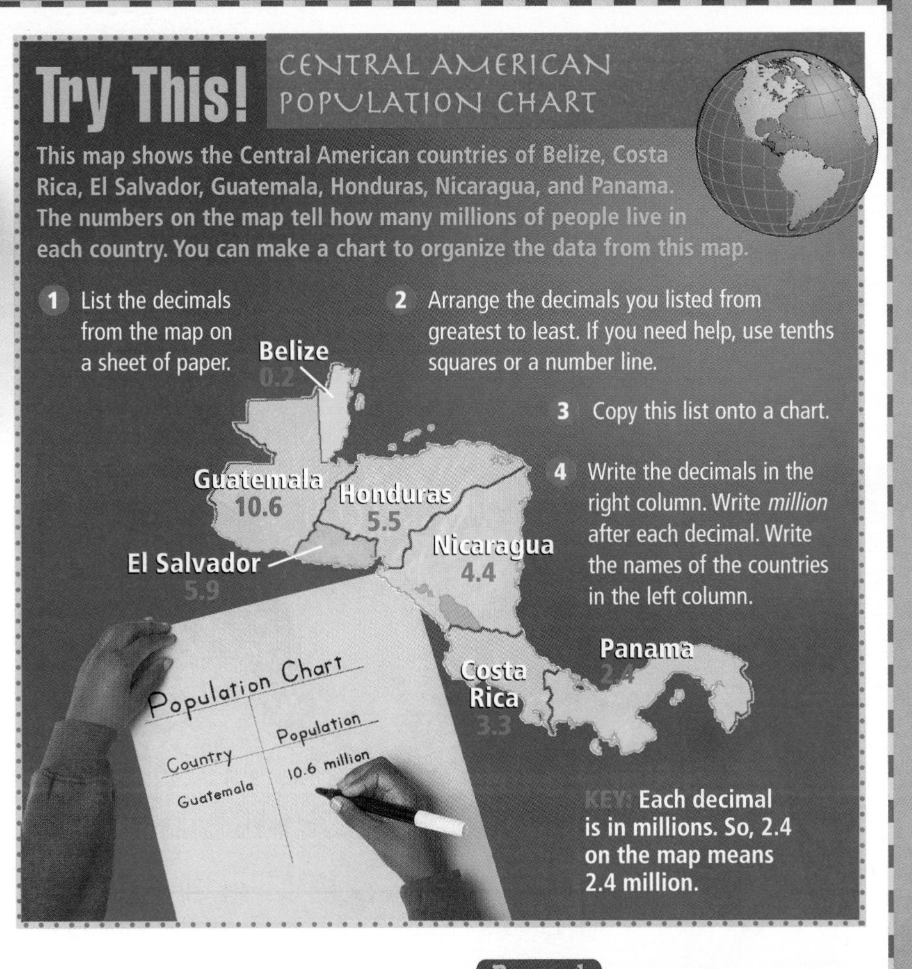

Try This! CENTRAL AMERICAN POPULATION CHART

This map shows the Central American countries of Belize, Costa Rica, El Salvador, Guatemala, Honduras, Nicaragua, and Panama. The numbers on the map tell how many millions of people live in each country. You can make a chart to organize the data from this map.

1. List the decimals from the map on a sheet of paper.
2. Arrange the decimals you listed from greatest to least. If you need help, use tenths squares or a number line.
3. Copy this list onto a chart.
4. Write the decimals in the right column. Write *million* after each decimal. Write the names of the countries in the left column.

Comma Sense

What do you notice about this radio station logo? It has a decimal comma instead of a decimal point. In many parts of South America, this is how people write all decimals.

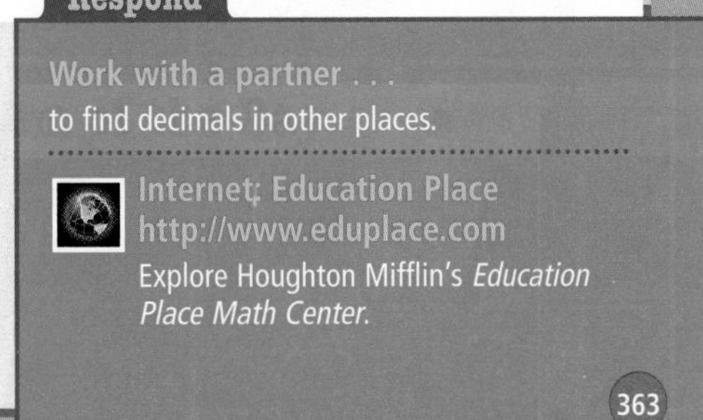

Respond

Work with a partner . . . to find decimals in other places.

Internet: Education Place
http://www.eduplace.com
Explore Houghton Mifflin's *Education Place Math Center.*

363

Tune In to Decimals

Background The decimal number identifying a radio station is a measure of how many times the radio wave that carries the station's signal vibrates in one second. The frequency of an FM station is measured in *megahertz* (MHz). A frequency of 96.1 means that the station produces a wave that vibrates 96,100,000 times per second. An AM station's frequency is measured in *kilohertz* (KHz). A frequency of 710 means that the station produces a wave that vibrates 710,000 times per second.

Activity: *Radio Decimals*

Have students list their favorite radio stations and their frequency numbers. Then have them write the number of times each second that each station's wave vibrates.

Central American Population Chart

Background Population data is an ideal way to reinforce concepts of place value and working with decimal numbers.

Activity: *Population Computation*

After students have completed Try This!:

- Ask students to use the data to write a problem involving adding or subtracting decimals. They can exchange problems with a partner, and solve.

Technology

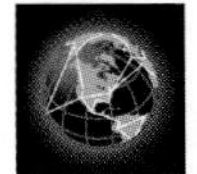

Internet: Education Place
http://www.eduplace.com
Houghton Mifflin Education Place **Mathematics Center** provides teacher and student support, such as links to other Internet sites.

Ultimate Writing & Creativity Center
Students can use the *Ultimate Writing & Creativity Center* for all their writing and publishing activities.

Kid to Kid

Project Ask students what they think Central American children learn in school. How could they share what they do with Central American students?

Suggest:

- *Remind students that most people in Central America speak Spanish. You could exchange pictures showing school activities.*
- *You could make a class tape with a greeting and music to exchange with children in Central America.*

Students could contact education agencies in Central American countries to find out how to do this.

Activity

Planning at a Glance

Objective To use a tenths model to investigate how to add and subtract decimals in tenths

Materials grid paper or number line paper (TR2, TR13)

Optional Resources

- Reteach 10.8; Practice 10.8; Enrichment 10.8
- Daily Cumul. Review, p. 137
- Math Center: How-To Card 37
- Every Day Counts
- **TAB**, TE pp. 346E–346F, 346J
- **Problem of the Day**, 137, p. 69; Flip Chart, p. 69b

MATHKEYS

Unlocking Fractions and Decimals 3–6, Level 3, Activity 17

Students Acquiring English

Elicit the verb *to jump* from students by sketching a small stream and asking how they would cross it without a bridge. Then create a number line on the board and ask a volunteer to demonstrate jumping ahead and jumping back on the number line.

Problem of the Day

Find the smallest number you can add to 123 that will give a sum whose only digits are 2's. 99

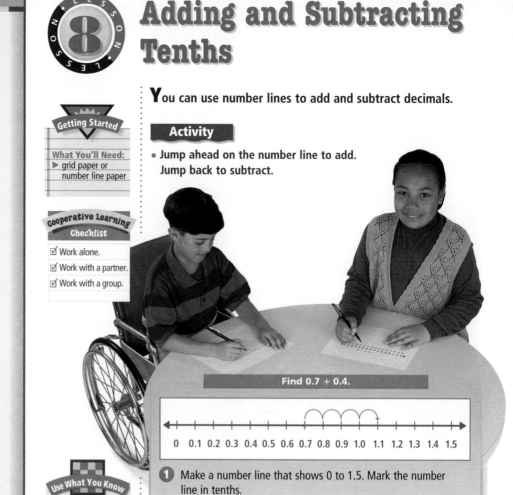

Lesson 8 Adding and Subtracting Tenths

You can use number lines to add and subtract decimals.

Getting Started

What You'll Need:
- grid paper or number line paper

Cooperative Learning Checklist

- ☑ Work alone.
- ☑ Work with a partner.
- ☑ Work with a group.

Activity

- Jump ahead on the number line to add. Jump back to subtract.

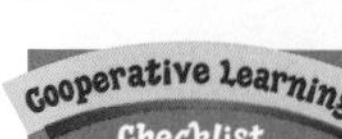

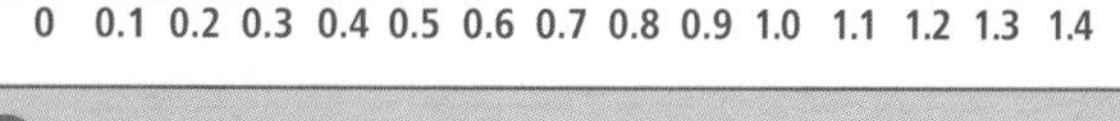

Find 0.7 + 0.4.

0 0.1 0.2 0.3 0.4 0.5 0.6 0.7 0.8 0.9 1.0 1.1 1.2 1.3 1.4 1.5

1. Make a number line that shows 0 to 1.5. Mark the number line in tenths.
2. Mark 0.7 on the line. To add 0.4, count on 4 tenths. Draw 4 arrows to show each tenth as you count. Where do you end? 1.1
3. Write an addition sentence to show the sum. 0.7 + 0.4 = 1.1
4. Use a number line to find the sum. Write the addition sentence.

   a. 0.9 + 0.5 (0.9 + 0.5 = 1.4) b. 0.2 + 0.8 (0.2 + 0.8 = 1.0) c. 0.4 + 1.0 (0.4 + 1.0 = 1.4) d. 0.5 + 0.5 (0.5 + 0.5 = 1.0)

Use What You Know

There are 10 tenths in 1 whole.

364 Chapter 10

1 Introduce

Motivate Make a number line in tenths from 0–1 on the floor using tape. Measure the tenths in "baby steps." Invite students to add and subtract tenths with their feet.

Teach: Activity

Emphasize these points:

- Move to the right to add tenths.
- Move to the left to subtract tenths.

Modeling Model a number line in tenths with a vertical arrow pointing to 0.9.

Ask:

- Do I move right or left to add 5 tenths to 9 tenths? to the right What is the sum? 1.4
- Which way to subtract 2 tenths from 9 tenths? to the left What is the difference? 0.7

2 Develop

Show What You Know!

- Guide students in counting tenths correctly along the number line.
- Remind students to move right to add and left to subtract.
- Have students discuss their answers for exercise 5.

3 Summarize

- Have students give examples of adding and subtracting tenths on a number line.

Ongoing Assessment Tim needs 2.5 meters of blue ribbon to make a costume for the school play. He has 1.3 meters. How can he find out how much more ribbon he needs to get? He can subtract 1.3 from 2.5 to find out that he needs to get 1.2 meters of ribbon.

Math Journal: *Communicating*

Explain how you would regroup tenths when adding eight tenths and seven tenths. The sum is 15 tenths, which is ten tenths plus five tenths, which is 1.5.

Find 1.5 − 0.6.

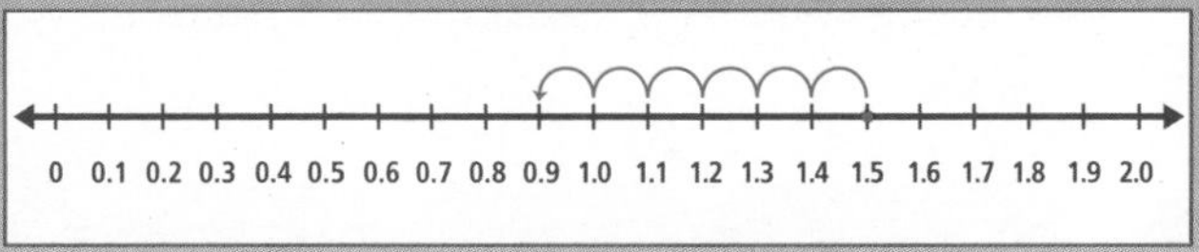

0 0.1 0.2 0.3 0.4 0.5 0.6 0.7 0.8 0.9 1.0 1.1 1.2 1.3 1.4 1.5 1.6 1.7 1.8 1.9 2.0

1. Make a number line that shows 0 to 2. Mark the number line in tenths.
2. Mark 1.5 on the line. To subtract 0.6, count back 6 tenths. Draw 6 arrows to show each tenth that you count. Where do you end? 0.9
3. Write a subtraction sentence to show the difference. 1.5 − 0.6 = 0.9
4. Make a number line to find the difference. Write the number sentence for each.

   a. 1.3 − 0.7 1.3 − 0.7 = 0.6 b. 1.0 − 0.9 1.0 − 0.9 = 0.1 c. 0.8 − 0.7 0.8 − 0.7 = 0.1 d. 1.1 − 0.9 1.1 − 0.9 = 0.2

Show What You Know!

Find the sum or difference. Then write a number sentence.

1. 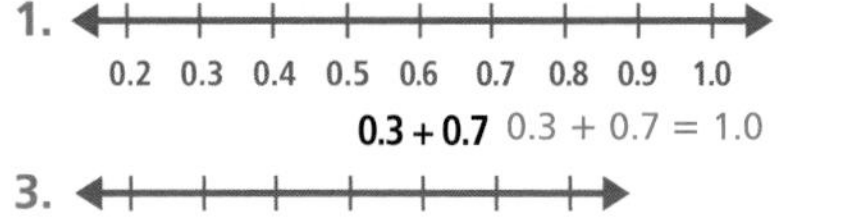
0.2 0.3 0.4 0.5 0.6 0.7 0.8 0.9 1.0
0.3 + 0.7 0.3 + 0.7 = 1.0

2. 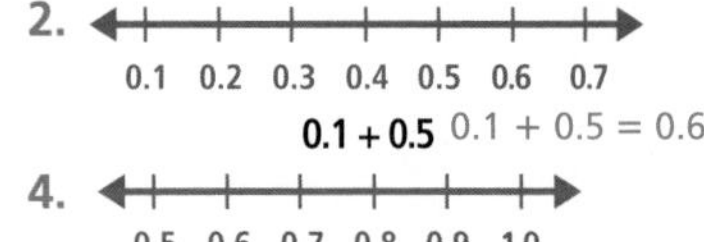
0.1 0.2 0.3 0.4 0.5 0.6 0.7
0.1 + 0.5 0.1 + 0.5 = 0.6

3. 0.9 1.0 1.1 1.2 1.3 1.4 1.5
1.4 − 0.3 1.4 − 0.3 = 1.1

4. 0.5 0.6 0.7 0.8 0.9 1.0
1.0 − 0.1 1.0 − 0.1=0.9

5. **Critical Thinking** How is adding and subtracting decimals on a number line like adding and subtracting whole numbers on a number line? How is it different? Answers will vary. Possible answer: You count to the right or left on the number line to add or subtract both decimals and whole numbers. You use different number lines.

Find each sum. Use a number line if needed.

6. 0.8 + 0.1 0.9 7. 0.5 + 0.7 1.2 8. 0.4 + 0.1 0.5 9. 1.0 + 0.2 1.2
10. 0.6 + 0.7 1.3 11. 0.2 + 0.1 0.3 12. 0.5 + 0.2 0.7 13. 0.4 + 0.6 1.0

Find each difference. Use a number line if you need to.

14. 1.2 − 0.1 1.1 15. 1.5 − 0.8 0.7 16. 1.3 − 0.9 0.4 17. 0.3 − 0.2 0.1
18. 0.1 − 0.1 0 19. 0.8 − 0.6 0.2 20. 1.5 − 1.4 0.1 21. 0.6 − 0.3 0.3

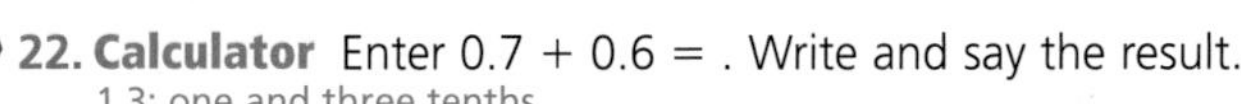

22. **Calculator** Enter 0.7 + 0.6 = . Write and say the result. 1.3; one and three tenths

Meeting Individual Needs

Extra Support

Tenths on the Line *(visual/kinesthetic)* Help pairs of students to create a number line on grid paper and use small counters, such as beans or buttons, to further explore adding and subtracting decimals in tenths. Let partners alternate posing examples and using the number line to find the sums and differences.

Alternate Approach

- Reteach Worksheet 10.8, Practice Worksheet 10.8
- **TAB** See TE p. 346E–346F.

Students Acquiring English

See Language Connections, Ch. 10.

Challenge

Write on the board: 6.3, 1.9, 3.7, 7.3. Tell students to use the decimals to answer the question: Who are we? If you add us together, our sum is 10. 6.3, 3.7

Practice

Math Center Use How-To Card 37, *Decimal Star*, to have students practice using a tenths model to investigate how to add and subtract decimals in tenths.

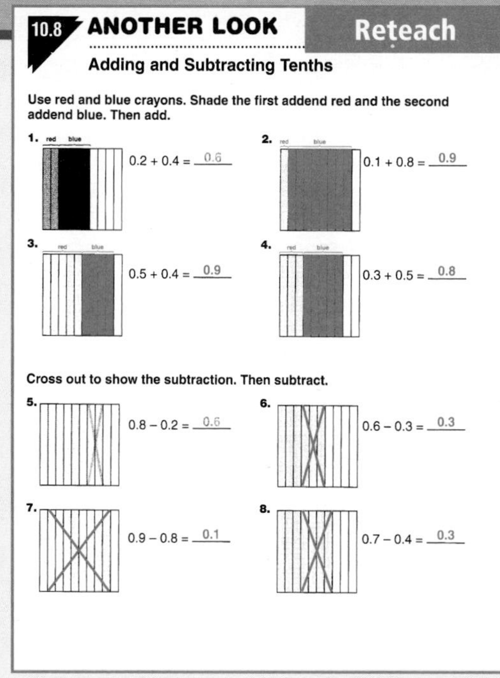

10.8 ANOTHER LOOK — **Reteach**

Adding and Subtracting Tenths

Use red and blue crayons. Shade the first addend red and the second addend blue. Then add.

1. 0.2 + 0.4 = 0.6
2. 0.1 + 0.8 = 0.9
3. 0.5 + 0.4 = 0.9
4. 0.3 + 0.5 = 0.8

Cross out to show the subtraction. Then subtract.

5. 0.8 − 0.2 = 0.6
6. 0.6 − 0.3 = 0.3
7. 0.9 − 0.8 = 0.1
8. 0.7 − 0.4 = 0.3

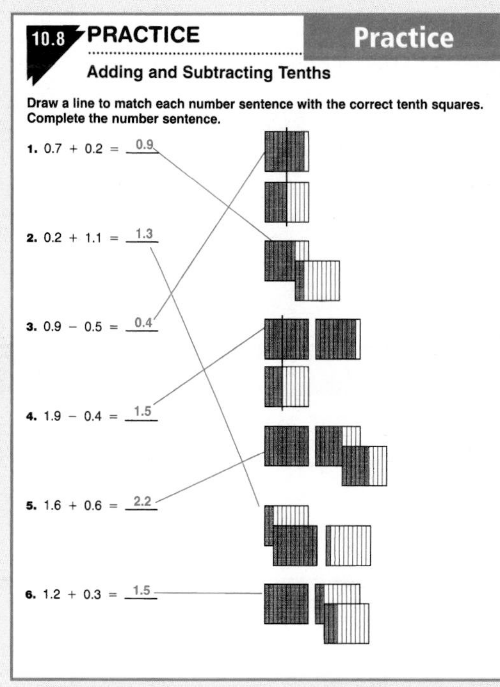

10.8 PRACTICE — **Practice**

Adding and Subtracting Tenths

Draw a line to match each number sentence with the correct tenth squares. Complete the number sentence.

1. 0.7 + 0.2 = 0.9
2. 0.2 + 1.1 = 1.3
3. 0.9 − 0.5 = 0.4
4. 1.9 − 0.4 = 1.5
5. 1.6 + 0.6 = 2.2
6. 1.2 + 0.3 = 1.5

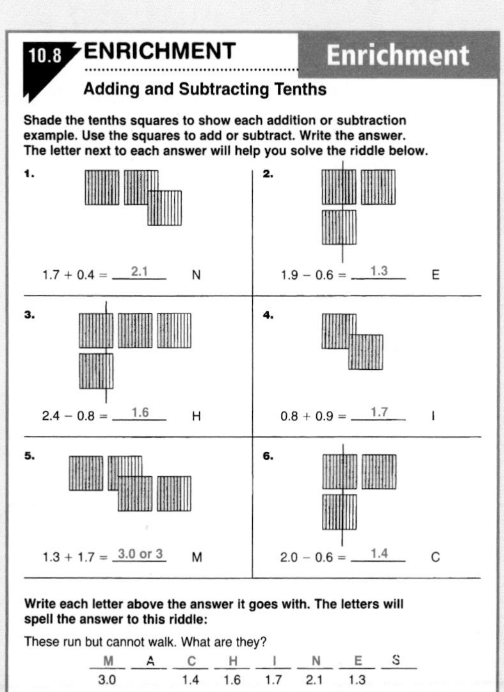

10.8 ENRICHMENT — **Enrichment**

Adding and Subtracting Tenths

Shade the tenths squares to show each addition or subtraction example. Use the squares to add or subtract. Write the answer. The letter next to each answer will help you solve the riddle below.

1. 1.7 + 0.4 = 2.1 N
2. 1.9 − 0.6 = 1.3 E
3. 2.4 − 0.8 = 1.6 H
4. 0.8 + 0.9 = 1.7 I
5. 1.3 + 1.7 = 3.0 or 3 M
6. 2.0 − 0.6 = 1.4 C

Write each letter above the answer it goes with. The letters will spell the answer to this riddle:

These run but cannot walk. What are they?

M A C H I N E S
3.0 1.4 1.6 1.7 2.1 1.3

Symbolic

Planning at a Glance

Objective To add and subtract tenths

Materials tenths squares (TR19)

Optional Resources

- Reteach 10.9; Practice 10.9; Enrichment 10.9
- Daily Cumul. Review, p. 138
- Math Center: Act. Card 59
- Every Day Counts
- **TAB**, TE pp. 346E–346F
- **Problem of the Day**, 138, p. 69; Flip Chart, p. 69b

Unlocking Fractions and Decimals 3–6, Level 3, Activity 17

Students Acquiring English

Draw a straight line on the chalkboard and elicit the word *line.* Ask several students to line up. Point out that by adding the word *up* to *line*, you get a verb meaning to arrange in a straight line. To line up numbers, they have to put the digits with the same place value in a straight line. Demonstrate. Then have students practice lining up numbers you give: 2.4 and .3, for example.

Problem of the Day

If you use at least one of each United States coin—except for a dollar coin—which ten coins give you exactly $1?
one half-dollar, 1 quarter, 1 dime, 2 nickels, and 5 pennies

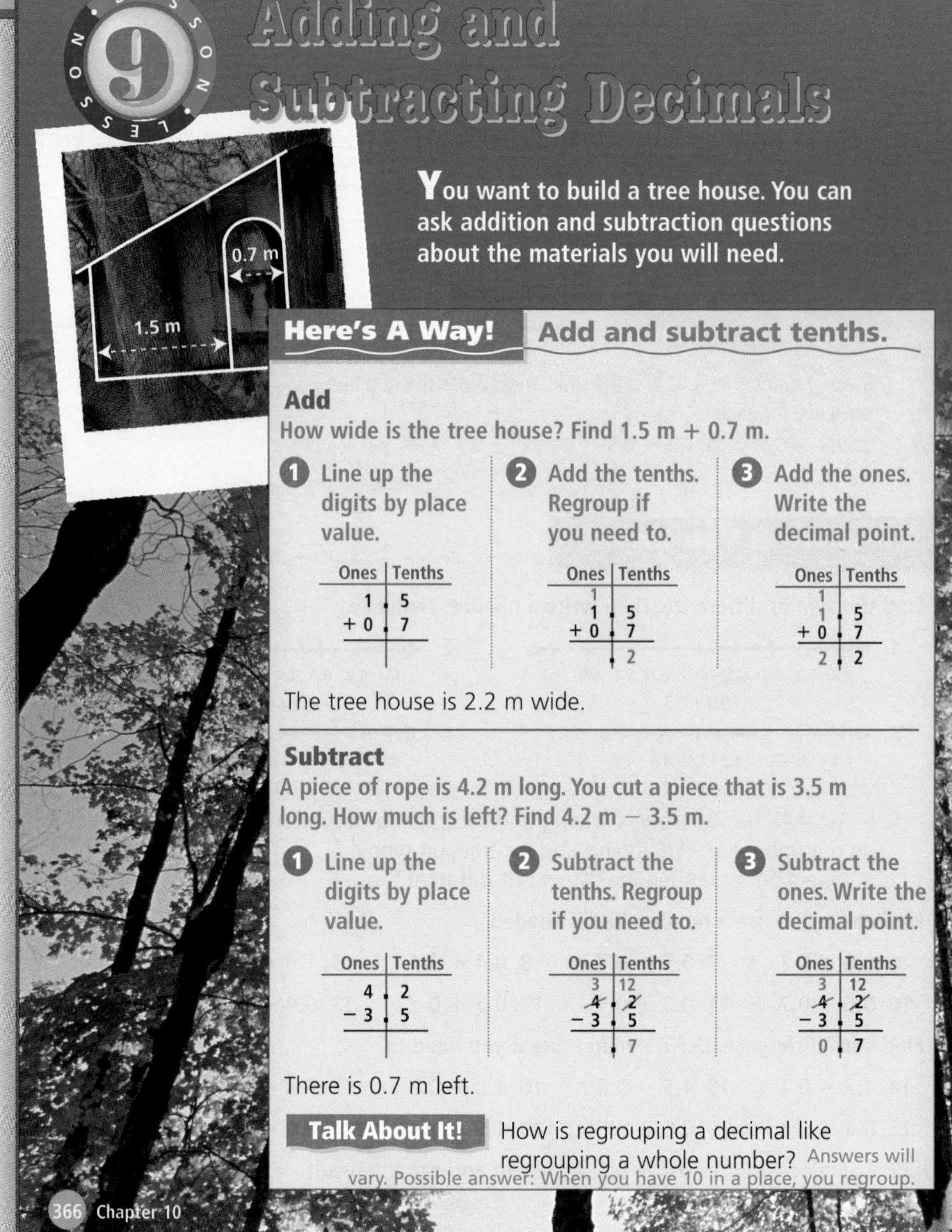

LESSON 9

Adding and Subtracting Decimals

You want to build a tree house. You can ask addition and subtraction questions about the materials you will need.

Here's A Way! Add and subtract tenths.

Add

How wide is the tree house? Find 1.5 m + 0.7 m.

1. Line up the digits by place value.
2. Add the tenths. Regroup if you need to.
3. Add the ones. Write the decimal point.

	Ones	Tenths
	1	5
+	0	7
	2	2

The tree house is 2.2 m wide.

Subtract

A piece of rope is 4.2 m long. You cut a piece that is 3.5 m long. How much is left? Find 4.2 m − 3.5 m.

1. Line up the digits by place value.
2. Subtract the tenths. Regroup if you need to.
3. Subtract the ones. Write the decimal point.

	Ones	Tenths
	~~4~~ 3	~~2~~ 12
−	3	5
	0	7

There is 0.7 m left.

Talk About It! How is regrouping a decimal like regrouping a whole number? Answers will vary. Possible answer: When you have 10 in a place, you regroup.

366 Chapter 10

Prior Knowledge Have students use or make tenths squares (TR19) to solve the following exercises.

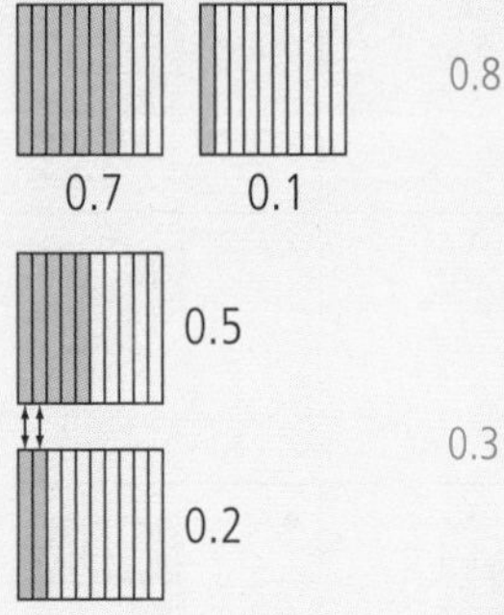

Teach: Here's A Way!

- Regroup decimals the same way as whole numbers. Twelve tenths is the same as 1 one and 2 tenths.

Show What You Know!

- Guide students in regrouping and in placing the decimal point correctly in their answers.
- Discuss with students their answers to exercise 8. Ask them to state the rule.

Work It Out!

- For exercises 14–17, remind students to line up the places correctly before they begin.
- Discuss students' answers for exercise 20. Some students may have allowed for the knot.

Using Reading Strategies Help students to use the Monitor strategy as they read the Problem Solving exercises. Have them work in pairs and discuss what each problem asks and how to answer it. See TE p. 346J.

- Remind students: 10 tenths equal 1 one.
- Ask students to discuss the mental math methods they used.
- Discuss with students what the 1 in 1.8 means. It means 1 one, or 1 whole.

Ongoing Assessment A boy ran the 100-meter dash in 13.5 seconds. If he needs to run it in 11.7 seconds to make the state competition, how much less time must he take?
1.8 seconds

Math Journal: *Communicating*

How is adding 1.2 + 3.0 like adding 12 + 30? How is it different? The digits in the sums are the same, but place values are different. The sum of 1.2 and 3.0 has a decimal point between the ones and the tenths.

Show What You Know!

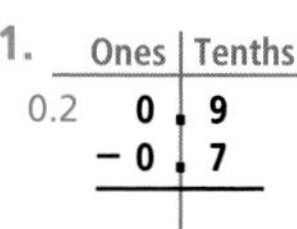

Add or subtract. Use a place-value chart to help you.

1.

	Ones	Tenths
	0 .	9
−	0 .	7

0.2

2.

	Ones	Tenths
	1 .	9
+	0 .	4

2.3

3.

	Ones	Tenths
	3 .	4
−	2 .	9

0.5

4. 0.7 + 0 0.7
5. 2.3 + 1.4 3.7
6. 2.6 − 1.8 0.8
7. 0.9 − 0 0.9
8. **Mental Math** What do you know about zero that helped you find the answer for exercises 4 and 7?
If you add or subtract zero from a number the sum or difference equals that number.

Work It Out!

Add or subtract. You may use a place-value chart to help you.

9. 4.7 + 4.8 = 9.5
10. 2.7 − 1.4 = 1.3
11. 0.4 + 0.5 = 0.9
12. 1.6 cm + 0.5 cm = 2.1 cm
13. 7.0 m − 1.4 m = 5.6 m
14. 4.5 + 2.8 7.3
15. 3.0 + 0.6 3.6
16. 1.9 − 0.6 1.3
17. 7.9 − 3.9 4.0
18. **Algebraic Reasoning** Copy and complete the tables.

a.

Number	Number + 0.5
1.0	1.5
1.5	? 2.0
2.0	? 2.5
? 2.5	3.0
3.5	? 4.0

b.

Number	Number − 1.3
6.6	5.3
5.6	? 4.3
? 4.6	3.3
2.6	1.3
? 1.6	0.3

Problem Solving

19. You have some fabric that is 3.2 m long. How much should be cut off the fabric to make it 2.5 m long?
0.7 m

20. You have ropes that are 1.6 m 1.9 m, and 2.6 m long. Which two ropes would you tie together to make a rope between 3 and 4 meters long? Explain.
the ropes measuring 1.6 m and 1.9 m

367

Meeting Individual Needs

Extra Support

By the Squares *(visual)* Have student pairs review some of the addition and subtraction exercises in this lesson by using tenths squares. Let partners discuss how they can use tenths squares to regroup.

Alternate Approach

- Reteach Worksheet 10.9, Practice Worksheet 10.9
- **TAB** See TE p. 346E–346F.

Students Acquiring English

See Language Connections, Ch. 10.

Challenge

Have student pairs add and subtract these decimals and whole numbers:

a. 12 + 0.9 12.9
b. 8 + 3.2 11.2
c. 6 − 0.2 5.8
d. 19 − 1.3 17.7
e. 7 + 2.7 9.7
f. 20 − 4.1 15.9

Have partners discuss their answers. Then have students create and exchange similar exercises.

Practice

Math Center Use Activity Card 59, *Magic Tenths Squares,* to have students practice adding and subtracting tenths.

Challenge Use Activity Card 59, and have students continue as described in Now Try This!

See **Just the Facts** Practice 10A, p. 138.

10.9 ANOTHER LOOK — Reteach

Adding and Subtracting Decimals

When you add or subtract decimals, be sure to line up the decimals by place value.

	Ones		Tenths
	(1)		
	1	.	4
+	0	.	7
	2	.	1

	Ones		Tenths
	(0)		(16)
	1	.	6
−	0	.	9
	0	.	7

Add.

1. 3.5 + 2.4 = 5.9
2. 6.1 + 0.7 = 6.8
3. 8.5 + 0.3 = 8.8
4. (1) 7.9 + 1.3 = 9.2
5. (1) 5.2 + 3.8 = 9.0
6. (1) 4.6 + 9.5 = 14.1

Subtract.

7. 3.7 − 2.6 = 1.1
8. 4.9 − 4.6 = 0.3
9. 8.2 − 6.1 = 2.1
10. (4) (13) 5.3 − 2.7 = 2.6
11. (8) (14) 9.4 − 3.6 = 5.8
12. (6) (18) 7.8 − 5.9 = 1.9

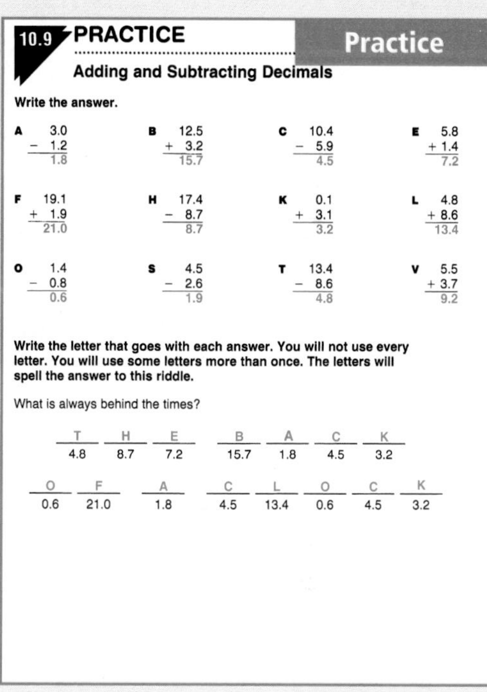

10.9 PRACTICE — Practice

Adding and Subtracting Decimals

Write the answer.

A 3.0 − 1.2 = 1.8
B 12.5 + 3.2 = 15.7
C 10.4 − 5.9 = 4.5
E 5.8 + 1.4 = 7.2
F 19.1 + 1.9 = 21.0
H 17.4 − 8.7 = 8.7
K 0.1 + 3.1 = 3.2
L 4.8 + 8.6 = 13.4
O 1.4 − 0.8 = 0.6
S 4.5 − 2.6 = 1.9
T 13.4 − 8.6 = 4.8
V 5.5 + 3.7 = 9.2

Write the letter that goes with each answer. You will not use every letter. You will use some letters more than once. The letters will spell the answer to this riddle.

What is always behind the times?

T	H	E		B	A	C	K
4.8	8.7	7.2		15.7	1.8	4.5	3.2

O	F		A		C	L	O	C	K
0.6	21.0		1.8		4.5	13.4	0.6	4.5	3.2

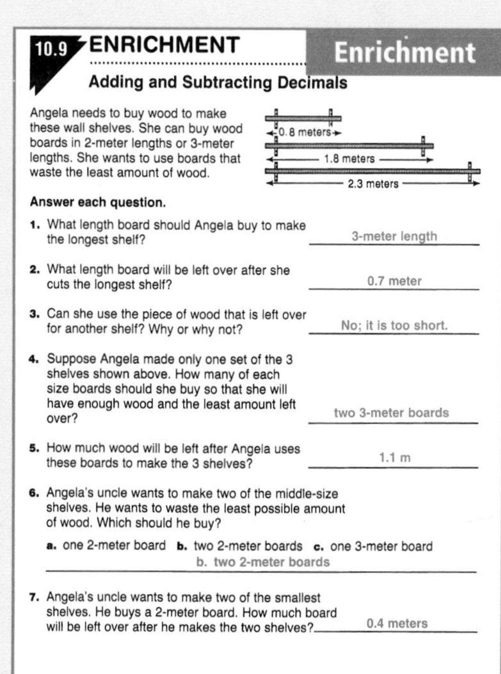

10.9 ENRICHMENT — Enrichment

Adding and Subtracting Decimals

Angela needs to buy wood to make these wall shelves. She can buy wood boards in 2-meter lengths or 3-meter lengths. She wants to use boards that waste the least amount of wood.

Answer each question.

1. What length board should Angela buy to make the longest shelf? 3-meter length
2. What length board will be left over after she cuts the longest shelf? 0.7 meter
3. Can she use the piece of wood that is left over for another shelf? Why or why not? No; it is too short.
4. Suppose Angela made only one set of the 3 shelves shown above. How many of each size boards should she buy so that she will have enough wood and the least amount left over? two 3-meter boards
5. How much wood will be left after Angela uses these boards to make the 3 shelves? 1.1 m
6. Angela's uncle wants to make two of the middle-size shelves. He wants to waste the least possible amount of wood. Which should he buy?
   a. one 2-meter board **b.** two 2-meter boards **c.** one 3-meter board
   b. two 2-meter boards
7. Angela's uncle wants to make two of the smallest shelves. He buys a 2-meter board. How much board will be left over after he makes the two shelves? 0.4 meters

Problem Solving

Planning at a Glance

Objective To use Make a List and other strategies to solve problems

Materials none

Optional Resources

- Reteach 10.10; Practice 10.10; Enrichment 10.10
- Daily Cumul. Review, p. 139
- Math Center: Project Card
- Every Day Counts
- **TAB**, TE pp. 346E–346F, 346J
- **Problem of the Day**, 139, p. 70; Flip Chart p. 70a

Students Acquiring English

To reinforce some of the vocabulary in this lesson, invite volunteers to provide a definition, synonym, or drawing for each of the following words: *pioneers, basic, structure, perimeter, rate, approximate*. Then ask other volunteers to use each word in a sentence.

Problem of the Day

Find a decimal that is exactly halfway between 2.8 and 8.2.
5.5

Problem Solving : Application

Problem Solving
Using Make a List and Other Strategies

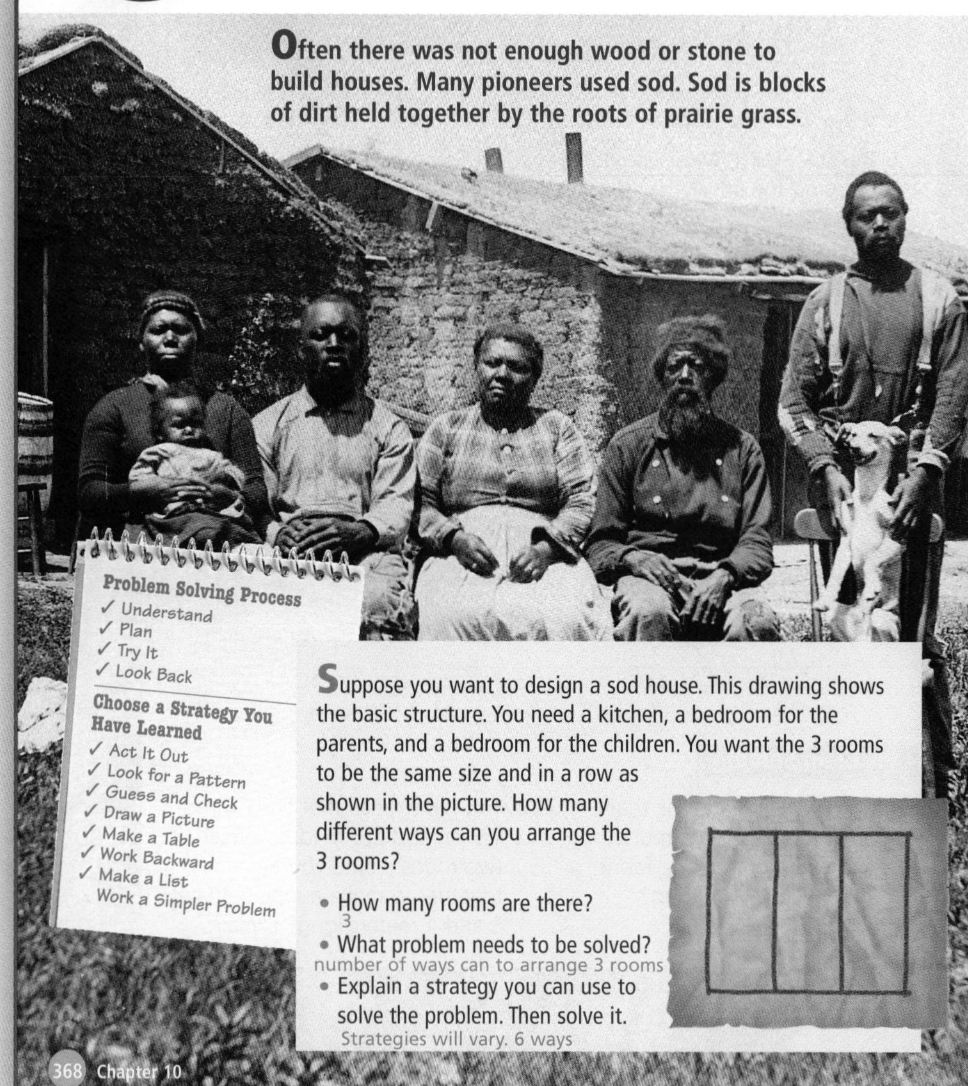

Often there was not enough wood or stone to build houses. Many pioneers used sod. Sod is blocks of dirt held together by the roots of prairie grass.

Suppose you want to design a sod house. This drawing shows the basic structure. You need a kitchen, a bedroom for the parents, and a bedroom for the children. You want the 3 rooms to be the same size and in a row as shown in the picture. How many different ways can you arrange the 3 rooms?

- How many rooms are there? 3
- What problem needs to be solved? number of ways can to arrange 3 rooms
- Explain a strategy you can use to solve the problem. Then solve it. Strategies will vary. 6 ways

368 Chapter 10

1 Introduce

Prior Knowledge At an ice cream stand, you can get a cone with 1, 2, or 3 scoops. Each scoop can be chocolate, strawberry, or vanilla. How many different combinations of flavors are possible? 19 combinations

Teach: ***Modeling***

Model the question above. Ask:

- What strategy can you use to solve the problem? Making a list is the most obvious strategy.
- How many flavor combinations can you make with a 1-scoop cone? 3 combinations
- How many flavor combinations can you make with a 2-scoop cone? 6 combinations
- How many flavor combinations can you make with a 3-scoop cone? 10 combinations
- How do you find the answer? Add 3 + 6 + 10.

2 Develop

Work It Out!

- Call on students to discuss their answers and the strategies they used to find them. For example, making a list could help them solve exercises 2, 5, and 6, while using a pattern would help them to make the list for exercise 2, and making a table would be more useful for exercise 3.
- Have students discuss their reasoning for exercise 7.

Using Reading Strategies Encourage students to use the Monitor strategy as they read the Problem Solving exercises. Ask them to share which problems they needed to reread, and why. See TE p. 346J.

3 Summarize

- Have students review the strategies they used to solve each problem.
- For each exercise, have someone suggest an alternate strategy that could be used.
- Remind students that there is no single correct strategy for solving any problem.

Math Journal: ***Communicating***

How does using a pattern to make a list help you? It helps to keep track of the combinations so that nothing is left out and nothing is listed twice.

Work It Out!

Use any strategy to solve the problem. Show your work.

1. Suppose each block of sod is 0.9 m long. Would 50 blocks be enough to build a row 50 m long? Explain. no; Each block is less than 1 m, so 50 blocks would be less than 50 m.

2. **Create Your Own** How many different 4-sided houses can you design? Each house should have a perimeter of 16 m. Answers will vary.

3. Many pioneers moved west in covered wagons. The wagon trains traveled an average of 29 km every day. At that rate, how many kilometers could a wagon train travel in 1 week? 203 km

Use the map to solve the following problems.

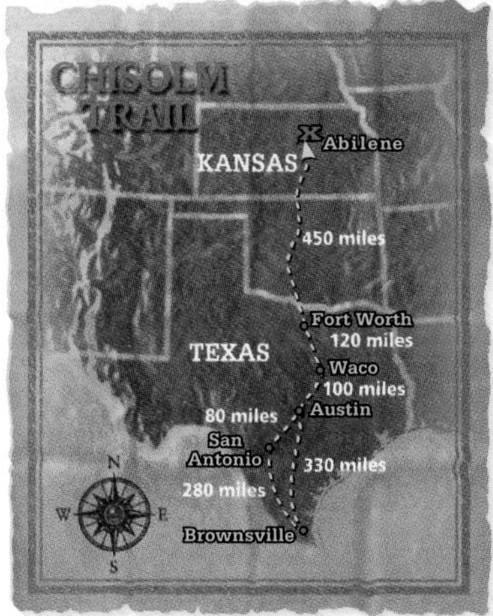

4. Your family wants to follow the Chisholm Trail, an old route for cattle drives. The first leg is from Brownsville to Austin. About how many extra miles will it take if you visit San Antonio on the way? Use one or more strategies to hep you to decide. Explain your thinking. About 30 miles; direct route is 330 miles; via San Antonio is 280 + 80 = 360 miles
5. Your family decide to drive close to 300 miles on one day of your trip on the Chisholm Trail. You plan to visit as many cities as you can that day. What route should you take? Explain. San Antonio, Austin, Waco, Fort Worth
6. In Abilene, cowboys sold their cattle for $40 each. How many different combinations of $5, $10, and $20 bills would make that amount? 9 combinations

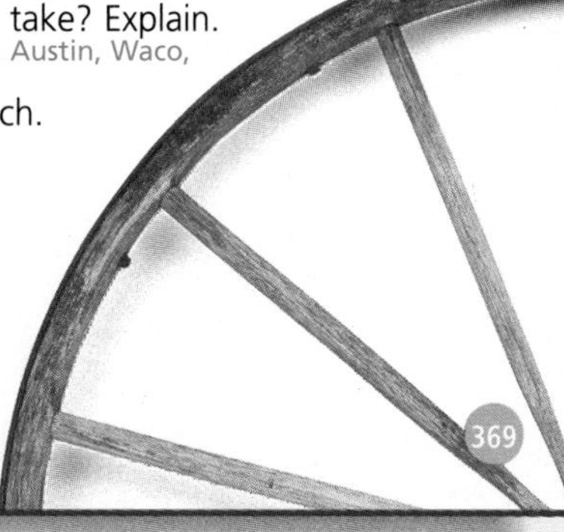

Share Your Thinking

7. For which problems did you use Make a List? How did it help you? See Additional Answers.

369

Meeting Individual Needs

Extra Support

Building Cars *(visual)* Have student pairs decide on a strategy and solve this problem: You're putting together a model car. There are three possible colors for the front and two possible colors for the back. How many different color combinations can you choose from? 6 combinations

Alternate Approach

- Reteach Worksheet 10.10
- **TAB** See TE pp. 346E–346F.

Students Acquiring English

See Language Connections, Ch. 10.

Challenge

Have students solve this problem: A dance company plans a dance with 2 dancers. Each will wear a mask. There are 5 masks to choose from: a feathered mask, a beaded mask, a velvet mask, a mask of lights, and a mirrored mask. How many possible pairs of masks can be used in the dance? 10 pairs

Practice

Math Center For more problem solving practice, see Project Card 10, *Newspaper Numbers.*

10.10 ANOTHER LOOK — Reteach

Using Make a List and Other Strategies

A friend writes two numbers on a card. The sum of the numbers is 12. When you multiply the numbers, you get 35. What are the mystery numbers?

1. Understand

- You want to find two numbers whose sum is 12 and whose product is 35.

2. Plan

- You need to make a list of the different sets of two numbers that add up to 12.
- You then need to multiply these pairs of numbers to see which sets have a product of 35.

3. Try It

- Make a list of the different sets of numbers that add up to 12. The list includes 0 and 12, 1 and 11, 2 and 10, 3 and 9, 4 and 8, 5 and 7, and 6 and 6.

4. Look Back

- The set of two numbers whose product is 35 is 5 and 7. So, 5 and 7 are the mystery numbers.

Solve. Use Make a List when you can.

1. A friend writes 2 different numbers on a card. The sum of the numbers is 10. When you multiply them you get 16. What numbers are on the card? 2, 8
2. Suppose you want to play tennis, baseball, and soccer on the first day of summer camp. In how many different orders can you do these activities? 6 different orders
3. There are 4 tables in the science classroom. Five students are measuring plants at each table. How many students are in the science classroom? 20 students

10.10 PRACTICE — Practice

Using Make a List and Other Strategies

Solve. Use Make a List when you can.

1. The Hernandez family is planning a picnic. They want sandwiches on rye bread and whole wheat bread. They like sandwiches made of peanut butter, chicken slices, and egg salad. Each sandwich will be made of one kind of bread and one filling. How many different kinds of sandwiches can the family make? 6 different sandwiches
2. Ms. Nugent wants to teach spelling, art, and math in the morning. In how many different orders can she teach these subjects? 6 different orders
3. There are 12 children at a birthday party. There is 1 adult for every 3 children. How many adults are at the party? 4 adults
4. Mr. Lange agreed to pay Marisa $10 for raking his entire lawn. Marisa only raked $\frac{1}{4}$ of the yard. How much should she be paid? $2.50
5. Four boys celebrated their birthdays during different months of the school year. Jeremy's birthday was in February and Simon's birthday was not in September. Lance celebrates his birthday a month after Jeremy. Ahmed is the first person in the third grade to celebrate his birthday in school. In what month are the boys birthdays? Complete the table to help you.

	Sept.	Nov.	Feb.	March
Jeremy	no	no	yes	no
Simon	no			
Ahmed				
Lance				

10.10 ENRICHMENT — Enrichment

Using Make a List and Other Strategies

Solve. Use Make a List when you can.

1. Use these decimals: 2.1, 4.4, 6.3.
   - Add two of them to make the smallest sum possible. 2.1 + 4.4 = 6.5
   - Add two of them to make the largest sum possible. 4.4 + 6.3 = 10.7
2. Make a true subtraction sentence with each set of numbers. One of the numbers should be the difference.
   - 10.5, 3, 7.5 — 10.5 − 3 = 7.5 or 10.5 − 7.5 = 3
   - 5.2, 8.2, 3 — 8.2 − 5.2 = 3 or 8.2 − 3 = 5.2
   - 23.4, 18.4, 5 — 23.4 − 5 = 18.4 or 23.4 − 18.4 = 5
3. Three objects are on a scale that reads 18.4 grams. Two of the objects are 4 grams each. How heavy is the third object? 10.4 grams
4. What is the mystery number? It is greater than 5.5. It is less than 10. If you add the number to itself you get 16.8. 8.4
5. Clare has half as much money as Tamala. Tamala has $.10 more than Latosha. Latosha has $.20. How much money do the 3 girls have altogether? Latosha has $.20, Tamala has $.30, and Clare has $.15 for a total of $.65.
6. Suppose you and a friend decide to share the cost of popcorn and a drink at a movie. The popcorn costs $1.50 and the soda is $1. How much will each of you pay? $1.25

Problem Solving

Planning at a Glance

Objective To use different strategies to solve problems

Materials none

Optional Resources

- Reteach 10.11; Practice 10.11; Enrichment 10.11
- Daily Cumul. Review, p. 140
- Math Center: Project Card 10
- Every Day Counts
- TAB, TE pp. 346E–346F, 346J
- Problem of the Day, 140, p. 70; Flip Chart, p. 70b

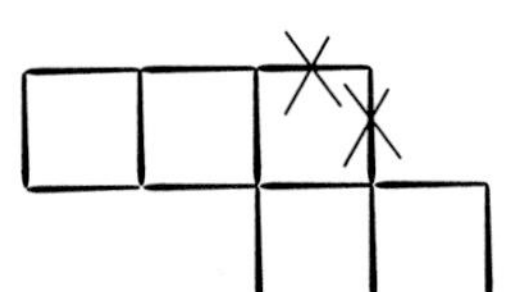

Unlocking Fractions and Decimals 3–6, Level 3, Activity 24, Circles Add/Subtract Mat

Students Acquiring English

Display or draw a picture of a baseball diamond that clearly shows all four bases. Elicit the names of the bases: first, second, third, and home. Then have students work in pairs. Ask a strong English speaker to describe the basic rules of baseball, especially how a run is scored. Then have each student acquiring English explain the game in his or her own words.

Problem of the Day

The 16 toothpicks form 5 equal squares. Which 2 toothpicks could you remove to leave only 4 squares?

One possible answer is shown.

Problem Solving : Application

LESSON 11

Problem Solving

Using Strategies

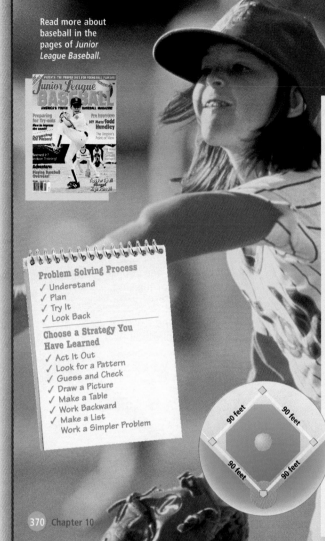

Read more about baseball in the pages of *Junior League Baseball.*

Problem Solving Process
✓ Understand
✓ Plan
✓ Try It
✓ Look Back

Choose a Strategy You Have Learned
✓ Act It Out
✓ Look for a Pattern
✓ Guess and Check
✓ Draw a Picture
✓ Make a Table
✓ Work Backward
✓ Make a List
Work a Simpler Problem

The first U.S. baseball game between two organized teams was played in Hoboken, New Jersey, in 1846. Perhaps you or some of your friends play Little League baseball.

It takes 10.8 seconds for a player to run 360 feet in a straight line. Why might it take the player more than 11 seconds to run around the bases?

- What is the question you have to answer? See Additional Answers
- What materials might help you to solve it? pencil and paper to draw a diagram
- How might this diagram of a baseball diamond help you? It shows the bases and the distance being run.

- Choose one or more strategies to use to solve the problem. Then solve it. See Additional Answers

90 feet
90 feet
90 feet
90 feet

370 Chapter 10

1 Introduce

Prior Knowledge **Ask, You are designing shirts for your softball team. The shirts will have 2 colors. You can choose from among red, blue, green, purple, and yellow. What are all the possible 2-color combinations?** R-B, R-G, R-P, R-Y, B-G, B-P, B-Y, G-P, G-Y, P-Y

Teach: *Modeling*

Model the problem above. Write the combinations on the chalkboard. Ask:

- Does it matter in which order we list the combinations? no
- Does it matter in which order we list the two colors in each combination? no
- Could there be both an R-B and a B-R combination? No; those are both the same combination.

2 Develop

Work It Out!

- Have students discuss the strategies they used to solve each problem. For example, they may make a list for exercises 2 and 6 and make a table for exercise 3.
- Call on students to discuss their answers for exercise 7.

Using Reading Strategies Encourage students to use the Monitor strategy as they read the Problem Solving exercises. Ask them how they kept track of information they got from rereading. See TE p. 346J.

3 Summarize

- Have students summarize the strategies they used to solve each problem.
- Call on students to suggest another strategy they could have used for each problem.

Ongoing Assessment The Blues softball team has 9 players in their regular lineup and one more who serves as a substitute. How many different combinations of players can the Blues put on the field? 10 combinations

Math Journal: *Communicating*

You can have 2 snacks. Your choices are pretzels, raisins, or an apple. What are all the possible combinations you can pick? There are 3 possible combinations: pretzels and raisins, pretzels and apple, and raisins and apple.

Work It Out!

Use any strategy to solve the problem. Show your work.

1. You have 30 baseball cards to trade. You give one-third of the cards to your sister. How many baseball cards do you have left? 20 cards
2. You have $8.50. You want to buy 3 baseball cards. The cards cost $4.50, $3.25, or $1.75. How many different combinations of cards can you buy? 4 combinations
3. A game lasts about 3 hours. Each team gets 3 outs in an inning. How many outs does each team get in 9 innings? 27 outs
4. Sometimes a game lasts more than 9 innings. This scoreboard shows a game that lasted for 18 innings. It was twice as long as a normal game. How many outs did each team get in the game? How long do you think it took to finish the game? Explain. 54 outs; probably about 6 hours, or twice as long as a normal game

INNING	1	2	3	4	5	6	7	8	9	10	11	12	13	14	15	16	17	18	
VISITOR	0	1	1	0	2	0	1	2	0	0	0	1	0	0	0	2	0	1	11
HOME	0	0	0	0	1	0	0	4	2	0	0	1	0	0	0	2	0	0	10

5. You are setting up a ticket booth, a snack booth, and a souvenir booth for the school Little League final. How many ways can you arrange the booths in a row? 6 ways
6. Suppose every player in Little League wears red or white caps, blue or red shirts, and white or black pants. How many different combinations of outfits are possible? 8 combinations

Share Your Thinking

7. Choose one of the problems above. Explain the strategy or strategies you used and how they helped you to solve the problem. Answers will vary.

371

Meeting Individual Needs

Extra Support

Spare Change ***(visual/kinesthetic)*** Have student pairs solve this problem and indicate the strategy they used: Lee has 2 quarters, 1 dime, and 3 pennies. Mia has 1 quarter, 1 dime, 3 nickels, and 1 penny. What coins must they give each other so that they each have an equal amount of money? Lee gives Mia 1 dime and 1 penny; Mia gives Lee 1 nickel. They will each have $0.57.

Alternate Approach

- Reteach Worksheet 10.11
- **TAB** See TE pp. 346E–346F.

Students Acquiring English

See Language Connections, Ch. 10.

Challenge

Challenge student pairs to extend the Ongoing Assessment problem on the previous page by finding the number of different combinations the Blues could put on the field if they had *two* substitute players instead of one. *Hint:* Make a list and look for a pattern. 55 combinations

Practice

Math Center For more problem solving practice, see Project Card 10, *Newspaper Numbers.*

See **Just the Facts** Practice 10B, p. 139.

10.11 ANOTHER LOOK — Reteach

Problem Solving: Using Strategies

Use any strategy to solve.

1. The fans at a baseball game sit on red, blue, or yellow seats. The first seat in a row is red, the second seat is blue, and the third seat is yellow. If this pattern continues, what color will the twelfth seat be? Yellow
2. The baseball game starts at 7:00 P.M. You stand up and stretch at 7:15 P.M. If you stand up to stretch every 15 minutes, how many times will you have stretched by 8:30 P.M.? 6 times
3. Jacob ate 25 peanuts by the fifth inning. He ate 5 peanuts each inning of the game. How many peanuts had he eaten by the third inning? 15 peanuts
4. There are 4 baseball diamonds on the practice fields. How many bases are there on the practice fields? 16 bases
5. There is a fence around the field. Four feet of each fence post is above the ground. Three feet of each post is in the ground. How long is each post? 7 feet
6. You are putting baseball cards into an album. Each page holds 5 cards. You have 32 cards. How many pages do you need? 7 pages

10.11 PRACTICE — Practice

Problem Solving: Using Strategies

Use any strategy to solve.

1996 World Series

Game 1	Atlanta 12	New York 1
Game 2	Atlanta 4	New York 0
Game 3	New York 5	Atlanta 2
Game 4	New York 8	Atlanta 6
Game 5	New York 1	Atlanta 0
Game 6	New York 3	Atlanta 2

1. The Atlanta Braves and the New York Yankees played in the 1996 World Series. The first team to win 4 games wins the Series. What team won the 1996 World Series? New York Yankees
2. What is the difference between the combined scores of Game 1 and Game 3? 6 runs
3. Rank the games in order of total runs from the most to the least. 4, 1, 3, 6, 2, 5
4. How many runs did New York have in the 1996 World Series? 18 runs
5. How many runs did Atlanta have? 26 runs
6. Suppose you have quarters, nickels, and dimes. What is the least number of coins you could use to buy the granola bar? 3 quarters
7. You buy a hot dog and a soda. You pay with a five-dollar bill. You receive 4 coins in change. What are the coins? 1 quarter, 2 dimes, 1 nickel

Concessions

Hot Dog	$2.50
Soda	$2
Pretzel	$1.50
Peanuts	$1.50
Granola Bar	75¢
Popcorn	$1.75

10.11 ENRICHMENT — Enrichment

Problem Solving: Using Strategies

Use any strategy to solve.

1996 World Series

Game 1	Atlanta: 12	New York: 1
Game 2	Atlanta: 4	New York: 0
Game 3	New York: 5	Atlanta: 2
Game 4	New York: 8	Atlanta: 6
Game 5	New York: 1	Atlanta: 0
Game 6	New York: 3	Atlanta: 2

1995 World Series

Game 1	Atlanta: 3	Cleveland: 2
Game 2	Atlanta: 4	Cleveland: 3
Game 3	Cleveland: 7	Atlanta: 6
Game 4	Atlanta: 5	Cleveland: 2
Game 5	Cleveland: 5	Atlanta: 4
Game 6	Atlanta: 1	Cleveland: 0

1. How many more runs did the Atlanta Braves score in the 1996 World Series than in the 1995 World Series? 3 runs
2. Look at the number of runs scored in each game. What games in the 1996 World Series had a total score of less than 10? Games 2, 3, 5, 6
3. Look at the total number of runs scored in the 1995 and 1996 World Series. Which series had a total number of runs which contains 2 numerals greater than 3? 1996 World Series with a total of 44 runs
4. There are 9 innings in a baseball game. An inning ends when each team makes 3 outs. How many outs are in a 9-inning baseball game? 54 outs
5. Six players all have different numbers on their jerseys. The first player wears the number 3, the second player wears the number 6, the third player wears the number 9, and the fourth player wears the number 12. If the jersey numbers continue in this pattern, what number will the sixth player wear? 18
6. Suppose a baseball game starts at 5:30 P.M. If each inning lasts approximately 30 minutes, at what time will a 9-inning baseball game end? 10:00 P.M.

Chapter 10 Chapter Test

Problem Solving

Give 0 to 5 points per answer, based on how well students meet the following criteria:

Problem 1

- There is use of a clear problem solving strategy.
- Work shows understanding that there are 10 other ways the stickers can be used so that each card has at least 1 sticker.

Problem 2

- There is use of a clear problem solving strategy.
- Work shows understanding that the mystery number is 15, because 1 + 5 = 6 and 15 falls between 8 and 23.

Concepts and Skills

If students need more help with concepts and skills in this chapter, use the following Reteaching Worksheets.

- 76 Writing Decimals from Tenths Squares, p. 212
- 77 Writing Decimals from Words and Fractions, p. 213
- 78 Counting with Decimals, p. 214
- 79 Comparing Decimals, p. 215
- 80 Ordering Decimals, p. 216
- 81 Placing the Decimal Point Correctly, p. 221
- 82 Regrouping When Adding Decimals, p. 222
- 83 Regrouping When Subtracting Decimals, p. 223

Chapter 10 Test

for Pages 346–371

Test-Taking Tips
Sometimes it helps to estimate an answer before looking at the multiple-choice options.

Problem Solving

Solve using any strategy. Show your work. (pages 354, 368)

1. Suppose you are making 2 valentine cards. You have 12 identical heart stickers. You could put 9 stickers on one card and 3 stickers on the other. How many other ways can you use all the stickers so each card has at least 1 sticker? 10 other ways
2. A mystery number is between 8 and 23. The sum of the ones digit and the tens digit is 6. What is the mystery number? 15

Concepts

Which decimal is greater? Use tenths squares to help you decide. (page 348)

3. 0.2 or 0.5 0.5 4. 0.7 or 0.6 0.7 5. 0.3 or 0.1 0.3 6. 0.8 or 0.9 0.9

Write a decimal to show the number. (pages 350, 358)

7. four and five tenths 4.5 8. nine and two tenths 9.2

9. five hundredths 0.05

How is the number written as a decimal? Write *a, b, c,* or *d*. (page 352)

10. six and seven tenths a. 7.6 b. 06.07 c. 6.07 d. 6.7 d

11.

Ones		Tenths
8	•	3

a. 0.83 b. 8.3 c. 38.0 d. 8.03 b

12. five and zero tenths a. 5.0 b. 5.5 c. 0.5 d. 50 a

372

Chapter Correlation to Standardized Tests

Math Central		Standardized Test Objectives						
Chapter Objective		**ITBS Form M**	**CAT/5**	**CTBS/4**	**Terra Nova (CTBS/5)**	**MAT 7th ed.**	**SAT 9th ed.**	**State/ Local**
10A	To explore and model decimals in tenths and hundredths	•	•	•	•	•	•	
10B	To relate decimals in tenths to fractions and mixed numbers in tenths	•	•	•	•	•	•	
10C	To read and write a decimal in word, table, and standard forms	•	•	•	•	•	•	
10D	To compare and order decimals using models	•	•	•	•	•	•	
10E	To add and subtract decimals with and without models	•	•	•	•	•	•	
10F	To use Make a List and other strategies to solve problems	•			•	•	•	

Skills

Compare the numbers. Write > or <. (page 356)

13. 4.0 ● 5 < 14. 5.4 ● 5.6 < 15. 0.1 ● 1 < 16. 0.7 ● 0.6 >

Write the decimals in order from least to greatest. (pages 356, 358)

17. 3.4, 2.4, 4.1 2.4, 3.4, 4.1 18. 5.1, 5.0, 0.5 0.5, 5.0, 5.1

19. 0.6, 0.1, 0.8 0.1, 0.8, 0.82 20. 0.7, 0.3, 0.4 0.3, 0.4, 0.7

Choose the correct sum. Write *a, b, c,* or *d*. (pages 364, 366)

21. 0.3 + 0.5	a. 0.6	b. 0.7	c. 0.8	d. 0.08	c
22. 0.4 + 1.0	a. 0.5	b. 1.4	c. 4.1	d. 1.04	b
23. 2.8 + 6.3	a. 8.1	b. 8.5	c. 9.1	d. 7.1	c
24. 1.7 + 0.7	a. 2.4	b. 2.7	c. 2.9	d. 1.4	a

Choose the correct difference. Write *a, b, c,* or *d*. (pages 364, 366)

25. 1.7 − 0.8	a. 0.5	b. 0.9	c. 1.0	d. 1.5	b
26. 0.9 − 0.7	a. 0.2	b. 1.0	c. 1.2	d. 2.0	a
27. 3.6 − 2.3	a. 0.3	b. 0.6	c. 1.3	d. 1.6	c
28. 5.0 − 1.9	a. 4.1	b. 0.31	c. 3.01	d. 3.1	d

Performance Task

(pages 350, 356)

- Copy the number line. Write the decimal number that belongs in each box. Explain how you decided which numbers to write. $\frac{8}{10}$, $1\frac{2}{10}$
- Draw the number line again and use fractions instead of decimals.

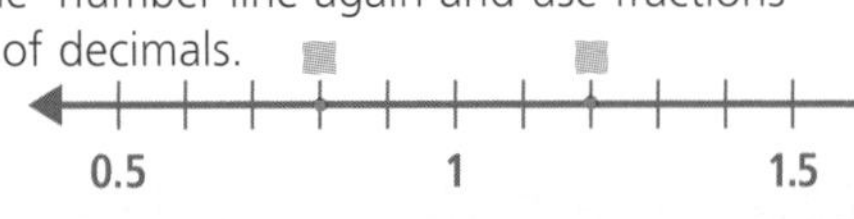

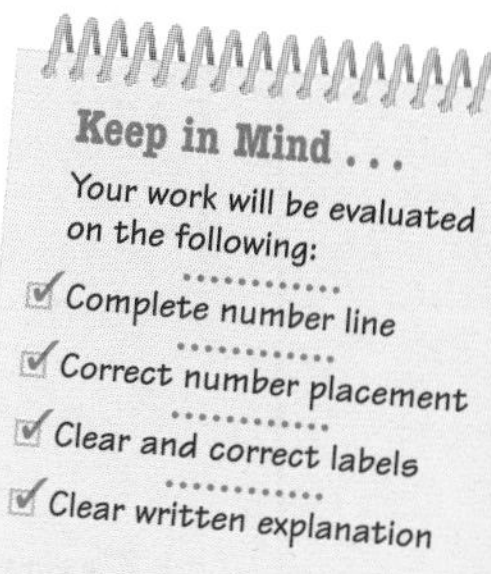

Keep in Mind . . .
Your work will be evaluated on the following:
Complete number line
Correct number placement
Clear and correct labels
Clear written explanation

373

Assessment Options

The following materials are found in your **Comprehensive Assessment Package:**

Formal Assessments
- Standardized-Format
- Free-Response Chapter Tests, Forms A and B
- Chapter Tests for Students Acquiring Language Proficiency
- Informal Learning Inventory

Performance Assessments
- Chapter Tasks
- Midyear and Final Project Tasks

Alternative Assessments
- Observation Checklist
- Student Attitude Assessment
- Student Self-Assessment *Individual and Group*

Standardized Testing: New Formats
- Enhanced Multiple-Choice
- Extended-Response
- Short-Response

Management
- Student Record Sheets
- Answer Keys

Standardized-Format Test
Fill in the circle of the correct answer.

- Standardized-Format Chapter Tests
- Free-Response Chapter Tests, Forms A and B
- Standardized-Format Midyear and Final Tests

Additional Assessment Resources

Test, Practice, Management Program
Use the *Test, Practice, Management Program* to create, administer, and score tests as well as generate practice sets. Questions are correlated to the Lesson Objectives.

Performance Task

Use the following criteria, each worth three points, to evaluate your students' responses. These criteria align with *Keep In Mind* in the Pupil Edition p. 251.

Criteria	
Shows a complete number line	Shows clear and correct labels
Shows correct number placement of 0.8 and 1.2	Writes a clear written explanation

Use this 4-level rubric to score students' responses. If you prefer a task with a 6-level rubric, use the Performance Assessment for this chapter.

3 points	Limited response
6 points	Acceptable
9 points	Capable
12 points	Superior

Common Error Alert

If your students are making frequent errors, see Analyzing Errors, TE pp. 373A–373B.

Scoring Chart

Item	Points
1–2	5 points each
3–28	3 points each
Performance Task	12 points
TOTAL	100 points or 100%

Item Analysis

Item	Objectives
1–2	Use Make a List and other strategies to solve problems (10F)
3–6	Compare and order decimals using models (10D)
7–12	Read and write a decimal in word, table, and standard forms (10C)
13–20	Compare and order decimals using models (10D)
21–28	Add and subtract decimals using models (10E)

Cumulative Test

For a cumulative review in the multiple-choice format, see TE pp. T80–T81.

Analyzing Errors

Strategies and Techniques for Reteaching

Errors in Basic Understanding of Decimal Place Value Whole number place value and decimal concepts are closely related. Their special denominators—10, 100, and so on—make decimals extremely helpful in reinforcing place-value relationships. Students who do not make the connection between whole numbers and decimals are likely to have difficulty understanding tenths and hundredths. Use tenths squares and a hundredths square to show students that the size relationship is important and that the unit can vary in size.

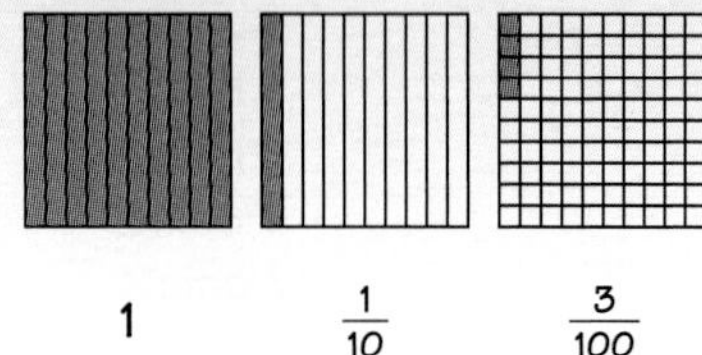

Comparing Place Value

Errors in Reading and Writing Decimals

Error Reads whole number and decimal only as decimal

Reteaching Use tenths squares to show 3 and 4 tenths: shade in three tenths squares to show 3; shade in 4 tenths strips on one tenth square to show 4 tenths.

Have the student look at the three fully shaded tenths squares and write 3. Then show the tenth square with 4 tenths shaded and tell the student to count the tenths. Note that although 3.4 can be thought of as 34 tenths, that is not the standard form of the decimal.

Error	Reteaching
Student reads 3.4 only as "34 tenths."	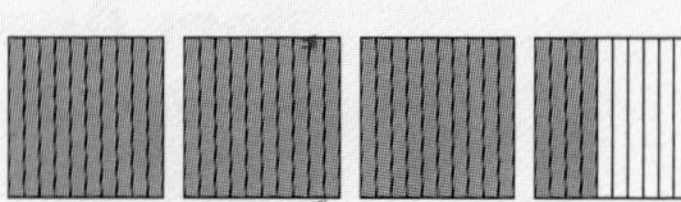 3 and 0.4 = 3.4

Error Cannot distinguish between tenths and hundredths

Reteaching Use money as a model to help students see that decimal place values are combined as a number in tenths and hundredths. Students should see that \$2.74 can be thought of as 2 dollars, 7 dimes and 4 pennies, but is read as 2 dollars and 74 cents, where cents names the hundredths. Then read the number without reference to money: two and seventy-four hundredths.

Error	Reteaching
2.74 = 2 and 74 tenths	\$2.74 2 dollars and 74 cents 2 and 74 hundredths

Error Writes zeros inappropriately in decimals

Reteaching Use tenths squares and a hundredths square to reinforce the idea that 5.4 and 5.04 are not equivalent. Have students compare models to verify that the numbers are not equal.

Error	Reteaching
5.4 = 5.04	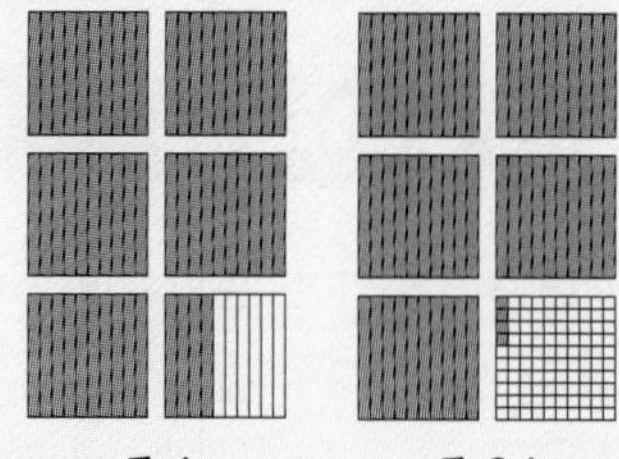 5.4 > 5.04

Analyzing Errors

Errors in Comparing Decimals

Error Compares decimals greater than 1 by examining tenths or hundredths first

Reteaching Use decimal squares to show the numbers being compared. Help students see that 4.2 is greater than 2.4. Remind them that decimals are compared in the same way as whole numbers, by first comparing the place with the greatest value.

Error

$2.4 > 4.2$

Reteaching

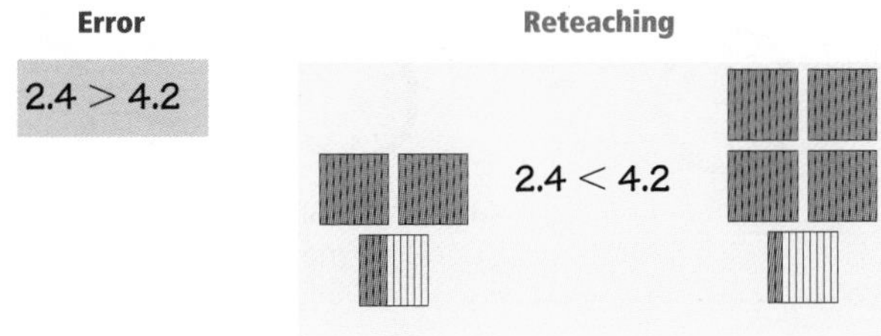

Error Does not line up the decimal points when comparing decimals vertically.

Reteaching Have students write the numbers in vertical format using a place-value chart. Then remind them to compare the numbers by first comparing the greatest place.

Error

```
4.2
  4
4.5
```

Reteaching

```
Ones.Tenths
   4.2
   4
   4.5
```

Adding and Subtracting Decimals

Errors in Adding and Subtracting

Error Does not write decimal point in answer

Reteaching Have students use lined paper turned sideways for decimal computation. Stress that each column can only take either one digit or a decimal point. Then have students place the decimal point in the answer before beginning computation.

Error

```
 3.7
+1.4
  51
```

Reteaching

		.	
	3	.	7
+	1	.	4
	5	.	1

Error in Subtracting

Error Subtracts lesser digit from greater digit

Reteaching Show a model of the greater number. Use the model to lead students through the steps for subtraction by asking the following questions:

How much do you want to subtract? 7 tenths How many tenths do you have? 3 tenths Do you have enough tenths? No What should you do? group a one as 10 tenths

Error

```
 6.3
-4.7
 2.4
```

Reteaching

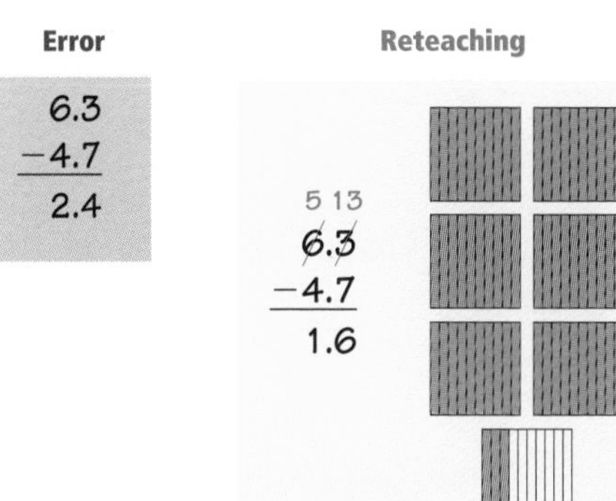

Cumulative Review

Two Ways to Use the Cumulative Review

Maintenance For those students whose results on the current Chapter Test show a good grasp of skills and concepts, you may wish to assign the Cumulative Review as homework. Students may also benefit from the specific review and practice opportunities listed in the Skills Maintenance chart.

Reassessment For those students whose results on the current Chapter Test show only a limited grasp of skills and concepts, you may wish to assign the Cumulative Review as class work. If it then appears that reassessment is needed, the Skills Reteaching chart on the opposite page identifies remedial minilessons in the Teacher's Resource Package.

Additional Assessment Resources

Test, Practice, Management Program

Use the *Test, Practice, Management Program* to create, administer, and score tests as well as generate practice sets. Questions are correlated to the Lesson Objectives.

Cumulative Review

Addition Properties (Chapter 1)
Find 6 + 5, 0 + 28, and 10 + 15 + 20.

Here's A Way!

Order property with doubles:
5 + 6 = 5 + 5 + 1 = 10 + 1
= 11
Zero property: 0 + 28 = 28
Grouping property:
10 + 15 + 20 = 45;
10 + 15 + 20 = 45

Find the sum. Tell how you found it. Answers will vary.
Correct sums and possible answers shown.

1. 21 + 0 — 21, zero property
2. 8 + 6 + 2 — 16, grouping property
3. 5 + 7 — 12, doubles
4. 9 + 4 + 11 — 24, grouping property
5. 0 + 38 — 38, zero property
6. 4 + 6 — 10, basic fact
7. Which property of addition did you find most helpful? Explain your choice. Answers will vary. Possible answer: the zero property. I can look at the addend to find the sum.

Telling Time (Chapter 2)
What time is it?

Here's A Way!

The short hand points to the hour, **10**.
Then, count by 5's up to the minute hand.

It is 10:35.

Write the time.

8. 2:15
9. 9:50
10. 12:20
11. 4:05
12. 7:35
13. 1:10
14. Divide an hour into 4 equal parts. How many minutes are in each part? 15 minutes

Division (Chapter 6)
Find 18 ÷ 6.

Here's A Way!

Use an array.
18 ÷ 6 = 3

Find the quotient. Use arrays or other models to help you.

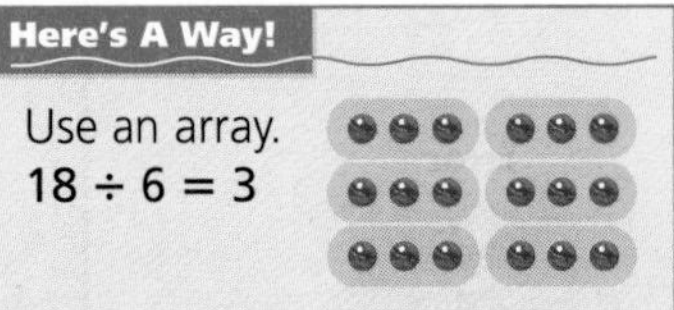

15. 72 ÷ 9 8
16. 63 ÷ 7 9
17. 42 ÷ 6 7
18. 56 ÷ 7 8
19. 48 ÷ 8 6
20. 64 ÷ 8 8
21. How could you check your answer to exercise 19? Multiply the quotient, 6, by the divisor, 8. If the answer is 48, it is correct.

374

Skills Maintenance

Chapter Objectives	Where taught in pupil book	More practice in pupil book
• To use the properties of addition to add three numbers (1C)	**Chapter 1**, pp. 18–19	More Practice Set 1.8, p. 439
• To write time shown on analog and digital clocks (2E)	**Chapter 2**, pp. 72–73	More Practice Set 2.15, p. 447
• To learn basic facts with 6 through 9 as factors and quotients (6B)	**Chapter 6**, pp. 210–211	More Practice Set 6.9, p. 459
• To compare and order fractions using models (8B)	**Chapter 8**, pp. 276–277	None
• To find the perimeter of a polygon (9B)	**Chapter 9**, pp. 308–309	More Practice Set 9.3, p. 466
• To use Make a List and other strategies (10F)	**Chapter 10**, pp. 368–369	None

Comparing Fractions (Chapter 8)

Which is greater, $\frac{1}{3}$ or $\frac{3}{6}$?

Here's A Way!

Use fraction models. Which has a greater shaded part?

$\frac{1}{3} > \frac{3}{6}$.

Compare the fractions. Write >, <, or =.

22. $\frac{4}{6}$ ● $\frac{1}{6}$ >　　**23.** $\frac{2}{8}$ ● $\frac{7}{8}$ <

24. $\frac{1}{5}$ ● $\frac{1}{2}$ <　　**25.** $\frac{1}{6}$ ● $\frac{1}{8}$ >

26. $\frac{2}{4}$ ● $\frac{4}{8}$ =　　**27.** $\frac{1}{3}$ ● $\frac{3}{5}$ <

28. Two apple pies are the same size. One is sliced into eighths. Another is sliced into sixths. Which is sliced into larger pieces? the pie in sixths

Measuring Perimeter (Chapter 9)

Find the perimeter.

Here's A Way!

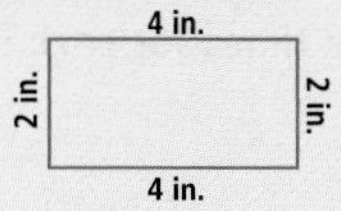

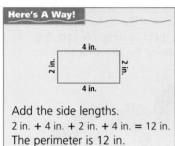

Add the side lengths.

2 in. + 4 in. + 2 in. + 4 in. = 12 in.

The perimeter is 12 in.

Write the perimeter.

29. 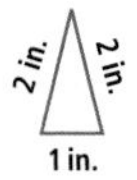

5 in.

30. 

16 in.

31. 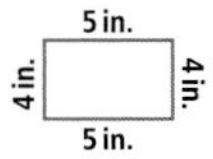

18 in.

32. 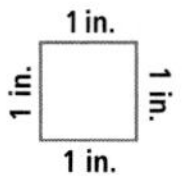

4 in.

33. 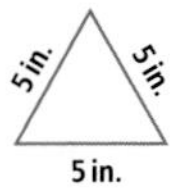

15 in.

34. 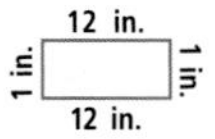

26 in.

Problem Solving

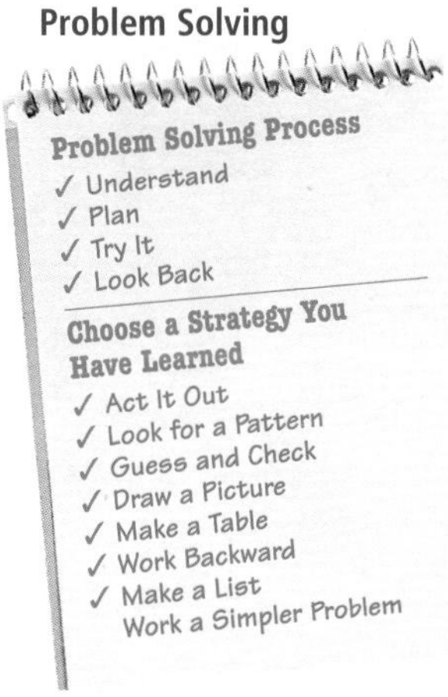

Solve the problem. Show your work.

35. You and 2 friends are going to blow up 16 balloons. Suppose one friend takes 6 balloons. You and the other friend each blow up half of the rest. Who would blow up the most balloons? the first friend

36. Your scout leader buys 3 packs of hot dogs and 3 packs of buns. The hot dogs cost \$2.95 a pack. The buns cost \$.95 a pack. Your scout leader gets \$.30 change. How much did she give the cashier? \$12.00

375

Students Acquiring English

Some students may need assistance on the Cumulative Review.

- Be prepared to read directions aloud to students.
- Focus special attention on word problems. Expect to paraphrase, diagram, or draw an explanation of the word problem.
- Review important vocabulary words that have been previously introduced.

Skills Reteaching

Chapter Objectives	Suggested materials for minilessons		
• To use the properties of addition to add three numbers (1C)	Reteach 1.8	Practice 1.8	Enrichment 1.8
• To write time shown on analog and digital clocks (2E)	Reteach 2.15	Practice 2.15	Enrichment 2.15
• To learn basic facts with 6 through 9 as factors and quotients (6B)	Reteach 6.9	Practice 6.9	Enrichment 6.9
• To compare and order fractions (8B)	Reteach 8.3	Practice 8.3	Enrichment 8.3
• To find the perimeter of a polygon (9B)	Reteach 9.3	Practice 9.3	Enrichment 9.3
• To use Make a List and other strategies (10F)	Reteach 10.10	Practice 10.10	Enrichment 10.10

INVESTIGATION

Management small groups
Materials chart paper, markers, stopwatches

Building Background

Students should be familiar with the concept of adding decimals.

Management Strategies Cooperative Learning

Introduce

- Establish rules for working in small groups. Post the rules in your classroom.

Guide

- If students have difficulty, ask them to restate what they know so far.
- Move students along by asking questions, not by giving answers.

Summarize

- Discuss the group outcome: What strategy did your group use? Why?

INVESTIGATION

Lickety-Split!

Keep In Mind . . .
Your work will be evaluated on the following:
- How well you add the decimals
- How clearly you lay out the race course
- How complete your chart is
- How well your group works together

Health Connection **With Your Group**

Have you ever been in a race or watched one? Here is your chance to design a race of your own. Decide how people will move in each different part, or leg, of the race. Have teams race. Use a stopwatch to time how long it takes them to complete each leg. Then, make a chart showing the times for each leg and for the whole race.

376

Investigation Support

Technology

Internet: Education Place
http://www.eduplace.com
Houghton Mifflin Education Place
Mathematics Center provides teacher and student support, such as links to other Internet sites.

Math Journal: *Communicating*

Let your students run some individual and relay races. Keep track of distances raced and winning times. Students can write about the results in their Math Journals.

Portfolio Opportunity

Make photocopies of each group's chart to include in student's portfolios. Ask students to describe their contributions to the chart.

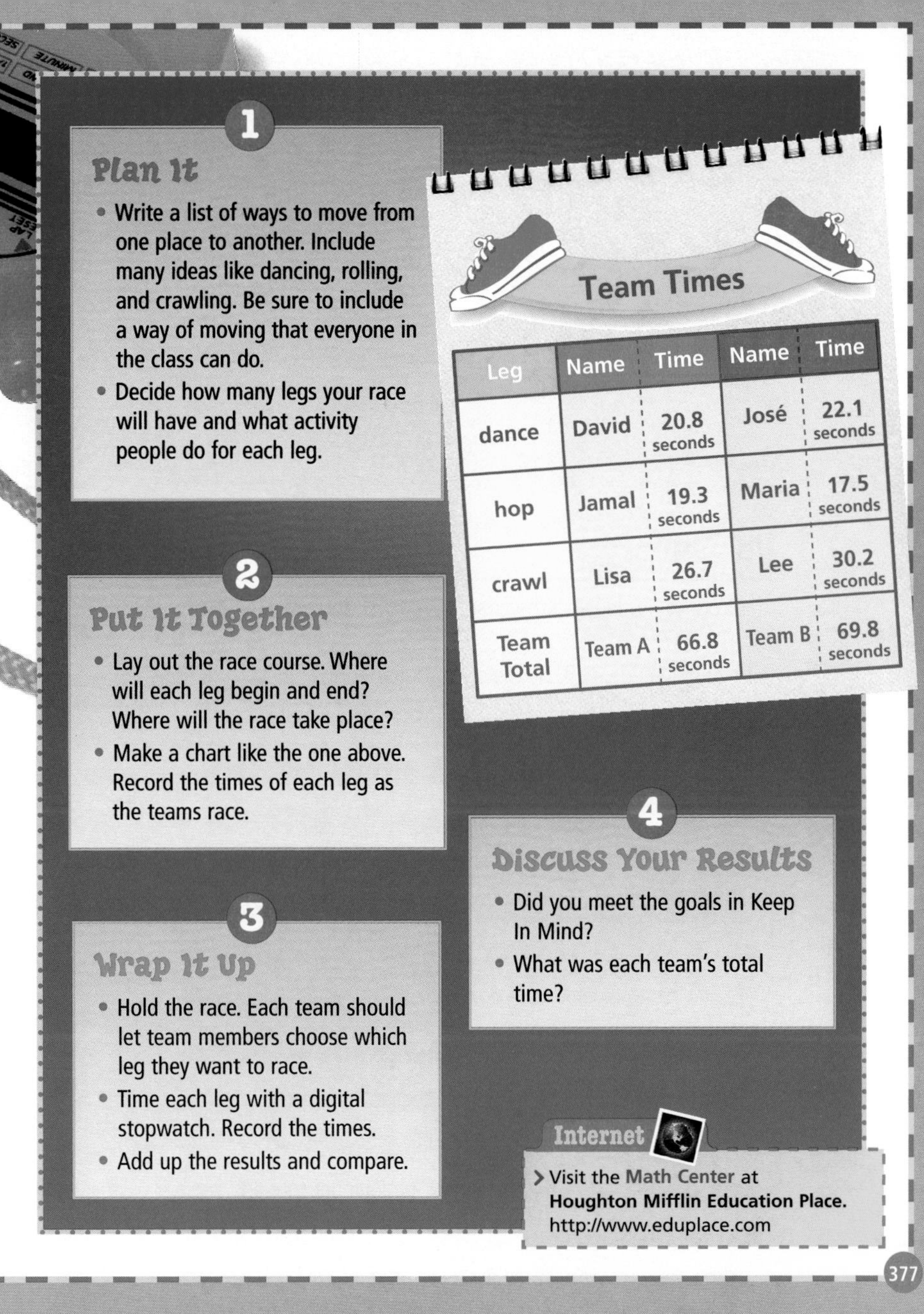

1
Plan It
Write a list of ways to move from one place to another. Include many ideas like dancing, rolling, and crawling. Be sure to include a way of moving that everyone in the class can do.
Decide how many legs your race will have and what activity people do for each leg.
Team Times
Leg | Name | Time | Name | Time
dance | David | 20.8 seconds | José | 22.1 seconds
hop | Jamal | 19.3 seconds | Maria | 17.5 seconds
crawl | Lisa | 26.7 seconds | Lee | 30.2 seconds
Team Total | Team A | 66.8 seconds | Team B | 69.8 seconds
2
Put It Together
Lay out the race course. Where will each leg begin and end? Where will the race take place?
Make a chart like the one above. Record the times of each leg as the teams race.
3
Wrap It Up
Hold the race. Each team should let team members choose which leg they want to race.
Time each leg with a digital stopwatch. Record the times.
Add up the results and compare.
4
Discuss Your Results
Did you meet the goals in Keep In Mind?
What was each team's total time?
Internet
Visit the Math Center at Houghton Mifflin Education Place. http://www.eduplace.com
377

Problem Solving Tip

Certain types of locomotion are more strenuous and slower than others. Student groups may take this into account when planning the lengths of their relays.

Completing the Investigation

Step 1 Some possible ways to move include, hopping, skipping, running, crawling, walking, rolling, dancing, galloping, somersaulting, seal walking, bear walking, and doing any of the above backwards or sideways.

Step 2 Help groups determine appropriate distances for each leg of the race.

Step 3 Model how to plan and draw the relay race course.

Step 4 Review rounding to the nearest hundredth using the stop watch display.

Extending the Investigation

Ask students to research the world record times for a variety of different types of races, auto races, horse races, swimming races, and running races. Students can make a table or graph to show their findings.

Assessment Scoring Rubric

These criteria align with *Keep In Mind* in the Pupil Edition on page 376.

Criteria	1 Limited response	2 Acceptable	3 Capable	4 Superior
Accuracy of calculations	Decimals are added inaccurately	Some of the decimals are added inaccurately	Most of the decimals are added accurately	All of the decimals are added accurately
Understanding of the math process	Lacks understanding of the math process	Can explain some of the math process	Understands most of the math process	Thoroughly understands the math process
Clarity and completeness of the chart	Chart is incomplete and disorganized	Chart shows an attempt to organize the information	Chart shows most of the information clearly and completely	Chart shows all of the information clearly and completely
Contribution to the group process	Makes no effort to contribute to the group	Makes some effort to contribute to the group	Contributes to the group most of the time	Contributes fully to the group

Use this 4-level rubric to score students' responses. If you prefer a task with a 6-level rubric, use the Performance Assessment for this chapter.

Multiplying by 1-Digit Numbers

Chapter Overview

Vocabulary

- Introduce students to the chapter with vocabulary minilesson, TAB p. 378J.
- Planning Guide, p. 378C, lists vocabulary for each lesson in the chapter.
- Use the SAE vocabulary support in Lessons 11.1, 11.3, 11.7, 11.9, and 11.10.

Rationale

Chapter Pacing: 10 days

- This chapter uses place-value blocks to develop the algorithm for multiplying by 1-digit numbers.
- Word problems review the meaning of multiplication and help students understand that multiplication means the combination of equal groups of things.
- In the Math World feature, students create a set of Napier's Bones and use them to solve a multiplication problem.
- In the Investigation, students use multiplying by 1-digit numbers in the context of time management and food preparation.

See **Daily Lesson Plans**, Chapter Management at a Glance, pp. 106–107; Suggested Weekly Plan, pp. 108–109.

Problem Solving

This chapter emphasizes the Work a Simpler Problem strategy for problem solving. It also reinforces strategies students have learned earlier and encourages them to choose and apply their own strategies.

Assessment

- The Chapter Introduction allows you to assess whether students are able to multiply by 1-digit numbers and have an understanding of place value.
- Observe students' abilities to model problems correctly, especially in the first part of the chapter where the underlying concepts are developed.
- When students move to paper and pencil, make sure they understand place value in the multiplicands.
- Use the Midchapter Review, the Chapter Test, and the Cumulative Review to assess students' needs for reinforcement or reteaching.

Reading Strategies

- Teach the Self-Question reading strategy minilesson on TAB p. 378J. Then, use the following as opportunities to reinforce the strategy.
  - Preparing for Tests, TE pp. 378G–378H
  - Problem Solving, Lessons 11.2–11.11
- Use the SAE reading support for Lesson 11.4.

Meeting Individual Needs

Students Acquiring English

Take time to demonstrate multiplication by 1-digit numbers.

- Demonstrate multiplication models to help students understand multiplying by 1-digit numbers.
- Help students verbalize the steps in the multiplication process.
- Provide several example problems and use manipulatives to model them.

See also **Language Connections** for additional support.

Extra Support

Students may have difficulty moving from 1-digit by 1-digit multiplication.

- Start with a few problems and use arrays to explain what takes place with the symbolic algorithms.
- Expanded algorithms and place value can increase students' understanding.
- Use the Basic Facts Workshop, p. 391A.
- Use the Analyzing Errors strategies, pp. 405A–405B.

Challenge

Many students may benefit from this extension activity.

- Have pairs solve 3-digit by 1-digit multiplication problems. One partner creates a problem. That partner multiplies the ones; the other partner multiplies the tens; and so on. Invite pairs to create additional problems.

Multi-Age Classroom

The chart below shows the chapters in books for levels 2 and 4 that can be used in conjunction with this chapter.

2	3	4
Chapter 10 *Multiplication and Division Readiness*	**Chapter 11** *Multiplying by 1-Digit Numbers*	**Chapter 6** *Multiplying by 1-Digit Numbers*

See **Daily Lesson Plans**, Multi-Age Classroom Concept and Skill Development, pp. 4–5.

Chapter Bibliography

Key

Multicultural ★	Social Studies
Science/Health	Music
Literature	Art

Technology

Students can explore multiplication with the electronic tools in *Unlocking Whole Numbers 3–5*. They can discover patterns and relationships by using sets, arrays, and place-value materials.

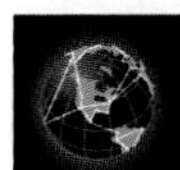

Internet: Education Place

http://www.eduplace.com

Visit the **Mathematics Center** in *Houghton Mifflin Education Place* to find activities, projects, games, and links to other valuable Internet sites.

Ultimate Writing & Creativity Center

Students can use the *Ultimate Writing & Creativity Center®* for all their writing and publishing activities. The software is available from The Learning Company® in Macintosh and Windows formats.

Larson's Leapfrog MATH™

Leapfrog Math includes mathematics skills and concepts for grades 3–6. Each grade is contained on a single CD-ROM. The software is available from Meridian Creative Group, a Division of Larson Texts, Inc.

Test, Practice, Management Program

Use the *Test, Practice, Management Program* to create, administer, and score tests as well as generate practice sets. Questions are correlated to Lesson Objectives.

Graphers Sunburst Communications, Inc.®

Using the friendly tools in *Graphers,* children can easily manipulate data that can be counted or sorted and represent their data in a table or with six types of graphs.

Books for Students

Houghton Mifflin Mathematics Bookshelf

The Giant Jam Sandwich
John Vernon Lord and Janet Burroway,
Houghton Mifflin, 1973.
Clever villagers make a giant jam sandwich to trap millions of wasps descending into their village. Students work with multiplication, money, and decimals while reading this humorous story.

Kids in the Kitchen: 100 Delicious, Fun and Healthy Recipes to Cook and Bake
Micah Pulleyn and Sarah Bracken,
Sterling Publication, 1995.
This recipe collection uses common ingredients and encourages experimenting with addition and subtraction of ingredients as well as the changing of baking and mixing times.

★ **Anno's Mysterious Multiplying Jar**
Masaichiro Anno and Mitsumasa Anno,
Philomel/Putnam, 1983.
A mysterious jar introduces readers to factorials.

The Case of the Willing Parrot
David D. Connell and Jim Thurman,
W.H. Freeman, 1995.
The Mathnet detectives use their mathematics skills to solve the mystery of a hidden fortune.

Menu-Math Presents the Hamburger Hut
Barbara Johnson and Kitty Scharf,
Remedial Publications, 1994.
Students practice multiplication and division skills while reading this interesting collection of story problems.

Math Wizardry for Kids
Margaret Kenda and Phyllis S. Williams,
Barron's Educational Series, 1995.
These puzzles, games, and ideas promote students to think like a mathematics wizard.

Multiplication
David Stienecker and Richard McCabe,
Marshall Cavendish, 1995.
Students perform experiments and other activities to explore multiplication concepts.

Books for Families

Mitch and Amy
Beverly Cleary,
Morrow Junior Books, 1991.
Parents can help their children read these adventures of a brother and sister who bicker and fight but support each other in learning, including multiplication and division facts.

Calculator Riddles
David A. Adler,
Holiday House, 1995.
A variety of fun word riddles are solved by performing operations on a calculator and then reading the display upside down. Good for familiarizing students with calculator keys.

From Head to Toe: Body Math
edited by Jean B. Crawford and Patricia Daniels,
Time-Life, 1993.
Parents and children can share these original stories, poems, riddles, and games that focus on mathematics related to the human body.

Reference Books for Teachers

The Development of Multiplicative Reasoning in the Learning of Mathematics
edited by Guershon Harel and Jere Confrey,
State University of New York Press, 1994.
From the Reform in Math Series, this book addresses how children develop effective thinking in the area of multiplication.

Math by All Means, Multiplication, Grade 3
Marilyn Burns,
Marilyn Burns Education Associates, 1991.
Teachers learn ways to teach multiplication from different approaches in geometric, numerical, and real-life situations.

Science in Action: The World of Numbers
compiled by Sue Lyons,
Marshall Cavendish, 1993.
These projects, experiments, and hands-on applications allow students to explore scientific principles of mathematics.

Planning Guide

	TE Pages	Lesson Objectives	Lesson Vocabulary	NCTM Standards
11.1 Exploring Multiplication	*380–381*	To explore multiplying a 2-digit number by a 1-digit number		Whole Number Concepts, Reasoning, Whole Number Computation, Communication, Connections
11.2 Estimating Products	*382–383*	To estimate products		Whole Number Concepts, Reasoning, Estimation, Communication, Connections
11.3 Work a Simpler Problem	*384–385*	To use the Work a Simpler Problem strategy to solve problems		Problem Solving, Whole Number Computation, Geometry, Measurement
11.4 Multiplying with an Array	*386–387*	To use arrays to multiply 2-digit numbers by 1-digit numbers, with and without regrouping		Whole Number Concepts, Communication, Connections, Reasoning
11.5 Multiplying 2-Digit Numbers	*388–389*	To multiply 2-digit numbers by 1-digit numbers, regrouping ones and tens		Connections, Estimation, Communication, Reasoning, Patterns and Functions
11.6 Choose a Computation Method	*390*	To decide whether to estimate or find an exact answer to solve problems		Problem Solving, Estimation, Whole Number Computation, Connections, Reasoning
11.7 Multiplying 3-Digit Numbers	*394–395*	To multiply 3-digit numbers by 1-digit numbers, with and without regrouping		Whole Number Concepts, Measurement, Estimation, Problem Solving, Reasoning, Communication
11.8 Work a Simpler Problem and Other Strategies	*396–397*	To use Work a Simpler Problem and other strategies to solve problems		Problem Solving, Whole Number Computation, Connections, Reasoning
11.9 Multiplying with Zeros	*398–399*	To multiply 3-digit numbers that include zeros by 1-digit numbers		Whole Number Concepts, Measurement, Reasoning, Estimation, Patterns and Functions
11.10 Multiplying Money	*400–401*	To multiply 3-digit money amounts by a 1-digit number		Whole Number Concepts, Fractions and Decimals, Problem Solving, Probability and Statistics
11.11 Using Strategies	*402–403*	To use different strategies to solve problems		Problem Solving, Measurement, Reasoning, Geometry and Spatial Sense, Communication

Chapter Objectives

11A To explore models for multiplying a 2-digit number by a 1-digit number
11B To estimate products
11C To multiply 2-digit numbers by 1-digit numbers
11D To multiply 3-digit numbers with and without zeros by 1-digit numbers
11E To multiply money amounts by 1-digit numbers
11F To use Work a Simpler Problem and other strategies to solve problems

Chapter Objectives	math center	State Requirements
11A	• *Think Multiplication!*, Activity Card 60; Number Card Deck	
11B	• *Taking Aim at Products*, Activity Card 61; Number Card Deck; Workmat 4	
11F	• *Giving a Party*, Project Card 11	
11A	• *Multiplication Arrays*, Activity Card 62; Number Card Deck	
11C	• *Rolling Products*, Activity Card 63; Gameboard 3	
11F	• *Giving a Party*, Project Card 11	
11D	• *Go, Products, Go!*, How-To Card 38; Gameboard 6	
11F	• *Giving a Party*, Project Card 11	
11D	• *Wheel of Products*, Activity Card 64	
11E	• *The $Money$ Game*, How-To Card 39; Money Card Deck; Gameboard 1	
11F	• *Giving a Party*, Project Card 11	

Integrating Reading Strategies

- Teach/review the Self-Question strategy using TAB p. 378J.
- Encourage students to practice the strategy in Lessons 11.2–11.11.

Technology

Unlocking Whole Numbers 3–5

Internet: Education Place
http://www.eduplace.com
Houghton Mifflin Education Place
Mathematics Center

Test, Practice, Management Program

Special Lessons

pp. 378–379
Chapter Introduction
The Introduction increases students' awareness of repeating multiplication patterns.

pp. 402–403

Students apply problem solving strategies in the context of investigating extreme weather conditions.

pp. 392–393
Math World
Multiplication Around the World
Use this feature to show students how multiplication is used all over the world.

pp. 408–409
Investigation
Craft Festival!
Students prepare and bake ornaments from salt dough to sell at a craft fair.

Assessment

Use the following assessment tools to help assess individual needs.

- Midchapter Review, p. 391
- Chapter Test, pp. 404–405
- Cumulative Review, pp. 406–407

Chapter

11 Multiplication Workshop

Whole and Decimal Numbers

Alternate Approach

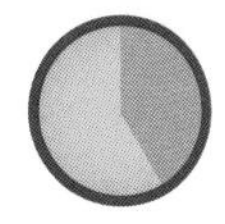

Use with page 388.

25 minutes

How Much Change?

Objective To model multiplication of 2-digit numbers

Management teacher directed; small groups
Materials several sets of coins, including pennies, nickels, dimes, and quarters, for each group
Advance Preparation Prepare a transparency as described below.
Modality *visual/kinesthetic*

Activity

- Label a transparency with the following column heads: *pennies, nickels, dimes, quarters.*
- Place 1 penny, 1 nickel, and 1 dime in the appropriate columns. Ask students how much money is shown. $ .16

pennies	nickels	dimes	quarters
1	5	10	

- Ask a volunteer to show how many coins there would be in all if 3 friends each had 16 cents. Have students tell you the total shown. $ .48

pennies	nickels	dimes	quarters
1	5	10	
1	5	10	
1	5	10	

- Ask, Is there more than one way to model $ .48? Invite volunteers to regroup the coins and show other possible combinations of coins. Answers will vary. Possible answers: 1 quarter, 2 dimes, 3 pennies; 1 quarter, 1 dime, 1 nickel, 3 pennies
- Model a few more examples on the overhead, changing the number of friends, and having groups of students model the problems and give you the answers. Encourage students to regroup coins to simplify problems and answers.

Meeting Individual Needs: *Modify*

Students Acquiring English Some students may have difficulty identifying the names and values of U.S. coins.

Extra Support

Use with page 382.

30 minutes

Count the Zeros

Objective To predict the number of places in a product; check using a calculator

Management teacher directed; pairs
Advance Preparation Make copies of the activity worksheet as shown.
Modality *visual*

Activity

- Distribute copies of the worksheet. Then, discuss how the problems in the first set and the problems in the second set differ. Have students complete the problems in the first set. Then have them predict the number of digits in the product for each problem in the second set and record their predictions.

Set 1	Product	Set 2	Prediction	Product
2 x 6		2 x 60		
3 x 5		300 x 5		
4 x 8		4 x 80		
5 x 7		5 x 700		
6 x 4		600 x 4		
5 x 8		50 x 8		
2 x 4		2 x 400		
7 x 3		7 x 300		
9 x 5		9 x 50		
3 x 9		300 x 9		

- Let students use a calculator to complete their worksheets after making their predictions.
- Discuss students' predictions about the number of digits in the products. Invite them to comment on the relationship between the two sets of problems and how they could use that information to predict the products.

For more practice **Using the Calculator,** see pp. T88–T90.

Meeting Individual Needs: *Modify*

Challenge Let students create their own problems, predict the number of places in the answers, and check their predictions with a calculator.

Multiplication Workshop

Game

Use with page 382.

30 minutes

Close to 100

Objective To estimate products

Management teacher monitored; small groups
Materials 9 blank cards for each student; a calculator for each group
Modality *visual/kinesthetic*

Activity

- Distribute blank cards and calculators to small groups of students. Ask each student to make one set of cards labeled 1 to 9.
- Have students combine cards, shuffle the deck, and deal four cards to each player.
- Tell students that the object of the game is to use the cards in their hand to create a multiplication problem (1-digit × 2-digit) with a product as close to 100 as possible.
- Have students record the problems they create and the product for each round. They can use the calculator if they need to.
- Products may be greater than or less than 100; the player closest to 100 on either side earns a point.
- Invite students to play several rounds by returning their cards to the deck, shuffling, and dealing again.

For more practice **Using the Calculator,** see pp. T88–T90.

1
4
2
5
Round
Cards
Problems
1
1, 4, 2, 5
54 x 2
42 x 5
24 x 5

Meeting Individual Needs: *Modify*

Extra Support Some students may benefit by using a calculator to find the products of various combinations of their cards before they "play" that round.

Challenge Students can deal 6 cards and make multiplication problems using 4 of them, for example, creating 2-digit × 2-digit or 3-digit × 1-digit problems.

Technology

MATHKEYS

Use with Lesson 11.5

Objective To model multiplication of 2-digit numbers by 1-digit numbers

Management teacher monitored; individuals
Materials *MathKeys: Unlocking Whole Numbers 3–5*, Lev. 3, Act. 21: How Many Apples?
Modality *visual*

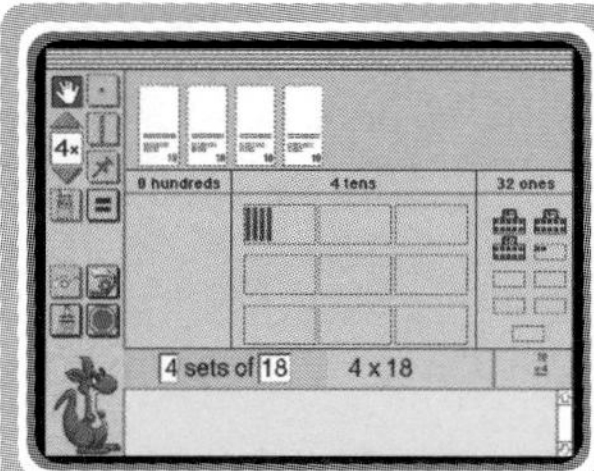

Activity

40 minutes

- Encourage students to use place-value blocks to solve the following problem: I went to the store and bought four containers of eggs. Each container had 18 eggs inside. How many eggs did I buy?
- Have students demonstrate their strategies and solutions.
- Invite students to open the *MathKeys* Base-Ten Blocks Multiplication Mat and experiment with it. Ask students to explain how they can tell when regrouping is necessary. A suitcase with a handle appears around the blocks, rods, or flats to be traded.
- Have students select How Many Apples? 1 from the Activities option on the Main menu and begin work. Students will solve a story problem.
- When students complete How Many Apples? 1, have them complete How Many Apples? 2, and How Many Apples? 3.

Meeting Individual Needs: *Modify*

Extra Support Offer students the opportunity to use hands-on place-value blocks to model each problem off-screen.

Challenge Have students record an estimate for each answer in the Notepad. Students can then record the actual answer as well and figure out how close their estimate was to the actual answer.

Chapter 11

Preparing for Tests

To develop students' test-taking strategies, model the following types of assessment items found in this program.

Standardized Tests

Write the following problem on the board.

You have $10.00. Comic books cost $1.75 each. Decide which is true:

- (A) You have enough money to buy 6 comic books.
- (B) To buy 4 comic books, you will need more money.
- (C) You have enough to buy 4 comic books. correct
- (D) You don't have enough to buy 5 comic books.

See also Standardized Testing: New Formats, Chapter 11.

Standardized tests usually require students to select a correct answer from a group of possible answers. In this problem, students must multiply a 3-digit by a 1-digit number to decide whether they have enough money.

Strategy

- What does the problem ask you to do? decide which statement is true
- How will you decide? use Guess and Check, multiply $1.75 × 4, then 5, then 6
- What might help you to model the problem? coins and dollars

Open-Ended Questions

Write the following problem on the board.

Give a reasonable estimate for 27 × 4.

Explain your reasoning.

See also Assessments, Chapter 11.

Open-ended questions can be answered in more than one way; they allow students to use a variety of concepts and processes. This problem allows students to determine a reasonable estimate to a multiplication problem.

Strategy

- What does the problem ask you to do? give a reasonable estimate for 27 × 4
- How can you estimate 27 × 4? substitute for 27 with a number close to 27 but easier to multiply
- What numbers can you substitute to get a reasonable estimate? Possible answers: 20; 25; 30
- So, what is a reasonable estimate of 27 × 4? Possible answers: 80; 100; 120

Preparing for Tests

Reading Strategies for Test-Taking

Self-Question: As I read, I ask myself questions, then read on or reread to find the answers.

Performance Tasks

Write the following direction on the board.

Use centimeter squared paper to create an array that will help you find the answer to this problem: 5×14.

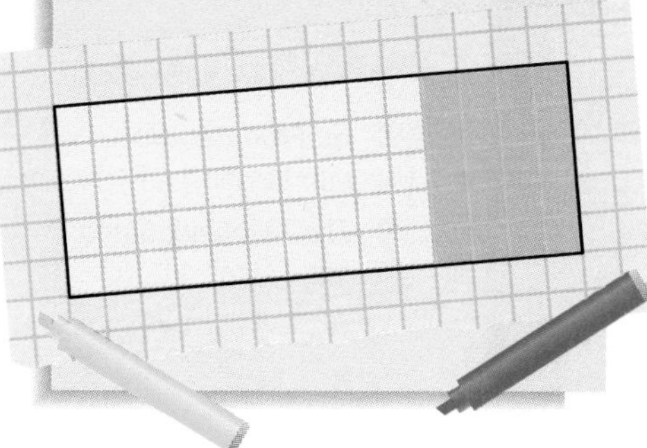

Performance assessments engage students in meaningful tasks that permit the teacher to observe their working procedures as well as the results they obtain. This task requires students to use squared paper to build an array.

Strategy

- What does the problem ask you to do? create an array that shows 5×14
- How many times will you need to show 14 in your array? 5 times
- How will you show 14? 10 squares of one color and 4 squares of another
- How will you use the array to find the answer? first multiply the ones, $5 \times 4 = 20$, then multiply the tens, $5 \times 10 = 50$, then add the products, $20 + 50 = 70$

Check the arrays to see whether they accurately represent 5×14. Evaluate whether students can clearly explain their use of arrays to multiply.

See also Performance Assessments, **Chapter 11.**

Test-Taking Tips

- Look back to see if your answer fits what the problem is asking.

Additional Assessment Resources

Test, Practice, Management Program

Use the *Test, Practice, Management Program* to create, administer, and score tests as well as generate practice sets. Questions are correlated to the Lesson Objectives.

Math Center

To meet individual needs, use the following resources from the Math Center. You may first wish to model activities for the whole class in order to demonstrate the rules for games and introduce procedures for independent tasks.

Gameboards

Gameboard 3
Use with Lesson 11.5.

Gameboard 6
Use with Lesson 11.7.

Gameboard 1
Use with Lesson 11.10.

Activity Cards

60 *Think Multiplication*
Use with Lesson 11.1.

61 *Taking Aim at Products*
Use with Lesson 11.2.

62 *Multiplication Arrays*
Use with Lesson 11.4.

63 *Rolling Products*
Use with Lesson 11.5.

64 *Wheel of Products*
Use with Lesson 11.9.

Project Card

11 *Giving a Party*
Use with Lessons 11.3, 11.6, 11.8, and 11.11.

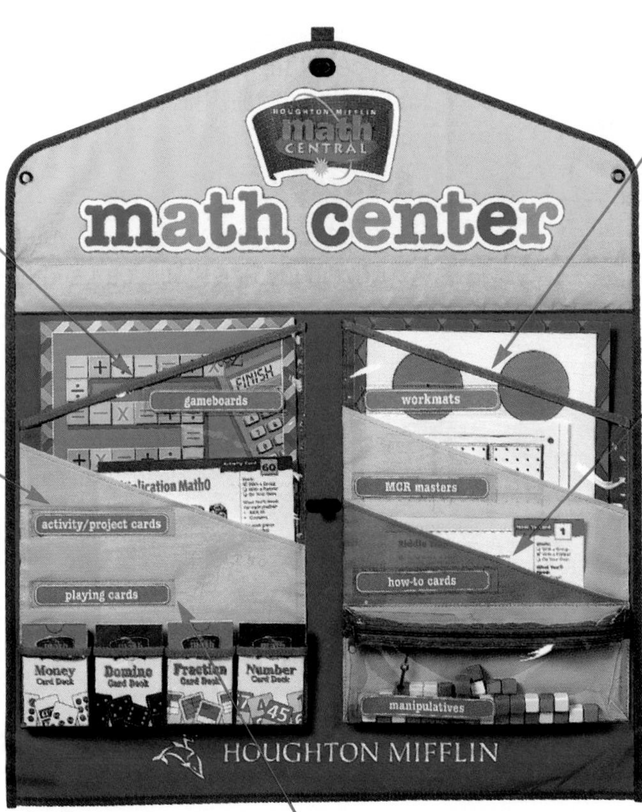

Workmats

Workmat 4
Use with Lesson 11.2.

How-To Cards

38 *Go Products, Go!*
Use with Lesson 11.7.

39 *The $Money$ Game*
Use with Lesson 11.10.

Card Decks

Number Card Deck
Use with Lessons 11.1, 11.2, and 11.4.

Money Card Deck
Use with Lesson 11.10.

Managing the Math Center

Manipulatives A variety of manipulatives can be used in Math Center activities. You might collect some on your own, or ask students to think creatively about useful materials. Common objects often used as manipulatives include egg cartons, paper clips, beans or noodles, and buttons or beads.

Vocabulary and Reading Strategies

Use these minilessons to strengthen vocabulary and reading skills.

Vocabulary

- digit

Linking Prior Knowledge and Vocabulary

Write the word **digit** on the board. Tell students that in mathematics, digit refers to numbers. In our number system, there are 10 digits (the numbers 0-9). We can make any number in our number system using only these digits. We call our system Hindu-Arabic. Talk about why ancient peoples in India and the Middle East might have created a system that has just 10 numerals. Students will likely suggest that we have 10 digits because we have 10 fingers, which very likely is the case. Demonstrate one method of finger counting.

Graphic Organizer: Diagram

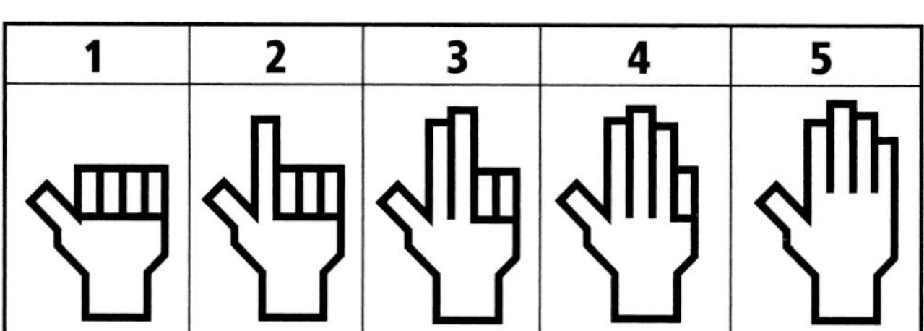

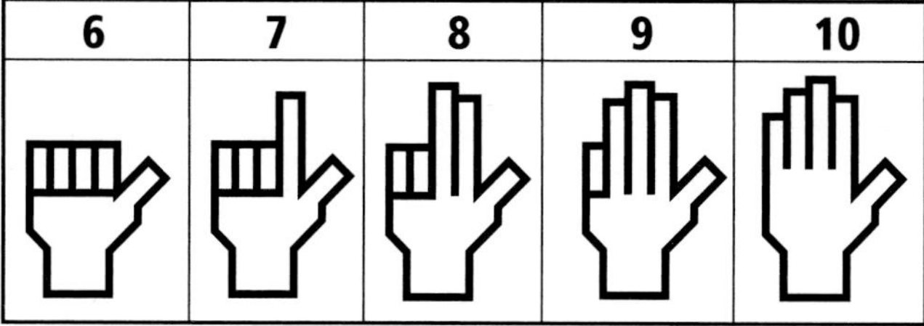

Reading Strategies

Strategy: Self-Question

As students read the problem, suggest they think of questions they would ask themselves to help them understand the problem. Lead them in using the Self-Question reading strategy for understanding direction lines throughout the chapter. Then model the Self-Question strategy.

Use the Thinking Aloud box and the graphic organizer to demonstrate the strategy with the following example.

> You used 4 rolls of film. Two rolls had 36 pictures each. The rest had 24 pictures each. How many pictures did you take?

Lesson 11.4, p. 387, Problem 22

Model by thinking aloud how to begin solving the problem.

Thinking Aloud

- I can reread the problem to be sure I understand it.
- I ask myself questions and use the answers to help me solve the problem. How many rolls did I use? How many rolls had 24 pictures? How many had 36? What operation will help me find how many in all?
- I can use the answers to make a table.

Graphic Organizer: Table

Film Used	Number of Rolls	Pictures Taken
36 picture roll	2	72
24 picture roll	2	48
	4 rolls total	**120 pictures total**

The reading strategies presented on this page can also apply to Lessons 11.2, 11.3, 11.4, 11.5, 11.6, 11.7, 11.8, 11.9, 11.10, and 11.11.

Objective

To use prior knowledge to explore multiplying by 1-digit numbers

Lesson Planning

Optional Resources

- Math Language Connections
- MATH KEYS *Unlocking Whole Numbers 3–5*

Every Day Counts Calendar Math

Multiplying

Students can explore the concepts of multiplying by 10 and estimating products by using the Computations and Connections activities in Every Day Counts, Level 3.

Assessing Prior Knowledge

Try This! Use this as a prechapter activity in the classroom or as a homework assignment.

Build confidence in using multiplication with this quick activity in which children look for patterns in the multiples of 3.

This activity

- assesses prior knowledge of multiplication and its relationship to addition

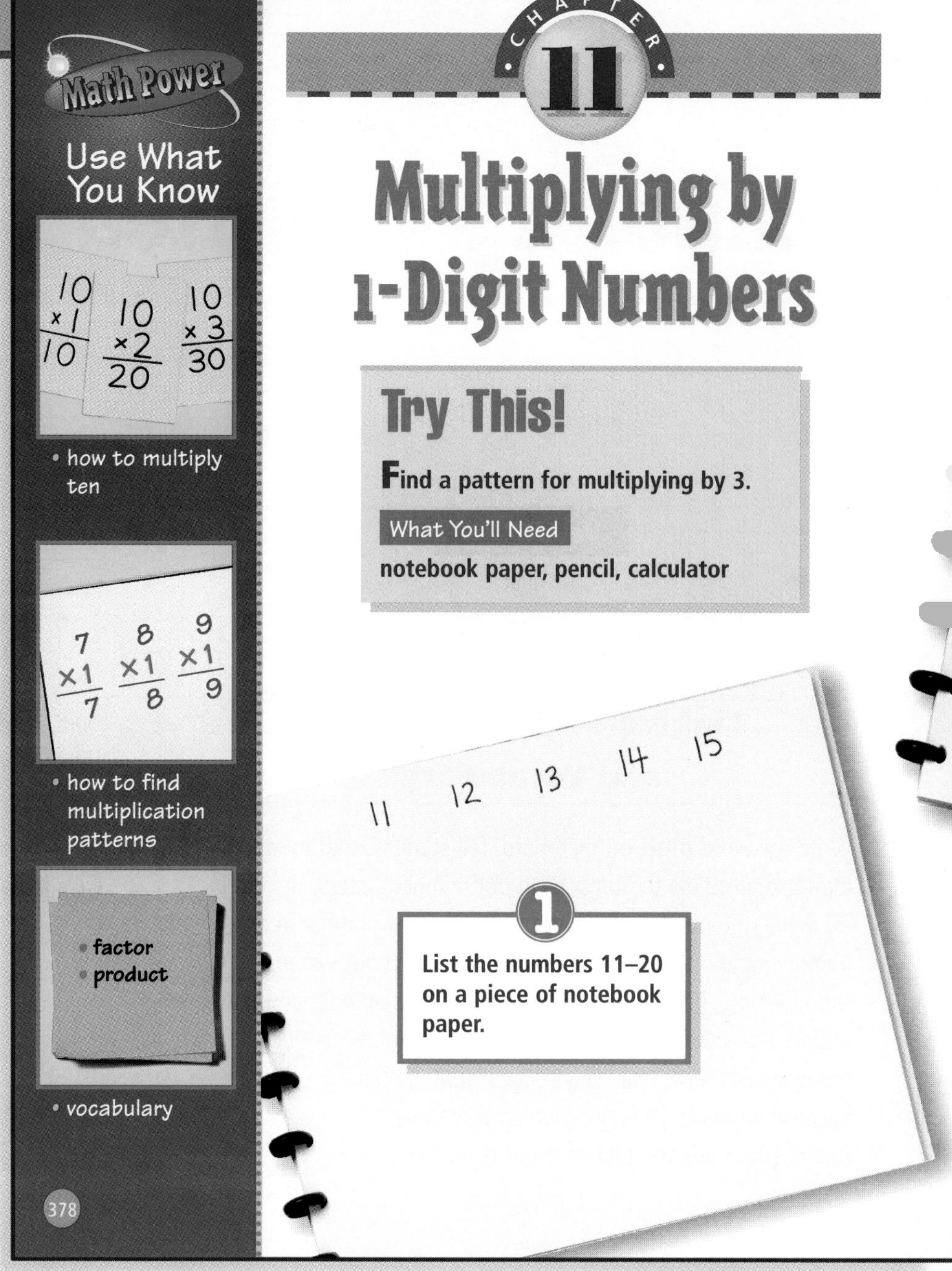

Chapter Connections

Math Links

Throughout this chapter, students will build on prior knowledge as they develop concepts and skills for problem solving with multiplication.

- **Number Sense** Lessons 11.3, 11.5, 11.7, 11.9, 11.10, 11.11
- **Arrays** Lessons 11.1, 11.4
- **Patterns and Relationships** Lessons 11.5, 11.11
- **Estimation** Lessons 11.2, 11.4, 11.6, 11.7, 11.8, 11.9, 11.10
- **Measurement** Lessons 11.3, 11.4, 11.7
- **Algebraic Reasoning** Lessons 11.1, 11.2, 11.4, 11.5, 11.10

Real *World*

Social Studies

- **Lesson 11.8, p. 396**
  The Special Olympics Students use problem solving strategies within the context of the Special Olympics World Games.
- **Lesson 11.9, p. 398**
  Trading Silk The silk trade of China in the 1300s provides a context for multiplication.

Science

- **Lesson 11.6, p. 390**
  Forest Rangers Estimation is a tool for keeping track of plant and animal populations.
- **Lesson 11.7, p. 394**
  Animal Eating Habits Students multiply to learn about the eating habits of elephants.
- **Lesson 11.11, p, 402**
  Weather Museum Students apply problem solving strategies and find out about weather.

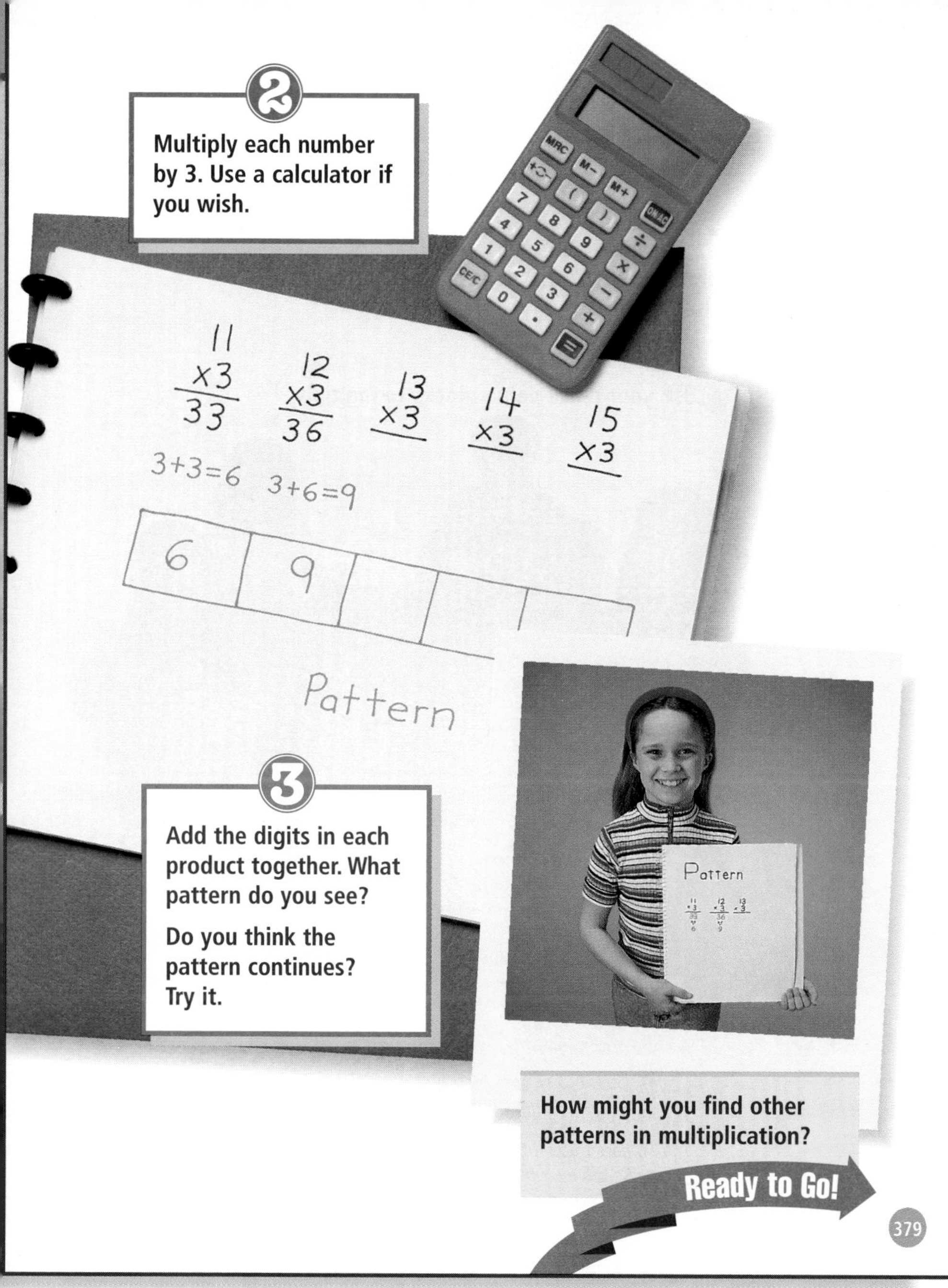

Multiply each number by 3. Use a calculator if you wish.
11 x3 33
12 x3 36
13 x3
14 x3
15 x3
3+3=6 3+6=9
6 9
Pattern
Add the digits in each product together. What pattern do you see?
Do you think the pattern continues? Try it.
How might you find other patterns in multiplication?
Ready to Go!
379

Assessing Prior Knowledge *(continued)*

- acts as a base for discussing how patterns can be used to decide whether an answer is reasonable
- provides a foundation for dividing by 1-digit numbers

Meeting Individual Needs

If students have trouble multiplying or skip-counting to make their charts, start with Quick Help. They may also need a brief teacher-guided review.

Quick Help Explain that in this activity students will use what they already know. Provide hundred charts and have students color every third square to find the multiples of 3. Repeat using a number line to 100 (a meter stick could be used). For more practice **Using the Calculator,** see pp. T88–T90.

Guided Review Refer to:

- **Lesson 5.7** Multiplying and Dividing by 3, Student Book p. 172
- **Multiplying and Dividing by 3** Practice Worksheet 5.7
- **Basic Facts** Review Basic Facts, TE p. 391A

Vocabulary Power

Use this graphic organizer to review vocabulary used in multiplying and place value.

Digits: The symbols 0–9 used in writing numbers. In a place-value system, the placement of the digit tells its value.

This three means 300.

This three means 3 ones.

Vocabulary Students can look in the dictionary for another meaning of the word *digit*. Discuss how these definitions are related. (People first used their fingers and toes for counting.)

Investigation Preview

Craft Festival!

Planning a school fund-raiser in which students sell salt-dough ornaments will help students apply multiplication in a real-world setting and explore successful management of resources. See the Investigation, TE pp. 408–409.

What They'll Do

- Decide how many ornaments to make.
- Find out how much of each ingredient will be needed to make the ornaments.
- Estimate the amount of time involved.
- Make a chart to show how the group will work together.

Technology

Students will enjoy looking for multiplication patterns by using ***MathKeys:*** *Unlocking Whole Numbers 3–5*. In the Hundred Chart Mat students can superimpose patterns of multiples up to fifteen. The Counter Multiplication Mat and Base-Ten Blocks Multiplication Mat each provide different models with which to examine patterns.

Activity

Planning at a Glance

Objective To explore multiplying a 2-digit number by a 1-digit number

Materials place-value blocks

Optional Resources

- Reteach 11.1; Practice 11.1; Enrichment 11.1
- Daily Cumul. Review, p. 141
- Math Center: Act. Card 60
- Every Day Counts
- **TAB**, TE pp. 378E–378F, 378J
- **Problem of the Day**, 141, p. 71; Flip Chart, p. 71a

MATHKEYS *Unlocking Whole Numbers 3–5*, Level 3, Activity 21

Students Acquiring English

To help with the Critical Thinking question, have students make a 2 × 3 array of counters and a 2 × 30 array of tens blocks. Ask what is the same (an array is an arrangement of rows and columns) and what is different (counters show ones, and place-value blocks show tens).

Problem of the Day

Theresa is making a chain using 10 large paper clips. Every paper clip is 5 centimeters long. She loses 0.1 centimeters of length every time she hooks two paper clips together. How long is Theresa's paper clip chain? 49.1 cm long

Exploring Multiplication

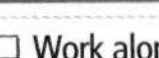

Cooperative Learning Checklist

- ☐ Work alone.
- ☑ Work with a partner.
- ☑ Work with a group.

Getting Started

What You'll Need:
▶ place-value blocks

Use What You Know

To multiply, you can use counters to make an array.

3 × 6 = 18

How would you find the product of 3 × 40? What about 4 × 15? Use your place-value blocks to try this activity.

Activity

- **Use your place-value blocks to multiply.**

Multiplying Tens

1. Use your place-value blocks. Show 1 row of 4 tens with tens blocks.
2. Show 2 more rows of 4 tens.
   a. How many rows of 4 tens do you have in all? 3 rows
   b. How many tens do you have in all? 12 tens
   c. How do you write 12 tens as a number? 120
3. To show the total, you can write a multiplication sentence.
   3 × 40 = 120

380 Chapter 11

1 Introduce

Motivate **Small groups each have a ones block, a tens block, a hundreds block, and a number cube. One student rolls the cube, another chooses a block, and a third records the number they have made. Then students switch roles.**

Teach: Activity

Emphasize these points:

- You can write a multiplication sentence for each array.
- As in addition, you may need to regroup ones as tens and tens as hundreds.

Modeling Model step 2 on student page 381. Ask:

- How do I write the number for 4 tens? 40

2 Develop

Show What You Know!

- Remind students that multiplication is a short way of adding equal addends.
- Guide students in setting up arrays correctly.
- To encourage cooperative learning, suggest that students record their answers individually but discuss them while they work.
- Have the class discuss their answers to exercise 20.

3 Summarize

- Discuss whether it would be easier to add or multiply to find the answers to exercises 9–12. Have students justify their ideas.

Ongoing Assessment You and two friends each have 24 model cars. What number sentences show how many model cars you have in all? 24 + 24 + 24 =72; 3 × 24 = 72

Math Journal: *Communicating*

Can you write a multiplication sentence for 21 + 21 + 23? No; to multiply, all the sets must be equal

Multiplying Tens and Ones

1. Use tens and ones to show 1 row of 15.
   a. How many ones are there? 5 ones
   b. How many tens? 1 ten
2. Show 3 more rows of 15.
   a. How many rows of 15 are there in all? 4 rows
   b. How many ones are there? 20 ones
   c. How many tens are there? 4 tens
   d. How do you write 4 tens as a number? 40
3. What is the product of 4 × 15?
   Write the multiplication sentence.
   4 × 15 = 60
   a. How did you get your answer? 40 + 20 = 60

Show What You Know!

Use your blocks. Find the product.

1. 3 × 29 87 **2.** 3 × 17 51 **3.** 4 × 14 56 **4.** 2 × 25 50

5. 5 × 21 105 **6.** 8 × 11 88 **7.** 5 × 29 145 **8.** 4 × 34 136

9. 7 × 27 189 **10.** 2 × 43 86 **11.** 9 × 16 144 **12.** 6 × 12 72

Use your blocks. Write a multiplication sentence about the arrays.

13. 6 rows of 45 6 × 45 = 270 **14.** 5 rows of 31 5 × 31 = 155 **15.** 8 rows of 19 8 × 19 = 152

Complete the multiplication sentence. Use blocks.

16. 5 × 12 = ■ 60 **17.** 5 × 31 = ■ 155 **18.** 7 × 16 = ■ 112

19. Critical Thinking How is multiplying with an array of place-value blocks like multiplying with counters? How is it different? Answers will vary. Possible answers: Alike, both help you show groups; different, place-value blocks show tens and ones and counters do not.

20. Write About It What are three ways you can find the product of 5 × 95? Answers will vary. Possible answer: skip-count by 100's, multiply with an array, add, use a calculator

Mixed Review **Write the quotient.**

21. 24 ÷ 6 4 **22.** 15 ÷ 3 5 **23.** 3)21 7 **24.** 2)8 4 **25.** 9)36 4

Meeting Individual Needs

Extra Support

Show It! *(kinesthetic)* Group students in pairs. Each student uses counters to create a multiplication array. Students name the multiplication sentence represented by their partner's array.

Alternate Approach

- Reteach Worksheet 11.1
- **TAB** See TE pp. 378E–378F.

MathZones

Understanding Multiplication

Students Acquiring English

See Language Connections, Ch. 11.

Challenge

Group students in pairs. Have each student write five repeated addition sentences, exchange papers with his or her partner, and rewrite the addition sentences as multiplication sentences.

Practice

Math Center Use Activity Card 60, *Think Multiplication!*, to have students practice multiplying 2-digit numbers by 1-digit numbers.

Challenge Use Activity Card 60 and have students continue as described in Now Try This!

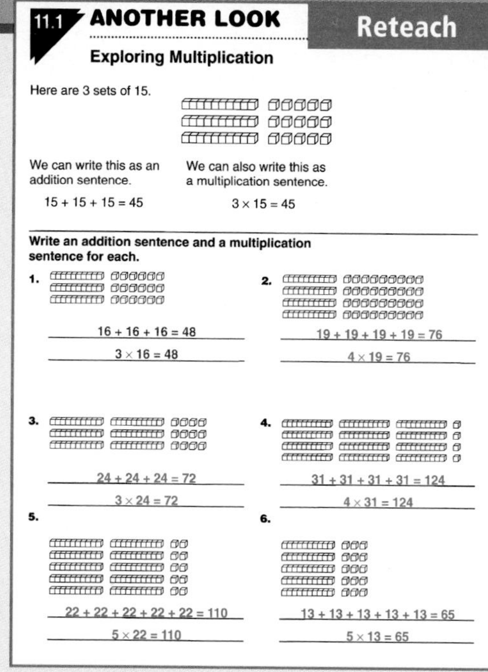

Reteach

11.1 ANOTHER LOOK
Exploring Multiplication

Here are 3 sets of 15.

We can write this as an addition sentence.
15 + 15 + 15 = 45

We can also write this as a multiplication sentence.
3 × 15 = 45

Write an addition sentence and a multiplication sentence for each.

1. 16 + 16 + 16 = 48; 3 × 16 = 48
2. 19 + 19 + 19 + 19 = 76; 4 × 19 = 76
3. 24 + 24 + 24 = 72; 3 × 24 = 72
4. 31 + 31 + 31 + 31 = 124; 4 × 31 = 124
5. 22 + 22 + 22 + 22 + 22 = 110; 5 × 22 = 110
6. 13 + 13 + 13 + 13 + 13 = 65; 5 × 13 = 65

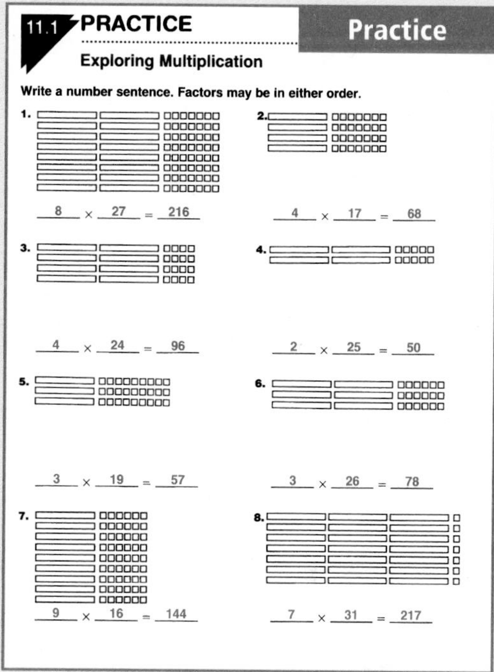

Practice

11.1 PRACTICE
Exploring Multiplication

Write a number sentence. Factors may be in either order.

1. 8 × 27 = 216
2. 4 × 17 = 68
3. 4 × 24 = 96
4. 2 × 25 = 50
5. 3 × 19 = 57
6. 3 × 26 = 78
7. 9 × 16 = 144
8. 7 × 31 = 217

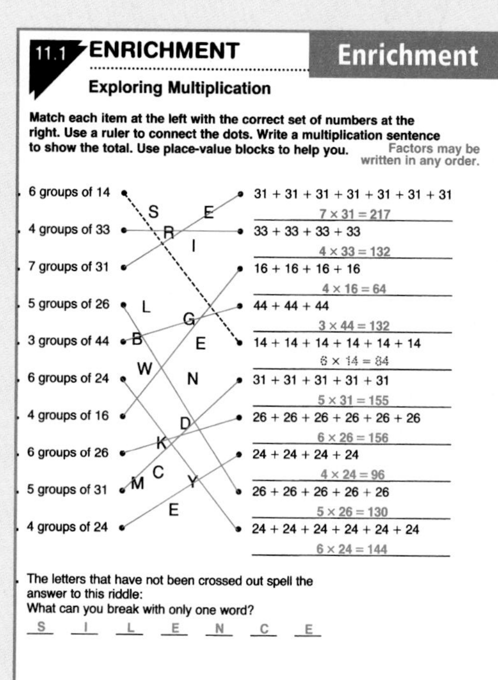

Enrichment

11.1 ENRICHMENT
Exploring Multiplication

Match each item at the left with the correct set of numbers at the right. Use a ruler to connect the dots. Write a multiplication sentence to show the total. Use place-value blocks to help you. Factors may be written in any order.

6 groups of 14	31 + 31 + 31 + 31 + 31 + 31 + 31 — 7 × 31 = 217
4 groups of 33	33 + 33 + 33 + 33 — 4 × 33 = 132
7 groups of 31	16 + 16 + 16 + 16 — 4 × 16 = 64
5 groups of 26	44 + 44 + 44 — 3 × 44 = 132
3 groups of 44	14 + 14 + 14 + 14 + 14 + 14 — 6 × 14 = 84
6 groups of 24	31 + 31 + 31 + 31 + 31 — 5 × 31 = 155
4 groups of 16	26 + 26 + 26 + 26 + 26 + 26 — 6 × 26 = 156
6 groups of 26	24 + 24 + 24 + 24 — 4 × 24 = 96
5 groups of 31	26 + 26 + 26 + 26 + 26 — 5 × 26 = 130
4 groups of 24	24 + 24 + 24 + 24 + 24 + 24 — 6 × 24 = 144

The letters that have not been crossed out spell the answer to this riddle:
What can you break with only one word?
S I L E N C E

LESSON 11.2

Symbolic

Planning at a Glance

Objective To estimate products

Materials none

Optional Resources

- Reteach 11.2; Practice 11.2; Enrichment 11.2
- Daily Cumul. Review, p. 142
- Math Center: Act. Card 61
- Every Day Counts
- **TAB**, TE pp. 378E–378F, 378J
- **Problem of the Day**, 142, p. 71; Flip Chart, p. 71b

Unlocking Whole Numbers 3–5, Level 3, Activity 19

Students Acquiring English

Build context for this lesson by showing or drawing a program. Discuss events that might have programs. Then ask: About how many programs would our class need? Can you estimate?

Problem of the Day

Margo, Nick, Omar, and Pam picked library books. They chose a joke book, a mystery, a biography, and a science book. For once, Nick is not reading about a president. Omar giggled as he picked his book. Margo loves to pretend she is a famous detective. Who chose which book? Margo chose a mystery, Nick chose a science book, Omar chose a joke book, and Pam chose a biography.

Estimating Products

You are making programs for a play. There will be 3 shows. Up to 64 people can come to each show. You have made 175 programs. Will that be enough?

Estimate to find out.

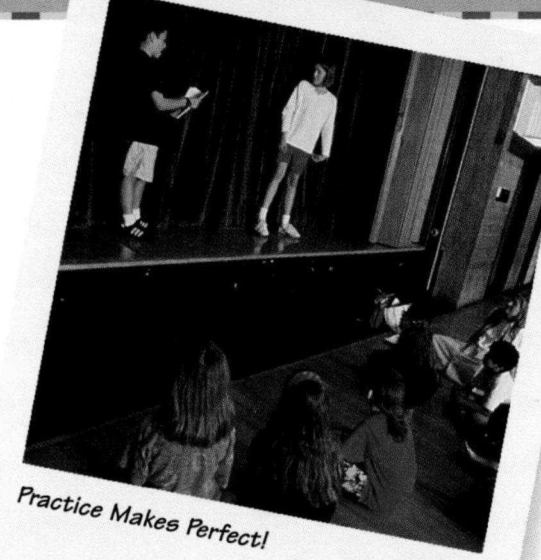

Practice Makes Perfect!

Here's A Way! Estimate 3 × 64.

1. Use rounding to estimate. Round one of the factors.
   3 × 64  3 × 60
2. Multiply.
   3 × 60 = 180
   So, 3 × 64 is about 180.
3. Think about the actual product.
   64 > 60   So, 3 × 64 > 3 × 60.
   So, the actual product will be greater than 180. More than 180 people can come to the shows. You do not have enough programs.

Talk About It! How do you know that 3 × 64 is greater than 180? 3 × 60 = 180, so 3 × 64 > 180

Other Examples Estimate 5 × $4.65.

Front-end estimation: 5 × $4 = $20

Rounding: 5 × $5 = $25

The product of 5 × $4.65 is between $20 and $25.

382 Chapter 11

1 Introduce

Prior Knowledge Have students solve: 5 X 70 350 5 X 700 3500 3 X 50 150

Teach: Here's A Way!
Emphasize these points:

- To find a product when one factor is a multiple of 10 or 100, first multiply the basic fact. Then put the same number of zeros in the product as there are in the factors.
- There can be more than one reasonable estimated answer.

Modeling Model the Other Example. Ask:

- Why did I use both $4 and $5? because the actual product will be somewhere in between the products of $4 × 5 and $5 × 5

2 Develop

Show What You Know!

Common Error Some students may not use the correct multiples of 10 and 100. Remind them to round to the nearest 10 or 100. See also Analyzing Errors, TE pp. 405A and 405B.

Work It Out!

- Ask students to discuss their reasoning for problems 23 and 24.
- Accept all reasonable answers, as student procedures for estimating may vary.

Using Reading Strategies Help students to use the Self-Question strategy as they read the exercises. Ask, How can asking questions help you use the table? See TE p. 378J.

3 Summarize

- Have students explain how they choose numbers that are easy to multiply mentally.
- Ask, When will an exact product be greater than the estimate?

Ongoing Assessment A roll of film holds 36 pictures. A photographer wants to take 100 pictures. Will 4 rolls be enough? Yes; an estimated 120–160 pictures can be taken.

Math Journal: *Communicating*

How can you predict how many digits an estimated product will have? by looking at the number of digits in the basic fact product and counting the zeroes in the factors

Show What You Know!

Estimate the product. Estimates will vary. Possible answers shown.

1. 3 × 67 210
2. 4 × 62 240
3. 7 × 82 560
4. 5 × $7.15 $35
5. 9 × $5.43 $45
6. 5 × 34 150
7. 6 × 273 1800
8. 6 × 216 1200

Estimate. Write < or > to make the number sentence true. Show your work.

9. 3 × 49 ● 4 × 32 >
10. 6 × 379 ● 5 × 514 <
11. 2 × 5079 ● 3 × 2895 >
12. 3 × 124 ● 2 × 225 <
13. **Critical Thinking** You know that one quarter is 25¢. Now estimate 2 × 23¢, 3 × 24¢, and 4 × 26¢. Explain how thinking about a quarter can help you estimate.
50¢; 75¢; $1.00; You can imagine you are counting quarters and skip-count by 25.

Work It Out!

Estimate the product. Estimates will vary. Possible answers shown.

14. 3 × 241 600
15. 6 × 83 480
16. 8 × 293 2400
17. 9 × 63 540

Estimate. Write < or > to complete the number sentence.

18. 6 × 30 ● 3 × 50 >
19. 4 × 59 ● 8 × 24 >
20. 9 × 19 ● 8 × 21 >
21. 4 × 12 ● 2 × 29 <
22. **Critical Thinking** Explain your answer to exercise 21.
12 rounds to 10, and 4 × 10 = 40; 29 rounds to 30, and 2 × 30 = 60; 40 < 60

Problem Solving Using Data

Estimate to solve the problem. Show how you estimated.

23. Which costs more, 7 pairs of shoes or 5 pirate shirts? 7 pairs of shoes
24. Your school play has 8 pirates. Will $200 be enough to buy each actor a pirate mask, a pirate hat, and a scarf?
Yes

Costumes

Item	Cost
Pirate Mask	$4
Pirate Hat	$7
Shoes	$28
Scarf	$13
Pirate Shirt	$36

More Practice Set 11.2, p. 474

383

Meeting Individual Needs

Extra Support

Find the Numbers *(visual)* Give student pairs this list of numbers: 2, 5, 34, 99. Have them work together to find the two numbers on the list whose estimated product is

a. about 60 34, 2
b. about 150 34, 5
c. about 500 99, 5
d. about 200. 99, 2

Alternate Approach

- Reteach Worksheet 11.2
- **TAB** See TE pp. 378E–378F.

MathZones

Understanding Multiplication

Students Acquiring English

See Language Connections, Ch. 11.

Challenge

Distribute 2 sets of number cards 1–9 and this list to student pairs: 29, 48, 57, 76, 88, 275, 361, 453. Students place cards facedown. Students take turns picking a card and a number from the list and estimating the product.

Practice

Math Center Use Activity Card 61, *Taking Aim at Products,* to have students practice estimating products.

Challenge Use Activity Card 61, and have students continue as described in Now Try This!

See **Just the Facts** Cumulative Practice 9, p. 272.

11.2 ANOTHER LOOK — Reteach

Estimating Products

Dillon bought 4 puzzles. Each puzzle has 46 pieces. About how many puzzle pieces are there altogether? Here are two ways to estimate the answer.

Use the 40 in 46. 40 × 4 = 160 or 50 × 4 = 200 46 is close to 50.

160 and 200 puzzle pieces are reasonable estimates.

Complete each to find an estimate. Answers may vary.

1. 37 students in a class, 3 classes. About how many students in all? 37 × 3 →
120 or 90 students are reasonable estimates.
2. 13 boxes of toys, 4 toys in each box. About how many toys in all? 13 × 4 →
40 toys is a reasonable estimate.
3. 26 puppets, 5 buttons needed for each. About how many buttons needed in all? 26 × 5 →
100 or 150 buttons are reasonable estimates.
4. 18 plants on a shelf, 6 shelves. About how many plants in all? 18 × 6 →
60 or 120 plants are reasonable estimates.
5. 42 players in a band, 7 bands in a parade. About how many players in all? 42 × 7 →
280 players is a reasonable estimate.

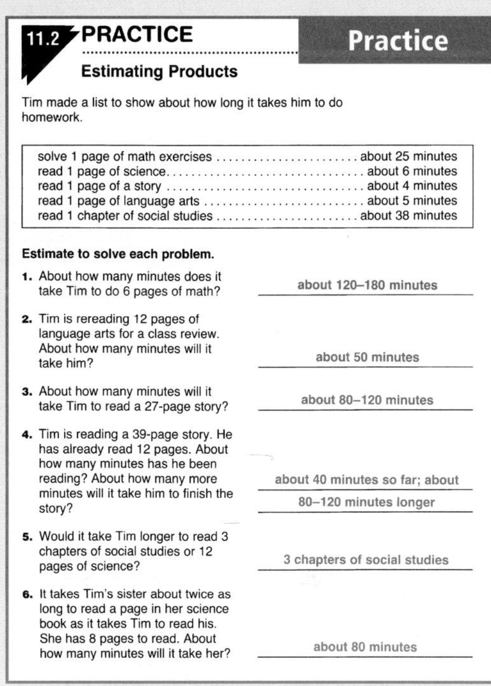

11.2 PRACTICE — Practice

Estimating Products

Tim made a list to show about how long it takes him to do homework.

solve 1 page of math exercises	about 25 minutes
read 1 page of science	about 6 minutes
read 1 page of a story	about 4 minutes
read 1 page of language arts	about 5 minutes
read 1 chapter of social studies	about 38 minutes

Estimate to solve each problem.

1. About how many minutes does it take Tim to do 6 pages of math? about 120–180 minutes
2. Tim is rereading 12 pages of language arts for a class review. About how many minutes will it take him? about 50 minutes
3. About how many minutes will it take Tim to read a 27-page story? about 80–120 minutes
4. Tim is reading a 39-page story. He has already read 12 pages. About how many minutes has he been reading? About how many more minutes will it take him to finish the story? about 40 minutes so far; about 80–120 minutes longer
5. Would it take Tim longer to read 3 chapters of social studies or 12 pages of science? 3 chapters of social studies
6. It takes Tim's sister about twice as long to read a page in her science book as it takes Tim to read his. She has 8 pages to read. About how many minutes will it take her? about 80 minutes

11.2 ENRICHMENT — Enrichment

Estimating Products

Circle the factors whose product is between the answers given.

1. (94 × 7 A) / 73 × 7 I — Product: 630–700
2. 53 × 2 R / (64 × 2 L) — Product: 120–140
3. (774 × 8 U) / 847 × 8 E — Product: 5600–6400
4. (78 × 3 N) / 64 × 3 R — Product: 210–240
5. 85 × 7 P / (77 × 7 C) — Product: 490–560
6. (947 × 6 H) / 821 × 6 A — Product: 5400–6000
7. (64 × 5 O) / 71 × 5 P — Product: 300–350
8. (91 × 2 R) / 88 × 2 T — Product: 180–200
9. 19 × 7 V / (28 × 7 D) — Product: 140–210
10. (88 × 8 I) / 92 × 8 S — Product: 640–720
11. 81 × 7 D / (73 × 7 N) — Product: 490–560
12. 28 × 5 A / (38 × 5 N) — Product: 150–200
13. (67 × 2 E) / 91 × 2 D — Product: 120–180
14. 378 × 6 S / (482 × 6 R) — Product: 2400–3000

Write the letter you circled on the line above each exercise number.

What can you never eat for breakfast?

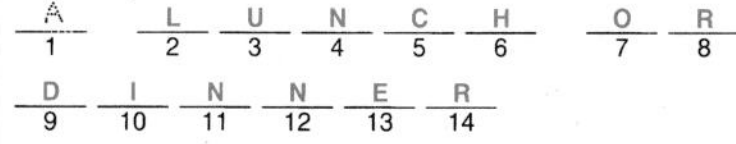

A (1) L (2) U (3) N (4) C (5) H (6) O (7) R (8)
D (9) I (10) N (11) N (12) E (13) R (14)

Planning at a Glance

Objective To use the Work a Simpler Problem strategy to solve problems

Materials none

Optional Resources

- Reteach 11.3; Practice 11.3; Enrichment 11.3
- Daily Cumul. Review, p. 143
- Math Center: Project Card 11
- Every Day Counts
- **TAB**, TE p. 378E–378F, 378J
- **Problem of the Day**, 143, p. 72; Flip Chart, p. 72a

Unlocking Whole Numbers 3–5, Level 3, Activity 13

Students Acquiring English
Have volunteers read problems 1–7. Discuss any unfamiliar terms or concepts.

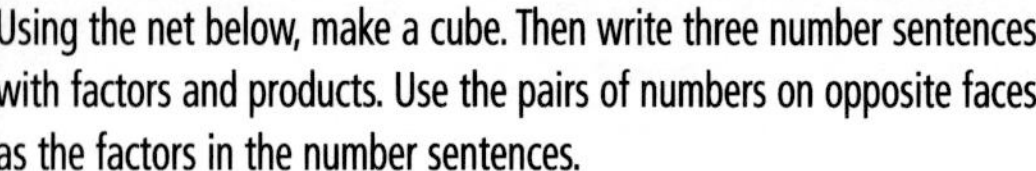

Problem of the Day

Using the net below, make a cube. Then write three number sentences with factors and products. Use the pairs of numbers on opposite faces as the factors in the number sentences.

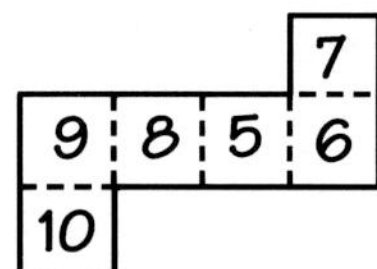

9 × 5 = 45, 6 × 8 = 48, 10 × 7 = 70

Problem Solving
Work a Simpler Problem

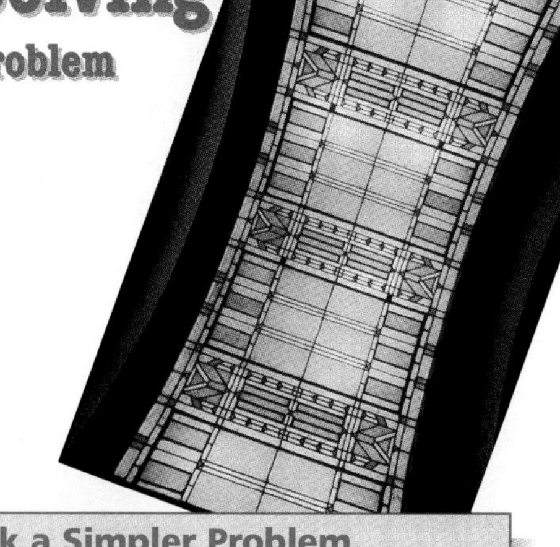

Architect Frank Lloyd Wright designed this window for a ceiling. Each wide section has 82 pieces of glass. How many pieces of glass would replace 3 wide sections?

Here's A Way! Use Work a Simpler Problem.

1 Understand
- How many pieces are in each wide section? 82 pieces
- How many sections do you need to replace? 3

2 Plan
- Use a simpler problem to solve this problem.

3 Try It
- Choose numbers that are easy to work with.
- What if there were 4 pieces in each section? Would there be 3 × 4 pieces altogether? yes

Pieces in 1 section	Pieces in 3 sections
4	3 × 4
82	

4 Look Back
- You would need 3 × 82, or 246, pieces of glass. How did the simpler problem help you to solve this problem? It showed how to set up the problem.

1 Introduce

Prior Knowledge **Write the following sequence on the board: 11, 15, 19, 23, 27, ____, ____. Ask, What numbers continue the pattern?** 31, 35 **What is the pattern?** add 4

Teach: Here's A Way!
Emphasize these points:

- You can make the problem simpler by choosing numbers that are easy to work with.
- Making a simpler problem can help you decide which operation to use.

Modeling Model the example. Ask:

- What did substituting the number 4 for 82 show you? that we needed to multiply by 3 to find the answer

2 Develop

Show What You Know!
Call on students to discuss their solutions to problem 1. Ask them to explain how they used simpler numbers to understand and to solve the problem.

Work It Out!
- Have students discuss the strategies they used. For example, they might work simpler problems for problems 3, 4, and 5 and work backwards for problem 6.

Using Reading Strategies Guide students to use the Self-Question strategy as they read the Problem Solving exercises. Ask them to share their questions with classmates. See TE p. 378J.

3 Summarize

- Have students review how to use simpler numbers to solve problems.
- Remind students that there is no one "correct" strategy for solving any problem.

Ongoing Assessment It takes Mr. Revenko 44 days to build a piano. How long does it take him to build 5 pianos? Explain your strategy. 220 days; one possible strategy: 4 ones × 5 plus 4 tens × 5

Math Journal: *Communicating*

What things about a problem suggest that it would be useful to use simpler numbers to solve it? Answers will vary. Students may indicate that the problem may seem confusing or use large numbers.

Show What You Know!

Use Work a Simpler Problem to solve the problem.

1. You buy 3 cans of soup for 45¢ each and 7 boxes of macaroni and cheese for 39¢ each. You pay the clerk $5.00. How much change should you receive? $.92

2. **Critical Thinking** How did simpler numbers help you make a plan for solving the problem? Answers will vary. Possible answer: They showed me that I needed to multiply, then add to find the total cost, and then subtract to find the amount of change.

Work It Out!

Use Work a Simpler Problem or any strategy to solve.

3. A school is holding a walkathon. People will pay $1.00 for every lap walked. There are 53 walkers. If each one walks 8 laps, will students reach their goal of $400? yes

4. The school bought 2 computer programs, 5 packs of disks, 2 mice, 3 mouse pads, and 2 keyboards. How much of the $400 is left? $15.00

Item	Price
Keyboard	$49.00
Program	$89.00
Disk 10 pack	$5.00
Mouse	$24.00
Mouse pad	$12.00

5. A fruitcake recipe needs 6 c dried fruit and nuts. You have $1\frac{1}{4}$ c cherries, $1\frac{1}{4}$ c apricots, $\frac{1}{2}$ c raisins, and $\frac{1}{2}$ c pecans. Do you have enough for the recipe? If not, how much more do you need? No; you need $2\frac{1}{2}$ more cups.

6. Exactly half of the people at a party wore red. The other 87 wore different colors. How many people were at the party? 174 people

7. A straight fence will have posts 6 ft apart. If 31 posts are used, how long will the fence be? 180 feet

Share Your Thinking

8. When did you decide to use a simpler problem? when working with greater numbers

9. Does everyone have to use the same simpler problem? Explain. no; the strategy works with any simpler numbers

Meeting Individual Needs

Extra Support

Plan Your Strategy *(auditory)* Let pairs of students work together to discuss how they used or could use the four steps of the problem solving process for problems 3–7. Remind students that the steps are listed on student page 384 and include understanding, planning, trying it, and looking back.

Alternate Approach

- Reteach Worksheet 11.3
- **TAB** See TE pp. 378E–378F.

MathZones
Understanding Multiplication

Students Acquiring English

See Language Connections, Ch. 11.

Challenge

Have students create problems that can be simplified for easier solution. They can exchange problems with a partner and solve.

Practice

Math Center For more problem solving practice, see Project Card 11, *Giving a Party.*

Reteach

11.3 ANOTHER LOOK

Problem Solving Strategy: Work a Simpler Problem

You have 6 decks of flash cards. There are 40 cards in each deck. How many cards should there be if all the decks are complete?

1. Understand

- You need to know how many flash cards are in 6 complete decks.

2. Plan

- Sometimes problems look difficult because they use large numbers or have extra information.
- You can use simpler numbers to help you decide how to solve the problem.

3. Try It

- Suppose there were only 4 flash cards in a full deck.
- You need to decide what operation to use to solve the simpler problem. You could multiply 4 by 6.
- You know that you can multiply to find the answer to the larger problem. Use place-value blocks to help you find 6 × 40.

4. Look Back

- You should have 240 cards if all 6 decks of flash cards are complete.

Solve. Use Work a Simpler Problem when you can.

1. A bookstore is open from 9 A.M. to 6 P.M. every day of the week. How many hours is it open each week? 63

2. There are 31 days in March. The bookstore is closed for vacation for 1 week but is open all the other days. How many hours is the bookstore open in March? 216 hours

Practice

11.3 PRACTICE

Problem Solving Strategy: Work a Simpler Problem

Solve. Use Work a Simpler Problem when you can.

Chart of Circus Admission Prices

Adults	$9
Students	$7
Children 5	$5
and under	$1.50

1. Mr. Alvarez has enough money for his ticket and 28 student tickets. How much money does Mr. Alvarez have? $205

2. The circus has 3 rings of circus acts that take place at one time. The first ring has 10 people performing in it, the second ring has 8 people performing in it, and the third ring has 12 people performing in it. How many people are performing? 30 people

3. There are 22 students in Ms. Wong's class, 22 students in Mr. Angel's class, 20 students in Mr. Wing's class, and 20 students in Mrs. Lilian's class. All the classes are allowed to bring a juice box, a granola bar, and a piece of fruit to the circus to snack on. How many food and drink items were brought to the circus by the students? 252 food and drink items

4. Souvenirs cost $5, $6.50, or $12. Olivia wants to buy four $12-souvenirs. How much money will she need? $48

5. There are 48 animals in the circus. Five are zebras, 10 are horses, 8 are tigers, 7 are lions, and the remaining animals are dogs. How many circus dogs are there? 18 dogs

6. The high-wire performance was the students' favorite circus act. There were 2 women and 3 men performing. Each performer did 15 flips in the air by the end of the performance. How many flips were performed? 75 flips

Enrichment

11.3 ENRICHMENT

Problem Solving Strategy: Work a Simpler Problem

Places Matt Visits	Distance from Matt's House
Jared's house	10 miles
Movie theater	12 miles
Shopping mall	31 miles
Jackie's house	5 miles
Swimming pool	4 miles
Grandfather's house	25 miles

Solve. Use Work a Simpler Problem when you can.

1. Matt visits his grandfather 2 times a month. His family drives there and back again. How many miles does Matt travel each month to visit his grandfather? 100 miles

2. Matt wants to buy a birthday gift for his mother. His father drives him to the shopping mall. Then his father drives to visit a friend that lives 3 miles from the mall. Then he returns to the mall to pick up Matt and drives home again. How many miles did Matt's father travel? 68 miles

3. Suppose all of the places Matt visits are on the same road. If he leaves his house and visits each place as he comes to it, where will his fourth stop be? Movie theater

4. Matt is on his way to Jared's house to spend the night. When he is halfway there, he has to return home to get his sleeping bag. How many miles in all will Matt have to travel to get to Jared's house? 20 miles

5. At the swimming pool Matt and his 4 friends dive for pennies. They find all the pennies that were in the water. The boys each have 23 pennies. How many pennies were in the water? 115 pennies

Connecting

Planning at a Glance

Objective To use arrays to multiply 2-digit numbers by 1-digit numbers, with and without regrouping

Materials place-value blocks, squared paper (TR2)

Optional Resources

- Reteach 11.4; Practice 11.4; Enrichment 11.4
- Daily Cumul. Review, p. 144
- Math Center: Act. Card 62
- Every Day Counts
- **TAB**, TE pp. 378E–378F, 378J
- **Problem of the Day**, 144, p. 72; Flip Chart, p. 72b

MATHKEYS *Unlocking Whole Numbers 3–5*, Level 3, Activity 14

Students Acquiring English

Building Reading Strategies Help with the Problem of the Day. Demonstrate what it means to "design an 8 × 8 grid." Ask students to point to "every 4th box" and "every 8th box." Put dots in some of the boxes and explain that the boxes without dots are "plain." Have students suggest a strategy for solving the problem, and then solve it.

Problem of the Day

Simon has an 8 × 8 grid to design. He plans to draw a red dot in every 4th box. He will make a border on every 8th box. How many boxes will be left plain? 48 boxes

Multiplying with an Array

Getting Started

What You'll Need:
- place-value blocks
- squared paper

Suppose you have 6 rolls of film. You can take 12 pictures with each roll. If you use all 6 rolls, how many pictures will you take?

You can use an array or an array diagram to find out.

Here's A Way! Find 6 × 12.

1. Multiply the ones.

$$\begin{array}{r} 12 \\ \times\ 6 \\ \hline 12 \end{array}$$ 6 × 2

2. Multiply the tens.

$$\begin{array}{r} 12 \\ \times\ 6 \\ \hline 12 \\ 60 \end{array}$$ 6 × 10

3. Add to find the product.

$$\begin{array}{r} 12 \\ \times\ 6 \\ \hline 12 \\ 60 \\ \hline 72 \end{array}$$

4. Explain what the answer means.

You will take 72 pictures.

Talk About It! How does putting the blocks into a ones and tens array help you find 6 × 12? The ones array shows 6 × 2 and the tens array shows 6 × 10.

386 Chapter 11

1 Introduce

Prior Knowledge **Ask, Which two of the numbers 53, 8, 98, and 5 have a product of about 800? About 250?** 98, 8; 53, 5

Teach: Here's A Way!

Emphasize this point:

- In step 2, make sure to add a zero to the right of the tens-place digit before you multiply.

Modeling Model 39 × 8. Ask:

- How many ones do I multiply by 8? 9
- What is the product? 72
- How many tens do I multiply by 8? 3
- What is the product? 240
- What do I do next to find the product of 8 × 39? find the sum of 72 + 240; 312

2 Develop

Show What You Know!

Common Error Some students may confuse the parts of the array. Remind them which part of the array shows the ones and which part shows the tens. See also Analyzing Errors, TE pp. 405A and 405B.

- Ask students to discuss exercise 9.

Work It Out!

- For exercise 21, have students discuss their mental math strategies.

Using Reading Strategies Help students to use the Self-Question strategy as they read the Problem Solving exercise. Ask, How can asking questions help you understand the problem? See TE. p. 378J

3 Summarize

- Have students explain how an array can help them multiply a 2-digit number by a 1-digit number.
- Emphasize that multiplication begins with the ones place.

Ongoing Assessment You have 5 packages of 35 stamps each. What multiplication sentence can you write to find out how many stamps you have? 5 × 35 = 175

Math Journal: *Communicating*

How can an array help you multiply? Students may say that an array shows them how many sets there are and how many ones and tens are in each set.

Show What You Know!

Use the array to answer the question.

1. Write a multiplication sentence for the array of blocks. 4 × 24
2. **Estimation** Is the product less than 100? How can you tell? Yes
   You can estimate by rounding. 4 × 20 = 80, and 80 < 100.
3. Draw a diagram of the array of blocks. Find the product. 96; See Additional Answers for the diagram.

Find the product. Use blocks or draw a diagram. Record. Check students' recording.

4. 3 × 16 48 5. 5 × 25 125 6. 9 × 13 117 7. 3 × 50 150 8. 4 × 25 100

9. **Critical Thinking** Do you need to use an array to find all of the products in exercises 4–8? Why or why not?
   Answers will vary. Possible answer: No; 5, 7, and 8 can be done with mental math.
10. **Create Your Own** Write a multiplication problem for a friend to solve. Answers will vary.

Work It Out!

Find the product. Show your work. Check students' recording.

11. 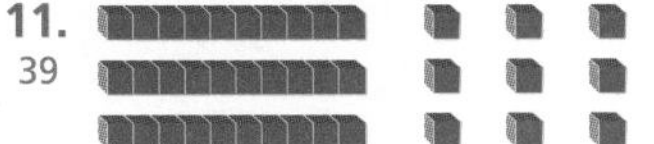 39

12. 78 (diagram: 3 by 20 and 6)

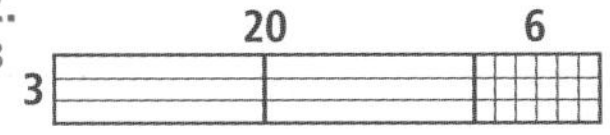

Find the product. Use a diagram, blocks, or mental math.

13. 3 × 19 57 14. 6 × 50 300 15. 7 × 12 84 16. 8 × 24 192

17. 6 × 20 120 18. 5 × 23 115 19. 8 × 10 80 20. 4 × 30 120

21. **Mental Math** In exercises 13–20, which products did you find by using mental math? Explain how you found them. Answers will vary. Possible answer: 14, 17, 19, 20; used basic facts and then wrote in a zero.
22. **Problem Solving** You used 4 rolls of film. Two rolls had 36 pictures each. The rest had 24 pictures each. How many pictures did you take? 120 pictures.

Mixed Review

Compare the two amounts. Write >, <, or =.

23. 2 c ● 1 qt < 24. 2 ft ● 18 in. > 25. 985 m ● 1 km < 26. 6 pt ● 3 qt =

More Practice Set 11.4, p. 474

Meeting Individual Needs

Extra Support

Arrays ***(visual/kinesthetic)*** Have students work in pairs to make arrays to solve the multiplication exercises below. For each exercise, have students model the 2-digit factor using place-value blocks. They can refer to the models as they make their arrays.

a. 6 × 23 138 d. 8 × 31 248

b. 3 × 77 231 e. 9 × 80 720

c. 4 × 65 260 f. 7 × 44 308

Alternate Approach

- Reteach Worksheet 11.4
- **TAB** See TE pp. 378E–378F.

MathZones
Understanding Multiplication

Students Acquiring English

See Language Connections, Ch. 11.

Practice

Math Center Use Activity Card 62, *Multiplication Arrays,* to have students practice using arrays to multiply 2-digit numbers by 1-digit numbers.

Challenge Use Activity Card 62 and have students continue as described in Now Try This!

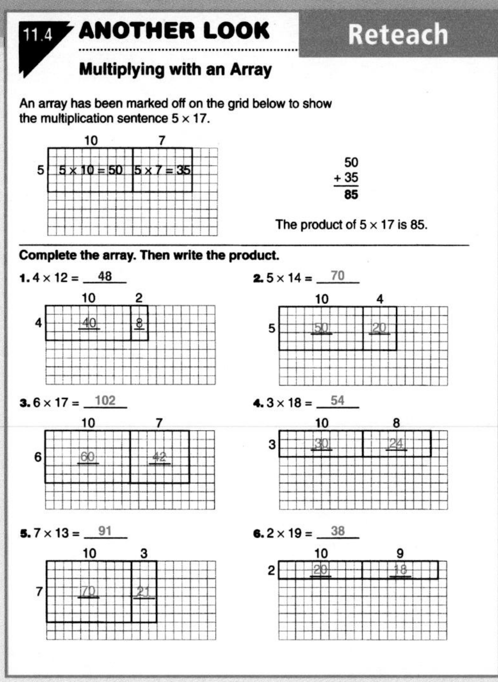

11.4 **ANOTHER LOOK** — Reteach

Multiplying with an Array

An array has been marked off on the grid below to show the multiplication sentence 5 × 17.

5 × 10 = 50 | 5 × 7 = 35; 50 + 35 = 85

The product of 5 × 17 is 85.

Complete the array. Then write the product.

1. 4 × 12 = 48 (40, 8)
2. 5 × 14 = 70 (50, 20)
3. 6 × 17 = 102 (60, 42)
4. 3 × 18 = 54 (30, 24)
5. 7 × 13 = 91 (70, 21)
6. 2 × 19 = 38 (20, 18)

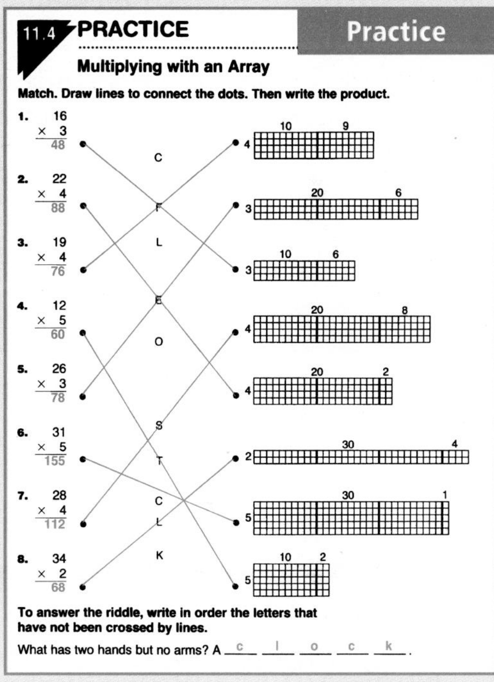

11.4 **PRACTICE** — Practice

Multiplying with an Array

Match. Draw lines to connect the dots. Then write the product.

1. 16 × 3 = 48
2. 22 × 4 = 88
3. 19 × 4 = 76
4. 12 × 5 = 60
5. 26 × 3 = 78
6. 31 × 5 = 155
7. 28 × 4 = 112
8. 34 × 2 = 68

Letters: C F L E O S T C L K

To answer the riddle, write in order the letters that have not been crossed by lines.

What has two hands but no arms? A c l o c k.

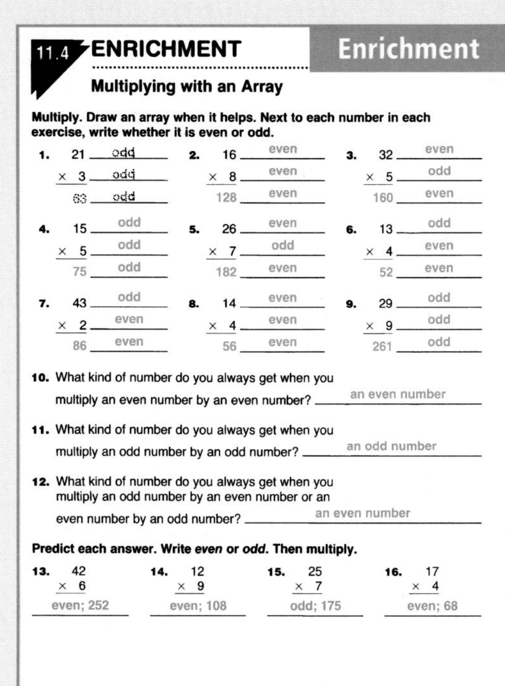

11.4 **ENRICHMENT** — Enrichment

Multiplying with an Array

Multiply. Draw an array when it helps. Next to each number in each exercise, write whether it is even or odd.

1. 21 odd × 3 odd = 63 odd
2. 16 even × 8 even = 128 even
3. 32 even × 5 odd = 160 even
4. 15 odd × 5 odd = 75 odd
5. 26 even × 7 odd = 182 even
6. 13 odd × 4 even = 52 even
7. 43 odd × 2 even = 86 even
8. 14 even × 4 even = 56 even
9. 29 odd × 9 odd = 261 odd

10. What kind of number do you always get when you multiply an even number by an even number? an even number
11. What kind of number do you always get when you multiply an odd number by an odd number? an odd number
12. What kind of number do you always get when you multiply an odd number by an even number or an even number by an odd number? an even number

Predict each answer. Write *even* or *odd.* Then multiply.

13. 42 × 6 even; 252
14. 12 × 9 even; 108
15. 25 × 7 odd; 175
16. 17 × 4 even; 68

LESSON 11.5

Connecting

Planning at a Glance

Objective To multiply 2-digit numbers by 1-digit numbers, regrouping ones and tens

Materials place-value blocks, squared paper (TR2)

Optional Resources

- Reteach 11.5; Practice 11.5; Enrichment 11.5
- Daily Cumul. Review, p. 145
- Math Center: Act. Card 63
- Every Day Counts
- **TAB**, TE pp. 378E–378F, 378J
- **Problem of the Day**, 145, p. 73; Flip Chart, p. 73a

Unlocking Whole Numbers 3–5, Level 3, Activity 21

Students Acquiring English

Display a checkerboard and checkers and invite students to share what they know about the game. Then read the question on student page 388, reviewing vocabulary as necessary.

Problem of the Day

The 4 on Jeremy's calculator does not work. How could he use the broken calculator to find 24 × 14? Explain your method.

One possible answer includes calculating 12 × 28, or calculating 8 × 3 × 7 × 2.

Multiplying 2-Digit Numbers

Getting Started
What You'll Need:
▶ place-value blocks
▶ squared paper

You have 3 checkerboards. You need 24 checkers to go with each board. How many checkers do you need to get?

You can multiply to find out. Estimate first to help you check your answer.

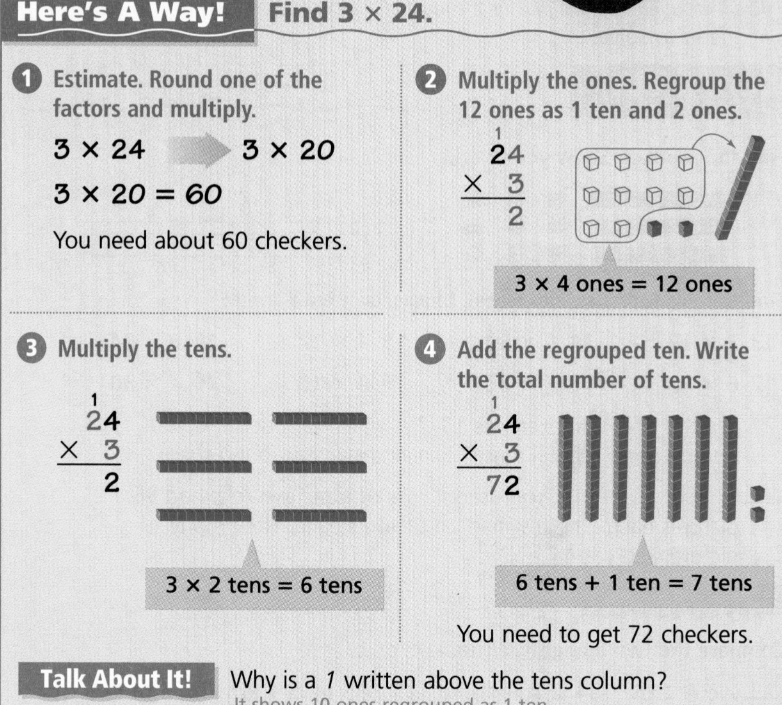

Here's A Way! Find 3 × 24.

1. Estimate. Round one of the factors and multiply.
   3 × 24 → 3 × 20
   3 × 20 = 60
   You need about 60 checkers.
2. Multiply the ones. Regroup the 12 ones as 1 ten and 2 ones.
   $\begin{array}{r} {}^{1}\\ 24 \\ \times\ 3 \\ \hline 2 \end{array}$
   3 × 4 ones = 12 ones
3. Multiply the tens.
   $\begin{array}{r} {}^{1}\\ 24 \\ \times\ 3 \\ \hline 2 \end{array}$
   3 × 2 tens = 6 tens
4. Add the regrouped ten. Write the total number of tens.
   $\begin{array}{r} {}^{1}\\ 24 \\ \times\ 3 \\ \hline 72 \end{array}$
   6 tens + 1 ten = 7 tens
   You need to get 72 checkers.

Talk About It! Why is a *1* written above the tens column?
It shows 10 ones regrouped as 1 ten.

388 Chapter 11

1 Introduce

Build Understanding **Have students tell how they are able to solve these problems:** by using basic facts

5 X □ = 250 50 **6 X □ = 60** 10
8 X □ = 240 30 **□ X 4 = 400** 100

Teach: Here's A Way!

Emphasize this point:

- Regroup 10 ones as 1 ten; regroup 10 tens as 1 hundred.

Modeling Model 61 × 4. Ask:

- Which place do I multiply first? ones
- Do I need to regroup the ones? The tens? The ones don't need regrouping; regroup 20 tens as 2 hundreds.

2 Develop

Show What You Know!

Common Error Some students may forget to add the regrouped number. Use place-value blocks and mats to review regrouping. See also Analyzing Errors TE pp. 405A and 405B.

- Have students discuss their answers to exercise 7.

Work It Out!

- Have students discuss their reasoning for exercises 23–25.

Using Reading Strategies Guide students to use the Self-Question strategy as they read the Problem Solving exercises. Ask them how asking questions can help them visualize the problem. See TE p. 378J.

3 Summarize

- Remind students that they may need to regroup ones as tens and tens as hundreds when multiplying a 2-digit number by a 1-digit number.

Ongoing Assessment There are 15 toy circus animals in a box. You sold 6 boxes. How many toy animals did you sell? 90 toy animals How many times did you have to regroup to find the product? once: 30 ones as 3 tens

Math Journal: *Communicating*

Answers will vary. Possible answers include multiplying one place value at a time and regrouping, making an array, multiplying 5 × 40 and subtracting 25, and using repeated addition.

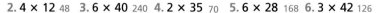

Show What You Know!

Find the product.

1. 34 × 3 = 102

2. 4 × 12 48 3. 6 × 40 240 4. 2 × 35 70 5. 6 × 28 168 6. 3 × 42 126

7. **Critical Thinking** What method would you use to find 9 × 99? Explain. Round 99 to 100; 9 × 100 = 900. Subtract 9. 9 × 99 = 891

Work It Out!

Multiply. Use any method you like.

8. 8 × 26 208 9. 7 × 39 273 10. 5 × 20 100 11. 6 × 17 102 12. 4 × 29 116

13. 45 × 7 315 14. 16 × 6 96 15. 84 × 4 336 16. 39 × 5 195 17. 25 × 6 150

18. 25 × 3 75 19. 25 × 9 225 20. 34 × 2 68 21. 44 × 3 132 22. 34 × 4 136

23. **Patterns** How can you use 3 × 15 and 6 × 15 to help you find 9 × 15? Answers will vary. Possible answers: To find 9 × 15, add 3 more groups of 15 to 6 × 15. Add the product of 3 × 15 to the product of 6 × 15.

24. **Algebraic Reasoning** Copy and complete the table.

Checkerboards	1	2	? (3)	? (4)	5	6	? (7)	8
Checkers	24	48	72	? (96)	? (120)	? (144)	168	? (192)

25. **Problem Solving** A checkerboard is 8 squares by 8 squares. When all 24 checkers are on the board, are more than half the squares covered? Explain. No; half would be 32.

More Practice Set 11.5, p. 475

Describe three ways to find 5 × 35. Answers will vary. Possible answers: repeated addition, arrays, multiplication

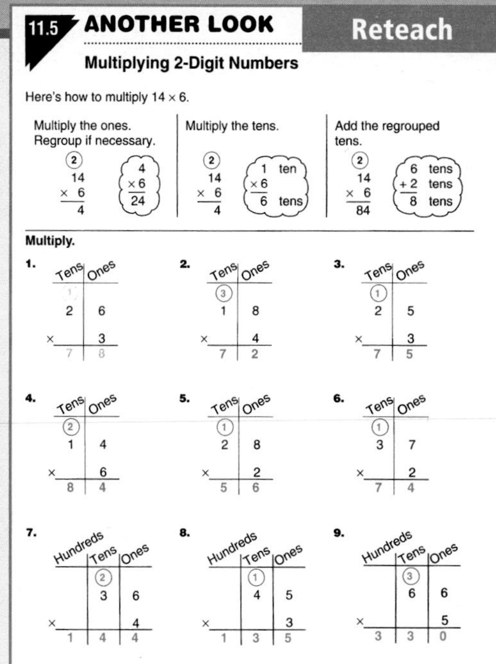

11.5 ANOTHER LOOK — Reteach

Multiplying 2-Digit Numbers

Here's how to multiply 14 × 6.

Multiply the ones. Regroup if necessary.	Multiply the tens.	Add the regrouped tens.
14 × 6 = 4 (2 regrouped); 4 × 6 = 24	14 × 6 = 4; 1 ten × 6 = 6 tens	14 × 6 = 84; 6 tens + 2 tens = 8 tens

Multiply.

1. 26 × 3 = 78
2. 18 × 4 = 72
3. 25 × 3 = 75
4. 14 × 6 = 84
5. 28 × 2 = 56
6. 37 × 2 = 74
7. 36 × 4 = 144
8. 45 × 3 = 135
9. 66 × 5 = 330

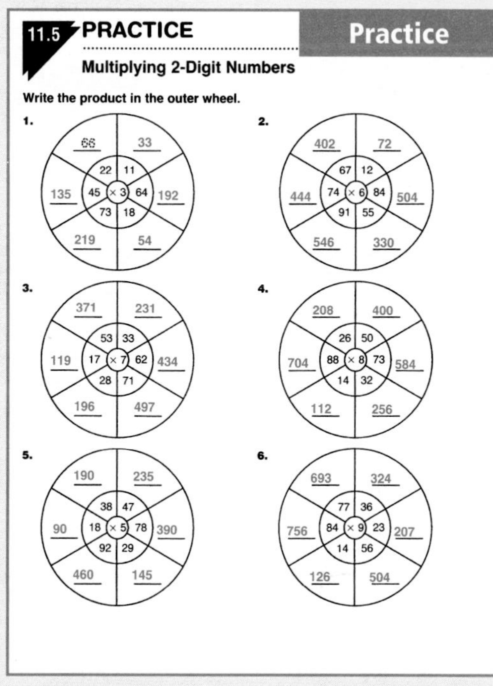

11.5 PRACTICE — Practice

Multiplying 2-Digit Numbers

Write the product in the outer wheel.

1. × 3: 22 → 66; 11 → 33; 64 → 192; 18 → 54; 73 → 219; 45 → 135
2. × 6: 67 → 402; 12 → 72; 84 → 504; 55 → 330; 91 → 546; 74 → 444
3. × 7: 53 → 371; 33 → 231; 62 → 434; 71 → 497; 28 → 196; 17 → 119
4. × 8: 26 → 208; 50 → 400; 73 → 584; 32 → 256; 14 → 112; 88 → 704
5. × 5: 38 → 190; 47 → 235; 78 → 390; 29 → 145; 92 → 460; 18 → 90
6. × 9: 77 → 693; 36 → 324; 23 → 207; 56 → 504; 14 → 126; 84 → 756

Meeting Individual Needs

Extra Support

Seeing Is Believing ***(visual/kinesthetic)*** Let pairs of students use place-value blocks to solve the following exercises. Then have them discuss how the place-value blocks help them understand the multiplication.

a. 55 × 6 330 c. 43 × 9 387

b. 27 × 8 216 d. 38 × 5 190

Alternate Approach

- Reteach Worksheet 11.5
- **TAB** See TE pp. 378E–378F.
- MATHKEYS Invite students to multiply with electronic base-ten blocks. They explore multiplying with and without trading in *Unlocking Whole Numbers 3–5,* Level 3, Activity 21.

MathZones

Understanding Multiplication

Students Acquiring English

See Language Connections, Ch. 11.

Challenge

Have students make up word problems using these factors: a. 6, 12 b. 27, 7

Invite students to trade papers and solve.

Practice

Math Center Use Activity Card 63, *Rolling Products,* to have students practice multiplying 2-digit numbers by 1-digit numbers, regrouping ones and tens.

Challenge Use Activity Card 63 and have students continue as described in Now Try This!

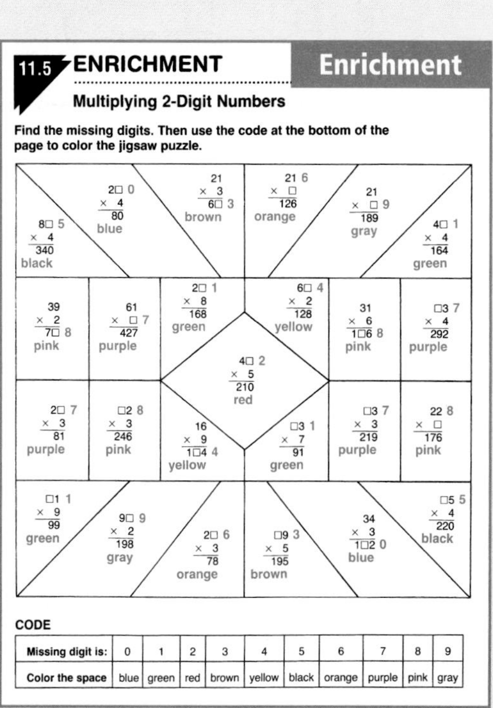

11.5 ENRICHMENT — Enrichment

Multiplying 2-Digit Numbers

Find the missing digits. Then use the code at the bottom of the page to color the jigsaw puzzle.

8□5 × 4 = 340 black; 2□0 × 4 = 80 blue; 21 × 3 = 6□3 brown; 21 × □ = 126 orange; 21 × □9 = 189 gray; 4□1 × 4 = 164 green;
39 × 2 = 7□8 pink; 61 × □7 = 427 purple; 2□1 × 8 = 168 green; 6□4 × 2 = 128 yellow; 31 × 6 = 1□6 8 pink; □3 7 × 4 = 292 purple;
4□2 × 5 = 210 red;
2□7 × 3 = 81 purple; □2 8 × 3 = 246 pink; 16 × 9 = 1□4 4 yellow; □3 1 × 7 = 91 green; □3 7 × 3 = 219 purple; 22 8 × □ = 176 pink;
□1 1 × 9 = 99 green; 9□ 9 × 2 = 198 gray; 2□ 6 × 3 = 78 orange; □9 3 × 5 = 195 brown; 34 × 3 = 1□2 0 blue; □5 5 × 4 = 220 black

CODE

Missing digit is:	0	1	2	3	4	5	6	7	8	9
Color the space	blue	green	red	brown	yellow	black	orange	purple	pink	gray

LESSON 11.6

Problem Solving

Planning at a Glance

Objective To decide whether to estimate or find an exact answer to solve problems

Materials none

Optional Resources

- Daily Cumul. Review, p. 146
- Math Center: Project Card 11
- Every Day Counts
- **TAB**, TE p. 378E–378F, 378J
- **Problem of the Day**, 146, p. 73; Flip Chart, p. 73b
- **Reteach, Practice, and Enrichment Worksheets for Lesson 11.6**

Unlocking Whole Numbers 3–5, Counters Multiply Mat

Students Acquiring English
To build meaning for the phrase *keep track of*, invite students to keep track of numbers of items in the classroom, or of the number of times a certain event occurs.

Problem of the Day

Use 15 counters. Put 1, 2, or 3 counters in each section of the figure. You may NOT put the same number of counters in sections that touch.
One possible answer is shown.

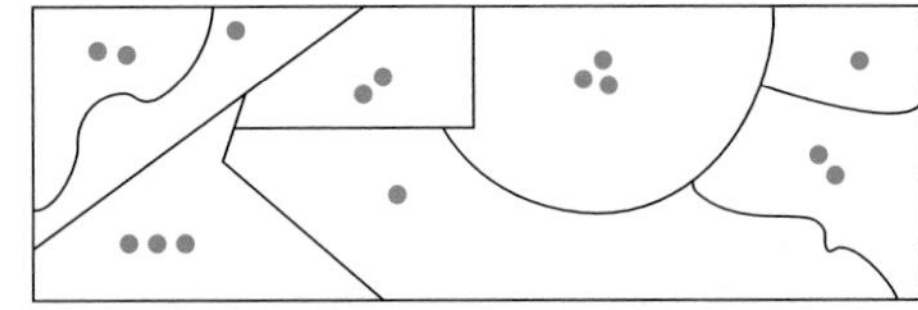

Problem Solving : Decisions

LESSON 6

Problem Solving

Choose a Computation Method

Choose a Computation Method

Ask Yourself:

- Do I need an exact answer or an estimate?
- Should I use a model, paper and pencil, mental math, or a calculator?
- What operation should I use?

Forest rangers keep track of plants and animals that live near them. You could keep track where you live. How could you find out how many fish live in a lake?

A Ranger at Work

You Decide

- Could you count all the fish? Explain. No; there are too many, they move around, and you cannot see them.
- Must you have an exact number, or could you use an estimate? Explain your decision. You can estimate. Explanations will vary.

Work It Out!

Decide whether to estimate or find an exact answer. Explain.

1. You are making rice pudding from a recipe. You need to know how much sugar to add. exact answer; The wrong amount will make it taste bad.
2. You want to buy a package of stickers and a drink. The stickers cost $1.98 and the drink costs $.75. Is $5.00 enough money? estimate; You can round and get a very close estimate.
3. You are inviting friends to your birthday party. You want to know how many invitations you will need. exact answer; You need enough invitations.
4. **Create Your Own** Write a problem for a friend to solve by estimating or finding an exact answer. Answers will vary.

Share Your Thinking

5. How do you know when to estimate? Answers will vary. Possible answer: You can estimate when it is not important to have an exact answer.

390 Chapter 11

1 Introduce

Prior Knowledge **Ask, You want to buy a jacket that costs $18.50 and a shirt that costs $7.95. Can you estimate to find out how much money you need?** yes; about $28.

Teach: You Decide
Emphasize this point:

- Estimation is useful when you need to know about how many.

Modeling Model the example. Discuss:

- Do you need an exact count of the fish? Why, or why not?
- How could you estimate the number of fish in a lake? count the fish in one part, and multiply

2 Develop

Work It Out!

- For problems 1–3, have students discuss why an exact answer is needed or why estimation is sufficient.
- For problem 4, invite students to share their problems with the class.
- Ask students to discuss problem 5.

Basic Facts Just the Facts Basic Facts Workshop 11, p. 118

Using Reading Strategies Encourage students to use the Self-Question strategy as they read the Problem Solving exercises. Ask, How can asking questions help you decide what computation method to use? See TE p. 378J.

3 Summarize

- Have students discuss how they decide whether to estimate or to find an exact answer to a problem.

Ongoing Assessment How would you find out how many times your heart beats in an hour? Answers may vary. Students will probably suggest counting heartbeats for a minute and then multiplying by 60, the number of minutes in an hour.

Math Journal: *Communicating*

How can you tell when an estimate will give you the answer you need without having to figure the exact answer? Answers may vary but should include the recognition that the kind of question asked gives a clue about what calculation method to use.

Problem Solving Workshop

Estimate or Find an Exact Answer?

Review

Use with page 390.

15 minutes

When Do You Estimate?

Management teacher directed; whole class

- Share problems such as the following and ask students to decide whether they should estimate or find an exact answer. Also ask what operation they would use and whether they would use a calculator, pencil and paper, or mental math.
  1. At the supermarket, your uncle is writing a check to pay for his groceries. Would he need an exact answer or an estimate? exact
  2. Your neighbor is going to plant new grass. The backyard is 75 feet by 40 feet. One bag of grass seed covers about 50 square feet of soil. Would she need an exact answer or an estimate? estimate
  3. The local taxi service charges $1.20 for the first mile and $0.25 for every additional $\frac{1}{4}$ mile. Your friend's house is 5 miles away. To make sure you have enough money to get there, would you need an exact answer or an estimate? exact, or find an overestimate
- Invite students to name other situations in which they could use estimates or exact answers. You might help them get started with the following examples: your uncle might want to *estimate* how much he spent on groceries last month; your cousin wants to know the *exact* price of a new pair of shoes; you need to *estimate* how many cookies to bring to a class party.

Activity

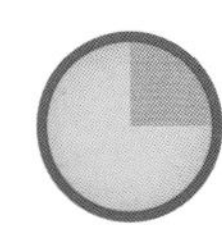

Use with page 390.

15 minutes

Do You Need Exact Answers?

Management small groups
Materials pencil and paper

- Tell students that they are in charge of taking the classroom inventory.
- Groups should choose items to include in their inventory (number of students, number of pencils, number of geoboards, etc.). Are there some classroom items you wouldn't find exact counts for? pieces of paper, rubber bands, paper clips, place-value blocks, etc.
- Then, group members decide whether to include exact answers or estimates for each item and find a way to record the results of their inventory in a table. The table should show whether numbers are estimates or exact counts.

How Many Are There?

Item	Exact Count	Estimate
pieces of paper		1,500
chairs	32	
students	24	
tables	7	
place-value blocks		300

- Post and discuss the results. Did any groups count the same items? How close were the numbers? Why might numbers vary between groups?

TAB Chapter 11

Teacher's Activity Bank

Basic Facts Workshop

Use with Lesson 11.6

Multiplying by 7

See also *Just the Facts*
- Support Masters
- Practice Worksheets
- Cumulative Practice

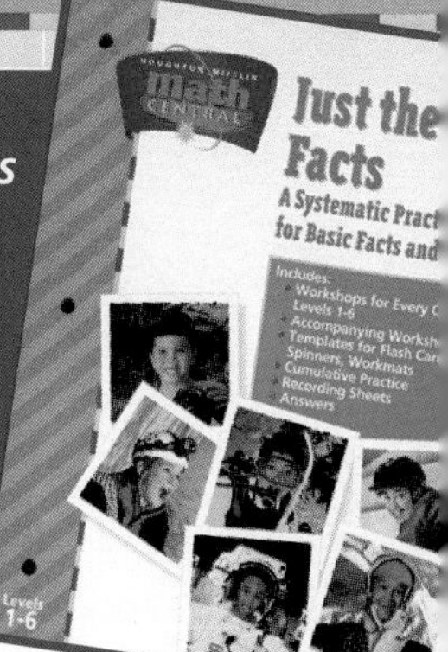

Review

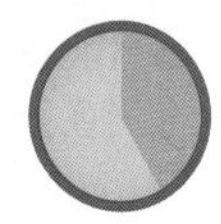

25 minutes

Use What You Know for 7's

Management whole class
Materials overhead projector; blank transparency; Just the Facts Support Master 7 (hundredths square) on p. 288; See also Practice 11A–11B on pp. 140–141 for use with Lessons 11.8–11.9, 11.11; Cumulative Practice 9 on p. 272 for use with Lesson 11.2.

- Remind the class that they have already practiced multiplying by 1's, 2's, 3's, 4's, 5's, 6's, and 9's. On a transparency write equations as shown. Have students determine the missing numbers. 2, 5, 1, 4, 3
- Ask students to identify which facts for 7 are missing from the list. $6 \times 7 = 42$, $7 \times 7 = 49$, $8 \times 7 = 56$, and $9 \times 7 = 63$
- Draw a 7×7 array on a grid transparency. Tell students that if they cannot remember the product of 7×7, they could use the facts they do know to find the answer. Discuss different ways they might split the array into parts to find the product for 7×7. 7×5 plus 7×2; 7×1 plus 7×6; 7×3 plus 7×4

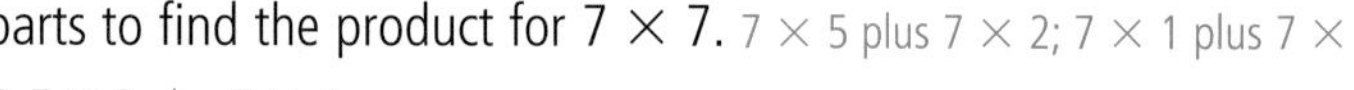

- Draw a 7×8 array on a grid transparency. In the event that students cannot remember the product, ask how they might split the array to use facts they do know to find 7×8. 7×4 plus 7×4; 7×2 plus 7×6; 7×3 plus 7×5

□ x 7 = 14
□ x 7 = 35
□ x 7 = 7
□ x 7 = 28
□ x 7 = 21

Practice

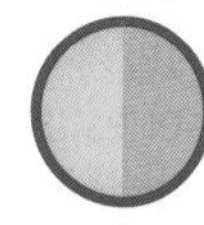

30 minutes

Make ×7 Flash Cards

Management individuals, then pairs
Materials for each student: 3 index cards; Just the Facts Support Masters 11, 15 (practice minutes, certificate) on pp. 292, 296; See also Practice 11A–11B on pp. 140–141 for use with Lessons 11.8–11.9, 11.11; Cumulative Practice 9 on p. 272 for use with Lesson 11.2.

- Distribute index cards to each student.
- Have students make flash cards for the 3 remaining multiplication facts for 7: 7×7, 7×8, and 8×7. Remind them to write their names or initials on the backs of their cards.
- After they complete their flash cards, have students work with partners to practice multiplying by 7.
- For additional practice, students should take their flash cards home. Remind them to keep a record of the minutes that they practice. Students may return completed records to school in exchange for a certificate.

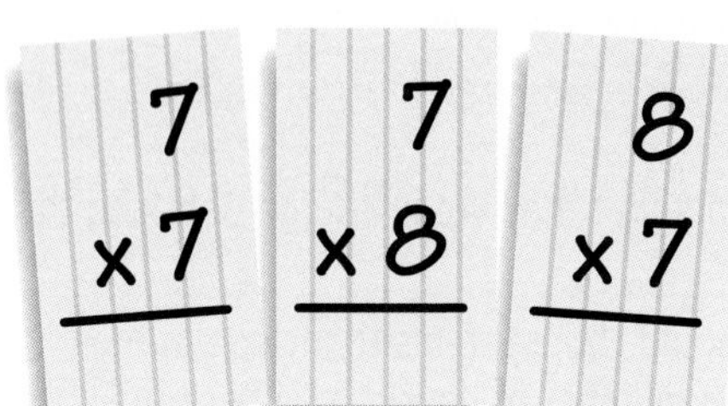

Midchapter Review

for Pages 378–390

Problem Solving

Use any strategy to solve the problem. Show your work. (page 384)

1. Suppose you want to buy 6 colored markers that cost 79¢ each and 2 black markers that cost 98¢ each. You have \$4.00. About how much more do you need to buy the markers? Answers will vary. Accept a range from \$2.70 to \$4.00
2. Some students from your school are going to the art museum. You fill 3 buses and half of another bus. There are 46 seats on each bus. How many people from your school are going on the trip? 161 people

Concepts

Write a multiplication sentence for the array. (page 380)

3. 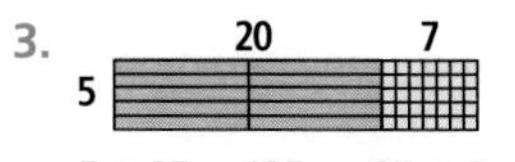

5 × 27 = 135, or 27 × 5 = 135

4. 30 2 / 4

4 × 32 = 128, or 32 × 4 = 128

Find the product. You may use arrays to help. (page 380)

5. 8 groups of 24 192
6. 19 × 3 57

Estimate. Write > or < to complete the number sentence. (page 382)

7. 21 × 3 ● 37 × 2 <
8. 8 × 50 ● 70 × 4 >
9. 9 × 31 ● 42 × 8 <
10. 69 × 4 ● 51 × 5 >

Skills

Find the product. (page 388)

11. 70 × 9 630
12. 8 × 13 104
13. 54 × 3 162
14. 5 × 99 495
15. 32 × 2 64

16.	17.	18.	19.	20.
76 × 6 = 456	51 × 8 = 408	69 × 4 = 276	28 × 3 = 84	17 × 2 = 34

391

Meeting Individual Needs

Students Acquiring English

Some students may need assistance on the Midchapter Review.

- Be prepared to read directions aloud to students.
- Focus special attention on word problems. Expect to paraphrase, diagram, or draw an explanation of the word problem.
- Review important vocabulary words that have been previously introduced.

Additional Assessment Resources

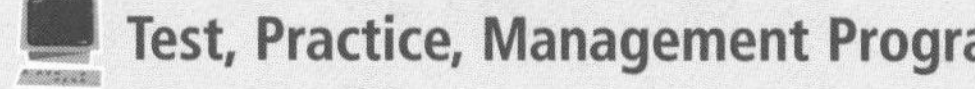

Test, Practice, Management Program

Use the *Test, Practice, Management Program* to create, administer, and score tests as well as generate practice sets. Questions are correlated to the Lesson Objectives.

Midchapter Review

Scoring Chart

Item	Points
1–2	10 points each
3–10	5 points each
11–20	4 points each
TOTAL	100 points or 100%

Problem Solving

Give from 0 to 10 points per answer, based on how well students meet the following criteria:

Problem 1

- Answer shows use of a particular strategy and a method for checking.
- Work is shown clearly.

Problem 2

- Answer shows use of a particular strategy and a method for checking.
- Answer shows that 161 people are on the trip.

Concepts and Skills

If students are having difficulty in particular areas, use the appropriate Reteaching Worksheets listed below.

- 84 Remembering to Regroup, p. 230
- 85 Regrouping Correctly, p. 231
- 86 Multiplying Three Factors, p. 232

Common Error Alert

If your students are making frequent errors, see Analyzing Errors, TE pp. 405A–405B.

Item Analysis

Item	Objectives
1–2	To use Work a Simpler Problem and other strategies to solve problems (11F)
3–6	To explore models for multiplying a 2-digit number by a 1-digit number (11A)
7–10	To estimate products (11B)
11–20	To multiply 2-digit numbers by 1-digit numbers (11C)

Math World

Iranian Multiplication

Background Here are some other ways that people around the world write mathematics differently than we do:

- Many countries use a 24-hour clock. (1:00 P.M., for example, becomes 13:00.)
- In many countries, when using numbers to write dates, people write the day before the month and use dots instead of slashes to separate numbers. (We would record October 5, 1999, for example, as 10/5/99, while a person in Senegal would write that date as 5.10.99.)

Critical Thinking Introduce the background information. Discuss: Does it matter which way we write a multiplication problem, the time, or a date?

Activity: *Alternative Expressions*

Have students practice using alternative ways of expressing mathematics:

- Students write 3 multiplication exercises in the Iranian way, exchange with a partner, and solve.
- Students use the 24-hour clock to write a schedule of their activities on a typical day.
- Students write their family members' birthdays using both ways of recording dates.

Multiplication Around the World

Math World

Learn about different kinds of multiplication problems, dollars, and calculators.

Get Your Money's Worth

Barbados (bahr BAY dohz) is an island in the Caribbean Sea. Barbados has its own money, but many stores, hotels, and restaurants also accept U.S. money. U.S. dollars are worth about twice as much as Barbados dollars. Suppose a hat costs \$6.00 in Barbados money. You have \$3.65 in U.S. money. Will this be enough to buy the hat? (Hint: How can you estimate 2 × \$3.65?)

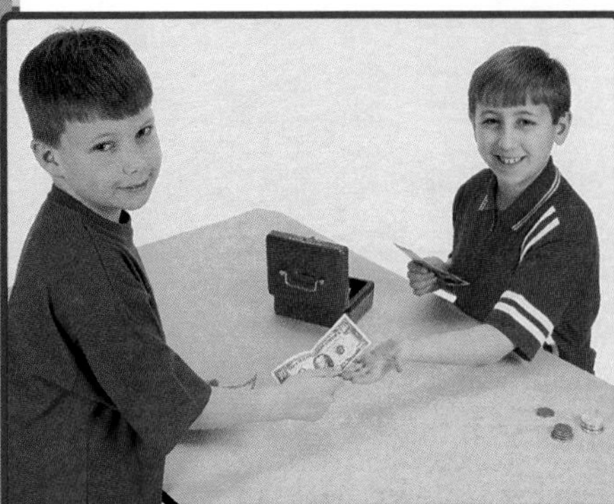

Writing Multiplication

Mathematics is a language that people all over the world can read and understand. Students in different parts of the world do not always write math problems exactly the same way. For example, someone who goes to school in Iran might write a multiplication problem with the multiplication sign to the right of the top number.

$$\begin{array}{r} 214^{\times} \\ 3 \\ \hline \end{array}$$

392

For More Information

Word Origins

dollar

From *taler* (TAH-ler), a silver coin once used in Germany; originally *Joachimstaler*, from *Joachimstal*, a town where similar coins were first minted.

In the 1700s, several countries issued coins called "thaler" or "dollar." The most common coin in the American Colonies was a large Spanish silver dollar.

Discuss with students why it is important for there to be standard units of money.

Literature

All Kinds of Money
Franklin Watts, 1988
David A. Adler

Cultural Atlas for Young People: Ancient Greece
Facts on File, 1989
Anton Powell

Enchantment of the World: Iran
Children's Press, 1991
Mary Virginia Fox

From Gold to Money
Lerner Group, 1985
Ali Mitgutsch

Money
Thomson Learning, 1995
Peggy Burns

The Story of Money
Troll Communications, 1993
Carolyn Kain

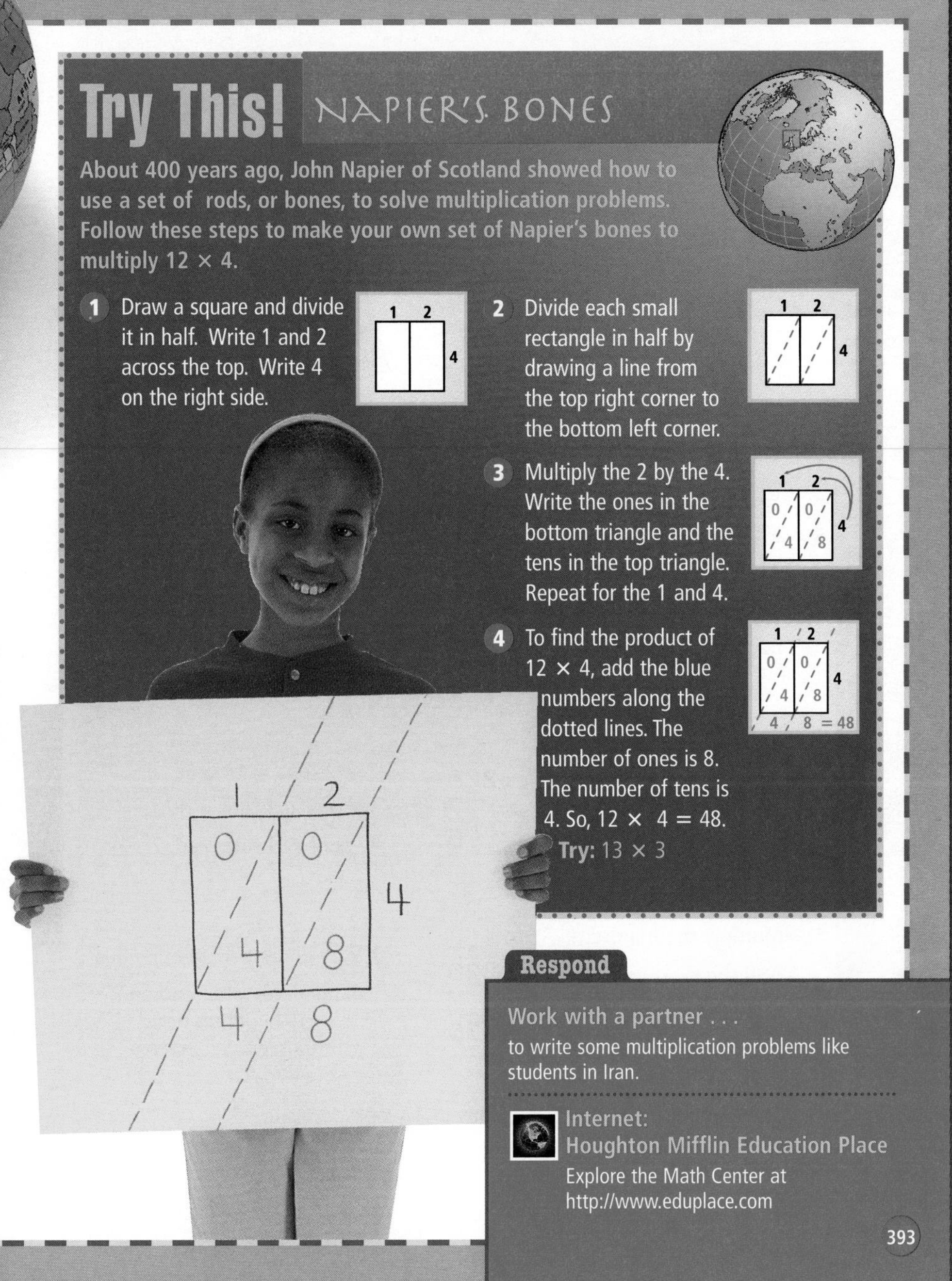

Try This! Napier's Bones

About 400 years ago, John Napier of Scotland showed how to use a set of rods, or bones, to solve multiplication problems. Follow these steps to make your own set of Napier's bones to multiply 12 × 4.

1. Draw a square and divide it in half. Write 1 and 2 across the top. Write 4 on the right side.
2. Divide each small rectangle in half by drawing a line from the top right corner to the bottom left corner.
3. Multiply the 2 by the 4. Write the ones in the bottom triangle and the tens in the top triangle. Repeat for the 1 and 4.
4. To find the product of 12 × 4, add the blue numbers along the dotted lines. The number of ones is 8. The number of tens is 4. So, 12 × 4 = 48.

Try: 13 × 3

Respond

Work with a partner . . .
to write some multiplication problems like students in Iran.

Internet:
Houghton Mifflin Education Place
Explore the Math Center at
http://www.eduplace.com

393

Multiply to Get Your Money's Worth

Background Students may find it interesting that foreign exchange rates are constantly in fluctuation. For example, an American traveler exchanging $100 in Japan on two consecutive days would have received the following amounts of money:

$100.00 U.S. in:	Feb. 12, 1997	Feb. 13, 1997
Japan	12420 yen	12440 yen

Activity: *Changing Exchange Rates*

- Ask: If you had been traveling in Japan that week, which day would have been better for you to pay in dollars?

Napier's Bones

Background Called "the next most important development in mechanical computation after the abacus," Napier's bones may have been based on an idea introduced in 1494 by the Italian mathematician Luca Pacioli. Napier was also one of the first mathematicians to use the decimal point the way we use it today.

Critical Thinking After completing the activity, discuss: How can you use what you know about place value to explain why Napier's bones work?

Technology

Internet: Education Place
http://www.eduplace.com
Houghton Mifflin Education Place **Mathematics Center** provides teacher and student support, such as links to other Internet sites.

Ultimate Writing & Creativity Center
Students can use the *Ultimate Writing & Creativity Center* for all their writing and publishing activities.

Kid to Kid

Project Ask: What would you want to buy if you were visiting other countries? Suggest:

- *You could exchange ideas with students in other countries.*
- *You could ask them how much the items cost in their money and figure out how much that is in dollars.*

Students could use the Internet or other international student exchange networks to contact foreign students.

Symbolic

Planning at a Glance

Objective To multiply 3-digit numbers by 1-digit numbers, with and without regrouping

Materials place-value blocks

Optional Resources

- Reteach 11.7; Practice 11.7; Enrichment 11.7
- Daily Cumul. Review, p. 147
- Math Center: How-To Card 38
- Every Day Counts
- **TAB**, TE pp. 378E–378F, 378J
- **Problem of the Day**, 147, p. 74; Flip Chart, p. 74a

Unlocking Whole Numbers 3–5, Level 3, Activity 21

Students Acquiring English

Model one of the prior knowledge examples emphasizing and demonstrating the terms *multiply* and *regroup*.

Problem of the Day

One of the numbers in the box does not belong. Why?

3515	428	6742	
8324	339	707	800

Possible answers include 800 because it is the only multiple of 10, 707 because it is the only palindrome or because it is the only one in which the last one or two digits are not the product of the first two digits.

Multiplying 3-Digit Numbers

You know that 1 week = 7 days.

An elephant at a zoo eats 225 lb of hay every day. How much hay does the elephant eat in 1 week?

You can multiply 225 by 7 to find out.

Here's A Way! Find 7 × 225.

1. Estimate by rounding to the nearest hundred.
   Since 7 × 200 = 1400, the elephant eats about 1400 lb of hay.
2. Multiply the ones. Regroup if needed.
   $\begin{array}{r} {}^{3}\\ 225 \\ \times\ \ 7 \\ \hline 5 \end{array}$
   7 × 5 ones = 35 ones
   35 ones = 3 tens, 5 ones
3. Multiply the tens. Add the regrouped tens. Regroup the tens if needed.
   $\begin{array}{r} {}^{1\,3}\\ 225 \\ \times\ \ 7 \\ \hline 75 \end{array}$
   7 × 2 tens = 14 tens
   14 tens + 3 tens = 17 tens
   17 tens = 1 hundred, 7 tens
4. Multiply the hundreds. Add the regrouped hundred. Regroup the hundreds if needed.
   $\begin{array}{r} {}^{1\,3}\\ 225 \\ \times\ \ 7 \\ \hline 1575 \end{array}$
   7 × 2 hundreds = 14 hundreds
   14 hundreds + 1 hundred is 15 hundreds or 1 thousand, 5 hundreds

The elephant eats 1575 lb of hay in 1 week.

Talk About It! Compare the answer to your estimate. The answer and the estimate are close.

394 Chapter 11

1 Introduce

Build Understanding Have students model 2 × 136 with place-value blocks.

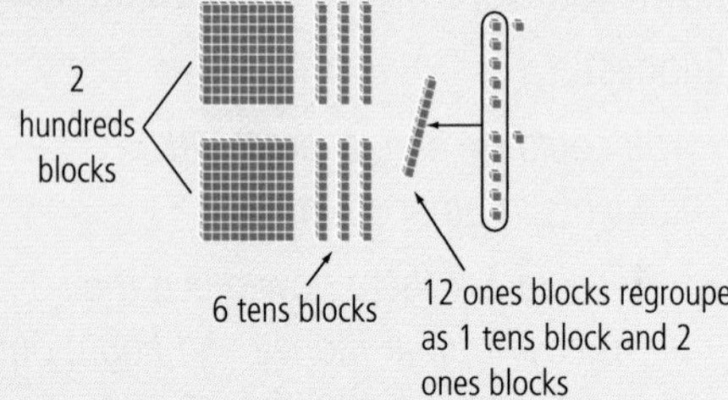

Ask, How many times did you regroup? once **What is the product?** 272

Teach: Here's A Way!

Emphasize this point:

- When multiplying a 3-digit number, you may need to regroup 0, 1, 2, or 3 times.

2 Develop

Show What You Know!

Common Error Some students may add a regrouped number before multiplying. Remind them of the correct procedure for regrouping. See also Analyzing Errors, TE pp. 405A and 405B.

Work It Out!

- Ask students to circle answers for which they used mental math.
- Have students discuss their solutions for problems 27–29.

Using Reading Strategies Help students to use the Self-Question strategy as they read the Problem Solving exercises. Discuss what questions they could ask. See TE p. 378J.

3 Summarize

- Have students discuss similarities and differences between multiplying a 3-digit number by a 1-digit number and multiplying a 2-digit number by a 1-digit number.
- Discuss mental math methods students used.

Ongoing Assessment You buy 5 packs of 144 paper napkins each for the school picnic. How many napkins do you buy? 720 napkins

Math Journal: *Communicating*

How can you use estimation to find out if 1125 is a reasonable product of 3 × 375? Multiply 3 × 300 and 3 × 400; compare the estimated products of 900 and 1200 to 1125. Since 1125 is greater than 900 and less than 1200, the product is reasonable.

Show What You Know!

Find the product. Use mental math if you can.

1.	2.	3.	4.	5.
434 × 4 1736	111 × 5 555	868 × 2 1736	256 × 6 1536	222 × 5 1110

6. **Critical Thinking** When do you need to regroup hundreds when you multiply? when you have more than 9 hundreds

Work It Out!

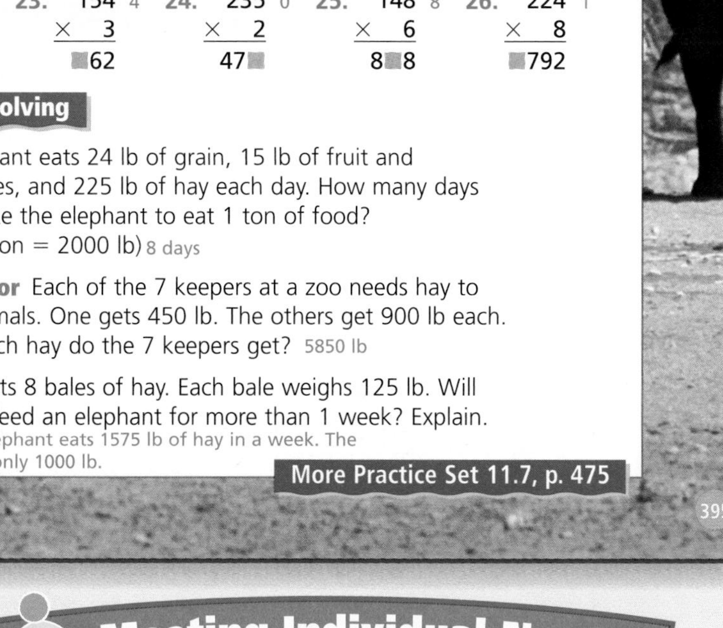

Estimate first. Then find the product. Estimates may vary. Possible estimates shown.

7. 419 × 2 800; 838	8. 423 × 2 800; 846	9. 263 × 6 1800; 1578	10. 363 × 3 1200; 1089	11. 421 × 4 1600; 1684
12. 129 × 6 600; 774	13. 324 × 5 1500; 1620	14. 193 × 4 800; 772	15. 100 × 7 700; 700	16. 221 × 2 400; 442
17. 518 × 4 2000; 2072	18. 197 × 2 400; 394	19. 132 × 5 500; 660	20. 513 × 2 1000; 1026	21. 345 × 3 900; 1035

Find the missing digit. Show your work.

22.	23.	24.	25.	26.
134 × 2 = 26■ 8	154 × 3 = ■62 4	235 × 2 = 47■ 0	148 × 6 = 8■8 8	224 × 8 = ■792 1

Problem Solving

27. An elephant eats 24 lb of grain, 15 lb of fruit and vegetables, and 225 lb of hay each day. How many days will it take the elephant to eat 1 ton of food? (Hint: 1 ton = 2000 lb) 8 days

28. **Calculator** Each of the 7 keepers at a zoo needs hay to feed animals. One gets 450 lb. The others get 900 lb each. How much hay do the 7 keepers get? 5850 lb

29. A zoo gets 8 bales of hay. Each bale weighs 125 lb. Will the hay feed an elephant for more than 1 week? Explain. no; An elephant eats 1575 lb of hay in a week. The zoo gets only 1000 lb.

More Practice Set 11.7, p. 475

395

11.7 ANOTHER LOOK — Reteach

Multiplying 3-Digit Numbers

Multiply 3 × 267.

Multiply the ones. Regroup?	Multiply the tens. Add the tens. Regroup?	Multiply the hundreds. Add the hundreds.
(2) 267 × 3 = 1	(2)(2) 267 × 3 = 01	(2)(2) 267 × 3 = 801

Multiply.

	Hundreds	Tens	Ones
1.	1	0	1
×			4
	4	0	4
2.		(2) 2	8
×			3
		8	4
3.	1	1	1
×			7
	7	7	7
4.	(1) 1	(1) 8	9
×			2
	3	7	8
5.	2	(3) 0	8
×			4
	8	3	2
6.	2	1	3
×			3
	6	3	9
7.	(1) 3	9	1
×			2
	7	8	2
8.		(3) 9	8
×			4
	3	9	2
9.	1	(1) 1	2
×			8
	8	9	6

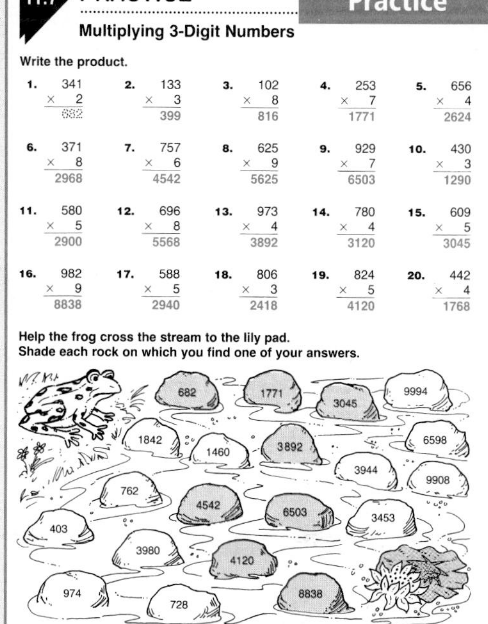

11.7 PRACTICE — Practice

Multiplying 3-Digit Numbers

Write the product.

1. 341 × 2 = 682	2. 133 × 3 = 399	3. 102 × 8 = 816	4. 253 × 7 = 1771	5. 656 × 4 = 2624
6. 371 × 8 = 2968	7. 757 × 6 = 4542	8. 625 × 9 = 5625	9. 929 × 7 = 6503	10. 430 × 3 = 1290
11. 580 × 5 = 2900	12. 696 × 8 = 5568	13. 973 × 4 = 3892	14. 780 × 4 = 3120	15. 609 × 5 = 3045
16. 982 × 9 = 8838	17. 588 × 5 = 2940	18. 806 × 3 = 2418	19. 824 × 5 = 4120	20. 442 × 4 = 1768

Help the frog cross the stream to the lily pad. Shade each rock on which you find one of your answers.

Meeting Individual Needs

Extra Support

Solve My Problem *(auditory)* Have students work in pairs. Working alternately, one partner orally gives step-by-step directions for the solution of one of the exercises below, while the other partner follows the steps to find the product.

a. 203 × 6 1218   d. 182 × 5 910

b. 454 × 3 1362   e. 830 × 4 3320

c. 425 × 9 3825   f. 727 × 7 5089

For more practice **Using the Calculator,** see pp. T88–T90.

Alternate Approach

- Reteach Worksheet 11.7
- **TAB** See TE pp. 378E–378F.

MathZones
Understanding Multiplication

Students Acquiring English

See **Language Connections**, Ch. 11.

Challenge

Provide number cards 0–9. Students shuffle the cards and place them facedown in a pile. Then they draw four cards to form a 3-digit factor and a 1-digit factor. Students arrange the digits to get the greatest possible product, then multiply.

Practice

Math Center Use How-To Card 38, *Go, Products, Go!,* to have students practice multiplying 3-digit numbers by 1-digit numbers, with and without regrouping.

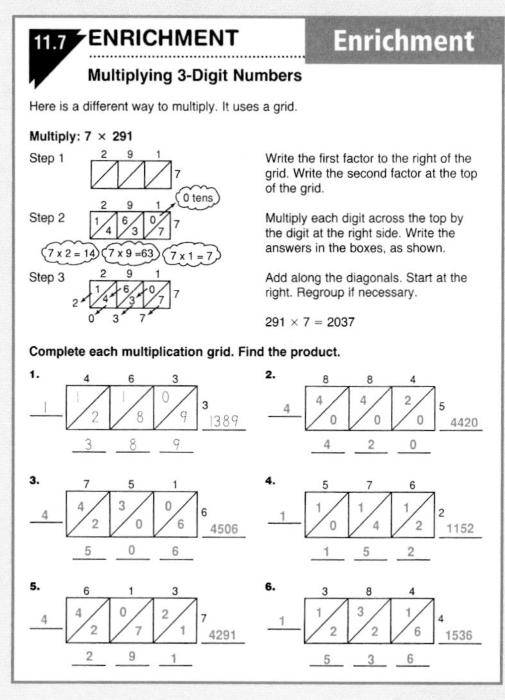

11.7 ENRICHMENT — Enrichment

Multiplying 3-Digit Numbers

Here is a different way to multiply. It uses a grid.

Multiply: 7 × 291

Step 1 — Write the first factor to the right of the grid. Write the second factor at the top of the grid. (0 tens)

Step 2 — Multiply each digit across the top by the digit at the right side. Write the answers in the boxes, as shown. (7 × 2 = 14) (7 × 9 = 63) (7 × 1 = 7)

Step 3 — Add along the diagonals. Start at the right. Regroup if necessary.

291 × 7 = 2037

Complete each multiplication grid. Find the product.

1. 463 × 3 = 1389
2. 884 × 5 = 4420
3. 751 × 6 = 4506
4. 576 × 2 = 1152
5. 613 × 7 = 4291
6. 384 × 4 = 1536

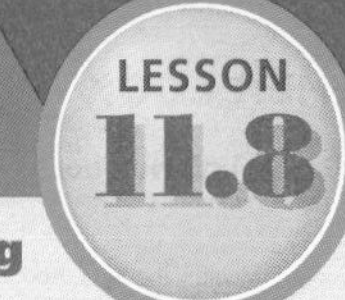

Problem Solving

Planning at a Glance

Objective To use Work a Simpler Problem and other strategies to solve problems

Materials none

Optional Resources

- Reteach 11.8; Practice 11.8; Enrichment 11.8
- Daily Cumul. Review, p. 148
- Math Center: Project Card 11
- Every Day Counts
- TAB, TE p. 378E–378F, 378J
- Problem of the Day, 148, p. 74; Flip Chart, p. 74b

Unlocking Whole Numbers 3–5, Level 3, Activity 19

Students Acquiring English

Discuss the term *Olympics*, and invite students to name sports and events that are included in the games. Ask, Which games are played in summer? Which in winter?

Problem of the Day

Olivia is playing a word game. She can use the letters A, T, and N. In how many different ways can she arrange her letters? Which arrangements form real words?

6 arrangements; real words are TAN, ANT, and if you count common names, NAT.

Problem Solving : Application

LESSON 8

Problem Solving

Using Work a Simpler Problem and Other Strategies

The Special Olympics World Games bring together athletes with disabilities from all over the world. They compete in 22 different events, including soccer, swimming, and track and field.

Problem Solving Process

- ✓ Understand
- ✓ Plan
- ✓ Try It
- ✓ Look Back

Choose a Strategy You Have Learned

- ✓ Act It Out
- ✓ Look for a Pattern
- ✓ Guess and Check
- ✓ Draw a Picture
- ✓ Make a Table
- ✓ Work Backward
- ✓ Make a List
- ✓ Work a Simpler Problem

At the 1995 World Games, 7 teams from Central and South America played with 11 players on the field for each team. Two teams had 15 players each (including substitutes). The rest had 14 players. How many soccer players were there?

- What problem needs to be solved? how many soccer players in all
- How many teams are there? 7 teams
- Can you make a simpler problem to help you solve the larger problem? yes; you might use 2 × 5 instead of 2 × 15 and 5 × 4 instead of 5 × 14
- What operations would you use to solve the simpler problem? multiplication and addition
- Explain a strategy you can use to solve the problem. Then, solve it. Work a Simpler Problem; 100 people

396 Chapter 11

1 Introduce

Prior Knowledge **Ask, How can using simpler numbers help you solve a problem?** by helping you see what operations you need to perform, and by making the computation easier

Teach: *Modeling*

Model the example. Discuss:

- If there were only one team of each size, how would you find the total number of players? add 14 + 15
- How would you solve if there were two teams of each size? find the products of 14 × 2 and 15 × 2; find the sum of the products
- How can you solve the problem with 2 teams of 15 and 5 teams of 14? find the products of 15 × 2 and 14 × 5; find the sum of the products

2 Develop

Work It Out!

- Ask students to discuss the strategies they used to solve problems 1–5. For example, for problem 3 they could use Work a Simpler Problem, while Make a Table could help solve problems 1 and 5. Work Backward is a useful strategy for problem 3.
- Have students discuss their reasoning for problem 8.

Using Reading Strategies Encourage students to use the Self-Question strategy as they read the Problem Solving exercises. Ask them what questions they could use to help them solve problem 2. See TE p. 378J.

3 Summarize

- Have students review their solution strategies for the problems.
- Ask students to discuss the kind of problems that can be solved by working a simpler problem.

Ongoing Assessment How can estimating help you use problem solving strategies? Possible answer: you can estimate to decide if an answer is reasonable, or use estimates to work a simpler problem

Math Journal: *Communicating*

Choose a problem in this lesson. Explain why working a simpler problem is a more useful strategy for solving it than drawing a picture. Responses should show understanding of these strategies.

Work It Out!

Use any strategy to solve the problem. Show your work.

1. Special Olympics World Games are held every two years. They alternate between Summer and Winter Sports. World Games for Summer Sports took place in 1995 and for Winter Sports in 1997. Will there be a World Games in the year you turn 13? Explain. Answers will vary.
2. Will the Special Olympics World Games ever happen in an even year? Explain. No; When you start with an odd number and count by 2's, you always end up with an odd number.
3. In Unified Sports, people with and without disabilities compete on the same teams. In Unified soccer, 5 people can play on a team at one time. In 1995, 210 people played Unified soccer. Thirty of those were extra players. How many teams of 5 were there? 36 teams
4. There were 40 athletes from Jamaica at the 1995 World Games. Suppose half won 1 gold medal each. If half of the rest won 1 silver medal each and the others won 2 bronze medals each, how many medals did the team win? 50 medals

Track and Field Athletes, 1995

Place	Number of Athletes
Africa	145
Asia	183
Europe	311
Central and South America	259
North America	469

5. One track and field event is the 4 × 100 relay. In it, 4 athletes on a team each run 100 yards. If 8 teams compete, how long is the race? 400 yards
6. **Estimation** Use the chart. Were there more than 1000 track and field athletes at the World Games in 1995? Explain. yes; a front-end estimate is 1100 athletes, and the actual total will be more.

7. **Create Your Own** Make up a problem about a Special Olympics sport. Ask a classmate to solve your problem. Answers will vary.

Share Your Thinking

8. What strategy did you use for problem 6? Explain why. Answers will vary.

397

Meeting Individual Needs

Extra Support

Problem Solving Practice *(visual)*

- Have student pairs solve this problem: A track has lanes for 9 runners. During a track meet, there are 26 races. If each athlete runs in 2 races, how many athletes compete in the track meet? 117 athletes
- Have students compare the strategy they used to solve the problem with other student pairs.

Alternate Approach

- Reteach Worksheet 11.8
- **TAB** See TE pp. 378E–378F.

MathZones
Understanding Multiplication

Students Acquiring English

See Language Connections, Ch. 11.

Challenge

Pose this problem: A boy is 7 years old. His sister is 19 years old. How many years from now will the sister be twice the boy's age? How old will they be that year? 5 years from now; The boy will be 12, the sister will be 24.

Practice

Math Center For more problem solving practice, see Project Card 11, *Giving a Party.*

See **Just the Facts** Practice 11A, p. 140.

Reteach

11.8 ANOTHER LOOK

Work a Simpler Problem and Other Strategies

The 8 members of a scout troop are having a recycling drive. After a week of collecting, 4 scouts collected 127 cans each. The other 4 collected 112 cans each. How many cans did the troop collect?

1. Understand
- You want to find the total number of cans.

2. Plan
- You can use simpler numbers to help you decide what operations to use.

3. Try It
- Suppose that 4 scouts collected 27 cans each and the other 4 collected 12 cans each.
- Decide what operations you need to use to solve the problem. If 4 scouts collected 27 cans each, they collected 4 × 27 cans. If 4 scouts collected 12 cans each, they collected 4 × 12 cans. Then, you could add the two products to find the total.
- So, now you know that you need to multiply and then add to find the total number of cans.

4. Look Back
- Since 4 × 127 = 508 and 4 × 112 = 448, the scouts collected 508 + 448 = 956 cans.

Solve. Use Work a Simpler Problem when you can.

1. The recycling center pays 55¢ for each pound of cans and 25¢ for each pound of glass bottles. If you bring in 5 pounds of glass bottles and 3 pounds of cans, how much money should you get? $2.90
2. The scout troop is building recycling bins for their school. They need 14 nails for each of the 2 bottle bins, and 13 nails each for the can bin and the newspaper bin. How many nails do they need? 54 nails

Practice

11.8 PRACTICE

Use a Simpler Problem and Other Strategies

Solve. Use Work a Simpler Problem when you can.

1. Mr. Pinski buys 3 boxes of glue sticks. Each box contains 101 glue sticks. How many glue sticks did Mr. Pinski buy? 303 glue sticks
2. Percy's dad, uncle, and cousin weigh approximately 185 pounds each. His mom and aunt weigh approximately 140 pounds each. They all want to jump on the trampoline. The maximum weight allowed on the trampoline is 450 pounds. If 2 men and 1 woman get on the trampoline, have they gone over the allowed weight? Yes
3. Leap year occurs every 4 years. The year 2000 is a leap year. Is the year 2008 a leap year? Yes
4. A book is open so the sum of the page numbers facing each other is 21. What are the page numbers? 10 and 11

5. The houses on Jenks Avenue are brown and yellow. There are twice as many brown houses as yellow houses. There are 8 brown houses. How many houses are there on Jenks Avenue? 12 houses
6. Juanita and her friends sell boxes of cookies. Juanita sells 55 boxes of cookies. Sasha sells 42 boxes of cookies, and Alicia sells twice as many cookies as Juanita. How many boxes of cookies did the girls sell? 207 boxes

Enrichment

11.8 ENRICHMENT

Use Work a Simpler Problem and Other Strategies

Solve. Use Work a Simpler Problem when you can.

1. A recipe for hot chocolate says you should mix 3 tablespoons of powder with 1 cup of hot water. If you want to make 8 cups of hot chocolate, how much mix do you need? 24 tablespoons
2. Coretta is testing Alex on her multiplication facts. Alex completes 5 problems in 8 seconds. How many problems can she complete in 40 seconds? 25 problems
3. You have 125 newspapers to distribute on your paper route. You travel 25 blocks to finish the route. You deliver to the same number of houses on each block. How many houses do you deliver to on each block? 5 houses
4. Mr. Brock, the school principal, bought 3 cartons of pencils. Each carton contained 110 pencils. He gave most of the pencils to his students. He found that he had 20 pencils left. How many pencils did he give to his students? 310 pencils
5. Hector puts $3 into his bank account each week. He now has $31. Suppose he continues to put $3 a week into the account. How much money will be in the bank account after 4 more weeks? $43

Symbolic

Planning at a Glance

Objective To multiply 3-digit numbers that include zeros by 1-digit numbers

Materials place-value blocks

Optional Resources

- Reteach 11.9; Practice 11.9; Enrichment 11.9
- Daily Cumul. Review, p. 149
- Math Center: Act. Card 64
- Every Day Counts
- TAB, TE pp. 378E–378F, 378J
- Problem of the Day, 149, p. 75; Flip Chart, p. 75a

Unlocking Whole Numbers 3–5, Level 3, Activity 21

Students Acquiring English
Have students hold up sets of objects that are the same size and ask them to describe what they are holding, using sentences such as, "These 2 books are the same size."

Problem of the Day

Aaron's telephone number starts with an 8 and ends with a 6. It has three 3's in it. It also has one other odd and one other even number. All seven digits in his phone number add up to 30. What might Aaron's phone number be?
one possible answer: 873-3036

Multiplying with Zeros

Use What You Know
The zero property says that 0 times any number equals 0.
$5 \times 0 = 0$

This picture from the 1300s shows people carrying silk across Asia. One roll of silk was 380 grams. How heavy were 7 rolls?

You can multiply to find out.

Here's A Way! Find 7×380.

1. Estimate by rounding to the nearest hundred.
   380 → 400
   $7 \times 400 = 2800$
   The rolls were about 2800 g.

2. Multiply the ones. Do you need to regroup?
   $$\begin{array}{r} 380 \\ \times\ \ 7 \\ \hline 0 \end{array}$$

3. Multiply the tens. Do you need to regroup?
   $$\begin{array}{r} ^{5}\ \ \\ 380 \\ \times\ \ 7 \\ \hline 60 \end{array}$$

4. Multiply the hundreds. Add the regrouped hundreds. Regroup.
   $$\begin{array}{r} ^{5}\ \ \ \\ 380 \\ \times\ \ 7 \\ \hline 2660 \end{array}$$
   The rolls were 2660 g.

Talk About It! Why is it important to record the zero?
It is important to fill the ones place so the other digits get written in the right place-value positions.

Other Examples

There are 0 tens in 309. Why are there 2 tens in the product?
The two tens are regrouped ones.

$$\begin{array}{r} ^{2}\ \ \\ 309 \\ \times\ \ 3 \\ \hline 927 \end{array}$$

398 Chapter 11

1 Introduce

Build Understanding Model 3×208 with place-value blocks.

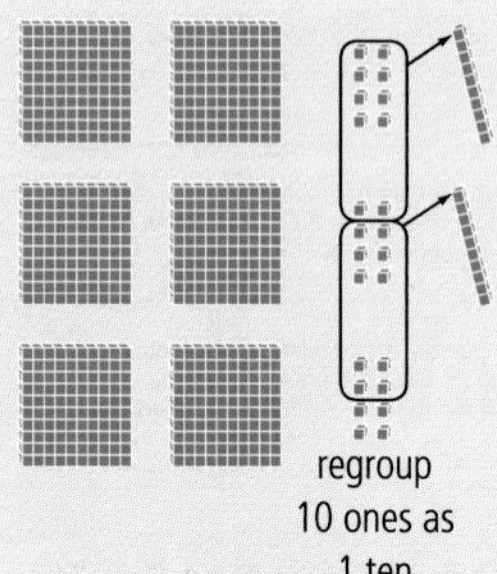

Ask, What is the product? 624

Teach: Here's A Way!

- When a 3-digit factor has a zero in the tens place and no ones are regrouped as tens, write a zero in the tens place of the product.

2 Develop

Show What You Know!

- Have students discuss their answers to exercise 1.
- Remind students to regroup correctly.
- Ask students to discuss their reasoning for exercise 7.

Work It Out!

- Have students circle the answers for which they used mental math.

Using Reading Strategies Help students to use the Self-Question strategy as they read the Number Sense and Problem Solving exercises. Ask them what kinds of questions are most helpful. See TE p. 378J.

3 Summarize

- Have students summarize the steps involved in finding the products: 3×670; 5×104.
- Discuss how mental math methods can help with multiplying 3-digit factors.

Ongoing Assessment On Monday, 306 children each eat 3 pieces of fruit. How many pieces of fruit do they eat in all? 918 pieces Why did you write a 1 in the tens place? There were 18 ones regrouped as 1 ten and 8 ones.

Math Journal: *Communicating*

How can place value and multiplication facts help you multiply 3-digit numbers? Facts and place value work together; for example, $3 \times 8 = 24$; $3 \times 800 = 2400$.

Show What You Know!

1. **Estimation** How can estimating the product first help you multiply greater numbers with zeros?
   It helps you know if your answer is reasonable.

Estimate. Then find the product. Estimates may vary. Possible estimates shown.

2. 140 × 7 — 700; 980
3. 508 × 4 — 2000; 2032
4. 209 × 6 — 1200; 1254
5. 610 × 3 — 1800; 1830
6. 290 × 5 — 1500; 1450

7. **Critical Thinking** If a 0 is in the ones place of a number, what will be in the ones place of the product? Explain.
   0; any number multiplied by zero equals zero

Work It Out!

Estimate. Then find the product. Compare the estimate to the product. Estimates may vary. Possible estimates shown.

8. 609 × 4 — 2400; 2436
9. 302 × 1 — 300; 302
10. 230 × 7 — 1400; 1610
11. 209 × 2 — 400; 418
12. 797 × 9 — 7200; 7173
13. 545 × 2 — 1000; 1090
14. 201 × 5 — 1000; 1005
15. 410 × 3 — 1200; 1230
16. 680 × 8 — 5600; 5440
17. 924 × 6 — 5400; 5544
18. 729 × 3 — 2100; 2187
19. 609 × 2 — 1200; 1218
20. 107 × 6 — 600; 642
21. 209 × 6 — 1200; 1254
22. 330 × 9 — 2700; 2970

Estimate the product. Write *a, b,* or *c.*

23. 5 × 102 b
   a. 50
   b. 500
   c. 5000
24. 4 × 510 c
   a. 20
   b. 200
   c. 2000
25. 2 × 190 b
   a. 40
   b. 400
   c. 4000
26. 2 × 509 c
   a. 10
   b. 100
   c. 1000

27. **Number Sense** Is the product of 3 × 409 closer to 1100 or to 1300? Explain.
   1300; 409 > 400, so 3 × 409 > 3 × 400
28. **Problem Solving** Marco Polo was an Italian explorer who visited China. He could buy 1 pair of geese and 2 pairs of ducks for 1 piece of silver. How many pairs of ducks and geese could he buy for 150 pieces of silver?
   150 pairs of geese and 300 pairs of ducks

399

Meeting Individual Needs

Extra Support

Surprise Products *(visual)* Make a set of ten index cards, each with a 3-digit number that has a zero either in the ones or tens place. Make a second set of 9 index cards, each with a single digit from 1 through 9. Have student pairs draw a number from each pile and work together to find the product. Have them discuss the steps they use, check their product with a calculator, and review the steps if the calculator does not match their answer. Let students repeat the procedure five times with different pairs of numbers.

For more practice **Using the Calculator,** see pp. T88–T90.

Alternate Approach

- Reteach Worksheet 11.9
- **TAB** See TE pp. 378E–378F.

MathZones

Understanding Multiplication

Students Acquiring English

See **Language Connections**, Ch. 11.

Practice

Math Center Use Activity Card 64, *Wheel of Products,* to have students practice multiplying 3-digit numbers that include zeros by 1-digit numbers.

Challenge Use Activity Card 64 and have students continue as described in Now Try This!

See **Just the Facts** Practice 11A, p. 140.

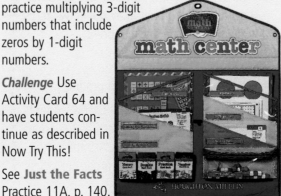

11.9 ANOTHER LOOK — Reteach

Multiplying with Zeros

Remember that 0 times any number equals 0.
Be sure to record the zeros when you multiply.

Multiply the ones. Regroup.	Multiply the tens. Add the regrouped number.		Multiply the hundreds.
208 × 5 = 0	208 × 5 = 40	5 × 0 = 0; 0 + 4 = 4	208 × 5 = 1040

Solve each problem.

1. Suppose it takes a person 305 hours to build a cabin. How many hours might it take to build 2 cabins? 610 hours
2. On a car trip, a family drives 401 miles in 1 day. How many miles might they drive in 3 days? 1203 miles
3. There are 180 school days in 1 year. How many school days are there in 4 years? 720 days
4. A football field is 100 yards long. How many yards long would 9 football fields be? 900 yards long
5. A large auditorium has 8 sections with 110 seats in each section. How many seats does the auditorium have in all? 880 seats
6. A package holds 6 oatmeal cookies. How many cookies would 207 packages hold? 1242 cookies

11.9 PRACTICE — Practice

Multiplying with Zeros

Solve each multiplication exercise to complete the crossnumber puzzle. Write each product in the number box.

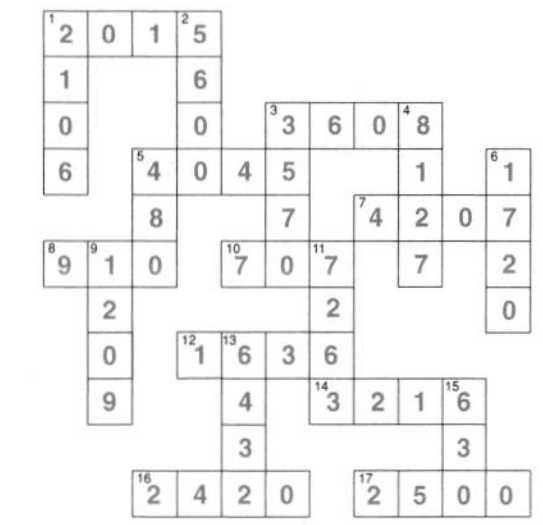

Across	Down
1. 5 × 403	1. 3 × 702
3. 4 × 902	2. 8 × 700
5. 5 × 809	3. 7 × 510
7. 7 × 601	4. 9 × 903
8. 5 × 182	5. 8 × 60
10. 7 × 101	6. 2 × 860
12. 4 × 409	9. 3 × 403
14. 4 × 804	11. 9 × 807
16. 4 × 605	13. 8 × 804
17. 4 × 625	15. 9 × 70

11.9 ENRICHMENT — Enrichment

Multiplying with Zeros

The Lightning Wheels Toy Car Company makes toy cars in 2 sizes. The chart below shows how many of each car are made in a day.

Toy Cars Made in 1 Day		
Kind of Car	Tiny Size	Regular Size
taxi	102	94
tow truck	90	65
bus	105	91
sports car	110	103
station wagon	109	108

Use the chart to solve each problem.

1. How many tiny sports cars are made in 5 days? 550 sports cars
2. How many regular station wagons are made in 4 days? 432 station wagons
3. In 6 days, how many more tiny taxis are made than regular taxis? 48 more tiny taxis
4. In 5 days, how many more tiny tow trucks are made than regular tow trucks? 125 more tiny tow trucks
5. In 7 days, how many tiny buses and regular buses are made? 1372 buses
6. In 3 days, how many tiny taxis and tiny buses are made? 621 tiny taxis and buses
7. Which is greater: the number of regular sports cars made in 6 days or the number of regular buses made in 7 days? How much greater? regular buses; 19
8. New workers made all the tiny tow trucks for 3 days. Then they made all the tiny station wagons for 5 days. How many toys is that in all? 815 toys in all
9. Use the chart to make up your own problem. Answers may vary.

Symbolic

Planning at a Glance

Objective To multiply 3-digit money amounts by a 1-digit number

Materials calculator

Optional Resources

- Reteach 11.10; Practice 11.10; Enrichment 11.10
- Daily Cumul. Review, p. 150
- Math Center: How-To Card 39
- Every Day Counts
- **TAB**, TE pp. 378E–378F, 378J
- **Problem of the Day**, 150, p. 75; Flip Chart, p. 75b
- MATHKEYS *Unlocking Whole Numbers 3–5, Level 3, Activity 21*

Students Acquiring English

Tell students you need to buy 3 apples. They are each $.45. Model how to find the total cost, emphasizing the phrase, "How much does it cost?"

Problem of the Day

Jamaal has 5 coins. He has twice as many dimes as quarters. He has half as many quarters as nickels. How much money does he have? 55¢

Multiplying Money

Getting Started

What You'll Need: ▶ calculator

How much would 6 boxes of crayons cost?

You can estimate to get an idea of what the amount would be. You can also use a calculator to find the exact cost.

Artist Supplies
Crayons $2.25
Paint Set $8.99

Here's A Way! Find 6 × $2.25.

1. **Round to the nearest dollar to estimate.**

   $2.25 → $2.00

   6 × $2.00 = $12.00

   You would need about $12.00.

2. **Press these keys:** 6 × 2 . 2 5 =

   Remember, a calculator does not have a $ key.

3. **Write the product shown on the calculator as dollars and cents.**

   The crayons would cost exactly $13.50. 

Talk About It! How can you use estimation to find out if you pressed the correct keys on the calculator? Compare the calculator's display with your estimate.

Other Examples

Compare the products. How is the calculator display like the written amount? How is it different? The calculator shows decimal points. It does not show dollar signs or a zero in the hundredths place.

a. $.75 × 3 = $2.25 (display: 2.25)

b. $8.90 × 3 = $26.70 (display: 26.7)

Explore **Display the following number sentence model: $□.□□ x □ = □. Have student pairs write 5–10 number sentences based on the model and solve them with a calculator.**

Teach: Here's A Way!

Emphasize these points:

- Regroup with money amounts just as you do with whole numbers.
- Always include two decimal places when writing money amounts in dollars and cents.

Modeling Model $.09 × 6. Ask:

- Why is the decimal point in the product between 0 and 5? factor has decimal in hundredths place

2 Develop

Show What You Know!

Common Error Some students may not place decimal points and zeros correctly. Review correct placement. See also Analyzing Errors, TE pp. 405A and 405B.

- Remind students that a calculator does not show a dollar sign and may not show zeros to the right of the decimal point.

Work It Out!

- Accept a range of estimated products.

Using Reading Strategies Guide students to use the Self-Question strategy as they read the Problem Solving exercises. Ask them to compare their questions with a partner's. See TE p. 378J.

- Have students compare multiplying money amounts with multiplying whole numbers.
- Ask students to review the use of the decimal point, dollar sign, and zeros in writing money amounts.

Ongoing Assessment Tim buys 3 model spaceships that cost $1.25 each. How much does he pay? $3.75 What did you regroup? 15 pennies as 1 dime and 5 pennies

Math Journal: *Communicating*

How is multiplying 3 × $.09 like multiplying 3 × 9? How is it different? The multiplication fact is the same, but the money product needs a dollar sign and a decimal point.

Show What You Know!

Write an estimate. Then use a calculator to find the product.
Estimates will vary. Possible estimates shown.

1. $1.27 × 3 — $3.00; $3.81
2. $2.00 × 5 — $10.00; $10.00
3. $.80 × 9 — $9.00; $7.20
4. $1.70 × 3 — $6.00; $5.10
5. $3.12 × 4 — $12.00; $12.48
6. 7 × $8.33 — $56.00; $58.31
7. 5 × $8.65 — $45.00; $43.25
8. 9 × $5.96 — $54.00; $53.64
9. 4 × $6.28 — $24.00; $25.12
10. **Critical Thinking** Describe how you estimated the product in exercises 8 and 9. rounded $5.96 to $6.00 and multiplied 9 × $6.00 = $54.00; rounded $6.28 to $6.00 and multiplied 4 × $6.00 = $24.00

Work It Out!

Estimate the product. Record your estimate. Then use a calculator to find the product.

11. $2.75 × 3 — $9.00; $8.25
12. $.25 × 8 — $.80; $2.00
13. $3.68 × 3 — $12.00; $11.04
14. $2.50 × 8 — $24.00; $20.00
15. $1.19 × 5 — $5.00; $5.95
16. 4 × $8.90 — $36.00; $35.60
17. 7 × $1.00 — $7.00; $7.00
18. 6 × $3.01 — $18.00; $18.06
19. 5 × $5.99 — $30.00; $29.95

Read the calculator display. Write the product.

20. 4 × $6.51 [26.04] $26.04
21. 2 × $8.90 [17.8] $17.80

Problem Solving Using Data

Use the prices shown on page 400.

22. Suppose you have $7.00. Can you buy 3 boxes of crayons? How do you know? yes, 3 × $2.25 = $6.75
23. Which costs more, 1 paint set or 4 boxes of crayons? Explain. 4 boxes of crayons; 4 × $2.25 = $9.00. $9.00 > $8.95

Mixed Review

Write the decimal.

24. 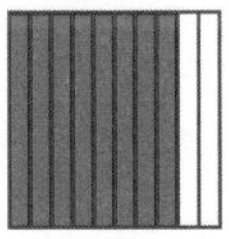 [grid model] 0.8
25. fifty hundredths 0.50
26. $3\frac{2}{10}$ 3.2

Write < or >.

27. 12.5 ● 21.2 <
28. 5.0 ● 4.9 >
29. 1.2 ● 1.9 <
30. 0.3 ● 0.1 >

More Practice Set 11.10, p. 476

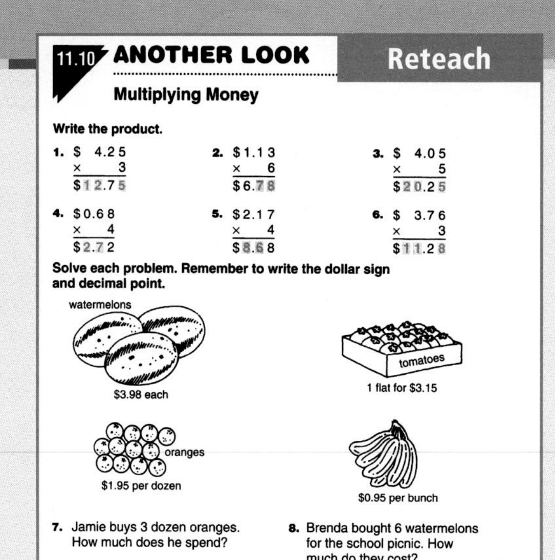

11.10 ANOTHER LOOK — Reteach
Multiplying Money

Write the product.

1. $4.25 × 3 = $12.75
2. $1.13 × 6 = $6.78
3. $4.05 × 5 = $20.25
4. $0.68 × 4 = $2.72
5. $2.17 × 4 = $8.68
6. $3.76 × 3 = $11.28

Solve each problem. Remember to write the dollar sign and decimal point.

watermelons $3.98 each

tomatoes 1 flat for $3.15

oranges $1.95 per dozen

$0.95 per bunch

7. Jamie buys 3 dozen oranges. How much does he spend? $5.85
8. Brenda bought 6 watermelons for the school picnic. How much do they cost? $23.88
9. What is the price of 6 flats of tomatoes? $18.90
10. Sal wants to buy 9 bunches of bananas to give to a homeless shelter. How much does he spend? $8.55

11.10 PRACTICE — Practice
Multiplying Money

Some children from Mr. O'Dill's class went to the circus. At the ticket booth, they saw this price chart:

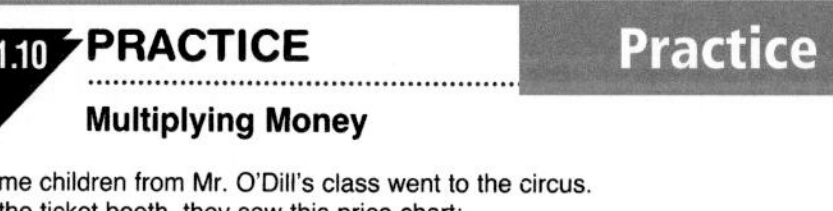

Circus Tickets/	Adult $5.10		T-shirts	$6.95
	Child $2.10			
arcade	$0.95		flashlights	$3.25
magazines	$0.85		pennants	$1.25
posters	$2.50		photo books	$5.50
binoculars	$9.95		peanuts	$0.50
sweatshirts	$8.50		popcorn	$1.70

Use the chart to write the price. Write the product to find the money spent.

1. Five parents helped Mr. O'Dill on the trip. How much did they spend on adult tickets? 5 (number bought) × $5.10 (price of item) Money spent $25.50
2. One of the parents bought 7 T-shirts to give as gifts. How much did he spend for the shirts? 7 (number bought) × $6.95 (price of item) Money spent $48.65
3. Four children bought arcade tickets. How much did the tickets cost? 4 (number bought) × $0.95 (price of item) Money spent $3.80
4. Mr. O'Dill bought 6 posters for his classroom. How much did he spend on the posters? 6 (number bought) × $2.50 (price of item) Money spent $15.00
5. Mrs. Oban, one of the parents, bought 5 pennants to give her nieces and nephews. How much did they cost her? 5 (number bought) × $1.25 (price of item) Money spent $6.25
6. Sweatshirts were bought by 5 children. How much did they spend on sweatshirts? 5 (number bought) × $8.50 (price of item) Money spent $42.50

11.10 ENRICHMENT — Enrichment
Multiplying Money

Handy Deli Menu			
cheese sandwich	$1.95	apple	$0.60
tuna sandwich	$2.75	banana	$0.45
turkey sandwich	$3.00	bagel	$0.70
bran muffin	$1.00	roll	$0.65
apple-nut muffin	$1.15	milk	$0.65
yogurt	$1.00	juice	$0.75

Use the menu to answer each question.

1. Brian bought 1 apple and 2 bran muffins. He gave the clerk a five-dollar bill. How much change did he get back? $2.40
2. Torie wants to buy a cheese sandwich, a turkey sandwich, and 2 juices. How much will all this cost? She has $6.25. Does she have enough money? $6.45; no
3. Mrs. Conklin ordered 4 bagels and 4 bananas. She gave the clerk a ten-dollar bill. How much change did she get back? $5.40
4. Ted spent $4.55 on a drink, a muffin, and a sandwich. What kind of drink, muffin, and sandwich did he order? milk, apple-nut, tuna
5. Blanca bought 6 tuna sandwiches for her family. She paid with $20.00. How much change did she get? $3.50 change
6. If you had $9.00 to spend on lunch for you and a friend, what would you buy? Answers may vary.
7. Make up a problem of your own. Tell what you bought, how much it cost, what bills you paid with, and how much change you got back. Answers may vary.

Meeting Individual Needs

Extra Support

Estimating Money ***(visual)*** Make two sets of index cards. On one, write money amounts in dollars and cents. (Include amounts less than $1.00.) On the other, write digits from 2 through 9. Students in small groups draw a card from each pile. Each student writes an estimate of the product and checks the product with a calculator. Score 3 points for a reasonable estimate, but lose 1 point for incorrect placement of a decimal point, dollar sign, or zero. The game ends when everyone has at least 10 points.

Alternate Approach

- Reteach Worksheet 11.10
- **TAB** See TE pp. 378E–378F.

MathZones
Understanding Multiplication

Students Acquiring English

See Language Connections, Ch. 11.

Challenge

Have pairs of students cut out food ads from newspapers. Each student has a shopping budget of $20.00. Students make a shopping list and trade their lists, calculating how much they will spend and how much change they should get back.

Practice

Math Center Use How-To Card 39, *The $Money$ Game*, to have students practice multiplying money amounts by a 1-digit number.

Problem Solving

Planning at a Glance

Objective To use different strategies to solve problems

Materials none

Optional Resources

- Reteach 11.11; Practice 11.11; Enrichment 11.11
- Daily Cumul. Review, p. 151
- Math Center: Project Card 11
- Every Day Counts
- **TAB**, TE pp. 378E–378F, 378J
- **Problem of the Day**, 151, p. 76; Flip Chart, p. 76a
- MATHKEYS *Unlocking Whole Numbers 3–5*, Level 3, Activity 12

Students Acquiring English

Build background for the context of this lesson by discussing storms. Identify the picture of the tornado on page 402. Ask students what other kinds of bad storms there are (hurricanes, thunder and lightning storms); explain those storms if necessary. Ask students to draw and label pictures of storms.

Problem of the Day

Oliver is playing a word game. He arranges the letters T, M, E, and A in any order. What real words can he form?
TEAM, MEAT, MATE, and TAME

Problem Solving : Application

LESSON 11

Problem Solving

Using Strategies

You can read more about weather in the pages of *Weatherwise.*

The Museum of American Weather in Haverhill, New Hampshire, has exhibits about all kinds of weather. One exhibit shows the Tri-State Tornado that tore through Missouri, Illinois, and Indiana in 1925.

Problem Solving Process
- ✓ Understand
- ✓ Plan
- ✓ Try It
- ✓ Look Back

Choose a Strategy You Have Learned
- ✓ Act It Out
- ✓ Look for a Pattern
- ✓ Guess and Check
- ✓ Draw a Picture
- ✓ Make a Table
- ✓ Work Backward
- ✓ Make a List
- ✓ Work a Simpler Problem

The Tri-State Tornado lasted $3\frac{1}{2}$ hours. If the tornado traveled about 1 mile every minute, about how far did it travel?

- What problem do you need to solve? how far did the Tri-State Tornado travel
- How many minutes are in 1 hour? 60 minutes
- How far would the tornado travel in 1 hour? 60 miles
- Explain a strategy you could use to solve the problem. Then solve it. Strategies will vary. $60 \times 3 = 180$; $\frac{1}{2}$ of $60 = 30$; $180 + 30 = 210$ miles

1 Introduce

Prior Knowledge Read the following: You and a friend are painting a fence that has 120 pickets. You can each paint 1 picket in 5 minutes. Ask, What strategy can help you figure out how long it will take you to paint the fence?
One possible answer: making a table

Teach: *Modeling*

Model the example. Discuss:

- How could you find the answer by solving a simpler problem first? figure out how many miles the storm travels in one hour, then add
- How could you solve the problem by making a table? make a table of miles traveled every 30 minutes
- What other strategies might help you solve the problem? Answers will vary.
- What is the answer? 210 miles

2 Develop

Work It Out!

- Call on students to discuss the strategies they used to solve problems 1–6.
- Ask students to identify information in the problems that they don't need to solve the problem.
- For problem 7, call on partners to explain each other's strategies to the class.
- Have students discuss any other strategies they suggested in problem 8.

Using Reading Strategies Encourage students to use the Self-Question strategy as they read the Problem Solving exercises. Ask, How can you use questions to get information from a table? See TE p. 378J.

3 Summarize

- Have students review the strategies they used to solve the problems.
- Ask students to cite an example of a problem that they solved with more than one strategy.

Ongoing Assessment Use any strategy: You're buying pizza for 15 people. Each pizza is cut into 8 slices. If each person eats 3 slices, how many pizzas do you need? How many slices will be left over? 6 pizzas; 3 slices

Math Journal: *Communicating*

Which problems in this lesson can be solved by working a simpler problem? How did you decide? Answers will vary. Students may choose any problem where simpler numbers allowed them to see the problem more clearly or compute the answer.

Work It Out!

Use any strategy to solve the problem. Show your work.

1. The chart shows the high temperature for 6 cities in January and July. Which city's temperature changes the most between January and July? Bismarck

High Temperatures

City	In Jan.	In July
Bismarck	20°F	84°F
Chicago	29°F	84°F
Honolulu	80°F	88°F
Miami	75°F	89°F
Detroit	30°F	83°F
Washington D.C.	42°F	89°F

2. St. Louis, Missouri, has a higher July temperature than Honolulu and a lower January temperature than Washington. Does the temperature change more in St. Louis than in Washington? Explain. yes; The June temperature must be at least 89°. The January temperature must be less than 42°. So the difference must be greater than 89° – 42°.

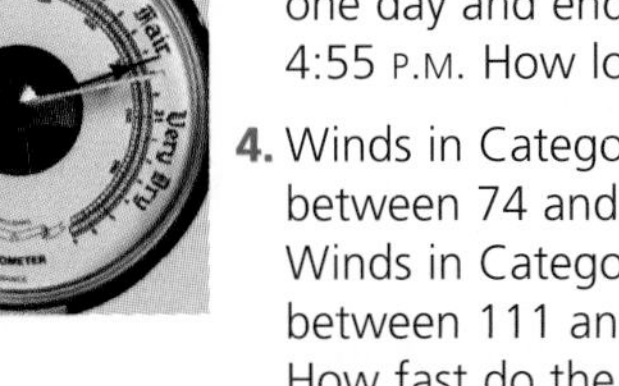

3. The Great New England Hurricane of 1938 had winds that blew 100 miles in an hour. It hit Connecticut at 4:10 P.M. one day and ended the same day at 4:55 P.M. How long did it last? 45 minutes

4. Winds in Category 1 hurricanes blow between 74 and 95 miles in an hour. Winds in Category 3 hurricanes blow between 111 and 130 miles in an hour. How fast do the winds in Category 2 hurricanes blow? between 96–110 miles per hour

5. You can tell how far away lightning is. Count the seconds between the lightning and the thunder. Lightning is 1 mile away for every 5 seconds. If you count 15 seconds, how far away is the lightning? 3 miles away

6. One inch of rain has as much water as 10 inches of snow. Which has more water, 2 feet of snow or 3 inches of rain? 3 inches of rain

Share Your Thinking

7. Compare your solution to problem 6 to a partner's. Did you use the same strategy? Answers will vary.

8. Explain how you could use a different strategy to solve problem 6. Answers will vary.

403

Meeting Individual Needs

Extra Support

Free T-Shirts *(visual)* Have student pairs use any strategy to solve this problem: You're buying 16 T-shirts for your soccer club. A local store offers 1 free T-shirt for every 3 you buy. How many of the 16 T-shirts will be free?

4 T-shirts

Alternate Approach

- Reteach Worksheet 11.11
- **TAB** See TE pp. 378E–378F.

MathZones

Understanding Multiplication

Students Acquiring English

See Language Connections, Ch. 11.

Challenge

Have students solve this problem: A pizza restaurant offers toppings on a whole or half pizza. You like sausage. One of your friends likes mushrooms or pepperoni. Another friend likes her pizza plain. A third friend likes mushrooms. All of you will eat plain. Each pizza is cut into 8 slices.

- If each person wants 3 slices, how many pizzas should you order? 2 pizzas
- What toppings would they have on each? Answers will vary.

Practice

Math Center For more problem solving practice, see Project Card 11, *Giving a Party.*

See **Just the Facts** Practice 11B, p. 141.

11.11 ANOTHER LOOK — Reteach

Problem Solving: Using Strategies

A bathroom floor is 14 tiles long and 8 tiles wide. In the middle, a bathtub takes up a space 6 tiles long by 2 tiles wide. How many tiles do you need to cover the floor?

1. Understand
- You need to find how many tiles will cover the part of the floor that is not covered by the bathtub.

2. Plan
- Decide what operations you will need to use.
- You will need to subtract the number of tiles covered by the bathtub from the number of tiles needed for the whole floor.

3. Try It
- Draw a picture of the bathroom. Use grid paper.
- Your drawing is like an array. You can find the number of tiles in the whole floor by finding 8 × 14. There would be 112 tiles in the whole floor.
- You can find the area of the bathtub in the same way. The bathtub takes up the space of 2 × 6 = 12 tiles.

4. Look Back
- To find the number of tiles needed, you can subtract. 112 – 12 = 100 tiles.

bathtub 2 6 14 8

Use any strategy to solve.

1. Red tiles cost $2 more each than white tiles. A package of 5 white tiles costs $10. How much would 2 packages of 5 red tiles cost? $40
2. Grout is used to hold tiles in place. If you need 1 gallon of grout to put 20 tiles in place, how many gallons would you need for the bathroom described in the explanation? 5 gallons

11.11 PRACTICE — Practice

Problem Solving: Using Strategies

Use any strategy to solve.

1. If Toni adds 5 to his age and then doubles it, he gets 30. How old is Toni? 10 years old
2. Claire has half as much money as May. May has 33¢ more than Hannah. Hannah has 25¢. How much money do May and Claire have? May has 58¢ and Claire has 29¢.
3. How much money do the 3 girls have in all? $1.12
4. You open your spelling book so that the sum of the page numbers on the facing pages is 49. What are the page numbers? 24 and 25
5. You test your friend on her multiplication facts. Your friend completes 5 problems in 8 seconds. How many problems can your friend complete in 40 seconds? 25 problems
6. Liam counts how many times Tamara and Ricky blink in 30 seconds. Tamara blinks 20 times and Ricky blinks 17 times. Approximately how many blinks might Tamara make in 1 minute? 40 blinks
7. How many blinks might Ricky make in 2 minutes? 68 blinks
8. You take a shower every day. You use about 50 gallons of water with each shower. You decide to start taking showers only 4 times a week to conserve water. How much water will you save in 1 week? 150 gallons
9. A typical raindrop falls an average of 600 feet every minute. How long does it take a raindrop to fall 2400 feet? 4 minutes

11.11 ENRICHMENT — Enrichment

Problem Solving: Using Strategies

Use any strategy to solve.

1. In 1972, the Hernandez family planted a pine tree that was 10 years old. How old will the tree be in the year 2000? 38 years old
2. The bus was scheduled to arrive at Webster School at 8:45 A.M. At 9:00 A.M., the bus was not at the school. Principal Jackson called the driver. The bus arrived 25 minutes after the call was made. How many minutes late was the bus? 40 minutes
3. In how many ways can the letters in the word READ be scrambled? Make as many real or nonsense words as you can. They must be 4 letters long, using each letter in READ only once. 23 words, 24 if you count READ
4. How many minutes are there in 5 hours? 300 minutes
5. There are 6 tables in Ms. Berg's classroom. There are 4 students each at 3 of the tables and 3 students at each of the remaining tables. How many students are there in Ms. Berg's class? 21 students
6. It takes about 17 muscles in your face to smile and 26 more muscles to frown. How many muscles does it take to frown? 43
7. Choose one of the problems above. Explain how a different strategy can be used to solve the same problem. Answers will vary.

Problem Solving

Give 0 to 6 points per answer, based on how well students meet the following criteria:

Problem 1

- There is use of a clear problem solving strategy.
- Work shows that $130 more is needed to reach the total of $500.

Problem 2

- There is use of a clear problem solving strategy.
- Work shows use of making a list or other organization of the data to see that 6 games take place.

Concepts and Skills

If students need more help with concepts and skills in this chapter, use the following Reteaching Worksheets.

- 84 Remembering to Regroup, p. 230
- 85 Regrouping Correctly, p. 231
- 86 Multiplying Three Factors, p. 232
- 87 Regrouping in Multiplication, p. 238
- 88 Regrouping Correctly, p. 239
- 89 Using the Zero Properties, p. 240

Chapter 11 Test

for Pages 378–403

Test-Taking Tips
If you are stuck, think about different strategies you have learned.

Problem Solving

Use any strategy to solve. Show your work. (pages 384, 396)

1. Your class puts on a play. You want to raise a total of $500.00 You sell 96 tickets the first night and 89 tickets the second night. Tickets are $2.00 each. How much more money does your class need? $130.00
2. You and 3 friends play each other in a one-on-one basketball tournament. Each person plays one game with every other person. How many games take place? 6 games

Concepts

Find the product. Use an array if you wish. (page 380)

3. 4 × 33 132
4. 5 × 19 95
5. 6 groups of 28 168
6. How could you use mental math to find 2 × 9 × 5? Use the grouping property and the order property: 2 × 5 = 10; 10 × 9 = 90.

Estimate. Write > or < to make the number sentence true. (page 382)

7. 32 × 6 ● 49 × 2 >
8. 6 × 61 ● 5 × 78 <
9. 412 × 4 ● 3 × 595 <
10. 188 × 2 ● 3 × 167 <

Find the product. Circle the product if you used mental math. Circles may vary. (pages 388, 394)

11. 41 × 4 = 164
12. 637 × 3 = 1911
13. 80 × 2 = 1600
14. 70 × 9 = 630
15. 294 × 2 = 588

404

Chapter Correlation to Standardized Tests

Math Central: Chapter Objective	ITBS Form M	CAT/5	CTBS/4	Terra Nova (CTBS/5)	MAT 7th ed.	SAT 9th ed.	State/ Local
11A To explore models for multiplying a 2-digit number by a 1-digit number	•	•	•	•	•	•	
11B To estimate products	•	•	•	•	•	•	
11C To multiply 2-digit numbers by 1-digit numbers	•	•	•	•	•	•	
11D To multiply 3-digit numbers with and without zeros by 1-digit numbers	•	•	•	•	•	•	
11E To multiply money amounts by 1-digit numbers	•	•	•	•	•	•	
11F To use Work a Simpler Problem and other strategies to solve problems	•			•	•	•	

Skills

Decide which statement is true. Write *a, b, c,* or *d.* (page 400)

16. You have \$20. Magazines cost \$3.85. b
    - a. You have enough to buy 6 magazines.
    - b. You have enough to buy 5 magazines.
    - c. You need more money to buy 4 magazines.
    - d. You don't have enough money to buy 5 magazines.
17. You have \$20. Large pizzas cost \$9.05. d
    - a. You have enough money for 3 large pizzas.
    - b. You have enough money for 4 large pizzas.
    - c. You don't have enough money for more than 1 pizza.
    - d. You have enough to buy 2 large pizzas.
18. You have \$20. Ice cream cones cost \$1.98. c
    - a. You can buy ice cream cones for 12 friends.
    - b. You can buy ice cream cones for 17 friends.
    - c. You need more money to buy ice cream for 12 friends.
    - d. You will get change if you buy cones for 12 friends.

Find the product. (pages 388, 394, 400)

19. 7 × 62 434 20. 86 × 8 688 21. 112 × 5 560 22. 341 × 4 1364

23. 3 × \$7.00 \$21.00 24. 6 × 19 114 25. 509 × 3 1527 26. 4 × \$2.99 \$11.96

Performance Task

(page 380)

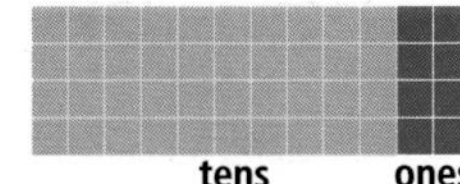

4 × 12 = 48

- Write a number sentence for the array.
- Explain the steps used in multiplying with an array.

Keep In Mind . . .
Your work will be evaluated on the following:
- ✓ Clearly written explanation
- ✓ Easy-to-follow steps
- ✓ True number sentence
- ✓ Number sentence that relates to the array

405

Performance Task

Use the following criteria, each worth four points, to evaluate your students' responses. These criteria align with *Keep In Mind* in the Pupil Edition, p. 405.

Criteria	
Includes a clear explanation	**Includes a true number sentence: 4 × 12 = 48**
Shows easy-to-follow steps	**Explains how the number sentence relates to the array**

Use this 4-level rubric to score students' responses. If you prefer a task with a 6-level rubric, use the Performance Assessment for this chapter.

4 points	**Limited response**
8 points	**Acceptable**
12 points	**Capable**
16 points	**Superior**

Common Error Alert

If your students are making frequent errors, see Analyzing Errors, TE pp. 405A–405B.

Scoring Chart

Item	Points
1–2	**6 points each**
3–26	**3 points each**
Performance Task	**16 points**
TOTAL	**100 points or 100%**

Item Analysis

Item	Objectives
1–2	Use Work a Simpler Problem and other strategies to solve problems (11F)
3–6	Explore models for multiplying a 2-digit number by a 1-digit number (11A)
7–10	Estimate products (11B)
11–26	Multiply 2-digit numbers, 3-digit numbers, and money amounts by 1-digit numbers (11C, 11D, 11E)

Assessment Options

The following materials are found in your **Comprehensive Assessment Package:**

Formal Assessments
- Standardized-Format
- Free-Response Chapter Tests, Forms A and B
- Chapter Tests for Students Acquiring Language Proficiency
- Informal Learning Inventory

Performance Assessments
- Chapter Tasks
- Midyear and Final Project Tasks

Alternative Assessments
- Observation Checklist
- Student Attitude Assessment
- Student Self-Assessment *Individual and Group*

Standardized Testing: New Formats
- Enhanced Multiple-Choice
- Extended-Response
- Short-Response

Management
- Student Record Sheets
- Answer Keys

Standardized-Format Test

- **Standardized-Format Chapter Tests**
- **Free-Response Chapter Tests, Forms A and B**
- **Standardized-Format Midyear and Final Tests**

Additional Assessment Resources

Test, Practice, Management Program

Use the *Test, Practice, Management Program* to create, administer, and score tests as well as generate practice sets. Questions are correlated to the Lesson Objectives.

Cumulative Test

For a cumulative review in the multiple-choice format, see TE pp. T82–T83.

Analyzing Errors

Strategies and Techniques for Reteaching

Errors in Multiplication Concepts
The multiplication algorithm requires students to successfully combine place-value concepts, accurate use of addition and multiplication facts. Lead students through the steps. Remind them to follow the steps in order. Encourage them to create their own flow charts and to refer to the charts as they work.

1. **Multiply the ones.**
2. **Regroup. Write the ones digit in the ones place.**
   Write the tens digit above the tens column.
3. **Multiply the tens.**
4. **Add the regrouped tens to this product.**
5. **Write the sum.**

Multiplying 2-Digit Numbers

Errors in Regrouping

Error Does not regroup ones for tens

Reteaching Show an example of multiplication as repeated addition. Model the multiplication with blocks to help students see that if they do not regroup, their answers may not be reasonable.

Error

26
× 3
618

Reteaching

26
26
+26
78

Error Forgets to add a regrouped number

Reteaching This is among the steps most easily forgotten. Have students circle a number as it is regrouped as a way of remembering to deal with it.

Error

2
36
× 4

Reteaching

②
36
× 4

Error Regroups ones digit rather than tens digit to tens place

Reteaching Use place-value models to help students see the concrete process of regrouping when multiplying a 2-digit number by a 1-digit number. Practice with physically regrouping will help them to work through the algorithm correctly.

Error

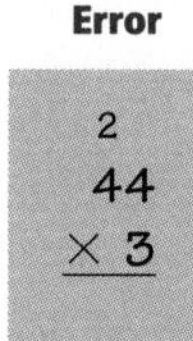

Reteaching

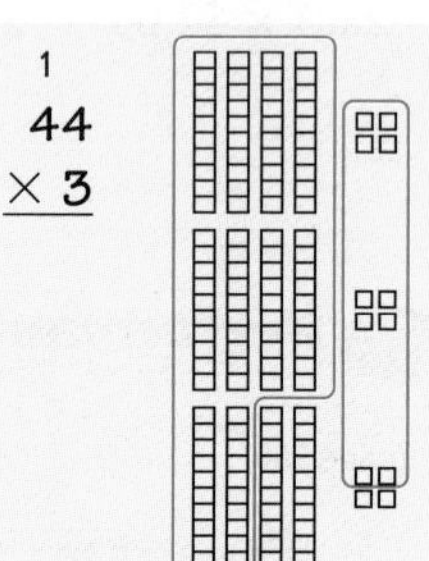

Error Adds a regrouped number before multiplying

Reteaching Review the algorithm step-by-step, modeling each step with place-value materials. Students should see that adding before multiplying does not make sense when compared to the model.

Error

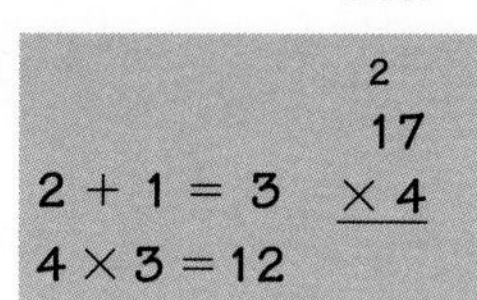

Reteaching

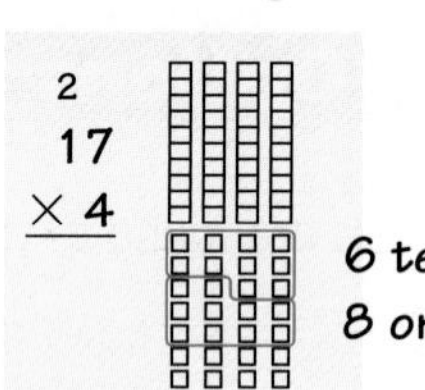

Error Adds rather than multiplies after regrouping

Reteaching Show the multiplication using expanded notation. Help students see that by using this procedure, they can tell whether their actual answer makes sense. Remind them that the 6 in 62, for example, means 6 tens and cannot be added to the regrouped ones.

Error

1
62
× 5
6 + 1 = 7

Reteaching

62   60 + 2
× 5   × 5   × 5
300 + 10 = 310

Analyzing Errors

Error Involving Place Value

Error Writes partial products incorrectly

Reteaching Have students estimate the product. Then work each step of the algorithm using both the short form and expanded notation. Help them see that the answer must be reasonably close to the estimate.

Error

```
  47
×  5

  35 (5 × 7)
+20 (5 × 4)
  55
```

Reteaching

```
 47   47 is close to 50.
× 5   50 × 5 = 250.
       40  +  7
      × 5   × 5
      200  + 35 = 235

      235 is close to 250.
      The answer makes sense.
```

Multiplying 3-Digit Numbers

Errors Involving Place Value

Error Disregards place value when multiplying

Reteaching Review expanded notation. Use expanded notation to multiply hundreds, tens, and ones independently. Then add the partial products.

Error

```
  174
×   3
32112
```

Reteaching

```
     174              174
100 + 70 + 4        ×   3
                       12 (3 × 4)
                      210 (3 × 70)
                      300 (3 × 100)
                      522
```

Error Does not align partial products correctly

Reteaching Although this error can be made when multiplying a 2-digit number, the error becomes more likely as the number of places increases. Have students use lined paper turned sideways to align the digits in the partial products.

Error

```
   327
×    5
   3 5
   100
+ 1500
 16305
```

Reteaching

```
   327
 ×   5
    35
   100
+ 1500
  1635
```

Error in Procedure

Error Omits steps in multiplying

Reteaching Prepare partially completed problems. Have students fill in the missing parts.

Error

```
   2
 324
×  6
 204
```

Reteaching

```
  1 2
  324
×   6
 □□44
```

Multiplying Money

Error in Placing Decimal Point

Error Always places the decimal to the left of the product when multiplying money

Reteaching Give students practice in estimating before multiplying. Remind them to compare their final answer to their estimate.

Error

```
 $.59
 ×  4
$.236
```

Reteaching

```
$.59   $.59 is about $.60
× 4    $.60 × 4 is $2.40
       So, $.59 × 4 is about $2.40.
       The answer must be $2.36.
```

Two Ways to Use the Cumulative Review

Maintenance For those students whose results on the current Chapter Test show a good grasp of skills and concepts, you may wish to assign the Cumulative Review as homework. Students may also benefit from the specific review and practice opportunities listed in the Skills Maintenance chart.

Reassessment For those students whose results on the current Chapter Test show only a limited grasp of skills and concepts, you may wish to assign the Cumulative Review as class work. If it then appears that reassessment is needed, the Skills Reteaching chart on the opposite page identifies remedial minilessons in the Teacher's Resource Package.

Additional Assessment Resources

Test, Practice, Management Program

Use the *Test, Practice, Management Program* to create, administer, and score tests as well as generate practice sets. Questions are correlated to the Lesson Objectives.

Cumulative Review

Subtracting with Zeros (Chapter 3)
Subtract 372 from 602.

Here's A Way!

Subtract the ones.
To subtract the tens, regroup the hundreds.
Subtract the hundreds.

```
  510
  602
− 372
  230
```

Find the difference.

1. 109 − 36 = 73
2. 203 − 85 = 118
3. 480 − 296 = 184
4. 802 − 348 = 454
5. 603 − 475 = 128
6. 520 − 189 = 331
7. Look at exercise 6. There are 0 ones in 520. How were you able to subtract 9 ones? by regrouping

Patterns in Basic Facts (Chapter 5)
Skip-count to find each answer.
3 × 5 and 20 ÷ 5

Here's A Way!

Skip-count by fives 3 times:
5, 10, 15; 3 × 5 = 15
Skip-count by fives to 20:
5, 10, 15, 20
You said 4 numbers.
20 ÷ 5 = 4

Find the answer.

8. 4 × 3 12
9. 5 × 3 15
10. 6 × 3 18
11. 12 ÷ 3 4
12. 15 ÷ 3 5
13. 18 ÷ 3 6
14. What number do you skip-count by in all of exercises 8–13? 3

Fact Families (Chapter 6)
Solve 8 × ■ = 24.

Here's A Way!

Use a fact family.
24 ÷ 3 = 8
24 ÷ 8 = 3
3 × 8 = 24
So, 8 × 3 = 24.

Find the missing factor.

15. ■ × 6 = 18 3
16. 18 ÷ 3 = ■ 6
17. 7 × ■ = 21 3
18. 21 ÷ 3 = ■ 7
19. 5 × ■ = 30 6
20. 30 ÷ 6 = ■ 5
21. Subtraction is related to addition. What is related to multiplication? division

406

Skills Maintenance

Chapter Objectives	Where taught in pupil book	More practice in pupil book
• To subtract 3-digit whole numbers with zeros (3D)	**Chapter 3**, pp. 110–111	More Practice Set 3.12, p. 451
• To identify patterns in fact families (5E)	**Chapter 5**, pp. 176–177	More Practice Set 5.9, p. 456
• To use inverse operations to complete fact families (6C)	**Chapter 6**, pp. 192–193	None
• To find simple equivalencies for customary and metric units (9D)	**Chapter 9**, pp. 314–315	More Practice Set 9.6, p. 468
• To relate decimals to fractions and mixed numbers (10D)	**Chapter 10**, pp. 352–353	More Practice Set 10.3, p. 472
• To use Work a Simpler Problem and other strategies (11F)	**Chapter 11**, pp. 396–397	None

Measurement (Chapter 9)
How many ounces are in 2 lb?

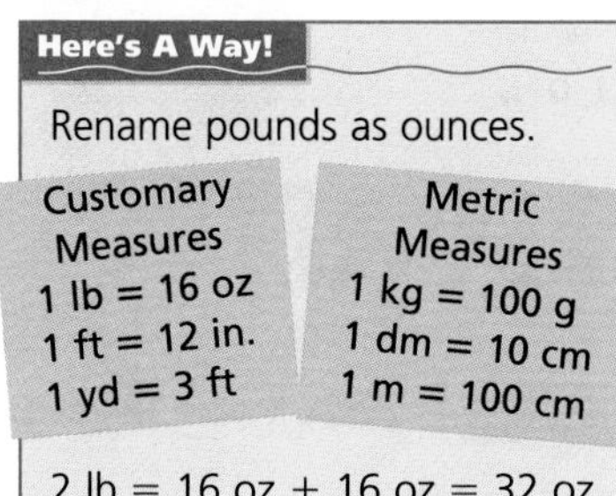

Here's A Way!
Rename pounds as ounces.
Customary Measures
1 lb = 16 oz
1 ft = 12 in.
1 yd = 3 ft
Metric Measures
1 kg = 100 g
1 dm = 10 cm
1 m = 100 cm
2 lb = 16 oz + 16 oz = 32 oz

Complete. Use the data on the charts.

22. 3 lb = ■ oz 48
23. ■ lb = 64 oz 4
24. 2 kg = ■ g 2000
25. 4000 g = ■ kg 4
26. 5 m = ■ cm 500
27. 7 dm = ■ cm 70
28. Would it make sense to measure your daily trip to school in centimeters? Why or why not? Answers will vary. Possible answer: No, because the units are too small to be meaningful for such a long distance.

Decimals (Chapter 10)
What fraction can you write for 0.6?

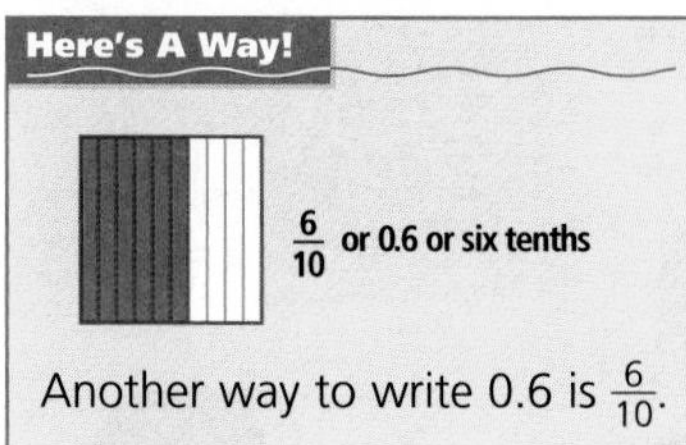

Here's A Way!
6/10 or 0.6 or six tenths
Another way to write 0.6 is 6/10.

Use models to write the decimal form of the fraction.

29. $\frac{1}{10}$ = ■ 0.1
30. $\frac{7}{10}$ = ■ 0.7
31. $\frac{9}{10}$ = ■ 0.9
32. $\frac{4}{10}$ = ■ 0.4
33. $\frac{5}{10}$ = ■ 0.5
34. $\frac{3}{10}$ = ■ 0.3
35. Draw a picture to show $\frac{2}{10}$. Label it three ways. Answers will vary. Check to be sure that the picture shows 10 equal parts with 2 parts shaded. Labels should state: $\frac{2}{10}$, 0.2, two tenths.

Problem Solving

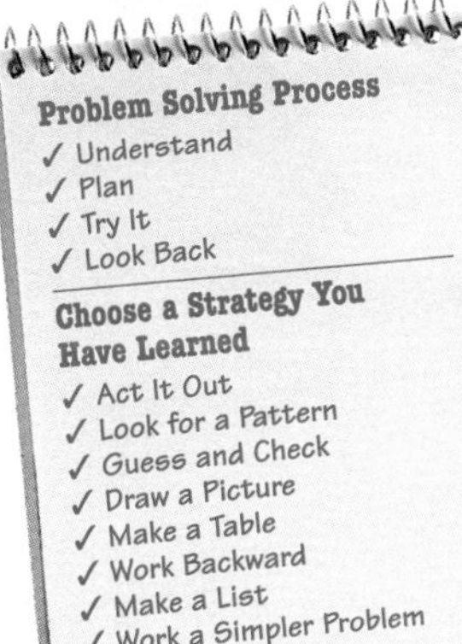

Solve the problem. Show your work.

36. Two whole numbers add up to 51. One number directly follows the other. What are they? 25 and 26
37. Suppose you have 4 pairs of shoes and 1 pair of boots. The shoes are each 3 inches wide. The boots are each 4 inches wide. A shoe rack is 24 inches across. Can you fit all the shoes and the boots side by side across the rack? Explain. No; You would need 32 inches across the rack. You only have 24 inches.

407

Skills Reteaching

Chapter Objectives	Suggested materials for minilessons		
• To subtract 3-digit whole numbers with zeros (3D)	Reteach 3.12	Practice 3.12	Enrichment 3.12
• To identify patterns in fact families (5E)	Reteach 5.9	Practice 5.9	Enrichment 5.9
• To use inverse operations to complete fact families (6C)	Reteach 6.1	Practice 6.1	Enrichment 6.1
• To find equivalencies for customary and metric units (9D)	Reteach 9.6	Practice 9.6	Enrichment 9.6
• To relate decimals to fractions and mixed numbers (10B)	Reteach 10.3	Practice 10.3	Enrichment 10.3
• To use Work a Simpler Problem and other strategies (11F)	Reteach 11.8	Practice 11.8	Enrichment 11.8

Students Acquiring English

Some students may need assistance on the Cumulative Review.

- Be prepared to read directions aloud to students.
- Focus special attention on word problems. Expect to paraphrase, diagram, or draw an explanation of the word problem.
- Review important vocabulary words that have been previously introduced.

INVESTIGATION

Management small groups
Materials chart paper, markers, salt dough ingredients (optional)

Building Background

Salt dough bakes into hard and inedible shapes that can be painted and decorated.

Management Strategies Cooperative Learning

Introduce

- Meet with the entire class to introduce the activity and assign students to small groups.

Guide

- If students have difficulty, ask them to restate the task.
- If a group is not working well together, review each student's role in the group.

Summarize

- Give students time to find solutions.
- Use small-group time to assess students' math skills.

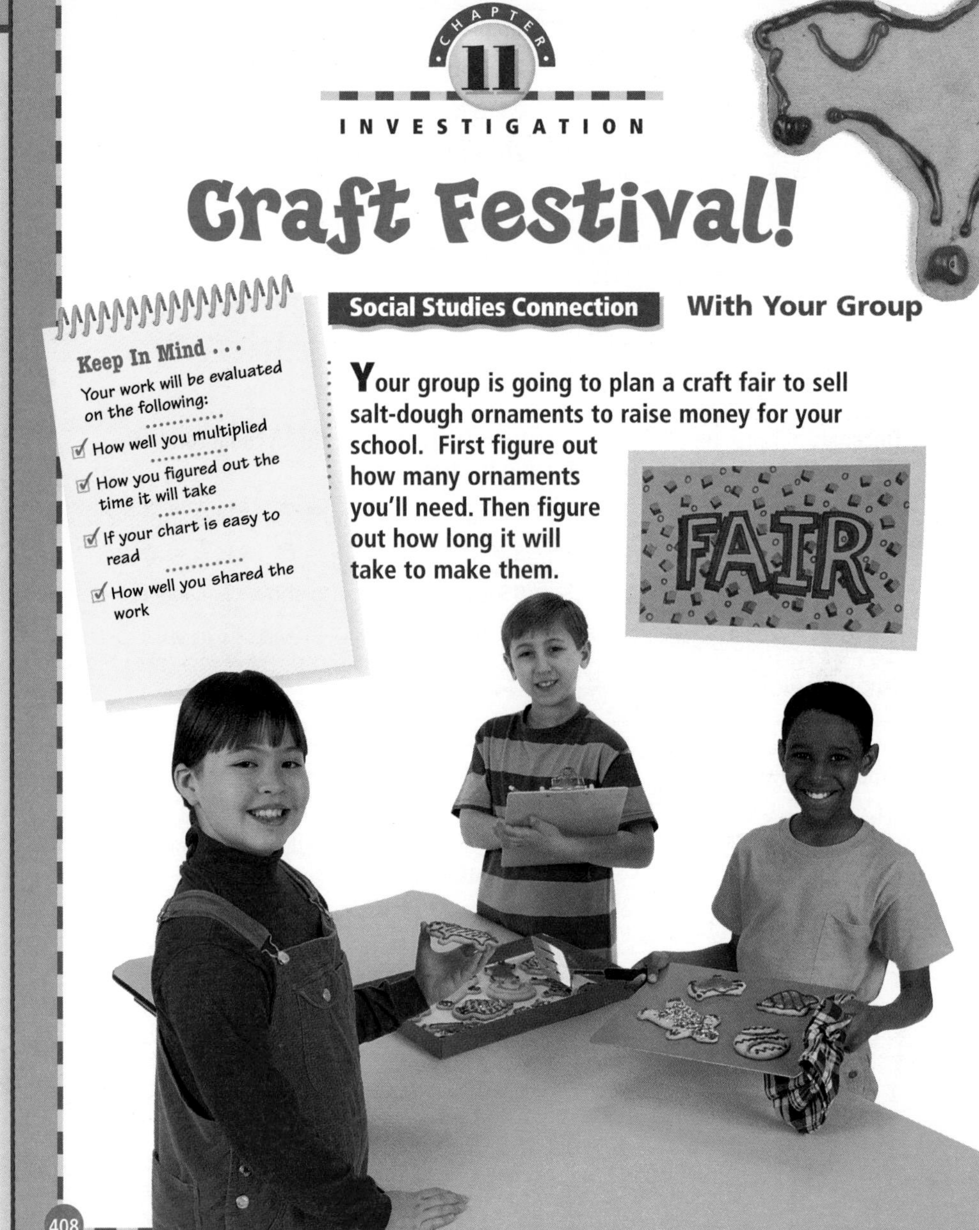

CHAPTER 11
INVESTIGATION
Craft Festival!
Keep In Mind . . .
Your work will be evaluated on the following:
How well you multiplied
How you figured out the time it will take
If your chart is easy to read
How well you shared the work
Social Studies Connection
With Your Group
Your group is going to plan a craft fair to sell salt-dough ornaments to raise money for your school. First figure out how many ornaments you'll need. Then figure out how long it will take to make them.
FAIR
408

Investigation Support

Technology

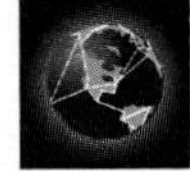

Internet: Education Place
http://www.eduplace.com
Houghton Mifflin Education Place **Mathematics Center** provides teacher and student support, such as links to other Internet sites.

Math Journal: *Communicating*

Ask students to bring in recipes for their favorite entree, vegetable and dessert. In their Math Journals, they can write the ingredients, cooking time, and a plan for preparing the entire meal.

Portfolio Opportunity

Make photocopies of each group's chart to put into individual portfolios.

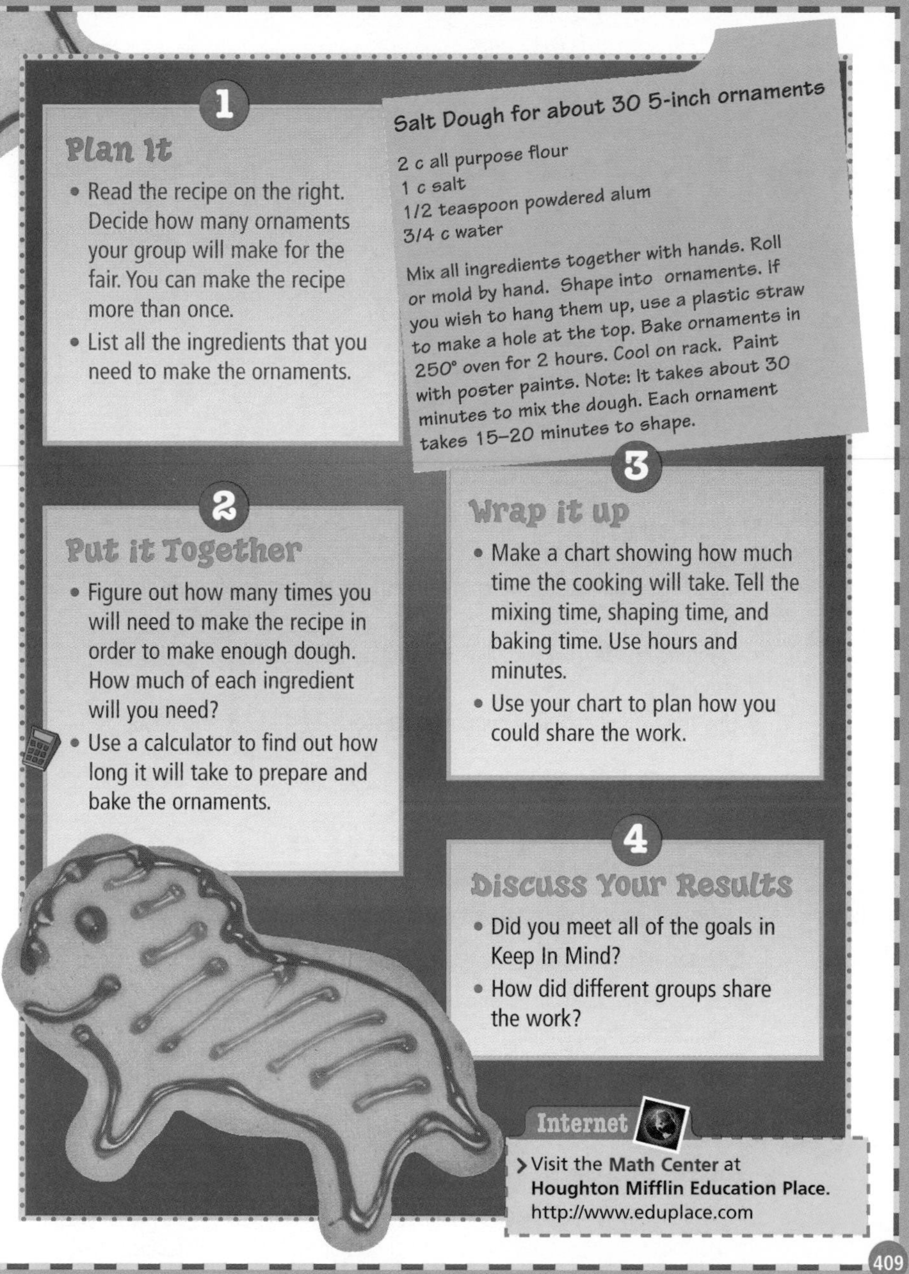

1 Plan It

- Read the recipe on the right. Decide how many ornaments your group will make for the fair. You can make the recipe more than once.
- List all the ingredients that you need to make the ornaments.

Salt Dough for about 30 5-inch ornaments

2 c all purpose flour
1 c salt
1/2 teaspoon powdered alum
3/4 c water

Mix all ingredients together with hands. Roll or mold by hand. Shape into ornaments. If you wish to hang them up, use a plastic straw to make a hole at the top. Bake ornaments in 250° oven for 2 hours. Cool on rack. Paint with poster paints. Note: It takes about 30 minutes to mix the dough. Each ornament takes 15–20 minutes to shape.

2 Put it Together

- Figure out how many times you will need to make the recipe in order to make enough dough. How much of each ingredient will you need?
- Use a calculator to find out how long it will take to prepare and bake the ornaments.

3 Wrap it up

- Make a chart showing how much time the cooking will take. Tell the mixing time, shaping time, and baking time. Use hours and minutes.
- Use your chart to plan how you could share the work.

4 Discuss Your Results

- Did you meet all of the goals in Keep In Mind?
- How did different groups share the work?

Internet

> Visit the Math Center at **Houghton Mifflin Education Place.** http://www.eduplace.com

409

Problem Solving Tip

How many people are you expecting to come to the craft fair? Discuss and come up with a realistic number, so that students can accurately plan the number of ornaments to make.

Completing the Investigation

Step 1 Encourage students to consider how many ornaments they think they could sell before they decide how many to make.

Step 2 Remind students that when adding amounts of time, 60 minutes = 1 hour.

Step 3 Charts can be illustrated with the shapes of the ornaments the group plans to make.

Step 4 Ask students to explain on their charts how the work could be shared between groups.

Extending the Investigation

Make the ornaments and have the craft fair as a classroom fund-raiser. Students can project the earnings based on numbers of ornaments sold and compare actual earnings after the sale.

For more practice **Using the Calculator,** see pp. T88–T90.

Assessment Scoring Rubric

These criteria align with *Keep In Mind* in the Pupil Edition on page 408.

Criteria	1 Limited response	2 Acceptable	3 Capable	4 Superior
Accuracy of calculations	Calculations are inaccurate	Some of the calculations are inaccurate	Most of the calculations are accurate	All of the calculations are accurate
Understanding of the math process	Lacks understanding of the time it takes to make ornaments	Can explain some of the math process	Understands most of the math process	Thoroughly understands the time it takes to make ornaments
Clarity and completeness of the chart	Chart is incomplete and disorganized	Chart shows an attempt to organize the information	Chart shows most information clearly and completely	Chart show all of the information clearly and completely
Contribution to the group process	Makes no effort to contribute to the group	Makes some effort to contribute to the group	Contributes to the group most of the time	Contributes fully to the group

Use this 4-level rubric to score students' responses. If you prefer a task with a 6-level rubric, use the Performance Assessment for this chapter.

Dividing by 1-Digit Numbers

Chapter Overview

Rationale

Chapter Pacing: 9 days

- This chapter carefully develops the division algorithm in several steps.
- By working with numbers that divide with "leftovers," students become aware that division may or may not yield a remainder.
- The Math World feature presents several ways of dividing a 24-hour period, and invites students to explore division in sports.
- In the Investigation, students use dividing by 1-digit numbers in the context of money management.

See **Daily Lesson Plans**, Chapter Management at a Glance, pp. 114–115; Suggested Weekly Plan, pp. 116–117.

Problem Solving

This chapter gives students the opportunity to choose from a variety of problem solving strategies to help them solve problems.

Assessment

- The Chapter Introduction allows you to assess whether students have a clear understanding of division.
- Observe student understanding at each step in the development of long division.
- Make sure that every student can accurately record the results of separating 40 counters into different groups, including remainders.
- Use the Midchapter Review, the Chapter Test, and the Cumulative Review to assess students' needs for reinforcement or reteaching.

Reading Strategies

- Teach the Evaluate reading strategy minilesson on TAB p. 410J. Then, use the following as opportunities to reinforce the strategy.
  - Preparing for Tests, TE pp. 410G–410H
  - Problem Solving Workshop, TE p. 420A
  - Problem Solving, Lessons 12.2, 12.4, 12.5, and 12.7–12.9
- Use the SAE reading support for Lessons 12.7 and 12.8.

Vocabulary

- Introduce students to the chapter with vocabulary minilesson, TAB p. 410J.
- Planning Guide, p. 410C, lists vocabulary for each lesson in the chapter.
- Use the SAE vocabulary support in Lessons 12.1–12.3 and 12.6.

Meeting Individual Needs

Students Acquiring English

Provide extra practice with dividing by 1-digit numbers.

- Allow time to explore models of division.
- Help students verbalize the process they use in dividing by 1-digit numbers.

See also **Language Connections** for additional support.

Extra Support

Students may lack understanding of division.

- Demonstrate the subtractive method of division with place-value blocks. Then, introduce regrouping using the same approach.
- Use the Basic Facts Workshop, p. 421A.
- Use the Analyzing Errors strategies, pp. 433A–433B.
- Use the Division Workshop's Extra Support activity.

Challenge

Many students may benefit from this extension activity.

- Give students the magic square shown. Have them divide each number in the magic square by 4 and write the quotient in the corresponding box in a blank magic square. Then, have them evaluate the new square. Is it a magic square? Can they make another one in a similar fashion? Why or why not?

162	146	272
296	192	92
122	242	216

Multi-Age Classroom

The chart below shows the chapters in books for levels 2 and 4 that can be used in conjunction with this chapter.

2	3	4
Chapter 10 *Multiplication and Division Readiness*	**Chapter 12** *Dividing by 1-Digit Numbers*	**Chapter 7** *Dividing by 1-Digit Numbers*

See **Daily Lesson Plans**, Multi-Age Classroom Concept and Skill Development, pp. 4–5.

Chapter Bibliography

Key

Multicultural	★	*Social Studies*	
Science/Health		*Music*	
Literature		*Art*	

Technology

Students can explore dividing with the electronic manipulatives in *Unlocking Whole Numbers 3–5*. The counters and base-ten materials, linked to symbolic notation, help students understand processes and relationships.

Internet: Education Place
http://www.eduplace.com

Visit the **Mathematics Center** in *Houghton Mifflin Education Place* to find activities, projects, games, and links to other valuable Internet sites.

Ultimate Writing & Creativity Center

Students can use the *Ultimate Writing & Creativity Center*® for all their writing and publishing activities. The software is available from The Learning Company® in Macintosh and Windows formats.

Larson's Leapfrog MATH™

Leapfrog Math includes mathematics skills and concepts for grades 3–6. Each grade is contained on a single CD-ROM. The software is available from Meridian Creative Group, a Division of Larson Texts, Inc.

Test, Practice, Management Program

Use the *Test, Practice, Management Program* to create, administer, and score tests as well as generate practice sets. Questions are correlated to Lesson Objectives.

Graphers Sunburst Communications, Inc.®

Using the friendly tools in *Graphers,* children can easily manipulate data that can be counted or sorted and represent their data in a table or with six types of graphs.

Books for Students

Houghton Mifflin Mathematics Bookshelf

Mush! Across Alaska in the World's Longest Sled-Dog Race
Patricia Seibert,
Millbrook Press, 1992.
Students learn about the Iditarod sled-dog race in this book, which also lets students explore estimation and division.

The Go-Around Dollar
Barbara Adams,
Simon and Schuster Children's Books, 1992.
This read-aloud picture book walks readers through a day in the life of a dollar bill. Text cites dollar facts about trading, making change, and detecting counterfeit bills.

One Hundred Hungry Ants
Elinor J. Pinczes,
Houghton Mifflin, 1993.
Students learn about division and number relationships as they read about an army of ants who march single file to a picnic, then divide and conquer.

A Remainder of One
Elinor J. Pinczes,
Houghton Mifflin, 1995.
When the queen of the bugs demands that her army march in even lines, Private Joe divides marchers into more lines so he will not be left out of the parade.

★ **Stories to Solve: Folktales from Around the World**
George Shannon,
Greenwillow Books, 1985.
This collection of folktales from around the world provides students with mysteries, puzzles, riddles, and problems to solve.

The Greatest Guessing Game: A Book About Dividing
Robert Froman,
Crowell, 1978.
The division process is explained by using the analogy that division is like a guessing game.

Books for Families

The Book of Classic Board Games
Sid Sackson,
Klutz Press, 1996.
Parents and children use mathematics skills while playing fifteen of the most popular board games from around the world dating back to 1400 B.C.

Helping Your Child Learn Math: With Activities for Children Aged 5 Through 13
Patsy F. Kanter,
DIANE Publishing, 1993.
This helpful guide presents a series of mathematics-based activities for parents and children to do together as a part of daily life. Good public sector resource.

Discovery Math: Division
David L. Stienecker,
Benchmark Books, 1996.
Together, families can do projects and experiments that explore division concepts.

Reference Books for Teachers

Math by All Means: Division, Grades 3–4
Susan Ohanian and Marilyn Burns,
Marilyn Burns Education Associates, 1995.
This five-week unit of instruction helps students construct their own understanding of division by examining patterns, analyzing statistical data, and investigating division from a geometric perspective.

Implicit and Explicit Knowledge: An Educational Approach
Dina Tirosh,
Ablex Publishing, 1994.
Speculations on the foundation of knowledge and intelligence, including multiplication and division, are shared in this book.

The Pattern Factory: Elementary Problem Solving Through Patterning
Ann Roper and Linda Harvey,
Idea School Supply, 1993.
This collection of exercises and problems based on patterns is designed to develop students' problem solving skills.

Planning Guide

	TE Pages	Lesson Objectives	Lesson Vocabulary	NCTM Standards
12.1 Exploring Division	*412–413*	To explore division, with and without remainders, using concrete materials	remainder	Whole Number Computation, Reasoning, Connections, Communication
12.2 Fractional Parts of a Set	*414–415*	To find a fraction of a set		Whole Number Concepts, Fractions and Decimals, Communication, Reasoning, Connections
12.3 Division with Remainders	*416–417*	To divide 1- and 2-digit dividends by 1-digit divisors, resulting in 1-digit quotients		Whole Number Concepts, Measurement, Problem Solving, Communication, Connections, Reasoning
12.4 Interpreting Remainders	*418–419*	To interpret remainders in word problems		Whole Number Concepts, Measurement, Reasoning, Communication, Connections
12.5 Is the Answer Reasonable?	*420*	To decide and to justify why an answer is reasonable		Problem Solving, Whole Number Concepts, Reasoning, Connections
12.6 Estimating Quotients	*424–425*	To estimate quotients of 2- and 3-digit dividends with 1-digit divisors		Whole Number Concepts, Patterns and Functions, Estimation, Measurement, Communication
12.7 2-Digit Quotients	*426–427*	To divide 2-digit dividends by 1-digit divisors, resulting in 2-digit quotients		Whole Number Concepts, Estimation, Communication, Reasoning, Connections
12.8 Dividing Greater Numbers	*428–429*	To divide 3-digit dividends by 1-digit divisors, resulting in 2-digit quotients		Whole Number Concepts, Estimation, Problem Solving, Communication, Connections
12.9 Using Strategies	*430–431*	To use different strategies to solve problems		Whole Number Concepts, Connections, Reasoning, Communication, Problem Solving

Chapter Objectives

12A To explore models for dividing a 2-digit number by a 1-digit number with remainders
12B To use division to find a fractional part of a set
12C To estimate quotients
12D To divide 2-digit numbers by 1-digit numbers
12E To divide 3-digit numbers by 1-digit numbers
12F To interpret remainders
12G To use a variety of strategies to solve problems

Chapter Objectives	math center	State Requirements
12A	• *Subtracting to Divide,* Activity Card 65	
12B	• *Divide and Move,* Activity Card 66; Gameboard 5	
12A, 12D	• *Remainders on the Move,* How-To Card 40; Number Card Deck; Gameboard 5	
12F	• *Remains to Be Seen,* Activity Card 67	
12G	• *Make a Musical Tape,* Project Card 12	
12C	• *Estimation Spin,* How-To Card 42; Workmat 4	
12D	• *Read the Signs,* How-To Card 42; Gameboard 8	
12E	• *Find the Missing Digits,* Activity Card 68	
12G	• *Make a Musical Tape,* Project Card 12	

Integrating Reading Strategies

- Teach/review the Evaluate strategy using TAB p. 410J.
- Encourage students to practice the strategy in Lessons 12.2, 12.4, 12.5, and 12.7–12.9.

Technology

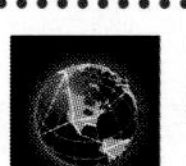

Unlocking Whole Numbers 3–5

Internet: Education Place
http://www.eduplace.com
Houghton Mifflin Education Place
Mathematics Center

Test, Practice, Management Program

Special Lessons

pp. 410–411

Chapter Introduction

The Introduction links prior knowledge of division to the concept of remainders.

pp. 430–431

Students apply problem solving strategies in the context of dogsled racing in Alaska.

pp. 422–423

Math World
Division Around the World

Use this feature to show students how division is used all over the world.

pp. 436–437

Investigation
Go, Team, Go!

Students figure out how much money it takes to supply a Little League team with uniforms and equipment.

Assessment

Use the following assessment tools to help assess individual needs.

- Midchapter Review, p. 421
- Chapter Test, pp. 432–433
- Cumulative Review, pp. 434–435

Chapter

12 Division Workshop

Whole and Decimal Numbers

Alternate Approach

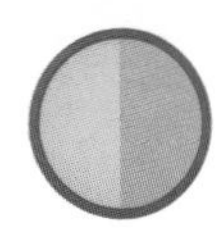

Use with page 412. **30 minutes**

Deck Division

Objective To model dividing a 2-digit number by a 1-digit number with remainders

Management teacher monitored; small groups
Materials for each student: 11 index cards
Modality *visual/kinesthetic*

Activity

- Distribute 11 index cards to each student.
- Divide the class into small groups and have them combine and shuffle their cards. Ask, How many cards are there in your group? Answers will vary.
- Help students identify the relationship between dealing cards and division.
- Invite 5 students to the front of the room, and deal out 3 sets of cards to them. Let volunteers suggest a number sentence that expresses what has happened. Make sure students understand how to record the remainder.

33 ÷ 5 is 6 R3

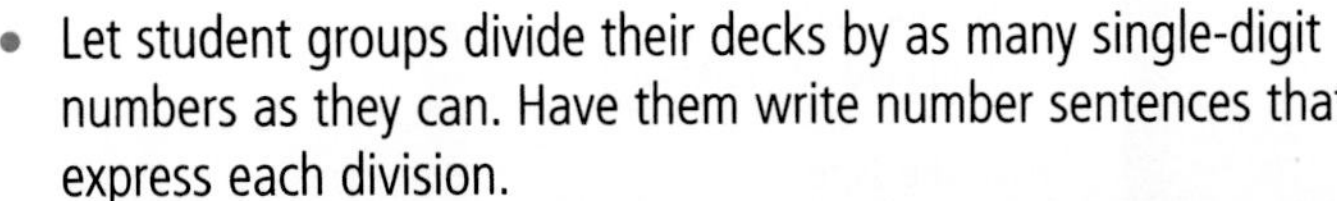

- Let student groups divide their decks by as many single-digit numbers as they can. Have them write number sentences that express each division.

Meeting Individual Needs: *Modify*

Challenge Ask students to determine how many cards should be in a deck if each group member is to receive 8 cards. How many for each class member?

Extra Support

Use with page 416. **25 minutes**

Repeated Subtraction

Objective To find quotients and remainders using a calculator

Management teacher directed; pairs
Modality *visual/verbal*

Activity

- Ask students to divide 37 by 5 on their calculators and tell you what they see. 7.4
- Remind students that 0.4 is $\frac{4}{10}$, not a remainder of 4. Explain that there is a way to find remainders with a calculator using repeated subtraction. Model the following keystroke sequence. Ask students to perform each step along with you. On your calculator enter 37 – 5. Then press the equals key. Continue pressing the equals key until the display reads 2. Tell students to make a tally mark each time they press the equals key. Tally each subtraction as you go.
- After 7 subtractions, the calculator will show 2. Tell students that since you cannot subtract 5 from 2, 2 is the remainder. Discuss how repeated subtraction and division are related.
- Assign several division problems with remainders for pairs to solve.
- For more practice **Using the Calculator,** see pp. T88–T90.

Meeting Individual Needs: *Modify*

Students Acquiring English Make sure that students understand the term *remainder.*

Game

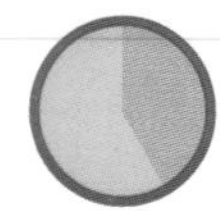

Use with page 426. **25 minutes**

Secret Quotient

Objective **To use multiplication to find a secret quotient**

Management teacher monitored; small groups
Materials calculator for each group
Modality *visual*

Activity

- Tell students they are detectives looking for a secret 2-digit quotient between 40 and 50.
- Begin by writing a 2-digit number between 40 and 50 on a slip of paper and hiding it.
- Small groups write a division problem with a quotient equal to the number they want to guess. Then each group asks if their quotient is correct. Tell them if the quotient is too high, too low, or the secret quotient.
- Have each group record all their guesses and responses. For a secret number of 43, a group's record sheet might look like this.
- When a group guesses the secret quotient, ask them to share their guessing strategy without giving away the number.
- Continue until all the groups have guessed the secret quotient.

Guess	Division problem	High/Low
50	100 ÷ 2	too high
40	80 ÷ 2	too low
45	90 ÷ 2	too high
41	82 ÷ 2	too low
43	86 ÷ 2	you guessed it!

Meeting Individual Needs: *Modify*

Extra Support Some students may succeed more readily if the secret quotient is easily divisible, for example, by 5. Or you may want to show students how to use a multiplication problem to write a division problem with a particular quotient.

Challenge Let groups take turns picking their own secret quotients.

Technology

MATHKEYS

Use with Lesson 12.4

Objective **To use division with remainders to solve realistic problems**

Management teacher monitored; pairs
Materials ***MathKeys**: Unlocking Whole Numbers 3–5,* Level 3, Act. 25: Sporty Divisions
Modality *visual*

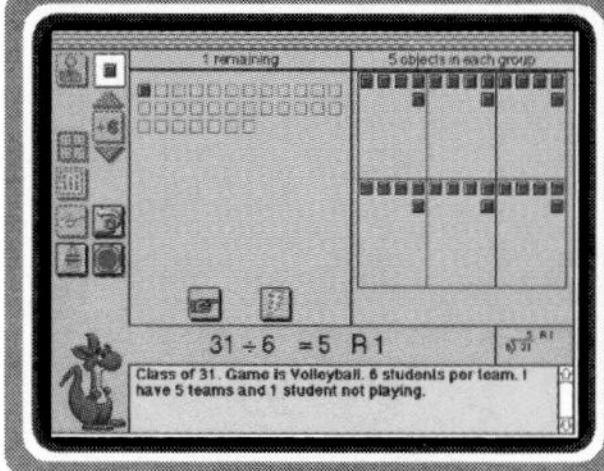

Activity

30 minutes

- Make a list of students' favorite gym activities. Discuss whether the entire class could participate in the activities at one time or whether some students will have to "sit out." Explain that students will use the computer to choose which sport would include the most people.
- Distribute Activity 25 Master and ask pairs of students to open the *MathKeys* Counters Division Mat.
- Tell students that for this activity, they will divide 31 students by the number of students on a team. The size of the team depends on the sport they select.
- Note that before students begin dividing, they must choose to share or group. Ask students to explain which one they chose and why.
- For each sport, students must determine how many games can be played between two teams, how many teams will not play, and the total number of students not playing.

Meeting Individual Needs: *Modify*

Extra Support Let students having difficulty fill in only the first two rows of the worksheet. They will determine the numbers of teams for each sport and how many students will not be on a team.

Challenge Ask students to answer this question in writing: If you could use any combination of sports, how could you include everyone in your class in a sport at one time?

Chapter 12

Preparing for Tests

To develop students' test-taking strategies, model the following types of assessment items found in this program.

Standardized Tests

Write the following problem on the board.

What is the best estimate for this quotient?
85 ÷ 2 = □

Ⓐ 80

Ⓑ 90

Ⓒ 45 correct

Ⓓ 50

Standardized tests usually require that students select the correct answer from a group of possible answers. In this problem, students select the best estimate for a quotient.

Strategy

- What should you do first? Possible answer: think of the problem as 2 × __ = 85
- What multiples of 10 will get you close to 85? 40 and 50
- How can you select the best estimate now? 40 gets closer than 50; 45 falls in the middle between 40 and 50.

See also Standardized Testing: New Formats, **Chapter 12.**

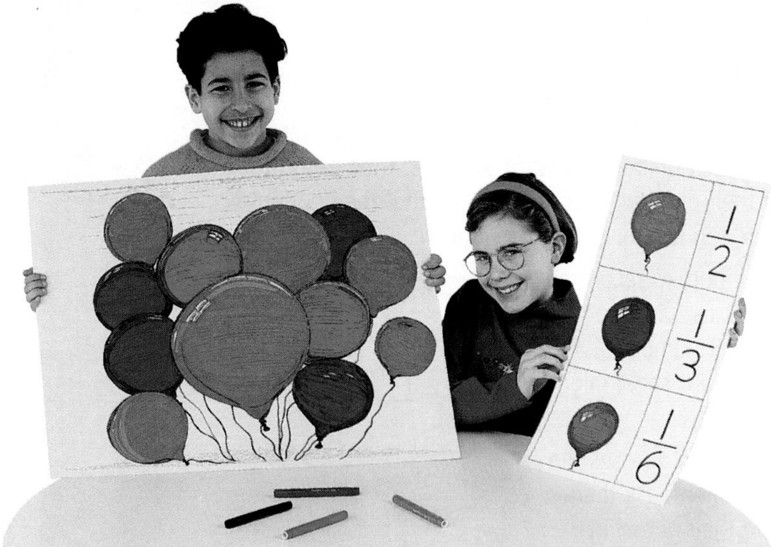

Open-Ended Questions

Write the following problem on the board.

You have 6 red, 4 purple, and 2 green balloons. Draw a picture of all the balloons. Make a chart showing what fraction of the balloons are red, what fraction are purple, and what fraction are green.

Open-ended questions can be answered in more than one way; they allow students to use a variety of concepts and processes. This problem requires students to draw pictures to determine fractional parts, and make a chart of the fractions.

Strategy

- What does the problem ask you to do? draw the balloons and make a chart to show what portion of the balloons are red, purple, and green
- What will the denominators show? the total number of parts, 12 parts
- What will the numerators show? how many balloons there are of each color: $\frac{6}{12}$ or $\frac{1}{2}$ are red; $\frac{4}{12}$ or $\frac{1}{3}$ are purple; $\frac{2}{12}$ or $\frac{1}{6}$ are green

See also Assessments, **Chapter 12.**

Preparing for Tests

Reading Strategies for Test-Taking

Evaluate: As I read, I make decisions about what information is and is not important and about what makes sense.

Performance Tasks

Write the following direction and problem on the board.

Solve the problem. Explain what to do with the remainder.

You are in a painting class with 16 students and 3 teachers. The class is going on a field trip to the art museum. The art school uses minivans for transportation, and 7 passengers can ride in each minivan. How many minivans will be needed for your trip?

Performance assessments engage students in meaningful tasks that permit the teacher to observe their working procedures as well as the results they obtain. This task requires that students divide and use remainders to solve a problem.

Strategy

- What does the problem ask you to do? tell how many minivans are needed for the field trip
- How will you decide? divide 19 members by 7 passengers in a van
- What is the answer? 2 R5
- Will 2 vans be enough for all the people? Why or why not? No, the remainder of 5 means there are 5 people left over. If you only use 2 vans, those 5 won't have any place to ride.
- So what do you have to do? use 3 vans
- What strategy did you use with the remainder in this problem? I included the remainder in the answer by writing the next whole number.
- Is this always the appropriate strategy for remainders? No, you have to look at each problem individually and decide what the remainder represents.

Check that students restate the problem as a number sentence, $19 \div 7 = \square$. They should explain why it makes sense to round the remainder up to the next whole number.

See also Performance Assessments, **Chapter 12.**

Test-Taking Tips

- Make notes or draw pictures to help you solve the problem.

Additional Assessment Resources

Test, Practice, Management Program

Use the *Test, Practice, Management Program* to create, administer, and score tests as well as generate practice sets. Questions are correlated to the Lesson Objectives.

Chapter 12

Math Center

To meet individual needs, use the following resources from the Math Center. You may first wish to model activities for the whole class in order to demonstrate the rules for games and introduce procedures for independent tasks.

Gameboards

Gameboard 5
Use with Lesson 12.2.

Gameboard 8
Use with Lesson 12.7.

Activity Cards

65 *Subtracting to Divide*
Use with Lesson 12.1.

66 *Divide and Move*
Use with Lesson 12.2.

67 *Remains to Be Seen*
Use with Lesson 12.4.

68 *Find the Missing Digits*
Use with Lesson 12.8.

Project Card

12 *Make a Musical Tape*
Use with Lessons 12.5 and 12.9.

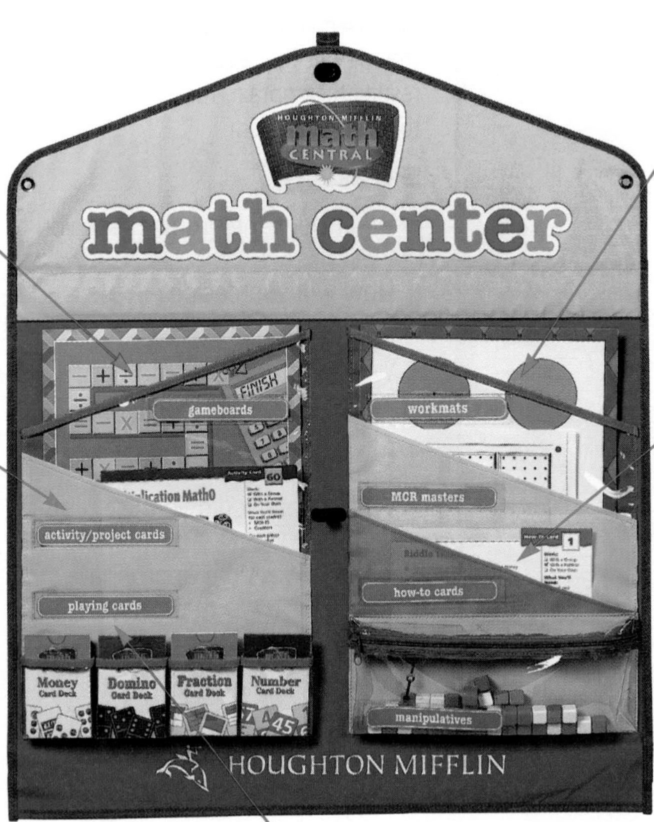

Workmats

Workmat 4
Use with Lesson 12.6.

How-To Cards

40 *Remainders on the Move*
Use with Lesson 12.3.

41 *Estimation Spin*
Use with Lesson 12.6.

42 *Read the Signs*
Use with Lesson 12.7.

Card Decks

Number Card Deck
Use with Lesson 12.3.

Managing the Math Center

Reinforcement If you observe students working as a group, be sure to note the particular competencies they display. Point them out specifically and publicly—this will have a powerful effect on a student's confidence. It also reinforces the idea that varying skills and perspectives are often vital for solving a problem.

Vocabulary and Reading Strategies

Use these minilessons to strengthen vocabulary and reading skills.

Vocabulary

- remainder

Linking Prior Knowledge and Vocabulary

Ask students to brainstorm the meaning of **remainder**. Record students' ideas. Then have them use a dictionary to verify the results, paying particular attention to the meaning in mathematics. Then work together to organize a semantic map.

Graphic Organizer: Semantic Map

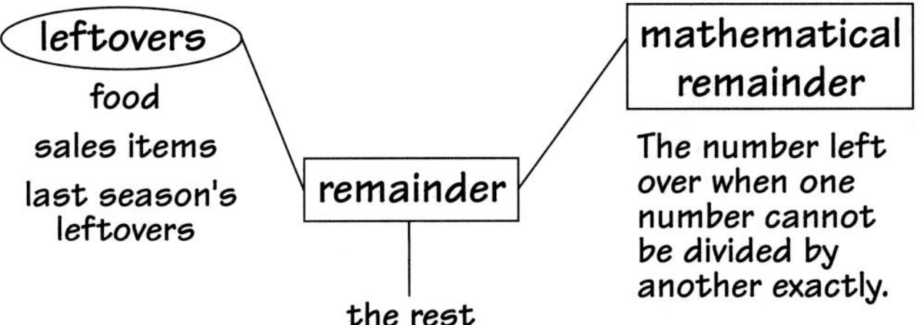

Reading Strategies

Strategy: Evaluate

Remind students that as they read, they can use the Evaluate Reading Strategy, seeing if the information makes sense. The strategy can be helpful with the graphs, tables, and word problems they encounter in the chapter.

Then point to the example problem. Suggest that they consider if there is enough information or too much. Then they can decide the best way to record the data and solve the problem.

Use the Thinking Aloud box and the graphic organizer to demonstrate how students can use the Evaluate reading strategy with the following example:

> A team of sled dogs ran from 10:15 A.M. to 11:55 P.M. Then they rested for 35 minutes and ran again from 12:30 P.M. to 2:50 P.M. How many hours did they run?

Lesson 12.9, p. 431, Problem 6

Model by thinking aloud how to begin solving the problem.

Thinking Aloud

- I can reread the problem to help me find out what the problem is about.
- I can evaluate the information and see that the time the dogs rested isn't important to the problem.
- I have to find out how many hours the sled dog team ran.
- I can use a timeline to figure it out.

Graphic Organizer: Time Line

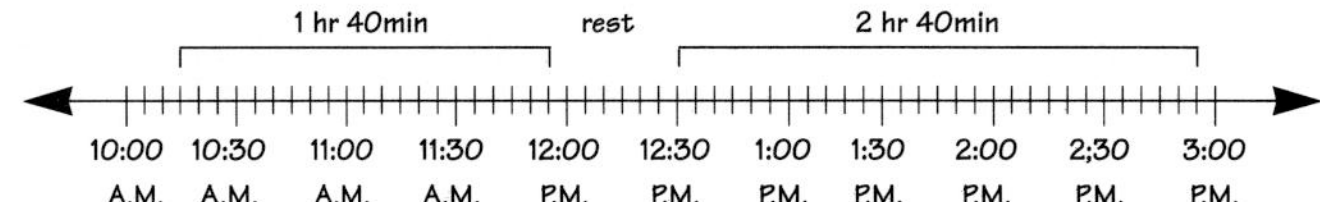

The dogs ran for 4 hours.

The reading strategies presented on this page can also apply to Lessons 12.2, 12.4, 12.5, 12.7, 12.8, and 12.9.

Objective

To use prior knowledge to explore dividing by 1-digit numbers

Lesson Planning

Optional Resources

- Math Language Connections
- MATHKEYS *Unlocking Whole Numbers 3–5*

Every Day Counts Calendar Math

Critical Thinking

To maximize students' critical thinking of division concepts, use Computations and Connections activities in Every Day Counts, level 3

Assessing Prior Knowledge

Try This! Use this as a prechapter activity in the classroom or as a homework assignment.

Build confidence in division concepts with this hands-on activity in which children model division problems using interlocking cubes.

This activity

- assesses prior knowledge of division
- acts as a base for discussing how division is related to multiplication

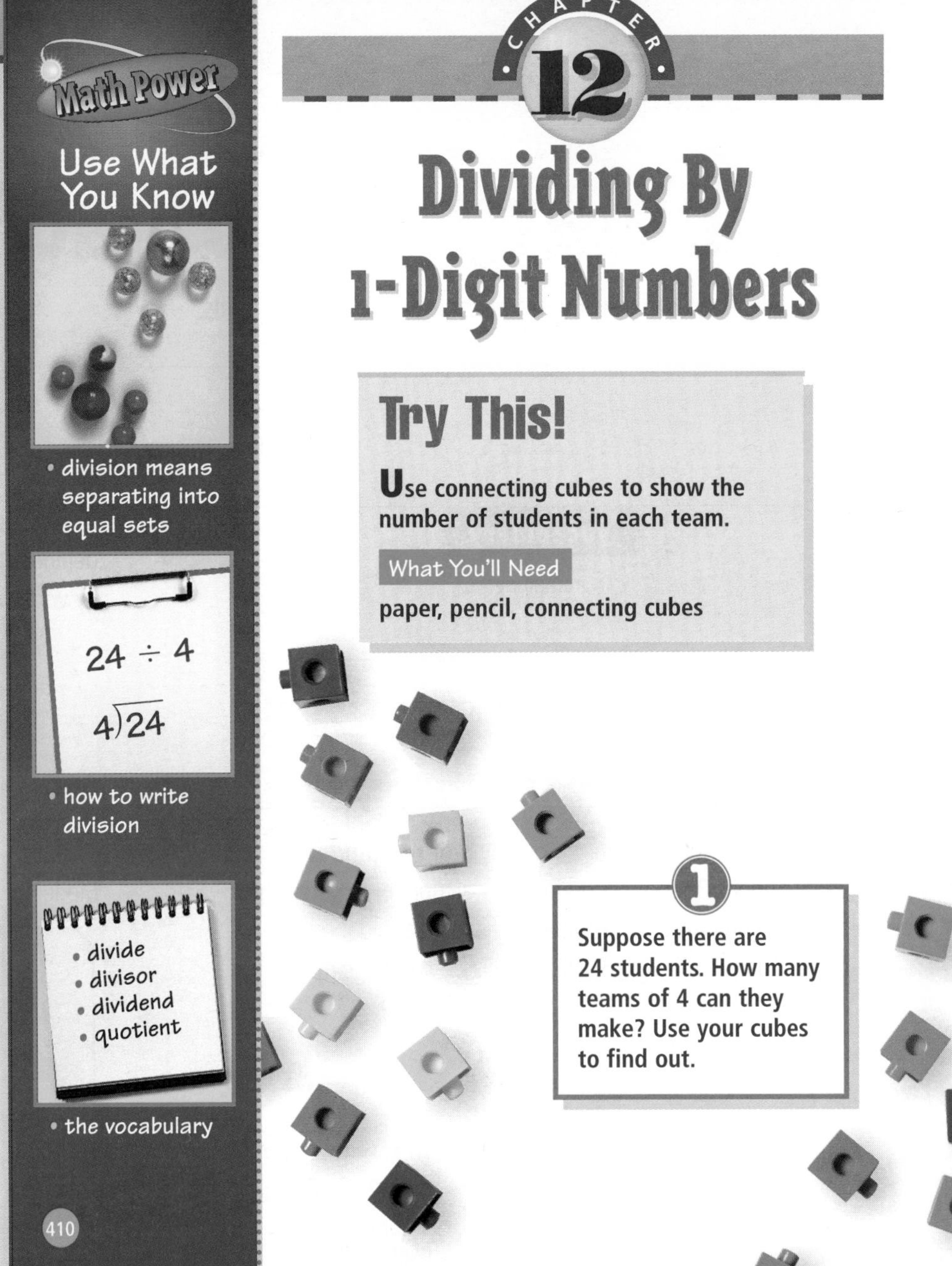

Math Power
Use What You Know
• division means separating into equal sets
24 ÷ 4
4)24
• how to write division
• divide
• divisor
• dividend
• quotient
• the vocabulary
410
CHAPTER
12
Dividing By 1-Digit Numbers
Try This!
Use connecting cubes to show the number of students in each team.
What You'll Need
paper, pencil, connecting cubes
1
Suppose there are 24 students. How many teams of 4 can they make? Use your cubes to find out.

Chapter Connections

Math Links

Throughout this chapter, students will build on prior knowledge as they develop concepts and skills for problem solving with division.

- **Number Sense** Lessons 12.1, 12.2, 12.3, 12.4, 12.5
- **Patterns and Relationships** Lessons 12.8, 12.9
- **Estimation** Lessons 12.6, 12.7, 12.8
- **Algebraic Reasoning** Lessons 12.1, 12.2, 12.6, 12.7

Real *World*

Social Studies

- **Lesson 12.4, p. 418**
  Rodeo Rodeo acts provide a context for interpreting remainders in division problems.
- **Lesson 12.7, p. 426**
  Community Service Students use facts about a toy drive for sick children to solve division problems with two-digit quotients.
- **Lesson 12.8, p. 428**
  Hot Air Balloons Students divide larger numbers as they solve problems about taking a trip on a hot air balloon.
- **Lesson 12.9, p. 430**
  Dogsled Races A lesson on dogsled races in Alaska is the setting for students to apply various problem solving strategies.

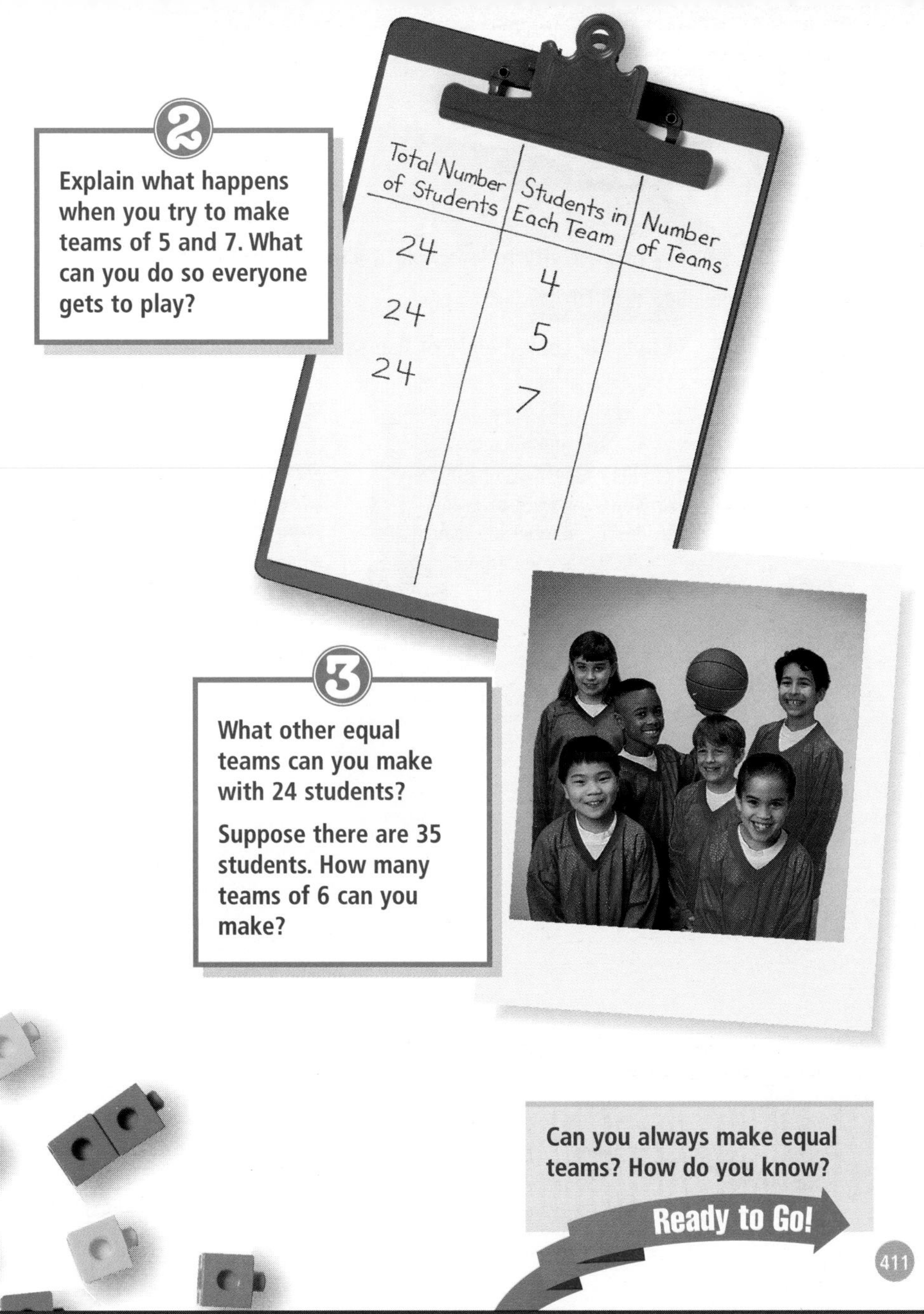

Explain what happens when you try to make teams of 5 and 7. What can you do so everyone gets to play?
Total Number of Students
Students in Each Team
Number of Teams
24
4
24
5
24
7
What other equal teams can you make with 24 students?
Suppose there are 35 students. How many teams of 6 can you make?

Can you always make equal teams? How do you know?

Ready to Go!

411

Assessing Prior Knowledge *(continued)*

- provides a foundation for division with remainders

Meeting Individual Needs

If students have trouble connecting the physical model to a division sentence, start with Quick Help. They may also need a brief teacher-guided review.

Quick Help Explain that in this activity students will use what they already know. To connect this activity to the students' understanding of multiplication, have students measure objects using an interlocking cube as a nonstandard unit of measure. Have students use multiplication language to write a sentence about the measurement: The length of the book is 12 times 1 cube. Then have students put cubes together to make the length and practice dividing it by 2, 3, and 4.

Guided Review Refer to:

- **Lesson 6.2** Activity: Rules for Division, Student Book p. 194
- **Rules for Division** Practice Worksheet 6.2
- **Basic Skills** Review Basic Facts, TE p. 421A

Vocabulary Power

Use this graphic organizer to review vocabulary used in division.

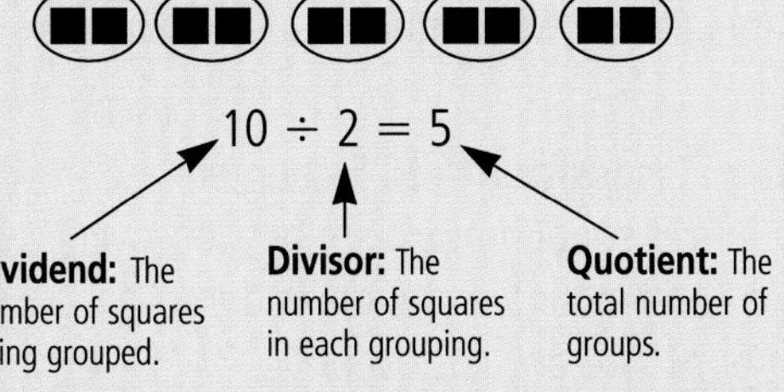

10 ÷ 2 = 5
Dividend: The number of squares being grouped.
Divisor: The number of squares in each grouping.
Quotient: The total number of groups.

Vocabulary Students can explore the meaning of the word *remainder* by looking up usages of *remain* in the dictionary. Discuss what these usages have in common with the definition of *remainder.*

Investigation Preview

Go, Team, Go!

Budgeting for the equipment for a Little League baseball team will give students practical experience in using multiplication and division operations to solve problems. See the Investigation, TE pp. 436–437.

What They'll Do

- Determine the needs of the team.
- Talk about ways to raise money.
- Make a chart of the estimated costs.
- Use division to find the amount that will be needed for one player.

Technology

Invite students to model these problems with the Counters Division Mat in ***MathKeys:*** *Unlocking Whole Numbers 3–5.* They can stamp 24 counters on the mat and then choose to group them into sets or share them into bins. Encourage students to explore dividing 24 and 35 using both methods.

LESSON 12.1

Activity

Planning at a Glance

Objective To explore division, with and without remainders, using concrete materials

Materials counters, Recording Sheet (Practice 12.1)

Optional Resources

- Reteach 12.1; Enrichment 12.1
- Daily Cumul. Review, p. 152
- Math Center: Act. Card 65
- Every Day Counts
- **TAB**, TE pp. 410E–410F
- **Problem of the Day**, 152, p. 76; Flip Chart, p. 76b
- MATHKEYS *Unlocking Whole Numbers 3–5*, Level 3, Activity 22

Students Acquiring English

Explain that *leftovers* usually means food that is not finished after a meal, but it can also mean anything that isn't used. Use counters to show a simple division problem with no remainder; have students say *No leftovers*. Then show one with a remainder of 2; have them say *2 leftovers, remainder of 2.*

Problem of the Day

Put a plus sign somewhere to form an addition sentence that has a sum of 466.

4 1 + 4 2 5

Exploring Division

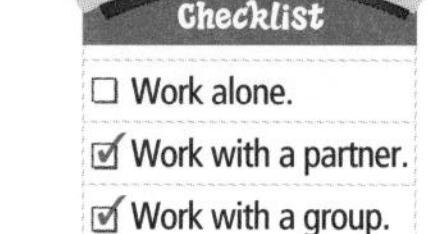

Cooperative Learning Checklist

- ☐ Work alone.
- ☑ Work with a partner.
- ☑ Work with a group.

Try this activity to learn more about division.

Getting Started

What You'll Need:
- 20 counters
- recording sheet

Vocabulary:
remainder
Glossary, p. 480

Activity

- **Copy the chart below or use the recording sheet.**

1 Divide 20 counters into 3 equal groups. If you have counters left over, push them aside. The number left over in division is called the **remainder.**

2 How many counters are in each group? How many are left over? Record the results. Write the division that shows what you did.

$3\overline{)20}$ 6R2 — R means Remainder

3 Push the counters together again. Repeat steps 1 and 2 six more times. Divide the 20 counters into 4, 5, 6, 7, 8, and 9 groups. Record the results. See Additional Answers.

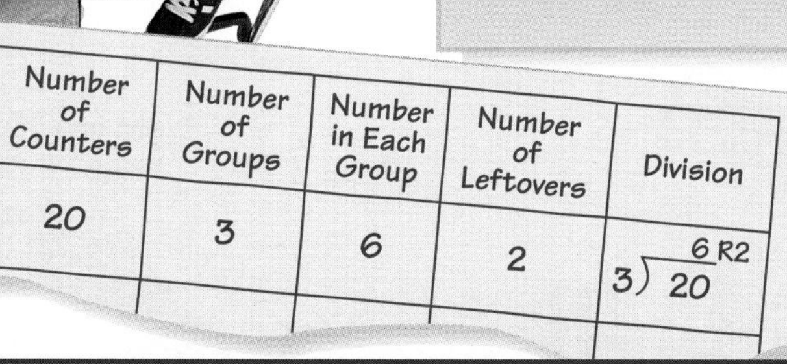

Number of Counters	Number of Groups	Number in Each Group	Number of Leftovers	Division
20	3	6	2	3) 20 6 R2

1 Introduce

Explore **Display 10 counters. Ask, Can these be separated into 3 equal groups?** no **Why not?** there is one left over

Teach: Activity

Emphasize these points:

- Not all numbers divide the counters *exactly* into equal groups.
- The number left over after items are divided equally among groups is called the *remainder*.

Modeling Model step 1. Ask:

- How many counters are in each group? 6
- How many are left over? 2

2 Develop

Show What You Know!

Common Error Some students may not know how to begin dividing their counters. Suggest they start with one counter for each of the groups they need, and add more counters one at a time to each group. See also Analyzing Errors, TE pp. 433A and 433B.

- Have students discuss their answers to exercise 3.
- Have students explain their reasoning for exercise 22. Guide them in expressing the relationship between multiplication facts and division facts.

3 Summarize

- Discuss the relationship between the remainder and the number of equal groups.
- Point out that multiplication facts can help students decide which numbers will divide exactly.

Ongoing Assessment If 25 counters are divided into 5 equal groups, are any left over? no Suppose the counters are divided into 4 equal groups. Are any left over? yes

Math Journal: *Communicating*

Can the remainder be equal to or greater than the number of equal groups? No; if it were, you could put at least 1 more into each of the equal groups.

Show What You Know!

1. Which numbers divided 20 with no remainder? 4, 5
2. Which numbers divided 20 with a remainder? 3, 6, 7, 8, 9

Use your counters to finish dividing. How many are in each group? How many are left over? Record what you do.

3. 4R1 $3\overline{)13}$

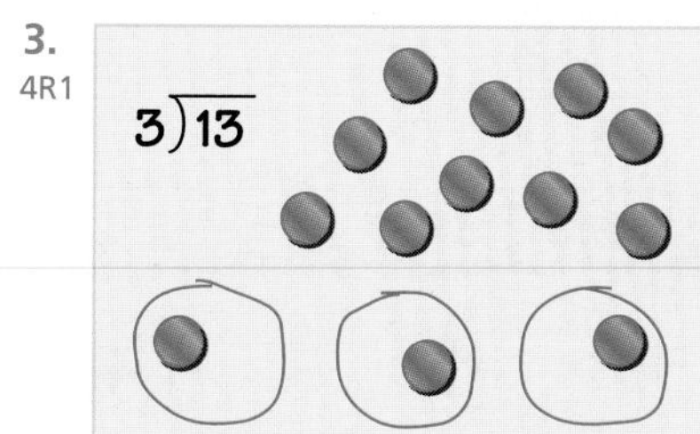

4. 4R1 $4\overline{)17}$

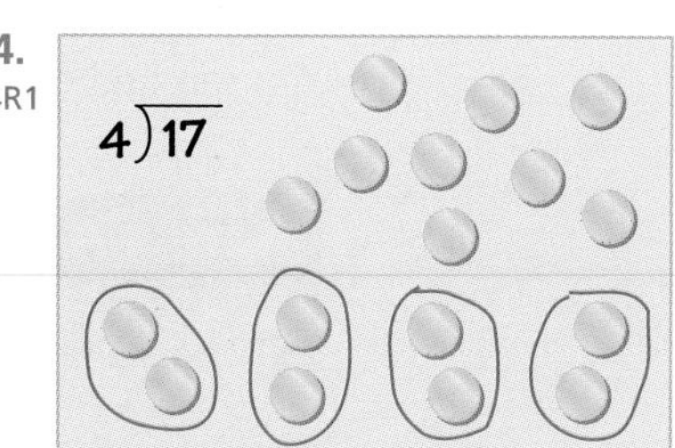

5. 3R2 $5\overline{)17}$

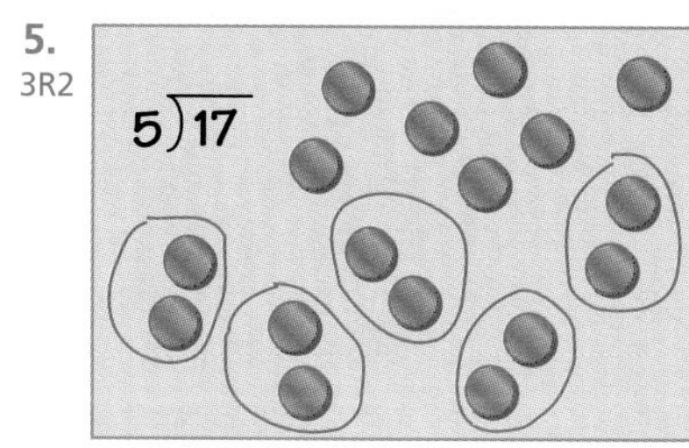

6. 3R1 $6\overline{)19}$

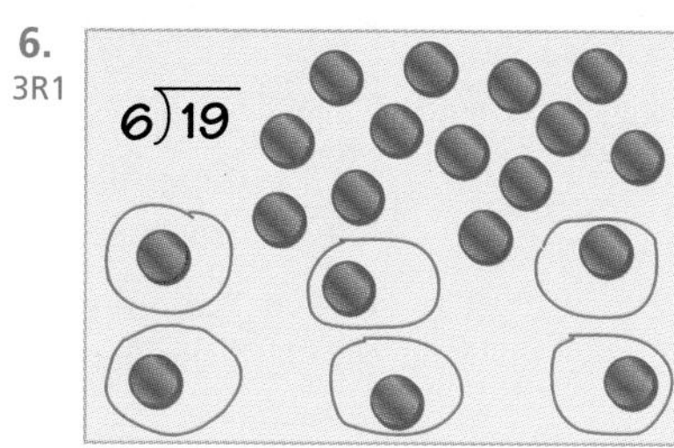

Solve. Use your counters.

7. $2\overline{)10}$ 5
8. $3\overline{)10}$ 3R1
9. $4\overline{)10}$ 2R2
10. $5\overline{)10}$ 2
11. $6\overline{)10}$ 1R4
12. $2\overline{)15}$ 7R1
13. $3\overline{)15}$ 5
14. $4\overline{)15}$ 3R3
15. $5\overline{)15}$ 3
16. $6\overline{)15}$ 2R3
17. $2\overline{)18}$ 9
18. $3\overline{)18}$ 6
19. $4\overline{)18}$ 4R2
20. $5\overline{)18}$ 3R3
21. $6\overline{)18}$ 3
22. **Critical Thinking** How can you check your answer to exercise 19 by multiplying and adding? Multiply 4 × 4 and add 2.
23. **Create Your Own** Write three division exercises with no remainder. Write three division exercises that have a remainder. Mix up the order. Trade papers with a classmate. Find the answers. Answers will vary.

Meeting Individual Needs

Extra Support

Equal Groups ***(visual, kinesthetic)*** Have pairs of students duplicate the activity with 30 counters. Have them make their own recording sheet. Suggest that they try to predict which numbers will divide 30 counters into equal sets without any left over, and which ones will not.

Alternate Approach

- Reteach Worksheet 12.1
- **TAB** See TE pp. 410E–410F.

MathZones

Understanding Division

Students Acquiring English

See Language Connections, Ch. 12.

Challenge

Have student pairs use counters to model division and then challenge each other to write a division sentence that describes the model.

Provide these instructions:

- Use counters to model a division sentence. You may choose to have a remainder or not.
- Challenge your partner to write a division sentence that shows what you have modeled.
- Compare and discuss your results.

Practice

Math Center Use Activity Card 65, *Subtracting to Divide*, to have students practice exploring division, with and without remainders.

Challenge Use Activity Card 65 and have students continue as described in Now Try This!

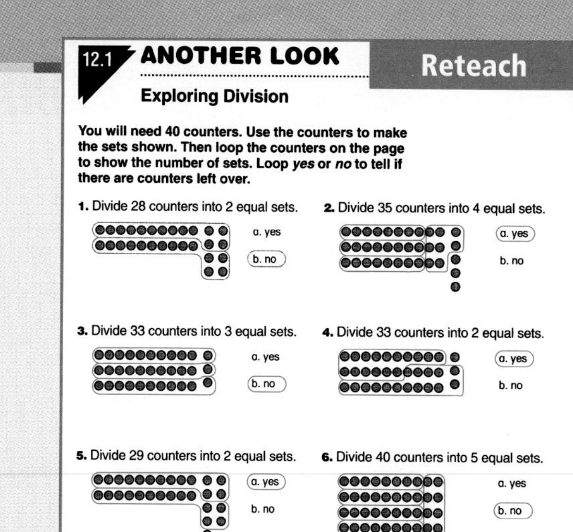

Reteach

12.1 **ANOTHER LOOK**

Exploring Division

You will need 40 counters. Use the counters to make the sets shown. Then loop the counters on the page to show the number of sets. Loop *yes* or *no* to tell if there are counters left over.

1. Divide 28 counters into 2 equal sets. a. yes (b. no)
2. Divide 35 counters into 4 equal sets. (a. yes) b. no
3. Divide 33 counters into 3 equal sets. a. yes (b. no)
4. Divide 33 counters into 2 equal sets. (a. yes) b. no
5. Divide 29 counters into 2 equal sets. (a. yes) b. no
6. Divide 40 counters into 5 equal sets. a. yes (b. no)
7. Divide 39 counters into 4 equal sets. (a. yes) b. no
8. Divide 36 counters into 3 equal sets. a. yes (b. no)

Practice

12.1 **PRACTICE/RECORDING SHEET**

Exploring Division

Number of Counters	Number of Groups	Number in Each Group	Number of Leftovers	Division
20	3	6	2	$3\overline{)20}$ 6 R2
20	4	5	0	$4\overline{)20}$ 5
20	5	4	0	$5\overline{)20}$ 4
20	6	3	2	$6\overline{)20}$ 3 R2
20	7	2	6	$7\overline{)20}$ 2 R6
20	8	2	4	$8\overline{)20}$ 2 R4
20	9	2	2	$9\overline{)20}$ 2 R2

Enrichment

12.1 **ENRICHMENT**

Exploring Division

You need 45 counters. Work with a partner to complete the chart. For the first row, first predict whether there will be a number left over. Then make the sets of 6. Record your results. Complete the table.

Number of Counters	Number in Each Set	Prediction	Number of Sets	Counters Left Over
45	6		7	3
45	5		9	0
45	7	Answers may vary.	6	3
45	8		5	5
45	11		4	1
45	15		3	0

Pick your own number of counters. Group them in different ways. Record your results in the table. Answers may vary.

Number of Counters	Number in Each Set	Prediction	Number of Sets	Number Left Over

Connecting

Planning at a Glance

Objective To find a fraction of a set

Materials pattern blocks

Optional Resources

- Reteach 12.2; Practice 12.2; Enrichment 12.2
- Daily Cumul. Review, p. 153
- Math Center: Act Card 66
- Every Day Counts
- **TAB**, TE pp. 410E–410F, 410J
- **Problem of the Day**, 153, p. 77; Flip Chart, p. 77a

MATHKEYS *Unlocking Fractions & Decimals 3–6,* Level 3, Activity 12

Students Acquiring English

Give students practice with constructions such as "$\frac{1}{3}$ of 6" by giving them counters and asking them to create groups to show $\frac{1}{3}$ of 6, $\frac{1}{2}$ of 8, and $\frac{1}{4}$ of 4. Ask them to describe their groups. Then, ask questions in the form "What fraction of 8 is 2?"

Problem of the Day

A hotel has 26 rooms on each floor. Odd-numbered rooms are across the hall from even-numbered rooms. The numbers on the top floor begin with 901. What is the number of the room in the middle of the even-numbered side of the hall on the top floor?
914

Lesson 2 Fractional Parts of a Set

Suppose you have 6 rubber stamps. You are going to give $\frac{1}{3}$ of them to your friend. How many stamps is that?

You can find $\frac{1}{3}$ of 6.

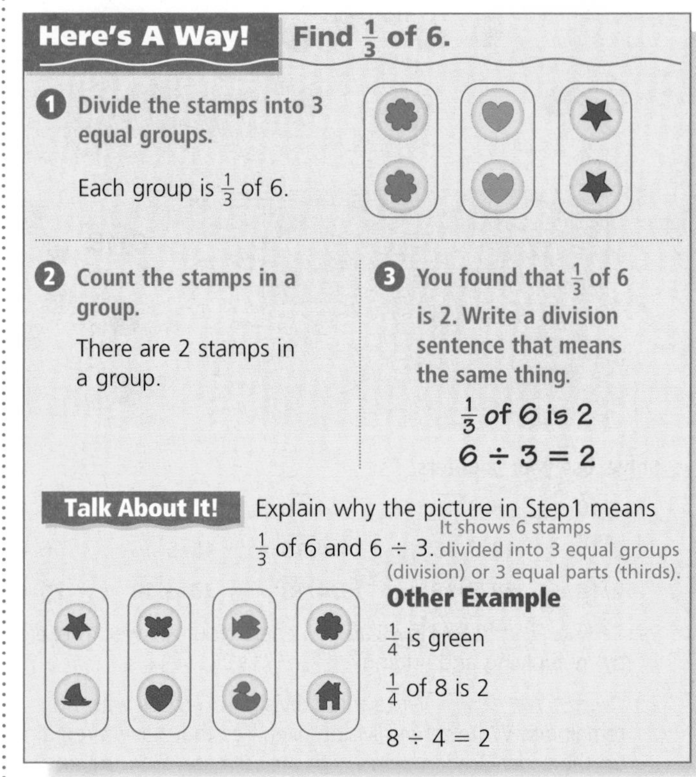

Here's A Way! Find $\frac{1}{3}$ of 6.

1. **Divide the stamps into 3 equal groups.** Each group is $\frac{1}{3}$ of 6.
2. **Count the stamps in a group.** There are 2 stamps in a group.
3. **You found that $\frac{1}{3}$ of 6 is 2. Write a division sentence that means the same thing.**
   $\frac{1}{3}$ of 6 is 2
   $6 \div 3 = 2$

Talk About It! Explain why the picture in Step1 means $\frac{1}{3}$ of 6 and $6 \div 3$. It shows 6 stamps divided into 3 equal groups (division) or 3 equal parts (thirds).

Other Example

$\frac{1}{4}$ is green

$\frac{1}{4}$ of 8 is 2

$8 \div 4 = 2$

1 Introduce

Build Understanding Each student takes 12 small parallelogram pattern blocks. Model finding $\frac{1}{2}$ of 12 by putting the blocks into 2 equal groups.

Then have students use the blocks to find $\frac{1}{3}$ of 12 4 **and $\frac{1}{4}$ of 12** 3

Teach: Here's A Way!

- $\frac{1}{3}$ of a group means one of 3 equal parts of the group.

2 Develop

Show What You Know!

Common Error Some students may not understand that each group of items equals one part of the whole. Make sure they understand that one *part of a group* (for example, $\frac{1}{4}$) can contain more than one *item*. See also Analyzing Errors, TE pp. 433A and 433B.

Work It Out!

- Have students discuss their reasoning for exercises 7 and 8.

Using Reading Strategies Help students to use the Evaluate strategy as they read the Problem Solving exercise. Ask, What information from the pictograph is important? See TE p. 410J.

3 Summarize

- Remind students that fractions, whether parts of a whole or parts of a group, refer to equal parts.
- Have students discuss the relationship between fractions and division.

Ongoing Assessment You have a package of 8 hamburger rolls. You use $\frac{1}{2}$ of them for a picnic. How many rolls did you use? 4 rolls

Math Journal: *Communicating*

Make up a problem that shows that $\frac{2}{3}$ of 12 equals 8.
Answers will vary but should use the numbers correctly in the problem.

Show What You Know!

Tell how many groups of marbles there are. What fraction is blue? Write the fraction. Then write the number of blue marbles.

1. 5, $\frac{1}{5}$, 2
2. 5, $\frac{1}{5}$, 3
3. **Critical Thinking** Explain why $\frac{1}{5}$ of the marbles in exercise 1 is a different amount than $\frac{1}{5}$ of the marbles in exercise 2.
   In exercise 1, the whole is 10; in exercise 2, the whole is 15.

Draw the picture. Shade one group. Write a fraction for the shaded group. Then write how many are in that group.

4. 6 circles in 3 equal groups $\frac{1}{3}$, 2
   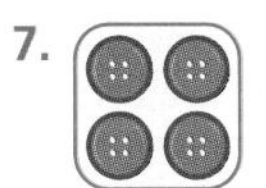 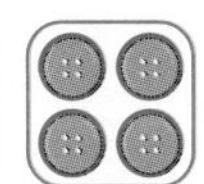 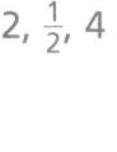
5. 10 circles in 2 equal groups $\frac{1}{2}$, 5
   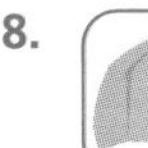 
6. Write the division sentence that goes with each picture you drew in exercises 4 and 5. $6 \div 3 = 2$; $10 \div 2 = 5$

Work It Out!

Tell how many groups of objects there are. What fraction is green? Write the fraction. Then write the number of green objects.

7. 2, $\frac{1}{2}$, 4
8. 2, $\frac{1}{2}$, 1

Draw the picture. Shade one group. Write a fraction for the shaded group. Then write how many are in that group.

9. 6 circles in 2 equal groups $\frac{1}{2}$, 3
10. 4 circles in 2 equal groups $\frac{1}{2}$, 2
11. 12 circles in 6 equal groups $\frac{1}{6}$; 2
12. 12 circles in 3 equal groups $\frac{1}{3}$; 4
13. Write the division sentence that goes with each picture you drew in exercises 9–12.
    $6 \div 2 = 3$; $4 \div 2 = 2$; $12 \div 6 = 2$; $12 \div 3 = 4$
14. **Problem Solving** If the rubber stamps in the chart are stored in boxes with two like stamps in each box, how many boxes are needed? What fraction of the boxes is whale stamps? 4; $\frac{1}{4}$

My Rubber Stamps

Whale	🖃🖃
Turtle	🖃🖃🖃🖃
Frog	🖃🖃

Key: 🖃 = 1 rubber stamp

More Practice Set 12.2, p. 476

Meeting Individual Needs

Extra Support

What Fraction? ***(visual/kinesthetic)*** Students working in pairs take turns dividing a pile of counters into equal groups and setting aside one or more of the groups. Partner must say a fraction that describes what part of the number of counters was set aside.

Alternate Approach

- Reteach Worksheet 12.2
- **TAB** See TE pp. 410–410F.

MathZones

Understanding Division

Students Acquiring English

See Language Connections, Ch. 12.

Challenge

Students work in pairs.

- Each student draws six pictures showing groups of objects that can be separated evenly into fractional parts, and writes a fraction next to each drawing.
- Partners challenge each other to mark off the fractional part of the drawing that represents the fraction written next to it.
- Partners compare and discuss their answers.

Practice

Math Center Use Activity Card 66, *Divide and Move,* to have students practice recognizing that fractions of a set refer to equal parts of a set.

Challenge Use Activity have students continue as described in Now Try This!

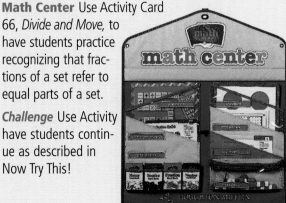

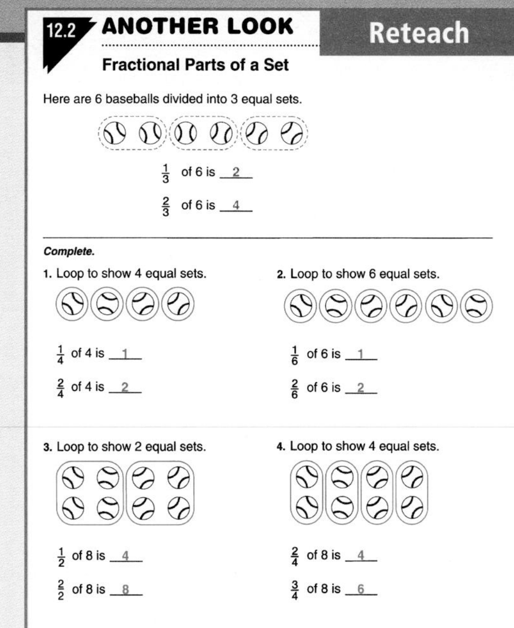

12.2 ANOTHER LOOK — Reteach

Fractional Parts of a Set

Here are 6 baseballs divided into 3 equal sets.

$\frac{1}{3}$ of 6 is 2

$\frac{2}{3}$ of 6 is 4

Complete.

1. Loop to show 4 equal sets.
   $\frac{1}{4}$ of 4 is 1
   $\frac{2}{4}$ of 4 is 2
2. Loop to show 6 equal sets.
   $\frac{1}{6}$ of 6 is 1
   $\frac{2}{6}$ of 6 is 2
3. Loop to show 2 equal sets.
   $\frac{1}{2}$ of 8 is 4
   $\frac{2}{2}$ of 8 is 8
4. Loop to show 4 equal sets.
   $\frac{2}{4}$ of 8 is 4
   $\frac{3}{4}$ of 8 is 6

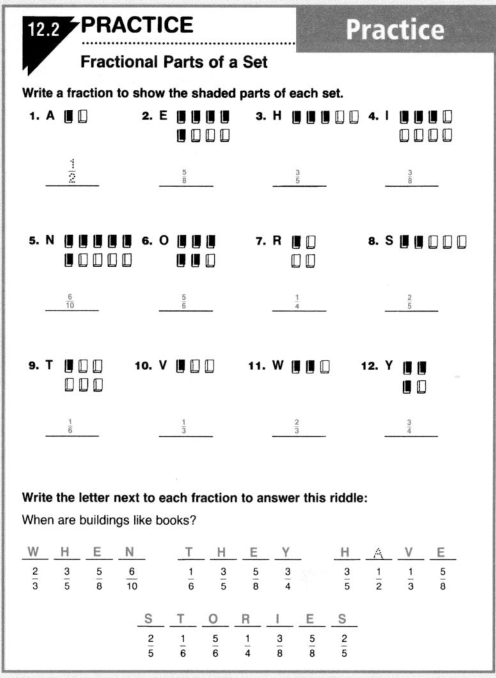

12.2 PRACTICE — Practice

Fractional Parts of a Set

Write a fraction to show the shaded parts of each set.

1. A $\frac{1}{2}$
2. E $\frac{5}{8}$
3. H $\frac{3}{5}$
4. I $\frac{3}{8}$
5. N $\frac{6}{10}$
6. O $\frac{5}{6}$
7. R $\frac{1}{4}$
8. S $\frac{2}{5}$
9. T $\frac{1}{6}$
10. V $\frac{1}{3}$
11. W $\frac{2}{3}$
12. Y $\frac{3}{4}$

Write the letter next to each fraction to answer this riddle:

When are buildings like books?

W H E N — $\frac{2}{3}$ $\frac{3}{5}$ $\frac{5}{8}$ $\frac{6}{10}$

T H E Y — $\frac{1}{6}$ $\frac{3}{5}$ $\frac{5}{8}$ $\frac{3}{4}$

H A V E — $\frac{3}{5}$ $\frac{1}{2}$ $\frac{1}{3}$ $\frac{5}{8}$

S T O R I E S — $\frac{2}{5}$ $\frac{1}{6}$ $\frac{5}{6}$ $\frac{1}{4}$ $\frac{3}{8}$ $\frac{5}{8}$ $\frac{2}{5}$

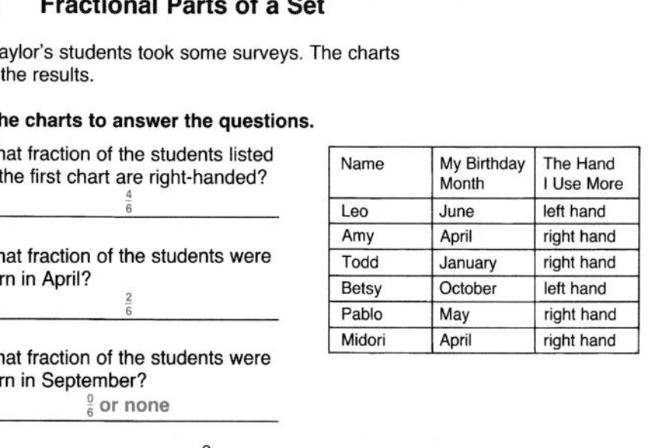

12.2 ENRICHMENT — Enrichment

Fractional Parts of a Set

Ms. Taylor's students took some surveys. The charts show the results.

Use the charts to answer the questions.

1. What fraction of the students listed in the first chart are right-handed? $\frac{4}{6}$
2. What fraction of the students were born in April? $\frac{2}{6}$
3. What fraction of the students were born in September? $\frac{0}{6}$ or none
4. Suppose you learned that $\frac{2}{3}$ of the students listed in the first chart are more than 120 cm tall. How many students is that? 4 students
5. What fraction of the students in the second chart like painting best? $\frac{5}{8}$
6. What fraction of the students like baseball best? $\frac{3}{8}$
7. What fraction of the students like a kind of ball game best? $\frac{7}{8}$

Name	My Birthday Month	The Hand I Use More
Leo	June	left hand
Amy	April	right hand
Todd	January	right hand
Betsy	October	left hand
Pablo	May	right hand
Midori	April	right hand

Name	Sport I Like to Play Most	Art I Like to Do Best
Margie	baseball	drawing
Diane	basketball	painting
Eddie	swimming	painting
Carmen	basketball	painting
Brad	basketball	pottery
Holly	baseball	painting
José	basketball	painting
Nico	baseball	drawing

Connecting

Planning at a Glance

Objective To divide 1- and 2-digit dividends by 1-digit divisors, resulting in 1-digit quotients, with and without remainders

Materials counters, color tiles

Optional Resources

- Reteach 12.3; Practice 12.3; Enrichment 12.3
- Daily Cumul. Review, p. 154
- Math Center: Act. Card 40
- Every Day Counts
- **TAB**, TE pp. 410E–410F, 410J
- **Problem of the Day**, 154, p. 77; Flip Chart, p. 77b

MATHKEYS *Unlocking Whole Numbers 3–5*, Level 3, Activity 24

Students Acquiring English

During the Build Understanding activity, be sure students are familiar with the meanings of *divide, equal groups,* and *remainders.*

Problem of the Day

Eric has a penny, a nickel, a dime, a quarter, and a half-dollar in his pocket. Find every possible price of items he could buy using two coins, without needing to get back change.

6¢, 11¢, 15¢, 26¢, 30¢, 35¢, 51¢, 55¢, 60¢, 75¢

Division with Remainders

What You'll Need:
- counters

Suppose you divide 35 by 4 with counters. You already know how to record the answer. Now find out how to record all the steps you do.

Here's A Way! Find 4)35.

1. Divide the counters into 4 equal groups. Record the number of counters in each group. 8 / 4)35
2. Multiply to record the total number of counters in the 4 groups. 8 / 4)35 / 32 (4 × 8)
3. Subtract to find the remainder. 8 / 4)35 / − 32 / 3 (Remainder)
4. Record the remainder next to the quotient. 8R3 / 4)35 / − 32 / 3 (Remainder)

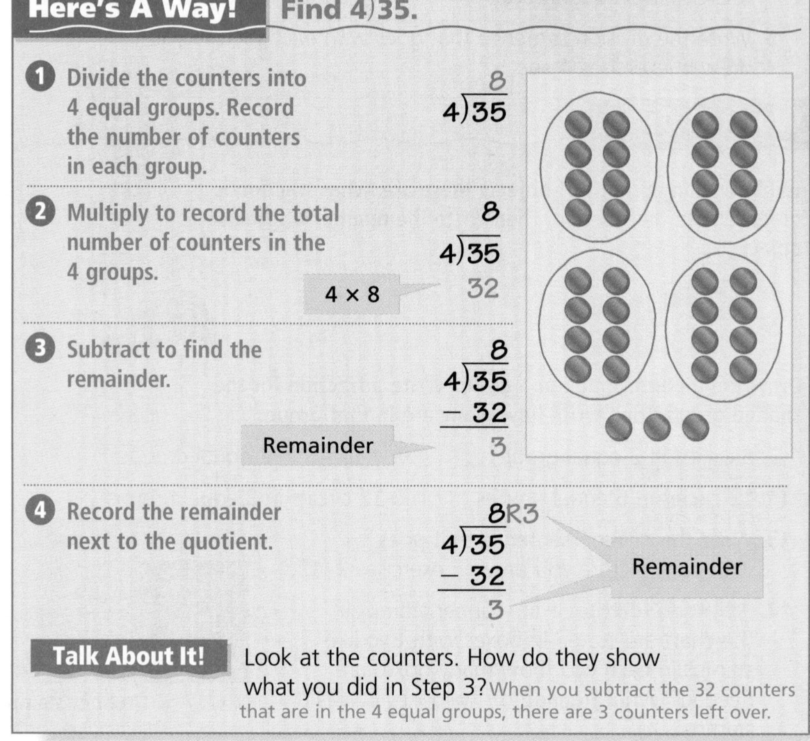

Talk About It! Look at the counters. How do they show what you did in Step 3? When you subtract the 32 counters that are in the 4 equal groups, there are 3 counters left over.

416 Chapter 12

1 Introduce

Build Understanding **Have each student take 10 color tiles and divide them into 2, 3, 4 and 5 equal groups. Then, have them record the results.**

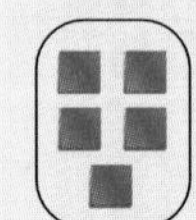  5 / 2)10

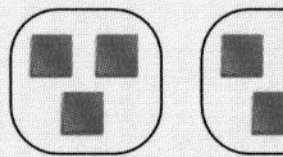    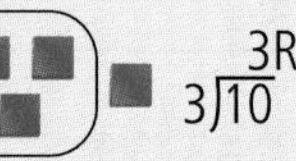 3R1 / 3)10

  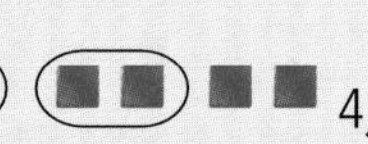 2R2 / 4)10

Teach: Here's A Way!

- Use multiplication facts to help you divide and to decide whether a quotient will have a remainder.

2 Develop

Show What You Know!

Common Error Some students may have a remainder greater than the divisor. Remind students that this shows they did not divide correctly. See also Analyzing Errors, TE pp. 433A and 433B.

- Have students discuss their answers to exercises 13 and 14.

Work It Out!

- Encourage students to use multiplication facts to check whether their division is correct and to predict whether there will be a remainder.

3 Summarize

- Call on students to review with the class the explanations they gave for exercise 37.
- Have students discuss whether mental math methods can help them find a quotient.

Ongoing Assessment You are dividing 23 by 3. How can you write the answer to the division? 7 R2 Discuss with students whether the remainder could be 3 or more.

Math Journal: *Communicating*

How can knowing multiplication and division facts help you divide? Answers should reflect an understanding of multiplication and division as related operations and of families of facts.

Show What You Know!

Look at the counters. Record what was done.

1. 3)17

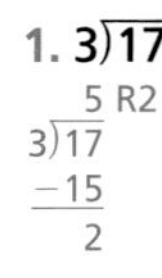

5 R2
3)17
−15
2

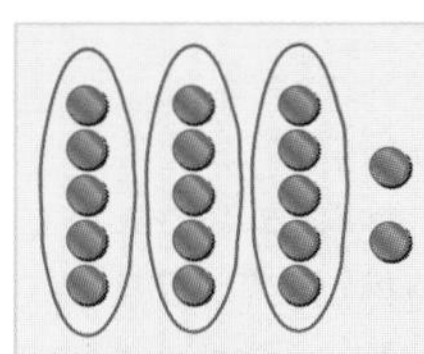

2. 5)23

4 R3
5)23
−20
3

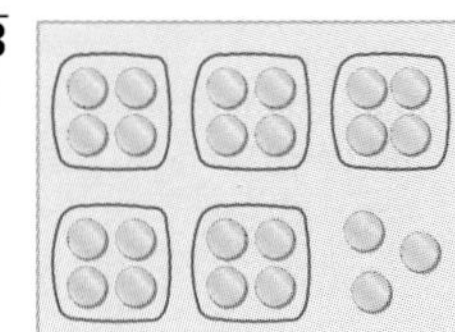

Use counters to divide. Then record. Check students' recording. Answers follow.

3. 5)18 3R3 4. 6)43 7R1 5. 4)39 9R3 6. 3)26 8R2 7. 2)13 6R1

8. 7)52 7R3 9. 8)49 6R1 10. 6)56 9R2 11. 9)60 6R6 12. 5)29 5R4

13. **Critical Thinking** If you divide a number by 5, can the remainder ever be 5 or greater? Explain. No; 5 can be divided into 5 equal parts. The remainder must be fewer.

14. **Critical Thinking** Sometimes division facts can help you know if a division problem has a remainder. Explain. They can tell you if the number divides evenly.

Work It Out!

Look at the counters. Record what was done.

15. 4)27

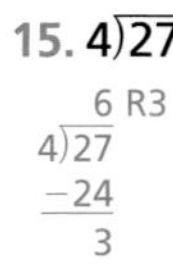

6 R3
4)27
−24
3

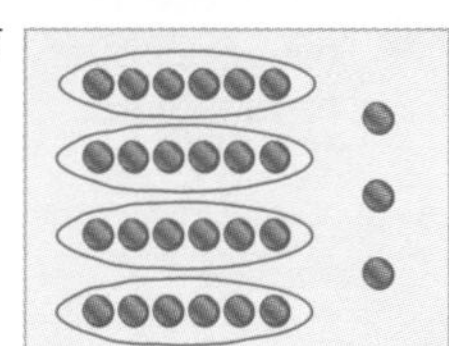

16. 6)32

5 R2
6)32
−30
2

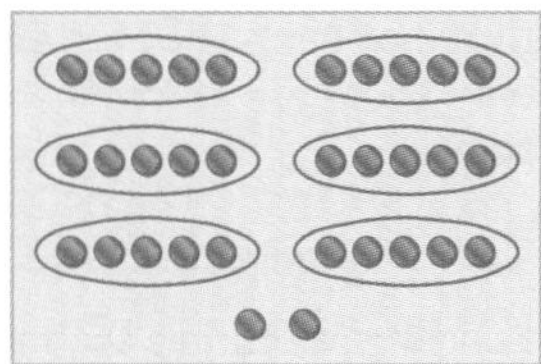

Use counters to divide. Then record. Check students' recording. Answers follow.

17. 3)22 7R1 18. 5)44 8R4 19. 2)15 7R1 20. 7)52 7R3 21. 9)62 6R8

22. 6)49 8R1 23. 8)54 6R6 24. 4)38 9R2 25. 5)24 4R4 26. 7)65 9R2

27. 2)17 8R1 28. 9)59 6R5 29. 3)28 9R1 30. 6)41 6R5 31. 6)33 5R3

32. 8)61 7R5 33. 5)32 6R2 34. 4)19 4R3 35. 7)47 6R5 36. 3)29 9R2

37. Use counters to divide 45 by 7. Then explain to a friend how to record what you did. 6R3; Answers will vary.

More Practice Set 12.3, p. 477

417

Meeting Individual Needs

Extra Support

Remainder, No Remainder *(visual)* Write random 2-digit numbers on 20 index cards. Student pairs draw a card. Each student predicts whether the quotient will have a remainder when the number is divided by 2. Students check their answers with place-value blocks. Repeat, having students divide by 3, then by 4.

Alternate Approach

- Reteach Worksheet 12.3
- **TAB** See TE pp. 410E–410F.

MathZones

Understanding Division

Students Acquiring English

See Language Connections, Ch. 12.

Challenge

Students create remainder quizzes for each other.

- Each student writes ten division examples. Some should have remainders.
- Partners exchange papers. Students predict which examples will have remainders and then solve.

Practice

Math Center Use Activity Card 40, *Remainders on the Move,* to have students practice dividing 1- and 2-digit dividends by 1-digit divisors.

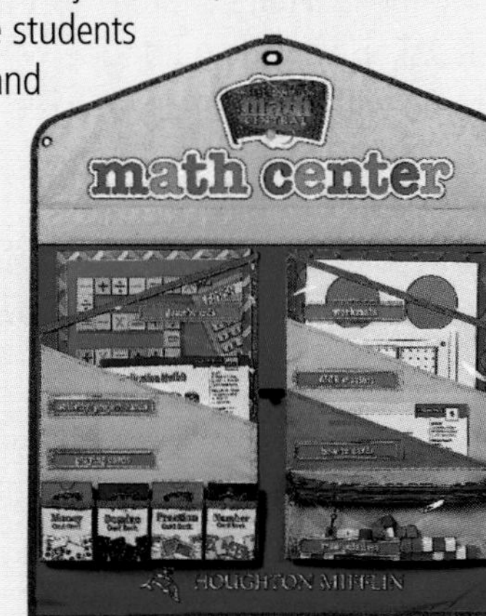

12.3 ANOTHER LOOK — Reteach

Division with Remainders

Complete the chart.

Problem	Loop the picture to show the sets.	Write the quotient and the remainder.
1. 22 peanuts divided among 6 students	6 sets	3 R4 6)22
2. 17 cherries divided among 3 children	3 sets	5 R2 3)17
3. 7 pencils divided among 2 students	2 sets	3 R1 2)7
4. 29 stickers divided among 4 classmates	4 sets	7 R1 4)29
5. 31 bananas divided among 6 monkeys	6 sets	5 R1 6)31

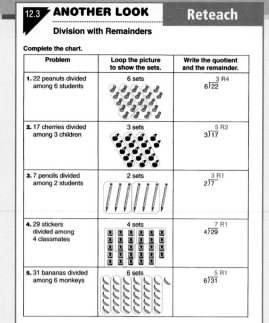

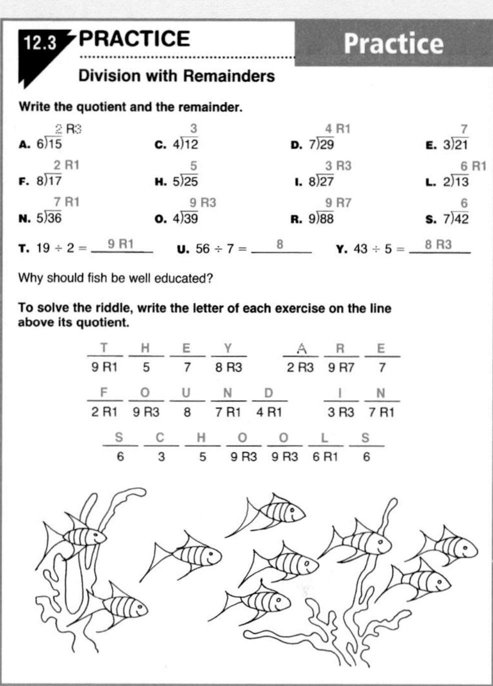

12.3 PRACTICE — Practice

Division with Remainders

Write the quotient and the remainder.

A. 6)15 2 R3 C. 4)12 3 D. 7)29 4 R1 E. 3)21 7

F. 8)17 2 R1 H. 5)25 5 I. 8)27 3 R3 L. 2)13 6 R1

N. 5)36 7 R1 O. 4)39 9 R3 R. 9)88 9 R7 S. 7)42 6

T. 19 ÷ 2 = 9 R1 U. 56 ÷ 7 = 8 Y. 43 ÷ 5 = 8 R3

Why should fish be well educated?

To solve the riddle, write the letter of each exercise on the line above its quotient.

T	H	E	Y		A	R	E
9 R1	5	7	8 R3		2 R3	9 R7	7

F	O	U	N	D		I	N
2 R1	9 R3	8	7 R1	4 R1		3 R3	7 R1

S	C	H	O	O	L	S
6	3	5	9 R3	9 R3	6 R1	6

12.3 ENRICHMENT — Enrichment

Division with Remainders

Write the missing digits.

1. 4)1 7 → [4] R [1]; Y − 1 6; [1]

2. 5)4 5 → [9]; B − [4][5]; 0

3. 6)4 4 → 7 R 2; A − [4][2]; 2

4. 8)6 [4] → 8; B − 6 [4]; 0

5. 9)[8][9] → 9 R 8; V − 8 1; 8

6. 7)4 [9] → [7]; B − 4 [9]; 0

7. 7)4 1 → 5 R [6]; P − 3 5; [6]

8. 3)[2] 7 → 9; B − [2] 7; 0

9. [8])7 1 → 8 R [7]; S − 6 4; [7]

10. 5)4 9 → [9] R [4]; N − 4 5; [4]

11. 8)[3][7] → 4 R 5; I − 3 2; 5

12. [5])2 8 → 5 R [3]; E − 2 5; [3]

Write the letter that goes with each remainder. The letters will spell the name of the state in which our country's first lending library was started.

P	E	N	N	S	Y	L	V	A	N	I	A
6	3	4	4	7	1		8	2	4	5	2

LESSON 12.4

Symbolic

Planning at a Glance

Objective To interpret remainders in word problems

Materials none

Optional Resources

- Reteach 12.4; Practice 12.4; Enrichment 12.4
- Daily Cumul. Review, p. 155
- Math Center: Act. Card 67
- Every Day Counts
- **TAB**, TE pp. 410E–410F, 410 J
- **Problem of the Day**, 155, p. 78; Flip Chart, p. 78b

MATHKEYS

Unlocking Whole Numbers 3–5, Level 3, Activity 25

Students Acquiring English

Have volunteers demonstrate the meanings of *include* and *ignore* through pantomime.

Problem of the Day

The ancient Maya Indians of Mexico had their own way to show numbers. Here are three Maya numbers. Find a pattern. Then use the patterns to write the numbers 2, 8, 11, and 19 the Maya way.

See answers below.

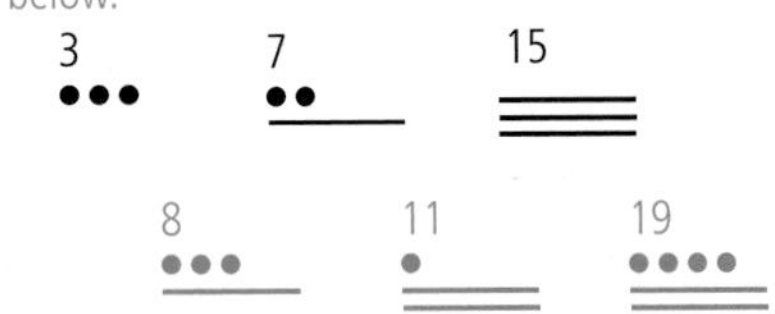

LESSON 4

Interpreting Remainders

Suppose you solve a division problem and there is a remainder. Does it make sense to use the remainder in your answer or to ignore it?

Here's A Way! Decide what to do with the remainder.

1 You can include the remainder in the answer.

There are 7 apples for 2 horses. Each horse gets an equal share. How many apples will each horse get?

$$2\overline{)7}\quad 3\text{ R}1$$

Each horse gets 3 apples and $\frac{1}{2}$ of the leftover apple.

2 You can ignore the remainder.

Cowhands at the rodeo are forming teams of 6 for a tug of war. There are 28 cowhands. How many teams can they form?

$$6\overline{)28}\quad 4\text{ R}4$$

They can form 4 teams. The 4 cowhands left over are not enough to form a team.

3 You can round the answer to the next whole number.

Ranchers will bring 16 horses to the rodeo in trailers. They put 3 horses in each trailer. How many trailers will they need?

$$3\overline{)16}\quad 5\text{ R}1$$

They need 6 trailers. One of the trailers will not be full.

Talk About It!

Why did you round to the next whole number to tell how many trailers the ranchers needed? So all horses could be put in trailers.

418 Chapter

1 Introduce

Prior Knowledge **Separate 14 counters into 5 equal sets. Ask, How many are in each set?** 2 **How many are left over?** 4

Teach: Here's A Way!

Emphasize these points:

- If a division word problem asks for a number left, use the remainder.
- If a problem asks for an exact number of groups or items in each group, drop the remainder.
- When a word problem asks for a number that includes all items in the dividend, round up to the next whole number.

Modeling Use drawings to model steps 1–3.

2 Develop

Show What You Know!

- Have students discuss their answers for exercise 1. Ask, how did you know to drop the remainder?

Using Reading Strategies Help students to use the Evaluate strategy as they read exercise 1. Ask, How did you decide what made sense to do with the remainder? See TE p. 410J.

Work It Out!

- Remind students to read each problem carefully before deciding how to interpret the remainder.
- For exercises 3–6, call on students to discuss their reasoning about what to do with the remainders.

3 Summarize

- Have students review three ways they can interpret a remainder in a division word problem.

Ongoing Assessment You have 29 peanuts. You want to share them equally with 2 friends.

- How can you do it? Divide 29 peanuts by 3 to get 9 peanuts per person.
- How many peanuts are left over? 2 peanuts

Math Journal: *Communicating*

Write your own division word problem for 20 ÷ 6. Word problems will vary but should illustrate 20 ÷ 6.

Show What You Know!

Divide. Tell what you did with the remainder.

1. You want to buy rodeo souvenirs for your friends at home. You have $14.00. How many key chains can you buy? 4 key chains; ignored the remainder

2. **Critical Thinking** Why did you need to think about the remainder to solve the exercise? to see if there was enough money for another key chain

Work It Out!

Divide. Decide what to do with the remainder.

3. Clowns at the rodeo will dress up as cows. Each cow costume needs 1 clown for the front legs and 1 clown for the back legs. There are 17 clowns. Will they be able to make 9 cows? No, only 8 cows; 1 clown will be left over
4. Six people can sit at a picnic table. How many picnic tables do you need to seat 32 people? Explain. 6 tables; 1 table will not be full.
5. Suppose there are 28 students in your class. Everyone will be working on a spring project. You form groups of 3. What can you do so no one is left out? form 8 groups of 3 and 1 group of 4
6. You want to frame 17 photographs. Four photos fit in each frame. How many frames do you need? 5 frames; 1 frame will have only 1 picture

Use division. Write a story problem about things at the rodeo. Then solve. Answers will vary.

7. 29 horses kept in 3 stables
8. 14 cowhands in teams of 4
9. 5 wagon rides, 26 passengers
10. 18 carrots, 4 ponies

419

Meeting Individual Needs

Extra Support

Visualizing Division *(kinesthetic)* Have student pairs review exercises 3–6 using place-value blocks. Have them say what the blocks and groups of blocks represent in each problem.

Alternate Approach

- Reteach Worksheet 12.4
- **TAB** See TE pp. 410E–410F.
-  Encourage students to divide with electronic manipulatives. They explore dividing with remainders as they solve realistic problems in *Unlocking Whole Numbers 3–5,* Level 3, Activity 25.

MathZones

Understanding Division

Students Acquiring English

See Language Connections, Ch. 12.

Challenge

Have student pairs make up three word problems that require division to solve. Each problem should require a different interpretation of a remainder. Let students trade and solve problems.

Practice

Math Center Use Activity Card 67, *Remains to Be Seen,* to have students practice interpreting remainders in word problems.

Challenge Use Activity Card 67 and have students continue as described in Now Try This!

12.4 ANOTHER LOOK — Reteach

Interpreting Remainders

Solve each problem.

1. Joe shows 6 rabbits at the State Fair. He has 56 carrots for the rabbits to share. He gives each rabbit an equal number of carrots.

   What is the greatest number of carrots each rabbit gets? 9 carrots

   How many carrots are left over? 2 carrots
2. Inez is raising 27 chickens for the fair. She is buying coops for them. Each coop can hold 8 chickens.

   How many coops should Inez buy? 4 coops

   Are all the coops full? no
3. A group of 33 acrobats will form human towers. Each tower needs 6 acrobats.

   How many towers can be made? 5 towers

   How many acrobats are not in the towers? 3 acrobats
4. Howie needs 3 balls of yarn to knit a puppet. He has 20 balls of yarn.

   How many puppets can he knit with this yarn? 6 puppets

   How many balls of yarn are not used? 2 balls of yarn
5. A group of 68 people are at the fun park. They all want to ride in the River Cars. Each car holds 9 riders.

   How many cars will be needed to hold all the people? 8 cars

   Are all the cars full? no

12.4 PRACTICE — Practice

Interpreting Remainders

Solve each problem.

1. At the Summer Learning Center, each cooking class has room for 8 students. How many cooking classes will there be if 70 people sign up? 9 classes N
2. In woodworking class, students will build model ships. Each ship needs 3 masts. There are 20 masts. How many ships can be built? 6 complete ships H
3. A softball team has 9 players. If 67 people sign up to play softball, how many teams can be formed? 7 complete teams C
4. The Center allows 7 students in each computer class. 53 students want to take computer classes. How many classes will be needed? 8 classes A
5. One crafts class of 4 people makes 41 button pictures. Each student plans to take home an equal number of buttons. How many buttons will be left to display in the main hall? 1 button S
6. The Acrobats Club will give a show. The 52 acrobats will form human pyramids. Each pyramid will be made up of 6 people. How many more people need to be in the show so that every acrobat can be part of a pyramid? 2 more people I
7. One group of 21 students and 2 teachers visit a nature park. The park's Raft Ride seats 8 people. How many rafts are needed for the group? 3 rafts W
8. A 60-minute tape will be used to record the stories of 7 students in a writing class. Tape time will be shared equally by the students. The teacher will also speak. For how many minutes can she speak? 4 minutes D

Write the letter on the line above the answer that goes with it.
What lunch food contains sand but tastes great?

A	S	A	N	D	W	I	C	H
	1	8	9	4	3	2	7	6

12.4 ENRICHMENT — Enrichment

Interpreting Remainders

Use the table to solve each problem. Decide what you will do with the remainder before you write your answer. You may draw pictures to help you.

Name of Ride	Number of Cars	Number of Seats in Each Car
Tilt-and-Spin	8	4
Terror Wheel	9	6
Twister Train	7	5
Moon Shot	10	2
Free Fall	2	4

1. A group of 37 people want to ride the Tilt-and-Spin. How many cars will they take up? How many times will the ride run? 10 cars; twice
2. A group of 17 people want to ride the Twister Train. The ride operator wants every car occupied with 2 or 3 people per car. How many cars will have only 2 people? How many cars will have 3 people? 4 cars with 2; 3 cars with 3
3. If 43 people rode the Moon Shot, how many times would the ride run? How many people would be left for the last ride? 3 times; 3 people left
4. The Free Fall lasts 3 minutes. How many people can ride it in 51 minutes? 136 people
5. A group of 63 people want to ride the Terror Wheel. How many cars will they take up? How many people will be in the last car? How many times will the ride need to run? 11 cars; 3 people; twice
6. How did you decide what to do with the remainders in these problems? Answers may vary.

LESSON 12.5

Problem Solving

Planning at a Glance

Objective To decide and to justify why an answer is reasonable

Materials none

Optional Resources

- Daily Cumul. Review, p. 156
- Math Center: Project Card 12
- Every Day Counts
- **TAB**, TE pp. 410E–410F, 410J
- **Problem of the Day**, 156, p. 78; Flip Chart, p. 78b
- **Reteach, Practice, and Enrichment Worksheets for Lesson 12.5**

MATHKEYS

Unlocking Whole Numbers 3–5, Level 3, Activity 25

Students Acquiring English

To develop meaning for the idiomatic expression *comes in*, display a catalog, and give examples such as *This dress comes in red.*

Problem of the Day

Use one geoboard and two rubber bands. Make a rectangle that touches 8 pins and a triangle that touches 6 pins, but let both figures touch only 1 pin together.

One possible answer is shown.

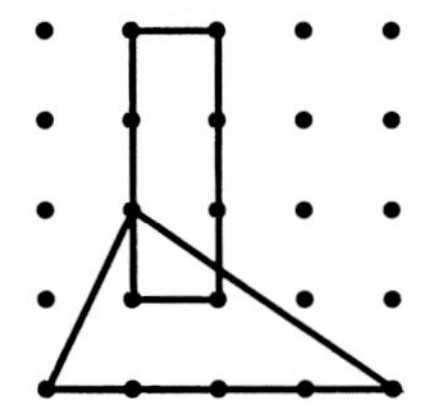

Problem Solving: Decisions

LESSON 5

Problem Solving

Is the Answer Reasonable?

Suppose you are inviting 13 friends to a party. The invitations come in packages of 5. How many packages should you buy?

Is the Answer Reasonable?

Ask Yourself:

- Did I answer the question?
- Did I divide correctly?
- Is the answer labeled with the right units?
- Did I use the remainder corrrectly?

You Decide

- Should you write a division problem to find the answer? yes; 13 ÷ 5
- What are the quotient and the remainder? 2R3
- If you buy 2 packages of invitations, how many people can you invite? 10 people; You need to buy 3 packages to invite 13 people.

Work It Out!

5. The photos should be in the album; It doesn't matter if the last page is full.

Solve the problem. Explain what you did with the remainder.

1. You want to serve a small can of fruit punch to each of the 14 people at your party. The cans come in packs of 6. How many packs do you need? 3 packs, 4 cans will be left over
2. You have 43 slices of bread. How many sandwiches can you make? Each sandwich has 2 slices of bread. 21 sandwiches; with the 1 slice left over, make half a sandwich
3. The principal is ordering a workbook for each of 61 third graders. The books come in packages of 8. How many packages must she order? 8 packages, 3 workbooks will be left over
4. Your teacher puts a photo of each of her 37 students in an album. She puts 8 photos on a page. How many photos will be on the last page she uses? it will only have 5 photos

Share Your Thinking

5. How did you decide what to do with the remainder in problem 4? See above.

1 Introduce

Prior Knowledge Ask, What is 21 ÷ 4? 5 R1

Teach: You Decide

Emphasize this point:

- To check if an answer is reasonable, make sure you used the remainder correctly.

Modeling Model the example. Discuss:

- How can I find the answer? divide the number of friends by the number of invitations in each package
- With 2 packages, how many people can you invite? 10
- Can you buy part of a package? No; you need to round the remainder up to the next whole number

2 Develop

Work It Out!

- Remind students that sometimes they should ignore the remainder, sometimes include it, and sometimes round their answer to the next highest whole number.
- Call on students to discuss how they handled the remainders in problems 1–4.
- Ask students to discuss their reasoning for problem 5.

Basic Facts Just the Facts Basic Facts Workshop 12, p. 119

Using Reading Strategies Encourage students to use the Evaluate strategy as they read the problems. Ask them what information they think is important in deciding whether an answer is reasonable. See TE p. 410J.

3 Summarize

- Remind students that they have to read a division word problem carefully to know what to do with the remainder.
- Have students give examples of three different ways of handling remainders.

Ongoing Assessment At a folk-dance festival, 51 people want to square dance. Each square needs 8 dancers. How many squares can be formed? 6 squares

Math Journal: *Communicating*

An album holds 4 pictures on each page. When it is almost full, how can you find the number of pictures by counting empty spaces? Answers may vary, but students should see that you can multiply the number of pages by 4 and subtract the empty spaces.

Problem Solving Workshop

What Do You Do with a Remainder?

Review

Use with page 420.

15 minutes

What Should We Do with the Remainder?

Management teacher directed; whole class

- Read the following problems to students. Ask them to solve the problems, identify the remainder, and to decide what to do with it.
  1. You are baking 5 batches of brownies for the school bake sale. Each batch requires 3 eggs. Eggs come packaged by the dozen. How many dozen eggs will you have to buy to make the brownies? 2 dozen; 9 extra eggs
  2. You need to mail 35 surprise party invitations. There are 8 invitations in a package. How many packages will you need to buy? 5 packages; 5 extra invitations

$$\begin{array}{r} 4\ R3 \\ 8\overline{)\ 35} \\ -32 \\ \hline 3 \end{array}$$

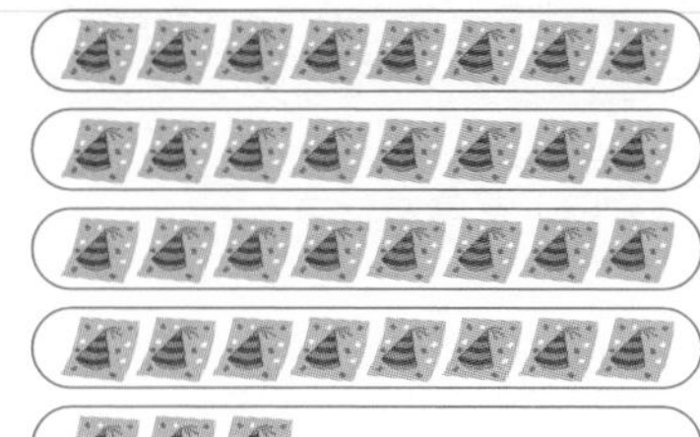

Include the remainder.

  3. You are purchasing paper products for the surprise party. Paper plates come 12 to a package and paper cups come 10 to a package. How many packages of each will you need to buy? 3 packages of paper plates; 1 extra plate; 4 packages of paper cups; 5 extra cups
  4. There are 137 students going on a field trip. Each bus holds 28 students. How many buses will be filled to capacity? 4 buses
- Ask students what they decided to do with their remainders in each problem. Ask, Why were the remainders important in each of these problems?

Activity

Use with page 420.

20 minutes

Using Remainders

Management small groups

- Read the following story to students.

  A river rafting trip is being planned for 12 students and 2 teachers. They need to make a list to figure out what items to bring and how much of each they will need. Extend the list shown, and help students decide what else to bring. Then, determine how many of each item is necessary for the trip.

We Need to Bring
- Bathing Suit
- Sunglasses
- Bagged Lunches
- Suntan Lotion
- Soap
- Toothbrush

3 towels/3 people 14 towels
1 lantern/4 people 4 lanterns
1 tent/4 people 4 tents
3 gallons water/2 people 21 gallons
1 first-aid kit/10 people 2 kits
1 backpack/2 people 7 backpacks
4 loaves bread/5 people 12 loaves

- Have small groups work together to add to the list.
- Invite groups to share their additions with the class.

Chapter 12

Basic Facts Workshop

Use with Lesson 12.5

Multiplying by 8

See also *Just the Facts*
- Support Masters
- Practice Worksheets
- Cumulative Practice

Review

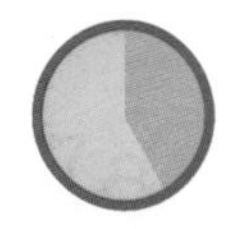

Only One 8

25 minutes

Management whole class
Materials overhead projector; blank transparency; Just the Facts Support Master 7 (hundredths square) on p. 288; See also Practice 12A–12B on pp. 142–143 for use with Lessons 12.7, 12.9; Cumulative Practice 9 on p. 272 for use with Lesson 12.8.

- Remind students that they have already practiced multiplying by 1's, 2's, 3's, 4's, 5's, 6's, 7's, and 9's. On a blank transparency, write equations as shown. Have students name the missing factors. 2, 7, 5, 4, 9, 3, 6
- Ask students to identify any facts for 8 other than 1 or 0 that are missing from the list. The only fact left to learn is 8×8.

$\square \times 8 = 16$
$\square \times 8 = 56$
$\square \times 8 = 40$
$\square \times 8 = 32$
$\square \times 8 = 72$
$\square \times 8 = 24$
$\square \times 8 = 48$

- Draw an 8×8 array on a grid transparency. Tell students that if they cannot remember the answer to 8×8, they might use facts that they already know to figure out the product.
- Discuss different ways they might split the array into parts to find the product for 8×8. Answers will vary. Possible answers: 4×8 plus 4×8; 1×8 plus 7×8; 2×8 plus 6×8; 3×8 plus 5×8.

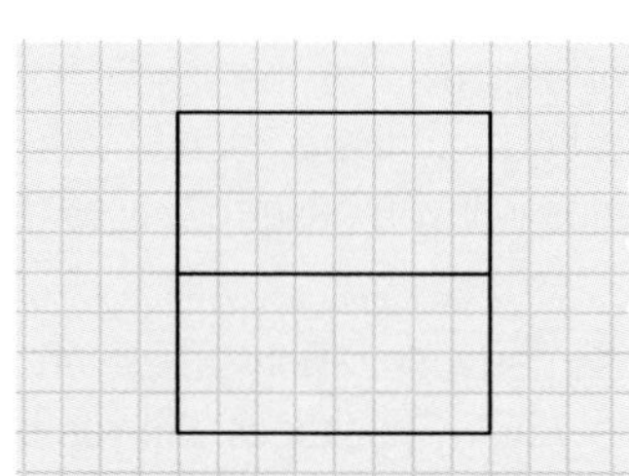

$4 \times 8 = 32$
$4 \times 8 = 32$

$$\begin{array}{r} 32 \\ +\ 32 \\ \hline 64 \end{array}$$

Practice

Make ×8 Flash Cards

30 minutes

Management individuals, then pairs
Materials for each student: 1 index card; Just the Facts Support Masters 11, 15 (practice minutes, certificate) on pp. 292, 296; See also Practice 12A–12B on pp. 142–143 for use with Lessons 12.7, 12.9; Cumulative Practice 9 on p. 272 for use with Lesson 12.8.

- Distribute index cards to students. Have them make flash cards as shown for the following fact: 8×8.
- Have students add this card to their previously made sets of 8's facts (8×1, 1×8, 8×2, 2×8, 8×3, 3×8, 8×4, 4×8, 8×5, 5×8, 8×6, 6×8, 8×7, 7×8, 8×9, and 9×8).
- Have students use their flash cards to practice 8's multiplication facts with a partner.
- For additional practice, students may want to take their flash cards home. Remind them to keep track of the number of minutes they practice. Students may return completed records to school in exchange for a certificate.

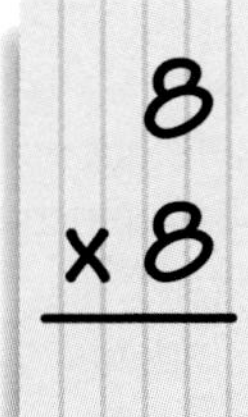

Midchapter Review

for Pages 410–420

Problem Solving

Solve using any strategy. Show your work. (pages 414, 416)

1. You plan to buy 12 cans of food for your kitten. You want $\frac{1}{2}$ of the cans of cat food to be tuna flavor, $\frac{1}{4}$ of the cans to be chicken, and the rest, seafood. How many cans of each kind should you buy? 6 tuna, 3 chicken, 3 seafood

2. You had a box of 30 dog biscuits. Your brother gave the dog the same number of biscuits each day. After 2 weeks, 2 biscuits are left. How many biscuits did he give the dog each day? 2 biscuits

Concepts

Use counters. Decide whether there will be a remainder. If there is a remainder, write it. (page 412)

3. 39 ÷ 6 yes, 3 4. 61 ÷ 8 yes, 5 5. 27 ÷ 3 no 6. 54 ÷ 9 no

Tell how many groups there are. Write a fraction for the blue group. Then write how many are in the blue group. (page 414)

7. 8; $\frac{1}{8}$, 1 8. 5; $\frac{1}{5}$, 2

9. 5; $\frac{1}{5}$, 1 10. 6; $\frac{1}{6}$, 2

Skills

Write the quotient and the remainder, if there is one. Check your answer by multiplying, then adding. Show your work. (page 416)

11. 16 ÷ 3 5R1 12. 48 ÷ 6 8 13. 49 ÷ 6 8R1 14. 27 ÷ 4 6R3

15. 5)32 6R2 16. 8)68 8R4 17. 8)64 8 18. 2)13 6R1

421

Meeting Individual Needs

Students Acquiring English

Some students may need assistance on the Midchapter Review.

- Be prepared to read directions aloud to students.
- Focus special attention on word problems. Expect to paraphrase, diagram, or draw an explanation of the word problem.
- Review important vocabulary words that have been previously introduced.
- Review titles and other elements of graphs and charts.

Additional Assessment Resources

Test, Practice, Management Program

Use the *Test, Practice, Management Program* to create, administer, and score tests as well as generate practice sets. Questions are correlated to the Lesson Objectives.

Scoring Chart

Item	Points
1–2	10 points each
3–10	6 points each
11–18	4 points each
TOTAL	100 points or 100%

Problem Solving

Give from 0 to 10 points per answer, based on how well students meet the following criteria:

Problem 1

- Answer shows use of a particular strategy and a method for checking.
- Answer shows that 6 of the cans are tuna, 3 are chicken, and 3 are seafood.

Problem 2

- Answer shows use of a particular strategy and a method for checking.
- Answer shows that the brother gave the dog 2 biscuits a day.

Concepts and Skills

If students are having difficulty in particular areas, use the appropriate Reteaching Worksheets listed below.

- 90 Writing the Remainder, p. 246
- 91 Comparing the Remainder and Divisor, p. 247
- 92 Reading the Division Sign, p. 248
- 93 Interpreting the Remainder, p. 249

Common Error Alert

If your students are making frequent errors, see Analyzing Errors, TE pp. 433A–433B.

Item Analysis

Item	Objectives
1–2	To use a variety of strategies to solve problems (12G)
3–6	To explore models for dividing a 2-digit number by a 1-digit number with remainders (12A)
7–10	To use division to find a fractional part of a set (12B)
11–18	To divide 2-digit numbers by 1-digit numbers (12D)

Math World

Sticking With Division

Background Different versions of lacrosse were played by Native Americans from Canada to Louisiana. The game today can be rough, but in earlier times, when entire tribes might play day-long matches, it was sometimes called "the younger brother of war."

Activity: *Lacrosse Division*

Pose these problems:

- Women's lacrosse teams play a 50-minute game, divided into two halves. How long is each half? 25 min
- A men's lacrosse field is 110 yd long, about twice as long as it is wide. How wide is the field? 55 yd
- Ben's lacrosse stick is 48 in. long. The head of the stick is 8 in. long. How many times longer than the head is the whole stick? 6 times
- Ben's lacrosse team scored 55 goals in 5 games. How many goals did it average for each game? 11 goals

Have students make up their own division problems involving a sport.

Division Around the World

Math World

Use division to think about sports, time, and thunderstorms. Then, divide a sheet of paper to make a paper windmill.

Sticking with Division

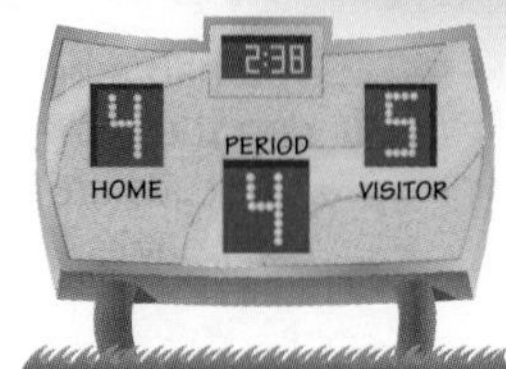

Canada's unofficial national sport is lacrosse (luh kraws). Native Americans made up the game more than 600 years ago. Today, lacrosse is played in schools and clubs throughout the world. Lacrosse games last 60 minutes. They are divided into four 15-minute periods. Think of some other sports. How are the games divided into time periods?

Lacrosse Hall of Fame Museum

Watch Out for Division

About 5000 years ago, the Sumerians divided the day into twelve 2-hour time periods. Today we divide each day into two 12-hour periods. A.M. and P.M. are used to name the two time periods. A.M. and P.M. come from Latin words meaning "before noon" and "after noon." Ships at sea divide the day into 6 time periods called *watches*. How long is each watch?

Lightning in Africa

422

For More Information

Word Origins

A.M.* and *P.M.

Abbreviations for *ante meridiem*, and *post meridiem*, Latin for "before noon" and "after noon."

The terms A.M. and P.M. came into use around 1500, when people were beginning to use mechanical clocks with 12-hour dials. These clocks did not keep time very well, and often had to be reset every sunny day at noon when the sun was directly overhead.

Discuss with students whether it makes sense to divide the day into two halves, before and after noon.

Literature

Energy Today: Wind Power
Gloucester Press, 1986
Mike Cross

Eyewitness Books: Sports
Alfred A. Knopf, Inc., 1988
Tim Hammond

Science Project: Sky and Weather
Franklin Watts, 1992
Alan Ward

The Super Science Book of Time
Thomson Learning, 1993
Kay Davies

Marshall Cavendish Illustrated Guide to Games Children Play Around the World: Ball Games
Marshall Cavendish Corp. 1989
Ruth Oakley

This Book Is About Time
Little, Brown and Co., 1978
Marilyn Burns

Try This! PAPER WINDMILLS

Children in China buy paper windmills, or pinwheels, to celebrate the beginning of spring. Try making a paper windmill of your own.

1. Fold a square piece of paper in half to make a triangle. Fold again to make a smaller triangle.
2. Unfold the paper to show the square divided into fourths. Color in the triangles.
3. Punch a hole in the center with a pencil.
4. Cut along the folds, stopping about an inch away from the hole.
5. Make a hole in the left corner of each triangle. Fold these corners down to the middle hole.
6. Push the pin through all of the holes and into the pencil's eraser. Give your pinwheel a try!

Wonder About Thunder?

You can use division to estimate how far away a thunderstorm is. Look for a flash of lightning. Then count the seconds until you hear the thunder. Divide the number of seconds by 5. The quotient tells you about how many miles away the storm is.

Respond

Work with a partner . . .
to find out more about windmills or keeping time.

Internet:
Houghton Mifflin Education Place
Explore the Math Center at http://www.eduplace.com

423

Watch Out for Division

Background The words *watch* and *awake* come from the same Old English word, meaning "to be alert." Crew members aboard ships were traditionally divided into two "watches," which alternated duty in 4-hour intervals, also called watches. Ships bells would sound every half hour, with "eight bells" signalling the end of a watch. The 1600–2000 watch (4:00–8:00 P.M.) was split into two halves, so that sailors would not have to stand the same watches every day. It was called the *dog watch*, a way for sailors to "dog," or dodge, the same daily routine.

Activity: *Duty Schedule*

Have the class imagine that they are a ship's crew. Have them work out a 48-hour duty schedule for two "watches," beginning with the "dawn watch" at 4:00 A.M. and including a dog watch.

Paper Windmills

Background The Chinese New Year corresponds calendrically to such festivals as Mardi Gras, celebrated in the Christian world the day before Lent begins, and is observed in much the same way.

Critical Thinking After students complete the activity, discuss the geometry of the pinwheels they have made.

Technology

Internet: Education Place
http://www.eduplace.com
Houghton Mifflin Education Place **Mathematics Center** provides teacher and student support, such as links to other Internet sites.

Ultimate Writing & Creativity Center
Children can use the *Ultimate Writing & Creativity Center* for all their writing and publishing activities.

Kid to Kid

Project Ask students how they could find out more about the game of lacrosse.

Suggest:

- *You could ask children in Canada about the game.*
- *You could exchange information other favorite sports.*

Students can use the Internet to contact Canadian school children or write to the education departments in the various Canadian provinces to ask about finding Canadian pen pals.

LESSON 12.6

Symbolic

Planning at a Glance

Objective To estimate quotients of 2- and 3-digit dividends with 1-digit divisors

Materials none

Optional Resources

- Reteach 12.6; Practice 12.6; Enrichment 12.6
- Daily Cumul. Review, p. 157
- Math Center: How-To Card 41
- Every Day Counts
- **TAB**, TE pp. 410E–410F, 410J
- **Problem of the Day**, 157, p. 79; Flip Chart, p. 79a

MATHKEYS *Unlocking Whole Numbers 3–5*, Level 3, Activity 23

Students Acquiring English

Review the term *quotient* with students.

Problem of the Day

The math machine takes a number in, changes it, then sends out a new number. Figure out how the numbers below were changed. Tell the rule, then give the four missing numbers.

one possible rule: multiply by 3, then add 2; 17, 26, 32, 101

In	Out
1	5
2	8
3	11
4	14
5	
8	
10	
33	

Estimating Quotients

You and 3 classmates need 115 paper flowers for a spring art project. About how many flowers should each of you make? You can estimate 115 ÷ 4 to find out.

Here's A Way! Estimate 115 ÷ 4.

1 Think of multiplication.

115 ÷ 4 = ■

4 × ■ = 115

2 Find out if the quotient will be less than or greater than 10.

4 × ■ = 115

4 × 10 = 40

40 < 115

The quotient will be greater than **10**. So, it has 2 digits.

3 Use multiples of 10 to get a closer estimate.

4 × 10 = 40

4 × 20 = 80

4 × 30 = 120

120 is close to 115, so the quotient is close to 30.

Each of you will make about 30 flowers.

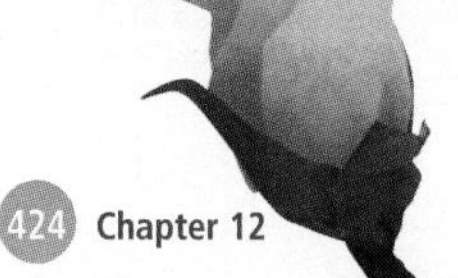

Talk About It! How do you know that 30 is a close estimate? 4 × 30 = 120, which is close to the total number of flowers

424 Chapter 12

1 Introduce

Prior Knowledge Have students solve by mental math:

3 x 10 30 **3 x 100** 300 **8 x 100** 800

Teach: Here's A Way!

Emphasize these points:

- To help find a quotient, think of a related multiplication sentence.
- Substituting 1, 10, and 100 for the quotient you are looking for can tell you if it will have 1, 2, or 3 digits.
- Use multiples of 10 or 100 to get a closer estimate.

Modeling Model how to check the estimate in step 3. Ask:

- How do you know 30 is a better estimate than 40? 40 × 4 = 160; 115 is closer to 120 than to 160

2 Develop

Show What You Know!

Common Error Some students may not correctly relate multiplication to division. Review basic multiplication and division fact families. See also Analyzing Errors, TE pp. 433A and 433B.

- Call on students to explain how they decided on an estimate for exercises 1–3.
- Have students discuss their answers for exercise 4.

Work It Out!

- Have students write the related multiplication sentence for each division exercise.
- Ask students to explain their reasoning for exercise 21.

3 Summarize

- Remind students that estimation helps them place a quotient within a *range* of numbers.
- Students think of a related multiplication sentence when estimating a quotient.

Ongoing Assessment Suppose you have 248 beads. You want to make 8 bracelets, each with the same number of beads. About how many beads can you put on a bracelet? 30–40

Math Journal: *Communicating*

Write a word problem that requires division and that has a quotient between 10 and 20. Answers will vary.

Show What You Know!

Write the letter of the better estimate.

1. 97 ÷ 3 b
   a. 20
   b. 30
2. 371 ÷ 4 b
   a. 80
   b. 90
3. 288 ÷ 9 a
   a. 30
   b. 40
4. **Critical Thinking** For $4\overline{)83}$, will the answer be closer to 20 or to 30? Explain. 20; 4 × 20 = 80, which is close to 83.

Work It Out!

Find a close estimate.

5. 84 ÷ 3 30	6. 255 ÷ 4 60	7. 96 ÷ 5 20	8. 626 ÷ 8 80
9. 169 ÷ 3 60	10. 51 ÷ 2 30	11. 425 ÷ 9 50	12. 198 ÷ 6 30
13. 331 ÷ 4 80	14. 230 ÷ 3 80	15. 27 ÷ 2 10	16. 521 ÷ 8 70
17. 126 ÷ 3 40	18. 84 ÷ 4 20	19. 262 ÷ 7 40	20. 416 ÷ 5 80

21. **Critical Thinking** For $2\overline{)63}$, will the answer be closer to 30 or to 40? Explain. 30; 2 × 30 = 60; 60 is closer to 63 than 2 × 40, or 80.

Algebraic Reasoning Copy the number sentence. Estimate and compare. Write > or <.

22. 73 ÷ 2 ● 73 ÷ 5 >
23. 112 ÷ 5 ● 212 ÷ 5 <
24. 550 ÷ 6 ● 101 ÷ 2 >

25. **Create Your Own** Write a division problem with a quotient between 30 and 40. Explain how you chose the divisor and the dividend. Answers will vary.

Mixed Review

26. 1.8 − 0.5 1.3	27. 3.5 + 8.8 12.3	28. 4.9 − 2.3 2.6	29. 12.8 − 6.9 5.9
30. 5.6 + 4.6 10.2	31. 2.5 − 1.7 0.8	32. 0.7 + 0.9 1.6	33. 8.2 + 0.8 9.0

More Practice Set 12.6, p. 477

Meeting Individual Needs

Extra Support

Quotient and Factors *(kinesthetic)* Provide place-value blocks and index cards with division problems. Have student pairs choose a card and model the product of the divisor × 1, 10, and 100 using ones, tens, and hundreds blocks. Which of their models shows a number that is closest to the dividend?

Alternate Approach

- Reteach Worksheet 12.6
- **TAB** See TE pp. 410E–410F.

MathZones

Understanding Division

Students Acquiring English

See Language Connections, Ch. 12.

Challenge

Write random 2- and 3-digit numbers on each of 20 index cards. Write the digits 2 through 9 on a second set of index cards. Pairs of students take turns drawing a card from each pile and estimating the quotient. Partners then check the estimate by dividing the numbers with a calculator. For more practice Using the Calculator, see pp. T88–T90.

Practice

Math Center Use How-To Card 41, *Estimation Spin,* to have students practice estimating quotients of 3-digit dividends with 1-digit divisors.

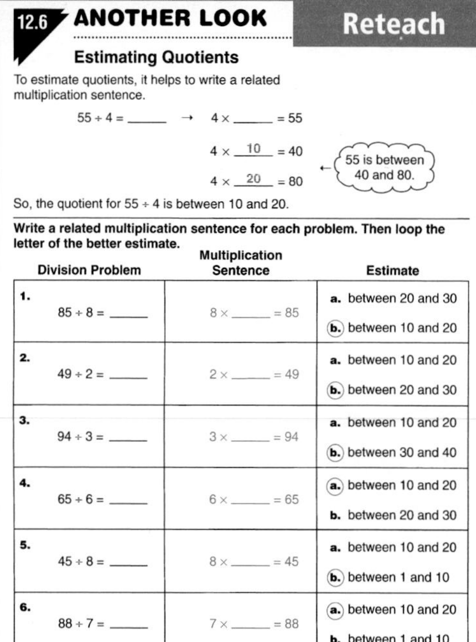

12.6 ANOTHER LOOK — Reteach

Estimating Quotients

To estimate quotients, it helps to write a related multiplication sentence.

55 ÷ 4 = ____ → 4 × ____ = 55

4 × 10 = 40
4 × 20 = 80
(55 is between 40 and 80.)

So, the quotient for 55 ÷ 4 is between 10 and 20.

Write a related multiplication sentence for each problem. Then loop the letter of the better estimate.

Division Problem	Multiplication Sentence	Estimate
1. 85 ÷ 8 = ____	8 × ____ = 85	a. between 20 and 30 (b.) between 10 and 20
2. 49 ÷ 2 = ____	2 × ____ = 49	a. between 10 and 20 (b.) between 20 and 30
3. 94 ÷ 3 = ____	3 × ____ = 94	a. between 10 and 20 (b.) between 30 and 40
4. 65 ÷ 6 = ____	6 × ____ = 65	(a.) between 10 and 20 b. between 20 and 30
5. 45 ÷ 8 = ____	8 × ____ = 45	a. between 10 and 20 (b.) between 1 and 10
6. 88 ÷ 7 = ____	7 × ____ = 88	(a.) between 10 and 20 b. between 1 and 10

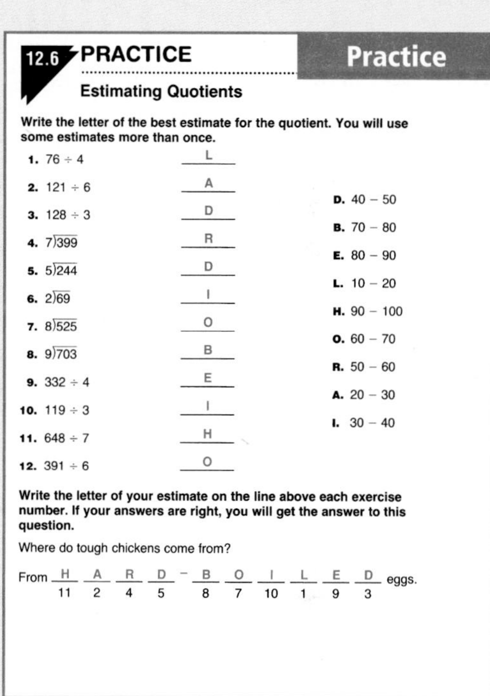

12.6 PRACTICE — Practice

Estimating Quotients

Write the letter of the best estimate for the quotient. You will use some estimates more than once.

1. 76 ÷ 4 L
2. 121 ÷ 6 A
3. 128 ÷ 3 D
4. $7\overline{)399}$ R
5. $5\overline{)244}$ D
6. $2\overline{)69}$ I
7. $8\overline{)525}$ O
8. $9\overline{)703}$ B
9. 332 ÷ 4 E
10. 119 ÷ 3 I
11. 648 ÷ 7 H
12. 391 ÷ 6 O

D. 40 – 50
B. 70 – 80
E. 80 – 90
L. 10 – 20
H. 90 – 100
O. 60 – 70
R. 50 – 60
A. 20 – 30
I. 30 – 40

Write the letter of your estimate on the line above each exercise number. If your answers are right, you will get the answer to this question.

Where do tough chickens come from?

From H(11) A(2) R(4) D(5) - B(8) O(7) I(10) L(1) E(9) D(3) eggs.

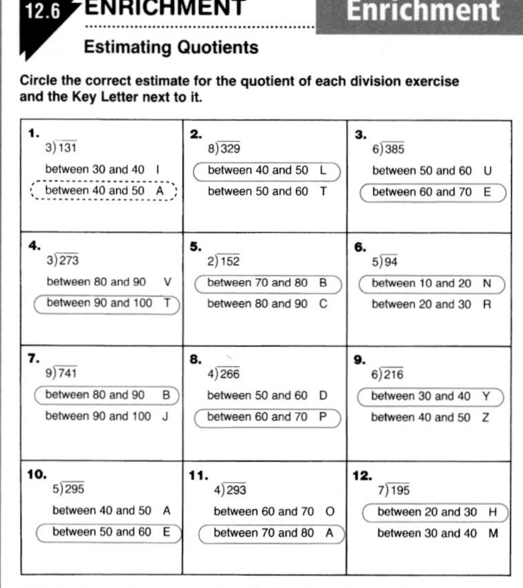

12.6 ENRICHMENT — Enrichment

Estimating Quotients

Circle the correct estimate for the quotient of each division exercise and the Key Letter next to it.

1. $3\overline{)131}$ between 30 and 40 I (between 40 and 50 A)	2. $8\overline{)329}$ (between 40 and 50 L) between 50 and 60 T	3. $6\overline{)385}$ between 50 and 60 U (between 60 and 70 E)
4. $3\overline{)273}$ between 80 and 90 V (between 90 and 100 T)	5. $2\overline{)152}$ (between 70 and 80 B) between 80 and 90 C	6. $5\overline{)94}$ (between 10 and 20 N) between 20 and 30 R
7. $9\overline{)741}$ (between 80 and 90 B) between 90 and 100 J	8. $4\overline{)266}$ between 50 and 60 D (between 60 and 70 P)	9. $6\overline{)216}$ (between 30 and 40 Y) between 40 and 50 Z
10. $5\overline{)295}$ between 40 and 50 A (between 50 and 60 E)	11. $4\overline{)293}$ between 60 and 70 O (between 70 and 80 A)	12. $7\overline{)195}$ (between 20 and 30 H) between 30 and 40 M

Write the Key Letter you circled on the line above the exercise number. The letters will spell the answer to this riddle.

What do elephants have that no other animal has?

B(7) A(11) B(5) Y(9) E(10) L(2) E(3) P(8) H(12) A(1) N(6) T(4) S

Connecting

Planning at a Glance

Objective To divide 2-digit dividends by 1-digit divisors, resulting in 2-digit quotients

Materials place-value blocks

Optional Resources

- Reteach 12.7; Practice 12.7; Enrichment 12.7
- Daily Cumul. Review, p. 158
- Math Center: How-To Card 42
- Every Day Counts
- **TAB**, TE pp. 410E–410F, 410J
- **Problem of the Day**, 158, p. 79; Flip Chart, p. 79b

Unlocking Whole Numbers 3–5, Level 3, Activity 23

Students Acquiring English

Building Reading Strategies Help with the Problem of the Day. Explain that to "chip in for a gift" means that all four cousins together buy one gift. Simplify the problem: How many cousins are there? How many cards does each cousin get? How many gifts? Encourage students to draw a diagram to help solve the problem.

Problem of the Day

There are five cousins in the Jones family. Every year each cousin makes a birthday card for every other cousin. For each cousin's birthday, the four other cousins chip in for a gift. In a year how many cards and gifts do the Jones cousins give? 20 cards, 5 gifts

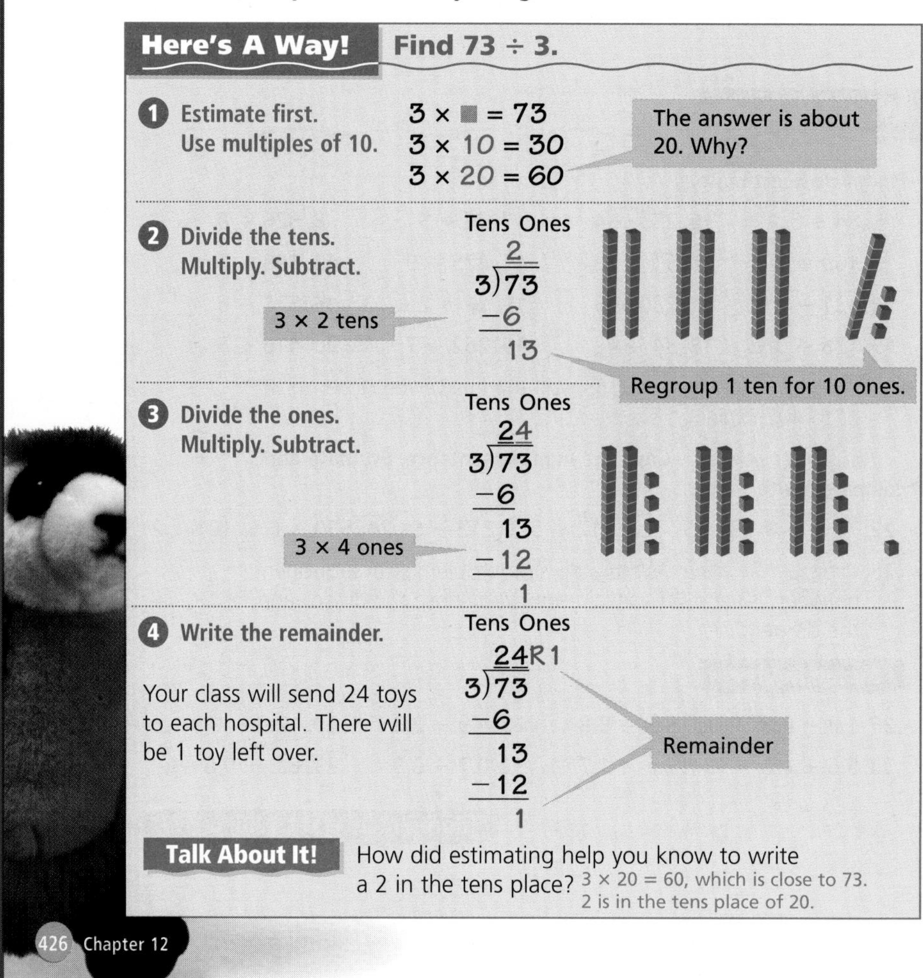

2-Digit Quotients

Your class collects 73 toys for children in 3 hospitals. You want to send the same number of toys to each hospital. How many will go to each? Divide to find out.

Here's A Way! **Find 73 ÷ 3.**

1. Estimate first. Use multiples of 10.
   $3 \times ■ = 73$
   $3 \times 10 = 30$
   $3 \times 20 = 60$
   The answer is about 20. Why?

2. Divide the tens. Multiply. Subtract.
   Tens Ones
   $3\overline{)73}$ quotient 2; -6; 13
   3 × 2 tens
   Regroup 1 ten for 10 ones.

3. Divide the ones. Multiply. Subtract.
   Tens Ones
   $3\overline{)73}$ quotient 24; -6; 13; -12; 1
   3 × 4 ones

4. Write the remainder.
   Tens Ones
   $3\overline{)73}$ quotient 24R1; -6; 13; -12; 1
   Remainder

   Your class will send 24 toys to each hospital. There will be 1 toy left over.

Talk About It! How did estimating help you know to write a 2 in the tens place? 3 × 20 = 60, which is close to 73. 2 is in the tens place of 20.

426 Chapter 12

1 Introduce

Build Understanding **Model how to find 26 ÷ 4 using place-value blocks.**

Regroup 2 tens as 20 ones → Make 4 equal groups → $4\overline{)26}$ 6R2

Then have students use blocks to solve 17 ÷ 3 5R2 **and 19 ÷ 5** 3R4.

Teach: Here's A Way!

- Estimating first can help you predict how many digits are in the quotient.

2 Develop

Show What You Know!

Common Error Some students may not regroup and divide to find the second digit in the quotient. Review the steps of division. See also Analyzing Errors, TE pp. 433A and 433B.

- Call on students to describe how they solved exercises 1–8.

Work It Out!

- Students can multiply the quotient by the divisor and add the remainder to check their answers.

Using Reading Strategies Guide students to use the Evaluate strategy as they read the Problem-Solving exercises. Ask them what information they think is important. See TE p. 410J.

3 Summarize

- Remind students that they can estimate a quotient to find the number of digits and the first digit in the quotient.

Ongoing Assessment You and some friends are going for Chinese food. There are 34 chopsticks. Each person will need 2 chopsticks. How many people can use chopsticks? 17 people

Math Journal: *Communicating*

How can estimation help you to tell whether 65 ÷ 3 has a 1- or 2-digit quotient? 3 × 10 = 30 and 3 × 100 = 300; 65 is between 30 and 300, so the quotient is between 10 and 100; it has 2 digits.

Show What You Know!

Estimation Estimate to tell which answer is greater. Write *a* or *b*.

1. a. $2\overline{)89}$ a b. $7\overline{)89}$
2. a. $3\overline{)96}$ a b. $4\overline{)96}$
3. **Critical Thinking** In exercise 1, how could you tell which answer would be greater without using multiples of 10? (Hint: Compare the dividends. Then compare the divisors.) When the dividends are the same, the smaller the divisor, the greater the quotient.

Estimate. Then divide.

4. $3\overline{)65}$ 20; 21R2
5. $4\overline{)90}$ 20; 22R2
6. $5\overline{)68}$ 10; 13R3
7. $2\overline{)25}$ 10; 12R1
8. $3\overline{)95}$ 30; 31R2

Work It Out!

Write the quotient. Write the remainder if there is one.

9. $8\overline{)48}$ 6
10. $8\overline{)96}$ 12
11. $6\overline{)83}$ 13R5
12. $6\overline{)84}$ 14
13. $7\overline{)78}$ 11R1
14. $5\overline{)91}$ 18R1
15. $2\overline{)77}$ 38R1
16. $3\overline{)96}$ 32
17. $2\overline{)81}$ 40R1
18. $3\overline{)68}$ 22R2
19. $4\overline{)94}$ 23R2
20. $5\overline{)85}$ 17
21. $2\overline{)93}$ 46R1
22. $6\overline{)72}$ 12
23. $2\overline{)69}$ 34R1
24. $50 \div 2$ 25
25. $5\overline{)22}$ 4R2
26. $75 \div 3$ 25
27. $6\overline{)80}$ 13R2
28. **Mental Math** In exercises 9–27, which can you solve with mental math? Answers will vary. Possible answers: 9, 24, 26

Problem Solving

29. A roll of paper wraps 4 toys. How many rolls will you need for 73 toys? (Hint: Think about the remainder.) 19 rolls
30. A sheet of wrapping paper is 17 in. long and 13 in. wide. How would you cut it to make a square? Cut 4 in. off the long side to make a 13 in. × 13 in. square.

Mixed Review

Write >, <, or =. Use a number line if you need to.

31. 0.1 < 1.0
32. 1.0 > 0.9
33. 5.8 > 5.5
34. 7 = 7.0
35. 5247 < 5369
36. 2001 > 1989
37. 974 < 1101
38. 8251 > 8238

More Practice Set 12.7, p. 478

Meeting Individual Needs

Extra Support

Share and Share Alike *(visual/kinesthetic)*

Have student pairs use place-value blocks to determine how many items are in one share, and how many are left over.

a. Five children share 85 marbles. 17 marbles

b. Three families share 22 fish caught on a fishing trip. 7 fish R1

c. Four hikers carry 84 pounds of gear among them. 21 pounds

Alternate Approach

- Reteach Worksheet 12.7
- **TAB** See TE pp. 410E–410F.

MathZones
Understanding Division

Students Acquiring English

See Language Connections, Ch. 12.

Challenge

Challenge students to make up problems using 2-digit quotients. Have pairs trade problems and solve.

Practice

Math Center Use How-To Card 42, *Read the Signs,* to have students practice dividing 2-digit dividends by 1-digit divisors.

See **Just the Facts** Practice 12A, p. 142.

12.7 ANOTHER LOOK — Reteach

Two-Digit Quotients

Follow these steps when you divide.

Write the tens. Multiply. Subtract. — $4\overline{)63}$: 1; − 40 (4 × 10); 23

Write the ones. Multiply. Subtract. — $4\overline{)63}$: 15; − 40; 23; − 20 (4 × 5); 3

Write the remainder if there is one.

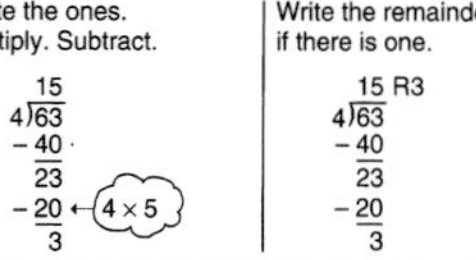

15 R3; $4\overline{)63}$; − 40; 23; − 20; 3

Complete each division problem. Write the quotient and remainder.

1. $3\overline{)64}$ = 21 R1; − 60 (3 × 20); 4; − 3 (3 × 1); 1

2. $7\overline{)85}$ = 12 R1; − 70 (7 × 10); 15; − 14 (7 × 2); 1

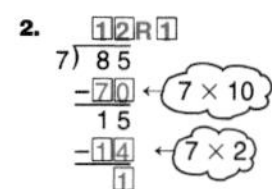

3. $6\overline{)99}$ = 16 R3; − 60 (6 × 10); 39; − 36 (6 × 6); 3

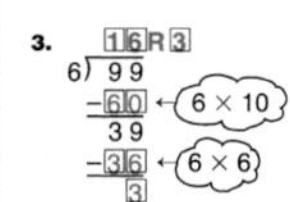

4. $8\overline{)117}$ = 14 R5; − 80 (8 × 10); 37; − 32 (8 × 4); 5

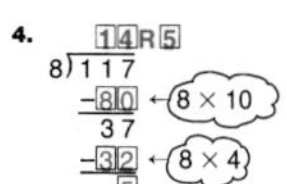

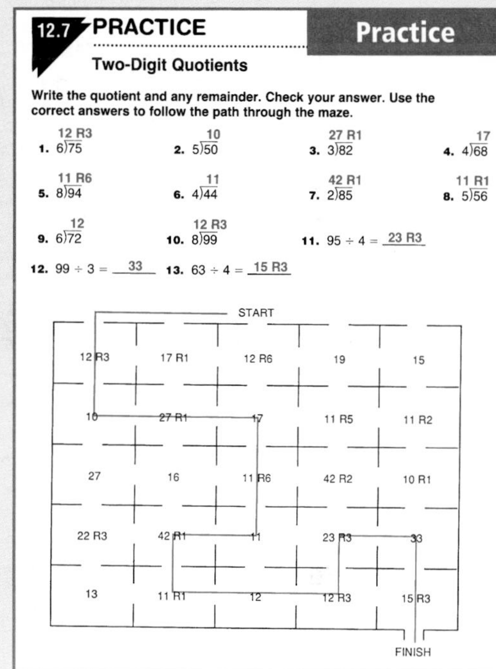

12.7 PRACTICE — Practice

Two-Digit Quotients

Write the quotient and any remainder. Check your answer. Use the correct answers to follow the path through the maze.

1. $6\overline{)75}$ 12 R3
2. $5\overline{)50}$ 10
3. $3\overline{)82}$ 27 R1
4. $4\overline{)68}$ 17
5. $8\overline{)94}$ 11 R6
6. $4\overline{)44}$ 11
7. $2\overline{)85}$ 42 R1
8. $5\overline{)56}$ 11 R1
9. $6\overline{)72}$ 12
10. $8\overline{)99}$ 12 R3
11. 95 ÷ 4 = 23 R3
12. 99 ÷ 3 = 33
13. 63 ÷ 4 = 15 R3

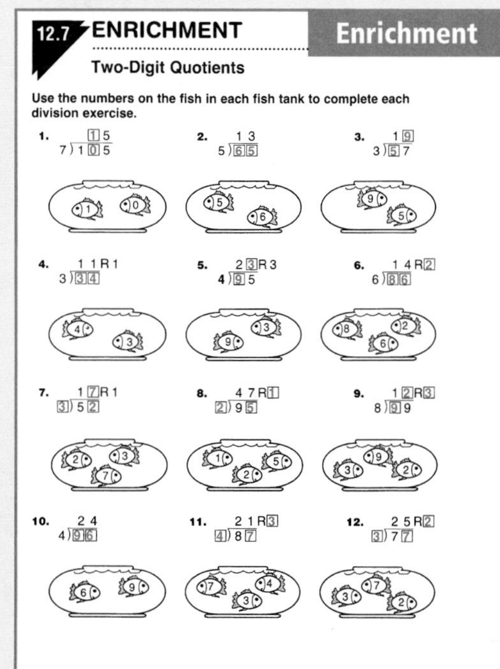

12.7 ENRICHMENT — Enrichment

Two-Digit Quotients

Use the numbers on the fish in each fish tank to complete each division exercise.

1. $7\overline{)105}$ = 15 (fish: 1, 0)
2. $5\overline{)65}$ = 13 (fish: 5, 6)
3. $3\overline{)57}$ = 19 (fish: 9, 5)
4. $3\overline{)34}$ = 11 R 1 (fish: 4, 3)
5. $4\overline{)95}$ = 23 R 3 (fish: 9, 3)
6. $6\overline{)86}$ = 14 R2 (fish: 8, 6, 2)
7. $3\overline{)52}$ = 17 R 1 (fish: 2, 3, 7)
8. $2\overline{)95}$ = 47 R1 (fish: 1, 2, 5)
9. $8\overline{)99}$ = 12 R3 (fish: 3, 9, 2)
10. $4\overline{)96}$ = 24 (fish: 6, 9)
11. $4\overline{)87}$ = 21 R3 (fish: 7, 4, 3)
12. $3\overline{)77}$ = 25 R2 (fish: 3, 7, 2)

Connecting

Planning at a Glance

Objective To divide 3-digit dividends by 1-digit divisors, resulting in 2-digit quotients

Materials place-value blocks

Optional Resources

- Reteach 12.8; Practice 12.8; Enrichment 12.8
- Daily Cumul. Review, p. 159
- Math Center: Act. Card 68
- Every Day Counts
- **TAB**, TE pp. 410E– 410F, 410J
- **Problem of the Day**, 159, p. 80; Flip Chart, p. 80a

MATHKEYS *Unlocking Whole Numbers 3–5*, Level 3, Activity 26

Students Acquiring English

Building Reading Strategies Help students understand what is being asked in problems 31 and 32. For 31, if 4 people go up each time, there can be no remainder. Have students do the problem and calculate how many more they need in order to have no remainder.

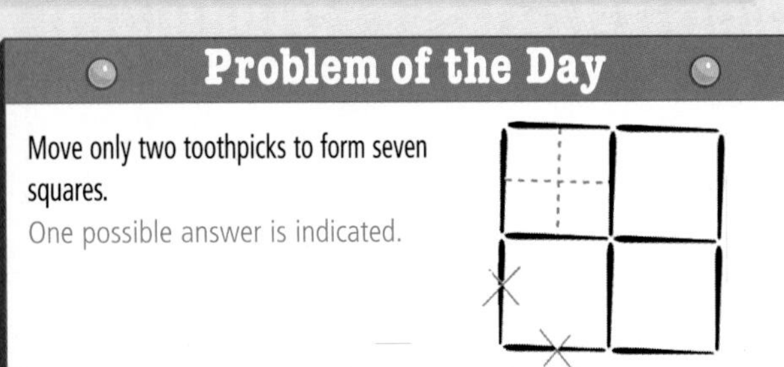

Problem of the Day

Move only two toothpicks to form seven squares.

One possible answer is indicated.

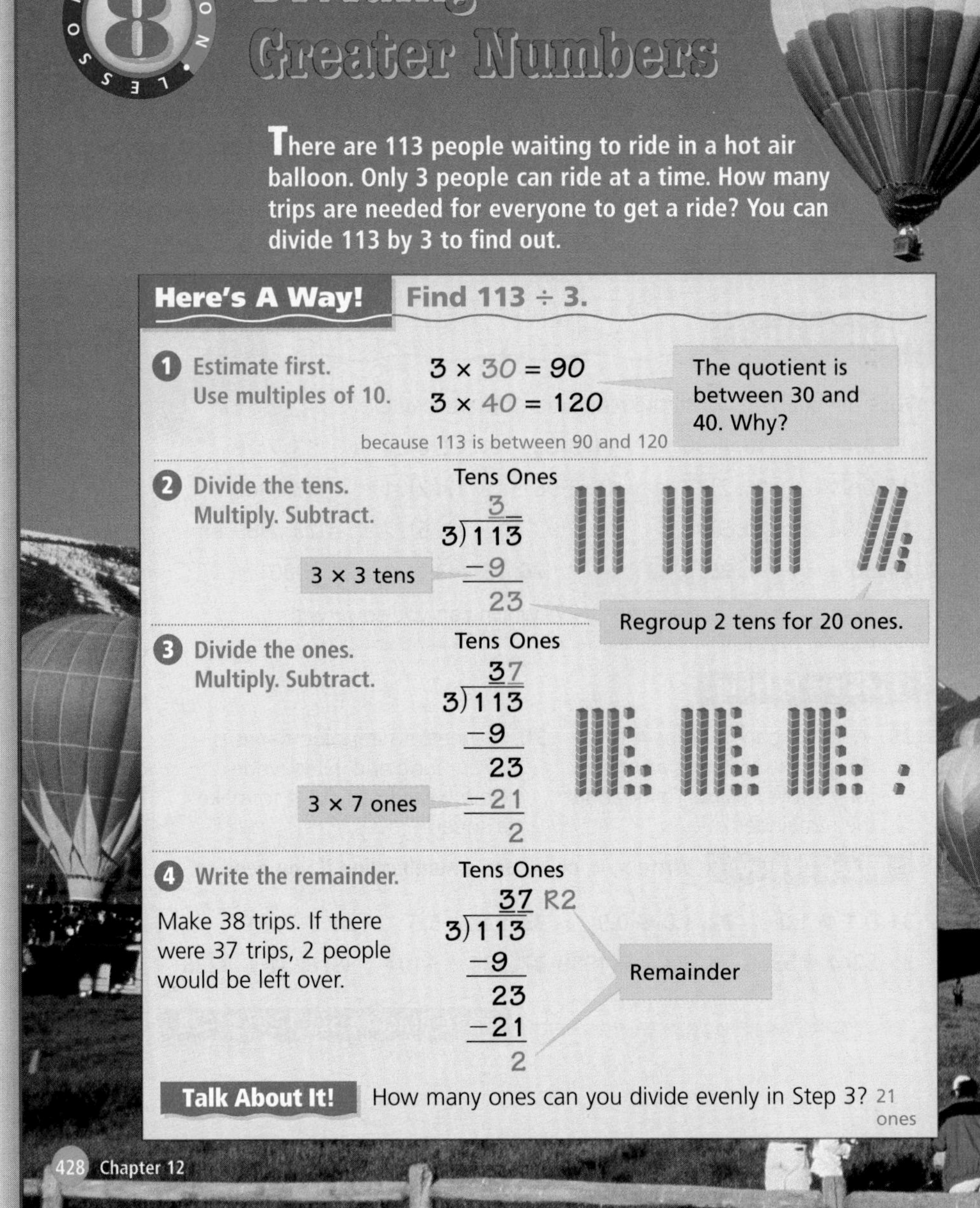

LESSON 8

Dividing Greater Numbers

There are 113 people waiting to ride in a hot air balloon. Only 3 people can ride at a time. How many trips are needed for everyone to get a ride? You can divide 113 by 3 to find out.

Here's A Way! Find 113 ÷ 3.

1. Estimate first. Use multiples of 10.
   $3 \times 30 = 90$
   $3 \times 40 = 120$
   The quotient is between 30 and 40. Why? because 113 is between 90 and 120
2. Divide the tens. Multiply. Subtract.
   Tens Ones
   3) 113 → 3; 3 × 3 tens: −9; 23
   Regroup 2 tens for 20 ones.
3. Divide the ones. Multiply. Subtract.
   Tens Ones
   3) 113 → 37; −9; 23; 3 × 7 ones: −21; 2
4. Write the remainder.
   Tens Ones
   3) 113 → 37 R2; −9; 23; −21; 2 (Remainder)
   Make 38 trips. If there were 37 trips, 2 people would be left over.

Talk About It! How many ones can you divide evenly in Step 3? 21 ones

428 Chapter 12

1 Introduce

Build Understanding Model how to find 113 ÷ 3 with place-value blocks.

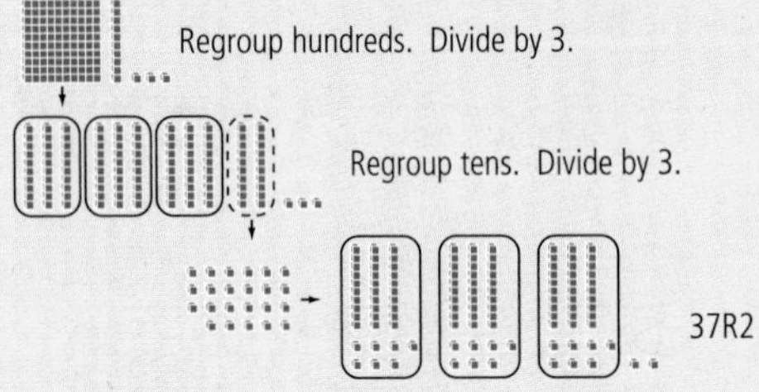

Ask, What did you regroup? 1 hundred as 10 tens; 2 tens as 20 ones **What is the quotient?** 37R2

Teach: Here's A Way!

Emphasize this point:

- Estimate to get the number of digits and the first digit in the quotient.

2 Develop

Show What You Know!

Common Error Some students may not complete the subtraction steps in long division. Review all the steps of long division with them. See also Analyzing Errors, TE pp. 433A and 433B.

Work It Out!

- For exercise 30, invite students to share the mental math methods they used.

Using Reading Strategies Guide students to use the Evaluate strategy as they read the Problem-Solving exercises. Ask them what information they will not need to solve the problems. See TE p. 410J.

3 Summarize

- Ask students to summarize the steps of dividing a 3-digit number by a 1-digit number.

Ongoing Assessment Jane has 147 T-shirts to pack. She packs 6 T-shirts to a box.

- How many boxes does she need? 25 boxes
- What did you do with the remainder? included it and wrote the next whole number
- Would all the boxes be full? No; one would contain 3 T-shirts.

Math Journal: *Communicating*

How can multiplying help you divide? Answers will vary but may include: Multiply the divisor by multiples of 10 to estimate; multiply to check the answer.

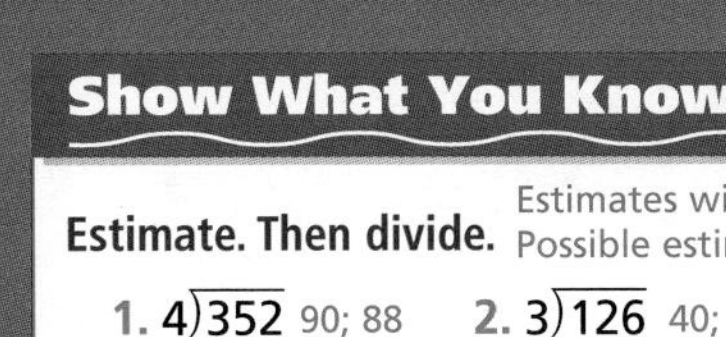

Show What You Know!

Estimate. Then divide. Estimates will vary. Possible estimate and the exact quotient shown.

1. 4)352 90; 88
2. 3)126 40; 42
3. 5)456 90; 91R1
4. 2)158 80; 79
5. 200 ÷ 5 40; 40
6. 201 ÷ 5 40; 40R1
7. 202 ÷ 5 40; 40R2
8. 320 ÷ 8 40; 40
9. 321 ÷ 8 40; 40R1
10. **Patterns** What patterns do you see in exercises 5–7? As the dividend increases by 1, the remainder increases by 1.

Work It Out!

Estimate. If the estimate is greater than 60, then divide. Estimates will vary. Possible estimate shown.

11. 2)119 50; so don't divide
12. 6)537 90; 89R3
13. 4)305 70; 76R1
14. 3)290 90; 96R2
15. 7)428 60; so don't divide
16. 9)843 90; 93R6
17. 5)486 90; 97R1
18. 8)724 90; 90R4
19. 4)231 50; so don't divide
20. 2)107 50; so don't divide

Divide.

21. 5)283 56R3
22. 4)264 66
23. 7)498 71R1
24. 8)368 46
25. 3)257 85R2
26. 360 ÷ 4 90
27. 729 ÷ 9 81
28. 153 ÷ 3 51
29. 488 ÷ 8 61
30. **Mental Math** Did you use mental math for any of the exercises? Explain. Answers will vary.

Problem Solving

31. Suppose a large hot-air balloon holds 4 people. There are 89 people waiting for a ride. How many more people must join the line so that 4 people can ride each time the balloon goes up? 3 people
32. Two ballons each carry 3 people. The riders' weights are 103 lb, 210 lb, 60 lb, 185 lb, 140 lb, and 40 lb. Each ballon can carry no more than 375 lb. Which people should ride together? 103 lb + 210 lb + 60 lb = 373 lb; 185 lb + 140 lb + 40 lb = 365 lb

More Practice Set 12.8, p. 478

429

Meeting Individual Needs

Extra Support

Division and Multiplication *(visual)* Have students make up and solve three multiplication problems, each of which has one 1-digit factor and one 2-digit factor. Then, have them exchange problems with a partner, and let the partner express each example as a related division problem.

Alternate Approach

- Reteach Worksheet 12.8
- **TAB** See TE pp. 410E–410F.

MathZones
Understanding Division

Students Acquiring English

See **Language Connections**, Ch. 12.

Practice

Math Center Use Activity Card 68, *Find the Missing Digits,* to have students practice dividing 3-digit dividends by 1-digit divisors resulting in 2-digit quotients.

Challenge Use Activity Card 68 and have students continue as described in Now Try This!

See **Just the Facts** Cumulative Practice 9, p. 272.

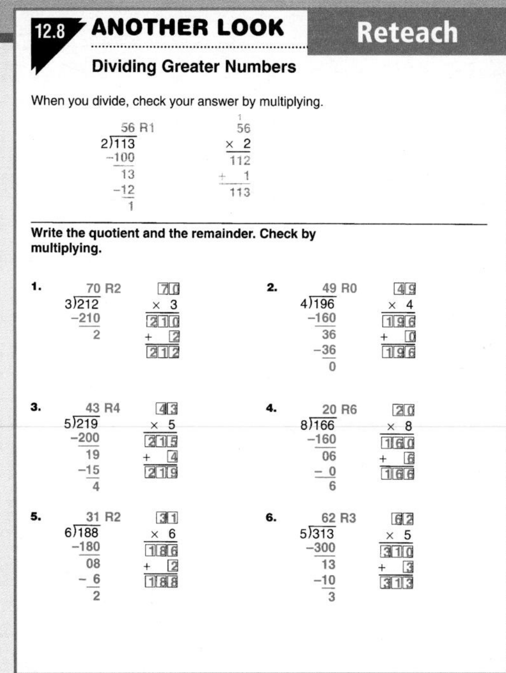

Reteach

12.8 ANOTHER LOOK
Dividing Greater Numbers

When you divide, check your answer by multiplying.

2)113 = 56 R1 (−100, 13, −12, 1); check: 56 × 2 = 112, + 1 = 113

Write the quotient and the remainder. Check by multiplying.

1. 3)212 = 70 R2 (−210, 2); check: 70 × 3 = 210, + 2 = 212
2. 4)196 = 49 R0 (−160, 36, −36, 0); check: 49 × 4 = 196, + 0 = 196
3. 5)219 = 43 R4 (−200, 19, −15, 4); check: 43 × 5 = 215, + 4 = 219
4. 8)166 = 20 R6 (−160, 06, −0, 6); check: 20 × 8 = 160, + 6 = 166
5. 6)188 = 31 R2 (−180, 08, −6, 2); check: 31 × 6 = 186, + 2 = 188
6. 5)313 = 62 R3 (−300, 13, −10, 3); check: 62 × 5 = 310, + 3 = 313

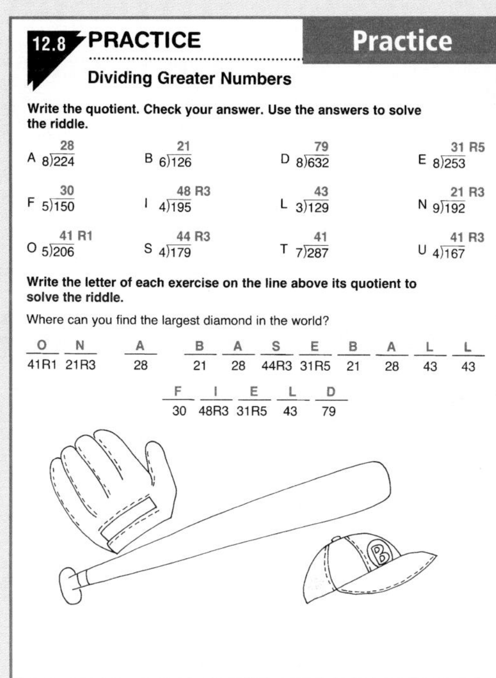

Practice

12.8 PRACTICE
Dividing Greater Numbers

Write the quotient. Check your answer. Use the answers to solve the riddle.

A 8)224 28   B 6)126 21   D 8)632 79   E 8)253 31 R5
F 5)150 30   I 4)195 48 R3   L 3)129 43   N 9)192 21 R3
O 5)206 41 R1   S 4)179 44 R3   T 7)287 41   U 4)167 41 R3

Write the letter of each exercise on the line above its quotient to solve the riddle.

Where can you find the largest diamond in the world?

O N (41R1 21R3) A (28) B A S E B A L L (21 28 44R3 31R5 21 28 43 43)
F I E L D (30 48R3 31R5 43 79)

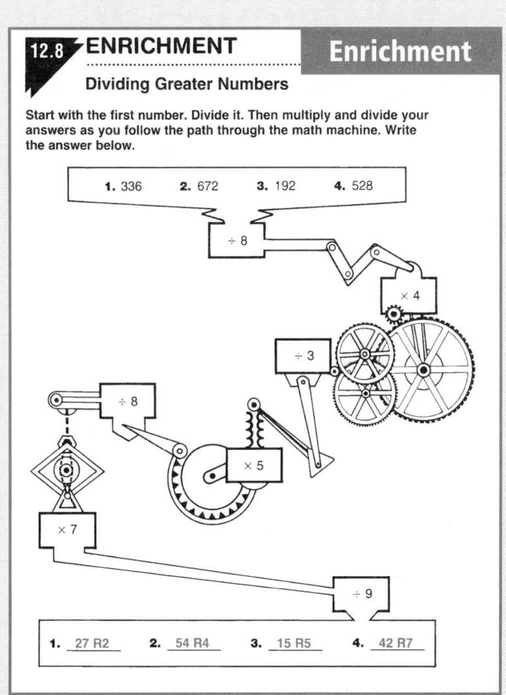

Enrichment

12.8 ENRICHMENT
Dividing Greater Numbers

Start with the first number. Divide it. Then multiply and divide your answers as you follow the path through the math machine. Write the answer below.

1. 336   2. 672   3. 192   4. 528

÷ 8, × 4, ÷ 3, × 5, ÷ 8, × 7, ÷ 9

1. 27 R2   2. 54 R4   3. 15 R5   4. 42 R7

LESSON 12.9

Problem Solving

Planning at a Glance

Objective To use different strategies to solve problems

Materials none

Optional Resources

- Reteach 12.9; Practice 12.9; Enrichment 12.9
- Daily Cumul. Review, p. 160
- Math Center: Project Card 12
- Every Day Counts
- TAB, TE pp. 410E–410F, 410J
- Problem of the Day, 160, p. 80; Flip Chart, p. 80b

MATHKEYS

To meet individual needs, use *Unlocking Whole Numbers 3–5*, Level 3, Activity 26.

Students Acquiring English

Students will need help with vocabulary: *race, racer, team, pair, single, lead, sled, relay*. After explaining *race, racer,* and *relay,* use a diagram to show how to organize a dog team, using the vocabulary words. Then let students write sentences in which these words are used.

Problem of the Day

In a magic square, every column, row, and diagonal has the same sum. Use the numbers 3 through 11 once each so that the magic square sum is 21.

One possible answer is shown.

10	3	8
5	7	9
6	11	4

Problem Solving : Application

LESSON 9

Problem Solving
Using Strategies

Read more about some sled dogs that saved a town in the pages of *Cricket* magazine.

In 1925, some people in Nome (nohm), Alaska, became very ill. Dog sleds sped across 674 miles of snow to bring medicine. A dog sled race takes place each year in Alaska to honor this event. The race is called the Iditarod (eye DIH tur ahd).

Problem Solving Process
- ✓ Understand
- ✓ Plan
- ✓ Try It
- ✓ Look Back

Choose a Strategy You Have Learned
- ✓ Act It Out
- ✓ Look for a Pattern
- ✓ Guess and Check
- ✓ Draw a Picture
- ✓ Make a Table
- ✓ Work Backward
- ✓ Make a List
- ✓ Work a Simpler Problem

Some racers use teams of 9 dogs. The dogs are arranged in 4 pairs. There is a single lead dog in front of the others. Each dog is about 4 feet long. Each pair of dogs is 2 feet from the next pair. The lead dog is 3 feet in front of the nearest pair. How long is the whole team of dogs?

- What question do you have to answer? how long is the whole dog team
- How are the dogs arranged? in pairs, except for the lead dog
- How long is each dog? about 4 feet long
- What is the spacing between the dogs? 2 feet, except 3 feet behind the lead dog
- Explain a strategy that can help solve the problem. Then solve it. Strategies will vary; 29 feet

430 Chapter 12

1 Introduce

Prior Knowledge **Ask, At a book fair, books are on sale for $3 each. How many can you buy with $25?** 8 books

Teach: ***Modeling***

Emphasize this point:

- Different kinds of problems require different kinds of strategies.

Model the example. Ask:

- Could you solve this problem with one operation? No; you need several additions, or multiplication and addition.
- What strategy did you use to solve the problem? Many students will choose drawing a picture or making a table.

2 Develop

Work It Out!

- For problems 1–6, have students discuss the strategies they used. For example, they could use Make a Table for problem 2 and Work a Simpler Problem for problem 4.
- Have students share their answers for problem 7.
- Call on students to compare their answers for problem 8.

Using Reading Strategies Encourage students to use the Evaluate strategy as they read the problems. Ask, Did any problems have unnecessary information? Which ones? See TE p. 410J.

3 Summarize

- Have students review their solution strategies for the problems.
- Remind students that there is no single "correct" strategy for any problem.

Ongoing Assessment An egg carton has spaces for a half-dozen eggs. In how many different ways can 5 eggs be arranged in the box? 6 ways

Math Journal: ***Communicating***

Which problem in this lesson was the hardest for you to solve? How did you figure out how to solve it? Answers should reflect an understanding of whatever method was used.

Work It Out!

Use any strategy to solve the problem. Show your work.

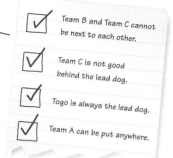

1. A dog sled racer must put together a team of 7 dogs. He wants 1 lead dog followed by 3 pairs of dogs. Look at his notes. How can he arrange the dogs so they will work well together? Togo, then Team B, Team A, Team C

Team B and Team C cannot be next to each other.
Team C is not good behind the lead dog.
Togo is always the lead dog.
Team A can be put anywhere.

2. A team of sled dogs ran 41 miles without stopping from 11:30 A.M. to 1:30 P.M. They traveled at about the same speed the whole way. About how many miles did they travel each hour? about 20 miles each hour

3. Suppose teams of sled dogs will will take turns carrying supplies 1044 miles across Alaska. Each team will run 36 miles of the distance. How many teams are needed? 29 teams

4. You are building a wall of snow blocks. A block is 1.5 ft on each side. The shaded parts of the wall are half blocks. If you want your wall to be 9 ft wide and 6 ft tall, how many more whole blocks do you need? How many more half blocks? 8 whole blocks, 2 half blocks

5. Suppose 3 racers take turns running a race. They go 90 miles altogether. They each go the same distance.How far did each racer go? 30 miles

6. A team of sled dogs ran from 10:15 A.M. to 11:55 A.M. Then they rested for 35 minutes and ran again from 12:30 P.M. to 2:50 P.M. How many hours did they run? 4 hours

Share Your Thinking

7. What strategy did you use to solve problem 6? How did the strategy help you? Answers will vary.

8. When a dog team has 1 lead dog followed by pairs of dogs, the number of dogs is always odd. Explain why. The pairs always add up to an even number. Adding the single lead dog makes the total number of dogs odd.

431

Meeting Individual Needs

Extra Support

What's It Worth? *(visual)* Have students solve this problem: Which is worth more, a stack of dimes 5 inches high or a stack of nickels 5 inches high? How do you know? A stack of dimes; dimes are worth more and are thinner than nickels, so there will be more of them in the stack.

Alternate Approach

- Reteach Worksheet 12.9
- **TAB** See TE pp. 410E–410F.

MathZones

Understanding Division

Students Acquiring English

See Language Connections, Ch. 12.

Challenge

Have students solve these problems:

- You're making a necklace with a pattern of 1 green bead alternating with 2 blue beads. The green beads are 1 inch long, and the blue beads are 2 inches long. How many beads of each color do you need to make a necklace 25 inches long? 10 blue beads, 5 green beads
- Now add 2 red beads on each side of every green bead. If you use 40 blue beads, how many red beads and how many green beads will you use? 40 red beads, 20 green beads

Practice

Math Center Use Project Card 12, *Make a Musical Tape,* to give students practice using different strategies to solve problems.

See **Just the Facts** Practice 12B, p. 143.

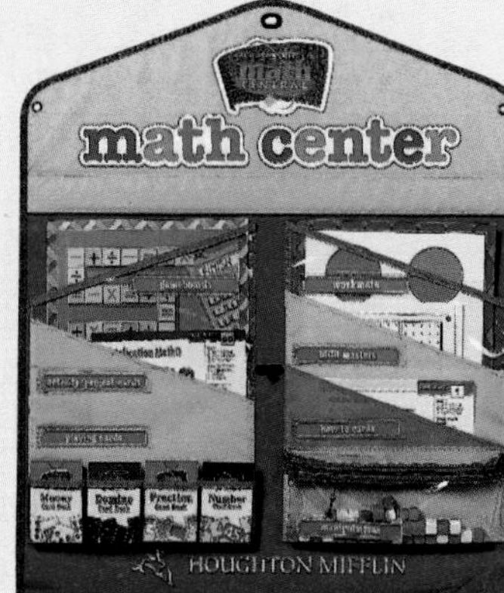

Reteach

12.9 ANOTHER LOOK

Problem Solving: Using Strategies

Use any strategy to solve.

1. A scout troop went fishing at a cabin for the weekend. One scout fished from 8:00 A.M. to 12:00 noon on Saturday and Sunday. He caught the same number of fish every hour and caught 24 fish altogether. How many fish did he catch the first hour? 3 fish
2. The cabin is 100 miles away. The troop drives halfway there and discovers they forgot the fishing poles. They go back and get the poles. How many miles did they drive by the time they reached the cabin? 200 miles
3. It is 5:00 P.M. and the troop just finished fishing for the day. They fished in Oak Bay for 45 minutes and in Spider Bay for 30 minutes. It took them 15 minutes to get to each bay and 15 minutes to return home. What time did they leave the cabin to go fishing? 3:00 P.M.
4. At lunch one day, you have a 48-ounce can of juice. You pour the juice into 6-ounce cups and fill each one to the top. How many cups can you fill? 8 cups
5. On the drive home, you want to listen to one hour of music. You have 3 tapes. One tape plays for 25 minutes. Another plays for 30 minutes. The third tape plays for 40 minutes. Which complete tapes can you listen to? the 2 shorter tapes

Practice

12.9 PRACTICE

Problem Solving: Using Strategies

Use any strategy to solve.

1. Ms. Elma's class is having a clean-up day. By 10:00 P.M., they washed $\frac{1}{3}$ of the 24 desks in the classroom. How many desks did they wash? 8 desks
2. Paco finds twice as many stickers in his desk as Vladimir. Vladimir has 4 fewer stickers than Jasmine who has 12. How many stickers do the 3 students have in all? 36 stickers
3. Ms. Bernstein is painting the wood frame around the bulletin board. (See the picture at right.) How many feet will she paint? 18 feet (SPRING; 3 ft; 6 ft)
4. Miguel takes $128 out of his savings account. He asks for as many $5 bills as possible and the remainder in $1 bills. How many $5 bills did he receive? How many $1 bills did he receive? 25 five-dollar bills, 3 one-dollar bills
5. You are thinking of a number. When you subtract 8 from the number you get 15. What do you get when you add 7 to the number? 30
6. Ten children are invited to a party. They are seated at square tables placed end to end to make one rectangular table. If only 1 person can sit on a side of a square table, how many square tables are needed to seat all 10 children? 4 tables
7. You are hiking on Saturday. You start at 9:15 A.M. and hike until 11:30 A.M. You rest for 45 minutes. You then hike from 12:15 P.M. to 3:00 P.M. How many hours did you hike? 5 hours

Enrichment

12.9 ENRICHMENT

Problem Solving: Using Strategies

Fill in the blank. Use any strategy to solve.

1. Mr. Wong has 15 ________. He eats $\frac{1}{3}$ of them. How many does he have left? $\frac{1}{3}$ of 15 is 5. Problems will vary.
2. ________ picks 17 apples from a tree. She also buys ________ apples at the store. How many apples does she have? Answers will vary.
3. It is now ________ P.M. Computer class begins at 8:30 P.M. How many minutes is it until computer class begins? Answers will vary.
4. Jake has $________. Video games cost $40.00 each. How many video games can he buy? Answers will vary.
5. How much money will Jake have left over? Answers will vary.
6. Every time Samantha puts 5 pennies in her bank, Zahara puts 10 pennies in her bank. If Samantha has ________ pennies in her bank. How many does Zahara have in hers? Answers will vary.

Chapter Test

Problem Solving

Give 0 to 8 points per answer based on how well students meet the following criteria:

Problem 1

- There is use of a clear problem solving strategy
- Correct answer is given

Problem 2

- There is use of a clear problem solving strategy
- Strategy is seen through to a correct solution
- Work shows use of a diagram, picture, or other organization to identify the pattern and solve

Concepts and Skills

If students need more help with concepts and skills in this chapter, use the following Reteaching Worksheets.

- 90 Writing the Remainder, p. 246
- 91 Comparing the Remainder and Divisor, p. 247
- 92 Reading the Division Sign, p. 248
- 93 Interpreting the Remainder, p. 249
- 94 Two-Digit Quotients, p. 254
- 95 Remainders with Two-Digit Quotients, p. 255

Chapter 12 Test

for Pages 410–431

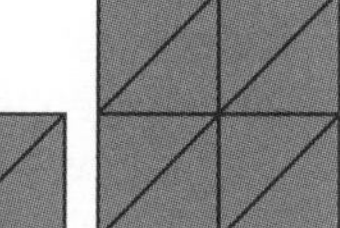

Test-Taking Tips
Unless you are sure of the answer, read all the choices before answering a multiple-choice question.

Problem Solving

Solve the problem using any strategy. Show your work. (page 430)

1. Your class is decorating the classroom door with bows. You need 4 feet of ribbon for each bow. How many bows can you make from 10 yards of ribbon? How much ribbon will be left over? (Hint: 1 yard = 3 feet) 7 bows with 2 feet left over
2. Suppose you use 2 congruent triangles to form a square. You add 6 more congruent triangles to make a larger square. How many triangles will you add to form a third square? 10 triangles

Concepts

Tell whether the division sentence has a remainder. Write the remainder if there is one. (page 412)

3. 72 ÷ 8 No
4. 43 ÷ 5 Yes, 3
5. 15 ÷ 4 Yes, 3
6. 24 ÷ 7 Yes, 3

Tell how many groups there are. Write a fraction for the blue group. Then write how many are in the blue group. (page 414)

7. 4, $\frac{1}{4}$, 1
8. 3, $\frac{1}{3}$, 2
9. 4, $\frac{1}{4}$, 3
10. 7, $\frac{1}{7}$, 1

What is the best estimate for the quotient? Write *a, b, c,* or *d*. (page 424)

11. 58 ÷ 4 a. 10 b. 20 c. 30 d. 15 d
12. 319 ÷ 5 a. 70 b. 60 c. 50 d. 40 b

432

Chapter Correlation to Standardized Tests

Math Central: Chapter Objective	ITBS Form M	CAT/5	CTBS/4	Terra Nova (CTBS/5)	MAT 7th ed.	SAT 9th ed.	State/Local
12A To explore models for dividing a 2-digit number by a 1-digit number with remainders	•	•	•	•	•	•	
12B To use division to find a fractional part of a set	•	•	•	•	•	•	
12C To estimate quotients	•	•	•	•	•	•	
12D To divide 2-digit numbers by 1-digit numbers	•	•	•	•	•	•	
12E To divide 3-digit numbers by 1-digit numbers	•	•	•	•	•	•	
12F To interpret remainders	•	•	•	•	•	•	
12G To use a variety of strategies to solve problems	•			•	•	•	

Skills

Solve. Choose the best answer. Write *a*, *b*, or *c*. (pages 416, 426, 428)

13. $9\overline{)82}$	a. 8	b. 9 R1	c. 9 R2 b
14. $7\overline{)30}$	a. 4 R2	b. 4 R3	c. 5 a
15. $6\overline{)546}$	a. 90	b. 90 R1	c. 91 c
16. 508 ÷ 7	a. 71 R4	b. 72 R4	c. 73 R4 b
17. 17 ÷ 6	a. 2 R3	b. 2 R4	c. 2 R5 c
18. 123 ÷ 4	a. 30	b. 30 R2	c. 30 R3 c

Find the answer. Check your answer by multiplying, then adding. Show your work. (pages 416, 426, 428)

19. 40 ÷ 5 8 20. 52 ÷ 8 6 R4 21. 300 ÷ 9 33 R3 22. 240 ÷ 3 80

23. $2\overline{)61}$ 30 R1 24. $5\overline{)372}$ 74 R2 25. $8\overline{)185}$ 23 R1 26. $4\overline{)25}$ 6 R1

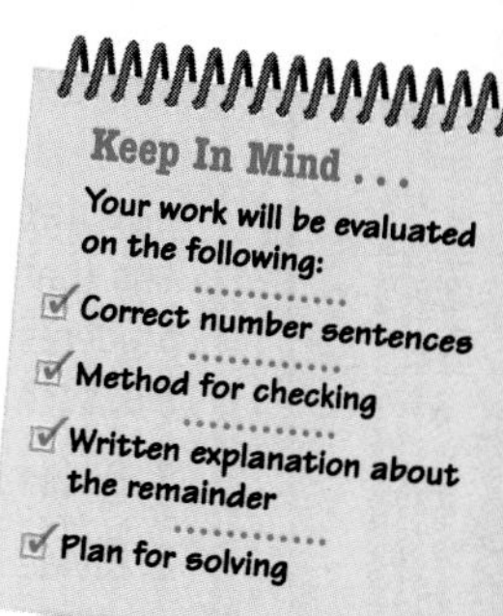

Keep In Mind . . .
Your work will be evaluated on the following:
Correct number sentences
Method for checking
Written explanation about the remainder
Plan for solving

Performance Task

Solve the problem using any strategy. Show your work. (pages 416, 418, 430)

You are making puppets. For each one, you need 3 pieces of felt. You have 11 pieces of felt in all. How many puppets can you make? 3 puppets

- Tell how you found the answer.
- Explain what you did with the remainder and why. The remainder can be dropped since no more puppets can be made from the 2 leftover pieces.
- Change the problem so that there is no leftover part or remainder to think about.
  Answers will vary. Possible answer: Use 12 pieces of felt.

433

Assessment Options

The following materials are found in your **Comprehensive Assessment Package:**

Formal Assessments
- Standardized-Format
- Free-Response Chapter Tests, Forms A and B

Performance Assessments
- Chapter Tasks
- Midyear and Final Project Tasks

Alternative Assessments
- Observation Checklist
- Student Attitude Assessment
- Student Self-Assessment
- *Individual and Group*

- Chapter Tests for Students Acquiring Language Proficiency
- Informal Learning Inventory

Standardized Testing: New Formats
- Enhanced Multiple-Choice
- Extended-Response
- Short-Response

Management
- Student Record Sheets
- Answer Keys

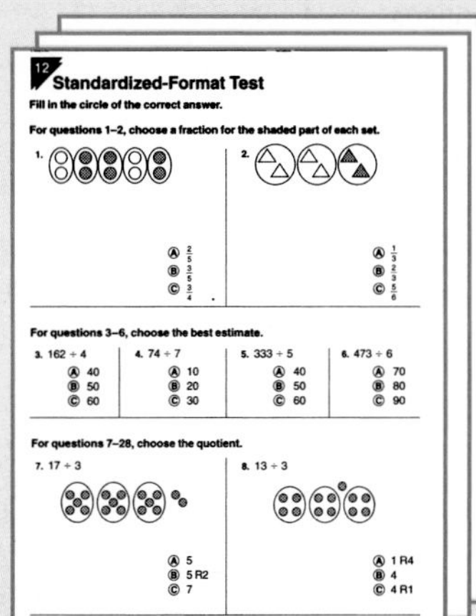

Additional Assessment Resources

Test, Practice, Management Program
Use the *Test, Practice, Management Program* to create, administer, and score tests as well as generate practice sets. Questions are correlated to the Lesson Objectives.

- Standardized-Format Chapter Tests
- Free-Response Chapter Tests, Forms A and B
- Standardized-Format Midyear and Final Tests

Performance Task

Use the following criteria, each worth four points, to evaluate your students' responses. These criteria align with *Keep In Mind* in the Pupil Edition, p. 433.

Criteria	
Shows a plan for solving	Shows a method for checking
Includes correct number sentences	Explains that you can only make 3 puppets

Use this 4-level rubric to score students' responses. If you prefer a task with a 6-level rubric, use the Performance Assessment for this chapter.

4 points	Limited response
8 points	Acceptable
12 points	Capable
16 points	Superior

Common Error Alert

If your students are making frequent errors, see Analyzing Errors, TE pp. 433A–433B.

Scoring Chart

Item	Points
1–2	8 points each
3–12	4 points each
13–26	2 points each
Performance Task	16 points
TOTAL	100 points or 100%

Item Analysis

Item	Objectives
1–2	To use a variety of strategies to solve problems (12G)
3–6	To explore models for dividing a 2-digit number by a 1-digit number with remainders (12A)
7–10	To use division to find a fractional part of a set (12B)
11–12	To estimate quotients (12C)
13–26	To divide 2-digit numbers and 3-digit numbers by 1-digit numbers (12D, E)

Cumulative Test

For a cumulative review in the multiple-choice format, see TE pp. T84–T85.

Analyzing Errors

Strategies and Techniques for Reteaching

Errors in Basic Understanding of Division The division algorithm incorporates the other three operations—addition, subtraction, and multiplication—as well as an understanding of place-value concepts. Students can benefit from modeling the steps in division using place-value materials. Students who carefully compare the place-value models to the algorithm will be able to associate the model with the quotient and to understand the meaning of the remainder.

```
  17 R1
2)35
 -2
  15
 -14
   1
```

Dividing by 1-Digit Numbers

Error Involving Place Value

Error Begins dividing in the greatest place without regard to the size of the dividend or divisor

Reteaching Students making this error probably have difficulty with place-value concepts. If they do not understand the relative sizes of the dividend and divisor, they will not recognize a reasonable answer. Remind students of the relationship between multiplication and division. Have them use that relationship to estimate the quotient before dividing.

Error

```
  50 R2
5)27
 -25
   2
  -0
   2
```

Reteaching

5 × ■ is about 27.

Answer should be about 5.

```
   5 R2
5)27
 -25
   2
```

Errors in Procedure

Error Divides each digit in the dividend separately; ignores remainders

Reteaching Help students recognize that there is an order to the steps and that the order must be followed. Students may wish to create a visual aid, such as a flow chart.

1. Divide the tens. Multiply. Subtract.
2. Divide the ones. Multiply. Subtract.

Write the remainder if there is one.

Error

```
  11
4)65
```

Reteaching

Step 1

```
  1
4)65
 -4
  2
```

Step 2

```
  16 R1
4)65
 -4
  25
 -24
   1
```

Error Divides the greater digit by the lesser digit

Reteaching Estimating the quotient will help students see that a quotient derived this way will not be reasonable.

Error

128 divided by 3.

128)3

Reteaching

Think of 1 hundred + 2 tens as 12 tens.

12 tens divided by 3 = 4 tens

```
  42 R2
3)128
 -12
   08
  - 6
    2
```

Error Does not divide fully when the dividend ends in zero

Reteaching Relate each step in the division algorithm to place-value models. Remind students to always divide tens, then ones, even when there are 0 ones.

Error

```
  1
4)40
 -4
  0
```

Reteaching

```
  10
4)40
 -4     4 × 1 ten
  00
 - 0    4 × 0 ones
   0
```

Analyzing Errors

Errors in Direction and Alignment

Error Does not keep columns aligned

Reteaching As with multiplication, have students turn lined paper sideways and use the vertical lines of the paper to delineate the places in a division algorithm. Remind them of the restriction that only one digit can be used per column.

Error

```
   25 R1
5)136
 -10
  26
 -25
   1
```

Reteaching

```
  27 R1
5)136
 -10
  36
 -35
   1
```

Error Writes quotients from right to left as with other operations

Reteaching Remind students that when you divide tens you get groups of tens, so if you can divide the tens, place the quotient above the tens. If you cannot divide the tens, begin the quotient in the ones place. Also use estimation to help students see the approximate size of the quotient.

Error

```
  31 R3
6)81
 -6
  21
 -18
   3
```

Reteaching

6)81

Estimate:

6 × ■ = 81

6 × 10 = 60

So, the answer must be greater than 10.

Begin writing in the tens place.

Errors Involving the Remainder

Error Leaves remainder that is greater than the divisor

Reteaching Remind students to ask themselves whether the remainder is greater than the divisor. If the answer is yes, the division is incomplete.

Error

```
  17 R8
5)93
 -5
  43
 -35
   8
```

Reteaching

8: •••••••• (circled)

```
  18 R3
5)93
 -5
  43
 -40
   3
```

Error Does not write the remainder

Reteaching Stress the importance of including the remainder in division problems through simple stories, such as 17 toys shared by 6 people. Also act out remainder situations with place-value models.

Error

```
   4
8)34
 -32
   2
```

Reteaching

34 ride tickets

8 people

4 rides each plus 2 extra rides

Error Confuses partial dividend with remainder

Reteaching Carefully review the steps in division, pointing out that the remainder is not written until all the needed places in the quotient have been filled.

Error

```
  32
7)212
 -21
   0
```

Reteaching

```
  30 R2
7)212
 -21
   02
   -0
    2
```

1. Divide 21 tens by 7.
2. Multiply. Subtract.
3. Can 2 ones be divided by 7? No.
4. Divide the ones.
5. Write the 0. Multiply. Subtract.
6. Write the remainder 2.

Cumulative Review

Two Ways to Use the Cumulative Review

Maintenance For those students whose results on the current Chapter Test show a good grasp of skills and concepts, you may wish to assign the Cumulative Review as homework. Students may also benefit from the specific review and practice opportunities listed in the Skills Maintenance chart.

Reassessment For those students whose results on the current Chapter Test show only a limited grasp of skills and concepts, you may wish to assign the Cumulative Review as class work. If it then appears that reassessment is needed, the Skills Reteaching chart on the opposite page identifies remedial minilessons in the Teacher's Resource Package.

Additional Assessment Resources

Test, Practice, Management Program

Use the *Test, Practice, Management Program* to create, administer, and score tests as well as generate practice sets. Questions are correlated to the Lesson Objectives.

Cumulative Review

Addition (Chapter 3)
Add. Find 318 + 119 + 57 + 42.

Here's A Way!

12 318 119 57 + 42 536	Add the ones. Ask, Do I need to regroup? Add the tens. Ask, Do I regroup? Add the hundreds.

Find the sum.

1.	2.	3.
41 33 170 + 254 498	86 72 412 + 110 680	90 66 14 + 37 207

4.	5.	6.
76 13 + 88 177	290 415 + 116 821	278 525 + 141 944

7. In exercise 4 what number did you write above the tens place? Why?
1, because 6 + 3 + 8 = 17; There is 1 ten to regroup in 17.

Rules for Division (Chapter 6)
Find 389 ÷ 389, 60 ÷ 1, 0 ÷ 26.

Here's A Way!

Any number divided by itself equals 1. **389 ÷ 389 = 1**
Any number divided by 1 equals itself. **60 ÷ 1 = 60**
Zero divided by any number equals zero. **0 ÷ 26 = 0**

Find the quotient. Use division rules.

8. 37 ÷ 37 1 **9.** 0 ÷ 249 0
10. 16 ÷ 16 1 **11.** 72 ÷ 1 72
12. 0 ÷ 54 0 **13.** 180 ÷ 1 180

14. What made it reasonable to use mental math to solve exercises 8–13? All the problems had a dividend of 0, a divisor of 1, or the same numbers for both. All the problems followed the rules for division.

Comparing Fractions (Chapter 8)
Does $\frac{3}{6}$ equal $\frac{4}{8}$?

Here's A Way!

Use models to compare.

Yes, $\frac{3}{6} = \frac{4}{8}$.

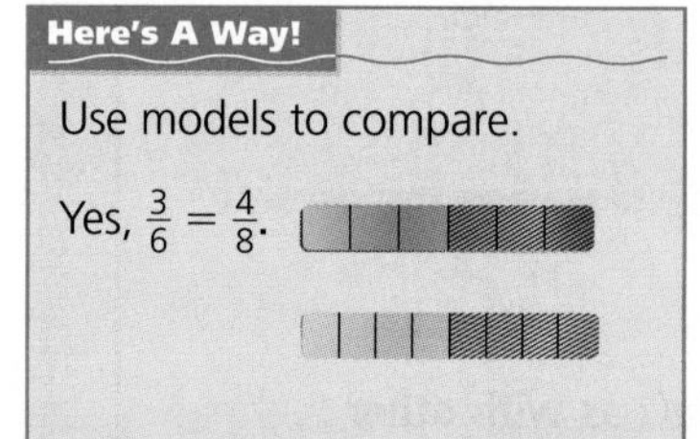

Write the fraction for each shaded part. Write >, <, or = between each pair of fractions.

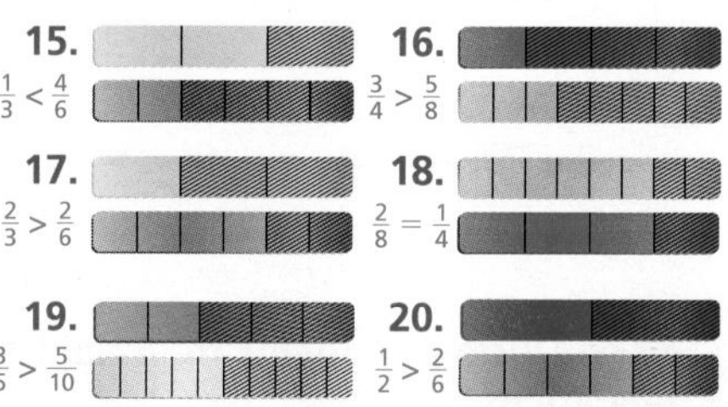

15. $\frac{1}{3} < \frac{4}{6}$
16. $\frac{3}{4} > \frac{5}{8}$
17. $\frac{2}{3} > \frac{2}{6}$
18. $\frac{2}{8} = \frac{1}{4}$
19. $\frac{3}{5} > \frac{5}{10}$
20. $\frac{1}{2} > \frac{2}{6}$

434

Skills Maintenance

Chapter Objectives	Where taught in pupil book	More practice in pupil book
• To add up to four whole numbers (3B)	**Chapter 3**, pp. 94–95	More Practice Set 3.5, p. 449
• To explore the rules for division (6A)	**Chapter 6**, pp. 194–195	None
• To compare and order fractions using models (8B)	**Chapter 8**, pp. 276–277	None
• To relate decimals to fractions and mixed numbers (10B)	**Chapter 10**, pp. 352–353	More Practice Set 10.3, p. 472
• To multiply 2-digit numbers by 1-digit numbers (11C)	**Chapter 11**, pp. 388–389	More Practice Set 11.5, p. 475
• To use a variety of strategies to solve problems (12G)	**Chapter 12**, pp. 430–431	None

Decimals (Chapter 10)
Write four tenths and seven hundredths as decimals.

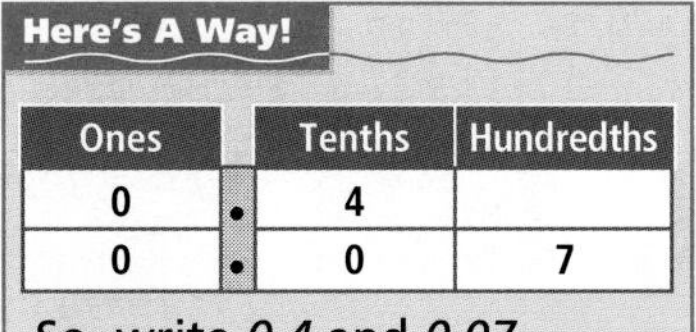

Here's A Way!

Ones		Tenths	Hundredths
0	•	4	
0	•	0	7

So, write *0.4* and *0.07*.

Write the decimal form of each number.

21.

Ones		Tenths	Hundredths
0	•	1	3

0.13

22. one tenth 0.1 **23.** three tenths 0.3

24. twenty-seven hundredths 0.27

25. Where did you write a zero in problem 24? Why? wrote zero in the ones to show that there are no ones

Multiplication (Chapter 11)
Multiply 3 by 12.

Here's A Way!

Use arrays.

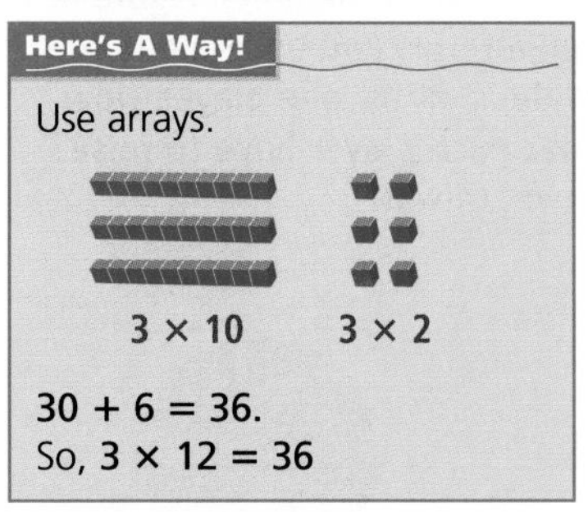

30 + 6 = 36.
So, 3 × 12 = 36

Use the arrays to find the products.

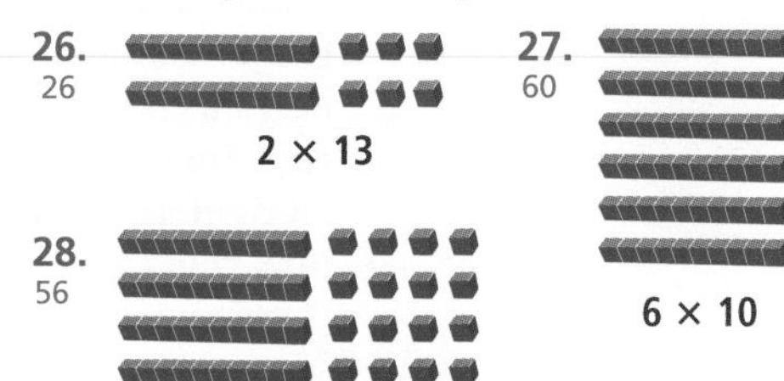

26. 26 2 × 13

27. 60 6 × 10

28. 56 4 × 14

29. Write an addition sentence for exercise 28. Why is the sum the same as the product? 14 + 14 + 14 + 14 = 56; The product is the same as adding 4 times.

Problem Solving

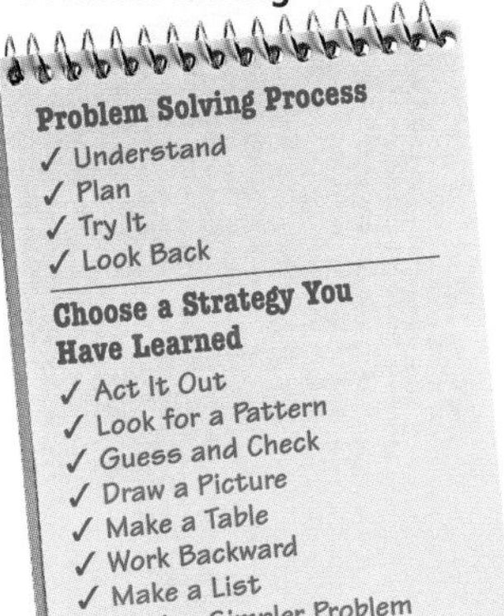

Solve the problem. Show your work.

30. Suppose you lost the combination for your bike lock. You know that the numbers are 17, 38, and 5. You just cannot remember the order. How many possible combinations can you try? 6 combinations

31. You and some friends are making puppets. Plastic eyes cost 15¢ each. You have 6 quarters, but you want to have at least $.50 left after you buy the eyes. How many eyes can you buy? 6 eyes

435

Students Acquiring English

Some students may need assistance on the Cumulative Review.

- Be prepared to read directions aloud to students.
- Focus special attention on word problems. Expect to paraphrase, diagram, or draw an explanation of the word problem.
- Review important vocabulary words that have been previously introduced.

Skills Reteaching

Chapter Objectives	Suggested materials for minilessons		
• To add up to four whole numbers (3B)	Reteach 3.5	Practice 3.5	Enrichment 3.5
• To explore the rules for division (6A)	Reteach 6.2	Practice 6.2	Enrichment 6.2
• To compare and order fractions using models (8B)	Reteach 8.3	Practice 8.3	Enrichment 8.3
• To relate decimals to fractions and mixed numbers (10B)	Reteach 10.3	Practice 10.3	Enrichment 10.3
• To multiply 2-digit numbers by 1-digit numbers (11C)	Reteach 11.5	Practice 11.5	Enrichment 11.5
• To use a variety of strategies to solve problems (12G)	Reteach 12.9	Practice 12.9	Enrichment 12.9

INVESTIGATION

Management small groups
Materials chart paper, markers, magazine pictures of baseball players

Building Background

Students should be familiar with multiplication and division facts to the number nine.

Management Strategies Cooperative Learning

Introduce

- Assign at least one student with strong math skills to each group.

Guide

- If students have difficulty, pose a simpler problem for them to solve.
- Remind students to check for agreement before writing.

Summarize

- Discuss the group process: What actions helped your group to work well? Why? What would you do differently next time?

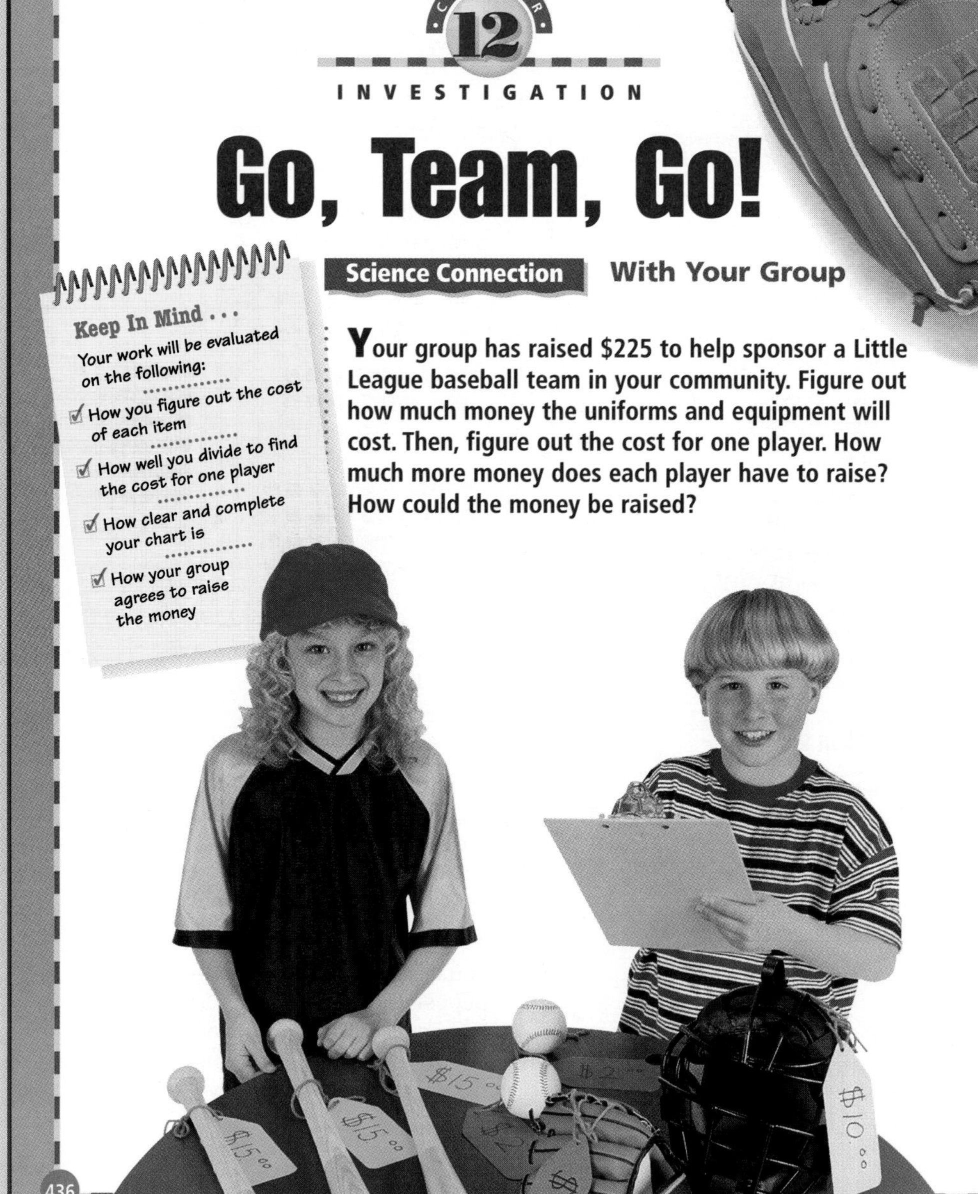

CHAPTER 12
INVESTIGATION
Go, Team, Go!
Keep In Mind . . .
Your work will be evaluated on the following:
How you figure out the cost of each item
How well you divide to find the cost for one player
How clear and complete your chart is
How your group agrees to raise the money
Science Connection
With Your Group
Your group has raised $225 to help sponsor a Little League baseball team in your community. Figure out how much money the uniforms and equipment will cost. Then, figure out the cost for one player. How much more money does each player have to raise? How could the money be raised?
$15.00
$15.00
$15.00
$20
$10.00
436

Investigation Support

Technology

Internet: Education Place
http://www.eduplace.com
Houghton Mifflin Education Place **Mathematics Center** provides teacher and student support, such as links to other Internet sites.

Math Journal: *Communicating*

One way of raising money for sports leagues is to ask local businesses to sponsor teams. In exchange for the donated money, players wear small advertisements on their uniforms that show which business supported each team. Ask students to write a letter to a local business asking for a donation. In their letter they can explain what the money will be used for, and explain their mathematical reasoning in figuring out how much to ask for. The letters can be written in their Math Journals.

Portfolio Opportunity

Make photocopies of each group's chart to place in individual portfolios.

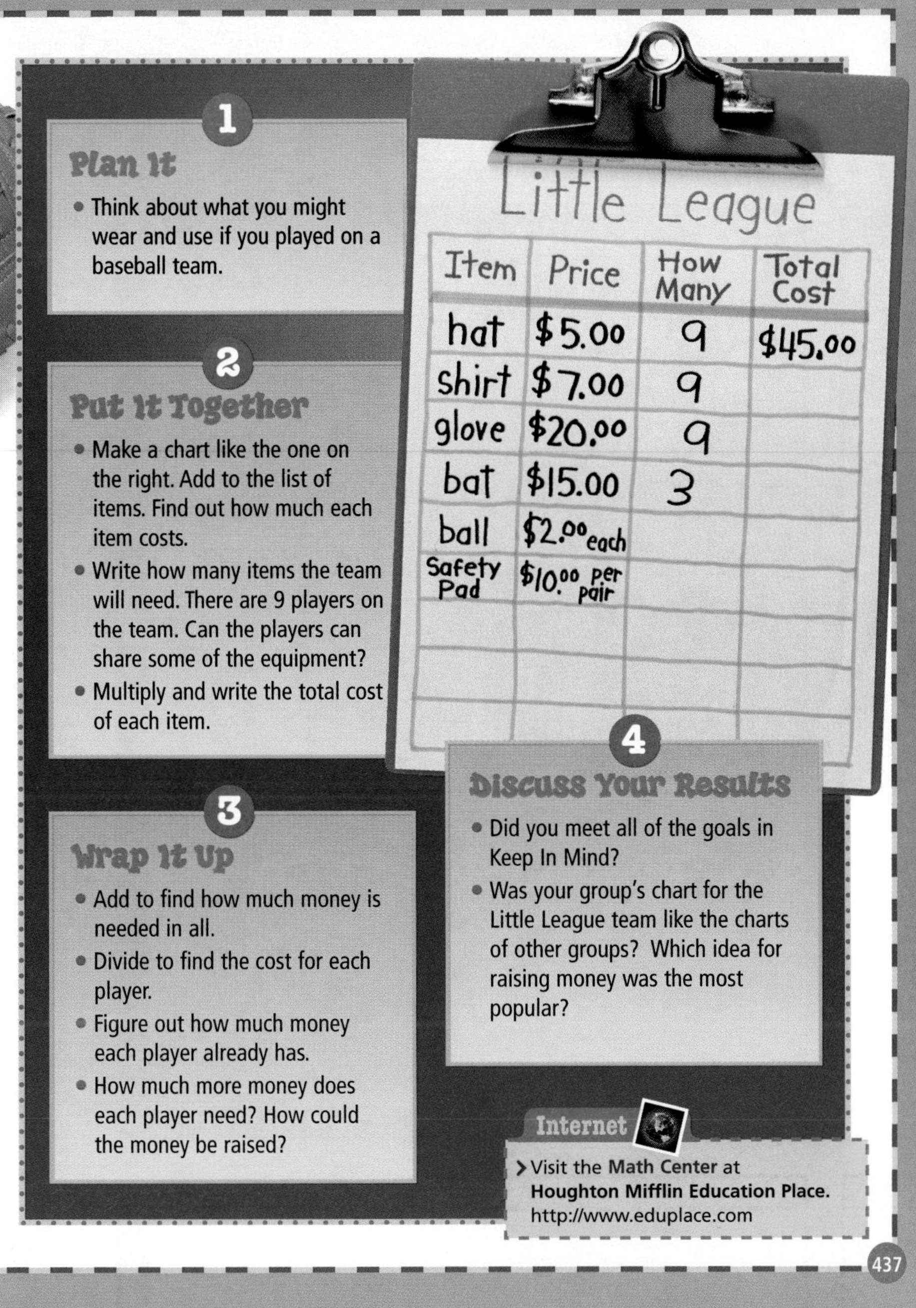

1
Plan It
• Think about what you might wear and use if you played on a baseball team.
2
Put It Together
• Make a chart like the one on the right. Add to the list of items. Find out how much each item costs.
• Write how many items the team will need. There are 9 players on the team. Can the players can share some of the equipment?
• Multiply and write the total cost of each item.
3
Wrap It Up
• Add to find how much money is needed in all.
• Divide to find the cost for each player.
• Figure out how much money each player already has.
• How much more money does each player need? How could the money be raised?
Little League
Item
Price
How Many
Total Cost
hat
$5.00
9
$45.00
shirt
$7.00
9
glove
$20.00
9
bat
$15.00
3
ball
$2.00 each
Safety Pad
$10.00 per pair
4
Discuss Your Results
• Did you meet all of the goals in Keep In Mind?
• Was your group's chart for the Little League team like the charts of other groups? Which idea for raising money was the most popular?
Internet
Visit the Math Center at Houghton Mifflin Education Place. http://www.eduplace.com
437

Problem Solving Tip

Which items do all players need, and which items will you need only one of? For example every player needs a uniform, a hat, shoes, and a glove, but each team needs only one set of catcher's equipment.

Completing the Investigation

Step 1 Brainstorm ways that groups can raise money for their teams. Car washes, bake sales, jog-a-thons, raffles, pancake breakfasts, and carnivals are just a few examples of fundraisers.

Step 2 Help students follow the steps for making accurate calculations.

Step 3 Discuss the different ways each group organized their chart.

Step 4 Suggest that students illustrate their charts with pictures of baseball players and equipment.

Extending the Investigation

Follow a local professional baseball team by cutting out box scores from the newspaper. The class can keep a chart of wins and losses, runs scored and runs given up, and hits made and hits allowed.

Assessment Scoring Rubric

These criteria align with *Keep In Mind* in the Pupil Edition on page 436.

Criteria	1 Limited response	2 Acceptable	3 Capable	4 Superior
Accuracy of calculations	Calculations are inaccurate	Some of the calculations are inaccurate	Most of the calculations are accurate	All of the calculations are accurate
Understanding of the cost of supplies	Lacks understanding of the cost of supplies	Can explain some of the cost of supplies	Understands most of the cost of the supplies	Thoroughly understands the cost of supplies
Clarity and completeness of the chart	Chart is incomplete and disorganized	Chart shows an attempt to organize the information	Chart shows most of the information clearly and completely	Chart shows all of the information clearly and completely
Contribution to the group process	Makes no effort to contribute to the group	Makes some effort to contribute to the group	Contributes to the group most of the time	Contributes fully to the group

Use this 4-level rubric to score students' responses. If you prefer a task with a 6-level rubric, use the Performance Assessment for this chapter.

More Practice

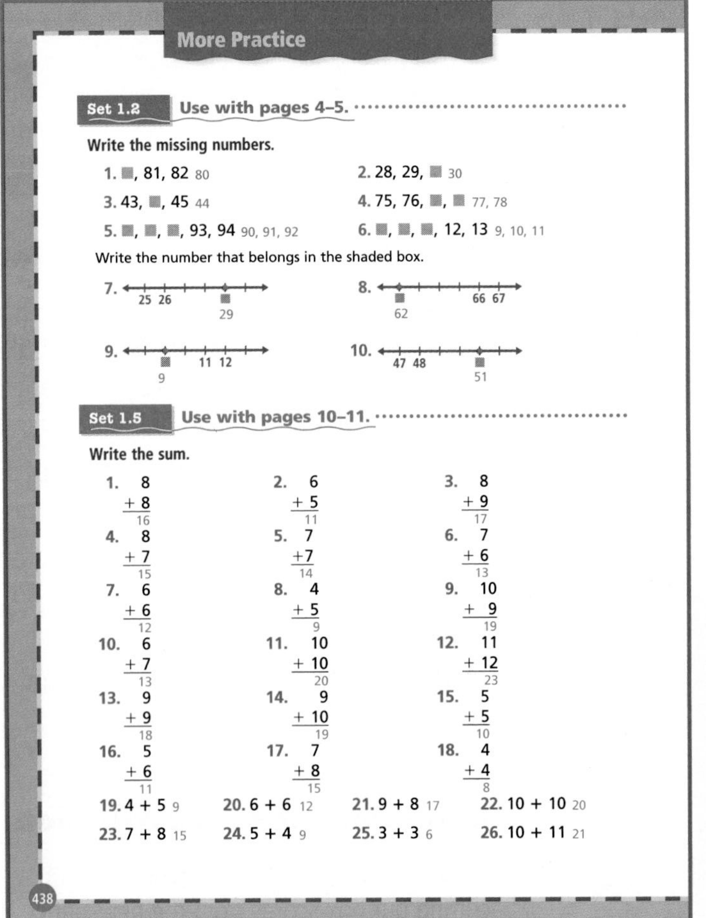

More Practice

Set 1.2 Use with pages 4–5.

Write the missing numbers.

1. ■, 81, 82 *80*
2. 28, 29, ■ *30*
3. 43, ■, 45 *44*
4. 75, 76, ■, ■ *77, 78*
5. ■, ■, ■, 93, 94 *90, 91, 92*
6. ■, ■, ■, 12, 13 *9, 10, 11*

Write the number that belongs in the shaded box.

7. 25 26 ■ *29*
8. ■ 66 67 *62*
9. ■ 11 12 *9*
10. 47 48 ■ *51*

Set 1.5 Use with pages 10–11.

Write the sum.

1. 8 + 8 *16*
2. 6 + 5 *11*
3. 8 + 9 *17*
4. 8 + 7 *15*
5. 7 + 7 *14*
6. 7 + 6 *13*
7. 6 + 6 *12*
8. 4 + 5 *9*
9. 10 + 9 *19*
10. 6 + 7 *13*
11. 10 + 10 *20*
12. 11 + 12 *23*
13. 9 + 9 *18*
14. 9 + 10 *19*
15. 5 + 5 *10*
16. 5 + 6 *11*
17. 7 + 8 *15*
18. 4 + 4 *8*
19. 4 + 5 *9*
20. 6 + 6 *12*
21. 9 + 8 *17*
22. 10 + 10 *20*
23. 7 + 8 *15*
24. 5 + 4 *9*
25. 3 + 3 *6*
26. 10 + 11 *21*

438

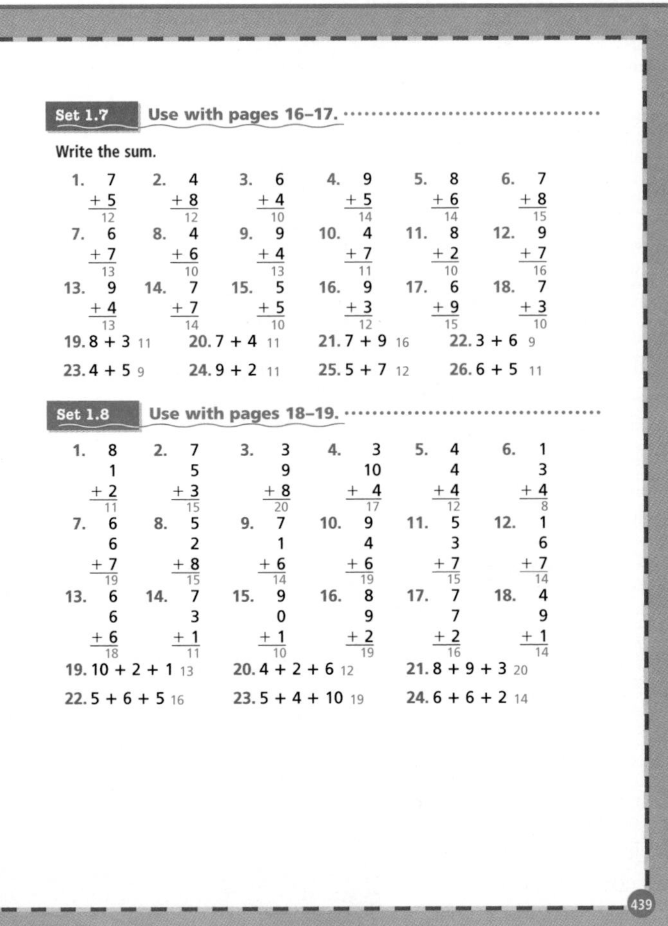

Set 1.7 Use with pages 16–17.

Write the sum.

1. 7 + 5 *12*
2. 4 + 8 *12*
3. 6 + 4 *10*
4. 9 + 5 *14*
5. 8 + 6 *14*
6. 7 + 8 *15*
7. 6 + 7 *13*
8. 4 + 6 *10*
9. 9 + 4 *13*
10. 4 + 7 *11*
11. 8 + 2 *10*
12. 9 + 7 *16*
13. 9 + 4 *13*
14. 7 + 7 *14*
15. 5 + 5 *10*
16. 9 + 3 *12*
17. 6 + 9 *15*
18. 7 + 3 *10*
19. 8 + 3 *11*
20. 7 + 4 *11*
21. 7 + 9 *16*
22. 3 + 6 *9*
23. 4 + 5 *9*
24. 9 + 2 *11*
25. 5 + 7 *12*
26. 6 + 5 *11*

Set 1.8 Use with pages 18–19.

1. 8 + 1 + 2 *11*
2. 7 + 5 + 3 *15*
3. 3 + 9 + 8 *20*
4. 3 + 10 + 4 *17*
5. 4 + 4 + 4 *12*
6. 1 + 3 + 4 *8*
7. 6 + 6 + 7 *19*
8. 5 + 2 + 8 *15*
9. 7 + 1 + 6 *14*
10. 9 + 4 + 6 *19*
11. 5 + 3 + 7 *15*
12. 1 + 6 + 7 *14*
13. 6 + 6 + 6 *18*
14. 7 + 3 + 1 *11*
15. 9 + 0 + 1 *10*
16. 8 + 9 + 2 *19*
17. 7 + 7 + 2 *16*
18. 4 + 9 + 1 *14*
19. 10 + 2 + 1 *13*
20. 4 + 2 + 6 *12*
21. 8 + 9 + 3 *20*
22. 5 + 6 + 5 *16*
23. 5 + 4 + 10 *19*
24. 6 + 6 + 2 *14*

439

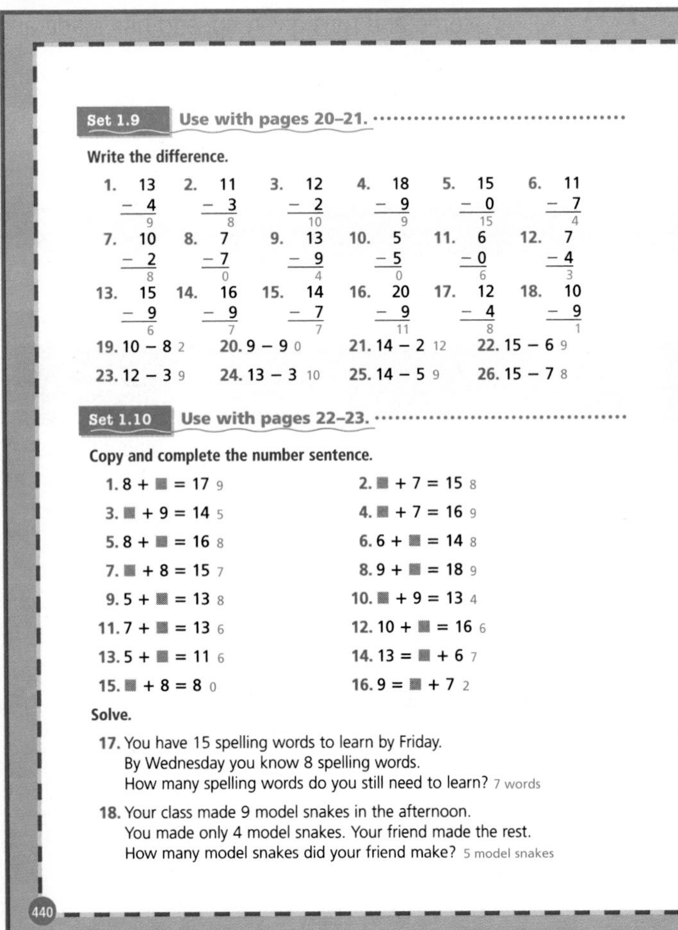

Set 1.9 Use with pages 20–21.

Write the difference.

1. 13 − 4 *9*
2. 11 − 3 *8*
3. 12 − 2 *10*
4. 18 − 9 *9*
5. 15 − 0 *15*
6. 11 − 7 *4*
7. 10 − 2 *8*
8. 7 − 7 *0*
9. 13 − 9 *4*
10. 5 − 5 *0*
11. 6 − 0 *6*
12. 7 − 4 *3*
13. 15 − 9 *6*
14. 16 − 9 *7*
15. 14 − 7 *7*
16. 20 − 9 *11*
17. 12 − 4 *8*
18. 10 − 9 *1*
19. 10 − 8 *2*
20. 9 − 9 *0*
21. 14 − 2 *12*
22. 15 − 6 *9*
23. 12 − 3 *9*
24. 13 − 3 *10*
25. 14 − 5 *9*
26. 15 − 7 *8*

Set 1.10 Use with pages 22–23.

Copy and complete the number sentence.

1. 8 + ■ = 17 *9*
2. ■ + 7 = 15 *8*
3. ■ + 9 = 14 *5*
4. ■ + 7 = 16 *9*
5. 8 + ■ = 16 *8*
6. 6 + ■ = 14 *8*
7. ■ + 8 = 15 *7*
8. 9 + ■ = 18 *9*
9. 5 + ■ = 13 *8*
10. ■ + 9 = 13 *4*
11. 7 + ■ = 13 *6*
12. 10 + ■ = 16 *6*
13. 5 + ■ = 11 *6*
14. 13 = ■ + 6 *7*
15. ■ + 8 = 8 *0*
16. 9 = ■ + 7 *2*

Solve.

17. You have 15 spelling words to learn by Friday. By Wednesday you know 8 spelling words. How many spelling words do you still need to learn? *7 words*
18. Your class made 9 model snakes in the afternoon. You made only 4 model snakes. Your friend made the rest. How many model snakes did your friend make? *5 model snakes*

440

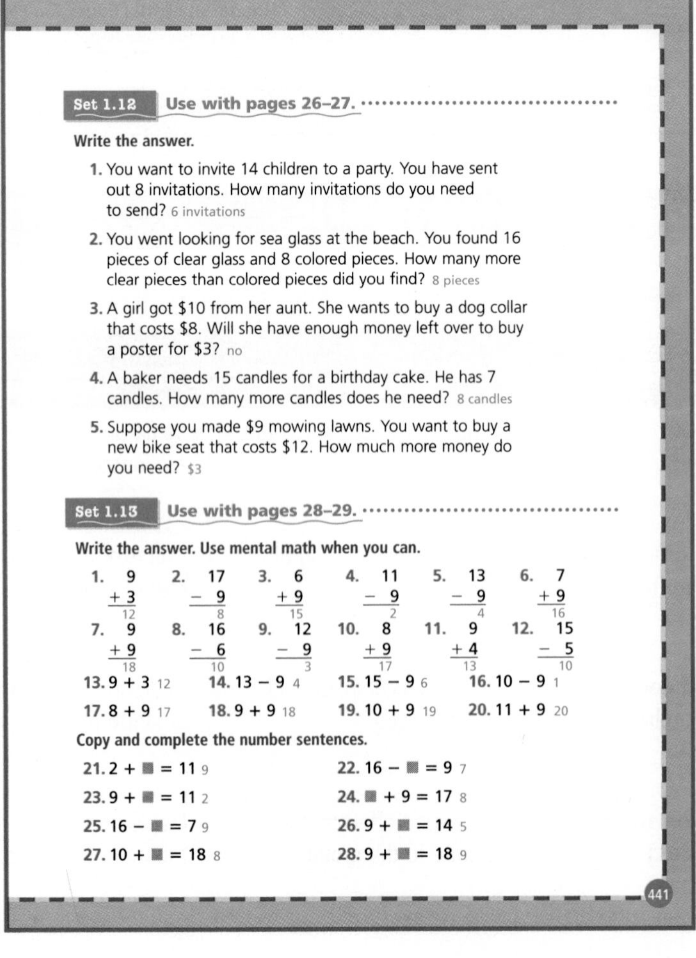

Set 1.12 Use with pages 26–27.

Write the answer.

1. You want to invite 14 children to a party. You have sent out 8 invitations. How many invitations do you need to send? *6 invitations*
2. You went looking for sea glass at the beach. You found 16 pieces of clear glass and 8 colored pieces. How many more clear pieces than colored pieces did you find? *8 pieces*
3. A girl got $10 from her aunt. She wants to buy a dog collar that costs $8. Will she have enough money left over to buy a poster for $3? *no*
4. A baker needs 15 candles for a birthday cake. He has 7 candles. How many more candles does he need? *8 candles*
5. Suppose you made $9 mowing lawns. You want to buy a new bike seat that costs $12. How much more money do you need? *$3*

Set 1.13 Use with pages 28–29.

Write the answer. Use mental math when you can.

1. 9 + 3 *12*
2. 17 − 9 *8*
3. 6 + 9 *15*
4. 11 − 9 *2*
5. 13 − 9 *4*
6. 7 + 9 *16*
7. 9 + 9 *18*
8. 16 − 6 *10*
9. 12 − 9 *3*
10. 8 + 9 *17*
11. 9 + 4 *13*
12. 15 − 5 *10*
13. 9 + 3 *12*
14. 13 − 9 *4*
15. 15 − 9 *6*
16. 10 − 9 *1*
17. 8 + 9 *17*
18. 9 + 9 *18*
19. 10 + 9 *19*
20. 11 + 9 *20*

Copy and complete the number sentences.

21. 2 + ■ = 11 *9*
22. 16 − ■ = 9 *7*
23. 9 + ■ = 11 *2*
24. ■ + 9 = 17 *8*
25. 16 − ■ = 7 *9*
26. 9 + ■ = 14 *5*
27. 10 + ■ = 18 *8*
28. 9 + ■ = 18 *9*

441

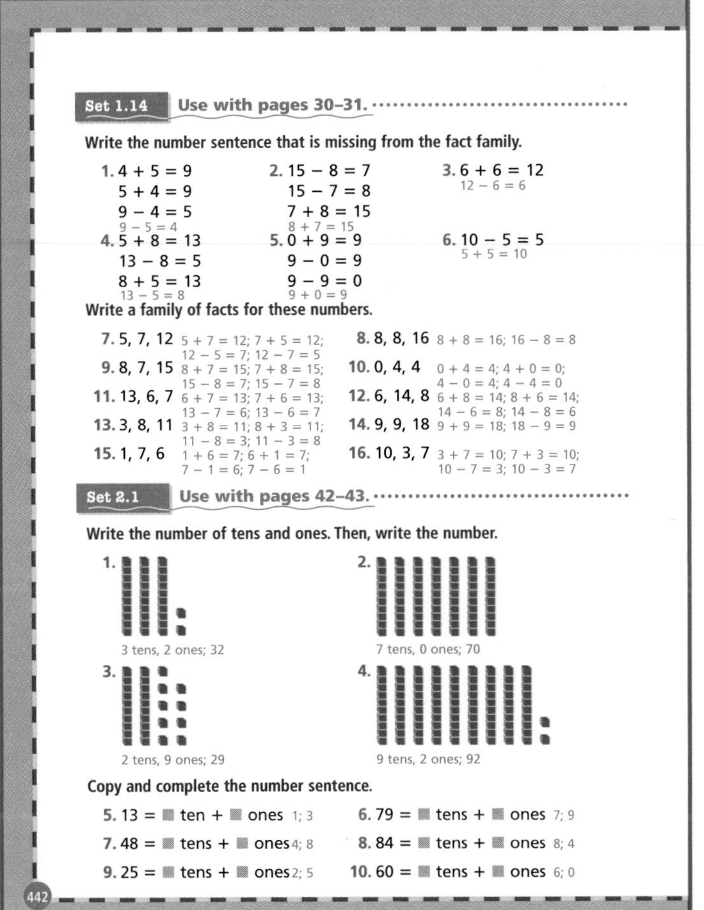

Set 1.14 Use with pages 30–31.

Write the number sentence that is missing from the fact family.

1. 4 + 5 = 9; 5 + 4 = 9; 9 − 4 = 5 — 9 − 5 = 4
2. 15 − 8 = 7; 15 − 7 = 8; 7 + 8 = 15 — 8 + 7 = 15
3. 6 + 6 = 12 — 12 − 6 = 6
4. 5 + 8 = 13; 13 − 8 = 5; 8 + 5 = 13 — 13 − 5 = 8
5. 0 + 9 = 9; 9 − 0 = 9; 9 − 9 = 0 — 9 + 0 = 9
6. 10 − 5 = 5 — 5 + 5 = 10

Write a family of facts for these numbers.

7. 5, 7, 12 — 5 + 7 = 12; 7 + 5 = 12; 12 − 5 = 7; 12 − 7 = 5
8. 8, 8, 16 — 8 + 8 = 16; 16 − 8 = 8
9. 8, 7, 15 — 8 + 7 = 15; 7 + 8 = 15; 15 − 8 = 7; 15 − 7 = 8
10. 0, 4, 4 — 0 + 4 = 4; 4 + 0 = 0; 4 − 0 = 4; 4 − 4 = 0
11. 13, 6, 7 — 6 + 7 = 13; 7 + 6 = 13; 13 − 7 = 6; 13 − 6 = 7
12. 6, 14, 8 — 6 + 8 = 14; 8 + 6 = 14; 14 − 6 = 8; 14 − 8 = 6
13. 3, 8, 11 — 3 + 8 = 11; 8 + 3 = 11; 11 − 8 = 3; 11 − 3 = 8
14. 9, 9, 18 — 9 + 9 = 18; 18 − 9 = 9
15. 1, 7, 6 — 1 + 6 = 7; 6 + 1 = 7; 7 − 1 = 6; 7 − 6 = 1
16. 10, 3, 7 — 3 + 7 = 10; 7 + 3 = 10; 10 − 7 = 3; 10 − 3 = 7

Set 2.1 Use with pages 42–43.

Write the number of tens and ones. Then, write the number.

1. 3 tens, 2 ones; 32
2. 7 tens, 0 ones; 70
3. 2 tens, 9 ones; 29
4. 9 tens, 2 ones; 92

Copy and complete the number sentence.

5. 13 = ■ ten + ■ ones 1; 3
6. 79 = ■ tens + ■ ones 7; 9
7. 48 = ■ tens + ■ ones 4; 8
8. 84 = ■ tens + ■ ones 8; 4
9. 25 = ■ tens + ■ ones 2; 5
10. 60 = ■ tens + ■ ones 6; 0

442

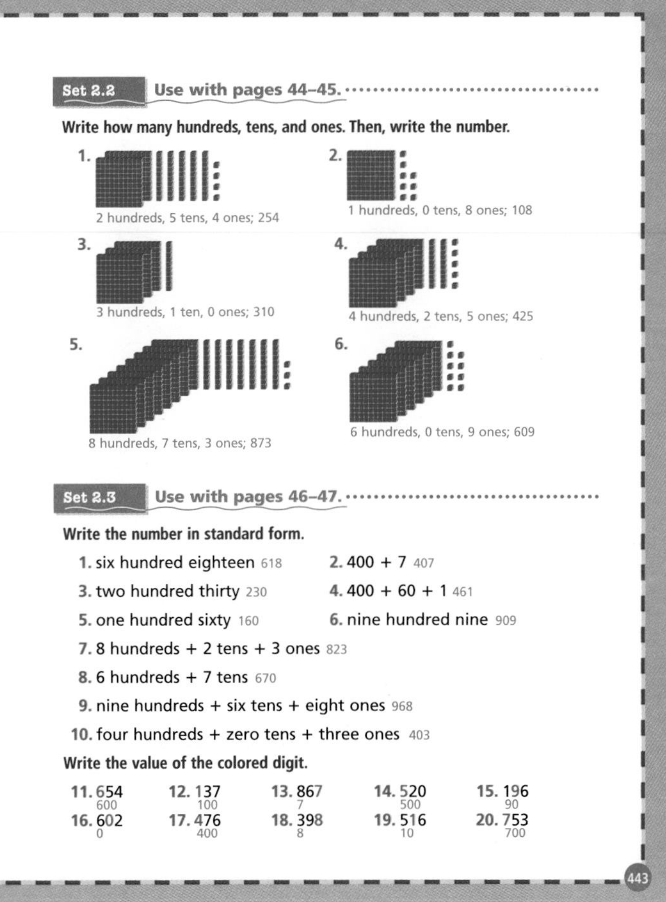

Set 2.2 Use with pages 44–45.

Write how many hundreds, tens, and ones. Then, write the number.

1. 2 hundreds, 5 tens, 4 ones; 254
2. 1 hundreds, 0 tens, 8 ones; 108
3. 3 hundreds, 1 ten, 0 ones; 310
4. 4 hundreds, 2 tens, 5 ones; 425
5. 8 hundreds, 7 tens, 3 ones; 873
6. 6 hundreds, 0 tens, 9 ones; 609

Set 2.3 Use with pages 46–47.

Write the number in standard form.

1. six hundred eighteen 618
2. 400 + 7 407
3. two hundred thirty 230
4. 400 + 60 + 1 461
5. one hundred sixty 160
6. nine hundred nine 909
7. 8 hundreds + 2 tens + 3 ones 823
8. 6 hundreds + 7 tens 670
9. nine hundreds + six tens + eight ones 968
10. four hundreds + zero tens + three ones 403

Write the value of the colored digit.

11. 654 600
12. 137 100
13. 867 7
14. 520 500
15. 196 90
16. 602 0
17. 476 400
18. 398 8
19. 516 10
20. 753 700

443

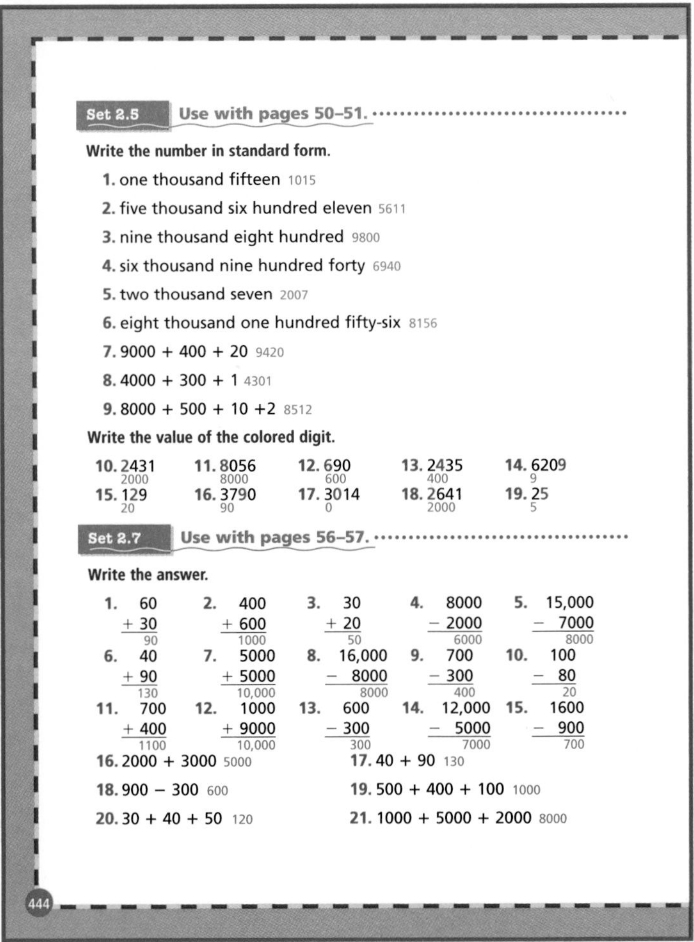

Set 2.5 Use with pages 50–51.

Write the number in standard form.

1. one thousand fifteen 1015
2. five thousand six hundred eleven 5611
3. nine thousand eight hundred 9800
4. six thousand nine hundred forty 6940
5. two thousand seven 2007
6. eight thousand one hundred fifty-six 8156
7. 9000 + 400 + 20 9420
8. 4000 + 300 + 1 4301
9. 8000 + 500 + 10 +2 8512

Write the value of the colored digit.

10. 2431 2000
11. 8056 8000
12. 690 600
13. 2435 400
14. 6209 9
15. 129 20
16. 3790 90
17. 3014 0
18. 2641 2000
19. 25 5

Set 2.7 Use with pages 56–57.

Write the answer.

1. 60 + 30 = 90
2. 400 + 600 = 1000
3. 30 + 20 = 50
4. 8000 − 2000 = 6000
5. 15,000 − 7000 = 8000
6. 40 + 90 = 130
7. 5000 + 5000 = 10,000
8. 16,000 − 8000 = 8000
9. 700 − 300 = 400
10. 100 − 80 = 20
11. 700 + 400 = 1100
12. 1000 + 9000 = 10,000
13. 600 − 300 = 300
14. 12,000 − 5000 = 7000
15. 1600 − 900 = 700
16. 2000 + 3000 5000
17. 40 + 90 130
18. 900 − 300 600
19. 500 + 400 + 100 1000
20. 30 + 40 + 50 120
21. 1000 + 5000 + 2000 8000

444

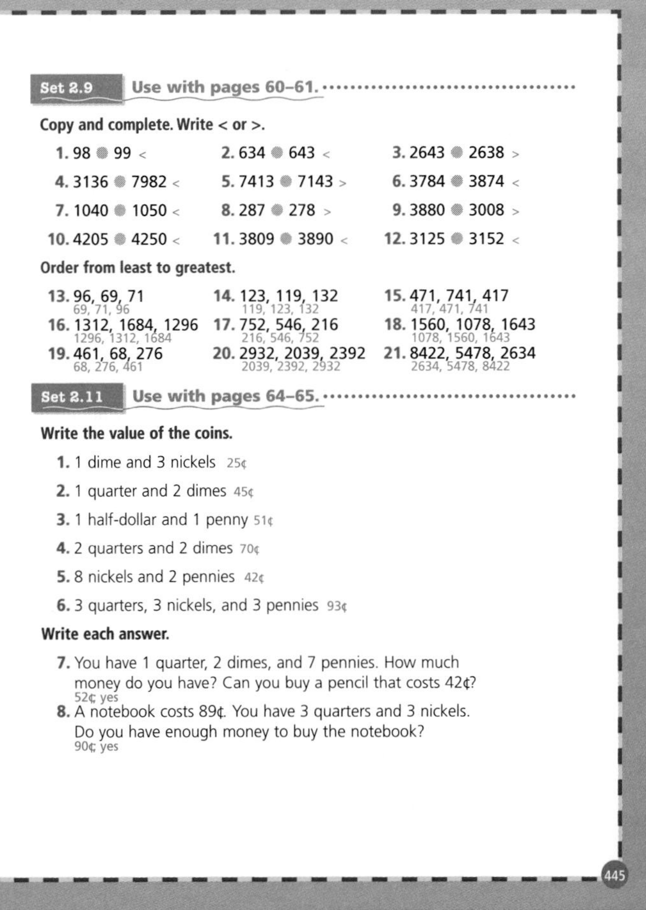

Set 2.9 Use with pages 60–61.

Copy and complete. Write < or >.

1. 98 ● 99 <
2. 634 ● 643 <
3. 2643 ● 2638 >
4. 3136 ● 7982 <
5. 7413 ● 7143 >
6. 3784 ● 3874 <
7. 1040 ● 1050 <
8. 287 ● 278 >
9. 3880 ● 3008 >
10. 4205 ● 4250 <
11. 3809 ● 3890 <
12. 3125 ● 3152 <

Order from least to greatest.

13. 96, 69, 71 — 69, 71, 96
14. 123, 119, 132 — 119, 123, 132
15. 471, 741, 417 — 417, 471, 741
16. 1312, 1684, 1296 — 1296, 1312, 1684
17. 752, 546, 216 — 216, 546, 752
18. 1560, 1078, 1643 — 1078, 1560, 1643
19. 461, 68, 276 — 68, 276, 461
20. 2932, 2039, 2392 — 2039, 2392, 2932
21. 8422, 5478, 2634 — 2634, 5478, 8422

Set 2.11 Use with pages 64–65.

Write the value of the coins.

1. 1 dime and 3 nickels 25¢
2. 1 quarter and 2 dimes 45¢
3. 1 half-dollar and 1 penny 51¢
4. 2 quarters and 2 dimes 70¢
5. 8 nickels and 2 pennies 42¢
6. 3 quarters, 3 nickels, and 3 pennies 93¢

Write each answer.

7. You have 1 quarter, 2 dimes, and 7 pennies. How much money do you have? Can you buy a pencil that costs 42¢? 52¢ yes
8. A notebook costs 89¢. You have 3 quarters and 3 nickels. Do you have enough money to buy the notebook? 90¢ yes

445

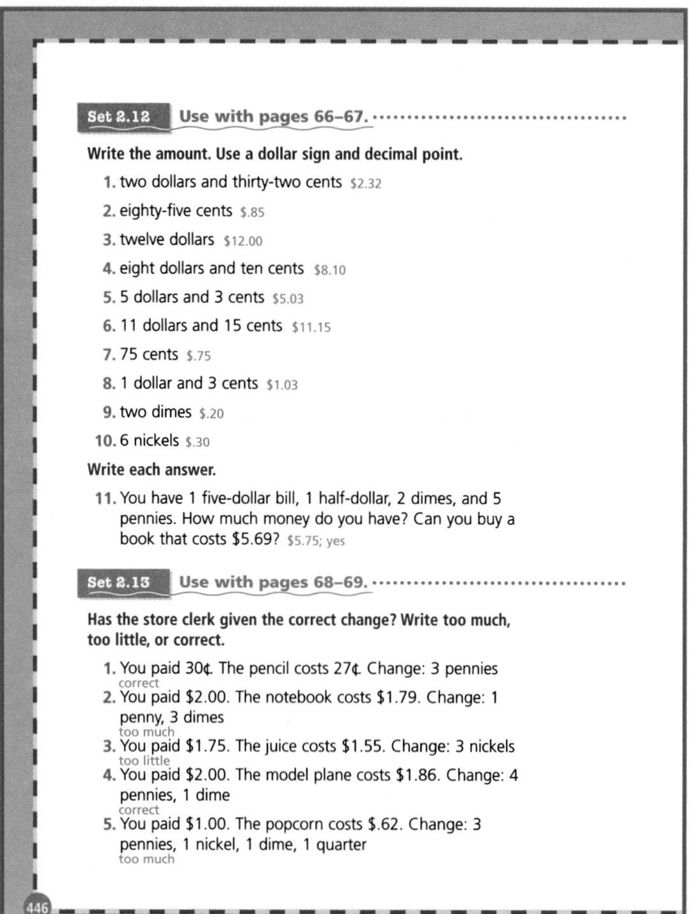

Set 2.12 Use with pages 66–67.

Write the amount. Use a dollar sign and decimal point.

1. two dollars and thirty-two cents $2.32
2. eighty-five cents $.85
3. twelve dollars $12.00
4. eight dollars and ten cents $8.10
5. 5 dollars and 3 cents $5.03
6. 11 dollars and 15 cents $11.15
7. 75 cents $.75
8. 1 dollar and 3 cents $1.03
9. two dimes $.20
10. 6 nickels $.30

Write each answer.

11. You have 1 five-dollar bill, 1 half-dollar, 2 dimes, and 5 pennies. How much money do you have? Can you buy a book that costs $5.69? $5.75; yes

Set 2.13 Use with pages 68–69.

Has the store clerk given the correct change? Write too much, too little, or correct.

1. You paid 30¢. The pencil costs 27¢. Change: 3 pennies correct
2. You paid $2.00. The notebook costs $1.79. Change: 1 penny, 3 dimes too much
3. You paid $1.75. The juice costs $1.55. Change: 3 nickels too little
4. You paid $2.00. The model plane costs $1.86. Change: 4 pennies, 1 dime correct
5. You paid $1.00. The popcorn costs $.62. Change: 3 pennies, 1 nickel, 1 dime, 1 quarter too much

446

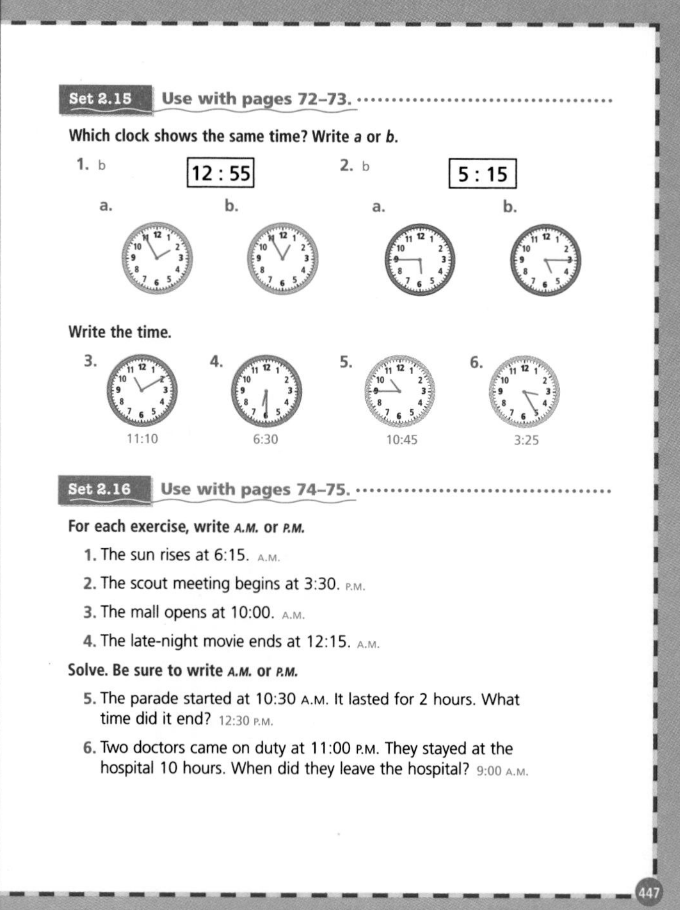

Set 2.15 Use with pages 72–73.

Which clock shows the same time? Write *a* or *b*.

1. b 12 : 55 a. b.
2. b 5 : 15 a. b.

Write the time.

3. 11:10
4. 6:30
5. 10:45
6. 3:25

Set 2.16 Use with pages 74–75.

For each exercise, write A.M. or P.M.

1. The sun rises at 6:15. A.M.
2. The scout meeting begins at 3:30. P.M.
3. The mall opens at 10:00. A.M.
4. The late-night movie ends at 12:15. A.M.

Solve. Be sure to write A.M. or P.M.

5. The parade started at 10:30 A.M. It lasted for 2 hours. What time did it end? 12:30 P.M.
6. Two doctors came on duty at 11:00 P.M. They stayed at the hospital 10 hours. When did they leave the hospital? 9:00 A.M.

447

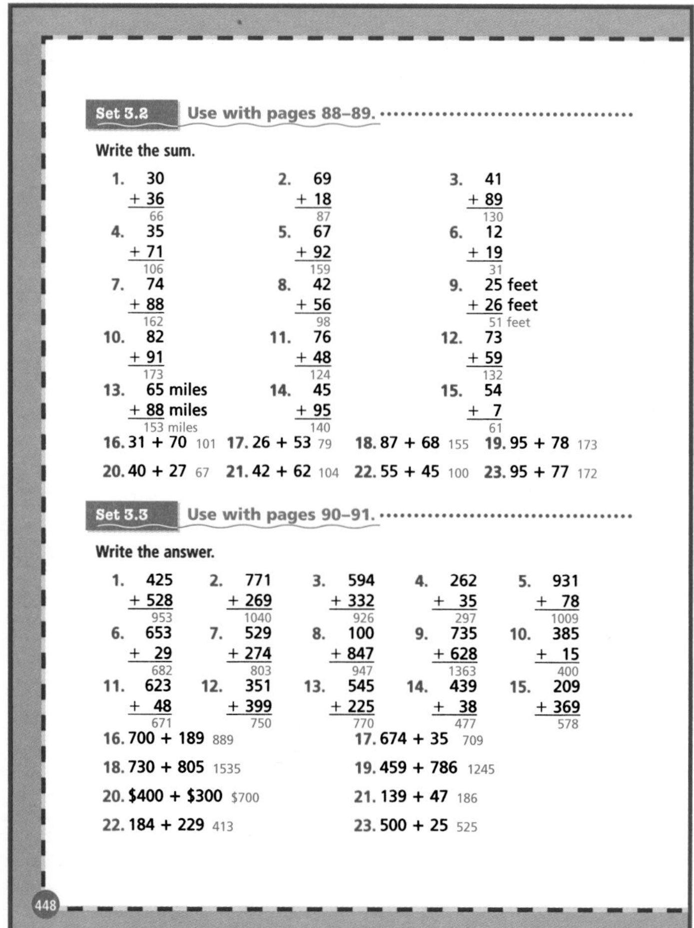

Set 3.2 Use with pages 88–89.

Write the sum.

1. 30 + 36 = 66
2. 69 + 18 = 87
3. 41 + 89 = 130
4. 35 + 71 = 106
5. 67 + 92 = 159
6. 12 + 19 = 31
7. 74 + 88 = 162
8. 42 + 56 = 98
9. 25 feet + 26 feet = 51 feet
10. 82 + 91 = 173
11. 76 + 48 = 124
12. 73 + 59 = 132
13. 65 miles + 88 miles = 153 miles
14. 45 + 95 = 140
15. 54 + 7 = 61
16. 31 + 70 101
17. 26 + 53 79
18. 87 + 68 155
19. 95 + 78 173
20. 40 + 27 67
21. 42 + 62 104
22. 55 + 45 100
23. 95 + 77 172

Set 3.3 Use with pages 90–91.

Write the answer.

1. 425 + 528 = 953
2. 771 + 269 = 1040
3. 594 + 332 = 926
4. 262 + 35 = 297
5. 931 + 78 = 1009
6. 653 + 29 = 682
7. 529 + 274 = 803
8. 100 + 847 = 947
9. 735 + 628 = 1363
10. 385 + 15 = 400
11. 623 + 48 = 671
12. 351 + 399 = 750
13. 545 + 225 = 770
14. 439 + 38 = 477
15. 209 + 369 = 578
16. 700 + 189 889
17. 674 + 35 709
18. 730 + 805 1535
19. 459 + 786 1245
20. $400 + $300 $700
21. 139 + 47 186
22. 184 + 229 413
23. 500 + 25 525

448

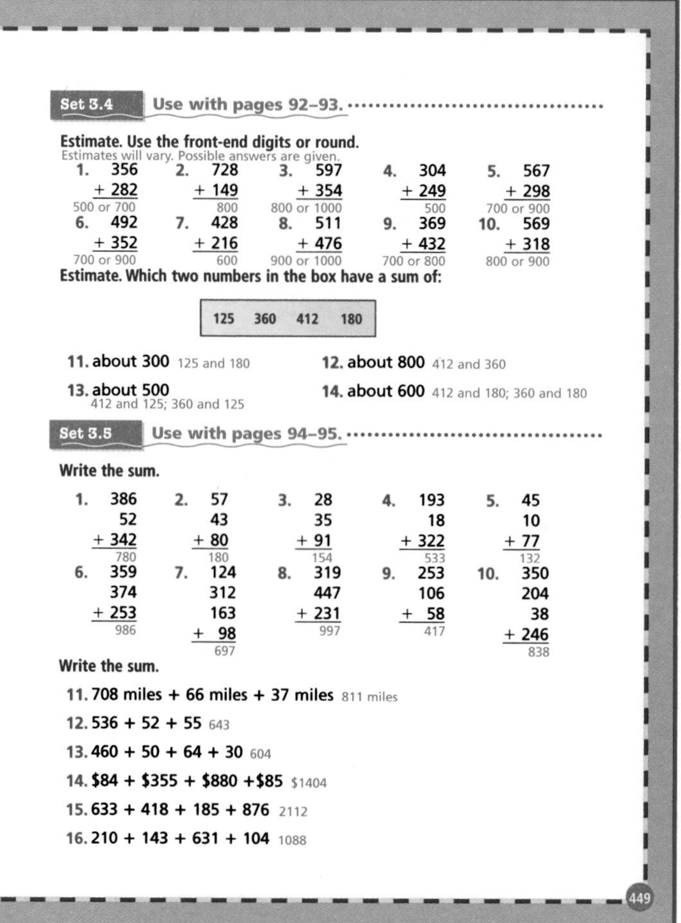

Set 3.4 Use with pages 92–93.

Estimate. Use the front-end digits or round.
Estimates will vary. Possible answers are given.

1. 356 + 282 500 or 700
2. 728 + 149 800
3. 597 + 354 800 or 1000
4. 304 + 249 500
5. 567 + 298 700 or 900
6. 492 + 352 700 or 900
7. 428 + 216 600
8. 511 + 476 900 or 1000
9. 369 + 432 700 or 800
10. 569 + 318 800 or 900

Estimate. Which two numbers in the box have a sum of:

125 360 412 180

11. about 300 125 and 180
12. about 800 412 and 360
13. about 500 412 and 125; 360 and 125
14. about 600 412 and 180; 360 and 180

Set 3.5 Use with pages 94–95.

Write the sum.

1. 386 + 52 + 342 = 780
2. 57 + 43 + 80 = 180
3. 28 + 35 + 91 = 154
4. 193 + 18 + 322 = 533
5. 45 + 10 + 77 = 132
6. 359 + 374 + 253 = 986
7. 124 + 312 + 163 + 98 = 697
8. 319 + 447 + 231 = 997
9. 253 + 106 + 58 = 417
10. 350 + 204 + 38 + 246 = 838

Write the sum.

11. 708 miles + 66 miles + 37 miles 811 miles
12. 536 + 52 + 55 643
13. 460 + 50 + 64 + 30 604
14. $84 + $355 + $880 + $85 $1404
15. 633 + 418 + 185 + 876 2112
16. 210 + 143 + 631 + 104 1088

449

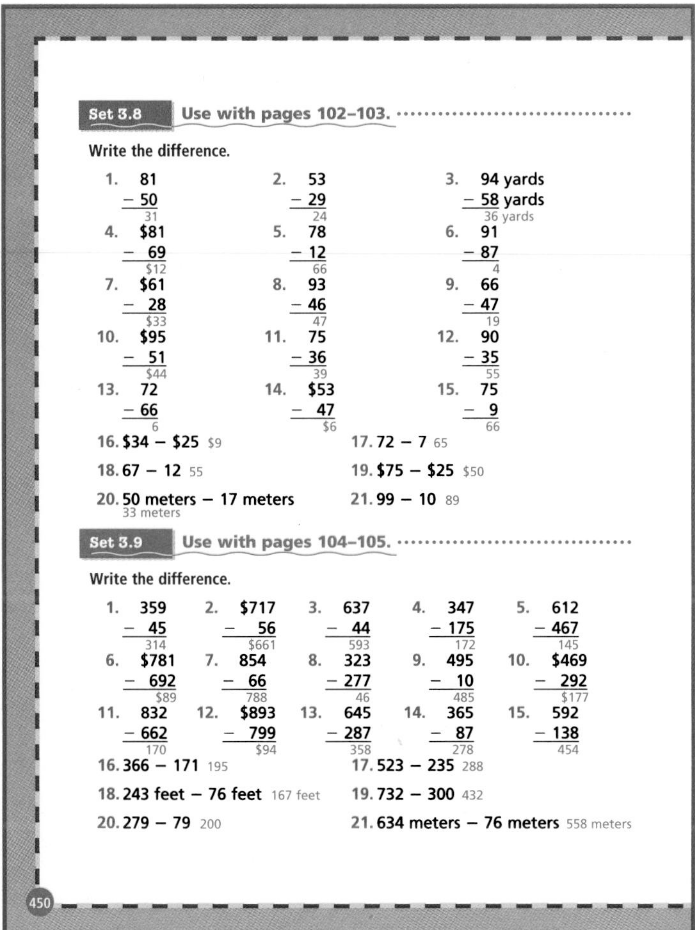

Set 3.8 Use with pages 102–103.

Write the difference.

1. 81 − 50 31
2. 53 − 29 24
3. 94 yards − 58 yards 36 yards
4. $81 − 69 $12
5. 78 − 12 66
6. 91 − 87 4
7. $61 − 28 $33
8. 93 − 46 47
9. 66 − 47 19
10. $95 − 51 $44
11. 75 − 36 39
12. 90 − 35 55
13. 72 − 66 6
14. $53 − 47 $6
15. 75 − 9 66
16. $34 − $25 $9
17. 72 − 7 65
18. 67 − 12 55
19. $75 − $25 $50
20. 50 meters − 17 meters 33 meters
21. 99 − 10 89

Set 3.9 Use with pages 104–105.

Write the difference.

1. 359 − 45 314
2. $717 − 56 $661
3. 637 − 44 593
4. 347 − 175 172
5. 612 − 467 145
6. $781 − 692 $89
7. 854 − 66 788
8. 323 − 277 46
9. 495 − 10 485
10. $469 − 292 $177
11. 832 − 662 170
12. $893 − 799 $94
13. 645 − 287 358
14. 365 − 87 278
15. 592 − 138 454
16. 366 − 171 195
17. 523 − 235 288
18. 243 feet − 76 feet 167 feet
19. 732 − 300 432
20. 279 − 79 200
21. 634 meters − 76 meters 558 meters

450

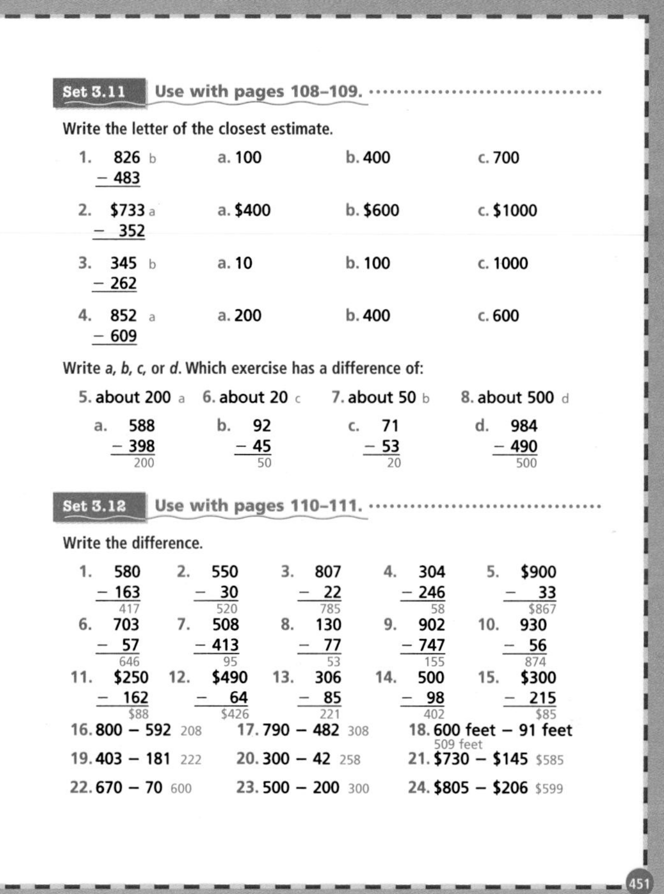

Set 3.11 Use with pages 108–109.

Write the letter of the closest estimate.

1. 826 − 483 b — a. 100 b. 400 c. 700
2. $733 − 352 a — a. $400 b. $600 c. $1000
3. 345 − 262 b — a. 10 b. 100 c. 1000
4. 852 − 609 a — a. 200 b. 400 c. 600

Write *a, b, c,* or *d*. Which exercise has a difference of:

5. about 200 a
6. about 20 c
7. about 50 b
8. about 500 d

a. 588 − 398 200
b. 92 − 45 50
c. 71 − 53 20
d. 984 − 490 500

Set 3.12 Use with pages 110–111.

Write the difference.

1. 580 − 163 417
2. 550 − 30 520
3. 807 − 22 785
4. 304 − 246 58
5. $900 − 33 $867
6. 703 − 57 646
7. 508 − 413 95
8. 130 − 77 53
9. 902 − 747 155
10. 930 − 56 874
11. $250 − 162 $88
12. $490 − 64 $426
13. 306 − 85 221
14. 500 − 98 402
15. $300 − 215 $85
16. 800 − 592 208
17. 790 − 482 308
18. 600 feet − 91 feet 509 feet
19. 403 − 181 222
20. 300 − 42 258
21. $730 − $145 $585
22. 670 − 70 600
23. 500 − 200 300
24. $805 − $206 $599

451

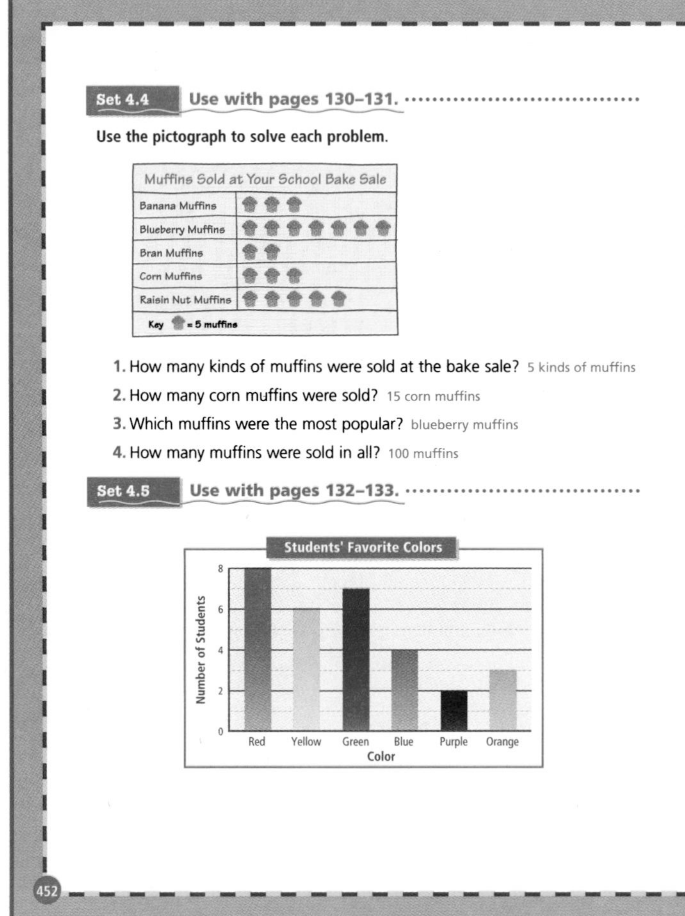

Set 4.4 Use with pages 130–131.

Use the pictograph to solve each problem.

Muffins Sold at Your School Bake Sale	
Banana Muffins	3 muffin symbols
Blueberry Muffins	7 muffin symbols
Bran Muffins	2 muffin symbols
Corn Muffins	3 muffin symbols
Raisin Nut Muffins	5 muffin symbols

Key: one muffin symbol = 5 muffins

1. How many kinds of muffins were sold at the bake sale? 5 kinds of muffins
2. How many corn muffins were sold? 15 corn muffins
3. Which muffins were the most popular? blueberry muffins
4. How many muffins were sold in all? 100 muffins

Set 4.5 Use with pages 132–133.

452

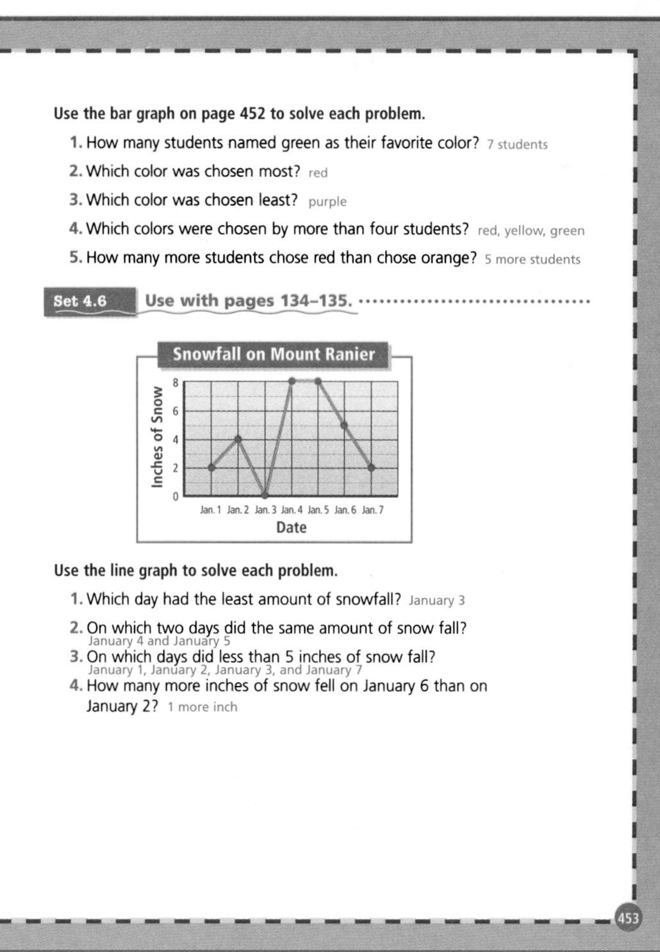

Use the bar graph on page 452 to solve each problem.

1. How many students named green as their favorite color? 7 students
2. Which color was chosen most? red
3. Which color was chosen least? purple
4. Which colors were chosen by more than four students? red, yellow, green
5. How many more students chose red than chose orange? 5 more students

Set 4.6 Use with pages 134–135.

Use the line graph to solve each problem.

1. Which day had the least amount of snowfall? January 3
2. On which two days did the same amount of snow fall? January 4 and January 5
3. On which days did less than 5 inches of snow fall? January 1, January 2, January 3, and January 7
4. How many more inches of snow fell on January 6 than on January 2? 1 more inch

453

More Practice

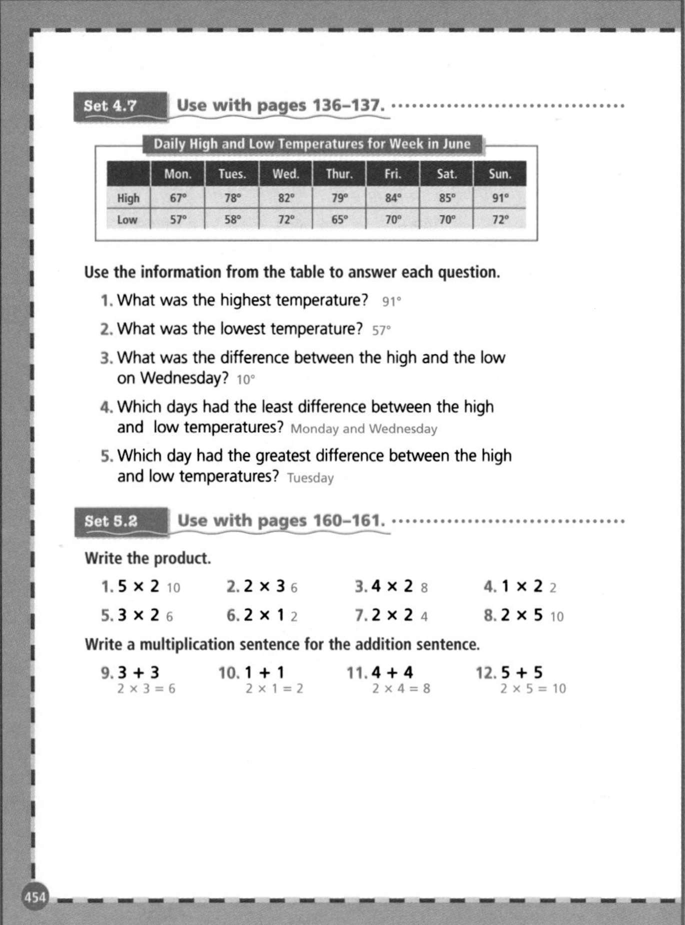

Set 4.7 Use with pages 136–137.

Daily High and Low Temperatures for Week in June							
	Mon.	Tues.	Wed.	Thur.	Fri.	Sat.	Sun.
High	67°	78°	82°	79°	84°	85°	91°
Low	57°	58°	72°	65°	70°	70°	72°

Use the information from the table to answer each question.

1. What was the highest temperature? 91°
2. What was the lowest temperature? 57°
3. What was the difference between the high and the low on Wednesday? 10°
4. Which days had the least difference between the high and low temperatures? Monday and Wednesday
5. Which day had the greatest difference between the high and low temperatures? Tuesday

Set 5.2 Use with pages 160–161.

Write the product.

1. 5 × 2 10 2. 2 × 3 6 3. 4 × 2 8 4. 1 × 2 2
5. 3 × 2 6 6. 2 × 1 2 7. 2 × 2 4 8. 2 × 5 10

Write a multiplication sentence for the addition sentence.

9. 3 + 3 2 × 3 = 6 10. 1 + 1 2 × 1 = 2 11. 4 + 4 2 × 4 = 8 12. 5 + 5 2 × 5 = 10

454

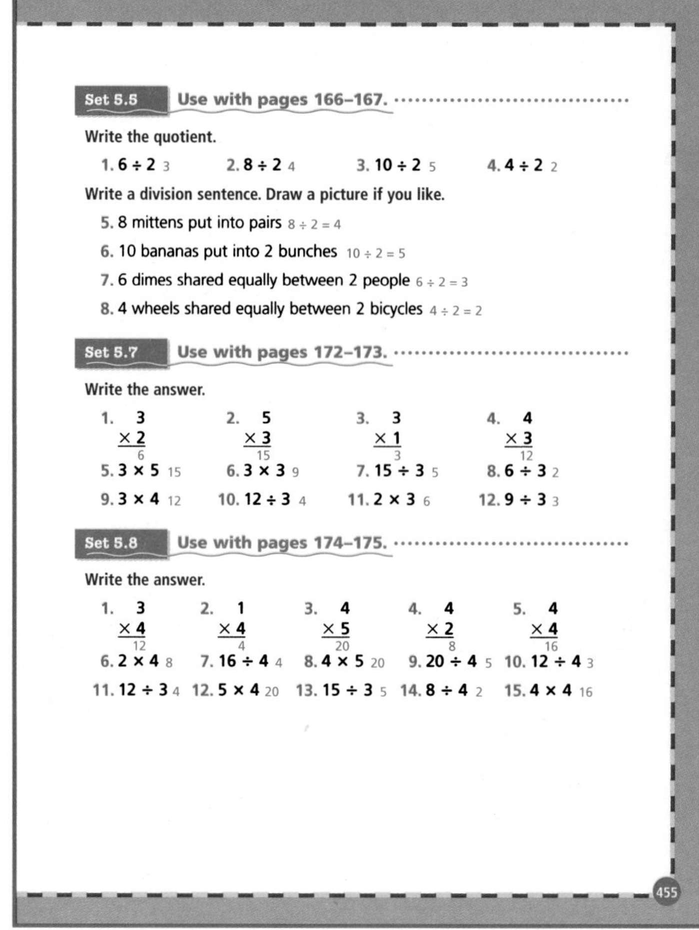

Set 5.5 Use with pages 166–167.

Write the quotient.

1. 6 ÷ 2 3 2. 8 ÷ 2 4 3. 10 ÷ 2 5 4. 4 ÷ 2 2

Write a division sentence. Draw a picture if you like.

5. 8 mittens put into pairs 8 ÷ 2 = 4
6. 10 bananas put into 2 bunches 10 ÷ 2 = 5
7. 6 dimes shared equally between 2 people 6 ÷ 2 = 3
8. 4 wheels shared equally between 2 bicycles 4 ÷ 2 = 2

Set 5.7 Use with pages 172–173.

Write the answer.

1. 3 × 2 6 2. 5 × 3 15 3. 3 × 1 3 4. 4 × 3 12
5. 3 × 5 15 6. 3 × 3 9 7. 15 ÷ 3 5 8. 6 ÷ 3 2
9. 3 × 4 12 10. 12 ÷ 3 4 11. 2 × 3 6 12. 9 ÷ 3 3

Set 5.8 Use with pages 174–175.

Write the answer.

1. 3 × 4 12 2. 1 × 4 4 3. 4 × 5 20 4. 4 × 2 8 5. 4 × 4 16
6. 2 × 4 8 7. 16 ÷ 4 4 8. 4 × 5 20 9. 20 ÷ 4 5 10. 12 ÷ 4 3
11. 12 ÷ 3 4 12. 5 × 4 20 13. 15 ÷ 3 5 14. 8 ÷ 4 2 15. 4 × 4 16

455

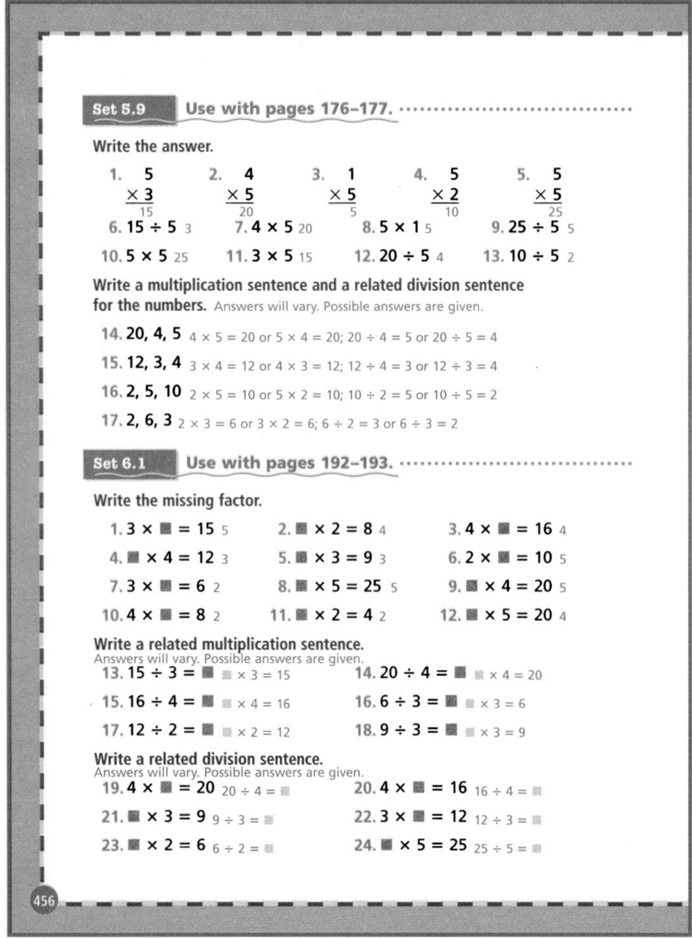

Set 5.9 Use with pages 176–177.

Write the answer.

1. 5 × 3 15 2. 4 × 5 20 3. 1 × 5 5 4. 5 × 2 10 5. 5 × 5 25
6. 15 ÷ 5 3 7. 4 × 5 20 8. 5 × 1 5 9. 25 ÷ 5 5
10. 5 × 5 25 11. 3 × 5 15 12. 20 ÷ 5 4 13. 10 ÷ 5 2

Write a multiplication sentence and a related division sentence for the numbers. Answers will vary. Possible answers are given.

14. 20, 4, 5 4 × 5 = 20 or 5 × 4 = 20; 20 ÷ 4 = 5 or 20 ÷ 5 = 4
15. 12, 3, 4 3 × 4 = 12 or 4 × 3 = 12; 12 ÷ 4 = 3 or 12 ÷ 3 = 4
16. 2, 5, 10 2 × 5 = 10 or 5 × 2 = 10; 10 ÷ 2 = 5 or 10 ÷ 5 = 2
17. 2, 6, 3 2 × 3 = 6 or 3 × 2 = 6; 6 ÷ 2 = 3 or 6 ÷ 3 = 2

Set 6.1 Use with pages 192–193.

Write the missing factor.

1. 3 × ■ = 15 5 2. ■ × 2 = 8 4 3. 4 × ■ = 16 4
4. ■ × 4 = 12 3 5. ■ × 3 = 9 3 6. 2 × ■ = 10 5
7. 3 × ■ = 6 2 8. ■ × 5 = 25 5 9. ■ × 4 = 20 5
10. 4 × ■ = 8 2 11. ■ × 2 = 4 2 12. ■ × 5 = 20 4

Write a related multiplication sentence.
Answers will vary. Possible answers are given.

13. 15 ÷ 3 = ■ ■ × 3 = 15 14. 20 ÷ 4 = ■ ■ × 4 = 20
15. 16 ÷ 4 = ■ ■ × 4 = 16 16. 6 ÷ 3 = ■ ■ × 3 = 6
17. 12 ÷ 2 = ■ ■ × 2 = 12 18. 9 ÷ 3 = ■ ■ × 3 = 9

Write a related division sentence.
Answers will vary. Possible answers are given.

19. 4 × ■ = 20 20 ÷ 4 = ■ 20. 4 × ■ = 16 16 ÷ 4 = ■
21. ■ × 3 = 9 9 ÷ 3 = ■ 22. 3 × ■ = 12 12 ÷ 3 = ■
23. ■ × 2 = 6 6 ÷ 2 = ■ 24. ■ × 5 = 25 25 ÷ 5 = ■

456

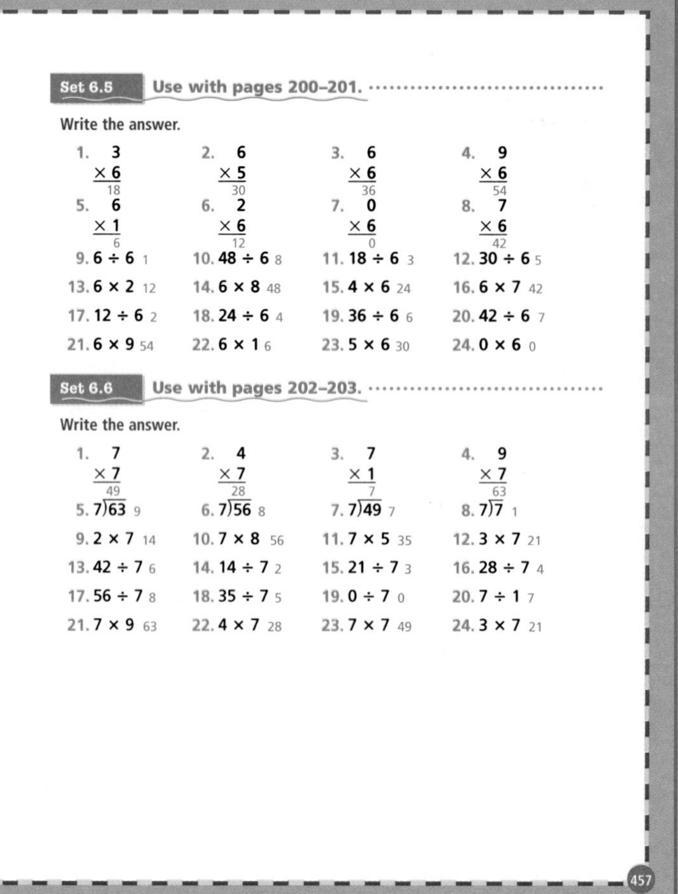

Set 6.5 Use with pages 200–201.

Write the answer.

1. 3 × 6 18 2. 6 × 5 30 3. 6 × 6 36 4. 9 × 6 54
5. 6 × 1 6 6. 2 × 6 12 7. 0 × 6 0 8. 7 × 6 42
9. 6 ÷ 6 1 10. 48 ÷ 6 8 11. 18 ÷ 6 3 12. 30 ÷ 6 5
13. 6 × 2 12 14. 6 × 8 48 15. 4 × 6 24 16. 6 × 7 42
17. 12 ÷ 6 2 18. 24 ÷ 6 4 19. 36 ÷ 6 6 20. 42 ÷ 6 7
21. 6 × 9 54 22. 6 × 1 6 23. 5 × 6 30 24. 0 × 6 0

Set 6.6 Use with pages 202–203.

Write the answer.

1. 7 × 7 49 2. 4 × 7 28 3. 7 × 1 7 4. 9 × 7 63
5. 7)63 9 6. 7)56 8 7. 7)49 7 8. 7)7 1
9. 2 × 7 14 10. 7 × 8 56 11. 7 × 5 35 12. 3 × 7 21
13. 42 ÷ 7 6 14. 14 ÷ 7 2 15. 21 ÷ 7 3 16. 28 ÷ 7 4
17. 56 ÷ 7 8 18. 35 ÷ 7 5 19. 0 ÷ 7 0 20. 7 ÷ 1 7
21. 7 × 9 63 22. 4 × 7 28 23. 7 × 7 49 24. 3 × 7 21

457

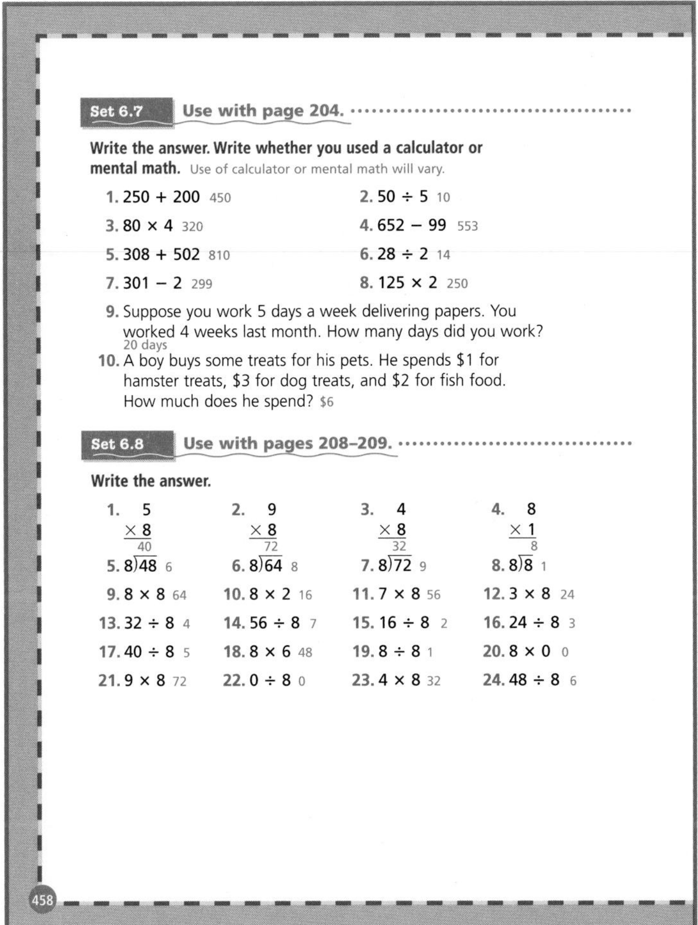

Set 6.7 Use with page 204.

Write the answer. Write whether you used a calculator or mental math. Use of calculator or mental math will vary.

1. 250 + 200 450
2. 50 ÷ 5 10
3. 80 × 4 320
4. 652 − 99 553
5. 308 + 502 810
6. 28 ÷ 2 14
7. 301 − 2 299
8. 125 × 2 250
9. Suppose you work 5 days a week delivering papers. You worked 4 weeks last month. How many days did you work? 20 days
10. A boy buys some treats for his pets. He spends $1 for hamster treats, $3 for dog treats, and $2 for fish food. How much does he spend? $6

Set 6.8 Use with pages 208–209.

Write the answer.

1. 5 × 8 = 40
2. 9 × 8 = 72
3. 4 × 8 = 32
4. 8 × 1 = 8
5. 8)48 6
6. 8)64 8
7. 8)72 9
8. 8)8 1
9. 8 × 8 64
10. 8 × 2 16
11. 7 × 8 56
12. 3 × 8 24
13. 32 ÷ 8 4
14. 56 ÷ 8 7
15. 16 ÷ 8 2
16. 24 ÷ 8 3
17. 40 ÷ 8 5
18. 8 × 6 48
19. 8 ÷ 8 1
20. 8 × 0 0
21. 9 × 8 72
22. 0 ÷ 8 0
23. 4 × 8 32
24. 48 ÷ 8 6

458

Set 6.9 Use with pages 210–211.

Write the answer.

1. 4 × 9 = 36
2. 7 × 9 = 63
3. 9 × 3 = 27
4. 9 × 2 = 18
5. 9)36 4
6. 9)9 1
7. 9)54 6
8. 9)63 7
9. 8 × 9 72
10. 9 × 0 0
11. 9 × 9 81
12. 5 × 9 45
13. 72 ÷ 9 8
14. 45 ÷ 9 5
15. 81 ÷ 9 9
16. 27 ÷ 9 3
17. 9 ÷ 1 9
18. 9 × 6 54
19. 18 ÷ 9 2
20. 9 × 1 9

Set 6.13 Use with pages 218–219.

1. During a basketball game, you made some field goals worth 2 points each and some foul shots worth one point each. You made 3 more field goals than foul shots. If you got 12 points, how many field goals did you make? 5 field goals
2. Two numbers added together give a sum of 30. One number is 2 more than the other number. What are the numbers? 14 and 16
3. At the store, an apple costs 55¢ and a pack of gum costs 45¢. You bought 4 items and received a dime in change from $2. What did you buy? 1 apple; 3 packs of gum
4. It takes three times as long for you to walk to your friend's house as it does for you to ride your bike. How much time will you save by riding your bike if it takes 18 minutes to walk? 12 min

459

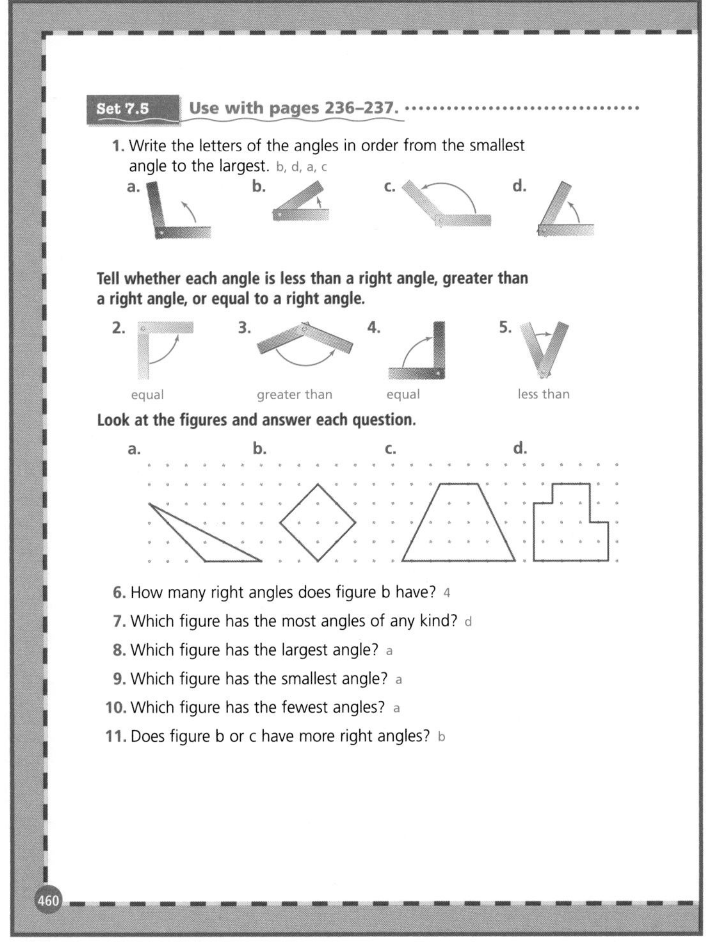

Set 7.5 Use with pages 236–237.

1. Write the letters of the angles in order from the smallest angle to the largest. b, d, a, c

a. b. c. d.

Tell whether each angle is less than a right angle, greater than a right angle, or equal to a right angle.

2. equal
3. greater than
4. equal
5. less than

Look at the figures and answer each question.

a. b. c. d.

6. How many right angles does figure b have? 4
7. Which figure has the most angles of any kind? d
8. Which figure has the largest angle? a
9. Which figure has the smallest angle? a
10. Which figure has the fewest angles? a
11. Does figure b or c have more right angles? b

460

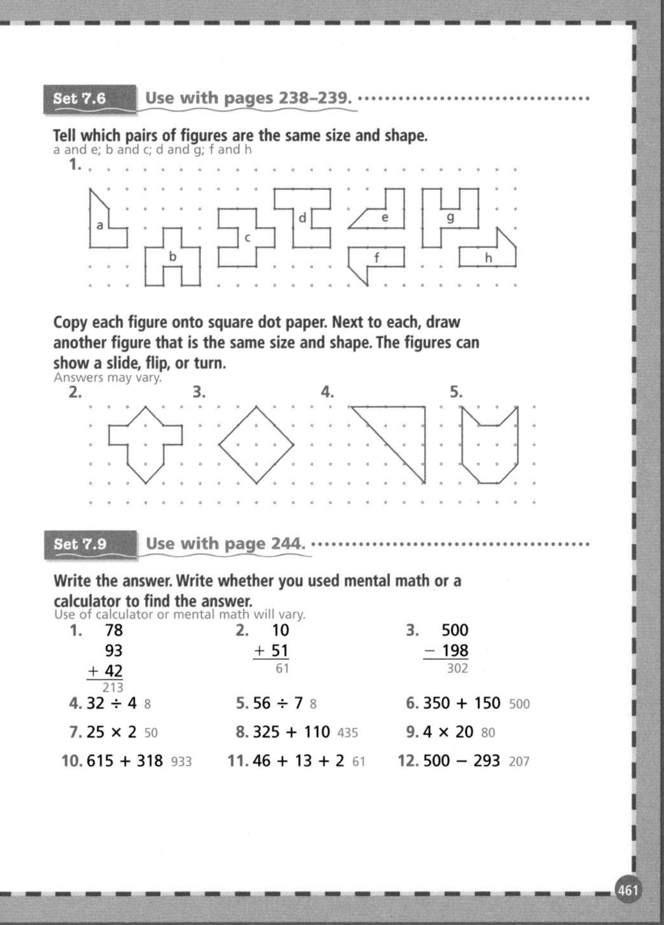

Set 7.6 Use with pages 238–239.

Tell which pairs of figures are the same size and shape. a and e; b and c; d and g; f and h

1.

Copy each figure onto square dot paper. Next to each, draw another figure that is the same size and shape. The figures can show a slide, flip, or turn. Answers may vary.

2. 3. 4. 5.

Set 7.9 Use with page 244.

Write the answer. Write whether you used mental math or a calculator to find the answer. Use of calculator or mental math will vary.

1. 78 + 93 + 42 = 213
2. 10 + 51 = 61
3. 500 − 198 = 302
4. 32 ÷ 4 8
5. 56 ÷ 7 8
6. 350 + 150 500
7. 25 × 2 50
8. 325 + 110 435
9. 4 × 20 80
10. 615 + 318 933
11. 46 + 13 + 2 61
12. 500 − 293 207

461

More Practice

Write the answer. Write whether you used mental math or paper and pencil to find the answer.

13. A librarian worked part time at the library. On Monday he worked 2 hours, on Tuesday he worked 3 hours, on Wednesday he worked 3 hours, and on Saturday he worked 6 hours. How many hours did the librarian work? 14 hours

Set 7.13 Use with pages 254–255.

Use the grid to solve each problem.

1. What is located at (1, 1)? picnic basket
2. What is located at (3, 2)? tree
3. Where is the picnic table located? (4, 4)

Use the grid to solve each problem.

4. Where is the circle located? (3, 6)
5. Which shape is closest to the circle? Where is it located? triangle; (4, 5)
6. What is located at (7, 1)? square
7. Where is the rectangle located? (1, 2)

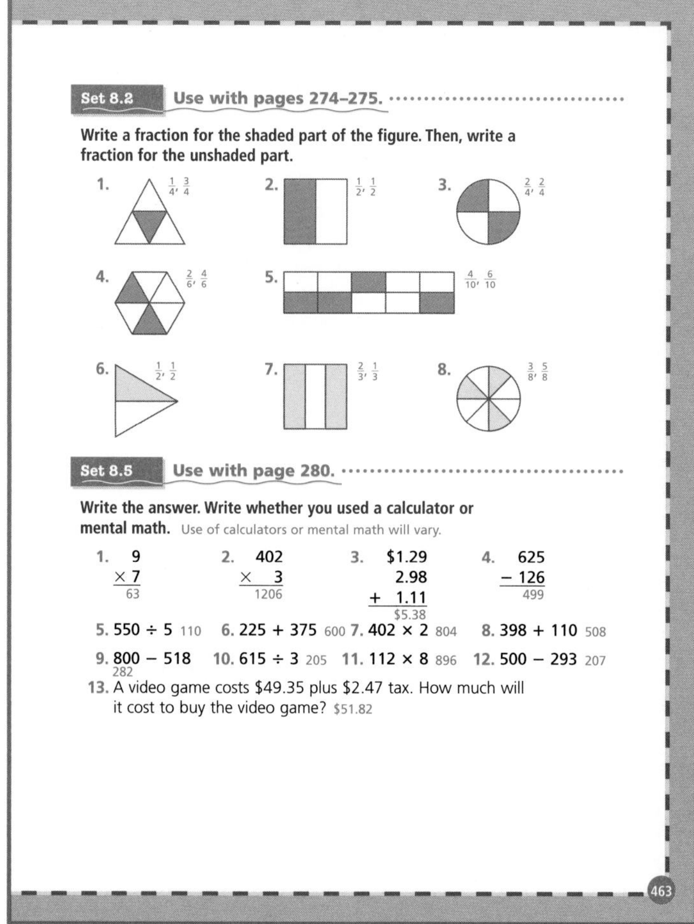

Set 8.2 Use with pages 274–275.

Write a fraction for the shaded part of the figure. Then, write a fraction for the unshaded part.

1. $\frac{1}{4}, \frac{3}{4}$
2. $\frac{1}{2}, \frac{1}{2}$
3. $\frac{2}{4}, \frac{2}{4}$
4. $\frac{2}{6}, \frac{4}{6}$
5. $\frac{4}{10}, \frac{6}{10}$
6. $\frac{1}{2}, \frac{1}{2}$
7. $\frac{2}{3}, \frac{1}{3}$
8. $\frac{3}{8}, \frac{5}{8}$

Set 8.5 Use with page 280.

Write the answer. Write whether you used a calculator or mental math. Use of calculators or mental math will vary.

1. 9×7 = 63
2. 402×3 = 1206
3. $\$1.29 + 2.98 + 1.11$ = \$5.38
4. $625 - 126$ = 499
5. 550 ÷ 5 110
6. 225 + 375 600
7. 402 × 2 804
8. 398 + 110 508
9. 800 − 518 282
10. 615 ÷ 3 205
11. 112 × 8 896
12. 500 − 293 207
13. A video game costs \$49.35 plus \$2.47 tax. How much will it cost to buy the video game? \$51.82

463

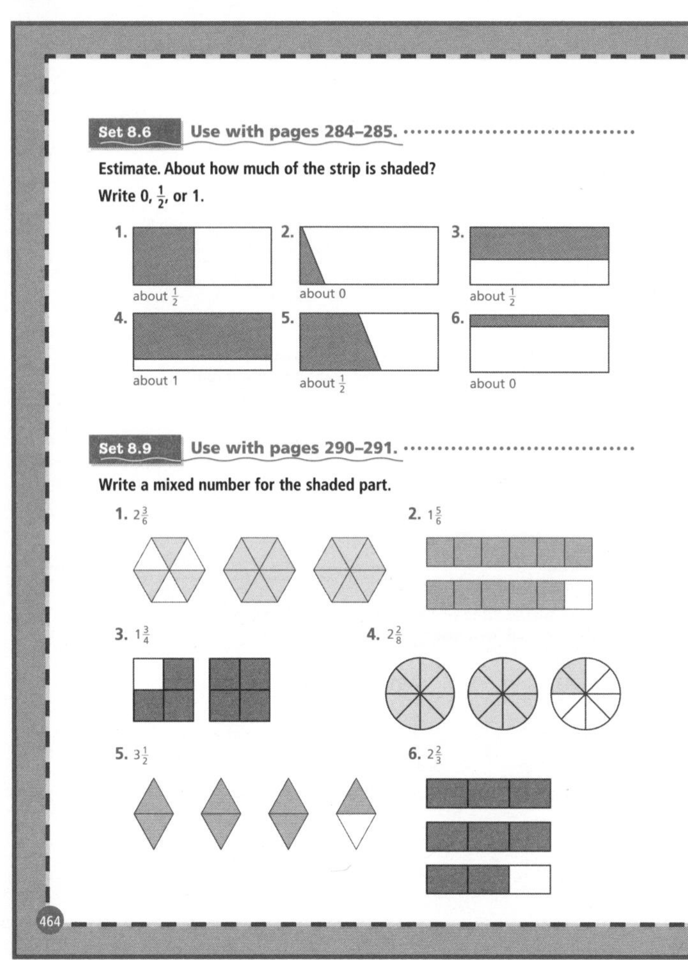

Set 8.6 Use with pages 284–285.

Estimate. About how much of the strip is shaded? Write 0, $\frac{1}{2}$, or 1.

1. about $\frac{1}{2}$
2. about 0
3. about $\frac{1}{2}$
4. about 1
5. about $\frac{1}{2}$
6. about 0

Set 8.9 Use with pages 290–291.

Write a mixed number for the shaded part.

1. $2\frac{3}{6}$
2. $1\frac{5}{6}$
3. $1\frac{3}{4}$
4. $2\frac{2}{8}$
5. $3\frac{1}{2}$
6. $2\frac{2}{3}$

464

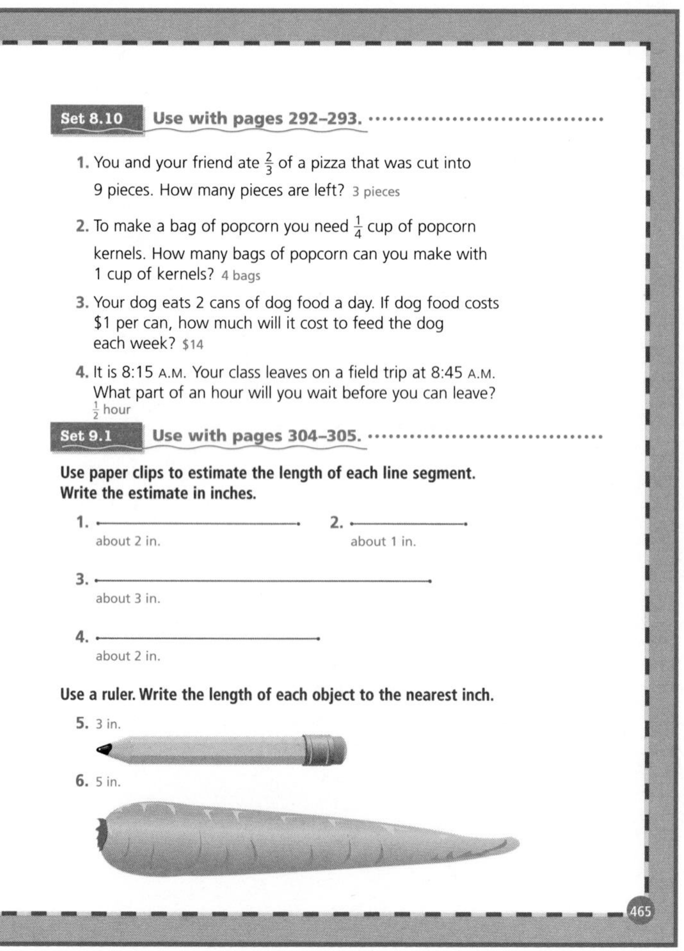

Set 8.10 Use with pages 292–293.

1. You and your friend ate $\frac{2}{3}$ of a pizza that was cut into 9 pieces. How many pieces are left? 3 pieces
2. To make a bag of popcorn you need $\frac{1}{4}$ cup of popcorn kernels. How many bags of popcorn can you make with 1 cup of kernels? 4 bags
3. Your dog eats 2 cans of dog food a day. If dog food costs \$1 per can, how much will it cost to feed the dog each week? \$14
4. It is 8:15 A.M. Your class leaves on a field trip at 8:45 A.M. What part of an hour will you wait before you can leave? $\frac{1}{2}$ hour

Set 9.1 Use with pages 304–305.

Use paper clips to estimate the length of each line segment. Write the estimate in inches.

1. about 2 in.
2. about 1 in.
3. about 3 in.
4. about 2 in.

Use a ruler. Write the length of each object to the nearest inch.

5. 3 in.
6. 5 in.

465

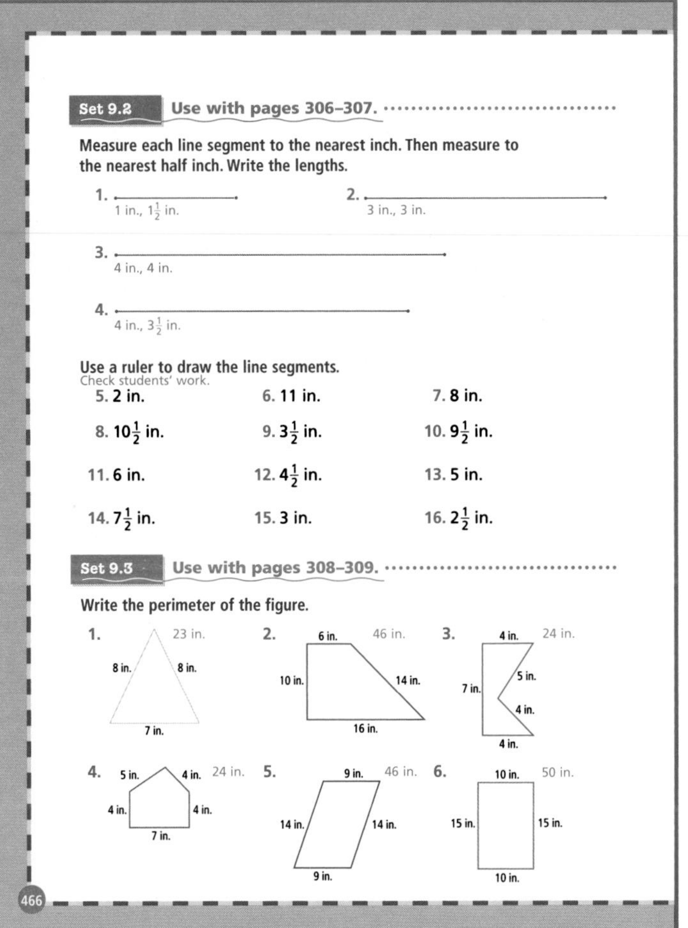

Set 9.2 Use with pages 306–307.

Measure each line segment to the nearest inch. Then measure to the nearest half inch. Write the lengths.

1. 1 in., $1\frac{1}{2}$ in.
2. 3 in., 3 in.
3. 4 in., 4 in.
4. 4 in., $3\frac{1}{2}$ in.

Use a ruler to draw the line segments.
Check students' work.

5. 2 in.	6. 11 in.	7. 8 in.
8. $10\frac{1}{2}$ in.	9. $3\frac{1}{2}$ in.	10. $9\frac{1}{2}$ in.
11. 6 in.	12. $4\frac{1}{2}$ in.	13. 5 in.
14. $7\frac{1}{2}$ in.	15. 3 in.	16. $2\frac{1}{2}$ in.

Set 9.3 Use with pages 308–309.

Write the perimeter of the figure.

1. 23 in. — 8 in., 8 in., 7 in.
2. 46 in. — 6 in., 10 in., 14 in., 16 in.
3. 24 in. — 4 in., 7 in., 5 in., 4 in., 4 in.
4. 24 in. — 5 in., 4 in., 4 in., 4 in., 7 in.
5. 46 in. — 9 in., 14 in., 14 in., 9 in.
6. 50 in. — 10 in., 15 in., 15 in., 10 in.

466

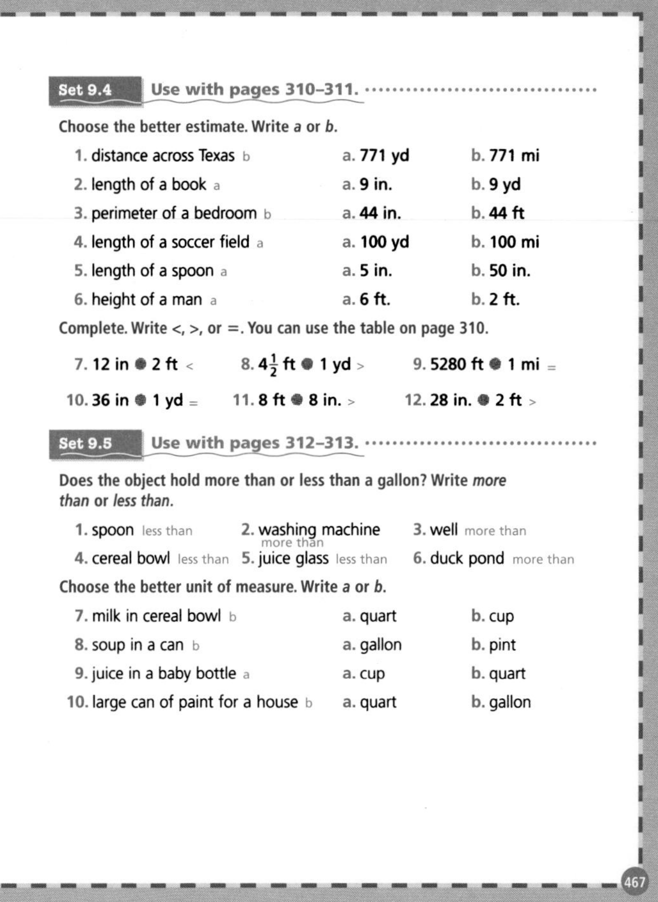

Set 9.4 Use with pages 310–311.

Choose the better estimate. Write *a* or *b*.

1. distance across Texas b	a. 771 yd	b. 771 mi
2. length of a book a	a. 9 in.	b. 9 yd
3. perimeter of a bedroom b	a. 44 in.	b. 44 ft
4. length of a soccer field a	a. 100 yd	b. 100 mi
5. length of a spoon a	a. 5 in.	b. 50 in.
6. height of a man a	a. 6 ft.	b. 2 ft.

Complete. Write <, >, or =. You can use the table on page 310.

7. 12 in ● 2 ft <	8. $4\frac{1}{2}$ ft ● 1 yd >	9. 5280 ft ● 1 mi =
10. 36 in ● 1 yd =	11. 8 ft ● 8 in. >	12. 28 in. ● 2 ft >

Set 9.5 Use with pages 312–313.

Does the object hold more than or less than a gallon? Write *more than* or *less than*.

1. spoon less than	2. washing machine more than	3. well more than
4. cereal bowl less than	5. juice glass less than	6. duck pond more than

Choose the better unit of measure. Write *a* or *b*.

7. milk in cereal bowl b	a. quart	b. cup
8. soup in a can b	a. gallon	b. pint
9. juice in a baby bottle a	a. cup	b. quart
10. large can of paint for a house b	a. quart	b. gallon

467

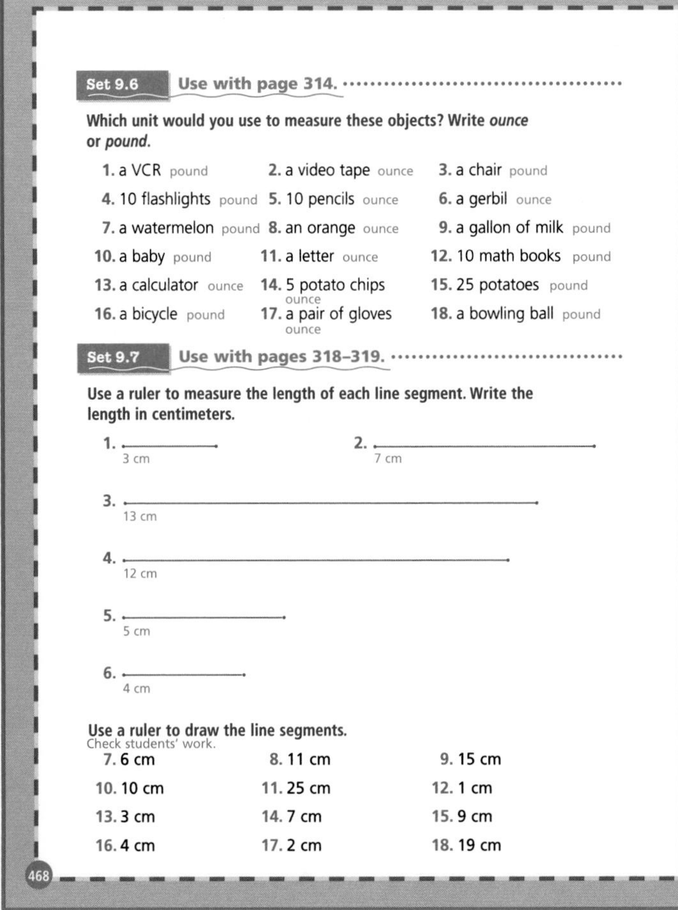

Set 9.6 Use with page 314.

Which unit would you use to measure these objects? Write *ounce* or *pound*.

1. a VCR pound	2. a video tape ounce	3. a chair pound
4. 10 flashlights pound	5. 10 pencils ounce	6. a gerbil ounce
7. a watermelon pound	8. an orange ounce	9. a gallon of milk pound
10. a baby pound	11. a letter ounce	12. 10 math books pound
13. a calculator ounce	14. 5 potato chips ounce	15. 25 potatoes pound
16. a bicycle pound	17. a pair of gloves ounce	18. a bowling ball pound

Set 9.7 Use with pages 318–319.

Use a ruler to measure the length of each line segment. Write the length in centimeters.

1. 3 cm
2. 7 cm
3. 13 cm
4. 12 cm
5. 5 cm
6. 4 cm

Use a ruler to draw the line segments.
Check students' work.

7. 6 cm	8. 11 cm	9. 15 cm
10. 10 cm	11. 25 cm	12. 1 cm
13. 3 cm	14. 7 cm	15. 9 cm
16. 4 cm	17. 2 cm	18. 19 cm

468

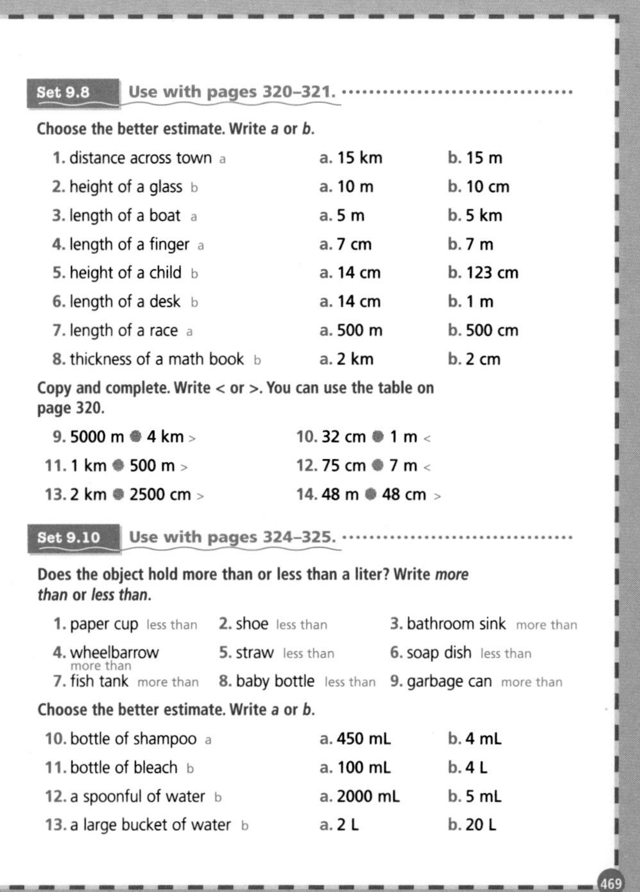

Set 9.8 Use with pages 320–321.

Choose the better estimate. Write *a* or *b*.

1. distance across town a	a. 15 km	b. 15 m
2. height of a glass b	a. 10 m	b. 10 cm
3. length of a boat a	a. 5 m	b. 5 km
4. length of a finger a	a. 7 cm	b. 7 m
5. height of a child b	a. 14 cm	b. 123 cm
6. length of a desk b	a. 14 cm	b. 1 m
7. length of a race a	a. 500 m	b. 500 cm
8. thickness of a math book b	a. 2 km	b. 2 cm

Copy and complete. Write < or >. You can use the table on page 320.

9. 5000 m ● 4 km >	10. 32 cm ● 1 m <
11. 1 km ● 500 m >	12. 75 cm ● 7 m <
13. 2 km ● 2500 cm >	14. 48 m ● 48 cm >

Set 9.10 Use with pages 324–325.

Does the object hold more than or less than a liter? Write *more than* or *less than*.

1. paper cup less than	2. shoe less than	3. bathroom sink more than
4. wheelbarrow more than	5. straw less than	6. soap dish less than
7. fish tank more than	8. baby bottle less than	9. garbage can more than

Choose the better estimate. Write *a* or *b*.

10. bottle of shampoo a	a. 450 mL	b. 4 mL
11. bottle of bleach b	a. 100 mL	b. 4 L
12. a spoonful of water b	a. 2000 mL	b. 5 mL
13. a large bucket of water b	a. 2 L	b. 20 L

469

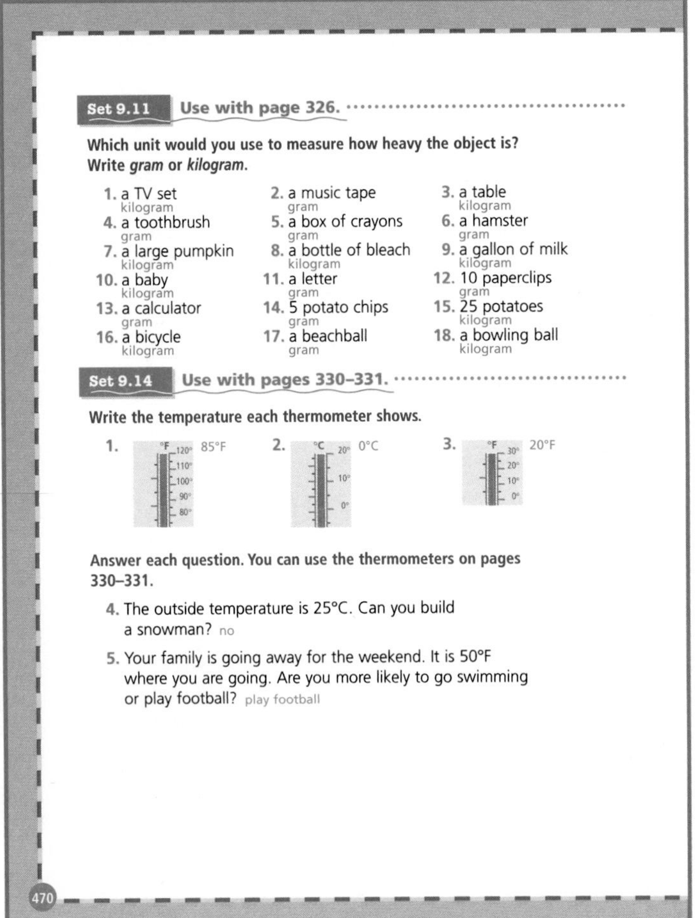

Set 9.11 Use with page 326.

Which unit would you use to measure how heavy the object is? Write *gram* or *kilogram*.

1. a TV set kilogram
2. a music tape gram
3. a table kilogram
4. a toothbrush gram
5. a box of crayons gram
6. a hamster gram
7. a large pumpkin kilogram
8. a bottle of bleach kilogram
9. a gallon of milk kilogram
10. a baby kilogram
11. a letter gram
12. 10 paperclips gram
13. a calculator gram
14. 5 potato chips gram
15. 25 potatoes kilogram
16. a bicycle kilogram
17. a beachball gram
18. a bowling ball kilogram

Set 9.14 Use with pages 330–331.

Write the temperature each thermometer shows.

1. 85°F
2. 0°C
3. 20°F

Answer each question. You can use the thermometers on pages 330–331.

4. The outside temperature is 25°C. Can you build a snowman? no
5. Your family is going away for the weekend. It is 50°F where you are going. Are you more likely to go swimming or play football? play football

470

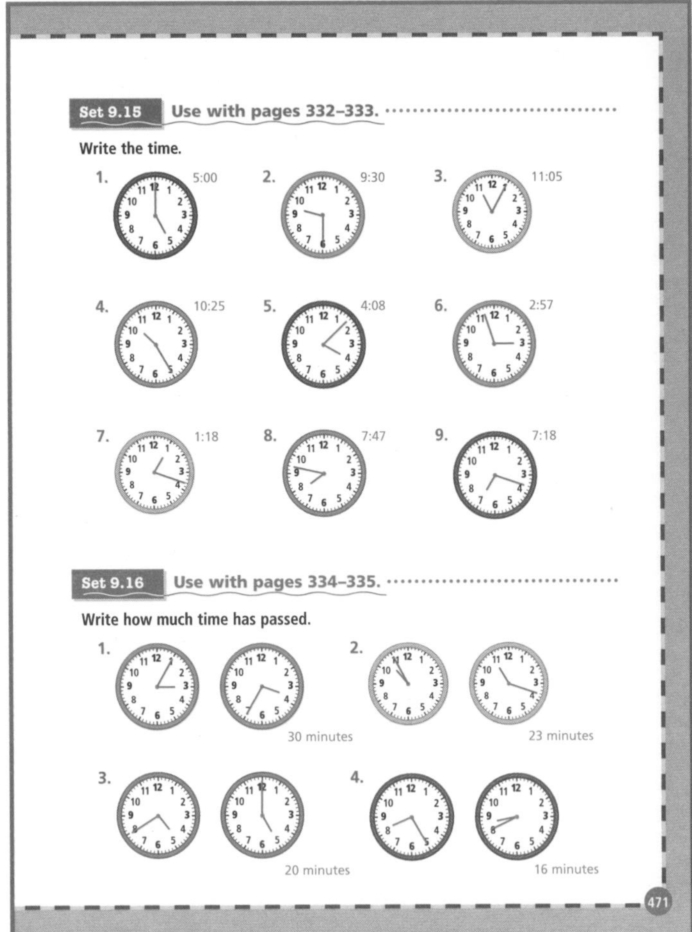

Set 9.15 Use with pages 332–333.

Write the time.

1. 5:00
2. 9:30
3. 11:05
4. 10:25
5. 4:08
6. 2:57
7. 1:18
8. 7:47
9. 7:18

Set 9.16 Use with pages 334–335.

Write how much time has passed.

1. 30 minutes
2. 23 minutes
3. 20 minutes
4. 16 minutes

471

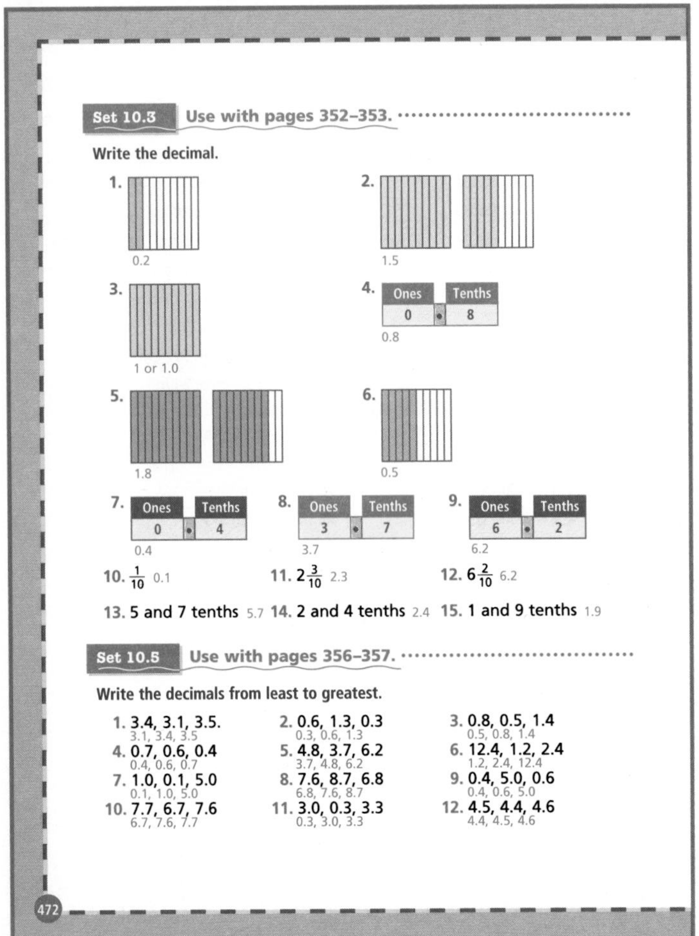

Set 10.3 Use with pages 352–353.

Write the decimal.

1. 0.2
2. 1.5
3. 1 or 1.0
4. Ones 0 . Tenths 8 — 0.8
5. 1.8
6. 0.5
7. Ones 0 . Tenths 4 — 0.4
8. Ones 3 . Tenths 7 — 3.7
9. Ones 6 . Tenths 2 — 6.2
10. $\frac{1}{10}$ 0.1
11. $2\frac{3}{10}$ 2.3
12. $6\frac{2}{10}$ 6.2
13. 5 and 7 tenths 5.7
14. 2 and 4 tenths 2.4
15. 1 and 9 tenths 1.9

Set 10.5 Use with pages 356–357.

Write the decimals from least to greatest.

1. 3.4, 3.1, 3.5. — 3.1, 3.4, 3.5
2. 0.6, 1.3, 0.3 — 0.3, 0.6, 1.3
3. 0.8, 0.5, 1.4 — 0.5, 0.8, 1.4
4. 0.7, 0.6, 0.4 — 0.4, 0.6, 0.7
5. 4.8, 3.7, 6.2 — 3.7, 4.8, 6.2
6. 12.4, 1.2, 2.4 — 1.2, 2.4, 12.4
7. 1.0, 0.1, 5.0 — 0.1, 1.0, 5.0
8. 7.6, 8.7, 6.8 — 6.8, 7.6, 8.7
9. 0.4, 5.0, 0.6 — 0.4, 0.6, 5.0
10. 7.7, 6.7, 7.6 — 6.7, 7.6, 7.7
11. 3.0, 0.3, 3.3 — 0.3, 3.0, 3.3
12. 4.5, 4.4, 4.6 — 4.4, 4.5, 4.6

472

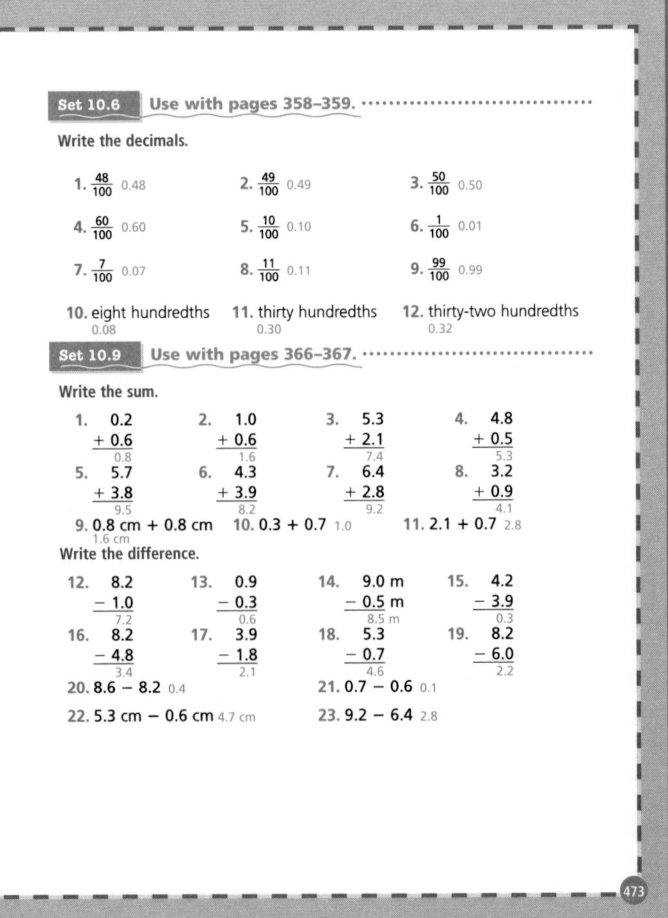

Set 10.6 Use with pages 358–359.

Write the decimals.

1. $\frac{48}{100}$ 0.48
2. $\frac{49}{100}$ 0.49
3. $\frac{50}{100}$ 0.50
4. $\frac{60}{100}$ 0.60
5. $\frac{10}{100}$ 0.10
6. $\frac{1}{100}$ 0.01
7. $\frac{7}{100}$ 0.07
8. $\frac{11}{100}$ 0.11
9. $\frac{99}{100}$ 0.99
10. eight hundredths 0.08
11. thirty hundredths 0.30
12. thirty-two hundredths 0.32

Set 10.9 Use with pages 366–367.

Write the sum.

1. 0.2 + 0.6 = 0.8
2. 1.0 + 0.6 = 1.6
3. 5.3 + 2.1 = 7.4
4. 4.8 + 0.5 = 5.3
5. 5.7 + 3.8 = 9.5
6. 4.3 + 3.9 = 8.2
7. 6.4 + 2.8 = 9.2
8. 3.2 + 0.9 = 4.1
9. 0.8 cm + 0.8 cm 1.6 cm
10. 0.3 + 0.7 1.0
11. 2.1 + 0.7 2.8

Write the difference.

12. 8.2 − 1.0 = 7.2
13. 0.9 − 0.3 = 0.6
14. 9.0 m − 0.5 m = 8.5 m
15. 4.2 − 3.9 = 0.3
16. 8.2 − 4.8 = 3.4
17. 3.9 − 1.8 = 2.1
18. 5.3 − 0.7 = 4.6
19. 8.2 − 6.0 = 2.2
20. 8.6 − 8.2 0.4
21. 0.7 − 0.6 0.1
22. 5.3 cm − 0.6 cm 4.7 cm
23. 9.2 − 6.4 2.8

473

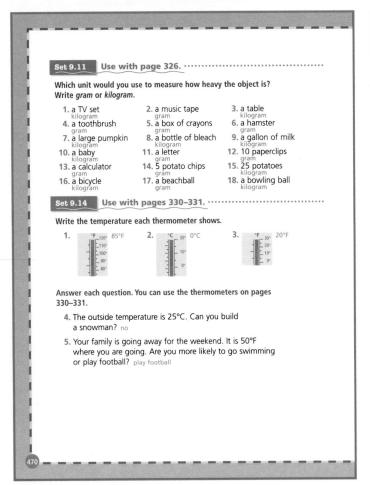

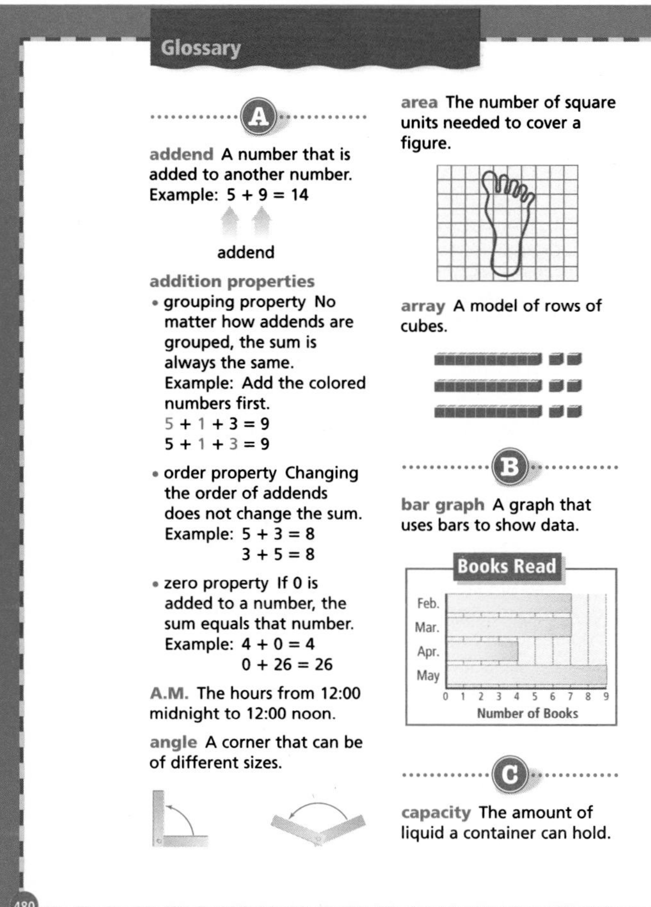

Glossary

A

addend A number that is added to another number.
Example: 5 + 9 = 14
addend

addition properties
- **grouping property** No matter how addends are grouped, the sum is always the same.
  Example: Add the colored numbers first.
  5 + 1 + 3 = 9
  5 + 1 + 3 = 9
- **order property** Changing the order of addends does not change the sum.
  Example: 5 + 3 = 8
  3 + 5 = 8
- **zero property** If 0 is added to a number, the sum equals that number.
  Example: 4 + 0 = 4
  0 + 26 = 26

A.M. The hours from 12:00 midnight to 12:00 noon.

angle A corner that can be of different sizes.

area The number of square units needed to cover a figure.

array A model of rows of cubes.

B

bar graph A graph that uses bars to show data.

C

capacity The amount of liquid a container can hold.

center The middle of a circle.

centimeter (cm) A metric unit of length. 100 centimeters equals 1 meter.

centimeter ruler A ruler marked in centimeters.

cone A solid that has a circular base and comes to a point.

congruent figures Figures that are the same size and shape.

cube A solid having six square faces the same size.

cup (c) A customary unit of capacity. 2 cups equal 1 pint.

customary system The measurement system that uses foot, quart, pound, and degree Fahrenheit.

cylinder A solid having circles of equal size at each end.

D

data Information, facts.

day A unit of time. 1 day equals 24 hours.
Example: Tuesday is the third day of the week.

decimal A number with one or more digits to the right of a decimal point.
Example: 0.9 and 1.08 are decimals.

decimal point A symbol used to separate dollars and cents in money amounts. A symbol used to separate ones and tenths in decimals.
Example: $1.50 1.3
decimal point

decimeter (dm) A metric unit of length. 1 decimeter equals 10 centimeters.

degree A unit for measuring temperature.

degree Celsius (°C) The metric unit for measuring temperature.

degree Fahrenheit (°F) The customary unit for measuring temperature.

denominator The number written below the bar in a fraction.
Example:
$\frac{1}{4}$ denominator

diameter A line that passes through the center of a circle.

difference The answer in a subtraction problem.
Example: 7 − 3 = 4
difference

digit Any of the symbols 0, 1, 2, 3, 4, 5, 6, 7, 8, or 9 used to write numbers.

dividend The number that is divided in a division problem.
Example: 12 ÷ 4 = 3
dividend

divisor The number to divide by in a division problem.
Example: 36 ÷ 9 = 4
divisor

dollar sign A symbol written to show dollars in money amounts.
Example: $1.50
dollar sign

E

edge Where two faces of a solid meet.

endpoint The point at an end of a line segment.
Example:

equivalent fractions Fractions that show the same amount.
Example:
$\frac{6}{8}$
$\frac{3}{4}$

estimate A number close to an exact amount. An estimate tells *about* how much.

even number A whole number ending in 0, 2, 4, 6, or 8.
Example: 12 56 704

expanded form A way to write a number to show the value of each digit.
Example: The way to expand 3962 is 3000 + 900 + 60 + 2.

F

face A flat surface of a solid.

fact family A group of facts that are related.
Example:
5 + 4 = 9 6 × 3 = 18
4 + 5 = 9 3 × 6 = 18
9 − 4 = 5 18 ÷ 6 = 3
9 − 5 = 4 18 ÷ 3 = 6

factor A number that is multiplied in a multiplication problem.
Example: 2 × 9 = 18
factor

flip A move that makes a figure face in the opposite direction.

foot (ft) A customary unit of length. 1 foot equals 12 inches.

fraction A number that names a part of a whole or a part of a set.

$\frac{2}{3}$ $\frac{1}{2}$ $\frac{1}{4}$

front-end estimation Using the digits with the greatest place value to find *about* how much.
Example:
230 → 200
+ 325 → + 300
500

G

gallon (gal) A customary unit of capacity. 1 gallon equals 4 quarts.

gram (g) A metric unit of mass, or heaviness. 1 gram equals 1000 milligrams.

graph A picture that shows information by using bars, lines, or symbols.

H

half turn A turn that causes a figure to point in a different direction.

The second figure is a half-turn image of the first.

hour A unit of time. 1 hour equals 60 minutes.

I

inch (in.) A customary unit of length. 12 inches equal 1 foot.

inch ruler A ruler marked in inches.

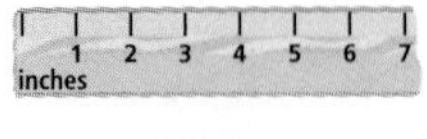

K

key Tells what each picture stands for in a pictograph.
Example:

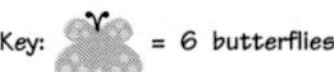

kilogram (kg) A metric unit of mass, or heaviness. 1 kilogram equals 1000 grams.

kilometer (km) A metric unit of length. 1 kilometer equals 1000 meters.

L

line A straight path that goes on forever in two directions.

line graph A graph that uses line segments to show changes over time.

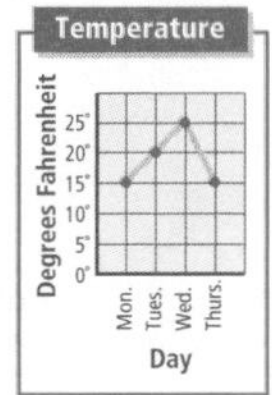

line of symmetry A line along which you could fold a figure so that both halves match.

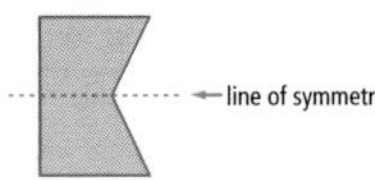

line segment Part of a line having two endpoints.

liter (L) The metric unit of capacity. 1 liter equals 1000 milliliters.

M

mass The heaviness of an object. Often measured with grams or kilograms.

meter (m) A metric unit of length. 1 meter equals 100 centimeters.

metric system The measurement system that uses units such as meter, liter, gram, and degree Celsius.

mile (mi) A customary unit of length. 1 mile equals 5280 feet.

milliliter (mL) A metric unit of capacity. 1000 milliliters equal 1 liter.

minute A unit of time. 1 minute equals 60 seconds.

missing addend An addend that is missing in an addition sentence.
Example: 5 + ■ = 9

missing addend

missing factor A factor that is missing in a multiplication sentence.

Example: 5 × ■ = 45

missing factor

mixed numbers Numbers that have a whole number and a fraction part.

Example: $3\frac{1}{2}$

multiplication properties

- order property Changing the order of factors does not change the product.
  Example: 6 × 4 = 24
  4 × 6 = 24
- property of one If 1 is a factor, the product always equals the other factor.
  Example: 6 × 1 = 6
  1 × 51 = 51
- zero property If 0 is a factor, the product is always 0.
  Example: 8 × 0 = 0
  0 × 17 = 0

N

number line A line showing numbers equally spaced and in counting order.

0 1 2 3 4 5 6 7 8 9 10

numerator The number written above the bar in a fraction.
Example: $\frac{1}{4}$ ← numerator

O

odd number A whole number ending in 1, 3, 5, 7, or 9.
Example: 13 67 429

ordered pair The numbers used to name a point on a grid.

ounce (oz) A customary measure of weight. 16 ounces equal 1 pound.

P

parallel lines Lines that are always the same distance apart.

perimeter The distance around a figure. The perimeter of the rectangle below is 12 cm.

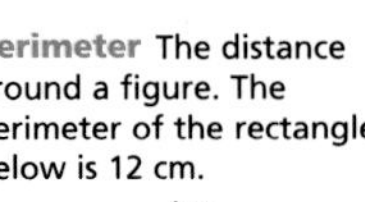

pictograph A graph that shows data with pictures.

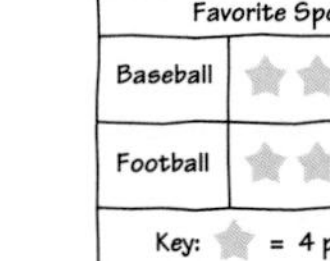

Favorite Sport	
Baseball	★★★★
Football	★★
Key: ★ = 4 people	

pint (pt) A customary unit of capacity. 2 pints equal 1 quart.

place value The value of each place in a number.
Example: In 7943, the digit 7 is in the thousands place.

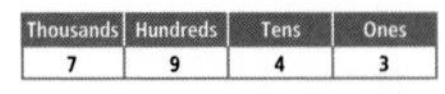

Thousands	Hundreds	Tens	Ones
7	9	4	3

P.M. The hours from 12:00 noon to 12:00 midnight.

point An exact place or position, marked by a dot.

pound (lb) A customary unit of weight. 1 pound equals 16 ounces.

prediction What someone thinks may happen.

prism A solid having 2 bases of equal size and shape at each end. The faces are all rectangles or a related shape.

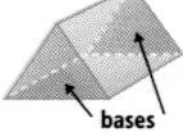

probability The chance that an event will happen.

product The answer in a multiplication problem.
Example: 5 × 3 = 15

product

property A rule for addition, multiplication, or another operation.

pyramid A solid having 1 base that varies in shape. The faces are triangles and meet at a point.

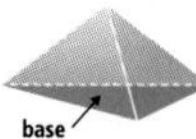

Q

quart (qt) A customary unit of capacity. 4 quarts equal 1 gallon.

quarter Another name for a fourth, 25¢, or $\frac{1}{4}$.

quotient The answer in a division problem.
Example: 54 ÷ 9 = 6

quotient

R

rectangle A figure having 4 sides and 4 square corners. A square is a kind of rectangle.

rectangular prism A prism with 2 rectangular bases and 4 rectangular faces.

remainder The number leftover when one number does not exactly divide another.
Example:
$9\overline{)38}$ = 4 R2 ← 2 is the remainder

right angle A square corner.

round To find the ten or the hundred nearest to an exact number.
Example: 436 rounded to the nearest hundred is 400.

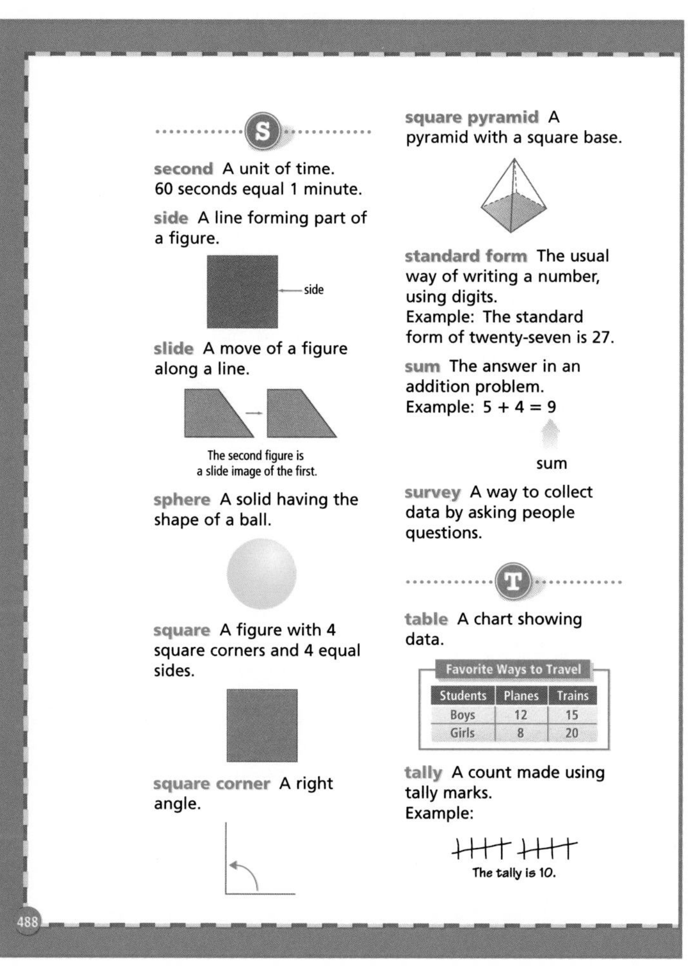

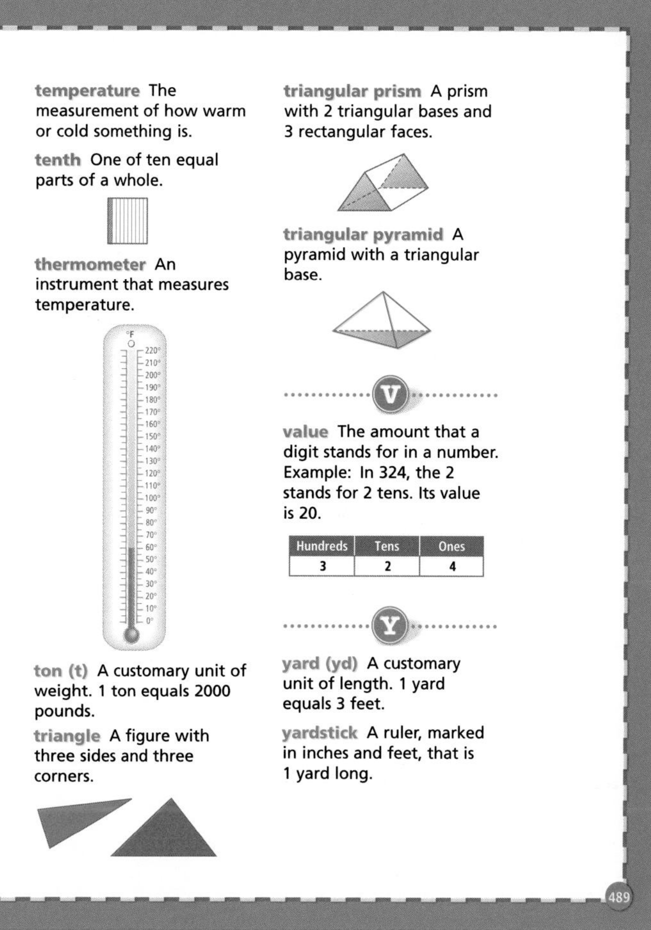

Test Prep Handbook

Contents

Test Prep Strategies

Cumulative Tests

Test Prep Handbook

Test Prep Strategies

This section of the handbook provides students with basic instruction in how to explain an answer on a free-response test or how to solve word problems in a multiple-choice test format.

Each lesson begins with a sample test item that takes students through the problem solving process while highlighting appropriate reading and problem solving strategies. Students then apply the problem solving process and strategies to complete the remaining practice test items.

Cumulative Tests

This section of the handbook provides practice in solving word problems in a multiple-choice test format and offers a review of the content throughout the grade level. Students have additional opportunities to work with estimation, representation, and reasonableness, which are key ideas or components on standardized tests.

Estimation Problems that focus on estimation require choosing an estimation strategy, finding the estimate, and interpreting the answer choices. Students may need to choose an answer from ranges, statements, or estimated quantities.

Representation Test items that focus on representation may include using a pictorial model, such as a graph, a number line, or a picture. Students may also be required to match a representation, such as an expression or an equation, to a problem.

Reasonableness In problems that focus on reasonableness, students are required to use number sense, logical reasoning, and conceptual understanding to choose the most appropriate answer.

Cumulative Tests: Additional Support

Minilessons

The Teacher's Book provides minilessons for use with test items that students typically have difficulty solving. The minilessons model how to use the problem solving process to answer one of the items on the Cumulative Test. The minilessons may be taught during or after the test to the entire class or to individuals, based on students' needs.

Reading Strategies

In this feature, the use of reading strategies, such as Predict/Infer, Self-Question, Monitor, Think About Words, Summarize, and Evaluate, reinforces students' understanding of test items. The teacher can use the suggestions in the Teacher's Book to model the use of these reading strategies during the test or after the test is administered.

Scoring Chart

A scoring chart is provided for the teacher's convenience.

Test Prep Strategies

Using the Self-Question and Draw a Picture Strategies

Type of Question
✓ Multiple-Choice
Enhanced Multiple-Choice
Free-Response
Extended-Response

Objectives

- **To express a solution using mathematical representation**
- **To develop strategies for answering multiple-choice test items**
- **To practice Self-Question reading strategy**

Explain that the Test Prep pages teach strategies that can be useful when taking tests. Read aloud the introduction, then have students read the sample problem. You can use the following ideas as you discuss each step of the solution process. (After students are familiar with the format of the Test Prep page, subsequent Test Prep pages can be done individually or in pairs.)

Sample Item

Understand Using Self-Question Strategy

Have the students state what the problem is asking.

- What does this mean: "Sam finds 2 more shells than Rosa"? Possible answer: Rosa has found 3 shells and Sam has found 3 shells plus 2 more.

Plan Choosing a Problem Solving Strategy

Tell students that once they understand what the problem is asking, they can choose a strategy to help them solve it. For this problem Draw a Picture will help.

- How will a picture show the information in this problem? Possible answer: A picture will show how many shells each person has.

Try It Using Draw a Picture

Have students look at the picture. Discuss the labels and what each one means.

- Which answer choice matches your solution? The answer should be C.

Look Back Checking for Reasonableness

Have students compare the picture to the information presented in the problem.

- Why could you rule out choices A and B? Possible answer: They do not include the fact that Sam had 3 shells, like Rosa did, plus two more.

Chapter 1 Test Prep Strategies

Read the problem slowly. As you are reading, ask yourself questions to help you understand how to solve the problem.

Sample Test Item

1 Rosa finds 3 shells at the beach. Sam finds 2 more shells than Rosa. What number sentence tells how many shells they have altogether?

- A 3 + 2 = ▪
- B 3 + 2 + 2 = ▪
- C 3 + 3 + 2 = ▪
- D 3 + 3 + 3 = ▪

1 Understand **Using Self-Question Strategy**

Reread the problem. Ask yourself questions about each sentence.

- What does this mean: "Sam finds 2 more shells than Rosa"?

2 Plan **Choosing a Problem Solving Strategy**

If you use Draw a Picture, you will be able to see the information in each sentence.

- How will a picture show the information in this problem?

3 Try It **Using Draw a Picture**

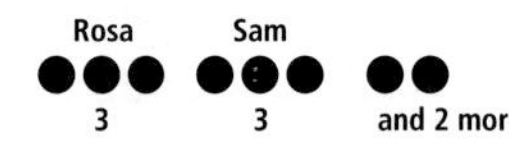

Together: 3 + 3 + 2 = ▪

- Which answer choice matches your solution?

4 Look Back **Checking for Reasonableness**

Reread the problem as you look at your picture. They should match.

- Why could you rule out choices A and B?

Try These!

2 A small dish holds 4 breadsticks. The large dish holds 5 more breadsticks than the small dish. Which sentence tells how many breadsticks are in both dishes?

- A 4 + 4 = ▪
- B 4 + 4 + 5 = ▪
- C 4 + 5 + 5 = ▪
- D 5 + 5 + 5 = ▪

3 Yuma collected 5 bottle caps last week. This week he collected 2 more than last week. What number sentence could be used to find how many bottle caps he has now?

- A 5 + 2 = ▪
- B 5 + 2 + 2 = ▪
- C 5 + 3 + 2 = ▪
- D 5 + 5 + 2 = ▪

492

Try These!

These questions are similar in format to the Sample Item. By Item 3, some students may be able to identify the correct solution sentence without pictorial representation.

Answers to Test Items

1. C **2.** B **3.** D

Additional Resources

- **Preparing for Tests,** pp. 1G–1H
- **Vocabulary and Reading Strategies,** p. 1J
- **Analyzing Errors,** pp. 39A–39B

Student Handbook Masters

The Test Prep Handbook pages can be found as blackline masters in the **Student Handbook Masters**.

Item Analysis

Item	1	2	3
Lesson	1.8	1.8	1.8

Test Prep Strategies

Chapter 2 Test Prep Strategies

As you read the problem, pay attention to the words. Think about the parts of the problem you might want to reread. Decide if you understand everything.

Sample Test Item

1 The chart shows the number of pages that 4 teachers read aloud in a week. Round each amount to the nearest ten. Which teacher read a rounded amount of 80 pages?

Teacher	Pages Read
Mr. Pago	73
Mrs. Lei	84
Mr. Toth	87
Miss Finn	91

A Mr. Pago
B Mrs. Lei
C Mr. Toth
D Miss Finn

1 **Understand** **Using Monitor Strategy**

Reread the problem. Notice that there is extra information.

- Which information is needed for solving the problem?

2 **Plan** **Choosing a Method for Solving**

Use rounding and mental math.

- When should you round up? down?
- How will you use mental math?

3 **Try It** **Using Rounding**

Round each number in the chart. So, 73 rounds down to 70; 84 rounds down to 80; 87 rounds up to 90; and 91 rounds down to 90.

- How did you decide whether to round up or down?

4 **Look Back** **Checking for Reasonableness**

Mrs. Lei read about 80 pages. Use number sense to be sure that this is the best answer.

- How do you know that you do not have to round "4 teachers"?

Try These!

2 The total pages read was 335. Round the number of pages to the nearest hundred.

A 300
B 330
C 340
D 400

3 Anita read 53 pages in a month. Round the number of pages to the nearest ten.

A 30
B 40
C 50
D 60

Test Prep Handbook

Using the Monitor Strategy and Rounding

Type of Question
- ✓ Multiple-Choice
- Enhanced Multiple-Choice
- Free-Response
- Extended-Response

Objectives

- **To find a solution by reading a chart and using rounding**
- **To develop strategies for answering multiple-choice test items**
- **To practice Monitor reading strategy**

This is a good Test Prep page to assign as individual work because not only is the student led through the solution method, but all of the answer choices are discussed as well. If the page is used as a whole-class activity, you can use the following ideas as you discuss each step.

Sample Item

Understand Using Monitor Strategy

Have students state the question they have to answer.

- Which information is needed for solving the problem? round to the nearest ten, the teachers' names, the number of pages read

Plan Choosing a Method for Solving

Once students understand the problem, they can make a plan to solve it (round the numbers).

- When should you round up? Down? If the ones digit is a 5 or greater, round up; If the ones digit is less than 5, round down.
- How will you use mental math? Possible answer: I will use it to round the numbers.

Try It Using Rounding

Students can begin rounding with choice A and work through to choice D, or they may decide to first test a choice that they think might be correct.

- How did you decide whether to round up or down? Possible answer: I looked at the number to the right of the tens place. If it was less than 5, I rounded down. If it was 5 or greater, I rounded up.

Look Back Checking for Reasonableness

Have students reread the problem to see if their answer makes sense.

- How do you know you do not have to round "4 teachers"? Possible answer: because I need to find out how many pages were read

ry These!

hese items offer additional practice in rounding numbers and answering multiple-choice ques-ons. Students should note that Item 2 involves rounding to the nearest hundred.

nswers to Test Items

. B **2.** A **3.** C

dditional Resources

Preparing for Tests, pp. 40G-40H
ocabulary and Reading Strategies, p. 40J
Analyzing Errors, pp. 79A–79B

tudent Handbook Masters

e Test Prep Handbook pages can be found as blackline masters in the **udent Handbook Masters.**

em Analysis

tem	1	2	3
esson	2.8	2.8	2.8

Test Prep Handbook

Test Prep Strategies

Using the Predict/Infer Strategy and Rounding

Type of Question
✓ Multiple-Choice
Enhanced Multiple-Choice
Free-Response
Extended-Response

Objectives

- To find a solution using estimation
- To develop strategies for answering multiple-choice test items
- To practice Predict/Infer reading strategy

Have students work in pairs. Students can benefit from thinking together and sharing ideas on how to tackle a math topic like estimation. If the page is used as a whole-class activity, you can use the following ideas as you discuss each step.

Sample Item

Understand Using Predict/Infer Strategy

Ask students to list the words that will help them decide which operation to choose to solve the problem.

- What operation can you use to compare? subtraction

Plan Choosing an Estimation Method

Point out that since the answer choices are to the nearest hundred, students should estimate the difference to the nearest hundred.

- Do you think this method will give you an answer like those shown in the answer choices? Why? Possible answer: Yes, because if the first two numbers in my subtraction sentence end in 00 so will my answer

Try It Using Rounding

Round the numbers, then subtract.

600 – 300 = 300

- Is this difference one of the answer choices? Yes, B

Look Back Checking for Reasonableness

Tell students to make sure when they look back that their answer is in the form asked for—in this case an estimate, not an exact answer.

- Why can choice D be ruled out? Possible answer: because choice D shows an estimate of the sum instead of the difference

Chapter 3 Test Prep Strategies

Read the problem to get a sense of what it is about. Reread to make a prediction about how it could be solved.

Sample Test Item

1 At a recycling center, Matt and his friends sorted 582 cans and 319 bottles. About how many more cans than bottles did they sort? Mark your answer.

- A 200
- B 300
- C 600
- D 900

❶ **Understand** **Using Predict/Infer Strategy**

Read the problem again. The question asks you to compare numbers. Try to predict what operation you will need and how large or small the answer will be.

- What operation can you use to compare?

❷ **Plan** **Choosing an Estimation Method**

Round each number to the nearest hundred, and then subtract.

- Do you think this method will give you an answer like those shown in the answer choices? Why?

❸ **Try It** **Using Rounding**

Round. 582 rounds up to 600 and 319 rounds down to 300.

Use mental math to find the difference.

600 − 300 = 300

- Is this difference one of the answer choices?

❹ **Look Back** **Checking for Reasonableness**

Reread the question to check if you did the right operation.

- Why can choice D be ruled out?

Try These!

2 A poultry farm has 281 chickens and 98 turkeys. About how many birds live at the poultry farm?

- A 100
- B 200
- C 300
- D 400

3 In July, 517 eggs were shipped to market. In August, 378 eggs were shipped. About how many more eggs were shipped in July?

- A 100
- B 200
- C 300
- D 400

494

Try These!

Students have to determine whether to estimate a sum or a difference in these problems. Answe choices are provided for whichever way students choose to estimate, so tell them not to settle fo an answer that looks right at first glance. Finding the correct answer choice needs more though

Answers to Test Items

1. B
2. D
3. A

Additional Resources

- **Preparing for Tests,** pp. 84G–84H
- **Vocabulary and Reading Strategies,** p. 84J
- **Analyzing Errors,** pp. 117A–117B

Student Handbook Masters

The Test Prep Handbook pages can be found as blackline masters in the **Student Handbook Masters.**

Item Analysis

Item	1	2	3
Lesson	3.9	3.9	3.9

Test Prep Strategies

Chapter 4 Test Prep Strategies

As you read a problem, be sure to read the labels on the charts, graphs, and diagrams. Think about the kinds of questions you could answer using the data.

1 Understand **Using Predict/Infer Strategy**
The question asks you to compare the data.
- How can you put the data in the graph in order?

2 Plan **Choosing a Method for Solving**
Study the graph. The lengths of the bars can help you make a prediction about the order of the colors.
- What other part of the graph can you use to tell how many of each color car passed by?

Sample Test Item

1 Sue looked out the classroom window for 5 minutes. She made a graph that showed the different colors of the cars that passed by.

Cars Passing By

Colors	Number of Cars
Blue	1
Red	9
White	6
Black	7

(Horizontal axis: Number of Cars, 2, 4, 6, 8, 10)

In order from greatest to least, how can Sue list the colors of the cars that passed by her window?

- **A** blue, red, white, black
- **B** black, white, red, blue
- **C** red, black, white, blue
- **D** red, white, black, blue

3 Try It **Using Data**
Begin with the longest bar. Then use the next longest bar, and so on.
- How can you keep track of the information you find?

4 Look Back **Checking for Reasonableness**
The answer choices are not numbers. The answer should be colors written from greatest to least number of cars.
- What information did you use to order the cars?

Try These!

Use Sue's graph to answer these questions.

2 How many blue cars passed by the window?
- **A** 1
- **B** 2
- **C** 4
- **D** 6

3 How many more red cars than white cars passed by the window?
- **A** 2
- **B** 3
- **C** 6
- **D** 9

Test Prep Handbook

495

Try These!

For these items students answer different types of questions using the bar graph. Ask students what other kinds of questions could be answered with information from the graph.

Answers to Test Items

1. C
2. B
3. B

Additional Resources

- **Preparing for Tests,** pp. 118G–118H
- **Vocabulary and Reading Strategies,** p. 118J
- **Analyzing Errors,** pp. 159A–159B

Student Handbook Masters

The Test Prep Handbook pages can be found as blackline masters in the **Student Handbook Masters.**

Item Analysis

Item	1	2	3
Lesson	4.5	4.5	4.5

Using the Predict/Infer Strategy and Data

Type of Question
✓ Multiple-Choice
Enhanced Multiple-Choice
Free-Response
Extended-Response

Objectives

- **To find a solution through reading and interpreting a graph**
- **To develop strategies for answering multiple-choice test items**
- **To practice Predict/Infer reading strategy**

Have students work in pairs to allow an exchange of ideas on reading and using a graph. If the page is used as a whole-class activity, you can use the following ideas as you discuss each step of the solution process.

Sample Item

Understand Using Predict/Infer Strategy
Discuss with the class the different parts of the graph: labels, bars, numbers, and title.
- How can you put the data in the graph in order?
  Possible answer: by using the lengths of the bars

Plan Choosing a Method for Solving
Students should see that computation is not needed to solve the first problem.
- What other part of the graph can you use to tell how many of each color car passed by? the numbers along the bottom of the graph

Try It Using Data
Encourage students to use scrap paper to keep track of their findings.
- How can you keep track of the information you find?
  Possible answer: I can make notes on scrap paper.

Look Back Checking for Reasonableness
Students should look back at the graph to check that their answer makes sense.
- What information did you use to order the cars?
  the lengths of the bars or the numbers on the graph

Test Prep Handbook

Test Prep Strategies

Using the Think About Words and Logical Reasoning Strategies

Type of Question
✓ Multiple-Choice
Enhanced Multiple-Choice
Free-Response
Extended-Response

Objectives

- To use multiplication, division, and number sense to determine the most reasonable answer
- To develop strategies for answering multiple-choice test items
- To practice Think About Words reading strategy

This is a good page to assign as individual work as the student is led in detail through the solution process. If the page is used as a whole-class activity, you can use the following ideas as you discuss each step.

Sample Item

Understand Using Think About Words Strategy

Emphasize the value of the three Understand questions posed on the student page

- What number word can you find? five
- Why is the word *least* important in this problem? Possible answer: It tells how to decide how much money Kara needs to bring.
- What does it mean to say "Each item costs either $1 or $2"? Kara will have to pay $1 or $2 for each item.

Plan Choosing a Problem Solving Strategy

Tell students that in order for their notes to be helpful, they need to be written in a legible, organized manner.

- What words or phrases from the problem should you use? Possible answers: buy 5 items; costs $1 or $2; least amount of money to bring

Try It Using Logical Reasoning

Have students think about how much money they would want in their pockets in the same situation.

- If all the items cost $2, how much money would Kara need? $10
- Should you choose an answer choice that is less than that amount? No, because if each item costs $2, Kara will not have enough money

Look Back Checking for Reasonableness

When students reread the problem, have them check to make sure they did not overlook any important words or phrases.

- Does your answer tell the least the items could cost or does it tell the most they could cost? the most they could cost

Chapter 5 Test Prep Strategies

As you read, look for math ideas that are said in words. Numbers said in word form are easily overlooked but are often an important part of the problem.

Sample Test Item

1 Kara has to buy five items at the store. Each item costs either $1 or $2. What is the least amount of money Kara needs to bring to make sure she has enough money?

A $5
B $7
C $10
D $12

1 Understand **Using Think About Words Strategy**

Read the problem. Look for important words.

- What number word can you find?
- Why is the word "least" important in this problem?
- What does it mean to say "Each item costs either $1 or $2"?

2 Plan **Choosing a Problem Solving Strategy**

If you use logical reasoning, you will be able to decide how much money Kara needs to bring. Write some sentences to organize your thoughts.

- What words or phrases from the problem should you use?

3 Try It **Using Logical Reasoning**

To know the least amount of money Kara might need, you have to find the most the items might cost.

- If all the items cost $2, how much money would Kara need?
- Should you choose an answer choice that is less than that amount?

4 Look Back **Checking for Reasonableness**

Reread the problem to make sure you answered the question.

- Does your answer tell the least the items could cost or does it tell the most they could cost?

Try These!

2 There are 3 tennis balls in a can. Ten children each need a tennis ball. What is the fewest number of cans that are needed?

A 3
B 4
C 5
D 6

3 Kyle and his 3 neighbors make sandwiches to take outside. If each person gets two sandwiches, how many should they make?

A 3
B 4
C 6
D 8

496

Try These!

Students get practice shifting their thinking between two different operations, as is often required on a standardized test. Discuss with students how they decided whether to add, subtract, multiply, or divide.

Answers to Test Items

1. C
2. B
3. D

Additional Resources

- **Preparing for Tests,** pp. 156G–156H
- **Vocabulary and Reading Strategies,** p. 156J
- **Analyzing Errors,** pp. 185A–185B

Student Handbook Masters

The Test Prep Handbook pages can be found as blackline masters in the **Student Handbook Masters.**

Item Analysis

Item	1	2	3
Lesson	5.2, 5.9	5.7	5.2, 5.7

Test Prep Strategies

Chapter 6 Test Prep Strategies

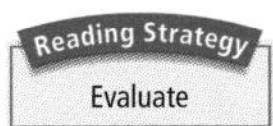

Read the problem and remember important numbers and words. See if the problem is about a familiar topic. This can also be helpful in solving the problem.

Sample Test Item

1 Mr. Ling separated an orange into 15 sections. He put the same number of sections on each of his 3 children's plates. Which picture shows how many orange sections each child got?

A

B

C

D

1 Understand **Using Evaluate Strategy**

Read the problem. You are familiar with the idea of sharing, or dividing, things.

- Which numbers will you use to solve the problem?

2 Plan **Choosing a Problem Solving Strategy**

If you draw a picture, you can show the orange sections divided up.

- From a picture, can you see if you divided equally?

3 Try It **Using Draw a Picture**

Think about the facts you know. Use those facts to draw a picture.

- Look at the answer choices. Which choice matches your drawing?

4 Look Back **Checking for Reasonableness**

You can check your answer by testing the other choices.

- How can you also check your answer by using multiplication?

Try These!

2 Seth has 4 bags. He wants to put 6 marbles in each bag. Which picture shows how many marbles Seth needs?

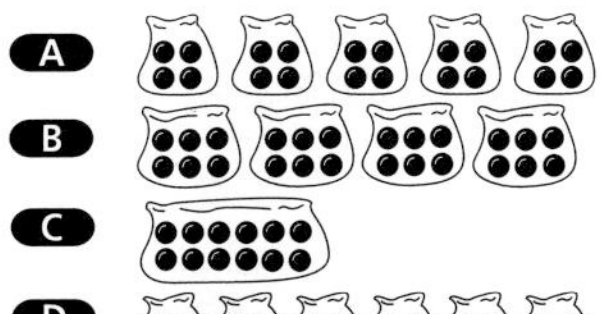

3 Jenna has 32 baseball cards. She puts 8 cards on each page of an album. Which picture shows how many pages Jenna will fill?

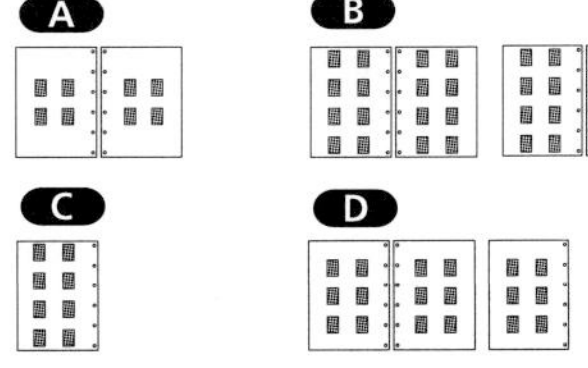

Test Prep Handbook

497

Try These!

Encourage students to use multiplication and division to check their answers. Have them explain why they can eliminate certain answer choices.

Answers to Test Items

1. D
2. B
3. B

Additional Resources

- **Preparing for Tests,** pp.190G–190H
- **Vocabulary and Reading Strategies,** p. 190J
- **Analyzing Errors,** pp. 221A–221B

Student Handbook Masters

The Test Prep Handbook pages can be found as blackline masters in the **Student Handbook Masters.**

Item Analysis

Item	1	2	3
Lesson	6.1	6.1, 6.5	6.1, 6.7

Using the Evaluate and Draw a Picture Strategies

Type of Question
✓ Multiple-Choice
Enhanced Multiple-Choice
Free-Response
Extended-Response

Objectives

- **To identify pictorial representations of word problems involving division**
- **To develop strategies for answering multiple-choice test items**
- **To practice Evaluate reading strategy**

Use the page as a whole-class activity. Read aloud the introduction, then have students read the sample problem. Use the following ideas as you discuss each step of the solution process.

Sample Item

Understand Using Evaluate Strategy

Ask students if they've ever been in a similar situation and how it was handled.

- Which numbers will you use to solve the problem? 15 and 3

Plan Choosing a Problem Solving Strategy

Tell students that sometimes a quick mental picture of what is happening helps in the planning. Suggest that students imagine 3 plates on a table.

- From a picture can you see if you divided equally? Yes, by counting how many there are on each plate

Try It Using Draw a Picture

Tell students to use a representation of an orange slice that does not take too long to draw. They do not want to use up time on unnecessary details.

- Look at the answer choices. Which choice matches your drawing? The answer should be D.

Look Back Checking for Reasonableness

Ask students to explain why they can eliminate choices A, B, and C.

- How can you also check your answer by using multiplication? 3 x 5 = 15

Test Prep Handbook

Test Prep Strategies

Using the Self-Question Strategy and Limiting Choices

Type of Question
✓ Multiple-Choice
Enhanced Multiple-Choice
Free-Response
Extended-Response

Objectives

- **To solve problems involving lines of symmetry, 3-dimensional solids, and congruent figures**
- **To develop strategies for answering multiple-choice test items**
- **To practice Self-Question reading strategy**

Have students work in pairs so that they can discuss the use of the word not and the different ways to check for congruence. If the page is used as a whole-class activity, you can use the following ideas as you discuss each step of the solution process.

Sample Item

Understand Using Self-Question Strategy

Have students look at the answer choices to help define what a line of symmetry is.

- Why is "NOT" in capital letters? Possible answer: because it's very important in understanding the question
- What is a line of symmetry? a line that divides a figure into 2 equal (congruent) parts

Plan Choosing a Method for Solving

Have students keep in mind the use of the word not in the problem.

- How can you tell whether or not the line is a line of symmetry? Possible answer: I can trace one part of the figure and then place it on top of the other part to see if they match.

Try It Limiting Choices

Caution students not to always trust what they see. They should prove symmetry by folding or tracing.

- Why should you test all of the choices? Possible answer: Because there are no numbers or operations within the problem itself, the only option for finding the answer is to test the choices.

Look Back Checking for Reasonableness

Emphasize that the word *not* plays a role in every step of this solution process.

- Does your choice match the correct use of the word *not* in the problem? Students should choose the figure that does not have a line of symmetry.

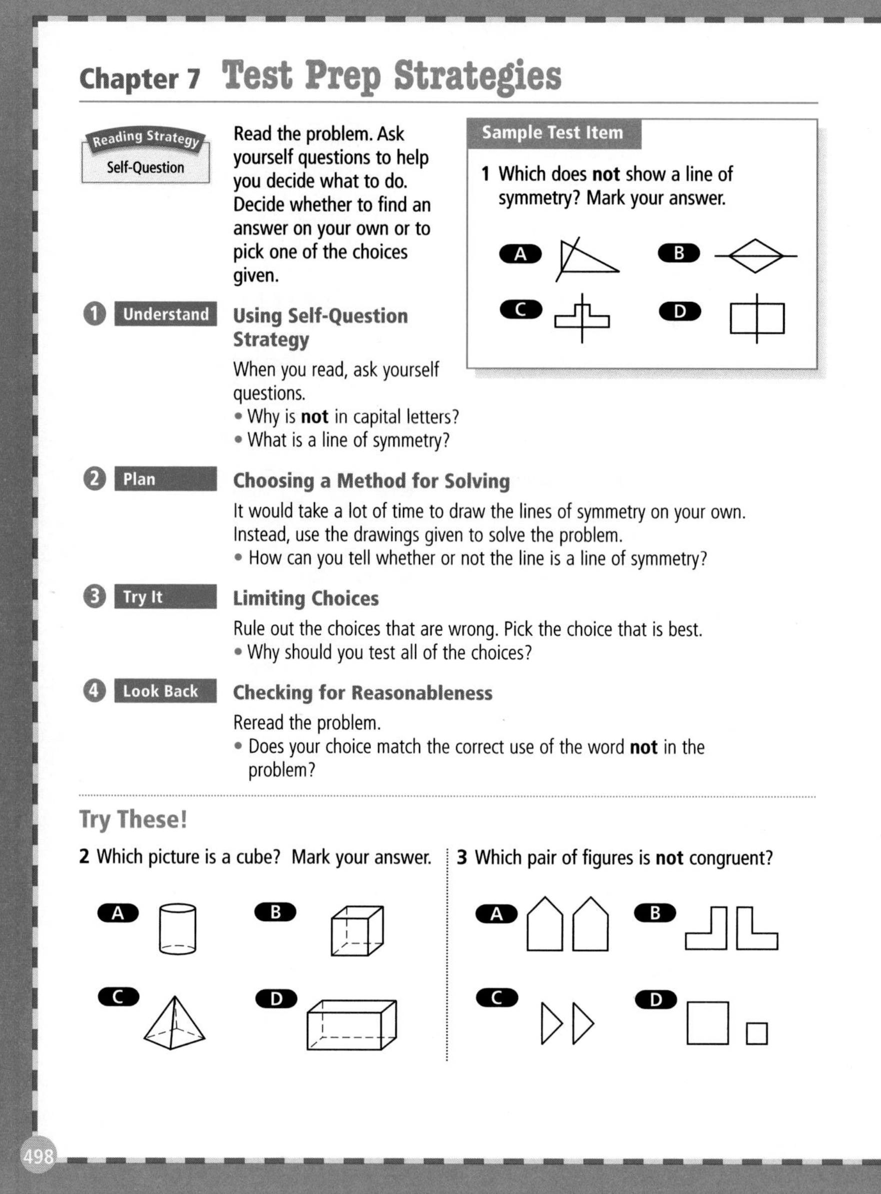

Chapter 7 **Test Prep Strategies**

Reading Strategy: Self-Question

Read the problem. Ask yourself questions to help you decide what to do. Decide whether to find an answer on your own or to pick one of the choices given.

Sample Test Item

1 Which does **not** show a line of symmetry? Mark your answer.

Ⓐ Ⓑ Ⓒ Ⓓ

1 **Understand** — **Using Self-Question Strategy**

When you read, ask yourself questions.
- Why is **not** in capital letters?
- What is a line of symmetry?

2 **Plan** — **Choosing a Method for Solving**

It would take a lot of time to draw the lines of symmetry on your own. Instead, use the drawings given to solve the problem.
- How can you tell whether or not the line is a line of symmetry?

3 **Try It** — **Limiting Choices**

Rule out the choices that are wrong. Pick the choice that is best.
- Why should you test all of the choices?

4 **Look Back** — **Checking for Reasonableness**

Reread the problem.
- Does your choice match the correct use of the word **not** in the problem?

Try These!

2 Which picture is a cube? Mark your answer.

Ⓐ Ⓑ Ⓒ Ⓓ

3 Which pair of figures is **not** congruent?

Ⓐ Ⓑ Ⓒ Ⓓ

498

Try These!

These examples give students practice in switching their direction of thought, for example, as with is and *is not* in standardized tests. Emphasize that students will encounter the use of *not* in many standardized tests that they will take.

Answers to Test Items

1. A
2. B
3. D

Additional Resources

- **Preparing for Tests,** pp. 226G–226H
- **Vocabulary and Reading Strategies,** pp. 226J
- **Analyzing Errors,** pp. 256A–265B

Student Handbook Masters

The Test Prep Handbook pages can be found as blackline masters in the **Student Handbook Masters.**

Item Analysis

Item	1	2	3
Lesson	7.7	7.10	7.6

Test Prep Strategies

Chapter 8 Test Prep Strategies

It is sometimes wise to read a problem more than once before you begin to solve it. Read it the first time to get an idea of what it is all about and to find out what is being asked. Then reread it to pay more attention to the math.

Sample Test Item

1 Leo got 3 ballons for his birthday. After a week, 2 of his balloons popped. Shade the balloons to show that $\frac{2}{3}$ of Leo's balloons popped.

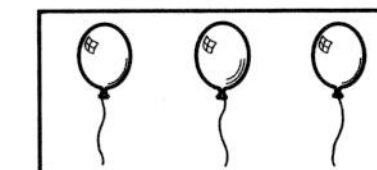

1 Understand **Using Summarize Strategy**
Read the problem. Then summarize it by noting the main points.
- What do you need to show?

2 Plan **Choosing a Problem Solving Strategy**
Use the model given to solve the problem.
- How will you show your answer on the model?

3 Try It **Making a Model**
Draw shading on the balloons.
- How does the number of balloons you shaded show the fraction $\frac{2}{3}$?

4 Look Back **Checking for Reasonableness**
Reread the problem.
- Do the numbers in the problem match your model?

Try These!

2 Megan was not very hungry last night. She only ate $\frac{1}{6}$ of a pizza. Shade the picture to show how much Megan ate.

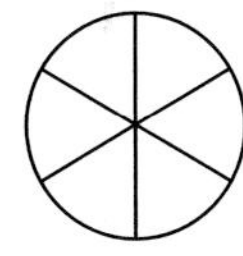

3 Shade $\frac{3}{5}$ of the stars.

Test Prep Handbook

499

Try These!

After students complete these items, have them go back to each item and name a fraction for the part that is not shaded. Have students explain how they knew how many objects to shade.

Answers to Test Items

1. 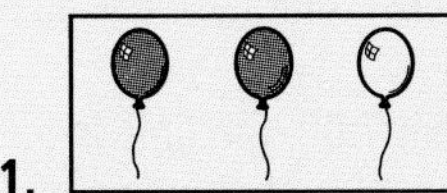

2. 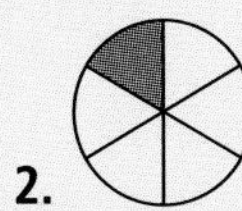

3. 

Additional Resources

- **Preparing for Tests,** pp. 270G–270H
- **Vocabulary and Reading Strategies,** p. 270J
- **Analyzing Errors,** pp. 297A–297B

Student Handbook Masters

The Test Prep Handbook pages can be found as blackline masters in the **Student Handbook Masters.**

Item Analysis

Item	1	2	3
Lesson	8.1, 8.2	8.1, 8.2	8.1, 8.2

Using the Summarize and Making a Model Strategies

Type of Question
Multiple-Choice
Enhanced Multiple-Choice
✓ Free-Response
Extended-Response

Objectives

- **To represent fractions using pictorial models**
- **To develop strategies for answering free-response test items**
- **To practice Summarize reading strategy**

Assign this page as individual work. Move through the classroom, checking students' progress. If the page is used as a whole-class activity, you can use the following ideas as you discuss each step of the solution process.

Sample Item

Understand Using Summarize Strategy
Have students name the information in the problem that is not necessary to solve it.
- What do you need to show? that 2 balloons popped

Plan Choosing a Problem Solving Strategy
Explain that there are different ways to represent that two balloons popped. Ask students to tell how the problem asks them to show what happened.
- How will you show your answer on the model? by shading 2 balloons

Try It Making a Model
Emphasize that the total number of balloons should be the denominator.
- How does the number of balloons you shaded show the fraction $\frac{2}{3}$? I shaded 2. Two is the numerator.

Look Back Checking for Reasonableness
Have students determine whether or not their answer fits the question.
- Do the numbers in the problem match your model? Two out of the 3 balloons should be shaded.

Test Prep Handbook

Test Prep Strategies

Using the Monitor and Work Backward Strategies

Type of Question
Multiple-Choice
Enhanced Multiple-Choice
Free-Response
✓ Extended-Response

Objectives

- To determine the reasonableness of a solution for problems involving time
- To develop strategies for answering extended-response test items
- To practice Monitor reading strategy

On this page, students will encounter a problem that requires a two-part answer. They will have to explain their choice to fully answer the problem. Lead students as a whole class through the introduction, sample problem, and solution process. You can use the following ideas as you discuss each step.

Sample Item

Understand Using Monitor Strategy

Ask students to identify the two questions they need to answer and to determine what kinds of answers are required.

Plan Choosing a Problem Solving Strategy

Tell students that although guessing and estimating are also possible plans, working backward would probably take less time.

- What time will you start with? I can start at 9:10 and work backward.

Try It Using Work Backward

- What information should you use about Tuesday? arrived 10 minutes earlier than Monday Monday? arrived 20 minutes early

  Lead students through a discussion that encompasses the following points: School begins at 9:10. When students count backward 10 minutes and then 20 minutes from 9:10, they will be at 8:40. Since Lani arrived at school at 8:30, the statement given is false. Have students offer their explanations for why the statement is false.

Look Back Checking for Reasonableness

Remind students to be sure that they have a true or false answer and an explanation.

- Do you get the same time that is shown on the clock? When students work backward from 9:10, they should end up at 8:40, so their answer should be no.

Chapter 9 Test Prep Strategies

As you read the problem, check that you understand the information and what you need to do to solve. At times it will be necessary to adjust your reading. You may need to slowly reread some parts in order to understand the problem.

Sample Test Item

1 On Monday, Lani arrived at school 20 minutes before school started. On Tuesday, Lani arrived 10 minutes earlier than she did Monday. On Tuesday, she arrived at.

School begins at 9:10.

Is this sentence true or false? How do you know?

1 Understand **Using Monitor Strategy**

When you read the problem, adjust your pace so you can understand it.
- Is the clock necessary to solve the problem?

2 Plan **Choosing a Problem Solving Strategy**

Work backward. Look for information that helps you get started.
- What time will you start with?

3 Try It **Using Work Backward**

Use the clock. It shows the time that Lani got to school.
- What information should you use about Tuesday? about Monday?

4 Look Back **Checking for Reasonableness**

Check your answer by working forward.
- Do you get the same time that is shown on the clock?

Try These!

2 On Saturday, the movie theater shows the movie 15 minutes later than Friday. On Friday, the movie is shown 15 minutes later than Thursday. The movie on Saturday starts at

The movie starts at 6:30 on Thursday.

True or false? How do you know?

3 Umi cleaned her room for 30 minutes, folded laundry for 15 minutes, and read to her younger brother for 15 minutes. She finished at

Umi started her chores at 3:00.

True or false? How do you know?

500

Try These!

Have students use the clock within each problem to help determine the answer and then check it. Students can use the clock to count forward and back.

Answers to Test Items

1. False, because if I count backward 10 minutes and then 20 minutes from 9:10, the time will be 8:40.
2. True, because if I count backward 30 minutes (15 + 15 = 30) from 7:00, the time is 6:30.
3. False; 30 + 15 + 15 = 60; 60 minutes = 1 hour; count back from 2:00; Umi began her chores at 1:00, not 12:30.

Additional Resources

- **Preparing for Tests,** pp. 302G–302H
- **Vocabulary and Reading Strategies,** p. 302
- **Analyzing Errors,** pp. 341A–341B

Student Handbook Masters

The Test Prep Handbook pages can be found as blackline masters in the **Student Handbook Masters.**

Item Analysis

Item	1	2	3
Lesson	9.16	9.16	9.16

Test Prep Strategies

Chapter 10 Test Prep Strategies

Read the problem slowly. Sometimes when you read slowly, you can pay closer attention to details and vocabulary.

Sample Test Item

1 Which decimal tells how much is shaded?

Ⓐ 2.4
Ⓑ 2.6
Ⓒ 3.4
Ⓓ 4.2

1 Understand **Using Monitor Strategy**
Reread the problem. Sometimes you may not remember the meaning of a math term in a problem.
- What part of the problem can help you remember what a decimal is?

2 Plan **Choosing a Method for Solving**
Use the model given in the problem to find the decimal that matches it.
- What does a totally shaded square stand for?

3 Try It **Using a Model**
Count how many wholes are shaded. Write the whole number.
Count how many tenths are shaded. Write the tenths.
- Which answer choice matches your solution?

4 Look Back **Checking for Reasonableness**
Reread the problem.
- Does it ask for how much is or how much is not shaded?

Try These!

2 Which decimal tells how much is shaded?

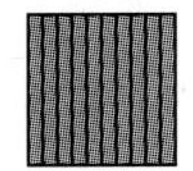
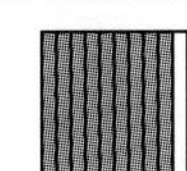

Ⓐ 0.9
Ⓑ 1.1
Ⓒ 1.9
Ⓓ 9.1

3 Which decimal tells how much is shaded?

Ⓐ 0.2
Ⓑ 0.8
Ⓒ 2
Ⓓ 8

Test Prep Handbook

501

Using the Monitor Strategy and Models

Type of Question
- ✓ Multiple-Choice
- Enhanced Multiple-Choice
- Free-Response
- Extended-Response

Objectives
- To identify the mathematical and pictorial representations of decimals to tenths
- To develop strategies for answering multiple-choice test items
- To practice Monitor reading strategy

This page is straightforward, so students should be able to complete the worksheet on an individual basis. Assign a partner to those students who might have difficulty. If the page is used as a whole-class activity, you can use the following ideas as you discuss each step.

Sample Item

Understand Using Monitor Strategy
Count with students by tenths from 0 to 1.
- What part of the problem can help you remember what a decimal is? Look at the picture or the answer choices.

Plan Choosing a Problem Solving Strategy
Tell students that if a picture is given in a problem, they need to determine if it is essential to finding the answer.
- What does a totally shaded square stand for? 1 whole

Try It Using Work Backward
Encourage students to be careful when counting tenths. They might want to point to each tenth with their pencil point so that they don't skip or recount a tenth.
- Which answer choice matches your solution? The answer is A.

Look Back Checking for Reasonableness
Remind students that if they misread the question, they may work out a wrong answer. It is likely that the wrong answer will be one of the answer choices, so they need to pay close attention to the words.
- Does it ask for how much is or how much is not shaded? how much is shaded

Try These!
Students are provided with more opportunities to match the mathematical and pictorial representations of decimals to tenths. Item 3 may be difficult for some students. Discuss what a zero in the ones place means.

Answers to Test Items
1. A
2. C
3. B

Additional Resources
- **Preparing for Tests,** pp. 346G–346H
- **Vocabulary and Reading Strategies,** p. 346J
- **Analyzing Errors,** pp. 373A–373B

Student Handbook Masters
The Test Prep Handbook pages can be found as blackline masters in the **Student Handbook Masters.**

Item Analysis

Item	1	2	3
Lesson	10.3	10.3	10.3

Test Prep Handbook

Test Prep Strategies

Using the Self-Question Strategy and Multiplication

Type of Question
Multiple-Choice
✓ Enhanced Multiple-Choice
Free-Response
Extended-Response

Objectives

- **To solve problems using a pictograph**
- **To develop strategies for answering enhanced-multiple choice test items**
- **To practice Self-Question reading strategy**

Have students work in pairs so they have the opportunity to share their ideas for using the graph to solve the problem. If the page is used as a whole-class activity, you can use the following ideas as you discuss each step.

Sample Item

Understand Using Self-Question Strategy

Ask students how many cones each 🍦 represents.

- What information can you get from the graph? the months; how many cones were bought each month; what amount the symbol represents

Plan Choosing a Computation Method

Some students might see another strategy that would help them to find the answer more quickly: Compare the number of cones for July and September (6 – 1 = 5), then multiply (5 x 15 = 75).

- How can you multiply to find the number for July? multiply the number of shown for July by 15

Try It Using Multiplication and Subtraction

Ask students to explain why they need to subtract.

- Which answer choice matches the difference? The answer is C.

Look Back Checking for Reasonableness

Ask students why the ones digit in the answer will be a 0 or a 5.

- Why can choice A be eliminated? Possible answer: Because July has several more cones than September, you know the answer is greater than 15.

Chapter 11 Test Prep Strategies

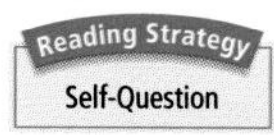

As you are reading the problem, ask yourself questions to help you understand the problem.

1 Understand **Using Self-Question Strategy**

Ask yourself questions about the problem and the graph.

- What information can you get from the graph?

2 Plan **Choosing a Computation Method**

The graph uses pictures to stand for numbers.

- How can you multiply to find the number for July?

3 Try It **Using Multiplication and Subtraction**

6 × 15 = 90 (July)
1 × 15 = 15 (September)
90 − 15 = 75

- Which answer choice matches the difference?

4 Look Back **Checking for Reasonableness**

Reread the problem and the question being asked.

- Why can choice A be eliminated?

Sample Test Item

1 The graph shows the number of cones sold each month this summer.

Ice Cream Cones

Month	Number of Cones
June	🍦🍦🍦
July	🍦🍦🍦🍦🍦🍦
August	🍦🍦🍦🍦🍦
September	🍦
Key: 🍦 = 15 cones	

How many more ice cream cones were sold in July in September?

A 15
B 45
C 75
D 90

Try These!

Use the graph above to answer these questions.

2 Last summer, 60 ice cream cones were sold during August. How many fewer cones were bought last August than this August?

A 15
B 30
C 45
D 60

3 Which months combined had a total sale of 120 cones?

A August, September
B June, August
C September, June
D June, August, September

502

Try These!

Before students begin these items, tell them that information from one item might be used in another, so they should keep a clear record of their work.

Answers to Test Items

1. C
2. A
3. B

Additional Resources

- **Preparing for Tests,** pp. 378G–378H
- **Vocabulary and Reading Strategies,** p. 378J
- **Analyzing Errors,** pp. 405A–405B

Student Handbook Masters

The Test Prep Handbook pages can be found as blackline masters in the **Student Handbook Masters.**

Item Analysis

Item	1	2	3
Lesson	11.5	11.5	11.5

Test Prep Strategies

Chapter 12 Test Prep Strategies

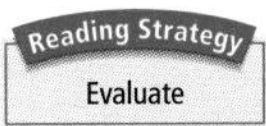

Read the problem slowly, paying attention to words that might offer important information for solving the problem. Sometimes the numbers in a problem seem more important than the words. You need to pay attention to both.

Sample Test Item

1 You have 84 pennies. You share them equally among 6 friends and yourself.

Which statement is true?

- **A** Each person gets 14 pennies.
- **B** Each person gets 12 pennies.
- **C** Each person gets less than 10 pennies.
- **D** Each person gets more than 20 pennies.

1 Understand **Using Evaluate Strategy**

Read the problem.

- What words tell you that the pennies will be shared among 7 people not 6 people?
- What does it mean "to share equally"?

2 Plan **Choosing a Computation Method**

You can divide and then compare your answer to the choices given.

- What is the division sentence you need to solve?

3 Try It **Using Division**

$84 \div 7 = 12$

Look at the quotient in your division sentence.

- Which choice describes the meaning of your quotient?

4 Look Back **Checking for Reasonableness**

Reread the question to see if your choice answers it.

- How could choices C and D be ruled out before you divide?

Try These!

Decide which statement is true.

2 You have 96 marbles. You and your 3 friends are going to play a game with the marbles. Each player needs the same number of marbles.

- **A** Each player will get 24 marbles.
- **B** Each player will get 32 marbles.
- **C** Each player will get less than 30 marbles.
- **D** Each player will get more than 40 marbles.

3 You have 176 acorns. You are going to give an equal amount to each of your 8 friends.

- **A** Each friend will get 18 acorns.
- **B** Each friend will get 25 acorns.
- **C** Each friend will get more than 20 acorns.
- **D** Each friend will get more than 30 acorns.

Test Prep Handbook

503

Try These!

After they complete these items, have students try to write their own multiple-choice item of the same type.

Answers to Test Items

1. B
2. A
3. C

Additional Resources

- **Preparing for Tests,** pp. 410G–410H
- **Vocabulary and Reading Strategies,** p. 410J
- **Analyzing Errors,** pp. 433A–433B

Student Handbook Masters

The Test Prep Handbook pages can be found as blackline masters in the **Student Handbook Masters.**

Item Analysis

Item	1	2	3
Lesson	12.2, 12.7	12.2, 12.7	12.2, 12.7

Using the Evaluate Strategy and Division

Type of Question
Multiple-Choice
✓ Enhanced Multiple-Choice
Free-Response
Extended-Response

Objectives

- To use division and number sense estimation to determine the most reasonable answer
- To develop strategies for answering enhanced multiple-choice test items
- To practice Evaluate reading strategy

Work through the page as a whole-class activity. Read aloud the introduction, then have students read the sample problem. You can use the following ideas as you discuss each step of the solution process and all of the answer choices.

Sample Item

Understand Using Evaluate Strategy

Have students look at the four answer choices. These types of answers can be confusing, so remind students that they need to choose the one that best fits the problem.

- What words tell you that the pennies will be shared among 7 people, not 6 people? "6 friends and yourself"
- What does it mean "to share equally"? Each person gets the same amount.

Plan Choosing a Computation Method

Ask students which words help them decide on the operation to use. Tell students that solving a division sentence and then comparing will take less time than checking all the choices (unless they are able to eliminate choices through estimation).

- What is the division sentence you need to solve? $84 \div 7 = ?$

Try It Using Division

Tell students that after they find a quotient, they must compare it to the answer choices.

- Which choice describes the meaning of your quotient? The answer is B.

Look Back Checking for Reasonableness

If it seems that more than one answer choice solves the problem, recheck your division and carefully reread the choices.

- How can choices C and D be eliminated before you divide? Possible answers: Estimate the quotient; Mentally multiply 7 by 10 and 7 by 20.

Test Prep Handbook

Minilesson for Item 2

Focus
- Solution Strategies
- Problem Solving
- Addition

Use with Item 2

Tell students you will solve Item 2 as a class. Explain that you will use the four-step problem solving process. Ask four students to each write the name of one of the steps on the board. Then ask a student to read Item 2 aloud.

Understand

What does the drawing show? the kinds of leaves Rita has
How many maple leaves does Rita have? 6 maple leaves
How many oak leaves does Rita have? 4 oak leaves
How many elm leaves does Rita have? 5 elm leaves
What is the problem asking you to find? the total number of leaves Rita has

Plan

Remind students that there are many ways to solve the problem. This time solve this problem by writing a number sentence.
What operation can you use to find a total? addition
How many types of leaves does Rita have? 3 types
How many addends should you have in the number sentence? 3

Try It

Ask students to write and solve the number sentence that will determine the number of leaves Rita has.
6 + 4 + 5 = 15

Look Back

Have students compare their number sentences with a partner's. If the sentences disagree, encourage students to explain their sentences and together come up with one number sentence. Then compare solutions as a class.

Check the Answer One way to check the answer to Item 2 is to draw a picture of all the leaves.
Remind students that on a multiple-choice test, they must fill in the bubble next to their answer choice.

Extra Support To review the mathematics in Item 2, use Lesson 1.8, Three or more Addends, pp. 18–19.

Chapter 1 Cumulative Test

Mark your answer on the answer sheet.

1. Which number line shows 1 more than 16? B

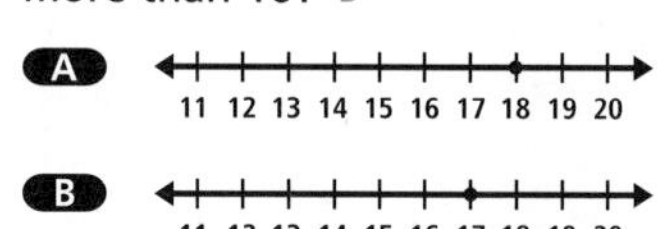

A ⟷ 11 12 13 14 15 16 17 18 19 20 (point at 18)
B ⟷ 11 12 13 14 15 16 17 18 19 20 (point at 17)
C ⟷ 11 12 13 14 15 16 17 18 19 20 (point at 16)
D ⟷ 11 12 13 14 15 16 17 18 19 20 (point at 15)

2. Rita has 6 maple leaves. She found 4 oak leaves and 5 elm leaves. How many leaves does Rita have? H

- F 6 + 5 − 4
- G 4 + 5
- H 6 + 5 + 4
- J 6 − 5

3. Which number goes into the box to make the sentence true?

3 + 6 = ■ + 3 D

- A 0
- B 1
- C 3
- D 6

4. What is the missing number?

10, 11, 12, ■ J

- F 16
- G 15
- H 14
- J 13

5. Todd bought a bag of 13 apples. There were 7 red apples in the bag. The rest were green apples. How many green apples were there? C

- A 1
- B 5
- C 6
- D 7

GO ON

504

Reading Strategies Use with Item 11

Remind students that they can use the Self-Question reading strategy by asking themselves questions as they work through a problem.

Thinking Aloud

What do I know already? *I know Bobby has 5 blue marbles, 5 yellow marbles, and 3 red marbles.*
What do I need to find out? *I need to find out which of the 4 answers is a reasonable answer for the number of marbles he has in all.*
What operation should I use to find a total? *I'll use addition.*
Do I have to find the actual total? *No, I just need to know if the total is less than 5, between 5 and 10, less than 10, or more than 10.*

Invite students to finish the problem and decide as a class which is the correct answer.

For More Practice Self-Question reading strategy minilessons, TE p. 1J.

Extra Support To review the mathematics in Item 10, use Lesson 1.8, Three or More Addends, pp. 18–19.

6. Sam has 10 counters. Ellen has 6 more counters than Sam. How many counters can Ellen give Sam so that they both have the same number? G

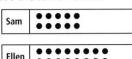

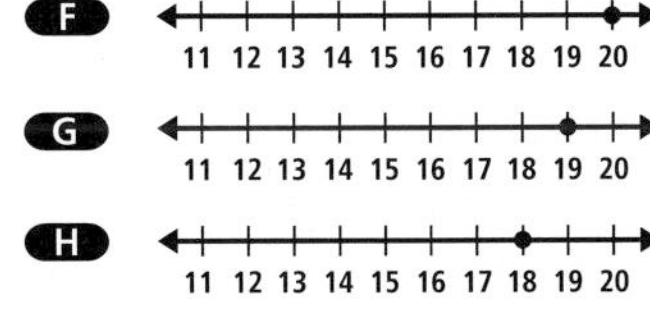

F 2
G 3
H 4
J 5

7. Which number goes into the box to make the sentence true?

5 + ■ = 5 A

A 0
B 1
C 10
D 25

8. Which number sentence is in the same fact family as

8 + 7 = 15? H

F 8 + 0 = 8
G 7 + 1 = 8
H 15 – 8 = 7
J 8 – 7 = 1

9. Miko is planting tulips in her garden. She will plant 3 rows of 5 tulips. Each row will have a white tulip at each end. The tulips in between will be red. How many of each color tulip will Miko need? D

A 4 white, 6 red
B 6 white, 3 red
C 6 white, 6 red
D 6 white, 9 red

10. Which number line shows 1 less than 19? H

F 11 12 13 14 15 16 17 18 19 20
G 11 12 13 14 15 16 17 18 19 20
H 11 12 13 14 15 16 17 18 19 20
J 11 12 13 14 15 16 17 18 19 20

11. Bobby has a marble collection with 5 blue marbles, 5 yellow marbles, and 3 red marbles. He wants to know how many marbles he has in all. What is a reasonable answer? A

A more than 10
B less than 10
C less than 5
D between 5 and 10

STOP

Test Prep Handbook

505

Student Handbook Masters

The Test Prep Handbook pages can be found as blackline masters in the **Student Handbook Masters**.

Scoring Chart

Number of Items Correct	1	2	3	4	5	6	7	8	9	10	11
Score	9	18	27	36	46	55	64	73	82	91	100

Item Analysis

Item	1	2	3	4	5	6	7	8	9	10	11
Lesson	1.2	1.8	1.4	1.2	1.12	1.3	1.4	1.14	1.15	1.2	1.2

Minilesson for Item 5

Focus

- Representation
- Problem Solving
- Subtraction with Models

Use with Item 5

Tell students that the class will solve Item 5 together. Ask students to read Item 5.

Understand

What is the problem asking you to find? how many green apples Todd bought

What information is given in the problem that will help you find the solution? Todd bought 13 apples; 7 of the apples were red.

Plan

Explain that there are many ways to solve any problem, but this time we are going to use a model to show subtraction.

How can you model this problem? apples

How many of the apples should you color red? 7 apples

Try It

Explain that there are many ways to model the problem. Ask several students to draw models on the board while the rest of the class draws models at their desk. Students will have different ways of modeling this problem, but their models should be similar to the following:

Step 1: Use 13 apples.

Step 2: Color 7 apples red.

Step 3: Color the remaining apples green.

Step 4: Students should count the green apples and find that Todd bought 6 green apples.

Look Back

Have students compare their models and solutions with those shown on the board. Make sure that all students agree that the correct answer is C, or 6 apples.

Check the Answer How can you check the answer? Possible answer: Write a number sentence. 13 – 7 = 6

Remind students that when taking a multiple-choice test, they should fill in the bubble next to their answer choice.

Extra Support To review the mathematics in Item 5, use Lesson 1.2, Using Subtraction, pp. 26–27.

Test Prep Handbook

Cumulative Test

Minilesson for Item 3

Focus
- Estimation
- Problem Solving
- Rounding

Use with Item 3

Tell students that, as a class, you will solve Item 3. Ask a student to write on the board the four steps followed in the four-step problem solving process. Then ask a student to read Item 3 aloud.

Understand

What does the question ask you to do? Round a number to the nearest hundred.

What does it mean to round a number? Possible answer: Find the closest ten, or in this case, the closest hundred.

Plan

Remember that when you are given multiple choices for an answer, you may want to start by eliminating some of the choices.

How do you know which choices to eliminate? Possible answer: Some choices are obviously incorrect.

Try It

Which answer choice is obviously incorrect? Why? 850; When a number is rounded to the nearest hundred, all the digits to the right of the hundreds place are zeros.

Instruct students to work in pairs. Have each pair choose at least one more answer choice they can eliminate.

Why could your choice be eliminated? Possible answer: Eliminate 700 because 860 is between 800 and 900, not between 700 and 800.

Have students agree in their pairs on which of the remaining two choices is correct. 900

Look Back

Explain how you made your choice. Possible reasoning: 860 is closer to 900 than 800.

Check the Answer Describe one way of checking the answer. Possible answer: Write 800–900 by tens or a number line; compare 860 to 800 and 900.

Remind students that on a multiple-choice test, they must fill in the bubble next to their answer choice.

Extra Support To review the mathematics in Item 3, use Lesson 2.8, Rounding, pp. 58–59.

Chapter 2 Cumulative Test

Mark your answer on the answer sheet.

1. Which number is shown in the picture of the model? D

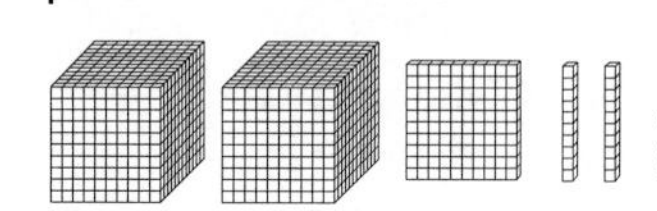

A 1,223
B 2,023
C 2,132
D 2,123

2. Which group of numbers is in order from greatest to least? J

F 498, 849, 894, 984
G 498, 894, 849, 984
H 894, 984, 849, 498
J 984, 894, 849, 498

3. Which number shows 860 rounded to the nearest hundred? D

A 700
B 800
C 850
D 900

4. The picture shows how much money Jen and Bob have. J

Jen

Bob

How much do they have together?

F $3.52
G $3.57
H $3.82
J $3.87

5. What are the next 2 numbers in this pattern? C

1, 2, 4, 7, 11, ■, ■

A 8, 6
B 15, 21
C 16, 22
D 16, 23

GO ON

506

Reading Strategies Use with Item 7

Remind students that they can use the Monitor reading strategy by asking themselves if the information given in a problem makes sense.

Thinking Aloud

What is the problem asking me to do? *I need to find a number which will make the number sentence true.*

What is the sum of the numbers on the left side of the equal sign? *The sum is 16.*

What should the sum of the numbers to the right of the equal sign be? Why? *The sum should be16. The value of the numbers on each side of an equal sign must be the same.*

Invite students to finish the problem and decide as a class which is the correct answer.

For More Practice Monitor reading strategy minilessons, TE p. 40J.

Extra Support To review the mathematics in Item 7, use Lesson 1.7, Using Tens to Add, pp. 16–17.

6. Which clock shows 20 minutes after 7 o'clock? F

F 

G 

H 

J 

7. Which number goes into the box to make the sentence true?

7 + 9 = 10 + ■ C

- A 2
- B 4
- C 6
- D 8

8. What is the value of 9 in the number 293,145? H

- F 900
- G 9,000
- H 90,000
- J 900,000

9. You buy a cap for $3.79. How much money do you have left? C

- A $0.21
- B $1.20
- C $1.21
- D $2.21

10. Nancy has about 400 beads. Ellen has about 300 beads. Sandy has 500 beads. Find out how many beads Nancy and Sandy have altogether. Which shows you how to find the answer using mental math? H

- F 4 − 3 + 5
- G 4 + 3 + 5
- H 4 + 5
- J 5 − 4 − 3

STOP

Test Prep Handbook

507

Student Handbook Masters

The Test Prep Handbook pages can be found as blackline masters in the **Student Handbook Masters.**

Scoring Chart

Number of Items Correct	1	2	3	4	5	6	7	8	9	10
Score	10	20	30	40	50	60	70	80	90	100

Item Analysis

Item	1	2	3	4	5	6	7	8	9	10
Lesson	2.5	2.9	2.8	2.12	2.4	2.15	1.7	2.5	2.13	2.7

Minilesson for Item 9

Focus

- **Reasonableness**
- **Problem Solving**
- **Making Change**

Use with Item 9

Tell students that you will solve Item 9 together.

Understand

What is the money amount given in the problem? $3.79

What does the money amount in the picture tell? the amount to start with

Plan

What operation can be used to solve the problem? subtraction

Could you add the two money amounts to find the change you will receive? Why or why not? No. The sum of the two money amounts will be greater than the amount I started with. I will have less than that if I spend some.

What operation will you use to find your change? Why? subtraction, because I need to find the amount remaining

Try It

How can you show subtraction on the picture? Cross off $3.79.

Is it reasonable for the answer to be greater than $1 or less than $1? Why? greater than $1; If you cross off $3 there is still a dollar and change left.

Look Back

Verify that every student correctly chose $1.21 as the solution.

Check the Answer One way to check the answer to Item 9 is to count on from $1.21. Add back $3.79 to see if you get $5.00.

Extension Have students find how much money would be left if the cap had cost $4.79.

For More Practice with reasonableness, ask students to describe how they would solve Item 4. See also Chapter 2 Chapter Test, Performance Task, p. 7–9.

Extra Support To review the mathematics in Item 9, use Lessons 2.12–2.13, Dollars and Cents or Making Change, pp. 66–67 or pp. 68–69.

Cumulative Test

Minilesson for Item 2

Focus

- Representation
- Problem Solving
- Addition

Use with Item 2

Tell students you will solve Item 2 as a class. Explain that you will use the four-step problem solving process. Have a student write the four steps on the board. Then ask a student to read Item 2 aloud.

Understand

What is the problem asking you to do? Find the number of stamps Robb has in all.

In which months does the problem say that Robb bought more? March, May, and June

How many stamps did Robb start with? 52 stamps

Plan

Remind students that there are many ways to solve the problem, but this time you are going to use a number sentence.

How could you represent this problem? Write an addition sentence.

How many addends will there be? 4

Try It

Ask several students to write an addition sentence on the board and solve it to find the solution to Item 2. Have the rest of the class write a number sentence at their desks. 52 + 16 + 18 + 14 = 100

Look Back

Compare your number sentences. Were the results all the same?

Check the Answer Another way to represent Item 2 is to use place-value blocks.

Remind students that on a multiple-choice test, they must fill in the bubble next to their answer choice.

For More Practice using number sentences, ask students to describe how they would solve Items 1 and 3. See also Chapter 4 Cumulative Test, p. 152.

Extra Support To review the mathematics in Item 2, use Lesson 3.5, Three or More Addends, pp. 94–95.

Chapter 3 Cumulative Test

Mark your answer on the answer sheet.

1. On Monday a truck driver drove 348 miles. On Tuesday he drove 212 miles. Which shows how many miles he drove both days? C

   A 348 − 212
   B 348 > 212
   C 348 + 212
   D 300 + 200

2. Robb had 52 stamps. In March he bought 16 more. In May he bought 18 more and in June he bought 14 more. How many stamps does Robb have in all? J

   F 80
   G 90
   H 99
   J 100

3. Mrs. Chang has flown 784 miles. She will get a free trip when she has flown 955 miles. How many more miles must she fly to get a free trip? B

   A 161 mi
   B 171 mi
   C 261 mi
   D 271 mi

4. Which flower is inside both the circle and the square? F

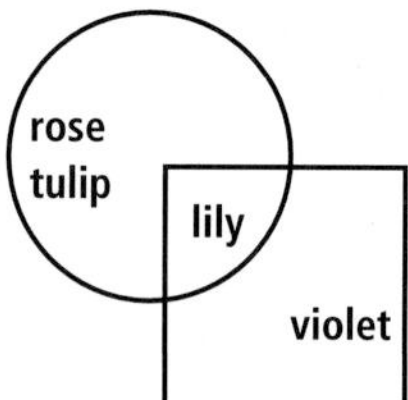

   F lily
   G tulip
   H violet
   J rose

5. The Sabata family drove 145 miles from San Antonio to Laredo. Then they drove 168 miles to Brownsville. Which is a reasonable way to estimate how many miles they drove altogether? B

   A 200 − 100 = ■
   B 100 + 200 = ■
   C 200 + 200 = ■
   D 200 + 300 = ■

GO ON

Reading Strategies Use with Item 7

Remind students that they can use the Predict/Infer reading strategy by reading carefully and looking for important information.

Thinking Aloud

What do I know after reading the problem? *I know there are 32 boxes of soap stacked on 4 shelves and each shelf has 4 more boxes than the one above it.*

Predict what shape all the boxes of soap together might look like on the shelves. *Since each shelf down has more boxes on it, I predict the shape is similar to a triangle.*

What do I need to find out? *I need to find out how many boxes of soap are on each shelf.*

Invite students to finish the problem and decide as a class which is the correct answer.

For More Practice Predict/Infer reading strategy minilessons, TE p. 84J.

Extra Support To review the mathematics in Item 7, use Lesson 2.4, Look for a Pattern, pp. 48–49.

6. There are 16 people in line to buy movie tickets. You are the 9th in line. How many people are behind you? G

- F 6
- G 7
- H 8
- J 25

7. In a store, boxes of soap are stacked on 4 shelves. Each shelf has 4 more boxes than the one above it. There are 32 boxes in all. How many boxes are on each shelf from top to bottom? D

- A 1, 5, 9, 13
- B 1, 5, 10, 16
- C 2, 4, 8, 14
- D 2, 6, 10, 14

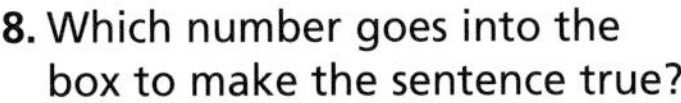

8. Which number goes into the box to make the sentence true?

$18 + 7 + 3 = 18 + \blacksquare + 7$ G

- F 2
- G 3
- H 7
- J 18

9. What is the standard form of eight hundred seventy-four thousand, one hundred twenty-nine? C

- A 800,740
- B 874,000
- C 874,129
- D 874,029

10. How is 121 written in word form? F

- F one hundred twenty-one
- G one hundred twelve
- H one hundred two one
- J one twenty-one

11. Which number line shows odd numbers greater than 10 *and* less than 20? A

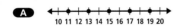

- A 10 11 12 13 14 15 16 17 18 19 20
- B 10 11 12 13 14 15 16 17 18 19 20
- C 10 11 12 13 14 15 16 17 18 19 20
- D 10 11 12 13 14 15 16 17 18 19 20

STOP

Test Prep Handbook

509

Student Handbook Masters

The Test Prep Handbook pages can be found as blackline masters in the **Student Handbook Masters.**

Scoring Chart

Number of Items Correct	1	2	3	4	5	6	7	8	9	10	11
Score	9	18	27	36	46	55	64	73	82	91	100

Item Analysis

Item	1	2	3	4	5	6	7	8	9	10	11
Lesson	3.3	3.5	3.9	2.6	3.4	1.2	2.4	1.8	2.5	2.3	1.2

Minilesson for Item 5

Focus

- Reasonableness
- Problem Solving
- Rounding

Use with Item 5

Tell students you will solve Item 5 together. Have a student read Item 5 aloud.

Understand

Where is the Sabata family driving? from San Antonio to Laredo and then to Brownsville

How many miles did they drive from Laredo to Brownsville? 168 miles

Plan

What is one way to solve this problem?
Possible answer: Start by eliminating answer choices.

Which answer choice can be eliminated immediately before rounding either distance? Why? Choice A; To find the total distance the Sabata family drove, we have to add.

To what place value do the numbers have to be rounded to match the answer choices? the nearest hundred

Is there another choice that can be eliminated just by considering the two distances? Why? Yes, Choice D; Both distances are between 100 and 200, so neither distance would round to 300.

Try It

Which number sentence will give a reasonable estimate? B Have pairs describe the method they used to round the two distances.

Look Back

Verify that each pair chose choice B as their answer. Have several students describe the rounding method they used.

Check the Answer Describe ways you could check the answer to Item 5. Possible answer: Make a number line from 100–200 with hundreds; see if the numbers are rounded correctly.

For More Practice with rounding, see Chapter 6 Cumulative Test (Items 15–21), p. 222.

Extra Support To review the mathematics in Item 5, use Lesson 3.4, Estimating Sums, pp. 92–93.

Test Prep Handbook

Cumulative Test

Minilesson for Item 3

Focus
- Representation
- Problem Solving
- Bar Graphs

Use with Item 3

Tell students you will solve Item 3 as a class. Ask four students to each describe one of the steps in the four-step problem solving process. Then ask students to read Item 3.

Understand
What type of graph is shown for Item 3? bar graph
What does the problem ask you to do? Find the number of students who worked at the most popular booth.

Plan
Ask students to describe ways they would solve this problem.
Which booth is the most popular? Explain your reasoning. The games booth is the most popular because it has the longest bar.
Find the longest bar. Draw a line from the top of the longest bar to the row of numbers along the graph.

Try It
Which number did the bar for the most popular game come closest to? 8
Which answer choice gives the correct solution? C

Look Back
Have students tell what kind of booth matches each of the remaining answer choices.

Check the Answer One way to check the answer to Item 3 is to use a ruler to make a straight line from the end of the longest bar to the number scale.
Remind students that on a multiple-choice test, they must fill in the bubble next to their answer choice.

Extension Ask the class which booth would have had the most students working at it if there were no games booth. food booth

For More Practice with bar graphs, see Chapter 6 Cumulative Test (Items 22–26), p. 223.

Extra Support To review the mathematics in Item 2, use Lesson 4.5, Bar Graphs, pp. 132–133.

Chapter 4 Cumulative Test

Mark your answer on the answer sheet.

1. The graph shows the number of snowy days each month last winter.

Snowy Days	
December	❄❄❄
January	❄❄❄❄❄
February	❄❄❄❄
March	❄❄
Key: ❄ = 2 days	

How many snowy days were there in February? D
- A 2 days
- B 4 days
- C 6 days
- D 8 days

2. In a bag there are 5 red cubes, 9 green cubes, 3 yellow cubes, and 1 blue cube. If you pick a cube, which color would you be most likely to pick? G
- F red
- G green
- H yellow
- J blue

3. The graph shows the number of students working at booths for the charity fair on Saturday.

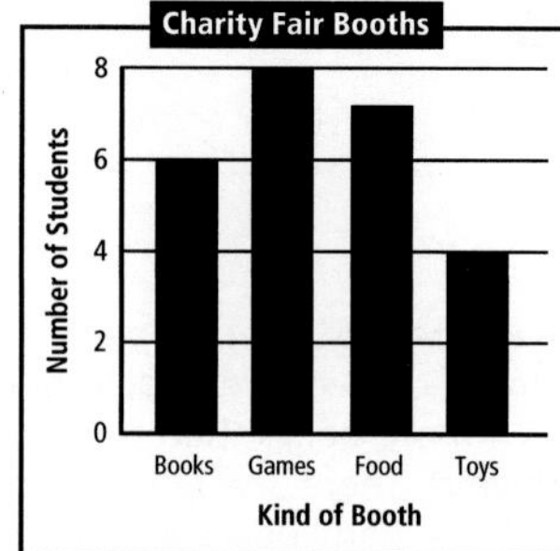

How many students worked at the most popular booth? C
- A 4
- B 0
- C 8
- D 6

4. The sum of 2 numbers is 30. Their difference is 6. What are the numbers? G
- F 11 and 19
- G 12 and 18
- H 13 and 17
- J 14 and 16

GO ON

510

Reading Strategies Use with Item 4

Remind students that they can use the Predict/Infer reading strategy by reading carefully and looking for important information.

Thinking Aloud
What do I know? *A sum is the answer to an addition problem. A difference is the answer to a subtraction problem.*
What does the problem ask me to find? *It asks me to find the pair of numbers.*
What do I predict I will need to do? *I predict I will need to add and subtract numbers to find the pair of numbers.*

Invite students to finish the problem and decide as a class which is the correct answer.

For More Practice Predict/Infer reading strategy minilessons, TE p. 122J.

Extra Support To review the mathematics in Item 4, use Lessons 3.2 and 3.8, Adding 2-Digit Numbers and Subtracting 2-Digit Numbers, pp. 88–89 and pp. 102–103.

5. The graph shows the number of videos rented at the video store for five days.

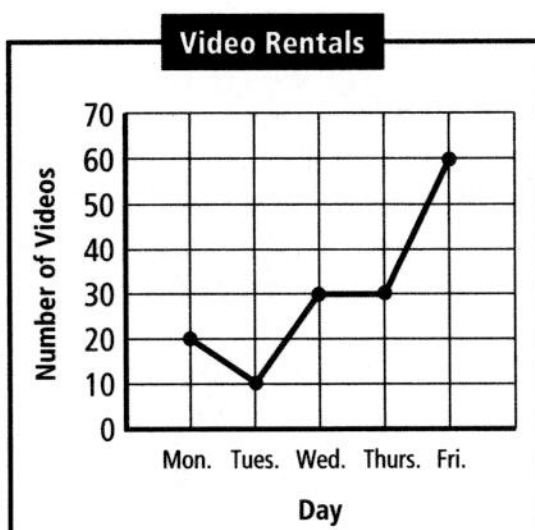

How many videos were rented on Wednesday, Thursday and Friday? B

- (A) 60
- (B) 120
- (C) 130
- (D) 150

6. On which spinner would the arrow be most likely to stop on white? F

(F) 

(G) 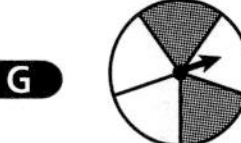

(H) 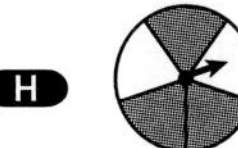

(J) 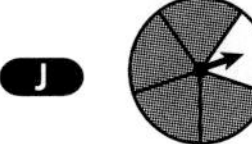

7. George read 24 pages of a book on Monday. He read 37 pages on Tuesday, 45 pages Wednesday, and 17 pages on Friday. How can you find the best estimate of the number of pages he read? B

- (A) round numbers down, add
- (B) round to the nearest ten, add
- (C) round numbers up, add
- (D) round to nearest hundred, add

8. Why is 17 **not** the next number in this pattern?

1, 4, 7, 10, 13,  G

- (F) It needs to be an even number.
- (G) It needs to be 3 more than 13.
- (H) It needs to be a 1-digit number.
- (J) It needs to be 3 less than 13.

STOP

Test Prep Handbook

Student Handbook Masters

The Test Prep Handbook pages can be found as blackline masters in the **Student Handbook Masters.**

Scoring Chart

Number of Items Correct	1	2	3	4	5	6	7	8
Score	13	25	38	50	63	75	88	100

Item Analysis

Item	1	2	3	4	5	6	7	8
Lesson	4.4	4.9	4.5	3.10	4.6	4.10	2.8	2.4

Minilesson for Item 2

Focus

- Representation
- Problem Solving
- Drawing a Picture

Use with Item 2

Tell students you will solve Item 2 together.

Understand

What does the problem ask you to do? Decide which color is most likely to be picked.

How many colors can you choose from? 4 colors

Plan

Remind students that there may be many ways to solve a problem. How could you use a picture or model to solve the problem? Draw a picture of the different-colored cubes.

Is it important to show the correct number of each color? Why or why not? Yes, because you have to know which color there is most of.

How many of each color will you show? 5 red, 9 green, 3 yellow, and 1 blue

Try It

Have students draw their own model of the blocks using crayons.

Which color is most likely to be picked? Explain your reasoning. green, because it is the most common color

Look Back

Why did using the drawing help you to solve the problem? Possible answer: I needed to see how many of each color there were.

Check the Answer Describe a way you could check Item 2. Possible answer: Make a model with real blocks. Remind students that on a multiple-choice test, they must fill in the bubble next to their answer choice.

Extension Have students determine the color most likely to be picked from 4 blue cubes, 6 red cubes, 2 yellow cubes, and 6 green cubes. Red and green are equally likely.

For More Practice using pictorial models, see Chapter 4 Chapter Test (Items 3–7), p. 150.

Extra Support To review the mathematics in Item 2, use Lesson 4.9, Experimenting with Chance, pp. 142–143.

Test Prep Handbook

Cumulative Test

Minilesson for Item 1

Focus
- Representation
- Problem Solving
- Addition and Multiplication

Use with Item 1

Tell students you will solve Item 1 together. Ask a volunteer to describe the four-step problem solving process. Then ask students to look over Item 1.

Understand

What does the question ask you to do? Find a number sentence that means the same as the one shown.

Plan

Remind students that there may be several ways to solve a problem. For this problem, you will use a picture or model.

How could you show 5 + 5 + 5 + 5 = 20? Possible answer: Draw 4 groups with 5 items in each group.

Ask volunteers to draw models of the number sentence on the board.

What other operation could this model represent? multiplication

How is the model for repeated addition similar to multiplication? There is the same number of items in each group and the same number of groups.

Try It

Tell students to choose the answer choice they think is correct. Then have them explain their reasoning.

Look Back

Why could you eliminate the division sentences? In division you start with the total and then divide the items into equal groups. In multiplication you start with the groups and find the total.

Ask students if they agreed with their partners. If there is a disagreement, have students describe their reasoning for the class and have the class explain why the answers differed. Then have them choose the answer that is correct.

Check the Answer Ask students to suggest ways to check the answer. Possible answer: Use skip-counting. Remind students that on a multiple-choice test, they must fill in the bubble next to their answer choice.

Extra Support To review the mathematics in Item 1, use Lesson 5.1, Using Multiplication, pp. 158–159.

Chapter 5 Cumulative Test

Mark your answer on the answer sheet.

1. Which number sentence means the same as

   5 + 5 + 5 + 5 = 20? C

   A 20 ÷ 5 = 4
   B 4 + 5 = 20
   C 4 × 5 = 20
   D 20 ÷ 4 = 5

2. Lita put her shell collection into boxes. She put 5 shells in each box. Use the table. How many shells are 5 boxes? H

Shell Collection					
Number of Boxes	1	2	3	4	5
Number of Shells	5	10	?	?	?

   F 15 shells
   G 20 shells
   H 25 shells
   J 30 shells

3. Tomo has 5 packs of trading cards. There are 3 cards in each pack. Which number sentence shows how many cards he has? C

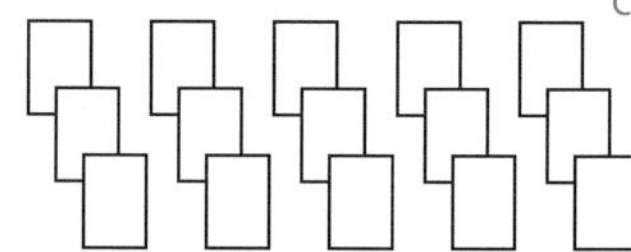

   A 4 × 3 = 12
   B 15 + 3 = 18
   C 5 × 3 = 15
   D 15 ÷ 3 = 5

4. Which example shows the order property of multiplication? G

   F 0 × 5 = 0
   G 5 × 2 = 10 and 2 × 5 = 10
   H 1 × 5 = 5
   J 2 × 5 = 10 and 5 + 5 = 10

GO ON

512

Reading Strategies Use with Item 4

Remind students that they can use the Think About Words reading strategy. They can find the meanings of unfamiliar words using the context and word parts.

Thinking Aloud

What word(s) are difficult to understand in Item 4? *The words "order" and "property" are hard words.*

Do you know what it means to put things in order? *It means to arrange them a certain way.*

What do you think the order property of multiplication says about multiplication sentences? *You can change the order of some numbers in a multiplication problem, and it will not change the answer.*

What else can you do when you cannot figure out a word's meaning from other words in the problem? *I can look up the word in the glossary or in a dictionary.*

Invite students to finish the problem and decide as a class which is the correct answer.

For More Practice Think About Words reading strategy minilessons, TE p. 156J.

Extra Support To review the mathematics in Item 4, use Lesson 5.11, Exploring Properties of Multiplication, pp. 180–181.

5. Which number sentence is in the same fact family as

$3 \times 4 = 12$? D

- (A) $4 \times 2 = 8$
- (B) $4 + 3 = 7$
- (C) $12 - 4 = 8$
- (D) $12 \div 4 = 3$

6. Sandra put her coin collection in groups of 4. She has 12 coins. Which picture shows how many groups she made? G

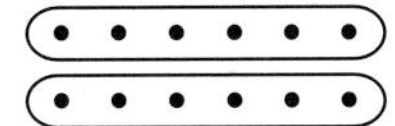

H 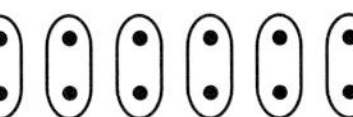

J 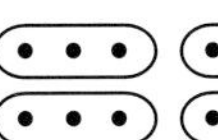 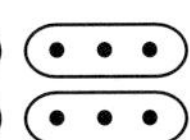

7. The post office sent out 150 boxes this week. They sent out 254 boxes last week. Which is the best way to estimate how many boxes were sent out altogether in the 2 weeks? D

- (A) 100 + 50
- (B) 200 + 200
- (C) 100 + 300
- (D) 200 + 300

8. There are 30 days in the month of April. Which graph shows that there are 4 birthdays in April in this class? G

F
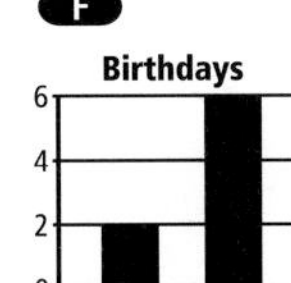

G

H
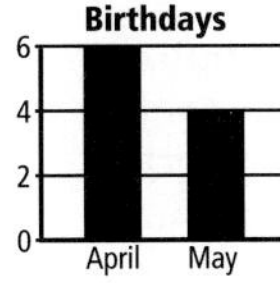

J
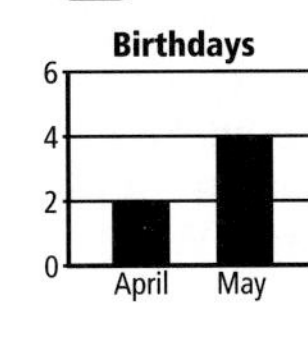

9. How would you write 63,514 in word form? C

- (A) sixty-three hundred, five fourteen
- (B) sixty-three thousand
- (C) sixty-three thousand, five hundred fourteen
- (D) sixty-three thousand, five hundred

10. Which is the value of the 4 in the number 407,926? J

- (F) 400
- (G) 4,000
- (H) 40,000
- (J) 400,000

STOP

Test Prep Handbook

Student Handbook Masters

The Test Prep Handbook pages can be found as blackline masters in the **Student Handbook Masters.**

Scoring Chart

Number of Items Correct	1	2	3	4	5	6	7	8	9	10
Score	10	20	30	40	50	60	70	80	90	100

Item Analysis

Item	1	2	3	4	5	6	7	8	9	10
Lesson	5.1	5.3	5.9	5.11	5.7	5.8	3.4	4.5	2.5	2.5

Minilesson for Item 3

Focus

- Solution Strategies
- Problem Solving
- Choosing the Number Sentence

Use with Item 3

Tell students you will solve Item 3 as a class.

Understand

What does the problem ask you to find? the number sentences that tell the number of trading cards Tomo has

How many packs of trading cards does Tomo have? 5 packs

How does the drawing show those packs? There are 5 groups and 3 cards in each group.

Plan

To solve this problem, students can use reasoning to eliminate answer choices.

Which numbers from the problem should be included in the number sentence? 5 and 3

Which choice does not have these numbers? A

How many trading cards does Tomo have as shown by the picture? 15 cards

What other choice can you eliminate? Why? B; 18 is too great a number.

Is Tomo dividing her cards into groups? Or is Tomo finding a total number? Tomo is finding a total number.

Try It

Ask students which of the remaining answer choices is correct. Have them explain their reasoning.

Look Back

For choice D to be correct, what would the problem have asked for? the number of groups or the number in each group, not how many cards in all.

Check the Answer Ask students to describe a way they can check their answer. Possible answer: Write an addition sentence for the drawing: 3 + 3 + 3 + 3 + 3 = 15. Then rewrite it as a multiplication sentence: 5 x 3 = 15.

For More Practice with reasonableness, ask students to describe how they would solve items 5 and 6. See also Chapter 9 Cumulative Test (Items 12–18), p. 342.

Extra Support To review the mathematics in Item 3, use Lesson 5.9, Multiplying and Dividing with 5, pp. 176–177.

Cumulative Test

Minilesson for Item 2

Focus
- **Solution Strategies**
- **Problem Solving**
- **Choosing a Number Sentence**

Use with Item 2

Tell students you will work on Item 2 as a class. Ask students to name the four steps in the problem solving process. Then ask a student to read Item 2 aloud.

Understand

What is the problem asking you to find? how many photos fit on 4 pages with the same number of photos on each page

Plan

Have students describe ways they could solve this problem. Then work through one possible method.

What operation could you use to take a whole and break it into equal groups? division

What number will be divided into groups? 24

Into how many groups does Ina want to divide her photos? Explain. 4 groups, for the 4 empty pages

By what number will you divide 24? 4

Try It

Have students work in pairs to choose the number sentence that will solve the problem. $24 \div 4 = 6$ Ask students why the remaining choices do not work.

Look Back

Why didn't you need to solve the problem to choose the correct answer? Only the number sentence that divides by 4 was asked for.

Check the Answer Ask students how they could check their answer by eliminating choices. Possible answer: by looking at the picture that shows the operation

Extension Have students describe a situation that could be solved using one of the remaining answer choices.

For More Practice using number sentences, ask students to describe how they would solve Items 3 and 5. See also Chapter 6 Chapter Test (Items 3–12), p. 220.

Extra Support To review the mathematics in Item 2, use Lesson 5.8, Multiplying and Dividing with 4, pp. 174–175.

Chapter 6 Cumulative Test

Mark your answer on the answer sheet.

1. Which number sentence is **not** true? B
   - A $0 \div 5 = 0$
   - B $5 \div 5 = 5$
   - C $5 \div 5 = 1$
   - D $5 \div 1 = 5$

2. Ina has 24 photos. She has 4 empty pages in her photo album. She wants the same number of photos on each page. Which sentence shows how many photos she can put on each page? H

   - F $24 \div 8 = 3$
   - G $24 \div 12 = 2$
   - H $24 \div 4 = 6$
   - J $24 \div 3 = 8$

3. Which number sentence is in the same fact family as

   $9 \times 6 = 54$? D
   - A $6 \times 7 = 42$
   - B $6 + 9 = 15$
   - C $54 - 9 = 45$
   - D $54 \div 6 = 9$

4. Look at the multiplication table.

X	1	2	3	4	5
1		2			?
2		4			?
3		6			?
4		8			?
5		10			?

   Which numbers will be in the column under 5? J
   - F 1, 2, 3, 4, 5
   - G 4, 8, 12, 16, 20
   - H 5, 5, 5, 5, 5
   - J 5, 10, 15, 20, 25

5. Which number sentence has the product 1,800? B
   - A $3 \times 6{,}000 = ■$
   - B $3 \times 600 = ■$
   - C $3 \times 60 = ■$
   - D $3 \times 6 = ■$

GO ON

514

Reading Strategies Use with Item 10

Remind students that they can use the Evaluate reading strategy by looking at what a problem tells and what a problem asks for.

Thinking Aloud

What does the problem tell? *It tells how much money the dress show took in on Monday, Tuesday, and Wednesday.*

What does the problem ask for? *It asks for the total amount the shop took in on all 3 days.*

Will I need all the numbers given in the problem? *Yes, I will.*

What word, or words, gives me a clue about the operation I will use to solve the problem? *The word "altogether" tells me I should use addition.*

Invite students to finish the problem and decide as a class which is the correct answer.

For More Practice Evaluate reading strategy minilessons, TE p. 190J.

Extra Support To review the mathematics in Item 10, use Lesson 3.3, Adding 3-Digit Numbers, pp. 90–91.

6. Which clock shows the same time? G

F 3:00
G 3:05
H 3:10
J 3:10

7. Which pair of rounded numbers is the most reasonable for estimating the sum? D

278 + 855

A 200 + 800
B 300 + 800
C 280 + 800
D 300 + 900

8. Matt's bookcase has 5 shelves. He can fit 8 books on a shelf. How many books can he put in the bookcase? Use the table. F

Number of Shelves	1	2	3	4	5
Number of Books	8	?	?	?	?

F 40
G 32
H 24
J 26

9. Three people can sit around a triangular table. If 5 tables are put together as shown, how many people can be seated? C

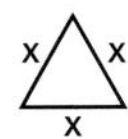

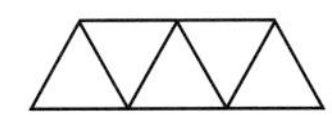

A 9
B 8
C 7
D 6

10. The dress shop took in $255 on Monday, $198 on Tuesday, and $312 on Wednesday. How much did the shop take in altogether? F

F $765
G $755
H $665
J $664

STOP

Test Prep Handbook

Student Handbook Masters

The Test Prep Handbook pages can be found as blackline masters in the **Student Handbook Masters**.

Scoring Chart

Number of Items Correct	1	2	3	4	5	6	7	8	9	10
Score	10	20	30	40	50	60	70	80	90	100

Item Analysis

Item	1	2	3	4	5	6	7	8	9	10
Lesson	6.1	5.8	6.5	6.4	6.11	2.15	3.4	5.3	4.2	3.3

Minilesson for Item 8

Focus

- Representation
- Problem Solving
- Patterns and Tables

Use with Item 8

Tell students you will solve Item 8 as a class.

Understand

What does the problem ask? how many books Matt can put in his bookcase

Plan

Remind students that there may be several ways to solve a problem. This time drawing a picture can help solve the problem.

How many shelves are in Matt's bookcase? 5 shelves

Draw a bookcase with 5 shelves on the board.

How many books can fit on each shelf? 8 books

Have a student draw 8 books on the first shelf.

How many books can fit on 2 shelves? 16 books

Have a student draw 8 books on the second shelf to verify the answer to the previous question.

How many books can fit on three shelves? 24 books

Have someone draw 8 books on the third shelf to verify the answer to the previous question.

Try It

Have students draw their own model to find the solution to the problem. Have the class agree that the bookcase holds 40 books, or choice F.

Look Back

How is drawing a picture similar to solving the problem using the table?

Check the Answer Ask students what multiplication sentence they could use to solve the problem? $5 \times 8 = 40$ or $8 \times 5 = 40$

Extension Have students find how many shelves would be filled if Matt had 32, 24, or 48 books. 4, 3, 8

For More Practice using pictorial models, ask students to describe how they would solve Item 9. See also Chapter 8 Cumulative Test (Items 15-21), p.298.

Extra Support To review the mathematics in Item 8, use Lesson 5.3, Make a Table, pp. 162–163.

Test Prep Handbook

Cumulative Test

Minilesson for Item 9

Focus

- **Solution Strategies**
- **Problem Solving**
- **Number Lines**

Use with Item 9

Tell students you will solve Item 9 together. Write the four steps of the problem solving process on the board. Then have students read Item 9 to themselves.

Understand

What is the question asking you to do? Choose the number line that shows all the numbers that are greater than 4 and less than 7.

Plan

Discuss ways of solving the problem. Explain that sometimes it's easier to eliminate answer choices.
Which answer is most obviously incorrect? Why? Possible answer: B. There are dots on numbers less than 4 and greater than 7.
Why can you eliminate A? You need to find all the numbers greater than 4 and less than 7, not just the numbers 4 and 7.

Try It

Have students determine which of the two remaining answer choices is correct.

Look Back

Discuss why C is incorrect. Because it includes 4 and 7. Item 9 asks for the numbers greater than 4 (not 4 itself) and less than 7 (not 7 itself).

Check the Answer Count and make a list of numbers that are greater than 4 and less than 7. Check that all of the numbers are on the number line.
Remind students that on a multiple-choice test, they must fill in the bubble next to their answer choice.

Extension Have students describe the numbers shown on the other number lines, such as which are odd or even.

For More Practice using number lines, see Chapter 7 Cumulative Test (Items 1–7), p. 266.

Extra Support To review the mathematics in Item 9, use Lesson 2.6, Logical Reasoning, p. 52.

Chapter 7 Cumulative Test

Mark your answer on the answer sheet.

1. Does this picture show a slide, flip, or turn? B

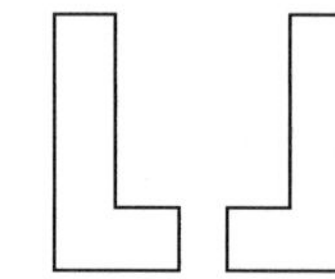

- A slide
- B flip
- C turn
- D half turn

2. Which picture shows congruent figures (have the same size and shape)? H

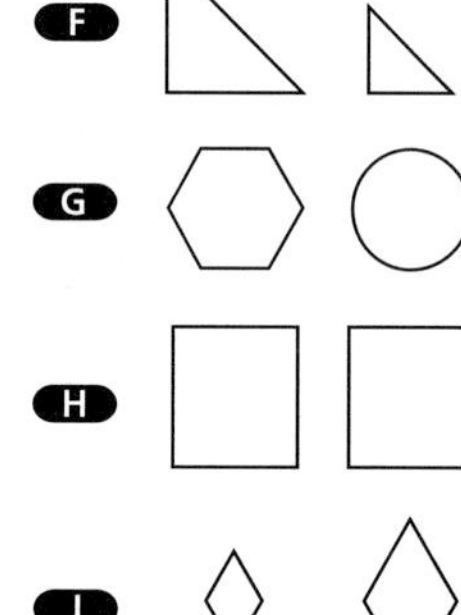

3. Sixty-three thousand people came to watch the football game. What is another way to write this number? C

- A 63
- B 630
- C 63,000
- D 6,300

4. Which pattern has **only** even numbers in it? J

- F 1 3 5 7 9
- G 5 10 15 20 25
- H 11 22 33 44 55
- J 10 20 30 40 50

5. Why is 64 **not** the next number in this pattern?

2, 4, 8, 16, ▒ B

- A It needs to be 4 more than 16.
- B It needs to be the double of 16.
- C It needs to be an odd number.
- D It needs to be less than 10.

GO ON

516

Reading Strategies Use with Item 1

Remind students that they can use the Self-Question reading strategy by asking themselves questions about what they have read.

Thinking Aloud

What does the question ask me to decide? *It asks me to decide if the drawing shows a slide, flip, or turn.*

What is a slide? *A slide is when you move a figure along a line.*

What is a flip? A flip is a move that makes a figure face in the opposite direction.

What is a turn? *A turn is a move that rotates a figure around a point.*

How can I make a model showing a flip, slide, and turn? *Possible answer: Trace the figure.*

Invite students to finish the problem and decide as a class which is the correct answer.

For More Practice Self-Question reading strategy minilessons, TE p. 226J.

Extra Support To review the mathematics in Item 1, use Lessons 7.1, 7.2, 7.3; Slides, Flips, Turns; pp. 228–233.

6. What is the shaded face on this pyramid? J

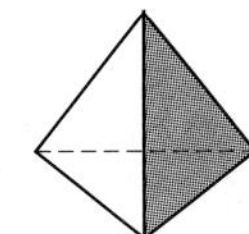

- F circle
- G square
- H hexagon
- J triangle

7. A redwood tree is 255 feet tall. A fir tree is 158 feet tall. An oak tree is 150 feet tall. How much taller is the redwood than the fir? C

- A 100 feet
- B 413 feet
- C 97 feet
- D 255 feet

8. How many lines of symmetry does this rectangle have? F

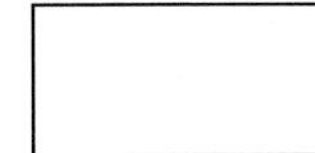

- F 2
- G 3
- H 4
- J 1

9. Which number line shows all the numbers that are greater than 4 **and** less than 7? D

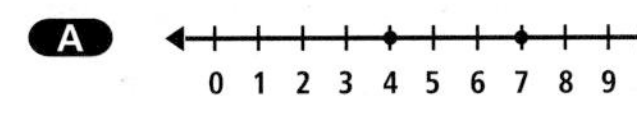

A 0 1 2 3 4 5 6 7 8 9

B 0 1 2 3 4 5 6 7 8 9

C 0 1 2 3 4 5 6 7 8 9

D 0 1 2 3 4 5 6 7 8 9

10. Three classes are going on a field trip. One class has 22 students, another class has 25 students, and a third class has 31 students. What is a reasonable way to estimate the total number of students? J

- F 20 + 20 + 20 = ▪
- G 20 + 25 + 30 = ▪
- H 200 + 300 + 300 = ▪
- J 20 + 30 + 30 = ▪

STOP

Test Prep Handbook

517

Student Handbook Masters

The Test Prep Handbook pages can be found as blackline masters in the **Student Handbook Masters**.

Scoring Chart

Number of Items Correct	1	2	3	4	5	6	7	8	9	10
Score	10	20	30	40	50	60	70	80	90	100

Item Analysis

Item	1	2	3	4	5	6	7	8	9	10
Lesson	7.2	7.6	2.5	7.4	7.4	7.10	3.9	7.7	2.6	3.4

Minilesson for Item 10

Focus

- Estimation
- Problem Solving
- Rounding

Use with Item 10

Tell students you will work on Item 10 as a class. Ask four students to each describe one of the steps in the four-step problem solving process. Then ask one student to read Item 10 aloud.

Understand

What is the question asking you to do? Find a reasonable estimate.

What data will you use to find the solution? 22, 25, and 31 students

Plan

Suggest that they round the data and write a number sentence.

What operation do you use to find the total number of students? addition

To what place should you round? Why? The numbers are all less than 100, so you can round to the nearest ten.

What answer choice can be eliminated now that you know to what place you will round? H

What number sentence would you use to find the exact number of students who went on the field trip?

22 + 25 + 31 = □

Try It

Have each student round the data to the nearest 10 and write a number sentence.

20 + 30 + 30 = □

Look Back

Verify that each student selected answer choice J. Ask students why estimates F and G are not as accurate.

Check the Answer Ask students to describe ways they can check their answers. Possible answer: Make a number line from 0–100 using tens; use it to round.

For More Practice rounding, see Chapter 8 Cumulative Test (Items 1–7), p. 298.

Extra Support To review the mathematics in Item 10, use Lesson 3.4, Estimating Sums, pp. 92–93.

Test Prep Handbook

Cumulative Test

Minilesson for Item 3

Focus
- Reasonableness
- Problem Solving
- Using Inverse Operations

Use with Item 3

Tell students you will solve Item 3 as a class.
What are the four steps we use to solve a problem? understand, plan, try it, and look back
Have each student read Item 3 to themselves.

Understand
What is this question asking you to do? Find the number sentence that solves a division problem.

Plan
Ask students for suggestions for solving item 3.
Since you don't have anything to solve before making your choice, solve Item 3 by elimination.
Which numbers would you expect to find in the correct number sentence? Why? 72 and 8; because they are the numbers in the division problem
What operation would be the most helpful? Why? multiplication, because it is in the same fact family

Try It
Have students work in pairs choosing answers that can be eliminated. Have students explain why C is the correct choice.

Look Back
Ask students to explain why it is reasonable to use multiplication when solving division problems.

Check the Answer Ask students to describe ways they can check their answer. Possible answer: Draw a picture to see if $72 \div 8 = 9$.

Extension Have students name number sentences that could be solved with the help of the remaining three choices.

For More Practice with reasonableness, ask students to describe how they would solve Items 4 and 7. See also Chapter 11 Cumulative Test (Items 15–21), p. 406.

Extra Support To review the mathematics in Item 3, use Lesson 6.8, Multiplying and Dividing with 8, pp. 208–209.

Chapter 8 Cumulative Test

Mark your answer on the answer sheet.

1. Look at the picture. Which fraction tells how much of the circle is shaded? D

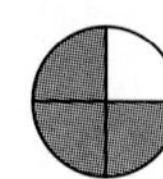

- A $\frac{1}{4}$
- B $\frac{1}{2}$
- C $\frac{3}{5}$
- D $\frac{3}{4}$

2. Which picture shows that

$\frac{1}{4} < \frac{2}{4}$? H

F 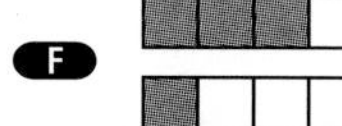

G 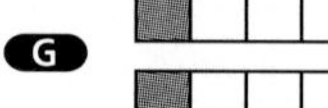

H 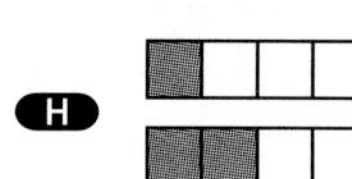

J 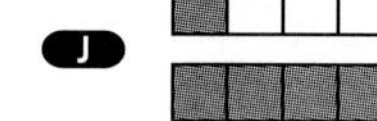

3. Which number sentence can help you find

$72 \div 8 = ■$? C

- A $8 \times 8 = 64$
- B $8 + 9 = 17$
- C $8 \times 9 = 72$
- D $72 - 8 = 64$

4. A friend has 2 more brothers than sisters. If your friend has 6 brothers and sisters in all, how many sisters are there? G

- F 5
- G 2
- H 3
- J 1

5. How much of the square is shaded? A

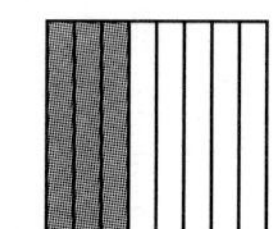

- A three eighths
- B one eighth
- C one half
- D three fourths

GO ON

518

Reading Strategies Use with Item 4

Remind students that they can use the Summarize reading strategy by writing a summary of a problem for a partner.

Thinking Aloud
After reading through the problem the first time, what do I need to find out? *Possible answer: A friend has some brothers and sisters and I need to find the number of sisters.*
After rereading the problem carefully, what do I know? *Possible answer: This friend has more brothers than sisters, but has 6 brothers and sisters altogether.*
What other information is important? *There are 2 more brothers than sisters.*
How would I summarize the problem for my partner? *Possible answer: I need to know how many sisters someone has. This person has 6 brothers and sisters, but 2 more brothers than sisters.*

Invite students to finish the problem and decide which answer is correct.

For More Practice Summarize reading strategy minilessons, TE p. 270J.

Extra Support To review the mathematics in Item 4, use Lesson 6.4, Guess and Check, pp. 198–199.

6. Which sentence tells about the fractions shown in the picture? J

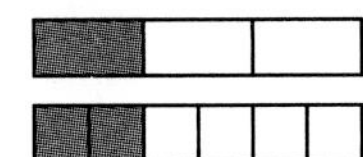

(F) $\frac{1}{2} = \frac{2}{4}$

(G) $\frac{1}{4} = \frac{2}{8}$

(H) $\frac{3}{4} = \frac{6}{8}$

(J) $\frac{1}{3} = \frac{2}{6}$

7. What is the difference? C

$$\begin{array}{r} 208 \\ -\ 19 \\ \hline \end{array}$$

(A) 199
(B) 181
(C) 189
(D) 89

8. Which number sentence means the same as

4 + 4 + 4 + 4 = 16? G

(F) 16 ÷ 2 = 8
(G) 4 × 4 = 16
(H) 16 + 4 = 20
(J) 8 + 8 = 16

9. Which picture shows $1\frac{2}{3}$? D

(A) 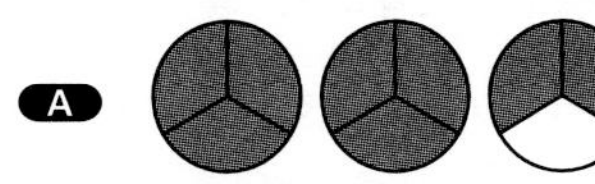

(B) 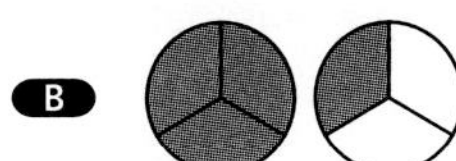

(C) 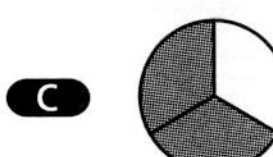

(D) 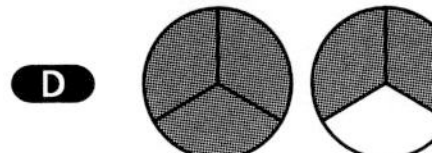

10. Three friends were playing a game. Jake got 22 points, Ann got 59 points and Bonnie got 76 points. About how many more points did Ann get than Bonnie? G

(F) 10
(G) 20 
(H) 50
(J) 60

STOP

Test Prep Handbook

519

Student Handbook Masters

The Test Prep Handbook pages can be found as blackline masters in the **Student Handbook Masters**.

Scoring Chart

Number of Items Correct	1	2	3	4	5	6	7	8	9	10
Score	10	20	30	40	50	60	70	80	90	100

Item Analysis

Item	1	2	3	4	5	6	7	8	9	10
Lesson	8.2	8.3	6.8	6.4	8.2	8.4	3.12	5.1	8.9	3.11

Minilesson for Item 6

Focus

- **Solution Strategies**
- **Problem Solving**
- **Fraction Models**

Use with Item 6

Tell students you will work on Item 6 as a class. Remind students that you will use the four-step problem solving process. Have each student read Item 6 to themselves.

Understand

What is this question asking you to do? Find the fraction sentence that describes the fractions shown in the drawing.

Plan

Could you use elimination to solve this problem? Explain. Yes, we can eliminate the fraction sentences as we look more carefully at the drawing.

Into how many parts is the top fraction model divided? 3

How many parts are shaded? 1

What fraction can you write for the shaded part? $\frac{1}{3}$

What fraction can you write for the shaded part of the other fraction model? $\frac{1}{6}$

Try It

Have students eliminate all the incorrect answer choices. Since there is only one answer choice with the fraction $\frac{1}{3}$, the answer is J.

Look Back

Have students explain why answer choice J is the correct answer.

Check the Answer Ask students to describe how they can check their answers.

Possible answer: I can write the fraction for the equivalent fraction model, $\frac{2}{6}$, and see if that's in the sentence too.

Remind students that on a multiple-choice test, they must fill in the bubble next to their answer choice.

For More Practice using models ask students to describe how they would solve Items 1, 2, and 9. See also Chapter 8 Cumulative Test (Items 6–9), p. 296.

Extra Support To review the mathematics in Item 6, use Lesson 8.4, Equivalent Fractions, pp. 278–279.

Test Prep Handbook

Cumulative Test

Minilesson for Item 2

Focus

- Representation
- Problem Solving
- Using a Table

Use with Item 2

Solve Item 2 as a class. Ask four students to write the four-step problem solving process on the board and explain what is done at each step. Then have every student read Item 2.

Understand

What is this question asking you to do? Find the perimeter of the rectangle shown.

What does the word "perimeter" mean? the distance around a figure

Plan

Ask students to explain some of the ways they could solve this problem.

Suggest that using a table can help them keep track of the length of all the sides.

How many sides does a rectangle have? 4

After you fill this in, what operation would you use to find the perimeter of a rectangle? addition

Draw the following table on the board.

side	A	B	C	D
length				

Try It

Have students copy the table and find the perimeter.

4in. + 8in. + 4in. + 8in. = 24in.

side	A	B	C	D
length	4 in.	8 in.	4 in.	8 in.

Look Back

Why isn't the perimeter 12 in.? 12 in. is only halfway around the rectangle; the perimeter is the complete distance around the rectangle.

Check the Answer Ask students how they can check their answer. Possible answer: I can double 8, double 4, and add 16 + 8 = 24.

Remind students that on a multiple-choice test, they must fill in the bubble next to their answer choice.

Extra Support To review the mathematics in Item 2, use Lesson 9.3, Perimeter, pp. 308– 309.

Chapter 9 Cumulative Test

Mark your answer on the answer sheet.

1. A paper clip is about 1 inch long. What is a reasonable estimate of the length of this pencil? C

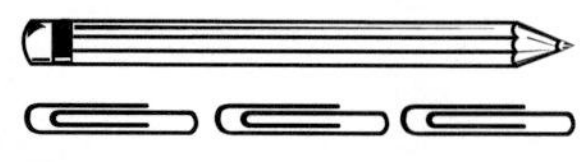

A 6 inches
B 8 inches
C 3 inches
D 1 inch

2. What is the perimeter of the rectangle? J

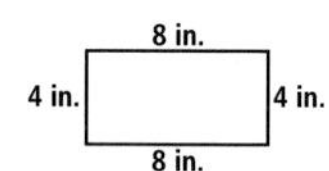

F 12 in.
G 32 in.
H 64 in.
J 24 in.

3. Which object would weigh less than 1 pound? D

A truck
B horse
C third grade student
D apple

4. How long is the key? G

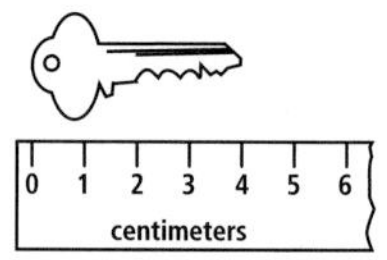

F 6 centimeters
G 4 centimeters
H 1 centimeter
J 2 centimeters

5. What temperature is shown on the thermometer? C

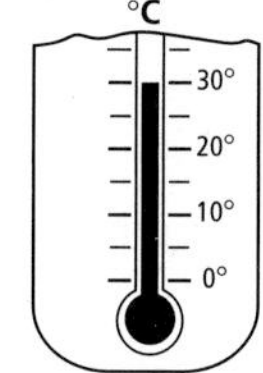

A 20° C
B 25° C
C 30° C
D 0° C

GO ON

520

Reading Strategies Use with Item 6

Remind students that they can use the Monitor reading strategy by rereading a problem and focusing on important information and details.

Thinking Aloud

What does the question ask me to find? *Find the amount of time that has elapsed.*

What does the word "elapsed" mean? *It means the number of minutes that pass between two given times.*

What times are shown on the two clocks? *3:45 and 4:10 are shown.*

Has a full hour elapsed? *No.*

What skip-counting pattern can I use between the two times? *Count by 5's.*

How many minutes elapsed from 3:45 to 4:10? *25 minutes elapsed.*

Invite students to finish the problem and decide as a class which is the correct answer.

For More Practice Monitor reading strategy minilessons, TE p. 302J.

Extra Support To review the mathematics in Item 6, use Lesson 9.16, Elapsed Time, pp. 334–335.

6. How much time has elapsed? H

- F 5 minutes
- G 35 minutes
- H 25 minutes
- J 55 minutes

7. At an art store, Rhea paid $8.00 for some watercolors. She also bought 3 paintbrushes that cost the same amount each. She spent $14.00. How much did each paintbrush cost? B

- A $1
- B $2
- C $3
- D $4

8. Adele sold 45 greeting cards at a school fair. Doug sold 28. How many greeting cards did Doug and Adele sell all together? F

- F 73
- G 63
- H 27
- J 17

9. Which group of numbers is in order from least to greatest? D

- A 1,248; 704; 790; 932
- B 790; 704; 932; 1,248
- C 704; 932; 790; 1,248
- D 704; 790; 932; 1,248

10. Which number shows 648 rounded to the nearest hundred? G

- F 500
- G 600
- H 650
- J 700

STOP

Test Prep Handbook

521

Student Handbook Masters

The Test Prep Handbook pages can be found as blackline masters in the **Student Handbook Masters**.

Scoring Chart

Number of Items Correct	1	2	3	4	5	6	7	8	9	10
Score	10	20	30	40	50	60	70	80	90	100

Item Analysis

Item	1	2	3	4	5	6	7	8	9	10
Lesson	9.1	9.3	9.6	9.7	9.14	9.16	9.9	3.2	2.9	2.8

Minilesson for Item 7

Focus

- **Representation**
- **Problem Solving**
- **Drawing a Picture and Money**

Use with Item 7

Tell students you will solve Item 7 together. Then ask a student to read Item 7 aloud.

Understand

What does this question expect you to find? the cost of each paintbrush

What information do you know? Watercolors cost $8.00; Rhea bought 3 paintbrushes, each costing the same amount; she spent $14.00.

Plan

Have a student draw 14 one-dollar bills on the board. Ask, How can drawing a picture help solve the problem? I can see how she spent the $14.

Try It

Have students use the drawing to model the solution.

How can you show that Rhea spent $8.00 on watercolors? Possible answer: Cross out 8 one-dollar bills on the board.

How can you show that Rhea bought 3 paintbrushes that all cost the same? Possible answer: Divide the remaining one-dollar bills into 3 equal sets.

Look Back

How much did each paintbrush cost? $2.00

Check the Answer One way to check the answer is to try all the answer choices. For example, if each paintbrush costs $1, three paint brushes would cost $3. So, the total cost would be $11, not $14.

Remind students that on a multiple-choice test, they must fill in the bubble next to their answer choice.

Extension Suppose Rhea paid $14.75. How would the answer change? Paintbrushes would cost $2.25 each.

For More Practice using pictorial models, ask students to describe how they would solve Item 9. See also Chapter 10 Cumulative Test (Items 22–28), p. 375.

Extra Support To review the mathematics in Item 7, use Lesson 9.9, Work Backward, pp. 322–323.

Test Prep Handbook

Cumulative Test

Minilesson for Item 6

Focus

- Reasonableness
- Problem Solving
- Comparing Decimals on a Number Line

Use with Item 6

Have students solve Item 6 as a class. Remind students that you will use the four-step problem solving process. Then ask students to read Item 6.

Understand

What is the question asking you to do? Choose the answer that describes the picture shown.

What decimals are given on the number line? 0.2 and 0.7

Plan

Which answer choices can you immediately eliminate now? Explain. J; the drawing shows 0.2 and 0.7, so both numbers should be in the answer.

What do you know about the order of numbers on a number line? The farther right you go on a number line, the greater the numbers are.

When using the < and > signs, does the pointed end point to the greater number or the lesser number? the lesser number

Try It

Ask students to share their answer and explain to the class why their answer is reasonable. Possible answer: G; 0.2 is to the left of 0.7 and it is not equal to 0.7.

Look Back

Remind students that points on a number line always show different values, that they are never equal.

Check the Answer Ask students how they could check their answers. Possible answer: Use decimal models.

Extension Have students draw a number line and mark two points. Instruct students to exchange drawings and compare the numbers.

For More Practice using reasonableness, ask students to describe how they would solve Items 3 and 4. See also Chapter 8 Cumulative Test (Items 25–30), p. 299.

Extra Support To review the mathematics in Item 6, use Lesson 10.5, Comparing and Ordering Decimals, pp. 356–357.

Chapter 10 Cumulative Test

Mark your answer on the answer sheet.

1. Which tenths square shows 0.5? C

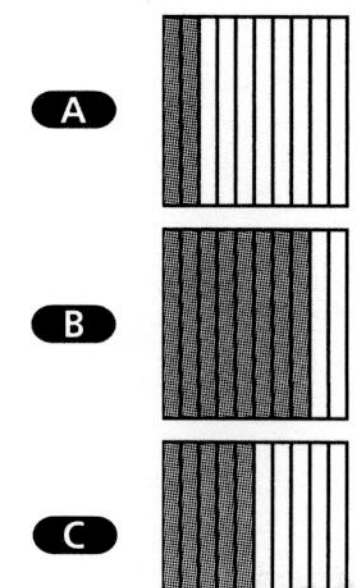

A
B
C
D

2. What are two ways to write the decimal for this hundredths square? J

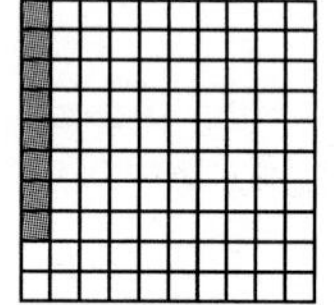

F 0.01 or one hundredth
G 0.15 or fifteen hundredths
H 0.50 or fifty hundredths
J 0.08 or eight hundredths

3. Which number sentence is in the same fact family as

10 ÷ 5 = 2? B

A 10 + 5 = 15
B 5 × 2 = 10
C 5 + 2 = 7
D 10 − 5 = 5

4. Which pattern has only odd numbers in it? J

F 100, 200, 300, 400, 500
G 32, 34, 36, 38, 40
H 98, 198, 298, 398, 498
J 21, 31, 41, 51, 61

5. Which shapes have 4 sides? C

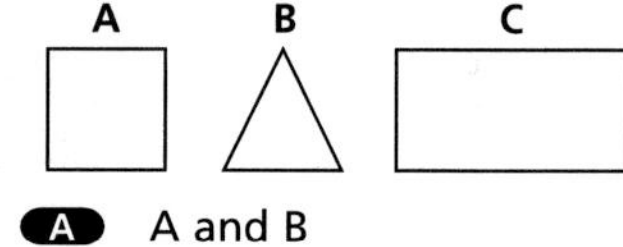

A A and B
B B and C
C A and C
D only A

GO ON

Reading Strategies Use with Item 8

Remind students they can use the Monitor reading strategy by asking themselves if they understand the question and if they know which details are important.

Thinking Aloud

How many seashells does Mary Ann have? *She has 12 seashells.*

Is the information about the rocks important? *No.*

What does she want to put into boxes? *She will put the seashells into the box.*

How many boxes does she have? *She has 3 boxes.*

Which operation do I use when I want to separate a set of items into equal groups? *I use division.*

What numbers from the problem should be in the division sentence? *I should use 12 and 3.*

Invite students to finish the problem and decide as a class which is the correct answer.

For More Practice Monitor reading strategy minilessons, TE p. 346J.

Extra Support To review the mathematics in Item 8, use Lesson 5.7, Multiplying and Dividing with 3, pp. 172–173.

6. Which number sentence does the picture show? G

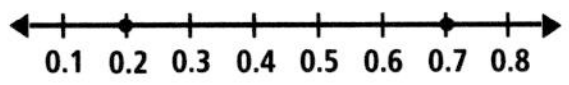

0.1 0.2 0.3 0.4 0.5 0.6 0.7 0.8

- F 0.2 < 0.2
- G 0.2 < 0.7
- H 0.2 = 0.7
- J 2 < 7

7. What does the 5 mean in 2.5? C

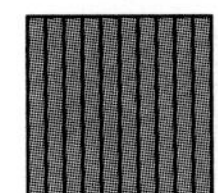
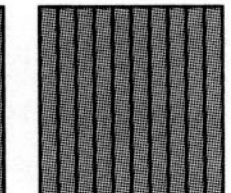
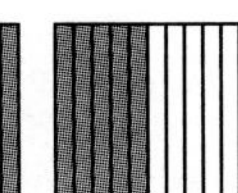
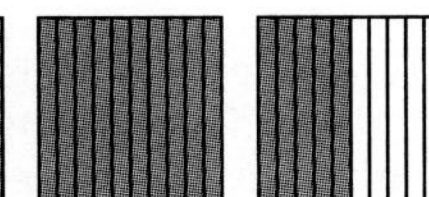

- A 5 hundredths
- B 5 wholes
- C 5 tenths
- D 5 ones

8. Mary Ann has 12 seashells and 2 rocks. She wants to divide up the seashells. She puts an equal number in each of 3 boxes. Which number sentence tells how many seashells are now in each box? H

- F 12 ÷ 2 = ■
- G 12 ÷ 12 = ■
- H 12 ÷ 3 = ■
- J 12 ÷ 6 = ■

9. Ed has 25 pennies. Sue has 74 pennies. Calvin has 98 pennies and Kim has 12 nickels. Which shows how to estimate the number of pennies they have altogether? C

- A 25 + 74 + 98 + 12
- B 30 + 70 + 100 + 10
- C 30 + 70 + 100
- D 20 + 70 + 90

10. The graph shows the number of backpacks sold at the sports store on six days. How many backpacks were sold on Friday and Saturday? H

Backpacks Sold	
Mon.	●
Tues.	● ● ●
Wed.	●
Thurs.	● ● ● ● ● ●
Fri.	● ● ● ●
Sat.	● ●
Key: ● = 5 backpacks	

- F 5
- G 60
- H 30
- J 6

STOP

Test Prep Handbook

523

Student Handbook Masters

The Test Prep Handbook pages can be found as blackline masters in the **Student Handbook Masters.**

Scoring Chart

Number of Items Correct	1	2	3	4	5	6	7	8	9	10
Score	10	20	30	40	50	60	70	80	90	100

Item Analysis

Item	1	2	3	4	5	6	7	8	9	10
Lesson	10.1	10.6	5.9	7.4	7.8	10.5	10.2	5.7	3.5	4.4

Minilesson for Item 10

Focus

- **Solution Strategies**
- **Problem Solving**
- **Pictographs and Skip-Counting**

Use with Item 10

Tell students you will solve Item 10 together. Then ask a student to read Item 10 aloud.

Understand

What is the question asking you to do? Find the number of backpacks sold on Friday and Saturday.

What does each symbol in the pictograph represent? 5 backpacks

Plan

Ask students to describe ways in which they could solve this problem.

How can skip-counting help you find the answer? Each symbol = 5 backpacks; skip-count by 5's to find how many.

Try It

Have students count by 5's to find the number of backpacks sold on Friday and Saturday. 30 Have them compare their answers with a friend.

Look Back

Remind students that a pictograph helps to compare the number of items easily and quickly. The more symbols shown, the greater the number.

Check the Answer One way to check the answer to Item 10 is to write one 5 for each symbol and then add. Remind students that on a multiple-choice test, they must fill in the bubble next to their answer choice.

Extension Ask students to find the number of backpacks sold on Mon., Tue., and Wed. combined. 25 backpacks

For More Practice with pictographs, see Chapter 5 Cumulative Test (Items 22–26), p. 187.

Extra Support To review the mathematics in Item 10, use Lesson 4.4, Pictographs, pp. 130–131.

Test Prep Handbook

Cumulative Test

Minilesson for Item 1

Focus
- Solution Strategies
- Problem Solving
- Arrays and Multiplication

Use with Item 1

Tell students you will solve Item 1 as a class. Ask four students to name one of each of the four steps in the problem solving process. Then have students read Item 1.

Understand

Discuss with students how an array represents multiplication. What is the question asking you to do? Choose the multiplication sentence that is modeled in the drawing.

Plan

This problem can be solved easily by eliminating answer choices that are not reasonable.
How many rows does the array have? 3 rows
What answer choice can you eliminate now? Why? C, because it does not have the number 3 in it
What number is being modeled in each row? 23

Try It

Have students eliminate other answer choices. What other answer choices can you eliminate? Possible answer: A and D can be eliminated because neither contain the number 23.

Look Back

Verify that each student chose answer choice B.

Check the Answer Have students check the answer by counting all the blocks in the drawing.
Remind students that on a multiple-choice test, they must fill in the bubble next to their answer choice.

Extension Have students draw an array of place-value blocks and exchange drawings. Each student writes the appropriate multiplication sentence for their drawing.

For More Practice using pictorial models, ask students to describe how they would solve Item 6. See also Chapter 6 Cumulative Test (Items 8–14), p. 222.

Extra Support To review the mathematics in Item 1, use Lesson 11.1, Exploring Multiplication, pp. 380–381.

Chapter 11 Cumulative Test

Mark your answer on the answer sheet.

1. Which multiplication sentence is shown by this array? B

   Ⓐ $3 \times 33 = 99$
   Ⓑ $3 \times 23 = 69$
   Ⓒ $2 \times 23 = 46$
   Ⓓ $3 \times 20 = 60$

2. Look at the figures. What will the next figure be? J

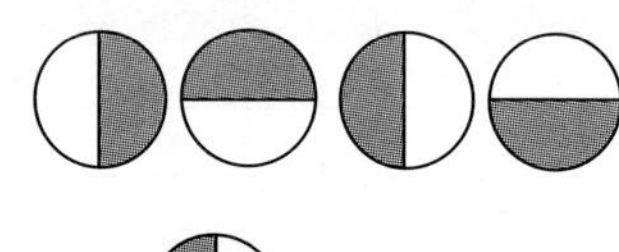

   Ⓕ 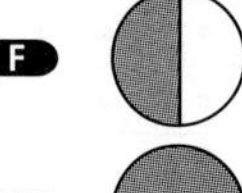
   Ⓖ
   Ⓗ 
   Ⓙ 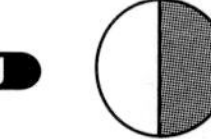

3. Use the nearest ten. Which is the best estimate of

   3×88? C

   Ⓐ 200
   Ⓑ 210
   Ⓒ 270
   Ⓓ 240

4. Ms. Alvarez's math class is studying division facts using flash cards. There are 30 cards put into 6 decks. Which sentence tells how many flash cards are in each deck? F

   Ⓕ $30 \div 6 = ■$
   Ⓖ $6 \times 30 = ■$
   Ⓗ $6 + 30 = ■$
   Ⓙ $30 - 6 = ■$

5. What is the perimeter of the triangle? D

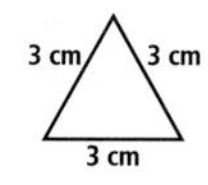

   Ⓐ 27 cm
   Ⓑ 6 cm
   Ⓒ 33 cm
   Ⓓ 9 cm

GO ON

Reading Strategies Use with Item 5

Remind students that they can use the Self-Question reading strategy by asking themselves questions about what they have read, what they know, and how they can apply what they know to solve the problem.

Thinking Aloud

What is the question asking me to do? *I need to find the perimeter of the triangle.*
What do I know about triangles? *They have 3 sides.*
What do I know about perimeter? *The perimeter of a shape is the total distance around the shape.*
How can I find the perimeter of a triangle? *I can add the lengths of all sides.*
How many numbers will I add? How do I know? *I will add 3, because triangles have 3 sides.*

Invite students to finish the problem and decide as a class which is the correct answer.

For More Practice Self-Question reading strategy minilessons, TE p. 378J.

Extra Support To review the mathematics in Item 5, use Lesson 9.3, Perimeter, pp. 308–309.

6. What is the product of

2 × 7? H

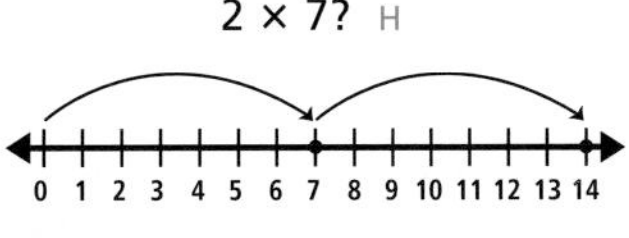

(F) 7
(G) 21
(H) 14
(J) 0

7. Which solids have a face that is a triangle? C

A  B   C 

(A) B and C
(B) only A
(C) A and C
(D) A and B

8. Randy has 43 crayons and 8 colored pencils. Alvin has 25 crayons and 6 colored pencils. Which shows how many crayons Randy and Alvin have together? F

(F) 43 + 25
(G) 43 + 8 + 25 + 6
(H) 43 + 25 − 8 − 6
(J) 43 − 25

9. There are four times as many apples as pears in a shopping cart. There are 20 apples and 5 pears. Which number sentence tells that there are more apples than pears? D

(A) 20 > 4
(B) 5 > 4
(C) 20 = 5
(D) 20 > 5

10. Which shapes are **not** congruent (have a different size or a different shape)? H

(F) 
(G) 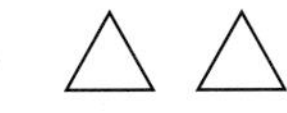
(H) 
(J) 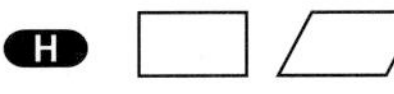

Test Prep Handbook

525

Student Handbook Masters

The Test Prep Handbook pages can be found as blackline masters in the **Student Handbook Masters.**

Scoring Chart

Number of Items Correct	1	2	3	4	5	6	7	8	9	10
Score	10	20	30	40	50	60	70	80	90	100

Item Analysis

Item	1	2	3	4	5	6	7	8	9	10
Lesson	11.1	7.14	11.2	6.5	9.3	6.6	7.10	3.4	2.9	7.6

Minilesson for Item 4

Focus

- Reasonableness
- Problem Solving
- Choosing a Number Sentence

Use with Item 4

Tell students you will solve Item 4 as a class. Then ask a student to read Item 4 aloud.

Understand

What is the problem asking you to do? Choose a number sentence that tells the number of flash cards in each deck.

Plan

Suggest students reread the problem and think about a number sentence they would use to solve it.
How many flashcards are there altogether? 30 flashcards
How many decks of flashcards are there? 6 decks
Which operation do you use when you want to break up a set into equal groups? division

Try It

Ask partners to write their number sentence on the board. Then compare them: 30 ÷ 6 = 5.

Look Back

Would 30 ÷ 5 = 6 also be a reasonable answer for this problem? Explain. No; this number sentence shows the number of cards in 5 equal decks.

Check the Answer Ask students to describe ways in which they could check this answer. Possible answer: Divide 30 slips of paper into 6 equal stacks and count the number of slips of paper in each stack.

Extension Instruct students to rewrite the problem for each of the remaining answer choices.

For More Practice using number sentences, ask students to describe how they would solve Item 9. See also Chapter 11 Cumulative Test (Items 15–21), p. 406.

Extra Support To review the mathematics in Item 4, use Lesson 6.5, Multiplying and Dividing with 6, pp. 200–201.

Test Prep Handbook

Cumulative Test

Minilesson for Item 5

Focus
- **Estimation**
- **Problem Solving**
- **Rounding Addends**

Use with Item 5

Tell students you will solve Item 5 as a class. Why do you use the four-step problem solving process? Possible answer: The steps help you understand the problem, organize your thoughts, and check your answers.
Have students read Item 5 to themselves.

Understand
What is the problem asking you to do? Choose the number sentence that will provide the best estimate for the addition problem.

Plan
Discuss how rounding can help them estimate the answer.
What is the largest place value of the addends in the problem? tens
To what place should we round the addends? tens

Try It
Have students round the numbers to the nearest ten and write a new number sentence. Have them compare the number sentences and find the correct answer choice.
C; 70 + 50 = 120

Look Back
If necessary, review the rules of rounding with the class.

Check the Answer Have students check the answer by discussing why the rules of rounding eliminate the other answer choices.
Remind students that on a multiple-choice test, they must fill in the bubble next to their answer choice.

Chapter 12 Cumulative Test

Mark your answer on the answer sheet.

1. You are going ice skating. You see on the thermometer that it is 30°F outside. What did you use the thermometer for? C

- A to find out that it is hot
- B to find out what time it is
- C to find out that it is cold
- D to see what day it is

2. Which number sentence can help you solve J

25 ÷ 5 = 5?

- F 25 + 5 = 30
- G 5 + 5 = 10
- H 25 − 5 = 20
- J 5 × 5 = 25

3. What fraction of the set of circles is shaded? B

- A $\frac{1}{5}$
- B $\frac{2}{5}$
- C $\frac{3}{5}$
- D $\frac{4}{5}$

4. Marco made 16 paper flowers for a party. When he finished making the flowers, he found that $\frac{1}{2}$ were red, $\frac{1}{4}$ were blue, and $\frac{1}{4}$ were green. How many flowers were blue? G

- F 16
- G 4
- H 8
- J 1

5. What is the best estimate of

72 + 54 = ■? C

- A 80 + 50 = 130
- B 80 + 60 = 140
- C 70 + 50 = 120
- D 70 + 60 = 130

GO ON

Reading Strategies Use with Item 7

Remind students that they can use the Evaluate reading strategy by looking at what a problem tells them and what it asks.

Thinking Aloud
What does the problem ask? *I need to write a money amount using a dollar sign and a decimal point.*
How much money did Rebecca take out of the bank? *She took out twelve dollars and seventy-five cents.*
What does the word "and" mean? *I need to place a decimal point because what follows is the cents.*

Invite students to finish the problem and decide as a class which is the correct answer.

For More Practice Evaluate reading strategy minilessons, TE p. 410J.

Extra Support To review the mathematics in Item 7, use Lesson 2.3, Place Value, pp. 46–47.

6. What are two ways to write the decimal for the shading? H

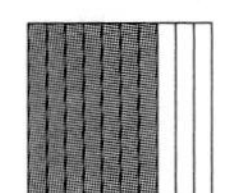

F 0.3 or three tenths
G 0.07 or seven hundredths
H 0.7 or seven tenths
J 0.03 or three hundredths

7. Rebecca took twelve dollars and seventy-five cents out of the bank. How is this money amount written with a dollar sign ($) and a decimal point (.)? D

A $1275
B $127.5
C 1275¢
D $12.75

8. Mike tried to stack 18 cubes in 4 equal piles. What result did he get? H

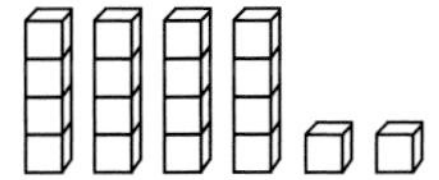

F 3 piles with 4 leftover cubes
G 2 piles with 2 leftover cubes
H 4 piles with 2 leftover cubes
J 8 piles with 2 leftover cubes

9. Colin has both nickels and dimes in his piggy bank. He has 5 coins altogether. How much could he have in his bank? C

A 20¢
B 25¢
C 45¢
D 60¢

10. You want to use mental math to find this difference. What is the first step you will take? C

$$\begin{array}{r} 99 \\ -\ 10 \\ \hline \end{array}$$

A regroup 1 ten
B round 10 to 9
C round 99 to 100
D subtract 9

STOP

Student Handbook Masters

The Test Prep Handbook pages can be found as blackline masters in the **Student Handbook Masters**.

Scoring Chart

Number of Items Correct	1	2	3	4	5	6	7	8	9	10
Score	10	20	30	40	50	60	70	80	90	100

Item Analysis

Item	1	2	3	4	5	6	7	8	9	10
Lesson	9.14	5.9	8.1	12.2	3.4	10.3	2.3	12.1	2.11	3.11

Minilesson for Item 6

Focus
- Solution Strategies
- Problem Solving
- Decimals

Use with Item 6

Tell students you will solve Item 6 as a class. Then have students read Item 6 to themselves.

Understand

What is this problem asking you to do? Name the two ways to write the decimal for the picture.
How can you write a decimal in two ways? in number form and in word form

Plan

Ask students to describe ways in which they could solve this problem.
How can you eliminate choices to solve the problem? Possible answer: I can use what I know about shading decimal models to eliminate unreasonable choices.
Describe the model in the picture. a model divided into 10 equal parts; 7 parts are shaded
Because of the number of parts that are shaded, which answer choices can be eliminated? F and J
What else can we look at to help us eliminate an answer choice? whether the models show tenths or hundredths

Try It

Have students determine which other answer to eliminate and which answer is correct. Possible answer: G can be eliminated because the model uses tenths, not hundredths. The correct answer is H.

Look Back

Have students describe how they could have solved the problem without using elimination.

Check the Answer One way to check the answer to Item 6 is to use the alternate methods students described above.

Extension Have several students draw models for the remaining answer choices.

For More Practice using pictorial models, ask students to describe how they would solve Items 2, 3, 8, and 9. See also Chapter 11 Cumulative Test (Items 29–35), p. 407.

Extra Support To review the mathematics in Item 6, use Lesson 10.3, Tenths, pp. 352–353.

Acknowledgments and Credits

Acknowledgments

For each of the selections listed below, grateful acknowledgment is made for permission to reprint copyrighted material as follows:

Cover of *Appalachian Mountain Club* magazine, March 1996 issue. Courtesy of AMC Outdoors, the magazine of the Appalachian Mountain Club.

Cover of *Children's Digest* magazine, December 1993 issue. Reprinted by permission of Children's Better Health Institute.

Cover of *Cobblestone* magazine, January 1996 issue: *A Historical Look at Washington, D.C.*, ©1996, published by Cobblestone Publishing Company, 7 School St., Peterborough, NH 03458.

Cover of *Cricket* magazine. Reprinted by permission of *Cricket* magazine, January 1996. Vol. 23, #5, ©1996 by Friso Henstra.

Cover of *Junior League Baseball* magazine, March 1997 issue. Reprinted by permission of 2D Publishing.

Cover of *Kids Discover: Flight* magazine, November 1991 issue. Reprinted by permission of Kids Discover.

Cover of *Kids Discover: Vikings* magazine, 1996 issue. Reprinted by permission of Kids Discover.

Cover of *National Geographic* magazine, October 1996 issue. Reprinted by permission of National Geographic Society.

Cover of *Newsweek* magazine, May 29, 1995 issue. ©1995, Newsweek, Inc. All rights reserved. Reprinted by permission.

Cover of *Ranger Rick* magazine. Reprinted from the July 1996 issue of *Ranger Rick* magazine, with the permission of the publisher, National Wildlife Federation. Copyright 1996 by NWF.

Cover of *Weatherwise* magazine, June/July 1996 issue. Reprinted by permission of Weatherwise.

Cover of *Zillions* magazine. Copyright 1996 by Consumers Union of U.S., Inc., Yonkers, NY 10703-1057. Referenced by permission from *Zillions*, September/October 1996.

Decimal Squares, Fraction Bars, and *Tower of Bars* were created by Professor Albert C. Bennett, Jr. and are registered trademarks of Scott Resources. They are used by permission of Scott Resources. All rights reserved.

Cover Photography

© Stuart Westmorland/Tony Stone Images (background)

Allan Landau Photography (front figure, screen inset)

Image Copyright © 1996 PhotoDisc, Inc. (inset)

Photography

i Stuart Westmorland/Tony Stone Images; iii Steve Grubman(l); vii Phil Schermeister/Corbis (t); ©1996 PhotoDisc, Inc. (b); xi Stephen Frisch/Stock Boston/PNI (l); Alon Reininger/Contact Press/PNI (r); 4-5 Alex Priest/Panoramic Images; 4 Galen Rowell/Corbis; 6 Colter Bay Indian Arts Musuem, Grand Tetons National Park, Wyoming, David T. Vernon Collection; 10 ©1996 PhotoDisc,Inc. (l,m); Steve Grubman (r); 11 ©1996 PhotoDisc, Inc.; 14 Bodleian Library, Oxford University (t); Mary Van de Ven/Pacific Stock (b); 16 Steve Grubman; 17 Norbert Wu/Tony Stone Images (l); Art Wolfe/Tony Stone Images (lm); Carl Roessler/Tony Stone Images (rm); Hal Beral/Photo Network/PNI (r); 18 Tony Freeman/PhotoEdit; 24 William R. Sallaz/Duomo; 32 Johnny Johnson/Animals Animals; ©1996 PhotoDisc, Inc. (inset) Steve Gorman (cover); 33 Pat and Tom Leeson/Photo Researchers (t); Wolfgang Bayer/Bruce Coleman, Inc./PNI (b); 48 Rosanne Olson/Allstock/PNI; 50-51 Gordon Joffrion/Stock South/PNI; 50 Michael Newman/PhotoEdit; 54 Corbis/Bettmann; 56-57 Courtesy of the United States Postal Service; 60 ©1996 PhotoDisc,Inc.; David Young Wolf/PhotoEdit (t); 62 Richard Nowitz/PhotoTake/PNI; 64-65 Mark Wyatt/Inside Track; 64 Gail Mooney/Corbis; 66 David Young Wolf/PhotoEdit; 67 ©1996 PhotoDisc, Inc.; 68 J.D. Schwalm/Stock South/PNI; 70 John White/Blackstar (bkgd); Craig Laughlin Collection; 75 Michael Matson/Allstock/PNI (l); Michael Newman/PhotoEdit/PNI (m); Lawrence Migdale/Stock Boston/PNI (r); 76 Phil Schermeister/Corbis; 90-91 Library of Congress/Corbis; 90 Corbis/Bettmann; 98 C M Dixon (t); Scala/Art Resource (l); Science and Society Picture Library (m,r); 99 Science and Society Picture Library (l); 102-03 Chris Harvey/Tony Stone Images; 102 Manoj Shah/Tony Stone Images (t); Chris Harvey/Tony Stone Images (b);104-05 NASA; 106 ©1996 PhotoDisc, Inc.(t); Lee Foster/Words & Pictures/PNI (b); 111 ©1996 PhotoDisc, Inc.; 112 Bob Daemmrich/Tony Stone Images; 114 Stuart Westmoreland/Tony Stone Images; Gail Shumway (cover); 115 Art Wolfe/Tony Stone Images; 125 Nik Wheeler/Corbis; 128 Tom Bean/Corbis (bkgd); Colter Bay Indian Arts Musuem, Grand Tetons National Park, Wyoming, David T. Vernon Collection; 129 Colter Bay Indian Arts Musuem, Grand Tetons National Park, Wyoming, David T. Vernon Collection; 130-31 Alon Reininger/Contact Press/PNI; 134-35 Tim Ribar/Stock South/PNI; 134 ©1996 PhotoDisc, Inc.; 135 ©1996 PhotoDisc, Inc.; 136-37 Mark Segal/Panoramic Images; 136 David Stover/Stock South/PNI; 138 Jose Azel/Aurora/PNI; 140 Brown Brothers (l); Owen Franken/Stock Boston (r); 148 Telegraph Colour Library/FPG; Clyde H. Smith/FPG (cover); 149 ©1996 PhotoDisc, Inc.; 160 Stephen Frisch/Stock Boston/PNI; 162-63 Merlin D. Tuttle/BCI; 162 Merlin D. Tuttle/BCI; 166 Casey B. Gibson; 168 ©1996 PhotoDisc, Inc.; 170 Corbis/Bettmann; 172 Greg Ryan/Allstock/PNI; 174 Darwin Wiggett/Westlight; 176 George Disario/The Stock Market; 178 Richard Pasley/Stock Boston/PNI; 182 Lester Sloan/Gamma Liaison; 200-01 A. Keuning/Panoramic Images; 202 Stanley M. Jay, Mandolin Bros., Inc.; 204 Jason Laure; 206 C M Dixon (l); 208-09 Kit Kittle/Corbis; 208 Kevin and Cat Sweeney/Tony Stone Images; 210-11 Paul Souders/Tony Stone Images; 210 Ned Gillette/Stock Market; 212 Mug Shots/The Stock Market; 217 ©1996 PhotoDisc, Inc.; 218 John Dunn; 219 John Dunn; 228 Joel Rogers/Corbis; 236 Peter Timmermans/Allstock/PNI; 247 Bowl with repeated feather motif, Courtesy of the Michael C. Carlos Museum, Emory University, Acc. No. 1994.6.2 (t); Owen Franken/Stock Boston/PNI (b); 254-55 Richard Nowitz/Phototake/PNI; 256 Lawrence Migdale; 260-61 David Muench/Corbis; 260 John Boykin; 262 ©1996 PhotoDisc, Inc. (bkgd); National Archives; 263 National Archives; 274-75 Adam Woolfitt/Corbis; 274 Kevin R. Morris/Corbis; 280 Gwyn M. Kibbe/Stock Boston; 284 Kevin Schafer/Allstock/PNI (t); ©1996 PhotoDisc, Inc. (l); 285 ©1996 PhotoDisc, Inc.; 286 Ellsworth Kelly, Blue Green Yellow Orange Red. 1966, Acrylic on canvas, each of five panels 5' x 4'. Solomon R. Guggenheim Museum, New York. Photograph by Sally Ritts ©The Solomon R. Guggenheim Foundation, New York. FN67.1833; 290 Triolo Burke/Foodpix/PNI; 292 Miro Vintoniv/Stock Boston/PNI; 293 Chris Brown/Stock Boston/PNI; 294 Randa Bishop/Uniphoto; Universitetets Oldsaksamling, Oslo (cover); 316 Arthur Beck/The Stock Market (t); Dallas & John Heaton/Westlight; 320 Woodward Payne/Photo 20-20/PNI; 327 Jim Pickerell/Westlight (t); © 1996 PhotoDisc, Inc. (b); 332 Greg L. Ryan/Allstock/PNI; 334-35 Bob Daemmrich/Stock Boston/PNI; 336 Tom McCarthy/PhotoEdit; 337 Tom McCarthy/PhotoEdit; 338 Brian Bahr/Allsport; 352-53 Dennis Kunkel/CNRI/Phototake/PNI; 352 Scott Camazine/Photo Researchers; 356 Kathi Lamm/Allstock/PNI (r); ©1996 PhotoDisc, Inc. (l); 357 ©1996 PhotoDisc, Inc.; 358 Peter Harholdt/Corbis (l); Buddy Mays/Corbis (r); 359 Roman Soumar/Corbis; 360 Courtesy of Pima Air & Space Museum, Tucson, Arizona (t,b); Roger/Tidman (m); 366-67 Charles Krebs/Tony Stone Images/PNI; 366 Gay Bumgarner/Allstock/PNI; 368 S.D. Butcher Collection, Nebraska State Historical Society, neg#B983-1231; 369 Archive Photos/American Stock Photography/PNI; 370 Scott Halleran/Allsport; 382 Frank Siteman/PhotoEdit; 384 Photograph by Thomas A Heinz, © Copyright Thomas A. Heinz; 386 ©1996 PhotoDisc, Inc.; 387 ©1996 PhotoDisc, Inc.; 390 Fredrik D. Bodin/Stock Boston/PNI (t); Johnny Johnson/Allstock/PNI (b); 394-95 Art Wolfe/Tony Stone Images; 394 Kevin Schafer/Tony Stone Images; 396 Bob Daemmrich/Stock Boston/PNI; 398-99 Paul Harris/Allstock/PNI; 398 e.t. archive/Bibliotheque National, Paris; 402 Howard Bluestein/Photo Researchers; Chuck Adcock (cover); 403 Jeffry Myers/Stock Boston; 419-20 K. Penovac/Sovfoto/Eastfoto/PNI; 422 Larry Sherer/High Impact Photography (l); Superstock (r); 428-29 Andrea Booher/Tony Stone Images; 430 Paul Souders/Tony Stone Images/PNI

Assignment Photography

170(l) Karen Ahola; 238, 246(l), 268, 312, 328-9(bkgd), 362, 363, 376(b), 392(l), 408, 409, 412, 423, 436(b) Petrisse Briel; 304(t), 424, 425 Dave Desroches; 268-9(t), 308 Fayfoto; iii(br), iv(bl), viii-ix(b),1(bl), 2-3, 15, 38, 39, 41(bl), 55, 82, 85(bl), 98(mr), 99(m), 120, 121, 122(bl, bm, br), 154, 224, 328(br) Allan Landau; vi, 2-3, 100,124,126(t), 230, 244(t), 256(br), 320(t), 320(m), 322(t), 324, 326, 354, 364, 380 Parker/Boon Productions; 188 Ilene Perlman; 83(b), 122(tl, ml), 123(bl), 140-141(b), 141(r), 156(tl, ml), 157(bl), 171(l), 189, 190(tl), 191(bl), 206(bl), 207(c), 224(t), 225(b), 227(bl), 246(br), 247(ml), 254(b, m), 269(r), 270(tl, ml), 271(bl), 282(l), 300, 303(bl), 347(bl), 379(bl), 393(bl), 411(bl) Tony Scarpetta; x(bl), 283, 316(l), 317(ml, mr) Tracey Wheeler

538

Using the Calculator

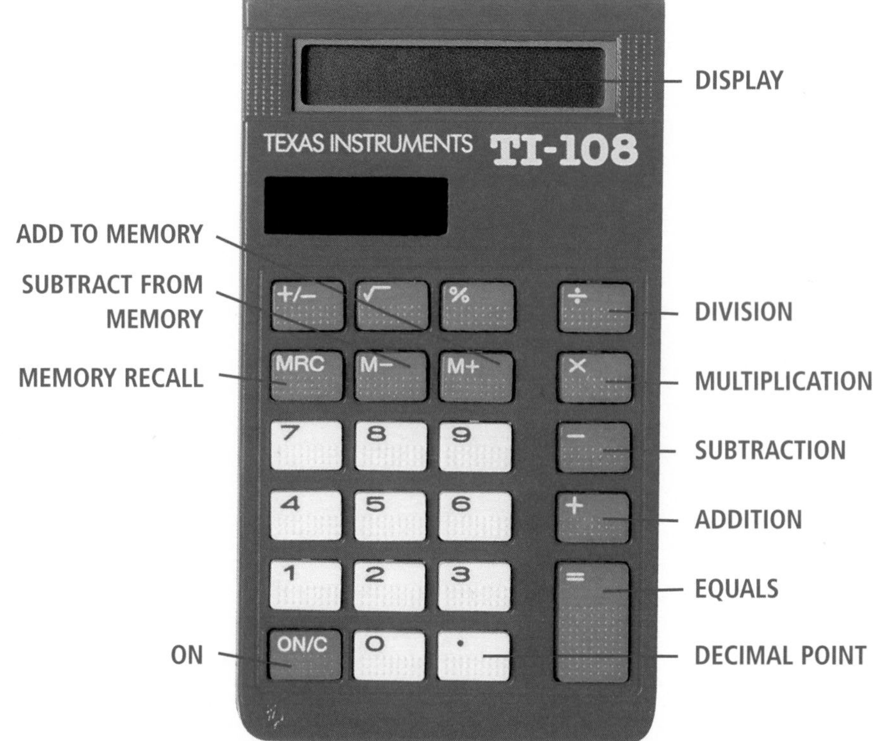

The information and activities that follow are designed to help students become familiar with the calculator.

Calculators Are Useful Show a calculator to the whole class or to small groups. Review the function of each key. Remind students that all calculators are not the same. The keys shown here, for example, may be found in different places on different calculators.

Remind Students . . .

- A calculator does not show commas.
- A calculator usually will not show more than eight digits.
- A calculator does not show a dollar sign. Use the decimal point to show money amounts.
- Care for your calculator. Cover the keyboard and display with the hard "slide cover" when the calculator is not in use.

The TI-108 The TI-108 is solar powered. The TI-108 can perform addition, subtraction, multiplication, division, constant and memory functions.

The Math Explorer The Math Explorer can perform addition, subtraction, multiplication, division, integer division, constant and memory functions. The Math Explorer also has a backspace button to allow you to erase the last number on the display.

The Memory Keys

TI-108

How can you add 14 to both 9 and 11? You can use the memory keys. Read below for practice.

M+ adds the displayed number to the memory.

M- subtracts the displayed number from the memory.

MRC displays the number stored in the memory.

MRC MRC clears the numbers stored in the memory.

Try it! Add 14 to 9 and then add 14 to 11.

Press	Display
1 4	**14**
M+	**M14**
9 +	**M9**
MRC	**M14**
=	**M23**
1 1 +	**M11**
MRC	**M14**
=	**M25**

So, 9 + 14 = 23 and 11 + 14 = 25.

The Constant Feature

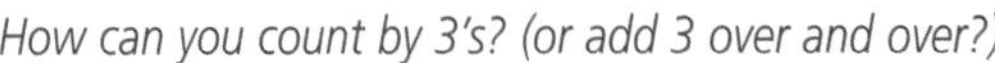

TI-108

How can you count by 3's? (or add 3 over and over?)

Use the equals key. Read below for practice.

= repeats the operation with the same number over and over again.*

Try it! Count by 3's.

Press	Display
3 +	**3**
3	**3**
=	**6**
=	**9**
=	**12**
=	**15**

So, the calculator adds 3 each time you press the = .

*If you are using the Math Explorer and you wish to repeat an operation with the same number, use the Cons .

On/Clear and Error Readings

TI-108

How can you make the number on the display go away?

How will you know if a number is too large to be shown on the display? (or if an operation is not possible?)

Use ON/C to make a number go away. If an operation is not possible or the number you are keying in is too large (the display will show up to eight digits), an E appears on the far left side of the display. E means error.

ON/C turns the calculator on, clears the display, and also removes the error reading.

Try it! Multiply 99999 by 99999.

Press	Display
9 9 9 9 9 ×	**99999**
9 9 9 9 9	**99999**
=	**E 0**

So the E tells you that the answer 9999800001 would not fit on the display. Now, can you clear the error condition and the display?

*Some calculators may round or truncate error answers.

Adding Numbers (and Entry Errors)

TI-108

How do you add 23, 61, and 131? What if you enter the wrong number?

Use the addition and equals keys. If you make a mistake entering a number, press the ON/C key once. Then reenter the number.

+ adds the digit that follows.

= completes the calculation.

ON/C clears the last value entered.

ON/C ON/C begins a new calculation.

Try it! Add 23, 61, and 131.

Press	Display
ON/C ON/C	**0**
2 3 +	**23**
6 1	**61**
+	**84**
1 3 1 =	**215**

So, 23 + 61 + 131 = 215.

Note to the teacher: You may want to use these activities to help students become familiar with using calculators.

Using the Calculator

Subtracting Numbers

TI-108

How can you subtract 549 from 706?

You can use the subtraction and equals keys. If you make a mistake entering a number, press the ON/C key once. Then reenter the number.

[−] subtracts the digit that follows.

[ON/C] [ON/C] begins a new calculation.

Try it! Subtract 549 from 706.

Press	Display
[ON/C] [ON/C]	**0**
[7] [0] [6] [−]	**706**
[5] [4] [9]	**549**
[=]	**157**

So, 706 – 549 = 157.

Multiplying Two Factors

TI-108

How can you multiply 45 by 7?

You can use the multiplication key.

[×] multiplies.

Try it! Multiply 45 by 7.

Press	Display
[ON/C] [ON/C]	**0**
[4] [5] [×]	**45**
[7]	**7**
[=]	**315**

So 45 x 7 = 315.

Dividing Numbers

TI-108

How can you divide 120 by 6?

You can use the division key. You know that 120 is the dividend and 6 is the divisor. Read below for practice.

[÷] divides.

Try it! Divide 120 by 6.

Press	Display
[ON/C] [ON/C]	**0**
[1] [2] [0] [÷]	**120**
[6]	**6**
[=]	**20**

So 120 ÷ 6 = 20.

Money Amounts

TI-108

How can you add $3.25 and $.50?

The calculator does not have a dollar key, but you can use the decimal key to show dollar amounts.

[.] enters a decimal point in a number.

Try it! Add $3.25 and $.50 ($3.25 + $.50).

Press	Display
[ON/C] [ON/C]	**0**
[3] [.] [2] [5]	**3.25**
[+]	**3.25**
[.] [5] [0]	**0.50**
[=]	**3.75**

So $3.25 + $.50 = $3.75.

Note to the teacher: You may want to use these activities to help students become familiar with using calculators.

Additional Answers

Chapter 1

Lesson 1.2, p. 4

Different: one is up and down, the other is left to right; Same: both show the numbers in order on a line with arrows at each end.

Lesson 1.3, p. 7

5.  

Lesson 1.6, p. 12

1. Not enough information. You need to know how long it takes to get from your house to the game.
2. Not enough information. You need to know how many pencils you each started out with and how many you gave away.
3. Yes; Yes; Since you have more than one dime, or at least 20 cents, you will get change.
4. Not enough information. Since you could have as little as 10 cents, you need to know how many nickels you have.

Lesson 1.14, p. 31

10. $8 + 4 = 12$
    $4 + 8 = 12$
    $12 - 4 = 8$
    $12 - 8 = 4$
11. $6 + 6 = 12$
    $12 - 6 = 6$
12. $5 + 7 = 12$
    $7 + 5 = 12$
    $12 - 7 = 5$
    $12 - 5 = 7$
13. $9 + 4 = 13$
    $4 + 9 = 13$
    $13 - 4 = 9$
    $13 - 9 = 4$
14. $5 + 4 = 9$
    $4 + 5 = 9$
    $9 - 4 = 5$
    $9 - 5 = 4$
15. $7 + 6 = 13$
    $6 + 7 = 13$
    $13 - 7 = 6$
    $13 - 6 = 7$
16. $10 + 10 = 20$
    $20 - 10 = 10$
17. $8 + 5 = 13$
    $5 + 8 = 13$
    $13 - 5 = 8$
    $13 - 8 = 5$

Chapter 2

Lesson 2.1, p. 43

9. 
10. 
11. 
12. 
13.
14. 
15.
16. 
17. 
18.

Lesson 2.3, p. 47

6. 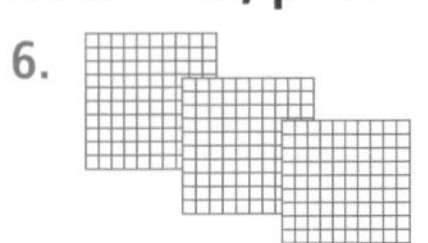

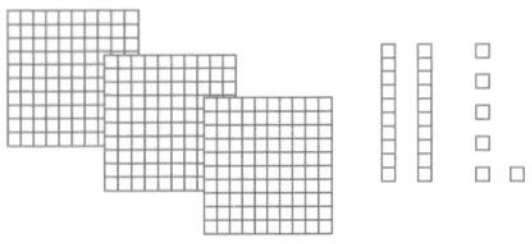

Lesson 2.4, p. 48

The rows of seats are labeled alphabetically. The seats in each row are numbered 1–10.

p. 49

1. 

Lesson 2.5, p. 51

5. 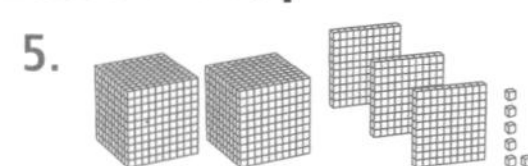

21. 

Lesson 2.6, p. 52

1. 

Lesson 2.10, p. 63

7. 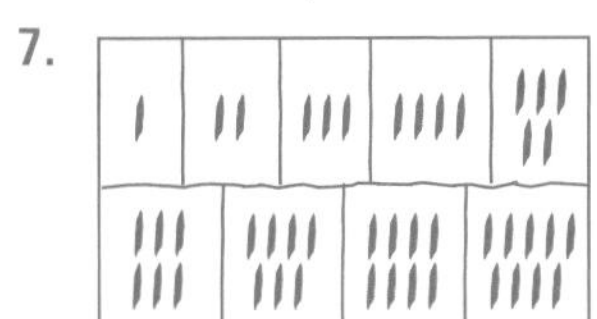

Lesson 2.11, p. 65

14.  

Lesson 2.12, p. 67

14.–25.

Garage Sale Cashbox

Numbers	Pictures	Words	Compare to \$3.50
\$3.75		three dollars and seventy-five cents	\$3.75 > \$3.50
\$2.09		two dollars and nine cents	\$2.09 < \$3.50
\$3.51		three dollars and fifty-one cents	\$3.51 > \$3.50
\$2.23		two dollars and twenty-three cents	\$2.23 < \$3.50
\$3.25		three dollars and twenty-five cents	\$3.25 < \$3.50

Chapter 3

Lesson 3.4, p. 92

5. 800, rounding; 700, front-end
6. 800, rounding; 700, front-end
7. 900, rounding; 900, front-end
8. 900, rounding; 800, front-end
18. 900, rounding; 800, front-end
19. 400, rounding; 300, front-end
20. 900, rounding; 800, front-end
21. 900, rounding; 900, front-end

Lesson 3.6, p. 96

Bullet 1: No. 10 eggs in a 12-egg carton means the carton is almost full. 10 raisins in a large bowl means the bowl is almost empty. You need to compare the amount you have with the maximum amount possible.

Bullet 3: Yes. Since 10 is close to 12, the egg carton is almost full.

8. Answers will vary. Possible answers: For question 5, you know you sleep between 7 and 10 hours a day, which is less than 83, so the answer is false. For question 6, there are hundreds of thousands of people living in each state, so the answer is true.

Lesson 3.13, p. 113

3. Yes. You can go 250 yards to the bumper cars, 200 yards to the carousel, 200 yards to the Ferris wheel, 300 yards to the Fun House, 350 yards to the Giant Slide, and 400 yards to the entrance.
4. Answers will vary. Possible answer: Go 300 yards to the Giant Slide, 350 yards to the Fun House, and 350 yards back to the carousel.
9. Answers will vary. Possible answer: You can use Guess and Check to solve the problem. Pick a first guess, such as the fun house ride. It takes longer than the slide; therefore, it cannot be the shortest ride. Your second guess should be the slide.

Lesson 3.14, p. 114

Bullet 2: You know that Jager can swim 150 yards in a minute, and that the dolphin can swim 600 yards in a minute.

Bullet 3: Act It Out. It would take the dolphin about 3 minutes to pass Jager. (The dolphin would be at 1800 yards and Jager would be at 1450 yards.)

p. 115

1. The leatherback sea turtle. It dives the least distance from the surface.

Chapter 4

Lesson 4.3, p. 128

You need to arrange the beads so that each row and column has 3 different shaped beads.

p. 129

5. Answers will vary. Possible answer: red, blue, blue, white, red, blue, blue, white, red, blue
9. Answers will vary. Possible answers: problem 1—Look for a Pattern, problem 2—Look for a Pattern, problem 5—Look for a Pattern/Act It Out

Lesson 4.5, p. 133

6. Alike: Both show how many of something; Different: A pictograph shows amounts with pictures, and a bar graph shows amounts with bars.
7. Alike: Both show the number of students; Different: Bars go in different directions; yes; One survey is about recess activities and the other is about how students get to school.

Lesson 4.8, p. 138

2. Yes. Using the graph, you can prove this by adding up the packs for each day.
4. Yes. Using the graph, you can see that 2 packs were collected on Tuesday and 4 on Wednesday. 4 is twice as many as 2.

Lesson 4.11, p. 147

2. Answers will vary, but should reflect understanding that there are fewer ways to get sums of 2, 3, 11, and 12.

Lesson 4.12, p. 149

10. Answers will vary. For problem 8, you can combine Look for a Pattern and Act It Out.

Chapter 5

Lesson 5.2, p. 161

1. $2 + 2 + 2 + 2 = 8$
   $2 + 2 + 2 + 2 + 2 = 10$ $\quad 5 \times 2 = 10$
   $2 + 2 + 2 + 2 + 2 + 2 = 12$ $\quad 6 \times 2 = 12$
2. Answers will vary. Possible answers: Answers are like skip-counting by 2; when another 2 is added in the addition sentence, the first number in the multiplication sentence increases by 1.

Lesson 5.3, p. 163

9.

Week	now	1	2	3	4	5
Exercises	4	6	8	10	12	14

Lesson 5.6, p. 168

3. No, because 10 X 3 = 30, which is more than your total of 20.
5. Yes, because the question asks for a number of hours and the answer gives a number of rehearsals.

Lesson 5.10, p. 179

1.

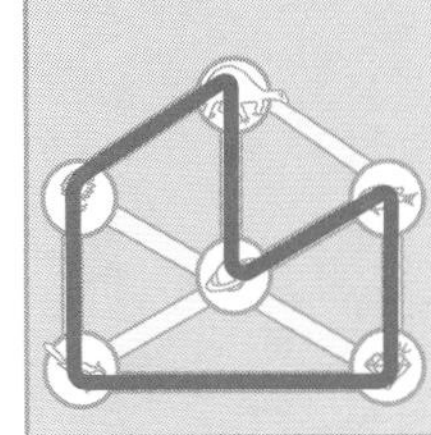

Lesson 5.11, p. 180

The Order Property

Step 3

The factors and products are the same. The factors are in a different order.

Step 4

a. $5 \times 7 = 35; 7 \times 5 = 35$
b. $3 \times 6 = 18; 6 \times 3 = 18$
c. $8 \times 2 = 16; 2 \times 8 = 16$

p. 181

14. In both, the answer stays the same even though the order of the other numbers changes.

Lesson 5.12, p. 183

1.

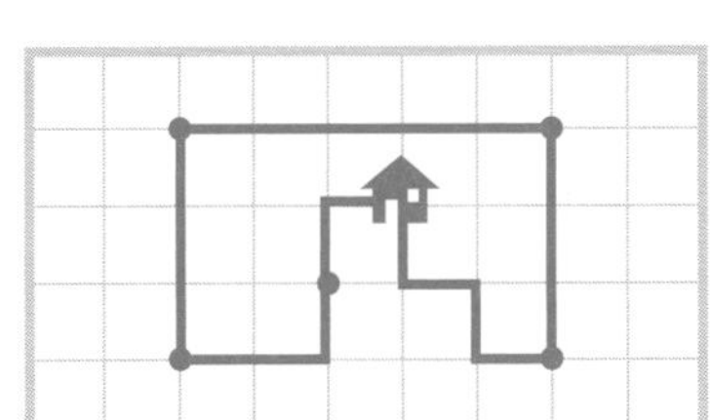

Chapter 6

Lesson 6.4, p. 198

6 is too high, so try 5. Therefore, 5 and 3 will be your next guess.

p. 199

8. Answers will vary. Possible answer: Use Guess and Check:
   step 1 — The difference between the number of brothers and sisters is 3.
   step 2 — first guess: 2, 3; $3 - 2 = 1$, and 1 is too low.
   step 3 — second guess: 1, 4; $4 - 1 = 3$
   Answer: 1 brother and 4 sisters

Lesson 6.7, p. 204

Bullet 3: No, because the numbers are simple enough to add mentally.

4. mental math, because the numbers are easy to work with; 7
5. Answers will vary. Possible answers should reflect the following: If the numbers are easy to work with and you are doing basic fact computation, use mental math.

Lesson 6.10, p. 212

There are 8 times as many red stars as blue stars.

Chapter 7

Lesson 7.1, p. 229

6.
7.
8.
9.

Lesson 7.2, p. 231

10.
11.
12.
13.

Lesson 7.3, p. 233

4.
5.

6.
7.
8.
9.

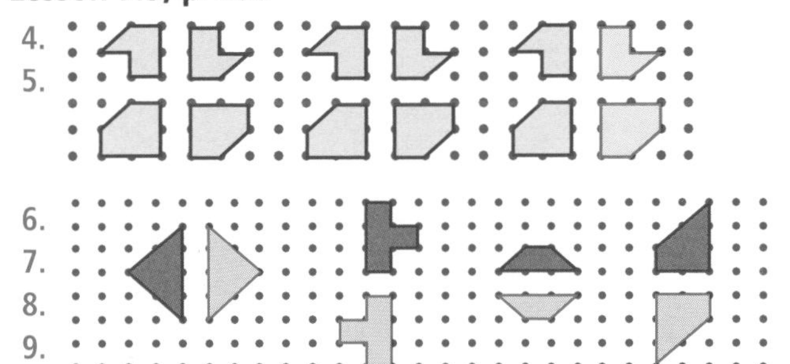

Lesson 7.10, pp. 248–249

For Steps 1–3

	Corners	Edges	Faces
Cube	8	12	6
Square pyramid	5	8	5
Triangular prism	6	9	5
Rectangular prism	8	12	6

Lesson 7.14, p. 257

1.

6.

Lesson 7.15, p. 259

14.

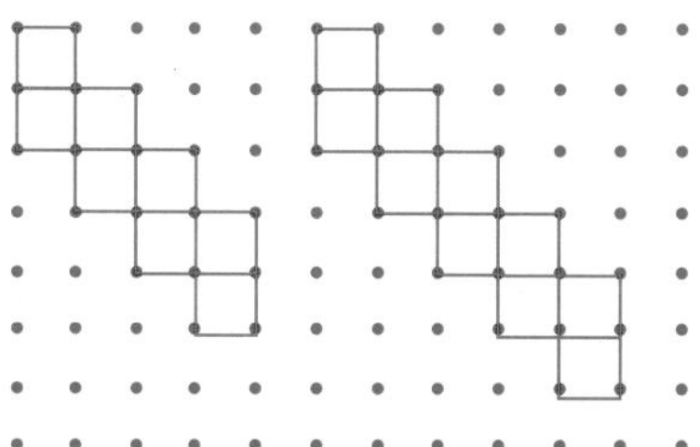

Lesson 7.16, p. 261

1. 4 square units
2. 28–29 square units
3. 1–2 square units
4. 12–15 square units

Chapter Test, p. 264

2.

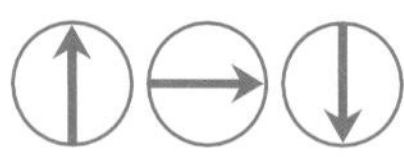

3.

4.

5.

Chapter 9

Lesson 9.9, p. 323

1. Leave the diner. Turn left and walk half a block. 2. Turn right and walk 2 blocks. 3. Turn right and walk 3 blocks. The theater will be on your left.

6.

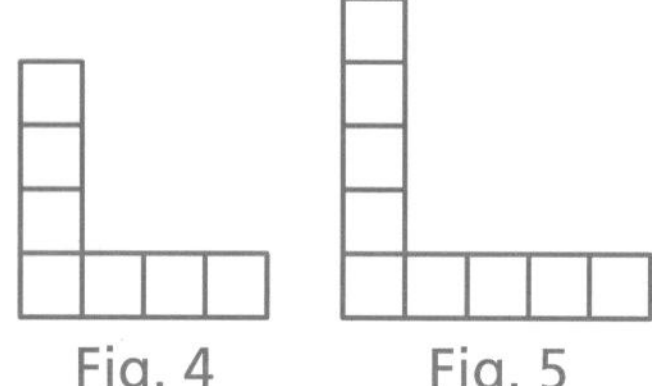

Lesson 9.10, p. 325

A — more than 1 liter
B — less than 1 liter
C — more than 1 liter
D — less than 1 liter
E — more than 1 liter
F — more than 1 liter

Chapter 10

Lesson 10.1, p. 349

12. less than
13. greater than
14. five tenths; equal to
15. 0.4, less than
16. six tenths; greater than

Lesson 10.4, p. 355

7. Answers will vary. Possible answer:

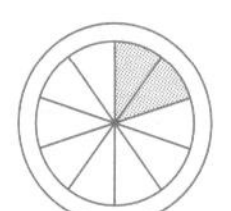 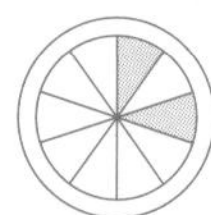 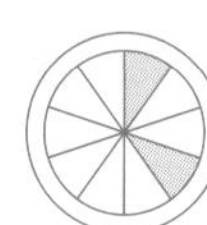  

Lesson 10.6, p. 359

11.

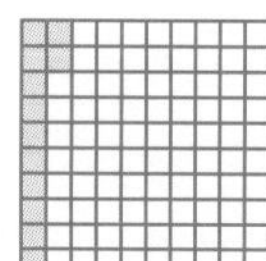

12.

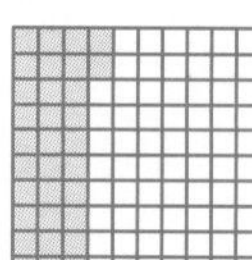

13.

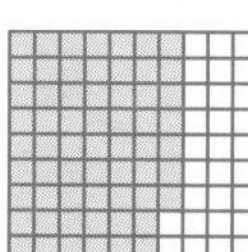

14.

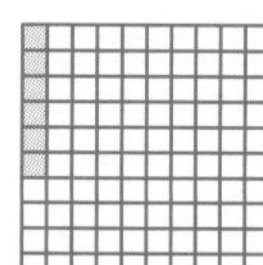

Lesson 10.10, p. 369

7. Answers will vary. Possible answer: It helped you to see all the possible combinations.

Lesson 10.11, p. 370

Bullet 1: Why might it take the player more than 11 seconds to run around the bases?

Bullet 4: Strategies will vary. The player has to turn corners and this will add to the running time.

Chapter 11

Lesson 11.4, p. 387

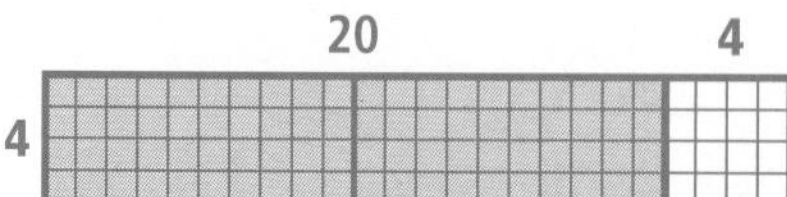

Chapter 12

Lesson 12.1, p. 412

Number of Counters	Number of Groups	Number in Each Group	Number of Leftovers	Division
20	4	5	0	$4\overline{)20}$ = 5
20	5	4	0	$5\overline{)20}$ = 4
20	6	3	2	$6\overline{)20}$ = 3 R2
20	7	2	6	$7\overline{)20}$ = 2 R6
20	8	2	4	$8\overline{)20}$ = 2 R4
20	9	2	2	$9\overline{)20}$ = 2 R2

Index

Index

Index

Index

Index